Teacher's Edition
Level 7

Heath Mathematics

Walter E. Rucker

Clyde A. Dilley

D. C. Heath and Company
Lexington, Massachusetts   Toronto

AUTHORS

Walter E. Rucker. Mr. Rucker is currently an author in residence for D.C. Heath and Company. He was formerly a Specialist in Education with the Curriculum Laboratory of the University of Illinois. He has been active in curriculum development and has served as teacher trainer in National Science Foundation Institutes. He has taught in elementary and secondary schools and is coauthor of successful elementary and junior high school mathematics programs.

Clyde A. Dilley. Professor of Education, University of Toledo, Toledo, Ohio. Dr. Dilley teaches methods courses in elementary and secondary mathematics. He was associated with the Curriculum Laboratory of the University of Illinois and served as teacher trainer in National Science Foundation Institutes. He has done research in comparing the effectiveness of long-division algorithms, has taught mathematics in public schools, and is coauthor of successful elementary and junior high school mathematics programs.

Consulting Author   Levels 1-6

J. Richard Dennis. Assistant Professor of Education, College of Education, University of Illinois. Dr. Dennis has been involved in the development and implementation of mathematics materials since 1963. He has also taught mathematics in public schools.

Authors of Teacher's Editions

Levels K, 1, and 2
Gary E. Cooke
Associate Professor of Education
Department of Elementary and
   Early Childhood Education
University of Toledo
Toledo, Ohio

Level 3
Gretchen M. Potter
Teacher
Champaign Public Schools
Champaign, Illinois

Level 4
Marjorie A. Jackson
Mathematics Consultant
Indianapolis Public Schools
Indianapolis, Indiana

Levels 5, 7, and 8
Melvin L. Thomas
Teacher of Mathematics
Foxboro High School
Foxboro, Massachusetts

Level 6
Jane Chaney
Principal
Edgewood Junior High School
Merritt Island, Florida

Authors of Calculator Worksheets

George Immerzeel
Teacher, Price Laboratory School
University of Northern Iowa
Cedar Falls, Iowa

Earl G. Ockenga
Teacher, Price Laboratory School
University of Northern Iowa
Cedar Falls, Iowa

Advisors

*Kindergarten and
Parent Involvement*
Linda Oldaker
Mathematics Supervisor
Washington School District
Phoenix, Arizona

Parent Involvement
Claire J. Zalewski
Mathematics Consultant
Lexington Public Schools
Lexington, Massachusetts

Level 7
Gary Tsuruda
Mathematics/Science Consultant
San Mateo City School District
San Mateo, California

Keep it simple. Most lessons ought to be complete using only the student's book. Extra practice books are great, but shouldn't be required.

LEVEL 3
(Also available in soft cover)

LEVEL 1

LEVEL 2

LEVEL K

We listened!

Everything you need is provided in the pupil's and teacher's editions. The ancillary materials can save you time in preparing classroom materials and help you accommodate a wide range of student ability.

- BASIC WORKSHEETS—Provide *extra practice* for every teaching lesson.

  Available as workbooks and duplicating masters for Levels 1–8, duplicating masters only for Level K.

- ENRICHMENT WORKSHEETS—Provide *extension activities* for every teaching lesson. Available as workbooks and duplicating masters for Levels 1–8, duplicating masters only for Level K.

- TESTS—Include *two tests* for every chapter. Duplicating masters Levels 1–8.

- PERSONALIZED LEARNING PACKETS—Provide a total *management package* for individualized instruction. Include Chapter Tests. Duplicating masters Levels 1–8.

- CALCULATOR WORKSHEETS—Use the hand-held calculator to help you teach mathematics. Duplicating masters Levels 3–8.

- PARENT INVOLVEMENT PACKETS—Provide teacher/parent/child interaction. Duplicating masters Levels K–8.

- CUMULATIVE RECORD FOLDERS—Provide a permanent record of students' progress.

Other Teaching Aids:

PROBLEM SOLVING WORKBOOKS—Levels 1–8
BIG BOOK—Kindergarten
ANSWER BOOKLETS—Levels 3–8

PRIMARY ACTIVITIES KIT—Manipulatives for Levels K–3.
INTERMEDIATE ACTIVITIES KIT—Manipulatives for Levels 4–8.
PRIMARY METRIC ACTIVITIES KIT—Measuring tools for Levels K–2.
CLASSROOM METRIC ACTIVITIES KIT—Measuring tools for Levels 3–8.
SCHOOL METRIC ACTIVITIES KIT—Measuring tools for Levels K–8.

LEVEL 5

LEVEL 8

LEVEL 7

LEVEL 6

LEVEL 4

"Teachers talked..."

A mathematics book should identify basic skills, teach them in a straightforward manner, and provide enough practice for the kids to master them.

And I want books with an open format and friendly tone written and designed to appeal to students.

We listened!

Visuals offer teaching support in the following ways:

- By stimulating interest.
- By clarifying the mathematics.
- By presenting problem-solving situations that are real.

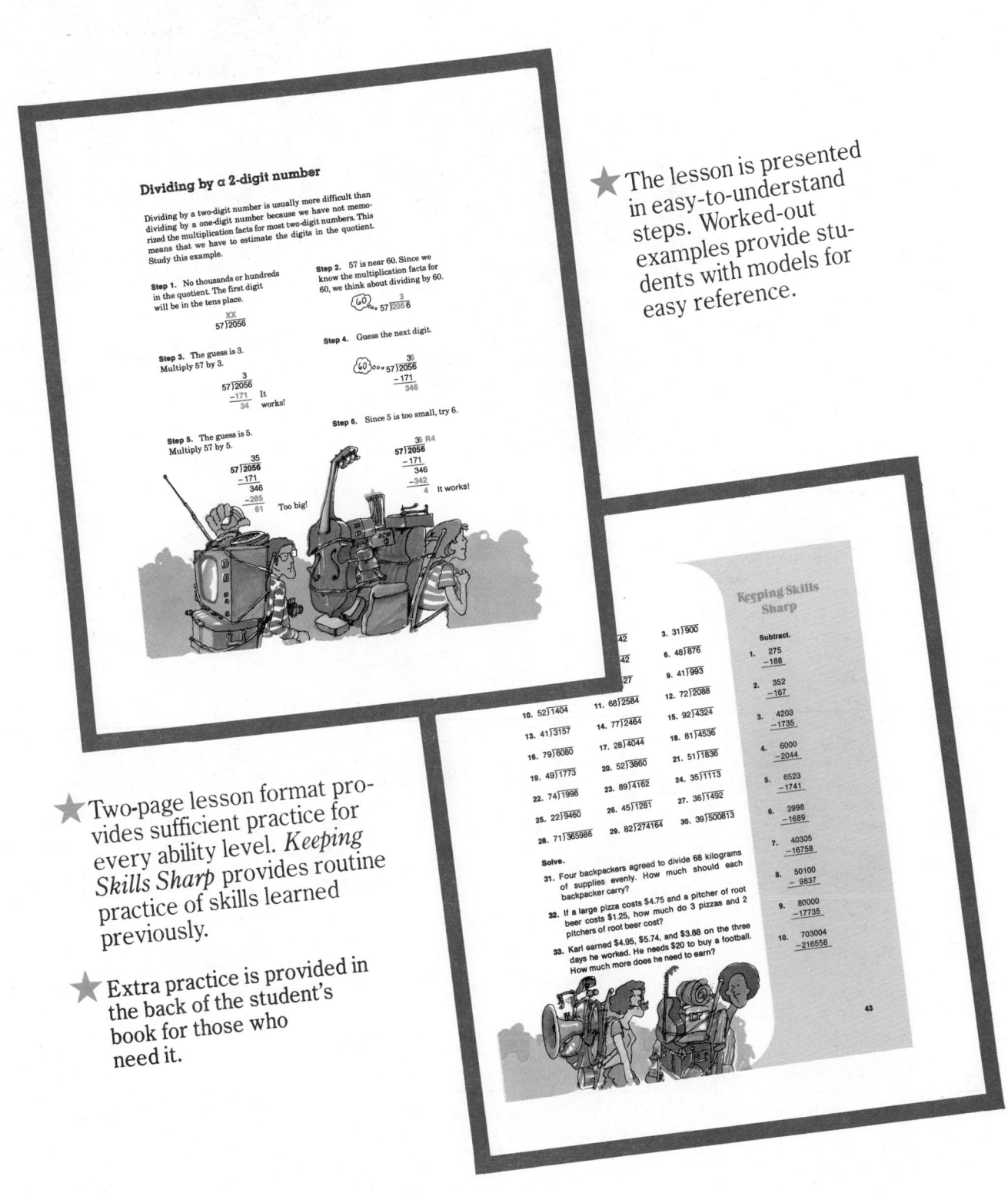

★ The lesson is presented in easy-to-understand steps. Worked-out examples provide students with models for easy reference.

★ Two-page lesson format provides sufficient practice for every ability level. *Keeping Skills Sharp* provides routine practice of skills learned previously.

★ Extra practice is provided in the back of the student's book for those who need it.

"Teachers talked..."

Evaluation material should help me keep track of each child's progress, and zero in on the areas where help is needed...

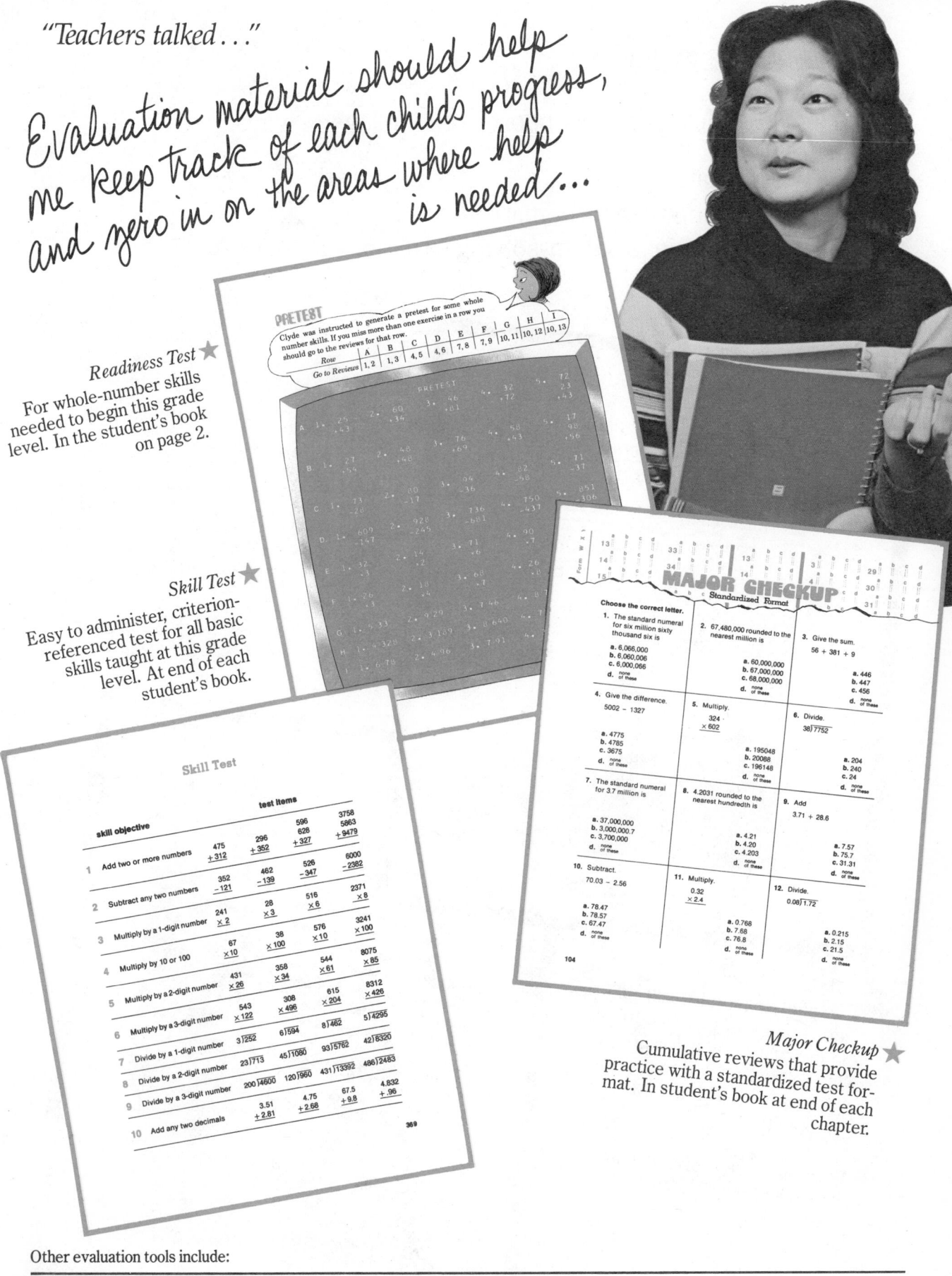

Readiness Test ★
For whole-number skills needed to begin this grade level. In the student's book on page 2.

Skill Test ★
Easy to administer, criterion-referenced test for all basic skills taught at this grade level. At end of each student's book.

Major Checkup ★
Cumulative reviews that provide practice with a standardized test format. In student's book at end of each chapter.

Other evaluation tools include:

- **Chapter Tests**
Two parallel tests for each chapter. In teacher's edition and as duplicating masters in TESTS and PERSONALIZED LEARNING PACKET.

- **Placement Test**
To place student in appropriate grade level material. In PERSONALIZED LEARNING PACKET.

- **Chapter Checkup**
Tests mastery of chapter, is keyed to learning objectives and text pages. In student's book at end of each chapter.

- **Final Checkup**
Review of all learning objectives of the level (with minimum objectives marked). In standardized test format. In the teacher's edition.

- **Midyear and Final Tests**
In Level 7 and Level 8 student books.

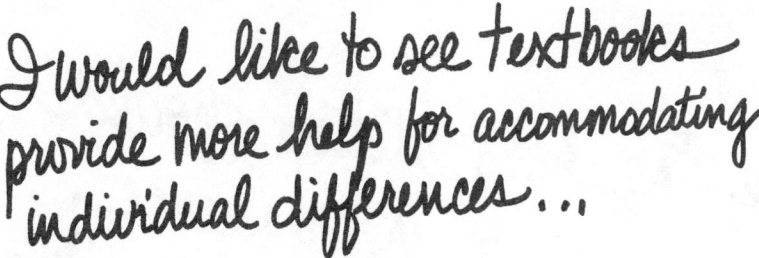

I would like to see textbooks provide more help for accommodating individual differences...

We listened!

★ *Projects* and *Skill Games* allow students of all ability levels to use their mathematics skills at their own level of understanding.

★ The Chapter Review allows the teacher to reteach and reinforce concepts and skills from the chapter based on needs identified by the chapter test.

★ *The Chapter Challenge* is for students who have mastered the objectives of the chapter.

More help on individual differences:
● Reinforcement and Enrichment activities are suggested in the teacher's editions for each lesson.
● BASIC and ENRICHMENT WORKSHEETS.
● *Excursions* to provide brain teasers.

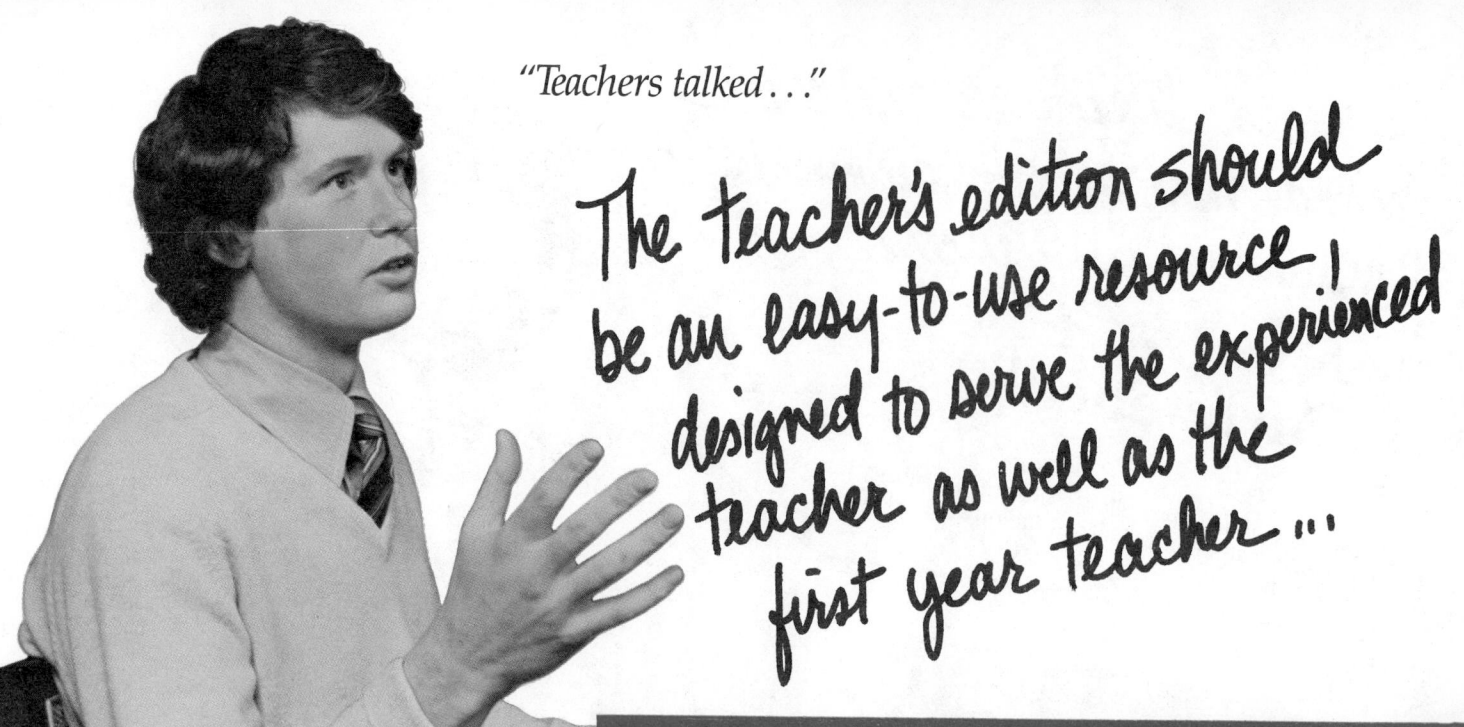

The teacher's edition should be an easy-to-use resource, designed to serve the experienced teacher as well as the first year teacher...

⭐ **Student Objectives**

Basic objectives are easily identified.

⭐ **Lesson Plans**

Pre-book and teaching strategies are suggested for every lesson.

⭐ **Three-Track Assignment Guide**

Suggests assignments for three ability levels and correlates the ancillary materials.

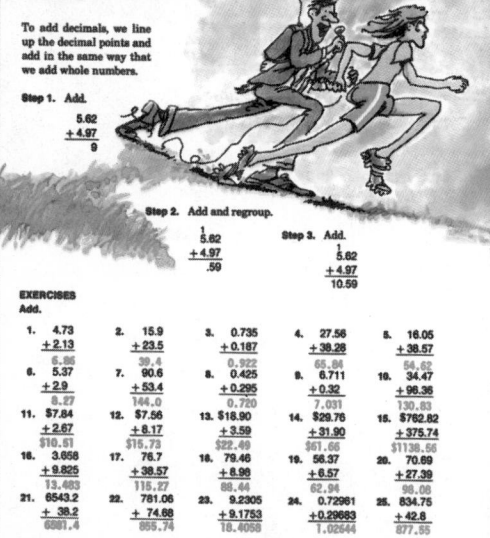

STUDENT OBJECTIVE
To add decimals.

Suggested Lesson Plan

Introduction Quickly write three whole numbers on the board and have a student come to the board and find their sum. Pick numbers that have a different number of digits and do not write them in position for adding. Call attention to the student's arrangement of the numbers starting from the right so that ones are added to ones, tens are added to tens, etc. Point out that we do the same thing when adding decimals except that we line up the decimal points.

Using the pages Use the exposition on page 66 to review addition, noting that we add decimals just as we add whole numbers. Discuss each step, noting how the work is recorded.

Assign exercises 1–40 for written work. Observe students when they encounter exercise 6. In this case, although they can add, many will be more comfortable if they write a 0 below the 7 before adding.

Assign the Keeping Skills Sharp to all students.

Adding decimals

To add decimals, we line up the decimal points and add in the same way that we add whole numbers.

Step 1. Add.
```
  5.62
+ 4.97
     9
```

Step 2. Add and regroup.
```
   1
 5.62
+4.97
  .59
```

Step 3. Add.
```
   1
  5.62
+ 4.97
 10.59
```

EXERCISES
Add.

1. 4.73 +2.13	2. 15.9 +23.5	3. 0.735 +0.187	4. 27.56 +39.28	5. 16.05 +38.57
6.86	39.4	0.922	66.84	54.62
6. 5.37 +2.9	7. 90.6 +53.4	8. 0.425 +0.295	9. 6.711 +0.32	10. 34.47 +96.36
8.27	144.0	0.720	7.031	130.83
11. $7.84 +2.67	12. $7.56 +8.17	13. $18.90 +3.59	14. $29.76 +31.90	15. $762.82 +375.74
$10.51	$15.73	$22.49	$61.66	$1138.56
16. 3.658 +9.825	17. 76.7 +38.57	18. 79.46 +8.98	19. 56.37 +6.57	20. 70.69 +27.39
13.483	115.27	88.44	62.94	98.08
21. 6543.2 +38.2	22. 781.06 +74.68	23. 9.2305 +9.1753	24. 0.72961 +0.29683	25. 634.75 +42.8
6581.4	855.74	18.4058	1.02644	677.55

66

Assignments

BASIC
page 66 exercises 1–25
page 67 exercises 26–38,
  Keeping Skills Sharp
Basic Worksheet 17

AVERAGE
page 66 exercises 1–25
page 67 exercises 26–40,
  Keeping Skills Sharp
Enrichment Worksheet 17

ENRICHED
page 66 exercises 1–25
page 67 exercises 26–40, Excursion
Enrichment Worksheet 17

EXTRA PRACTICE
page 380 set 31

66 Lesson 25 (core)

We listened!

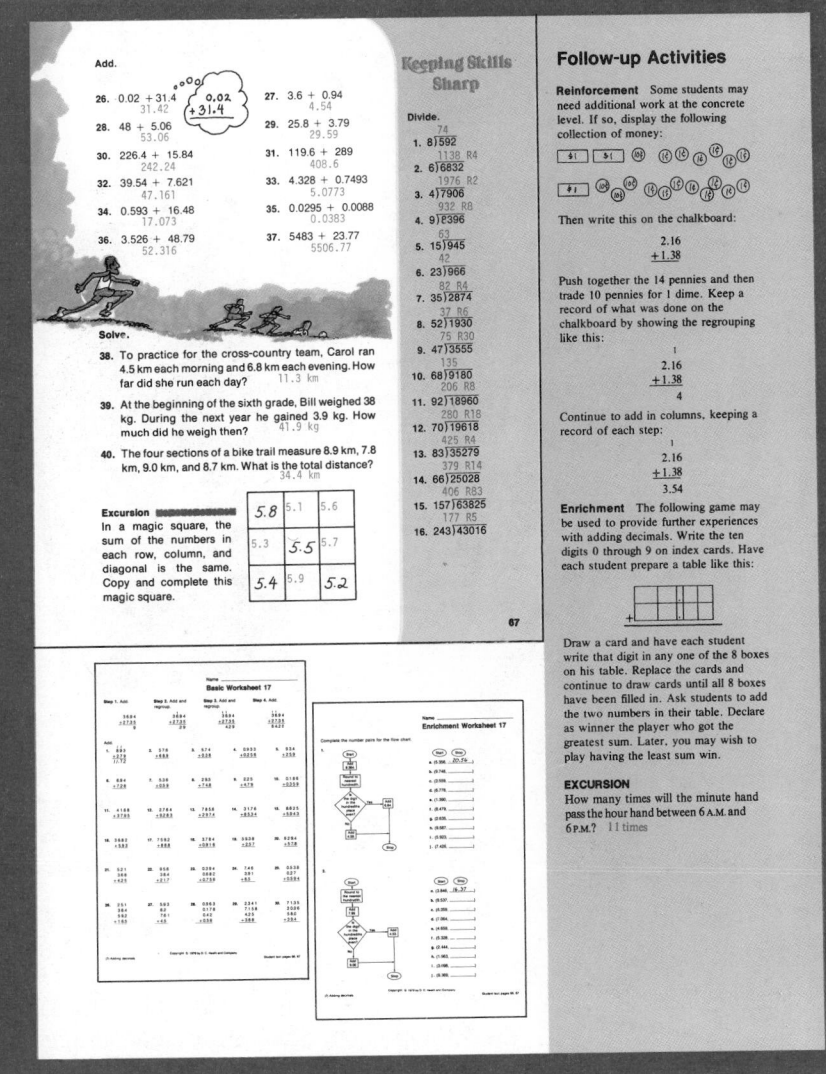

★ *Lesson Follow-Up*

Reinforcement and enrichment for every lesson.

★ *Excursions*

Provide change of pace.

★ *Core lessons* are identified.

BASIC and ENRICHMENT WORKSHEETS

Provided for every teaching lesson—extra practice for all students.

"*Teachers talked...*"

Many of my students master the computational skills but just can't seem to develop any competence in using those skills to solve problems...

Extra Problem Solving

Set 1

1. Jean had 277 coins in her collection. Her grandfather gave her 58 coins from his large collection. How many coins did Jean have then?

2. Jean went to a coin show where she sold 26 of her coins and bought 34. How many coins did she have then? (See exercise 1.)

3. At one time Jean had 172 United States coins and 86 foreign coins. How many more U.S. coins did she have?

At another time Jean had 329 coins. At a coin show she traded a 1973 Eisenhower silver dollar and a 1939 Jefferson nickel for 13 other coins that she needed. How many coins did she have then?

years ago an 1884 Liberty Head dollar was bought for $2975. ly it sold for $7000. How rofit was made?

years ago a coin dealer roll (20 coins) of 1976 Ei- silver dollars for $95. Re- d the coins individually ow much profit did he

Mathematics in careers

Oceanographers are scientists who study the ocean. They study the physical and chemical properties of the ocean, as well as all forms of life in the ocean.

1. a. Which ocean is the largest?
   b. Which ocean is the smallest?
   c. How much larger is the Pacific Ocean than the Atlantic Ocean?
   d. What is the total area of the oceans?
   e. The total area of the earth's surface is 509,917,870 square kilometers. How much of the earth's surface area is not ocean?

2. The deepest known spot in the Pacific Ocean is Challenger Deep. It is 11,033 meters below the surface. The deepest known spot in the Atlantic Ocean is in the Puerto Rico Trench, 8648 meters below the surface. How much deeper is Challenger Deep?

3. The highest mountain in the world is Mount Everest, which is 8848 meters high. If Mount Everest were put into Challenger Deep, how far below the surface of the water would the top of Mount Everest be?

Areas of Oceans	
Ocean	Area (in square kilometers)
Pacific	165,200,000
Atlantic	81,662,000
Indian	73,441,700
Antarctic	13,000,000
Arctic	14,090,000

47

We listened!

HEATH MATHEMATICS stresses problem-solving skills with a common-sense approach. Students are encouraged to think the problem through, to visualize it in their minds, and to make a *real* problem out of it. *Then* they select the appropriate tools and work out the solution. Well-chosen themes make the problems real.

Other problem-solving tools include:

● *Extra Problem Solving—*
Sets of additional problem solving exercises correlated to appropriate lessons. In the back of the pupil's book.

● *Creative Problem Solving*
Fourteen problems that require careful thought and analysis. Detailed suggestions for using these problems and several methods for solving the problems are introduced. In the teacher's edition.

Additional teaching support in the teacher's editions:

★ Record and Assignment Charts—If you wish to individualize instruction with each student progressing at his own rate, these charts provide a complete and simple management system. Also available on duplicating masters in the PERSONALIZED LEARNING PACKET.

★ Simple, five-step approach to individualizing classroom instruction:
1. Administer chapter pretest.
2. Record test results here.
3. Make appropriate assignments here.
4. Administer chapter posttest.
5. Make reteaching assignments here.

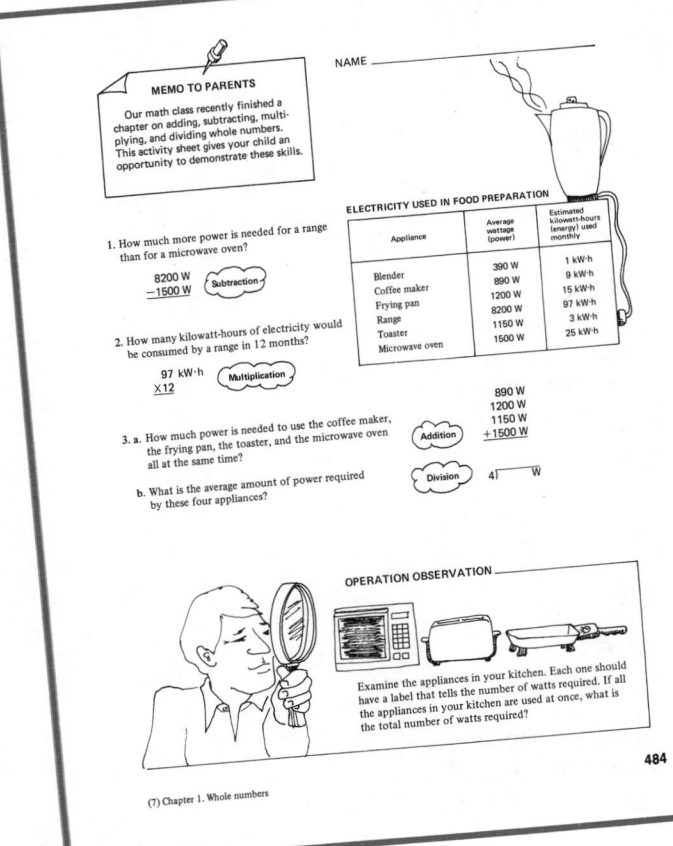

★ *Parent Involvement Worksheets*—
Activity sheets for students to do with parents and family. There is also a Parent Report of Student Progress.
Available on duplicating masters, Levels K–8.

Contents

Introduction

The development team for the HEATH MATHEMATICS PROGRAM was carefully selected to provide balance in all aspects of curriculum development. It includes authors, classroom teachers, professors of mathematics education, curriculum specialists, and consultants in specialized areas. Their collective classroom experience totals more than 135 years. Additionally, six members have been active participants in curriculum projects and teacher training. The team established five major premises that guided the development of the program. These premises incorporate recent insights into the nature of mathematics instruction as well as understandings based on experience.

PREMISE 1 A mathematics program should provide a balanced approach in developing proficiency in basic mathematical skills.

HEATH MATHEMATICS recognizes the importance of building a solid foundation in basic facts and skills. The vast majority of the lessons at every level concentrate on computational skills. Each lesson and subsequent review and maintenance exercises provide sufficient practice to assure an appropriate level of mastery for each student. A careful sequencing of the skills allows each student to achieve a sense of accomplishment and success.

However, *basic skills must include more than computational skills*. A recent position paper from the National Council of Supervisors of Mathematics states:

"Any list of basic skills must include computation. However, the role of computational skills in mathematics must be seen in the light of the contribution they make to one's ability to use mathematics in everyday living. In isolation, computational skills contribute little to one's ability to participate in mainstream society. Combined effectively with the other skill areas, they provide the learner with the basic mathematical ability needed by adults."

HEATH MATHEMATICS recognizes this need for balance and provides an appropriate number of lessons dealing with problem solving, estimating, geometry, interpreting and organizing data, measuring, predicting, and applying mathematics to everyday situations. Levels 7 and 8 include all the topics and skills considered prerequisite for high school mathematics.

PREMISE 2 Understanding can best be achieved by teaching mathematics concepts and skills in a way that is reasonable to students.

Mathematics is the most sophisticated invention of man and has been a highly refined science for hundreds of years. "Modern math" yielded to the temptation of developing mathematics in terms of its abstract structure. This confused and distorted its basic simplicity for many students.

A new wave of instructional materials is also causing confusion, but for entirely different reasons. These materials depend on rote learning. Rote learning is not reasonable to students, and merely showing the steps for a computation process and providing an abundance of practice does not achieve or promote understanding.

HEATH MATHEMATICS presents each new topic by drawing on the student's past experience and understanding to make it reasonable. When appropriate, an instructional model involves the student in the lesson pages. A carefully structured, step-by-step development leads the student through the exposition, provides examples of the final form of the process, and is followed by ample lesson practice. The end result is proficiency with understanding—achieved in a setting both motivational and reasonable.

PREMISE 3 Students should be made aware of the usefulness of mathematics and how it relates to their daily lives.

Although students see and use numbers every day, they often do not make the connection between their daily lives and what goes on in their mathematics classroom. The concerned teacher uses many techniques to make students aware of the application of mathematics to life skills. Consumer mathematics, for instance, is emphasized throughout each level of HEATH MATHEMATICS and Levels 5 through 8 have an entire chapter devoted to this important topic. There are also many pages entitled Mathematics and Science and Mathematics in Careers.

PREMISE 4 The textbook presentation of a mathematical process should be compatible with and reinforce the classroom teacher's style of presentation.

A major shortcoming of many textbooks is that their development of key processes, such as the steps involved in long division, bear little resemblance to the final form the classroom teacher is working towards. HEATH MATHEMATICS utilizes a direct approach that provides students with examples that are just like their teacher's. There are no confusing intermediate steps. Notations that aid teaching are shown in the same way that the teacher does them.

PREMISE 5 Teaching support for each lesson should be complete and easily accessible.

The teacher's edition provides comprehensive lesson plans for every teaching lesson. It provides step-by-step suggestions for initiating the lesson, for using the lesson pages, and for reinforcing the lesson. An easy-to-use assignment guide coordinates every component designed for use with the lesson. The Basic and Enrichment Worksheets that support the lesson are reduced in size and shown on the teacher's page for easy reference.

The HEATH MATHEMATICS teacher's edition has the same basic format and teaching support at every level. This is especially helpful for teachers who teach more than one grade level.

Notes on Planning

The preceding pages point out the major features of the program and the basic premises on which it was developed. Here are some suggestions for putting the program to work in *your* classroom.

Planning the Year

The learning objectives for Level 7 are listed on page T3. This manageable list gives you a quick overview of the content of each chapter. The objectives for Levels 7 and 8 focus on the minimal skill competencies and concepts considered prerequisite for high school mathematics.

You can easily correlate HEATH MATHEMATICS to your own school's course of study. The amount of time you spend on each two-page lesson should be based on the needs of your class. You may omit noncore lessons without interrupting the flow of the program. Chapters 11 and 12 may be considered noncore for Level 7; the content of these chapters will be covered thoroughly in Level 8.

Getting Started

You can use the test on page 2 to diagnose each student's readiness to begin Level 7. The Review Chapter (pages 2–16) provides review and practice of these critical entry skills. Once you've completed your overview of the year's work and decided whether or not to use the Review chapter, you'll be ready to plan Chapter 1.

Planning the Chapters

Each chapter introduction provides you with useful background information and teaching suggestions. This information is organized in the same way for each chapter and includes: (1) chapter learning objectives, (2) mathematics background, (3) teaching the chapter, (4) vocabulary, and (5) materials list.

You will find the chapters easy to use because each chapter is organized in the same way and provides you with all the teaching support you need, regardless of the ability range of your students and whether you are teaching one section of mathematics or five sections. The teaching/learning features that are a part of each chapter are listed below. The page references locate the items in Chapter 1 and the teacher commentary about them.

Chapter Introduction, pages 17a and 17b
Pretest, pages 17c and 17d
Record and Assignment Chart, pages 17e and 17f
Chapter Lessons, pages 17 to 54
Chapter Checkup, page 50
Project, page 51
Chapter Review, page 52
Chapter Challenge, page 53
Major Checkup, page 54
Posttest, page 54a
Parent Involvement, pages 478 to 491

Planning the Daily Lesson

The discussion so far has focused on long-range planning. However, the primary purpose of any teacher's edition is to provide practical suggestions that will help you on a day-to-day basis. Each two-page lesson provides you with in-depth teaching support. The daily suggested lesson plans (in the yellow areas) include: (1) learning objectives, (2) a list of materials needed, (3) a mathematics vocabulary list of new words, (4) suggestions for introducing the lesson, (5) suggestions to guide the presentation of the lesson, and (6) an assignment guide for three ability levels that coordinates all the worksheets and extra practice for use with the lesson.

After your students have finished the lesson pages, you have several options to choose from in the Follow-up section (blue area). There are suggestions for both reinforcement and enrichment. *Excursions* and *Calculator Activities* provide a change of pace. BASIC WORKSHEETS and ENRICHMENT WORKSHEETS are reproduced in reduced size for every teaching lesson to show the available lesson support.

Planning for Individual Differences

Most teachers have all students study the same topic at one time and accommodate differences in ability by providing activities at various levels of difficulty. HEATH MATHEMATICS has many features and components that help make this task manageable. For slower students: easy practice exercises with each lesson, extra practice exercises (pages 374–397), suggestions for reteaching and reinforcement with each lesson, Basic Worksheets, Keeping Skills Sharp, and Chapter Reviews. For better students: enrichment activities with each lesson, Excursions, Enrichment Worksheets, Projects, and Chapter Challenges.

Teachers who wish to have each student progress at an individual rate will find that the Record and Assignment Charts (see page 17f), tests, and other components of the PERSONALIZED LEARNING PACKET greatly simplify the management and record keeping for this type of instruction.

Planning for Testing

Readiness Test	In the student's book on page 2. Determines readiness to begin Level 7. A parallel test on page 16.
Chapter Checkups	In student's text. Correlated to objectives and text pages.
Chapter Tests	In teacher's edition (see page 17d) and as duplicating masters in both TESTS and PERSONALIZED LEARNING PACKET. Two parallel forms for each chapter. Correlated to objectives and text pages.
Midyear Test **Final Test**	In the student's book, pages 201–202 and pages 367–368. Test the major objectives by chapter.
Skill Test	In student's text (see pages 369–373). A criterion-referenced test for all basic computational skills taught in Level 7.
Final Checkup	In teacher's edition (see pages 439–445). A final test in standardized format covering the year's work.

Learning Objectives

The following is a list of learning objectives for Level 7 of the **Heath Mathematics Program.** It is important to note, however, that these objectives refer only to those things that are relatively easy to test. There are other important objectives that are not readily stated in behavioral terms. Some of these deal with attitude, appreciation, self-reliance, and initiative. These are long-range objectives of the whole program and are not measured by paper and pencil tests. You can chart progress in reaching these objectives in anecdotal records.

Chapter 1

1-1   Read and write numerals for large numbers. [pages 18–19]

1-2   Round whole numbers. [pages 20–23]

1-3   Add any two or more whole numbers. [pages 26–27, 30]

1-4   Subtract any two whole numbers. [pages 28–30]

1-5   Multiply any two whole numbers. [pages 32–39, 46]

1-6   Divide any two whole numbers. [pages 40–46]

1-7   Solve word problems that involve whole numbers. [pages 31, 47–49]

Chapter 2

2-1   Write decimals in word and standard form. [pages 56–61]

2-2   Determine which of two decimals is greater. [pages 62–63]

2-3   Round decimals. [pages 64–65]

2-4   Add and subtract decimals. [pages 66–69]

2-5   Show how to estimate sums and differences of decimals. [pages 70–71]

2-6   Solve word problems that involve addition and subtraction of decimals. [pages 72–75]

Chapter 3

3-1   Multiply any two decimals. [pages 82–84, 86–87, 98–99]

3-2   Divide any two decimals. [pages 90–93, 96–99]

3-3   Solve word problems that involve multiplication or division of decimals. [pages 88–89, 94–95]

Chapter 4

4-1   Tell whether one set is a subset of another set. [pages 106–107]

4-2   Give the intersection and the union of two sets. [pages 108–109]

4-3   Give the greatest common factor of two numbers. [pages 110–111]

4-4   Give the least common multiple of two numbers. [pages 114–115]

4-5   Substitute numbers into variable expressions and simplify. [pages 118–119, 126–127]

4-6   Solve simple equations. [pages 120–121, 124–125]

Chapter 5

5-1   Measure lengths to the nearest millimeter. [pages 134–135]

5-2   Make conversions among metric units. [pages 134–137, 154–155]

5-3   Compute perimeters and circumferences. [pages 138–139, 157]

5-4   Compute areas. [pages 140–144, 158–159]

5-5   Compute surface areas of prisms and cylinders. [pages 146–149, 159]

5-6   Compute volumes of prisms and cylinders. [pages 150–153, 162–163]

5-7   Make conversions among customary units. [pages 156–157, 164–165]

Chapter 6

6-1   Reduce fractions to lowest terms. [pages 172–177]

6-2   Determine which of two fractions is greater. [pages 178–179]

6-3   Add and subtract fractions. [pages 180–184]

6-4   Change fractions to mixed numbers and vice versa. [pages 186–187]

6-5   Add mixed numbers. [pages 188–189, 192]

6-6   Subtract mixed numbers. [pages 190–192]

6-7   Solve word problems that involve fractions. [pages 194–195]

Chapter 7

7-1 Multiply any two fractions. [pages 204–209, 214, 216]

7-2 Divide any two fractions. [pages 210–214, 217, 220–221]

7-3 Change fractions to terminating decimals and vice versa. [pages 222–223]

7-4 Change fractions to repeating decimals and vice versa. [pages 224–225]

7-5 Multiply mixed numbers. [pages 226–227]

7-6 Divide mixed numbers. [pages 228–229]

7-7 Solve word problems that involve multiplication and division of mixed numbers. [pages 218–219, 231–233]

Chapter 8

8-1 Write the ratio of two quantities. [pages 240–241]

8-2 Solve proportions. [pages 242–243, 250]

8-3 Make conversions among fractions, decimals, and percents. [pages 252–257]

8-4 Find what percent one number is of another. [pages 256–257]

8-5 Find a given percent of a number. [pages 258–261, 264]

8-6 Find a number when a given percent of it is known. [pages 262–264]

8-7 Solve word problems that involve percents. [pages 257, 259, 263, 265–267]

Chapter 9

9-1 Compute total earnings for various ways of being paid. [pages 274–275]

9-2 Solve problems involving budgets, discounts, and unit prices. [pages 276–283]

9-3 Write checks and balance checking accounts. [pages 284–285]

9-4 Compute simple interest. [pages 286–287]

9-5 Compute installment prices. [pages 288–289]

Chapter 10

10-1 Measure angles to the nearest degree. [pages 298–303]

10-2 Determine whether two lines are parallel or perpendicular. [pages 304–305]

10-3 List corresponding parts of congruent figures. [pages 306–307]

10-4 State important properties of common figures. [pages 308–316]

Chapter 11

11-1 Count outcomes of simple and compound events. [pages 324–327]

11-2 Compute probabilities for outcomes. [pages 328–329]

11-3 Read graphs. [pages 334–335]

11-4 Compute means, medians, and ranges. [pages 336–337]

Chapter 12

12-1 Add integers. [pages 346–348, 352]

12-2 Subtract integers. [pages 350–352]

12-3 Multiply integers. [pages 354–355, 358]

12-4 Divide integers. [pages 356–358]

12-5 Graph ordered pairs of integers in the coordinate plane. [pages 360–361]

Scope and Sequence

The following charts indicate the scope and sequence of topics for Levels 6, 7, and 8 of the **Heath Mathematics Program**. This scope and sequence will help you understand how the preceding text leads into this one and how this text leads into the following one. **Bold** type indicates that a topic is being introduced for the first time. You can easily determine which topics should be familiar to students who have previously used Level 6, which topics are new in this level, and which topics will be reviewed in Level 8. The selected student page references for each topic make it convenient for you to find examples of how the various concepts and skills are taught.

6

Place value and counting

Thousands, 2, 3
Millions, billions, 8, 9
Rounding to the nearest ten,
   hundred, thousand, 6, 7, 9, 23
Comparing numbers, 4, 19
Roman numerals, 10, 11
Place value of decimals, 176−180
Base two numerals, 31
Place value in the metric system,
   234, 235
Practice, 30

Addition of whole numbers

Basic facts, 13
Properties of addition, 12
Addends with two to six digits,
   16−19
Adding three or more addends, 18,
   19
Checking by estimation, 24, 25
Practice, 30, 45, 54, 83, 155

Subtraction of whole numbers

Basic facts, 14
Find the missing addends, 15
Subtracting numbers with two to
   five digits, 20−23
Checking by estimation, 24, 25
Practice, 30, 51, 54, 155

7

Place value to trillions, 18, 19
Expanded numerals, 21
Counting by multiples of 10, 100, and
   1000, 20, 21
Rounding numbers, 22, 23, 27
Comparing numbers through hundred
   thousands, 24, 25
Reading numbers in text, 61
Place value of decimals, 56−58
Base five, 53
Practice, 52

Pretest for basic skills, 2
Properties of addition, 3
Posttest (after review and practice),
   16
Addends with two to six digits, 26, 27
Adding three and four addends, 27
Finding missing digits, 27
Estimating sums, 26, 27
Grouping symbols, 30
Practice, 3−5, 30, 35, 52

Pretest for basic skills, 2
Posttest (after review and practice),
   16
Subtraction with numbers to five
   digits, 28, 29
Shortcut for subtracting from
   hundreds, thousands, and ten
   thousands, 29
Estimating differences, 28
Grouping symbols, 30
Practice, 6−8, 30, 43, 52

8

Place value to trillions, 3
Place value of decimals, 20, 21
Rounding decimals, 22, 23
Comparing decimals, 24, 25
Place value in the metric system, 118,
   120

Pretest for basic skills, 2
Adding two whole numbers, 5
Adding three or more addends, 6
Posttest for basic skills, 18
Properties of addition, 60
Grouping symbols, 60
Using addition to solve subtraction
   equations, 68, 69, 72, 73
Practice, 5, 6, 9

Pretest for basic skills, 2
Subtraction with numbers to five
   digits, 7, 8
Posttest for basic skills, 18
Using subtraction to solve addition
   equations, 68, 69, 72, 73
Practice, 7, 8, 9

Problem solving and applications

REVIEW CHAPTER
Basic Skills

Pages 1–16

Learning Objectives

After completing this chapter, all students should be able to do the following:

- Recall from memory the basic addition facts.
- Add 2-digit numbers.
- Recall from memory the basic subtraction facts.
- Subtract 3-digit numbers with one regrouping.
- Recall from memory the basic multiplication facts.
- Multiply a 2-digit number by a 1-digit number.
- Recall from memory the basic division facts.
- Divide a 2-digit number by a 1-digit number.

This chapter provides a brief review of whole-number operations for students who need it. The Pretest pinpoints the areas where help is needed, and the Review Lessons focus on those skills. Most students will not require extensive reteaching of these skills, but many may benefit from reviewing them.

The students who require reteaching will probably be low achievers or have a low aptitude for learning mathematics. For this reason, most of the teaching suggestions in the lesson plans are intended for such students.

vi

By now you have studied a great deal of mathematics. You've learned to add, subtract, multiply, and divide whole numbers, fractions, and decimals. These skills are often called the **basic skills** because they help us learn more about other topics in mathematics.

The first part of this book helps you find out which whole number skills you might need to review and then provides practice exercises for each of them. We used our computer (we call it "Clyde" around school) to generate these review and practice lessons. We hope you enjoy working with Clyde as much as we do.

Lesson Structure

This chapter contains a Pretest, 13 Review Lessons, and a Posttest. The teaching support for each lesson is organized as follows:

1. *Student Objectives* are listed for easy reference.

2. The *Suggested Lesson Plan* has teaching strategies intended primarily for low achievers.

3. The *Lesson Exercises* are given in a computer-type format to provide an interesting theme for the review material and help emphasize the importance of basic computational skills.

4. *Reinforcement* is provided by the Extra Practice exercises in the back of the student text and additional Extra Practice exercises given in the teacher's edition for most of the lessons. Also, many Skill Games are suggested in the teacher's edition that can be used throughout the year to provide a variation from pencil-and-paper drills.

5. *Answers* are provided on the students' page for most of the lessons. You will need to familiarize the students with the technique used, since the answers are not given in order.

STUDENT OBJECTIVE
To demonstrate whole-number entry skills in addition, subtraction, multiplication, and division. (See page 1a for the list of objectives.)

Suggested Lesson Plan

- Have students do the Pretest on page 2.
- Any student who misses more than one exercise in each section will probably benefit from work on the related Review Lesson. The chart at the top of page 2 identifies the lessons that should be completed. For example, a student who misses two exercises in row C should do Review Lessons 4 and 5.
- After students have completed the test, analyze the results carefully.
- The chart at the top of the page will place students in appropriate Review Lessons.
- Any student missing two or more exercises in any one row should receive some reteaching. To make this more manageable, you may wish to group students who have the same difficulties.
- Assign selected Review Lessons for practice or as speed drills for better students.

PRETEST

Clyde was instructed to generate a pretest for some whole number skills. If you miss more than one exercise in a row you should go to the reviews for that row.

Row	A	B	C	D	E	F	G	H	I
Go to Reviews	1, 2	1, 3	4, 5	4, 6	7, 8	7, 9	10, 11	10, 12	10, 13

PRETEST

A.
1. 25 +43
2. 60 +34
3. 46 +81
4. 32 +72
5. 72 23 +43

B.
1. 27 +54
2. 48 +48
3. 76 +69
4. 58 +43
5. 17 98 +56

C.
1. 73 -28
2. 80 -17
3. 94 -36
4. 82 -58
5. 71 -37

D.
1. 609 -147
2. 928 -245
3. 736 -681
4. 750 -437
5. 851 -306

E.
1. 32 ×3
2. 14 ×2
3. 71 ×6
4. 90 ×7
5. 61 ×4

F.
1. 26 ×3
2. 18 ×4
3. 68 ×7
4. 26 ×8
5. 46 ×9

G.
1. 5)33
2. 9)29
3. 7)46
4. 8)71
5. 6)49

H.
1. 4)328
2. 3)189
3. 8)640
4. 7)217
5. 2)166

I.
1. 6)78
2. 4)96
3. 7)91
4. 3)84
5. 5)80

2

Answers for Pretest.

A. 1. 68 2. 94 3. 127 4. 104
   5. 138
B. 1. 81 2. 96 3. 145 4. 101
   5. 171
C. 1. 45 2. 63 3. 58 4. 24
   5. 34
D. 1. 462 2. 683 3. 55 4. 313
   5. 545
E. 1. 96 2. 28 3. 426 4. 630
   5. 244
F. 1. 78 2. 72 3. 476 4. 208
   5. 414
G. 1. 6 R3 2. 3 R2 3. 6 R4
   4. 8 R7 5. 8 R1
H. 1. 82 2. 63 3. 80 4. 31
   5. 83
I. 1. 13 2. 24 3. 13 4. 28
   5. 16

REVIEW 1   Addition properties and basic addition facts

Clyde was instructed to search its data bank for two properties that help us remember addition facts. Here is the printout.

ADDING ZERO PROPERTY

THE SUM OF A NUMBER AND ZERO IS THAT SAME NUMBER.

$$6 + 0 = 6 \qquad\qquad 0 + 3 = 3$$

COMMUTATIVE PROPERTY OF ADDITION

YOU CAN CHANGE THE ORDER OF TWO ADDENDS WITHOUT CHANGING THE SUM.

$$3 + 4 = 4 + 3 \qquad\qquad 7 + 2 = 2 + 7$$

THERE ARE 36 PAIRS OF BASIC ADDITION FACTS SUCH AS $\begin{array}{r}7\\+3\\\hline\end{array}$

AND $\begin{array}{r}3\\+7\\\hline\end{array}$. IF YOU KNOW ONE FACT IN A PAIR AND THE COMMUTA-

TIVE PROPERTY, THEN YOU KNOW THE OTHER FACT.

Clyde generated 30 practice exercises. Time yourself to see how quickly you can do them. Memorize the facts you missed. Repeat the exercise in a day or so to see if you have improved your speed and accuracy.

ADD.

1. $\begin{array}{r}2\\+6\\\hline\end{array}$	2. $\begin{array}{r}4\\+7\\\hline\end{array}$	3. $\begin{array}{r}5\\+8\\\hline\end{array}$	4. $\begin{array}{r}3\\+7\\\hline\end{array}$	5. $\begin{array}{r}4\\+3\\\hline\end{array}$	6. $\begin{array}{r}7\\+7\\\hline\end{array}$
7. $\begin{array}{r}1\\+8\\\hline\end{array}$	8. $\begin{array}{r}5\\+3\\\hline\end{array}$	9. $\begin{array}{r}8\\+6\\\hline\end{array}$	10. $\begin{array}{r}2\\+7\\\hline\end{array}$	11. $\begin{array}{r}5\\+5\\\hline\end{array}$	12. $\begin{array}{r}8\\+4\\\hline\end{array}$
13. $\begin{array}{r}9\\+9\\\hline\end{array}$	14. $\begin{array}{r}7\\+5\\\hline\end{array}$	15. $\begin{array}{r}0\\+7\\\hline\end{array}$	16. $\begin{array}{r}8\\+8\\\hline\end{array}$	17. $\begin{array}{r}6\\+3\\\hline\end{array}$	18. $\begin{array}{r}9\\+1\\\hline\end{array}$
19. $\begin{array}{r}3\\+8\\\hline\end{array}$	20. $\begin{array}{r}6\\+6\\\hline\end{array}$	21. $\begin{array}{r}8\\+9\\\hline\end{array}$	22. $\begin{array}{r}5\\+4\\\hline\end{array}$	23. $\begin{array}{r}7\\+8\\\hline\end{array}$	24. $\begin{array}{r}4\\+4\\\hline\end{array}$
25. $\begin{array}{r}5\\+6\\\hline\end{array}$	26. $\begin{array}{r}8\\+2\\\hline\end{array}$	27. $\begin{array}{r}6\\+7\\\hline\end{array}$	28. $\begin{array}{r}4\\+6\\\hline\end{array}$	29. $\begin{array}{r}1\\+7\\\hline\end{array}$	30. $\begin{array}{r}6\\+0\\\hline\end{array}$

COMPUTER CHECK

26.10 27.13 28.10 29.8 30.6
14.12 15.7 16.16 17.9 18.10 19.11 20.12 21.17 22.9 23.15 24.8 25.11
1.8 2.11 3.13 4.10 5.7 6.14 7.9 8.8 9.14 10.9 11.10 12.12 13.18

3

Answers for Review 1.

1. 8   2. 11   3. 13   4. 10   5. 7
6. 14   7. 9   8. 8   9. 14   10. 9
11. 10   12. 12   13. 18   14. 12
15. 7   16. 16   17. 9   18. 10
19. 11   20. 12   21. 17   22. 9
23. 15   24. 8   25. 11   26. 10
27. 13   28. 10   29. 8   30. 6

STUDENT OBJECTIVE
To recall from memory the basic addition facts.

Suggested Lesson Plan

- Review the addition properties in the printout.

- Assign the exercises. Timing the student is a good way to encourage self-improvement.

- Identify students who need additional work on the basic facts. Assign Set 1 on page 374 and one or more of the following activities.

  1. Make an addition-facts table like this:

+	0	1	2	3	4	5	6	7	8	9
0										
1										
2										
3										
4										
5										
6										
7										
8										
9										

     The facts in the blue area are the ones that frequently cause difficulty. Have students list their own "demons" and work on mastery independently.

  2. Make a table similar to this one:

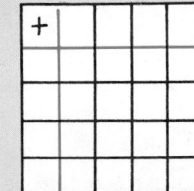

     For individual practice, fill in the first row and first column with the numbers that the student needs work on. For example, this table focuses on the facts for 6, 7, 8, and 9:

+	9	7	6	8
8				
6				
9				
7				

  3. Repeat the addition-table activity frequently for students who need the practice.

Suggested Lesson Plan

- Review the process of regrouping.

- You may find this demonstration of regrouping useful with some of your students.

  1. Write this exercise on the chalkboard:

     85
     +42

  2. Use place-value materials such as bundles of sticks to represent the numbers:

     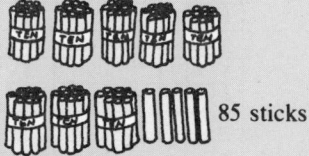 85 sticks

      42 sticks

  3. Ask, "How many single sticks are there?"

  4. Ask, "How many bundles of ten are there?" Since there are more than 9 of them, we group 10 of them together to make a bundle of 100.

  5. Make a record of what happened in a place-value chart.

Hundreds	Tens	Ones
	8	5
	4	2
1	2	7

- Demonstrate other combinations (e.g., 64 + 73, 52 + 91).

- Assign the exercises. Point out that the answers at the bottom of the page are listed in numerical order.

Reinforcement
Students who need additional practice should do Set 2 on page 374 and the Extra Practice on this page.

4 Review Lesson 2

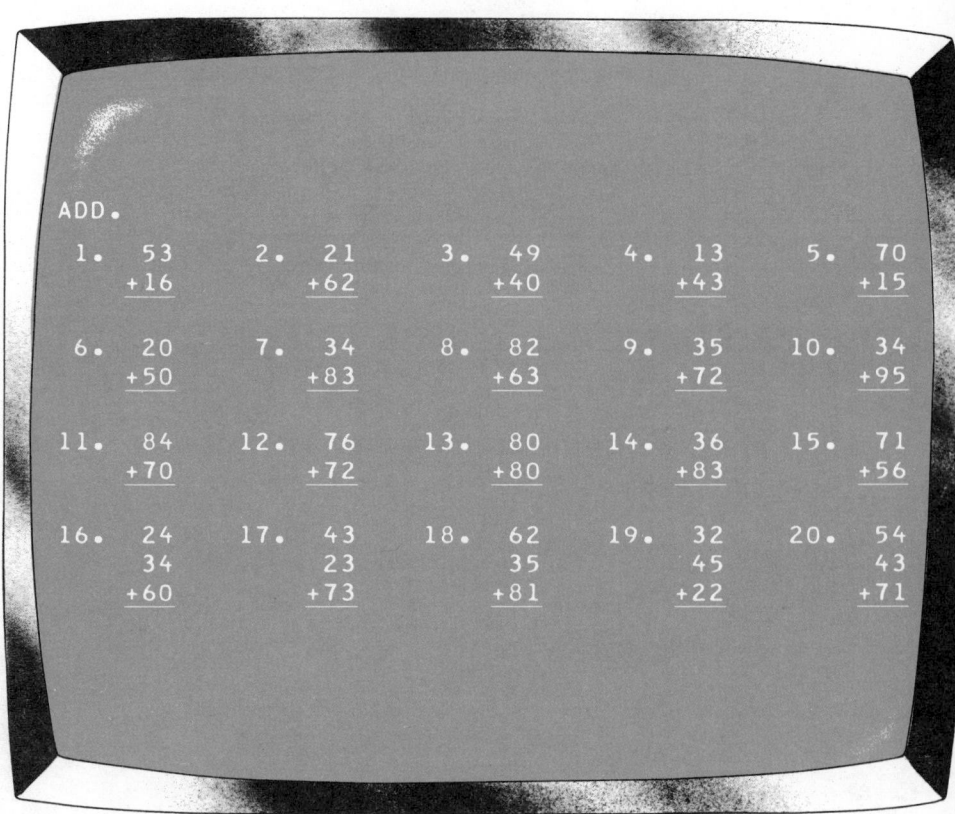

REVIEW 2 Adding 2–digit numbers

MEMORY RETRIEVAL—ADDING IN COLUMNS

	ADD ONES.	ADD TENS.
72	72	72
+51	+51	+51
	3	123

ADD.

1. 53 +16	2. 21 +62	3. 49 +40	4. 13 +43	5. 70 +15
6. 20 +50	7. 34 +83	8. 82 +63	9. 35 +72	10. 34 +95
11. 84 +70	12. 76 +72	13. 80 +80	14. 36 +83	15. 71 +56
16. 24 34 +60	17. 43 23 +73	18. 62 35 +81	19. 32 45 +22	20. 54 43 +71

COMPUTER CHECK
YOU SHOULD BE ABLE TO FIND EACH ANSWER IN THIS LIST:
4   56 69 70 83 85 89 99 107 117 118 119 127 129 139 145 148 154 160 168 178

Answers for Review 2.

1. 69   2. 83   3. 89   4. 56   5. 85
6. 70   7. 117   8. 145   9. 107
10. 129   11. 154   12. 148   13. 160
14. 119   15. 127   16. 118   17. 139
18. 178   19. 99   20. 168

Extra Practice

53 +54	65 +72	81 +77
93 +35	97 +52	36 +82
83 +56	23 +92	74 +45
64 +84	91 +65	68 +61
52 31 +64	40 53 +41	72 22 +42

Answers for Extra Practice.

107	137	158
128	149	118
139	115	119
148	156	129
147	134	136

REVIEW 3 Adding 2–digit numbers

MEMORY RETRIEVAL—ADDING WITH REGROUPING

ADD ONES, THEN REGROUP.		ADD TENS.
27 +88	$\overset{1}{27}$ +88 ——— 5	$\overset{1}{27}$ +88 ——— 115

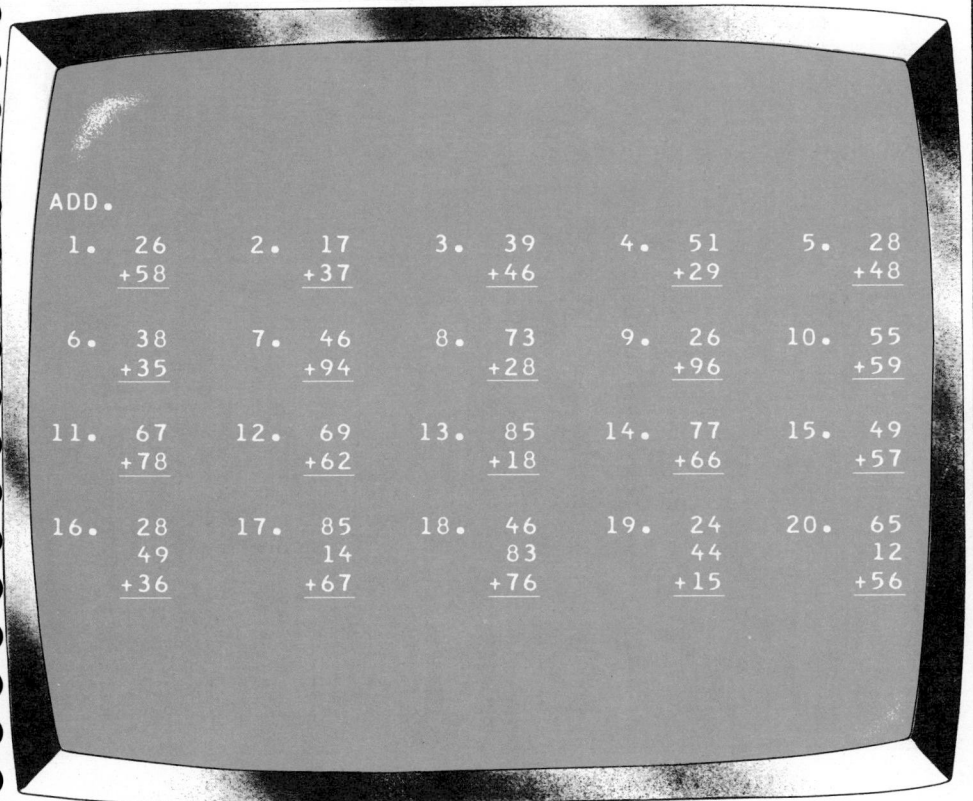

ADD.

1. 26 +58	2. 17 +37	3. 39 +46	4. 51 +29	5. 28 +48
6. 38 +35	7. 46 +94	8. 73 +28	9. 26 +96	10. 55 +59
11. 67 +78	12. 69 +62	13. 85 +18	14. 77 +66	15. 49 +57
16. 28 49 +36	17. 85 14 +67	18. 46 83 +76	19. 24 44 +15	20. 65 12 +56

COMPUTER CHECK
YOU SHOULD BE ABLE TO FIND EACH ANSWER IN THIS LIST:
54 73 76 80 83 84 85 101 103 106 113 114 122 131 133 140 143 145 166 205

5

Extra Practice

62 +71	85 +73	15 +98
82 +48	96 +26	49 +75
58 +81	75 +39	47 +96
68 +53	58 +39	77 +54
75 +27	41 +76	38 +67

Answers for Review 3.

1. 84 2. 54 3. 85 4. 80 5. 76
6. 73 7. 140 8. 101 9. 122
10. 114 11. 145 12. 131 13. 103
14. 143 15. 106 16. 113 17. 166
18. 205 19. 83 20. 133

Answers for Extra Practice.

133	158	113
130	122	124
139	114	143
111	97	131
102	117	105

STUDENT OBJECTIVE
To add any 2-digit numbers.

Suggested Lesson Plan

- Review the regrouping from ones to tens using the strategy from Review Lesson 2.

- Assign the exercises. Remind students that the answers are at the bottom of the page.

Reinforcement

- Assign Set 3 on page 374 and the Extra Practice on this page to students who miss more than four exercises.

- The following Skill Game may be used frequently with students who are still having trouble with addition.

  1. Make ten digit-cards:

     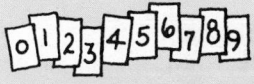

  2. Have students make a form like this:

     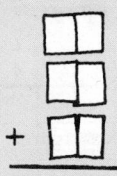

  3. Mix the cards thoroughly and select one at random; then write the digit in any one of the boxes:

     first card drawn ⬚6

     entered in the
     form here

  4. Repeat until all six boxes are filled.

  5. Have the students find the sum of their three 2-digit numbers. The student with the greatest sum wins.

Suggested Lesson Plan

- Remind students of the relationship between addition and subtraction: Every addition fact has two related subtraction facts. Discuss the example in the Data Bank, then repeat with several other facts, such as these:

$$
\begin{array}{r} 7 \\ +6 \\ \hline 13 \end{array}
\qquad
\begin{array}{r} 13 \\ -6 \\ \hline 7 \end{array}
\text{ and }
\begin{array}{r} 13 \\ -7 \\ \hline 6 \end{array}
$$

- Assign the exercises. Timing the students is a good way to encourage self-improvement.

- You may want to have the students repeat Review 1 as a timed test at this time.

Reinforcement

- Students who are having difficulty memorizing the basic facts will benefit from completing the following addition table.

+	0	1	2	3	4	5	6	7	8	9
0										
1										
2										
3										
4										
5										
6										
7										
8										
9										

- You can provide addition and subtraction drill quickly and efficiently with smaller addition tables that have missing entries:

+	8	5	9
7	15	12	16
6	14	11	15
9	17	14	18

+	6	4	9
9	15	13	18
4	10	8	13
7	13	11	16

This allows you to focus on the facts that are causing difficulty.

- For remedial practice, you may want to use this Skill Game:

  1. Make up a set of subtraction flashcards. Index cards are especially good for this. One of your students who can print neatly can make the cards—you should have at least 40. Be sure all ten digits are represented as answers.

  2. Have students draw this form and fill in the boxes using any of the digits 0–9. They may repeat any digit as many times as they wish.

  3. Mix the cards and draw them one at a time. If the players have the answer in their table, they cross it out. If it appears more than once, they may cross off only one square.

  4. The winner is the first player to cross off four boxes in a row, column, or diagonal.

- Assign Set 4 on page 374.

REVIEW 4   Basic subtraction facts

SUBTRACTION   DATA BANK

IF YOU KNOW THE ADDITION FACTS AND REMEMBER THAT ADDITION AND SUBTRACTION ARE RELATED, YOU SHOULD HAVE LITTLE TROUBLE RECALLING THE SUBTRACTION FACTS.

EXAMPLE:
$$\begin{array}{r} 5 \\ +9 \\ \hline 14 \end{array}$$
THIS ADDITION FACT HAS TWO RELATED SUBTRACTION FACTS,

$$14 - 9 = 5 \quad \text{AND} \quad 14 - 5 = 9$$

Time yourself to see how quickly you can do the 35 exercises below. Memorize the facts you missed. Repeat the exercises in a day or so to see if you have improved your speed and accuracy.

SUBTRACT.

1. $\begin{array}{r}12\\-4\\\hline\end{array}$	2. $\begin{array}{r}15\\-7\\\hline\end{array}$	3. $\begin{array}{r}13\\-8\\\hline\end{array}$	4. $\begin{array}{r}12\\-9\\\hline\end{array}$	5. $\begin{array}{r}14\\-8\\\hline\end{array}$
6. $\begin{array}{r}11\\-7\\\hline\end{array}$	7. $\begin{array}{r}16\\-9\\\hline\end{array}$	8. $\begin{array}{r}11\\-2\\\hline\end{array}$	9. $\begin{array}{r}17\\-8\\\hline\end{array}$	10. $\begin{array}{r}13\\-4\\\hline\end{array}$
11. $\begin{array}{r}11\\-6\\\hline\end{array}$	12. $\begin{array}{r}15\\-8\\\hline\end{array}$	13. $\begin{array}{r}12\\-7\\\hline\end{array}$	14. $\begin{array}{r}16\\-8\\\hline\end{array}$	15. $\begin{array}{r}13\\-9\\\hline\end{array}$
16. $\begin{array}{r}15\\-6\\\hline\end{array}$	17. $\begin{array}{r}12\\-3\\\hline\end{array}$	18. $\begin{array}{r}18\\-9\\\hline\end{array}$	19. $\begin{array}{r}14\\-6\\\hline\end{array}$	20. $\begin{array}{r}13\\-7\\\hline\end{array}$
21. $\begin{array}{r}11\\-8\\\hline\end{array}$	22. $\begin{array}{r}14\\-9\\\hline\end{array}$	23. $\begin{array}{r}12\\-5\\\hline\end{array}$	24. $\begin{array}{r}11\\-9\\\hline\end{array}$	25. $\begin{array}{r}11\\-3\\\hline\end{array}$
26. $\begin{array}{r}16\\-7\\\hline\end{array}$	27. $\begin{array}{r}13\\-5\\\hline\end{array}$	28. $\begin{array}{r}14\\-7\\\hline\end{array}$	29. $\begin{array}{r}17\\-9\\\hline\end{array}$	30. $\begin{array}{r}12\\-8\\\hline\end{array}$
31. $\begin{array}{r}11\\-5\\\hline\end{array}$	32. $\begin{array}{r}13\\-6\\\hline\end{array}$	33. $\begin{array}{r}14\\-5\\\hline\end{array}$	34. $\begin{array}{r}15\\-9\\\hline\end{array}$	35. $\begin{array}{r}11\\-4\\\hline\end{array}$

COMPUTER CHECK

9

1. 8 2. 8 3. 5 4. 3 5. 6 6. 4 7. 7 8. 9 9. 9 10. 9 11. 5 12. 7 13. 5 14. 8
15. 4 16. 9 17. 9 18. 9 19. 8 20. 6 21. 3 22. 5 23. 7 24. 2 25. 8 26. 9
27. 8 28. 7 29. 8 30. 4 31. 6 32. 7 33. 9 34. 6 35. 7

Answers for Review 4.

1. 8	2. 8	3. 5
4. 3	5. 6	6. 4
7. 7	8. 9	9. 9
10. 9	11. 5	12. 7
13. 5	14. 8	15. 4
16. 9	17. 9	18. 9
19. 8	20. 6	21. 3
22. 5	23. 7	24. 2
25. 8	26. 9	27. 8
28. 7	29. 8	30. 4
31. 6	32. 7	33. 9
34. 6	35. 7	

REVIEW 5 Subtracting 2–digit numbers, one regrouping

MEMORY RETRIEVAL— 2–DIGIT SUBTRACTION

	NOT ENOUGH ONES, SO REGROUP A TEN.	SUBTRACT ONES, SUBTRACT TENS.
82 −53	7 8̸2 −53	7 8̸2 −53 29

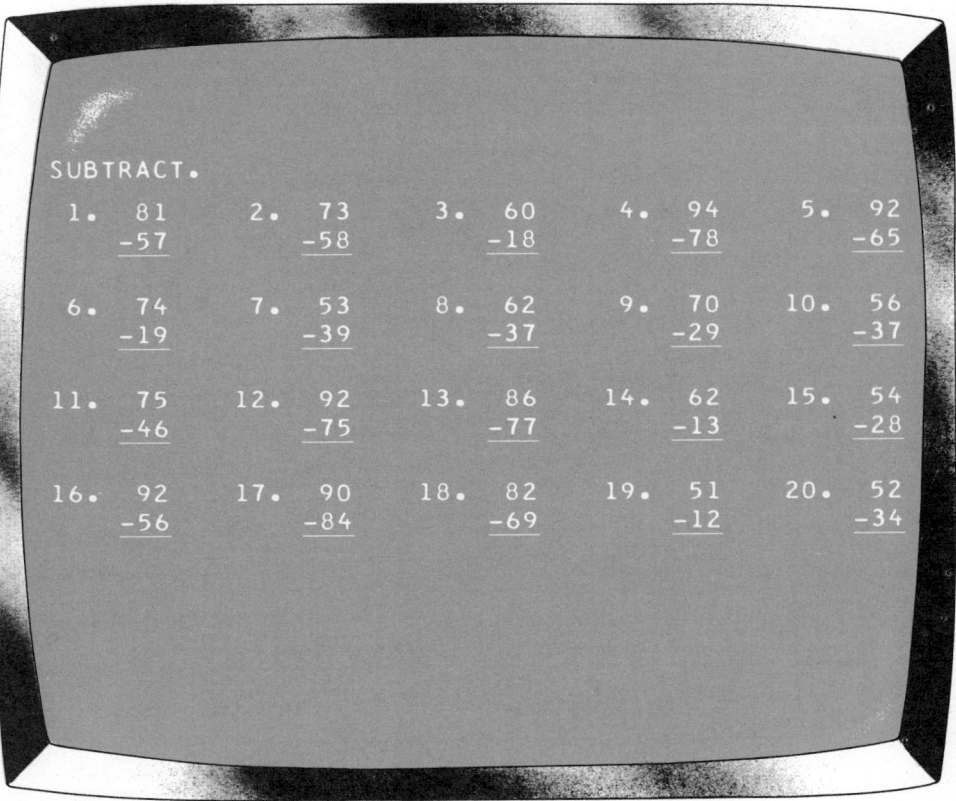

SUBTRACT.

1. 81 −57	2. 73 −58	3. 60 −18	4. 94 −78	5. 92 −65
6. 74 −19	7. 53 −39	8. 62 −37	9. 70 −29	10. 56 −37
11. 75 −46	12. 92 −75	13. 86 −77	14. 62 −13	15. 54 −28
16. 92 −56	17. 90 −84	18. 82 −69	19. 51 −12	20. 52 −34

COMPUTER CHECK
YOU SHOULD BE ABLE TO FIND EACH ANSWER IN THIS LIST:
6   9   13   14   15   16   17   18   19   24   25   26   27   29   36   39   41   42   49   55   **7**

Extra Practice

23 −14	56 −17	81 −24
35 −18	48 −39	60 −43
73 −56	91 −48	50 −34
42 −27	84 − 9	36 −18
67 −38	75 −26	43 −17

Answers for Extra Practice.

9	39	57
17	9	17
17	43	16
15	75	18
29	49	26

Answers for Review 5.

1. 24 2. 15 3. 42 4. 16 5. 27
6. 55 7. 14 8. 25 9. 41 10. 19
11. 29 12. 17 13. 9 14. 49
15. 26 16. 36 17. 6 18. 13
19. 39 20. 18

STUDENT OBJECTIVE
To subtract 2-digit numbers when one regrouping is required.

Suggested Lesson Plan

- Review the process of regrouping in subtraction with the following demonstration:

    1. Write this exercise on the chalkboard:

        62
        −37

    2. Use place-value materials such as bundles of sticks to represent 62 sticks:

    3. You want to remove 7 ones, but there are only 2, so separate a bundle of ten into 10 ones:

        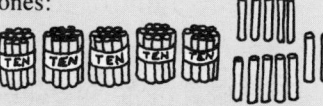

        Now there are 12 loose sticks.

    4. Take away 7 sticks, leaving 5. You now have 5 bundles of ten and 5 loose sticks:

    5. Take away 3 tens. Now there are 2 tens and 5 ones left:

    6. Make a record of what happened in a place-value chart:

Step 1.		Step 2.		Step 3.	
Tens	Ones	Tens	Ones	Tens	Ones
5̸ 6̸	12 2̸	5̸ 6̸	12 2̸	5̸ 6̸	12 2̸
−3	7	−3	7	−3	7
			5	2	5

    7. Write the same exercise without using a table:

Step 1.	Step 2.	Step 3.
5 6̸¹2 −3 7	5 6̸¹2 −3 7 5	5 6̸¹2 −3 7 2 5

Reinforcement

- Assign Set 5 on page 375 and the Extra Practice on this page to any students who miss four or more exercises.

Review Lesson 5   7

Subtracting 3–digit numbers, one regrouping

STUDENT OBJECTIVE
To subtract 3-digit numbers when one regrouping is required.

Suggested Lesson Plan

- Review regrouping. Use the demonstration from Review Lesson 5 extended to include hundreds. For example:

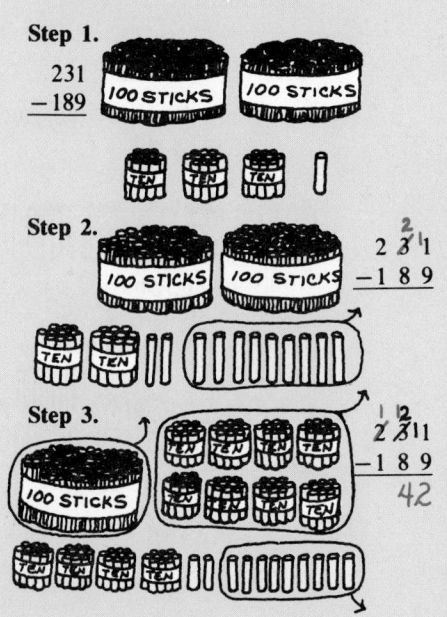

Step 1.
$$231 - 189$$

Step 2.
$$2\overset{2}{3}^{1} - 189$$

Step 3.
$$\overset{1}{2}\overset{12}{3}^{1}1 - 189 = 42$$

- Assign the exercises.

Reinforcement
- Students missing four or more exercises should do Set 6 on page 375 and the Extra Practice on this page.

MEMORY RETRIEVAL— 3-DIGIT SUBTRACTION

SUBTRACT ONES.		NOT ENOUGH TENS, SO REGROUP A HUNDRED.	SUBTRACT TENS, SUBTRACT HUNDREDS.
$427 - 253$	$427 - 253 = 4$	$\overset{3}{4}\cancel{}27 - 253 = 4$	$\overset{3}{4}\cancel{}27 - 253 = 174$

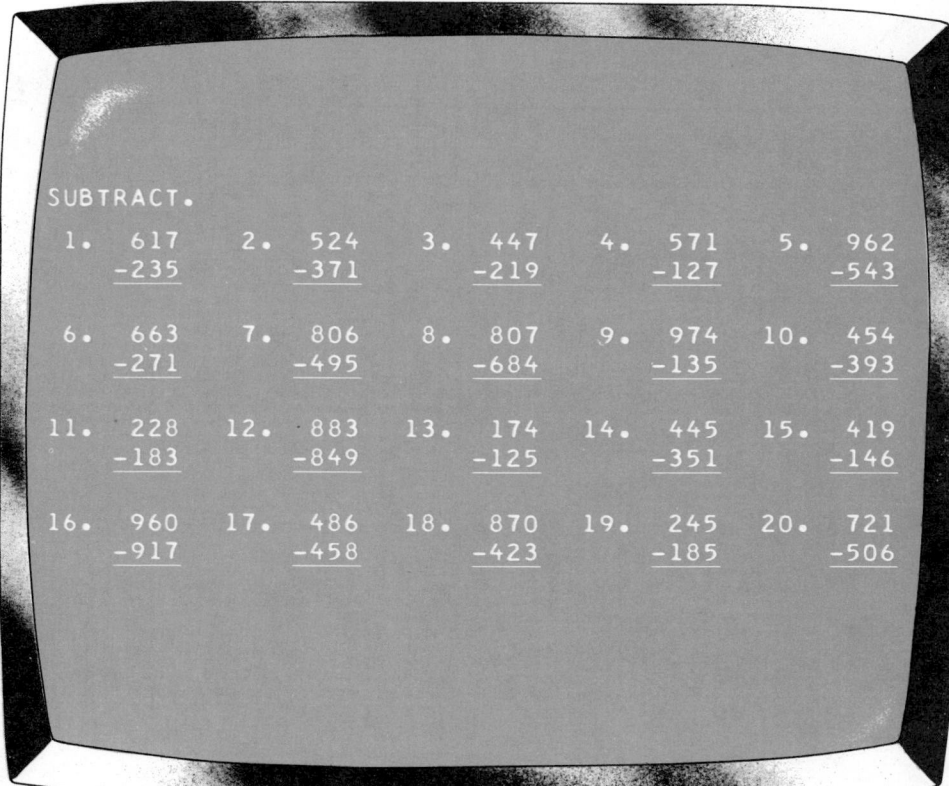

SUBTRACT.

1. 617 −235
2. 524 −371
3. 447 −219
4. 571 −127
5. 962 −543

6. 663 −271
7. 806 −495
8. 807 −684
9. 974 −135
10. 454 −393

11. 228 −183
12. 883 −849
13. 174 −125
14. 445 −351
15. 419 −146

16. 960 −917
17. 486 −458
18. 870 −423
19. 245 −185
20. 721 −506

COMPUTER CHECK
YOU SHOULD BE ABLE TO FIND EACH ANSWER IN THIS LIST:

8   28 34 43 45 49 60 61 94 123 153 215 228 273 311 382 392 419 444 447 839

Answers for Review 6.

1. 382   2. 153   3. 228   4. 444
5. 419   6. 392   7. 311   8. 123
9. 839   10. 61   11. 45   12. 34
13. 49   14. 94   15. 273   16. 43
17. 28   18. 447   19. 60   20. 215

Extra Practice

676 −557	569 −483	633 −421
231 −228	493 −205	774 −484
537 −261	664 −236	935 −853
641 −325	816 −421	540 −432
167 −128	292 −144	858 −419

Answers for Extra Practice.

119	86	212
3	288	290
276	428	82
316	395	108
39	148	439

REVIEW 7 — Multiplication properties and basic multiplication facts

Clyde was instructed to search its data bank for three properties that help us remember the multiplication facts. Here is the printout.

MULTIPLYING BY ZERO PROPERTY

THE PRODUCT OF A NUMBER AND ZERO IS ZERO.

$$6 \times 0 = 0 \qquad 0 \times 3 = 0$$

MULTIPLYING BY ONE PROPERTY

THE PRODUCT OF A NUMBER AND ONE IS THAT SAME NUMBER.

$$6 \times 1 = 6 \qquad 1 \times 3 = 3$$

COMMUTATIVE PROPERTY OF MULTIPLICATION

YOU CAN CHANGE THE ORDER OF TWO FACTORS WITHOUT CHANGING THE PRODUCT.

$$3 \times 4 = 4 \times 3 \qquad 7 \times 2 = 2 \times 7$$

THERE ARE 36 PAIRS OF BASIC MULTIPLICATION FACTS SUCH AS $\begin{array}{r}7\\ \times 3\end{array}$ AND $\begin{array}{r}3\\ \times 7\end{array}$. IF YOU KNOW ONE FACT IN A PAIR AND THE COMMUTATIVE PROPERTY, THEN YOU KNOW THE OTHER FACT.

Clyde generated the following practice exercises. Time yourself to see how quickly you can do them. Memorize the facts you missed. Repeat the exercises in a day or so to see if you have improved your speed and accuracy.

MULTIPLY.

1. $\begin{array}{r}5\\ \times 6\end{array}$	2. $\begin{array}{r}9\\ \times 4\end{array}$	3. $\begin{array}{r}5\\ \times 7\end{array}$	4. $\begin{array}{r}8\\ \times 6\end{array}$	5. $\begin{array}{r}4\\ \times 5\end{array}$	6. $\begin{array}{r}9\\ \times 8\end{array}$
7. $\begin{array}{r}6\\ \times 7\end{array}$	8. $\begin{array}{r}4\\ \times 6\end{array}$	9. $\begin{array}{r}3\\ \times 9\end{array}$	10. $\begin{array}{r}7\\ \times 9\end{array}$	11. $\begin{array}{r}8\\ \times 8\end{array}$	12. $\begin{array}{r}7\\ \times 4\end{array}$
13. $\begin{array}{r}5\\ \times 5\end{array}$	14. $\begin{array}{r}9\\ \times 6\end{array}$	15. $\begin{array}{r}7\\ \times 8\end{array}$	16. $\begin{array}{r}4\\ \times 8\end{array}$	17. $\begin{array}{r}6\\ \times 6\end{array}$	18. $\begin{array}{r}5\\ \times 8\end{array}$
19. $\begin{array}{r}9\\ \times 9\end{array}$	20. $\begin{array}{r}1\\ \times 8\end{array}$	21. $\begin{array}{r}7\\ \times 7\end{array}$	22. $\begin{array}{r}0\\ \times 9\end{array}$	23. $\begin{array}{r}5\\ \times 9\end{array}$	24. $\begin{array}{r}4\\ \times 4\end{array}$

COMPUTER CHECK

1. 30 2. 36 3. 35 4. 48 5. 20 6. 72 7. 42 8. 24 9. 27 10. 63
11. 64 12. 28 13. 25 14. 54 15. 56 16. 32 17. 36 18. 40 19. 81 20. 8 21. 49 22. 0 23. 45 24. 16

Figure 1

X	0	1	2	3	4	5	6	7	8	9
0										
1										
2										
3										
4										
5										
6										
7										
8										
9										

Figure 2

X	7	4	6	8
4				
7				
6				
8				

X	5	8	4	9
9				
6				
3				
7				

Answers for Review 7.

1. 30 2. 36 3. 35 4. 48 5. 20
6. 72 7. 42 8. 24 9. 27 10. 63
11. 64 12. 28 13. 25 14. 54
15. 56 16. 32 17. 36 18. 40
19. 81 20. 8 21. 49 22. 0 23. 45
24. 16

STUDENT OBJECTIVE
To recall from memory the basic multiplication facts.

Suggested Lesson Plan

- Review the three properties shown in the printout on page 9. Stress the usefulness of the commutative property in memorizing 36 pairs of multiplication facts.

- Assign the exercises. Timing the students is a good way to encourage self-improvement.

- Identify the students who need additional work on the basic facts.

Reinforcement

Assign one or more of the following activities.

- Make a multiplication-facts table as in Figure 1 below.

- Use the multiplication table to help students diagnose their own "demons" to work on.

- Here are five tips for using the multiplication table:

  1. Cross out the 0 and 1 columns and rows—nearly everyone knows these.

  2. Most students know the facts for 2—cross these out as well.

  3. You may want to discuss a special property for the products of 3:
  For each product, the sum of the digits is 3, 6, or 9. For examples 12, 15, 18, 21, 24, and 27: $1 + 2 = 3$, $1 + 5 = 6$, $1 + 8 = 9$, $2 + 1 = 3$, $2 + 4 = 6$, and $2 + 7 = 9$.

  4. A similar pattern is formed by the products of 9. For each product, the sum of the digits is 9.

  5. Most students know their facts for 5. This leaves 4, 6, 7, and 8 as the facts that need the most emphasis.

- Make smaller multiplication charts for special emphasis as in Figure 2.

- Repeat the multiplication-table activity frequently with students who need the practice.

- Assign Set 7 on page 375.

- You may want to repeat the speed drills for addition and subtraction at this time.

STUDENT OBJECTIVE
To multiply a two-digit number by a
1-digit number when there is no
regrouping from ones to tens.

Suggested Lesson Plan

- Discuss the steps shown in the
Memory Retrieval on page 10. Work
out as many examples as necessary.

- Assign the exercises. You may have a
few students who will need to use a
multiplication table.

Reinforcement
- Assign Set 8 on page 375 and the
Extra Practice on this page to
students who miss four or more
exercises.

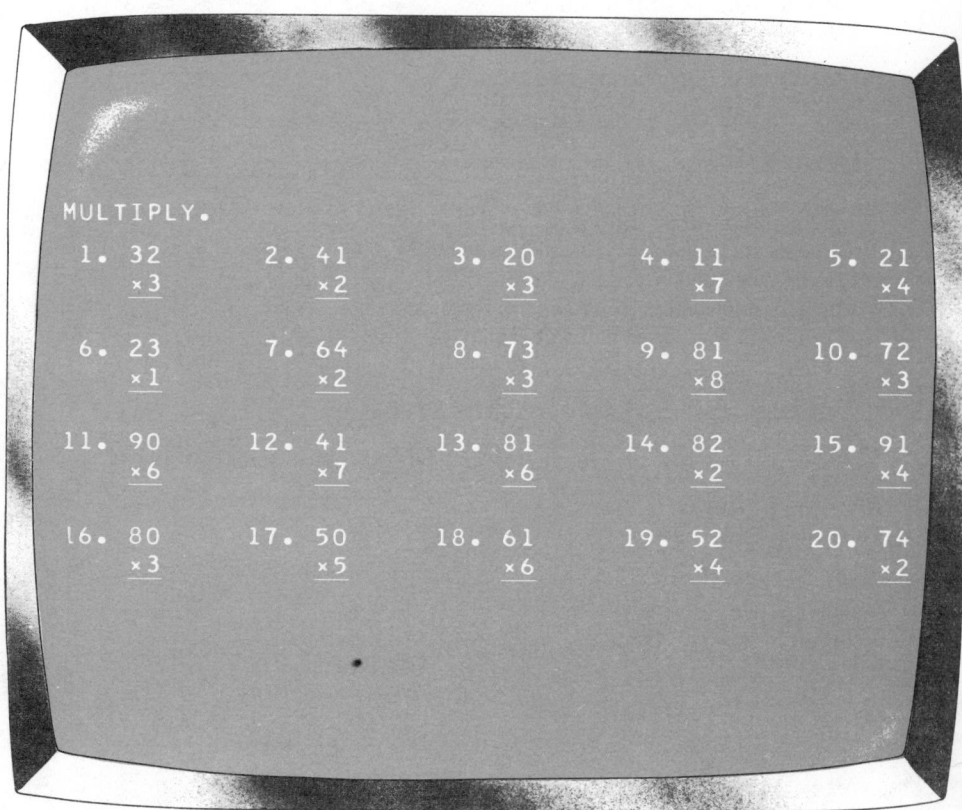

REVIEW 8 — Multiplying a 2–digit number by a 1–digit number

MEMORY RETRIEVAL— MULTIPLICATION IN COLUMNS

	MULTIPLY ONES.	MULTIPLY TENS.
74 ×2	74 ×2 8	74 ×2 148

MULTIPLY.

1. 32 ×3	2. 41 ×2	3. 20 ×3	4. 11 ×7	5. 21 ×4
6. 23 ×1	7. 64 ×2	8. 73 ×3	9. 81 ×8	10. 72 ×3
11. 90 ×6	12. 41 ×7	13. 81 ×6	14. 82 ×2	15. 91 ×4
16. 80 ×3	17. 50 ×5	18. 61 ×6	19. 52 ×4	20. 74 ×2

COMPUTER CHECK
YOU SHOULD BE ABLE TO FIND EACH ANSWER IN THIS LIST:
10   23 60 77 82 84 96 128 148 164 208 216 219 240 250 287 364 366 486 540 648

Answers for Review 8.

1. 96   2. 82   3. 60   4. 77   5. 84
6. 23   7. 128   8. 219   9. 648
10. 216   11. 540   12. 287   13. 486
14. 164   15. 364   16. 240   17. 250
18. 366   19. 208   20. 148

Extra Practice

93 ×3	93 ×2	81 ×4
52 ×4	73 ×3	20 ×7
60 ×8	62 ×4	41 ×8
61 ×7	72 ×4	54 ×2
53 ×3	83 ×3	91 ×6

Answers for Extra Practice.

279	186	324
208	219	140
480	248	328
427	288	108
159	249	546

REVIEW 9 — Multiplying a 2–digit number by a 1–digit number

MEMORY RETRIEVAL— MULTIPLICATION WITH REGROUPING

MULTIPLY ONES AND REGROUP.	MULTIPLY TENS AND ADD.

$$\begin{array}{r} 54 \\ \times 3 \\ \hline \end{array}$$

$$\begin{array}{r} {}^{1}\;\;\\ 54 \\ \times 3 \\ \hline 2 \end{array}$$

$$\begin{array}{r} {}^{1}\;\;\\ 54 \\ \times 3 \\ \hline 162 \end{array}$$

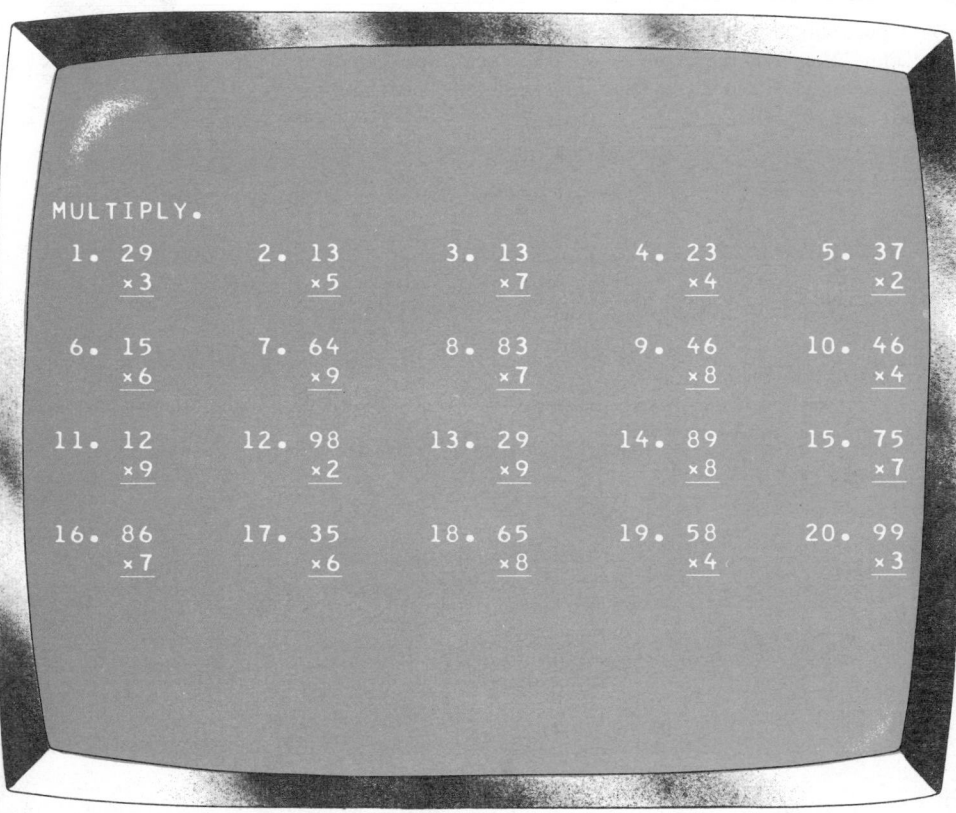

MULTIPLY.

1. 29 ×3	2. 13 ×5	3. 13 ×7	4. 23 ×4	5. 37 ×2
6. 15 ×6	7. 64 ×9	8. 83 ×7	9. 46 ×8	10. 46 ×4
11. 12 ×9	12. 98 ×2	13. 29 ×9	14. 89 ×8	15. 75 ×7
16. 86 ×7	17. 35 ×6	18. 65 ×8	19. 58 ×4	20. 99 ×3

COMPUTER CHECK
YOU SHOULD BE ABLE TO FIND EACH ANSWER IN THIS LIST:
65 74 87 90 91 92 108 184 196 210 232 261 297 368 520 525 576 581 602 712   11

Extra Practice

54 ×3	65 ×2	52 ×6
84 ×5	34 ×6	79 ×2
87 ×5	28 ×6	82 ×7
27 ×6	85 ×4	65 ×9
58 ×6	73 ×6	22 ×7

Answers for Extra Practice.

162	130	312
420	204	158
435	168	574
162	340	585
348	438	154

Answers for Review 9.

1. 87 2. 65 3. 91 4. 92 5. 74
6. 90 7. 576 8. 581 9. 368
10. 184 11. 108 12. 196 13. 261
14. 712 15. 525 16. 602 17. 210
18. 520 19. 232 20. 297

Suggested Lesson Plan

- Discuss the steps shown in the Memory Retrieval on page 11. You will need to do several more examples where the number "carried" is larger than 1.

EXAMPLE.

Step 1.

$$\begin{array}{r} 4 \\ 37 \\ \times 6 \\ \hline 2 \end{array}$$

Multiply ones and regroup. In this case the product of the ones is 42 and we "carry" the 4 tens.

Step 2.

$$\begin{array}{r} 4 \\ 37 \\ \times 6 \\ \hline 222 \end{array}$$

Multiply tens and add. Remind the students to multiply first, then add the 4.

- Assign the exercises. Since the multiplication process is quite complicated, you should check the students' work carefully to be sure they understand each step.

Reinforcement

- Assign Set 9 on page 376 and the Extra Practice on this page to students who miss four or more exercises.

- The following Skill Game will be useful throughout the year to provide multiplication practice.

  1. Use the digit cards from Review Lesson 3.

  2. Have the students draw a form like this: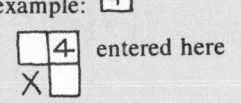

  3. Thoroughly mix the ten digit-cards, select one at random, and write the number in any box.
     For example: ④

     ④ entered here

  4. Repeat until all three boxes are filled.
     For example:

     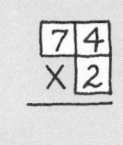

     ④ ⑦ ②
     first second third

  5. Find the product. Largest product wins. In the example, the product is 148. Is this the largest product possible? The smallest?

Review Lesson 9   11

Suggested Lesson Plan

- Discuss the property shown in the Division Data Bank on page 12. Point out the similarities between addition-subtraction and multiplication-division: Every multiplication fact has two related division facts. Provide several examples.

- Assign the exercises. Timing the students is a good way to encourage self-improvement.

- You may want to have some of the students also do Reviews 1, 4, and 7 again at this time.

Reinforcement

- Students who are having difficulty memorizing the basic facts will benefit from completing the following multiplication table. Students must use division facts to fill in the missing entries.

×	3	7	5	8	6	4	4	2
7	21	49	35	56	42	63	28	14
4	12	28	20	32	24	36	16	8
9	27	63	45	92	54	81	36	18
3	9	21	15	29	18	29	12	6
5	15	35	25	40	30	45	20	10
2	6	14	10	16	12	18	8	4
8	24	56	40	64	48	72	48	16
6	18	42	30	48	36	54	24	12

- You can provide multiplication and division drill quickly and efficiently with smaller multiplication tables that have missing entries:

×	4	7	9
6	24	42	54
8	32	56	72
3	12	21	27

×	4	7	8
5	20	35	40
4	16	28	32
8	32	56	64

This allows you to focus on the facts that are causing difficulty.

REVIEW 10 Basic division facts

DIVISION DATA BANK

IF YOU KNOW THE MULTIPLICATION FACTS AND REMEMBER THAT MULTIPLICATION AND DIVISION ARE RELATED, YOU SHOULD HAVE LITTLE TROUBLE RECALLING THE DIVISION FACTS.

EXAMPLE:

$$\begin{array}{r} 3 \\ \times 7 \\ \hline 21 \end{array}$$

THIS MULTIPLICATION FACT HAS TWO RELATED DIVISION FACTS.

$$3\overline{)21} \quad \text{(result 7)} \qquad 7\overline{)21} \quad \text{(result 3)}$$

Time yourself to see how quickly you can do the 40 exercises below. Memorize the facts you missed. Repeat the exercises in a day or so to see if you have improved your speed and accuracy.

DIVIDE.

1. $4\overline{)20}$	2. $5\overline{)35}$	3. $6\overline{)18}$	4. $7\overline{)49}$	5. $5\overline{)15}$
6. $8\overline{)32}$	7. $2\overline{)16}$	8. $8\overline{)24}$	9. $3\overline{)27}$	10. $6\overline{)6}$
11. $5\overline{)40}$	12. $4\overline{)16}$	13. $5\overline{)45}$	14. $8\overline{)64}$	15. $2\overline{)14}$
16. $9\overline{)72}$	17. $2\overline{)18}$	18. $5\overline{)0}$	19. $9\overline{)36}$	20. $6\overline{)12}$
21. $4\overline{)28}$	22. $8\overline{)16}$	23. $7\overline{)21}$	24. $8\overline{)48}$	25. $2\overline{)12}$
26. $6\overline{)24}$	27. $9\overline{)81}$	28. $4\overline{)24}$	29. $7\overline{)63}$	30. $3\overline{)12}$
31. $8\overline{)56}$	32. $1\overline{)8}$	33. $3\overline{)18}$	34. $6\overline{)42}$	35. $4\overline{)12}$
36. $9\overline{)54}$	37. $5\overline{)25}$	38. $3\overline{)24}$	39. $6\overline{)36}$	40. $9\overline{)18}$

COMPUTER CHECK

12

1.5 2.7 3.3 4.7 5.3 6.4 7.8 8.3 9.9 10.1 11.8 12.4 13.9 14.8 15.7 16.8 17.9 18.0 19.4 20.2 21.7 22.2 23.3 24.6 25.6 26.4 27.9 28.6 29.9 30.4 31.7 32.8 33.6 34.7 35.3 36.6 37.5 38.8 39.6 40.2

- For remedial practice, you may want to use this Skill Game.

  1. Make up a set of division flashcards. Index cards are especially good for this. One of your students who can print neatly can make the cards—you should have at least 40. Be sure all ten digits are represented as answers.

27 ÷ 3	36 ÷ 4	48 ÷ 8

  2. Have students draw this form and fill in the boxes using any of the digits 0–9. They may repeat any digit as many times as they wish.

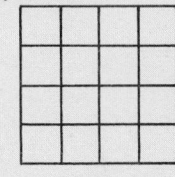

3. Draw cards at random. If the players have the answer in their table, they cross it out. If it appears more than once, they may cross off only one square.

4. The winner is the first player to cross off four boxes in a row, column, or diagonal.

- Assign Set 10 on page 376.

Answers for Review 10.

1. 5 2. 7 3. 3 4. 7 5. 3 6. 4
7. 8 8. 3 9. 9 10. 1 11. 8 12. 4
13. 9 14. 8 15. 7 16. 8 17. 9
18. 0 19. 4 20. 2 21. 7 22. 2
23. 3 24. 6 25. 6 26. 4 27. 9
28. 6 29. 9 30. 4 31. 7 32. 8
33. 6 34. 7 35. 3 36. 6 37. 5
38. 8 39. 6 40. 2

REVIEW 11 Dividing by a 1–digit number

MEMORY RETRIEVAL— DIVIDING WITH A REMAINDER

	RECALL FACTS.	DIVIDE, THEN MULTIPLY.	SUBTRACT TO GET REMAINDER.

$$8\overline{)34}$$

RECALL FACTS.

$$\begin{array}{ccc} 3 & 4 & 5 \\ \times 8 & \times 8 & \times 8 \\ \hline 24 & 32 & 40 \end{array}$$
(TOO BIG)

DIVIDE, THEN MULTIPLY.
$$8\overline{)34} \quad \frac{4}{32}$$

SUBTRACT TO GET REMAINDER.
$$8\overline{)34} \quad \begin{array}{r} 4\,R2 \\ -32 \\ \hline 2 \end{array}$$

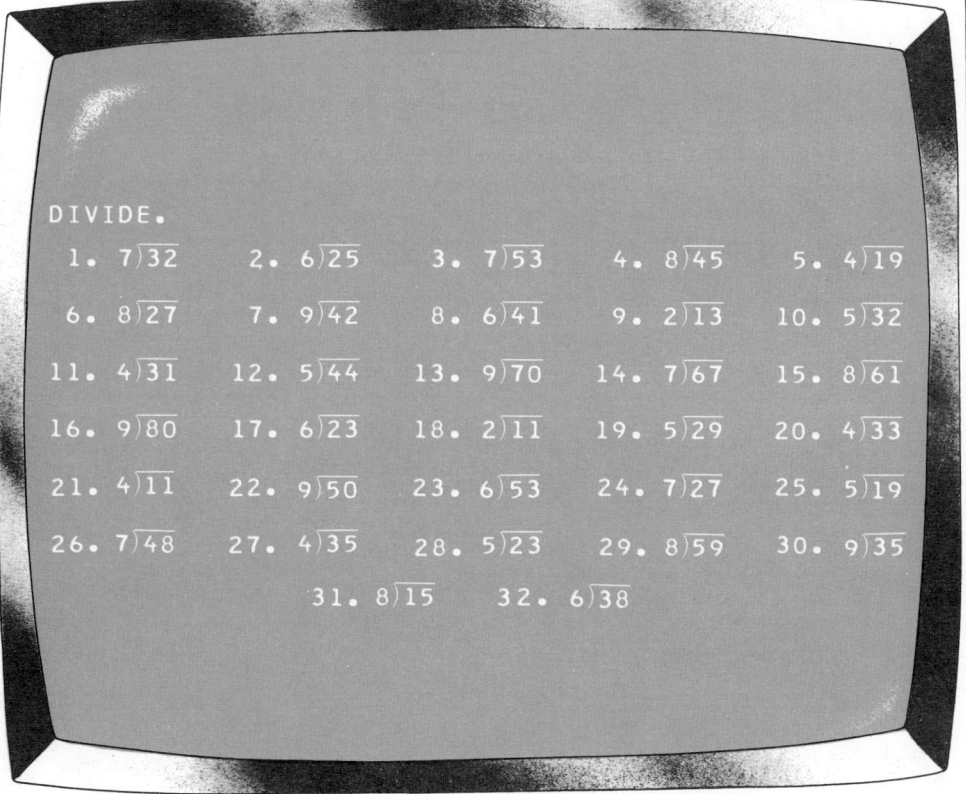

DIVIDE.

1. $7\overline{)32}$ 2. $6\overline{)25}$ 3. $7\overline{)53}$ 4. $8\overline{)45}$ 5. $4\overline{)19}$

6. $8\overline{)27}$ 7. $9\overline{)42}$ 8. $6\overline{)41}$ 9. $2\overline{)13}$ 10. $5\overline{)32}$

11. $4\overline{)31}$ 12. $5\overline{)44}$ 13. $9\overline{)70}$ 14. $7\overline{)67}$ 15. $8\overline{)61}$

16. $9\overline{)80}$ 17. $6\overline{)23}$ 18. $2\overline{)11}$ 19. $5\overline{)29}$ 20. $4\overline{)33}$

21. $4\overline{)11}$ 22. $9\overline{)50}$ 23. $6\overline{)53}$ 24. $7\overline{)27}$ 25. $5\overline{)19}$

26. $7\overline{)48}$ 27. $4\overline{)35}$ 28. $5\overline{)23}$ 29. $8\overline{)59}$ 30. $9\overline{)35}$

31. $8\overline{)15}$ 32. $6\overline{)38}$

COMPUTER CHECK
YOU SHOULD BE ABLE TO FIND EACH ANSWER IN THIS LIST:
1 R7   2 R3   3 R3   3 R4   3 R5   3 R6   3 R8   4 R1   4 R3   4 R4   4 R6   5 R1   5 R4   5 R5
6 R1   6 R2   6 R5   6 R6   7 R3   7 R4   7 R5   7 R7   8 R1   8 R3   8 R4   8 R5   8 R8   9 R4

13

STUDENT OBJECTIVE
To do division-with-remainder problems that involve only basic division facts.

Suggested Lesson Plan

- Discuss the example in the Memory Retrieval on page 13. Work out several additional examples of division-with-remainder such as these:

$$3\overline{)17} \qquad 5\overline{)27}$$

- Assign the exercises, reminding students that the answers are given at the bottom of the page.

Reinforcement

- Students who missed four or more exercises should do Set 11 on page 376 and the Extra Practice on this page.
- Write this riddle and Decoder on the board or use an overhead projector.

"What does the gorilla football team call its trainer?"

DECODER

$7\overline{)36}$	$6\overline{)50}$	$7\overline{)47}$	$9\overline{)57}$	$8\overline{)73}$
T	E	U	A	P
$5\overline{)32}$	$3\overline{)22}$	$8\overline{)53}$	$4\overline{)29}$	$9\overline{)85}$
R	E	S	A	T
$7\overline{)46}$	$6\overline{)34}$	$4\overline{)39}$	$9\overline{)49}$	$3\overline{)28}$
O	V	P	C	E

Cross out all letters where the remainder is 2, 4, or 5.
The remaining letters answer the riddle.

Extra Practice

$8\overline{)70}$ $7\overline{)69}$ $4\overline{)29}$

$7\overline{)30}$ $5\overline{)39}$ $4\overline{)35}$

$9\overline{)40}$ $7\overline{)62}$ $6\overline{)49}$

$9\overline{)83}$ $7\overline{)44}$ $7\overline{)64}$

$8\overline{)36}$ $8\overline{)74}$ $7\overline{)37}$

Answers for Extra Practice.

8 R6	9 R6	7 R1
4 R2	7 R4	8 R3
4 R4	8 R6	8 R1
9 R2	6 R2	9 R1
4 R4	9 R2	5 R2

Answers for Review 11.

1. 4 R4   2. 4 R1   3. 7 R4   4. 5 R5
5. 4 R3   6. 3 R3   7. 4 R6   8. 6 R5
9. 6 R1   10. 6 R2   11. 7 R3   12. 8 R4
13. 7 R7   14. 9 R4   15. 7 R5
16. 8 R8   17. 3 R5   18. 5 R1
19. 5 R4   20. 8 R1   21. 2 R3
22. 5 R5   23. 8 R5   24. 3 R6
25. 3 R4   26. 6 R6   27. 8 R3
28. 4 R3   29. 7 R3   30. 3 R8
31. 1 R7   32. 6 R2

Review Lesson 11   **13**

Suggested Lesson Plan

- Discuss the example in the Memory Retrieval on page 14. Work out several more examples.

- Some of your students may benefit from the following physical demonstration of division.

    1. Write the following exercise on the chalkboard and construct a physical model using place-value materials such as bundles of sticks:

    2. Divide the sticks into four piles. There are not enough hundreds for each pile, so separate the hundred into 10 tens:

    3. There are now 16 tens, and they can be divided evenly into 4 piles. Demonstrate this by placing the bundles of ten in piles, one at a time:

    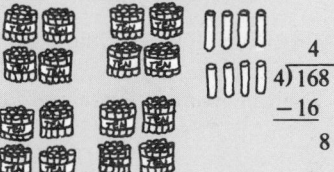

    4. Now divide the 8 loose sticks into 4 piles:

- Division is a very difficult operation for many students, so this physical demonstration of division should be repeated using other examples.

Reinforcement

- Students who miss more than four exercises should do Set 12 on page 376 and the Extra Practice on this page.

REVIEW 12 Dividing by a 1–digit number

MEMORY RETRIEVAL—DIVIDING IN COLUMNS

	REGROUP, THEN DIVIDE TENS.	DIVIDE ONES.
6)246	6)246 → 4	6)246 → 41

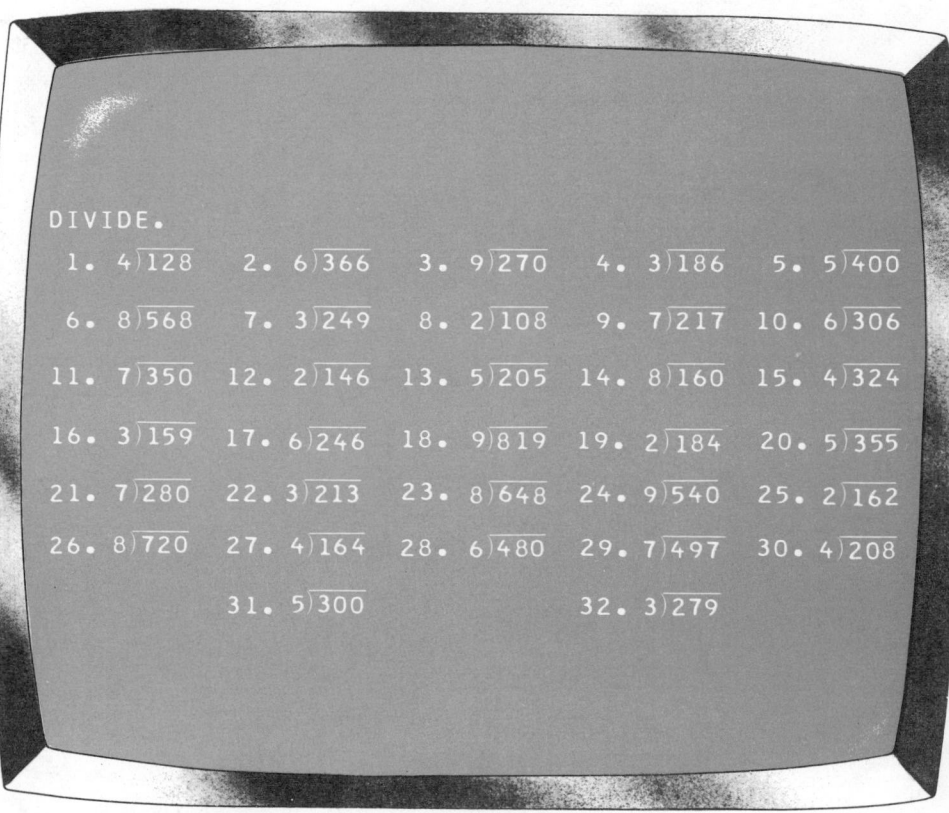

DIVIDE.

1. 4)128   2. 6)366   3. 9)270   4. 3)186   5. 5)400

6. 8)568   7. 3)249   8. 2)108   9. 7)217   10. 6)306

11. 7)350   12. 2)146   13. 5)205   14. 8)160   15. 4)324

16. 3)159   17. 6)246   18. 9)819   19. 2)184   20. 5)355

21. 7)280   22. 3)213   23. 8)648   24. 9)540   25. 2)162

26. 8)720   27. 4)164   28. 6)480   29. 7)497   30. 4)208

31. 5)300   32. 3)279

COMPUTER CHECK
YOU SHOULD BE ABLE TO FIND EACH ANSWER IN THIS LIST:

14   20 30 31 32 40 41 50 51 52 53 54
      60 61 62 71 73 80 81 83 90 91 92 93

Answers for Review 12.

1. 32   2. 61   3. 30   4. 62   5. 80
6. 71   7. 83   8. 54   9. 31   10. 51
11. 50 12. 73 13. 41 14. 20
15. 81 16. 53 17. 41 18. 91
19. 92 20. 71 21. 40 22. 71
23. 81 24. 60 25. 81 26. 90
27. 41 28. 80 29. 71 30. 52
31. 60 32. 93

Extra Practice

3)126	4)248	6)186
9)540	3)276	5)305
3)153	8)720	2)102
9)360	7)357	6)126
4)164	2)188	5)300

Answers for Extra Practice.

42	62	31
60	92	61
51	90	51
40	51	21
41	94	60

REVIEW 13 Dividing by a 1-digit number

MEMORY RETRIEVAL— DIVIDING WITH REGROUPING

STUDENT OBJECTIVE
To divide any 2-digit number by a 1-digit number.

$$2\overline{)76}$$

DIVIDE TENS.

$$\begin{array}{r} 3 \\ 2\overline{)76} \\ -6 \\ \hline 1 \end{array}$$

REGROUP, THEN DIVIDE ONES.

$$\begin{array}{r} 38 \\ 2\overline{)76} \\ -6 \\ \hline 16 \\ -16 \\ \hline 0 \end{array}$$

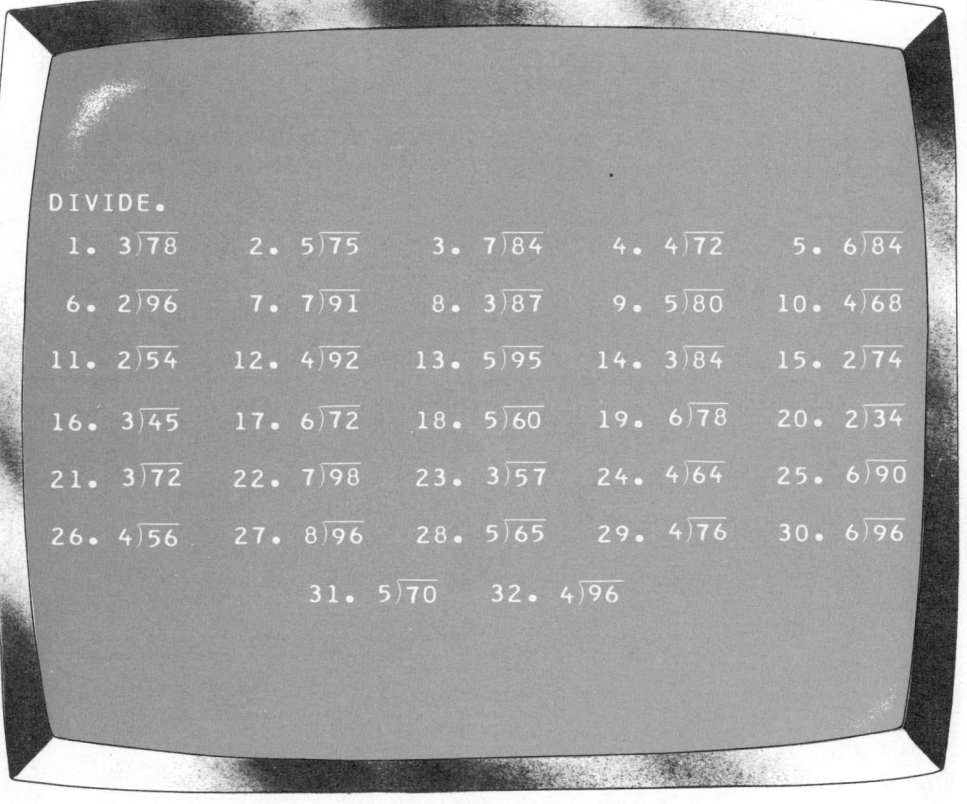

DIVIDE.

1. $3\overline{)78}$	2. $5\overline{)75}$	3. $7\overline{)84}$	4. $4\overline{)72}$	5. $6\overline{)84}$
6. $2\overline{)96}$	7. $7\overline{)91}$	8. $3\overline{)87}$	9. $5\overline{)80}$	10. $4\overline{)68}$
11. $2\overline{)54}$	12. $4\overline{)92}$	13. $5\overline{)95}$	14. $3\overline{)84}$	15. $2\overline{)74}$
16. $3\overline{)45}$	17. $6\overline{)72}$	18. $5\overline{)60}$	19. $6\overline{)78}$	20. $2\overline{)34}$
21. $3\overline{)72}$	22. $7\overline{)98}$	23. $3\overline{)57}$	24. $4\overline{)64}$	25. $6\overline{)90}$
26. $4\overline{)56}$	27. $8\overline{)96}$	28. $5\overline{)65}$	29. $4\overline{)76}$	30. $6\overline{)96}$

31. $5\overline{)70}$ 32. $4\overline{)96}$

COMPUTER CHECK
YOU SHOULD BE ABLE TO FIND EACH ANSWER IN THIS LIST:
12 13 14 15 16 17 18 19 23 24 26 27 28 29 37 48

15

Suggested Lesson Plan

- Discuss the example in the Memory Retrieval on page 15. Work out several more examples where it is necessary to regroup tens to ones.

  $4\overline{)76}$ $7\overline{)84}$

- The following physical demonstration of dividing with regrouping is a good follow-up to the suggested demonstration in Lesson 12.

  1. Write this exercise on the board and represent the dividend with 5 bundles of ten and 1 single stick:

  $3\overline{)51}$

  2. Divide the tens into 3 piles, placing 1 bundle at a time:

  3 bundles have been used, with 2 bundles and a single stick remaining.

  3. Regroup the 2 bundles of ten. There are now 21 loose sticks. Distribute the loose sticks one at a time to the 3 piles:

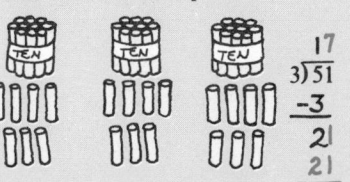

  Repeat with several other examples. Be sure students see the relationship between the manipulation and the written work.

- Assign the exercises.

Reinforcement

- Students who miss more than four exercises should do Set 13 on page 376 and the Extra Practice on this page.

Extra Practice

$5\overline{)85}$	$4\overline{)68}$	$4\overline{)92}$
$2\overline{)38}$	$7\overline{)98}$	$3\overline{)78}$
$6\overline{)96}$	$2\overline{)68}$	$3\overline{)45}$
$3\overline{)81}$	$5\overline{)75}$	$8\overline{)96}$
$7\overline{)84}$	$6\overline{)72}$	$5\overline{)90}$

Answers for Extra Practice.

17	17	23
19	14	26
16	34	15
27	15	12
12	12	18

Answers for Review 13.

1. 26 2. 15 3. 12 4. 18 5. 14
6. 48 7. 13 8. 29 9. 16 10. 17
11. 27 12. 23 13. 19 14. 28
15. 37 16. 15 17. 12 18. 12
19. 13 20. 17 21. 24 22. 14
23. 19 24. 16 25. 15 26. 14
27. 12 28. 13 29. 19 30. 16
31. 14 32. 24

STUDENT OBJECTIVE
To demonstrate mastery of the skills
reviewed in this chapter. (See page 1a
for the list of objectives.)

You should establish criteria for mastery
for each of the nine skills tested.
Students who need additional practice
and/or reteaching should be dealt with
individually.

Suggested Lesson Plan

- Results of the posttest should be
  analyzed very carefully. The
  whole-number skills required for
  starting Chapter 1 are covered on this
  test. You will be able to pinpoint
  specific areas of need and assign
  additional work based on these
  identified needs.

POSTTEST

Clyde generated this posttest based on the 13 reviews of whole number skills. A good score on this test means you are ready to start Chapter 1.

POSTTEST

	1.	2.	3.	4.	5.
A.	46 +12	36 +40	54 +74	82 +63	61 52 +34
B.	36 +17	35 +35	74 +89	78 +28	32 94 +97
C.	84 −36	70 −24	71 −67	73 −36	92 −58
D.	908 −127	437 −282	546 −474	720 −316	893 −547
E.	21 ×4	23 ×3	41 ×6	80 ×4	61 ×7
F.	28 ×3	16 ×6	74 ×8	39 ×6	87 ×7
G.	3)26	8)43	4)37	7)61	5)48
H.	6)126	4)288	5)350	2)146	3)249
I.	8)96	3)81	5)85	6)84	7)98

16

Answers for Posttest.

A. 1. 58 2. 76 3. 128 4. 145
   5. 147
B. 1. 53 2. 70 3. 163 4. 106
   5. 223
C. 1. 48 2. 46 3. 4 4. 37
   5. 34
D. 1. 781 2. 155 3. 72 4. 404
   5. 346
E. 1. 84 2. 69 3. 246 4. 320
   5. 427
F. 1. 84 2. 96 3. 592 4. 234
   5. 609
G. 1. 8 R2 2. 5 R3 3. 9 R1
   4. 8 R5 5. 9 R3
H. 1. 21 2. 72 3. 70 4. 73
   5. 83
I. 1. 12 2. 27 3. 17 4. 14
   5. 14

Chapter 1
Whole Numbers

Pages 17—54

Learning Objectives

After completing this chapter, all students should be able to do the following:

1-1 Write numbers with up to 15 digits in words and standard numerals.

1-2 Round whole numbers.

1-3 Add any two or more whole numbers.

1-4 Subtract any two whole numbers.

1-5 Multiply any two whole numbers.

1-6 Divide any two whole numbers.

1-7 Solve word problems that involve whole numbers.

First, students learn to write numbers into the trillions, and then they learn to round and compare any whole numbers. Next, the addition, subtraction, multiplication, and division algorithms are carefully reviewed and much practice is provided. In all cases students are taught and encouraged to use estimation as a check on their work. Finally, throughout the chapter students are given many opportunities to learn to solve practical problems stated in word form.

Mathematics

Computation algorithms. In the students' text, the techniques of computing are reviewed with little explanation about why the algorithms work as they do. If you wish to give explanations, there are several that work reasonably well. Here are examples of two—an abstract explanation involving the structure of the whole number system, and a physical explanation involving the natural manipulation of objects. We use an addition example and a subtraction example, but similar examples can be found for the other operations. (See the Suggested Lesson Plans for lessons in which those operations are taught.)

Abstract explanation.

$$\begin{array}{r} 41 \\ +27 \\ \hline \end{array}$$

$$
\begin{aligned}
41 + 27 &= (4 \times 10 + 1) + (2 \times 10 + 7) \quad \text{place-value} \\
&\qquad\qquad\qquad\qquad\qquad\qquad\quad \text{definitions} \\
&= (4 \times 10 + 2 \times 10) + (1 + 7) \quad \text{commutative} \\
&\qquad\qquad\qquad\qquad\qquad\qquad\qquad \text{and} \\
&\qquad\qquad\qquad\qquad\qquad\qquad\qquad \text{associative} \\
&\qquad\qquad\qquad\qquad\qquad\qquad\qquad \text{properties} \\
&= (4 + 2) \times 10 + (1 + 7) \quad \text{distributive property} \\
&= (6 \times 10) + (1 + 7) \quad \text{basic addition fact} \\
&= 6 \times 10 + 8 \quad \text{basic addition fact} \\
&= 68 \quad \text{place-value definition}
\end{aligned}
$$

Physical objects explanation.

$$\begin{array}{r} 203 \\ -86 \\ \hline \end{array}$$

Students can think about 2 bundles of 100 sticks, and 3 single sticks.

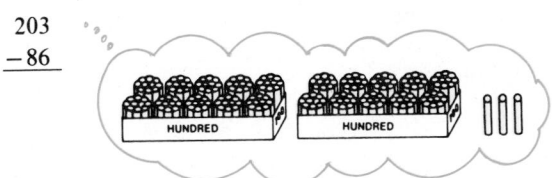

Now, in order to take away 86 sticks, they must regroup—take a bundle of 100 apart to get 10 bundles of 10. Then they must regroup again—take a bundle of 10 apart to get 10 single sticks.

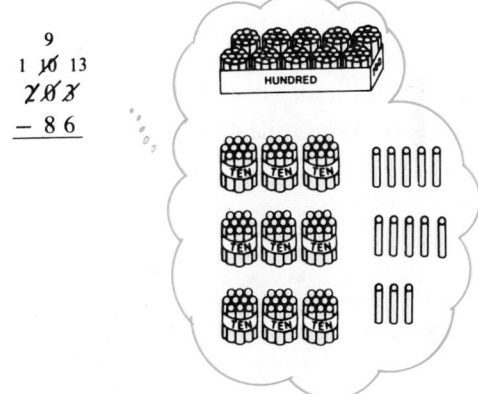

Now they can take away 8 tens and 6 single ones. This leaves 1 hundred, 1 ten, and 7 ones.

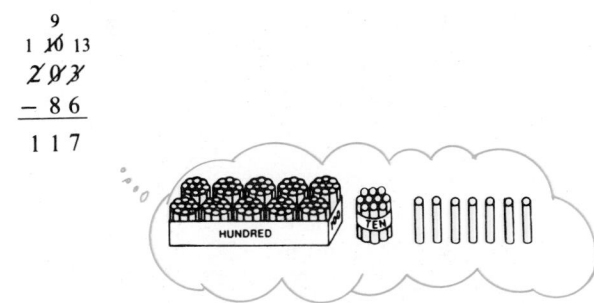

Notice that the sticks are manipulated in a very natural way and that the algorithm mirrors that manipulation. This makes the algorithm seem natural and clear.

17a

Teaching the Chapter

Students must have many different kinds of experiences to learn to solve story problems. Among the important experiences are those that force the student to think about the processes used in finding solutions rather than the solutions themselves. Estimating and using hand-held calculators are two methods. Here are some others that you may wish to try.

Ask students to find as many ways of solving a problem as they can. It is important in such an activity that students clearly understand that they are not interested in the answer to the problem, only in the methods of solution. Here is an example of a simple problem that has at least four reasonable, different methods of solving it:

56 band members are marching in 4 rows.
How many members in each row?

Method 1. Divide.

$$\begin{array}{r} 14 \\ 4\overline{)56} \end{array}$$

Method 2. Multiply.

... 10 rows	11 rows	12 rows	13 rows	14 rows
$\times 4$	$\times 4$	$\times 4$	$\times 4$	$\times 4$
40	44	48	52	56

Method 3. Subtract.

$56 - 4 = 52$ 1 row and 52 left
$52 - 4 = 48$ 2 rows and 48 left
$48 - 4 = 44$ 3 rows and 44 left
$44 - 4 = 40$ 4 rows and 40 left

$8 - 4 = 4$ 13 rows and 4 left
$4 - 4 = 0$ 14 rows

Method 4. Add.

$4 + 4 = 8$ in 2 rows
$8 + 4 = 12$ in 3 rows
$12 + 4 = 16$ in 4 rows
$16 + 4 = 20$ in 5 rows

$48 + 4 = 52$ in 13 rows
$52 + 4 = 56$ in 14 rows

Another strategy to try with your students is to give them some computation that has been performed and ask them to make up problems that go with the computation.

Example 1. Here is a computation that someone did to solve a problem. What might the problem have been?

$$6(3 + 4) = 42$$

Possible solution: Six carloads of students went on a field trip. In each car there were 3 boys and 4 girls. How many students were there in all?

Possible solution: Mrs. Harte bought each of her 6 nephews a shirt-and-tie combination for Christmas. Each shirt cost $4 and each tie cost $3. How much did she spend in all?

Try this! Give a situation and ask students to make up problems. For example, give this situation:

A 6-pack of cola costs $1.56.

Then ask students to make up problems. Here are three simple examples:

1. How much would 1 bottle cost?
2. How much would 15 bottles cost?
3. How much change would you get if you paid for the 6-pack with two $1 bills?

You can also ask for a specific kind of problem such as one that can be solved by multiplication or one that can be solved by subtraction.

It should be pointed out that making up problems that fit situations is not a skill that students are likely to use, but such an activity helps students to see the relationships between the way words are used in problems and the computations that can be used to solve the problems.

Remember that students do not learn to solve problems by being exposed to a chapter on problem solving. They learn by having many experiences over a long period of time. Therefore, you should continue to use the activities above throughout the year to supplement the problem-solving activities described in the text.

Vocabulary

addend	million
billion	product
consecutive multiples	quotient
difference	rounding
digit	standard numeral
divisor	sum
factor	trillion

Materials

hand calculators
newspaper and magazine ads
old telephone book
digit cards
road atlas

Chapter Tests

There are two equivalent tests for each chapter, a pretest and a posttest. They are given full size in this teacher's edition, before and after each chapter. (See page 17d and page 54b for the Chapter 1 tests.) You may reproduce these tests or you may purchase them as duplicating masters in either of the two booklets, TESTS or PERSONALIZED LEARNING PACKET. Each section of these tests is keyed to a learning objective and to the relevant student text pages. To individualize your teaching, use the pretest with the Record and Assignment Chart (see page 17f). If you are maintaining a class-paced program, you may not wish to administer a pretest. In that case, you can use the pretest as an alternative posttest for makeup and retesting.

Chapter 1 Pretest

Name _____

Date _____

Write in standard numerals. [Obj. 1-1, pages 18–19]

1. sixteen thousand four hundred _____

2. twenty-four million _____

3. four billion, five hundred twenty-six thousand _____

Write in words.

4. 5324 _____

5. 400,000,000 _____

6. 8,000,000,153 _____

Round [Obj. 1-2, pages 20–23]

7. 47,583 to the nearest hundred. _____

8. 9754 to the nearest ten. _____

9. 86,500 to the nearest thousand. _____

10. 95,499,999 to the nearest million. _____

Add. [Obj. 1-3, pages 26–27, 30]

11. 37	12. 957	13. 35,794	14. 29	15. 482
+ 48	+ 688	+ 9,866	87	675
			+ 63	+ 448

Subtract. [Obj. 1-4, pages 28–30]

16. 83	17. 703	18. 57,341	19. 29,424	20. 80,000
– 46	– 286	– 26,887	– 6,958	– 27,543

Multiply. [Obj. 1-5, pages 32–39, 46]

21. 483	22. 604	23. 37	24. 5236	25. 3217
× 8	× 5	× 61	× 245	× 603

Divide. [Obj. 1-6, pages 40–46]

26. 3)423   27. 5)777   28. 28)2016   29. 48)24144   30. 521)40638

Solve. [Obj. 1-7, pages 31, 47–49]

31. Sam saved $1500. Then he bought a snow-mobile for $989. How much did he have left? _____

32. Joan bought a dog for $98 plus $6 tax. She also bought a collar and leash for $7. How much did she spend? _____

17d

Chapter 1
Record and Assignment Chart

Name _____

Pretest Date _____   Posttest Date _____

Objectives

		Pretest Score Mark number correct	Posttest Score Mark number correct
1-1	Write numbers with up to 15 digits in words and standard numerals.	0-1 | 2 | 3 | 4 | 5 | 6	0-1 | 2 | 3 | 4 | 5 | 6
1-2	Round whole numbers.	0 | 1 | 2 | 3 | 4	0 | 1 | 2 | 3 | 4
1-3	Add any two or more whole numbers.	0-1 | 2 | 3 | 4 | 5	0-1 | 2 | 3 | 4 | 5
1-4	Subtract any two whole numbers.	0-1 | 2 | 3 | 4 | 5	0-1 | 2 | 3 | 4 | 5
1-5	Multiply any two whole numbers.	0-1 | 2 | 3 | 4 | 5	0-1 | 2 | 3 | 4 | 5
1-6	Divide any two whole numbers.	0-1 | 2 | 3 | 4 | 5	0-1 | 2 | 3 | 4 | 5
1-7	Solve word problems that involve whole numbers.	0 | 1 | 2	0 | 1 | 2

Unsatisfactory Score | Satisfactory Score (Pretest and Posttest)

TEACHING ASSIGNMENTS*

	Student Page	Basic Assignment	Average Assignment	Enriched Assignment	Problem Solving	RETEACHING ASSIGNMENTS†
1-1	18, 19	1–18, 24–26	1–28, EW 1	1–28, EW 1		page 377 Set 14, BW 1
1-2	20, 21	1–64	1–74, EW 2	1–82, EW 2		page 377 Set 15, BW 2
1-2	22, 23	1–26	1–27, EW 3	1–28, EW 3		page 377 Set 16, BW 3
	24, 25	1–16	1–16, EW 4	1–16, EW 4	17, 18	page 377 Set 17, BW 4
1-3	26, 27	1–39	1–46, EW 5	1–49, EW 5		page 378, Set 18, BW 5
1-4	28, 29	1–38	1–41, EW 6	1–41, EW 6		page 378 Set 19, BW 6
1-3 1-4	30	1–30	1–35, EW 6	1–40, EW 6		BW 6
1-7	31	1–3	1–3	1–3		BW 6
	32, 33	1–20	1–31, EW 7	1–31, EW 7	32, 33, 34	page 378 Set 20, BW 7
1-5	34, 35	1–39	1–39, EW 8	1–39, EW 8	40, 41, 42	page 378 Set 21, BW 8
	36, 37	1–25	1–25, EW 9	1–25, EW 9	26, 27, 28, 29	page 379 Set 22, BW 9
	38, 39	1–34	1–34, EW 9	1–34, 39–40, EW 9	35, 36, 37, 38	page 379 Set 23, BW 9
	40, 41	1–50	1–50, EW 10	1–50, EW 10	51, 52, 53, 54	page 379 Set 24, BW 10
1-6	42, 43	1–30	1–30, EW 11	1–30, EW 11	31, 32, 33	page 379 Set 25, BW 11
	44, 45	1–23	1–30, EW 11	1–36, EW 11		page 379 Set 26, BW 11
1-3 1-5	46	1–9	1–9, EW 12	1–9, EW 12		BW 12
1-7	47	1–2	1–3	1–3		BW 12
1-7	48, 49	1–4	1–6, EW 12	1–6, EW 12		BW 12
1-7	398-401	Extra Problem Solving, Sets 1 and 2				
	50	Chapter Checkup				
	51	Project				
	52	Chapter Review				
	53	Chapter Challenge				
	54	Major Checkup				

*Check assignments for objectives with unsatisfactory pretest scores.   BW = Basic Worksheet

†Check assignments for objectives with unsatisfactory posttest scores.   EW = Enrichment Worksheet

17e

Record and Assignment Chart

The Record and Assignment charts provide a management system for individualized instruction. They are given in this teacher's edition at the beginning of each chapter. You may reproduce these charts or you may purchase them as duplicating masters in the booklet entitled PERSONALIZED LEARNING PACKET.

To provide individualized instruction, administer the chapter pretest to each student and enter the scores on the Record and Assignment Chart. In this example,

Chapter 1
Record and Assignment Chart

Name _Sara Cobb_

Pretest Date _9/15/81_ Posttest Date _____

Objectives

		Pretest Score Mark number correct	Posttest Score Mark number correct
1-1	Write numbers with up to 15 digits in words and standard numerals.	0-1 2 3 4 ✓5 6	0-1 2 3 4 5 6
1-2	Round whole numbers.	0 1 ✓2 3 4	0 1 2 3 4
1-3	Add any two or more whole numbers.	0-1 2 ✓3 4 5	0-1 2 3 4 5
1-4	Subtract any two whole numbers.	0-1 2 3 ✓4 5	0-1 2 3 4 5

Sara Cobb has a satisfactory score for objective 1-1 and an unsatisfactory score for objective 1-2. You can give teaching assignments for objective 1-2 by checking the appropriate rows in the lower part of the chart. You can indicate average assignments for Sara like this:

TEACHING ASSIGNMENTS*

	Student Page	Basic Assignment	Average Assignment	Enriched Assignment	Problem Solving	RETEACHING ASSIGNMENTS†
1-1	18, 19	1–18, 24–26	1–28, EW 1	1–28, EW 1		page 377 Set 14, BW 1
	20, 21	1–64	1–74, EW 2	1–82, EW 2		page 377 Set 15, BW 2
1-2	22, 23	1–26	1–27, EW 3 ✓	1–28, EW 3		page 377 Set 16, BW 3
	24, 25	1–16	1–16, EW 4	1–16, EW 4	17, 18 ✓	page 377 Set 17, BW 4
1-3	26, 27	1–39	1–46, EW 5 ✓	1–49, EW 5		page 378, Set 18, BW 5
1-4	28, 29	1–38	1–41, EW 6 ✓	1–41, EW 6		page 378 Set 19, BW 6
1-3 1-4	30	1–30	1–35, EW 6 ✓	1–40, EW 6		BW 6
				1–3		BW 6
						page 378 Set 20, BW 7

Sara has also been assigned the problem-solving exercises on page 25 since she needs practice in this skill. Another student can be given enriched assignments by checking assignments in the *Enriched* column. These assignments include the harder exercises. A student who works at a slower pace can be given the basic assignments which do not include harder exercises or Enrichment Worksheets.

You may also accommodate individual differences by modifying the scores considered satisfactory—superior students could be required to achieve nearly perfect scores while slower students might be allowed to progress to another chapter even though they have a lower score on some objectives.

There are several other choices you can make to adapt the program to individuals. You can selectively assign the Project, the Chapter Review, and the Chapter Challenge.

After a student has completed the assignments in a chapter, administer the posttest (see page 54a), enter the posttest scores on the Record and Assignment Chart, and assign reteaching assignments for objectives with unsatisfactory posttest scores.

1
Whole Numbers

STUDENT OBJECTIVE
To read and write numerals for large
  numbers.

VOCABULARY
billion, million, standard numeral, trillion

Suggested Lesson Plan

Introduction Remind students that in our system of naming numbers the value of each digit increases by 10 times as you move to the left. For this reason, our system is called a *base ten system*. The places are grouped in threes. Each three places is called a *period*. The names at the top of the chart on page 18 name these periods. Remind students that to read a numeral for a large number, they read the three digits within a period and say the period name, starting at the left. Commas are inserted for every three digits as visual clues for the period.

  For example, for the numeral in the chart on page 18, show students that they read "148" and then say the name of the period "million," then "731" and say the name of the next period, "thousand." Note that we do not say "ones" for the ones period; and, although the name of the period is plural, for example "millions," we say the name as if it were singular— "million."

  Try to have students read numerals without saying "and" between the names of the periods. This common practice is not correct since the proper function of "and" is to differentiate between the whole number part and the decimal part of a numeral. For example, 642 is read "six hundred forty-two" while 600.42 is read "six hundred and forty-two hundredths." Although students may continue to read the large numerals with "ands" you should try not to say the "and" in order to set a correct example.

Using the pages Have students turn to pages 18 and 19 in their books. Go over the exposition on page 18, noting the place-value chart and the numeral illustrated. Point out to students that the term "standard numeral" is generally used to refer to such numerals as 148,731,000. Other types of numerals are "expanded numerals," "exponential numerals," etc.

  Draw the place-value chart on the board and write several standard numerals below it so that the digits line up in the proper columns. Call on

students in turn to read the numerals aloud. As they read, point with your finger to the digits being read and the name of the period when you come to a comma.

  Continue having students read the numerals aloud for exercises 1—23. Have each student read at least one numeral by going back over some exercises out of order.

  Have students do exercises 24—28 for written work, writing standard numerals for numbers written with words.

Large numbers

You need only the ten digits 0, 1, 2, 3, 4, 5, 6, 7, 8, 9 to write a numeral for any whole number, *no matter how large*. The average number of kilometers between the earth and the sun is shown in this place-value table.

Trillions			Billions			Millions			Thousands			Ones		
hundreds	tens	ones	hundreds	tens	ones	hundreds	tens	ones	hundreds	tens	ones	hundreds	tens	ones
						1	4	8	7	3	1	0	0	0

Standard numeral: **148,731,000**

Starting at the right, each group of three digits (called a **period**) is usually set off with a comma.

  Read as: **"one hundred forty-eight million,** seven hundred thirty-one thousand**"**

To read a large number, first think about the value of each period.

trillions	billions	millions	thousands	ones
4,	372,	053,	007,	203

  four trillion, three hundred seventy-two billion, **fifty-three** million, seven thousand, **two hundred three**

18

Assignments

BASIC
page 18 Discuss
page 19 exercises 1—18, 24—26
Basic Worksheet 1

AVERAGE
page 18 Discuss
page 19 exercises 1—28
Enrichment Worksheet 1

ENRICHED
page 18 Discuss
page 19 exercises 1—28
Enrichment Worksheet 1

EXTRA PRACTICE
page 377 set 14

EXERCISES
Read aloud.

1. 58,374   2. 195,396   3. 528,030   4. 401,006

5. 7,821,534   6. 9,060,358   7. 923,465   8. 178,025

9. 5,273,456   10. 8,392,051   11. 38,297,438   12. 51,703,004

13. 952,360,000   14. 538,412,073   15. 3,825,506,142

16. 7,020,350,413   17. 79,003,000,580   18. 391,000,000,000

19. 385,700,000,000   20. 521,361,782,534   21. 5,820,000,000,000

22. 48,036,742,100,000   23. 593,120,000,590,000

Here are some number facts about the sun.
Give the standard numeral.

24. Its mass is three hundred thirty-one thousand, nine hundred fifty *times* the mass of the earth.   331,950

25. The diameter is one million, three hundred eighty-four thousand kilometers.   1,384,000

26. The temperature at the center is about nineteen million, nine hundred eighty thousand degrees Celsius.   19,980,000

27. It gives the earth about ninety-four trillion kilowatts of energy.   94,000,000,000,000

28. The star closest to our solar system is about forty trillion, six hundred eighty-one billion, one hundred forty-seven million kilometers away.   40,681,147,000,000

19

Name _____
Basic Worksheet 1

trillions billions millions thousands ones
432, 571, 065, 289, 146

Give the digit in the
1. hundreds place. _____   2. ten thousands place. _____
3. millions place. _____   4. hundred thousands place. _____
5. billions place. _____   6. hundred trillions place. _____
7. ten millions place. _____   8. ten billions place. _____
9. ten trillions place. _____   10. hundred millions place. _____

Match.
_____ 11. 382,051,060   a. thirty-eight million, two hundred five thousand, one hundred sixty
_____ 12. 380,251,600   b. three hundred eighty-two million, five thousand, one hundred sixty
_____ 13. 38,205,160   c. three hundred eighty-two million, fifty-one thousand, sixty
_____ 14. 382,051,600   d. three hundred eighty million, two hundred fifty-one thousand, sixty
_____ 15. 382,005,160   e. three hundred eighty million, two hundred fifty-one thousand, six hundred
_____ 16. 38,251,060   f. three hundred eighty-two million, fifty thousand, sixteen
_____ 17. 380,251,060   g. three hundred eighty-two million, fifty-one thousand, six hundred
_____ 18. 38,250,160   h. three hundred eighty million, two hundred fifty thousand, sixteen
_____ 19. 382,050,016   i. thirty-eight million, two hundred fifty-one thousand, sixty
_____ 20. 380,250,016   j. thirty-eight million, two hundred fifty thousand, one hundred sixty

(7) Large numbers   Copyright © 1979 by D. C. Heath and Company   Student text pages 18, 19

Name _____
Enrichment Worksheet 1

What number is
1. 1 thousand greater than 5269? _____
2. 4 thousand greater than 6208? _____
3. 2 thousand less than 36,782? _____
4. 10 thousand less than 596,832? _____
5. 100 thousand greater than 460,082? _____
6. 100 thousand greater than 900,000? _____
7. 10 thousand less than 600,000? _____
8. 3 million greater than 5,381,000? _____
9. 2 million less than 2,684,000? _____
10. 1 billion greater than 568,000,000? _____
11. 10 billion less than 12,678,000,000? _____

What whole number is "halfway" between
12. 0 and 1000? _____
13. 9000 and 10,000? _____
14. 9500 and 10,000? _____
15. 24,000 and 24,050? _____
16. 99,000 and 100,000? _____
17. 125,600 and 126,000? _____
18. 3,821,000 and 3,822,000? _____
19. 5,160,000 and 5,166,000? _____
20. 18,404,000 and 18,404,250? _____

(7) Large numbers   Copyright © 1979 by D. C. Heath and Company   Student text pages 18, 19

Follow-up Activities

Reinforcement This game provides further experiences with reading "large numbers." Divide the students into two well-balanced teams. Have a player from one team go to the chalkboard and write a large number (15 digits or fewer). Have a volunteer from the other team read the numeral. If he is correct, his team is awarded one point. If he is incorrect, the player who wrote the numeral on the board can earn a point by reading the numeral correctly. Next, call on a player from the other team to go to the chalkboard and write a numeral. Play continues until a team has a total of 12 points and thus wins the game.

Enrichment Ask students to determine how many different 3-digit numbers they can "build" using all these digits:

4 7 9   Answer: 6

Ask, "How many different 4-digit numbers can be built with these digits?"

6 1 8 6   Answer: 12

"How many different 4-digit numbers can be built with these digits?"

9 2 7 4   Answer: 24

CALCULATOR ACTIVITY
Provide one calculator for every two students. One student reads the numbers for exercises 1−3 on page 19 aloud. The other student enters the numbers in the calculator as he or she hears them and finds the sum of the three numbers. If the sum is correct, the students have read and entered the numbers correctly. If the sum is not correct, they try the three numbers again. Continue for every three numbers through exercise 12.

Exercises 1−3, sum 781,800;
Exercises 4−6, sum 17,282,898;
Exercises 7−9, sum 6,374,946;
Exercises 10−12, sum 98,392,493.

Answers.
24. 331,950   25. 1,384,000
26. 19,980,000
27. 94,000,000,000,000
28. 40,681,147,000,000

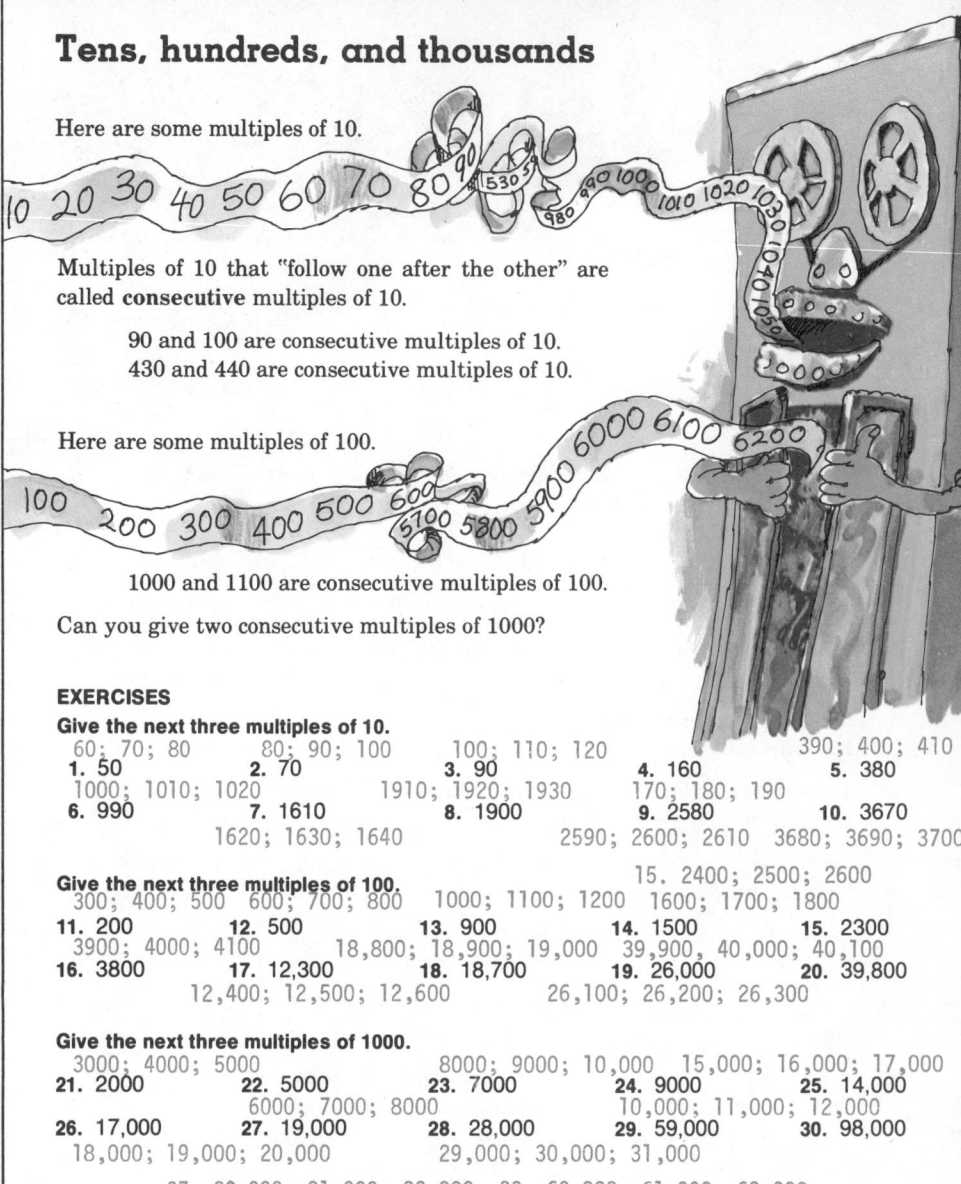

STUDENT OBJECTIVES
To identify consecutive multiples of 10, 100, and 1000.
To write standard numerals as expanded numerals.

VOCABULARY
consecutive multiples, expanded numeral

Suggested Lesson Plan

Introduction Write these sequences of numbers on the board and ask what numbers come next:

40, 50, 60, ___, ___, ___
460, 470, 480, ___, ___, ___
1230, 1240, 1250, ___, ___, ___

1600, 1700, 1800, ___, ___, ___
2400, 2500, 2600, ___, ___, ___
4800, 4900, 5000, ___, ___, ___

16,000, 17,000, 18,000, ___, ___, ___
120,000, 121,000, 122,000, ___, ___, ___
518,000, 519,000, 520,000, ___, ___, ___

Explain that the first three sequences that students completed are called *consecutive multiples* of 10. Ask what the second sequences would be called (consecutive multiples of 100) and the third sequences of numbers (consecutive multiples of 1000.)

Direct students to the exposition on page 21. Explain that a standard numeral can be expressed as an expanded numeral by writing each digit as a multiple of the place value it occupies. For example, in 642, the 6 really means 600, and the 4 means 40. Thus 642 in expanded form is 600 + 40 + 2.

Write 4 or 5 numerals on the board and have students write expanded numerals.

Using the pages Use the exposition on page 20 to reinforce the introduction to consecutive multiples. Have students give examples of consecutive multiples of 10, 100, and 1000.

Next write a two-digit number on the board and have students name the consecutive multiples of 10 that the number is between. For example, 48 is between 40 and 50.

Write several three- and four-place numerals on the board and have students name the consecutive multiples of 100 that the number is between. For example, 642 is between 600 and 700. Do more examples for consecutive multiples of 1000.

Assign exercises 1–82 for written work.

Tens, hundreds, and thousands

Here are some multiples of 10.

Multiples of 10 that "follow one after the other" are called **consecutive** multiples of 10.

90 and 100 are consecutive multiples of 10.
430 and 440 are consecutive multiples of 10.

Here are some multiples of 100.

1000 and 1100 are consecutive multiples of 100.

Can you give two consecutive multiples of 1000?

EXERCISES
Give the next three multiples of 10.
60; 70; 80   80; 90; 100   100; 110; 120   390; 400; 410
1. 50 **2.** 70 **3.** 90 **4.** 160 **5.** 380
1000; 1010; 1020 1910; 1920; 1930 170; 180; 190
6. 990 **7.** 1610 **8.** 1900 **9.** 2580 **10.** 3670
1620; 1630; 1640 2590; 2600; 2610 3680; 3690; 3700

Give the next three multiples of 100.
15. 2400; 2500; 2600
300; 400; 500 600; 700; 800 1000; 1100; 1200 1600; 1700; 1800
11. 200 **12.** 500 **13.** 900 **14.** 1500 **15.** 2300
3900; 4000; 4100 18,800; 18,900; 19,000 39,900; 40,000; 40,100
16. 3800 **17.** 12,300 **18.** 18,700 **19.** 26,000 **20.** 39,800
12,400; 12,500; 12,600 26,100; 26,200; 26,300

Give the next three multiples of 1000.
3000; 4000; 5000 8000; 9000; 10,000 15,000; 16,000; 17,000
21. 2000 **22.** 5000 **23.** 7000 **24.** 9000 **25.** 14,000
6000; 7000; 8000 10,000; 11,000; 12,000
26. 17,000 **27.** 19,000 **28.** 28,000 **29.** 59,000 **30.** 98,000
18,000; 19,000; 20,000 29,000; 30,000; 31,000

27. 20,000; 21,000; 22,000 29. 60,000; 61,000; 62,000
20 30. 99,000; 100,000; 101,000

Assignments

BASIC
page 20 exercises 1–30
page 21 exercises 31–64
Basic Worksheet 2

AVERAGE
page 20 exercises 1–30
page 21 exercises 31–74
Enrichment Worksheet 2

ENRICHED
page 20 exercises 1–30
page 21 exercises 31–82
Enrichment Worksheet 2

EXTRA PRACTICE
page 377 set 15

Write the two consecutive multiples of 10 that the given number is between.

31. 53 (Answer 50, 60)
32. 82 80; 90
33. 95 90; 100
34. 236 230; 240
35. 758 750; 760
36. 996 990; 1000
37. 137 130; 140
38. 297 290; 300
39. 599 590; 600
40. 1235 1230; 1240
41. 1364 1360; 1370
42. 2375 2370; 2380
43. 4991 4990; 5000
44. 6998 6990; 7000

Write the two consecutive multiples of 100 that the given number is between.

45. 358 300; 400
46. 526 500; 600
47. 908 900; 1000
48. 1542 1500; 1600
49. 1973 1900; 2000
50. 2713 2700; 2800
51. 2974 2900; 3000
52. 7820 7800; 7900
53. 1529 1500; 1600
54. 9280 9200; 9300
55. 11,248 11,200; 11,300
56. 15,943 15,900; 16,000
57. 23,993 23,900; 24,000
58. 96,421 96,400; 96,500
59. 84,601 84,600; 84,700

Write the two consecutive multiples of 1000 that the given number is between.

60. 2816 2000; 3000
61. 5601 5000; 6000
62. 9309 9000; 10,000
63. 12,386 12,000; 13,000
64. 51,742 51,000; 52,000
65. 52,174 52,000; 53,000
66. 68,031 68,000; 69,000
67. 74,395 74,000; 75,000
68. 80,861 80,000; 81,000
69. 99,376 99,000; 100,000
70. 123,452 123,000; 124,000
71. 215,395 215,000; 216,000
72. 109,465 109,000; 110,000
73. 596,645 596,000; 597,000
74. 899,904 899,000; 900,000

Here is how to write a standard numeral as an **expanded numeral**. Notice the multiples that are used.

$$526,378 = 500,000 + 20,000 + 6000 + 300 + 70 + 8$$

A multiple of:	100,000	10,000	1000	100	10	1

Give the expanded numeral.

75. 758 700 + 50 + 8
76. 2356 2000 + 300 + 50 + 6
77. 4829 4000 + 800 + 20 + 9
78. 6238 6000 + 200 + 30 + 8
79. 39,274 30,000 + 9000 + 200 + 70 + 4
80. 83,261 80,000 + 3000 + 200 + 60 + 1
81. 295,378 200,000 + 90,000 + 5000 + 300 + 70 + 8
82. 563,174 500,000 + 60,000 + 3000 + 100 + 70 + 4

21

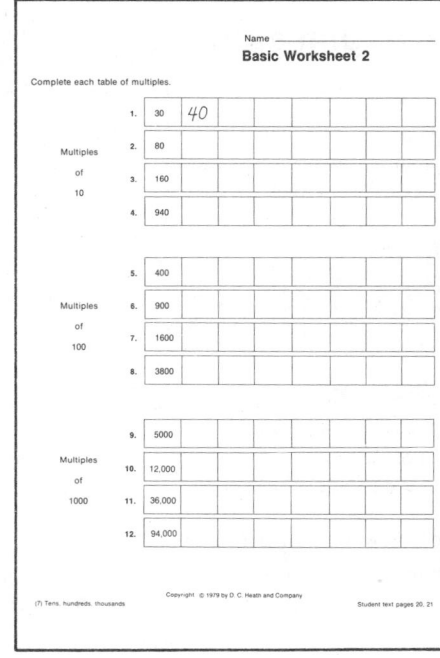

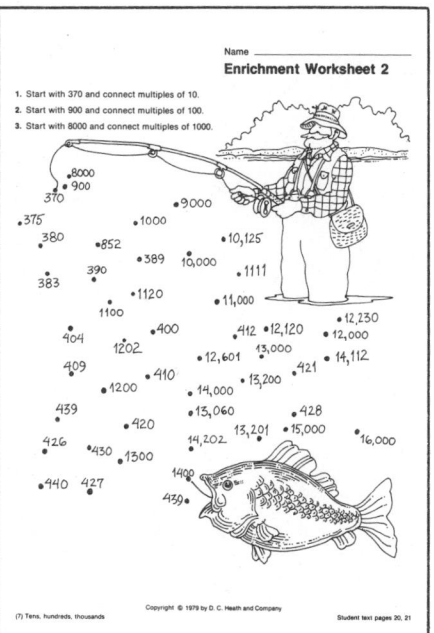

STUDENT OBJECTIVE
To round numbers to the nearest 10,
nearest 100, and nearest 1000.

VOCABULARY
rounding

Suggested Lesson Plan

Introduction Find in a newspaper or magazine advertisement or news report some examples of the use of approximations in place of actual counts or measurements. Show the examples to your class and ask them to make some educated guesses about the real values for which the approximations are given. Ask students to suggest other examples.

Introduce the concept of rounding by writing a 3-digit number on the board. Ask a student to name the consecutive multiples of 10 that the number is between. Write these multiples above and below the number to be rounded.

$$640$$
Example: 643
$$650$$

Now ask which multiple of 10 the number is nearer to. Thus, 643 is rounded to 640.

Repeat with several numbers, moving to multiples of 100 and 1000.

Write a number, say 750, that is to be rounded to the nearest hundred. After listing the multiples of 100 above and below 750, have students note that 750 is exactly halfway between 700 and 800. Explain that in these instances it is the general custom to round up to the larger multiple. Thus, 750 is rounded to 800.

Using the pages Use the exposition on page 22 to summarize the introduction to the lesson.

Work through the shortcut described on page 23. Explain to students that instead of listing the multiples of 1000, we can think of the multiples by just looking at the digit in the thousands place. The digit in the hundreds place will tell us whether the number is to be rounded "up" or "down."

Assign exercises 1–13 to be done in class before discussing the shortcut method. After allowing a few minutes for students to round the numbers, read the answers so they can correct their own work.

After explaining the shortcut method, assign exercises 14–28 for written work.

22   Lesson 3 (core)

Rounding

Sometimes rounded numbers are used instead of exact numbers.

When we use the nearest multiple of 10 as the rounded number, we are **rounding to the nearest 10.**

38 | Round to nearest 10 >40

51 | Round to nearest 10 >50

When we use the nearest multiple of 100 as the rounded number, we are **rounding to the nearest 100.**

576 | Round to nearest 100 >600

621 | Round to nearest 100 >600

When a number to be rounded is half way between two multiples, round up to the greater multiple.

75 | Round to nearest 10 >   80

850 | Round to nearest 100 >   900

4500 | Round to nearest 1000 >5000

EXERCISES
Round to the nearest 10.

1. 71 70   2. 88 90   3. 97   4. 155
                              100   160

Round to the nearest 1000.

9. 7586   10. 997   11. 376,500
   8000   1000   377,000

22

Round to the nearest 100.

5. 631   6. 641   7. 1550   8. 3050
   600   600   1600   3100

Round to the nearest million.

12. 5,432,671   13. 5,583,675
    5,000,000   6,000,000

About 400,000 kg of fish were caught today

Assignments

BASIC
page 22 exercises 1–13
page 23 exercises 14–26
Basic Worksheet 3

AVERAGE
page 22 exercises 1–13
page 23 exercises 14–27
Enrichment Worksheet 3

ENRICHED
page 22 exercises 1–13
page 23 exercises 14–28
Enrichment Worksheet 3

EXTRA PRACTICE
page 377 set 16

Here is how I round 67,523 to the nearest 1000.

Step 1. Find the thousands place.

67,523
   ↑

Step 2. Look 1 place to the right. If the digit is 5 or greater, round "up."

67,523 ⟶ 68,000
    ↑

Use the shortcut to round the following numbers.
Round to the nearest 100.

14. 780   800   15. 923   900   16. 5280   5300   17. 650   700   18. 14,350

                                                                    14,400

Round to the nearest 1000.

19. 8500   20. 27,499   21. 186,501   22. 399,846
     9000   27,000   187,000   400,000

Round to the nearest 100,000.

23. 386,543   24. 2,867,321   25. 14,977,000   26. 16,450,000
     400,000   2,900,000   15,000,000   16,500,000

The table shows the findings of a recent census.

27. Round each population to the nearest 100,000.

28. Round to the nearest million.

Eight Most Populous States

State	Population
California	19,953,134
New York	18,190,740
Pennsylvania	11,793,909
Texas	11,196,730
Illinois	11,113,976
Ohio	10,652,017
Michigan	8,875,083
New Jersey	7,168,164

23

Follow-up Activities

Reinforcement The following game provides further practice in rounding. Divide the students into two well-balanced teams. Write the number 458,316 on the chalkboard. A player from one of the teams comes to the chalkboard and rounds the number to the nearest 10. If the player is correct, that team is awarded a point. A player from the other team comes to the chalkboard and rounds the number to the nearest 100. Continue in this way, having students round the number to the nearest 1000, to the nearest 10,000, and to the nearest 100,000. Write a larger number on the chalkboard and continue to play the game. The first team to earn a total of 12 points wins the game.

Enrichment The game described above may also be used with more able students. You may wish to encourage them to work with larger numbers and have them round to the nearest 1,000,000, to the nearest 10,000,000, and so on.

CALCULATOR ACTIVITY
Have students round exercises 1−4 to the nearest 10. As they round the numbers they enter them in the calculator and add. The sum of the rounded numbers for exercises 1−4 is 420. If they round all 4 numbers correctly, they should get the correct sum.

Exercises 1−4, sum 420

Rounded to the nearest 100
Exercises 5−8, sum 5900

Rounded to the nearest 1000
Exercises 9−11, sum 386,000

Answers.

27. 20,000,000   28. 20,000,000
    18,200,000   18,000,000
    11,800,000   12,000,000
    11,200,000   11,000,000
    11,100,000   11,000,000
    10,700,000   11,000,000
     8,900,000   9,000,000
     7,200,000   7,000,000

Suggested Lesson Plan

Introduction Begin this lesson with a quick discussion of the sport of hot-air ballooning. Try to involve students in the lesson by looking for their personal knowledge or experiences with the sport. Before straying too far from the lesson, point out that in this sport, as in many others, the winner is determined by comparing measurements. Ask for other sports where the winner is determined by comparing measurements. Some examples will be shot put, broad jump, high jump, pole vault, pass and kick football, cross country team scores, etc.

Of course, most students can compare numbers, but often they have not identified efficient ways to do so. List on the board, in flow-chart fashion, the organized steps in comparing numbers: First, if the numbers have a different number of digits, the number having more digits is greater. Second, if they have the same number of digits, start at the left and compare the digits in the same place. The first number having a greater digit is the greater number.

Put these examples on the board and work through the steps for comparison.

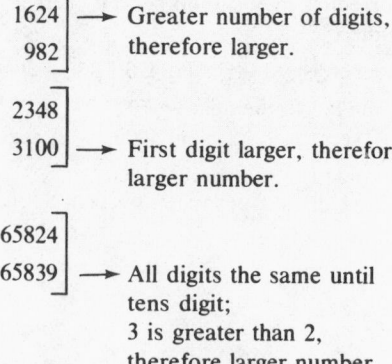

$$\left.\begin{array}{c} 1624 \\ 982 \end{array}\right\} \longrightarrow$$ Greater number of digits, therefore larger.

$$\left.\begin{array}{c} 2348 \\ 3100 \end{array}\right\} \longrightarrow$$ First digit larger, therefore larger number.

$$\left.\begin{array}{c} 65824 \\ 65839 \end{array}\right\} \longrightarrow$$ All digits the same until tens digit; 3 is greater than 2, therefore larger number.

As you list these numbers and compare on the board, review the use of > "is greater than" and < "is less than." Remind students that the closed end of the symbol always points to the smaller number.

Using the pages After having students try a few comparisons you have put on the board, assign exercises 1–18 for written work.

Comparing numbers

The first hot-air balloon was built in 1783 by two Frenchmen. Today hot-air ballooning is a sport enjoyed by many.

Hot-air balloonists compete in several events. One event is spot-landing. The balloons must take off and land during a specified time and land near a specified spot. The balloon that lands closest to the spot wins.

Suppose one balloon missed the spot by 1526 m and another missed by 1578 m. To determine which balloon won, the numbers are compared.

Since both have the same number of digits, we start at the left and compare the digits that are in the same place.

$$\overset{\boxed{\text{Since } 2 < 7}}{\underset{\text{is less than}}{1526 \quad < \quad 1578}}$$

$$\overset{\boxed{\text{Since } 7 > 2}}{\underset{\text{is greater than}}{1578 \quad > \quad 1526}}$$

EXERCISES
< or >?

1. 864 ● 865
   <
2. 700 ● 699
   >
3. 999 ● 1000
   <
4. 907 ● 970
   <

5. 6493 ● 6385
   >
6. 4863 ● 987
   >
7. 88,235 ● 91,740
   <
8. 64,291 ● 64,289
   >

9. 71,892 ● 53,461
   >
10. 80,007 ● 78,999
    >
11. 354,621 ● 703,945
    <
12. 406,735 ● 406,673
    >

24

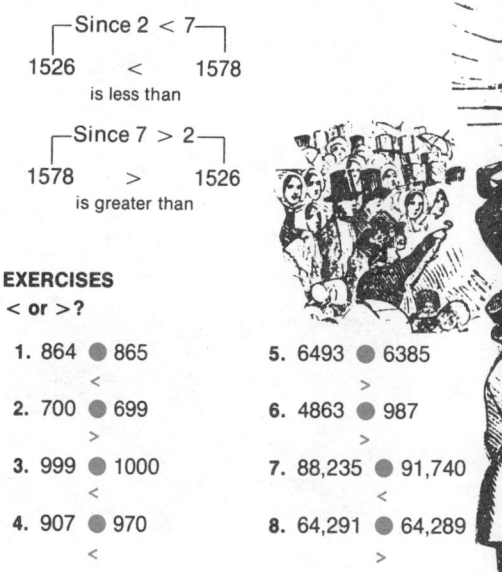

Assignments

BASIC
page 24 exercises 1–12
page 25 exercises 13–16
Basic Worksheet 4

AVERAGE
page 24 exercises 1–12
page 25 exercises 13–16
Enrichment Worksheet 4

ENRICHED
page 24 exercises 1–12
page 25 exercises 13–18
Enrichment Worksheet

EXTRA PRACTICE
page 377 set 17

17. Here are the results of a spot-landing event. Rank the balloons from 1 through 6. First place (least number) gets a rank of 1.

Name of balloon	Meters landed from spot	
America	786	3
Big Apple	770	2
Easy Floater	909	5
Explorer	859	4
Free Spirit	913	6
High Rise	768	1

18. The winner of a cross-country event is the balloon that floats the farthest during a specified time. Rank the balloons from 1 through 6. First place (greatest number) gets a rank of 1.

Name of balloon	Kilometers traveled	
America	1380	2
Big Apple	1275	5
Easy Floater	1363	3
Explorer	1196	6
Free Spirit	1394	1
High Rise	1282	4

13. 488,183 ● 487,997
>

14. 745,835 ● 745,853
<

15. 800,000 ● 799,000
>

16. 99,999 ● 100,000
<

25

Follow-up Activities

Reinforcement Prepare a deck of digit cards or playing cards with the face cards removed. Organize students in pairs. As the students are dealt one card at a time, the student plays the card in a place-value position to make the largest number possible. After a card is placed, it cannot be moved. Each student can be dealt different cards or they can both play the same cards without letting each other see where they have played the card.

Enrichment Give each student part of a page from an old telephone book. Have each student circle twenty consecutive numbers in one column. Students then look in their list of numbers for "winners." They should use only the last 4 digits in the telephone number. For example, "Who has the largest 4-digit number? Who has the smallest 4-digit number? Who has the number closest to 5000?", etc.

EXCURSION

1. What is the greatest number of small squares that can be shaded so that no two are in the same row, column, or diagonal?

   Answer.   1

2. Repeat with this 3-by-3 square.   2

3. Repeat with a 4-by-4 square.   4

4. Can you find a rule?

For $n > 3$, in an $n \times n$ square n small squares can be shaded.

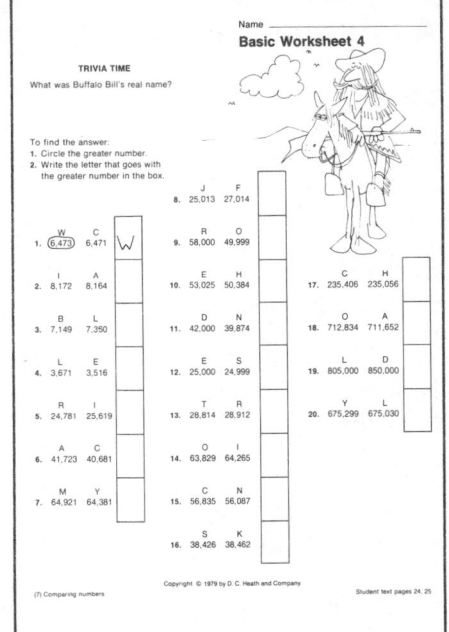

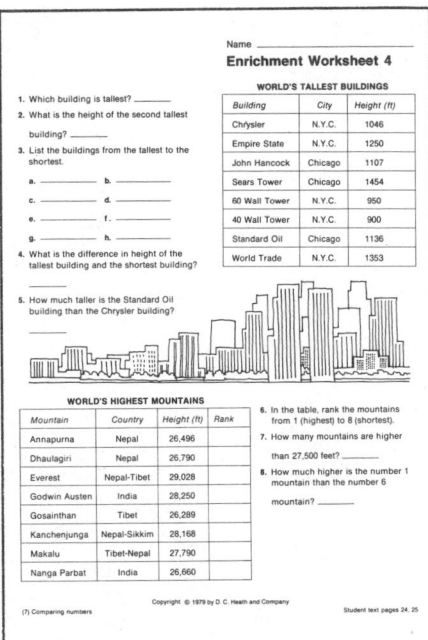

Suggested Lesson Plan

Introduction   A few of your students may have difficulty adding whole numbers. All of them will profit from a review and practice of addition of large whole numbers.

The students who are having difficulty will probably have one or more of these problems: (1) they have not memorized the basic addition facts; (2) they do not know how to regroup; (3) they have trouble keeping consecutive sums "in their heads" when they have more than two addends. In the first case, they need more practice; some addition games or drill with basic-fact cards would probably be best. For difficulty with regrouping, the use of sticks to show regrouping may help. For the third problem, regular mental arithmetic drill will help. Give oral exercises such as the following, pausing after each operation to give students time to do the computation. Start with 5, add 4, add 12, subtract 6, add 3. What is the end number?

Using the pages   Go over the exposition on page 26, discussing the need to estimate before proceeding to the sum. Point out that by estimating students can identify gross errors. Work through the addition examples, showing each step on the board. Put several more examples on the board and, as students work the problems, circulate around the room to note the ones having difficulty.

Assign exercises 1−49 for written work. Point out to students that they should estimate the sum for exercises 1−12 before adding. For exercises 40−46, students do not have to add; they match the correct sum by estimating.

Adding whole numbers

If you estimate a sum before you add, you will know whether your answer is reasonable. You can round each addend to the nearest 100 to estimate the sum.

600   300
589 + 323

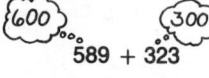

The sum is near 900

To find the sum, we add in each column.

Step 1. Add ones and regroup.

$$\begin{array}{r} 1 \\ 589 \\ +323 \\ \hline 2 \end{array}$$

Step 2. Add tens and regroup.

$$\begin{array}{r} 11 \\ 589 \\ +323 \\ \hline 12 \end{array}$$

Step 3. Add hundreds.

$$\begin{array}{r} 11 \\ 589 \\ +323 \\ \hline 912 \end{array}$$

EXERCISES

First estimate the sum. Then add.

1. 373 **900**	2. 287 **900**	3. 675 **900**	4. 858 **1000**	5. 467 **1000**	6. 897 **1300**
+499	+566	+184	+79	+465	+399
872	853	859	937	932	1296
7. 742 **1600**	8. 868 **1600**	9. 879 **1400**	10. 656 **1200**	11. 363 **1000**	12. 367 **1100**
+935	+733	+464	+455	+570	+678
1677	1601	1343	1111	933	1045

Add.

13. $8.26	14. $6.85	15. $8.31	16. $9.76	17. $6.74
+1.37	+2.37	+5.46	+3.85	+3.21
$9.63	$9.22	$13.77	$13.61	$9.95
18. 6482	19. 5761	20. 9473	21. 4235	22. 2058
+7358	+3897	+6745	+3849	+3979
13,840	9658	16,218	8084	6037
23. 56248	24. 51742	25. 80375	26. 503498	27. 736429
+39746	+39165	+29654	+128745	+167893
95,994	90,907	110,029	632,243	904,322

26

Assignments

BASIC
page 26   exercises 1−27
page 27   exercises 28−39,
       Keeping Skills Sharp
Basic Worksheet 5

AVERAGE
page 26   exercises 1−27
page 27   exercises 28−46,
       Keeping Skills Sharp
Enrichment Worksheet 5

ENRICHED
page 26   exercises 1−27
page 27   exercises 28−49,
       Keeping Skills Sharp
Enrichment Worksheet 5

EXTRA PRACTICE
page 378   set 18

Add.

28.	952 163 +798 **1913**	29.	521 630 +708 **1859**	30.	521 835 +477 **1833**	31.	623 507 + 31 **1161**
32.	703 259 384 +801 **2147**	33.	591 538 322 +960 **2411**	34.	124 202 419 +716 **1461**	35.	218 162 907 +669 **1956**
36.	5258 3940 7132 +8679 **25,009**	37.	5366 2170 8422 +7359 **23,317**	38.	7436 2918 3756 +2943 **17,053**	39.	5234 7183 6129 +7438 **25,984**

Match. Find the sums by estimating.

40. 1536 + 294   d   a. 1185
41. 399 + 582   f   b. 1422
42. 908 + 695   g   c. 1297
43. 911 + 386   c   d. 1830
44. 620 + 314 + 488   b   e. 2080
45. 375 + 529 + 281   a   f. 981
46. 692 + 575 + 813   e   g. 1603

Find the missing digits.

47.
```
      2
   38■9
 + 4■6■5
   8094
      2
```
48.
```
    7 3 2
   ■9■8■
 + 6■7■9
  141131
     1 4
```
49.
```
          8
   563■25
 4+3■796■6
    ■1■7■1
    9 1 9
```

Round to the nearest 100.

1. 496 — 500
2. 506 — 500
3. 739 — 700
4. 850 — 900
5. 967 — 1000
6. 1421 — 1400
7. 1530 — 1500
8. 2674 — 2700
9. 3961 — 4000
10. 5382 — 5400
11. 6250 — 6300
12. 8109 — 8100
13. 9950 — 10,000
14. 10,072 — 10,100
15. 26,439 — 26,400
16. 37,825 — 37,800
17. 48,954 — 49,000
18. 59,500 — 59,500
19. 60,972 — 61,000
20. 79,036 — 79,000

27

Follow-up Activities

Reinforcement This game may be used to provide further practice with the addition algorithm. Write the ten digits 0–9 on cards and have students draw a table like this:

```
   □ □ □
 + □ □ □
 ‾‾‾‾‾‾‾
```

As you draw and replace the cards, have students fill in their tables with the digits. When all 6 cells have been filled, have students add the two numbers in their tables. The player with the greatest sum wins the game.

Enrichment Write on the chalkboard:

```
  three
  three
 +three
 ‾‾‾‾‾‾
  seven
```

Explain to students that different letters are to be replaced by different digits and that the same letters are to be replaced by the same digit. Have students reconstruct the addition problem.

Answer:
```
  23199
  23199
 +23199
 ‾‾‾‾‾‾
  69597
```

EXCURSION
Follow the path to find the end number.

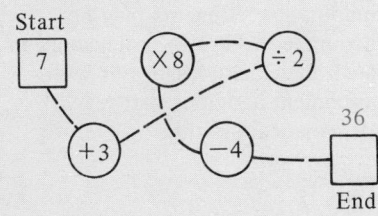

Start [7] ×8 ÷2 +3 −4 36 End

(core) Lesson 5   **27**

Name _____
Basic Worksheet 5

Step 1. Add and regroup. | Step 2. Add. | Step 3. Add and regroup. | Step 4. Add.
```
  4837        4837        4837        4837
 +1645       +1645       +1645       +1645
 ‾‾‾‾‾‾      ‾‾‾‾‾‾      ‾‾‾‾‾‾      ‾‾‾‾‾‾
      2          82         482        6482
```

Add.
1. 567 +278 = 845
2. 359 +514
3. 638 +298
4. 585 +369
5. 142 +463
6. 346 +518
7. 280 +495
8. 439 +186
9. 255 +698
10. 369 +187
11. 5973 +8382
12. 9065 +6597
13. 8082 +5986
14. 7934 +8490
15. 8499 +7983
16. 25631 +74289
17. 78205 +39648
18. 27381 +46958
19. 43975 +72568
20. 93421 +63687
21. 321 746 +825
22. 594 375 +294
23. 758 299 +642
24. 2174 3859 +6052
25. 4387 2165 +9340
26. 591 238 256 +721
27. 927 818 150 +436
28. 431 655 583 +77
29. 8206 5300 7429 +2605
30. 5241 7382 6251 +3433

(7) Adding whole numbers   Copyright © 1979 by D. C. Heath and Company   Student text pages 26, 27

Name _____
Enrichment Worksheet 5

```
 5 8 6
+ 3 4 7
‾‾‾‾‾‾‾
 9 3 3
```

Fill in the missing digits.
1. 3 4□ / +1□9 / □31
2. □6□8 / +4□5□ / 1 2 3 9 7
3. 8 3 2□ / +□□□ / □4□0 0
4. 8□9□5 / +□7□8□ / □0 1 4 5 1
5. 9 5 / 6□ / +□3 / 2 4 5
6. 5 9□ / 2□7 / +□4 9 / 1 0 1 4
7. 6 2□ / □9 8 / +5□9 / 1 5 9 6
8. □3□2 / 9□8 1 / +7 3 2□ / 2 5 3 5 2

Like letters are replaced by the same digit.
Each letter stands for a digit. What are the digits?
9. ME +MY = EYE
10. SEND +MORE = MONEY

(7) Adding whole numbers   Copyright © 1979 by D. C. Heath and Company   Student text pages 26, 27

Suggested Lesson Plan

Introduction Not all your students will need the redevelopment of the subtraction algorithm, but all of them will benefit from practice. Put several examples on the board and have students work through them while you record the work on the board. Before working the problems, have students estimate the differences by rounding to the nearest 100 or 1000 and then subtracting mentally. The problems should increase in difficulty, from some requiring just one regrouping to others requiring two or three regroupings. Also have students try some that have zeros in the minuend—for example, 803 − 624 or 3006 − 1697.

Using the pages Use the exposition on pages 28 and 29 to reinforce the examples already worked on the board. Call on individual students to explain the steps while you record the work on the board. Assign exercises 1−36 for written work. Work through the shortcut illustrated on page 29. (Do not expect all students to benefit from it.)

Encourage students to try the Calculator Activity if they have their own calculators. You may want to have several calculators available for use during free time on problems assigned computation. Students may be encouraged to use the calculators to check their daily lessons or with enrichment activities that reveal mathematical insight.

Subtracting whole numbers

You can estimate a difference by rounding each number to the nearest 100.

823 − 294

The difference is near 500.

To find the difference, we subtract in each column.

Step 1. Not enough ones.
Regroup 1 ten for 10 ones.

$$8\,\overset{1}{2}\,\overset{1}{3}$$
$$-2\,9\,4$$

Step 2. Subtract ones.

$$8\,\overset{1}{\cancel{2}}\,\overset{1}{3}$$
$$-2\,9\,4$$
$$9$$

Step 3. Not enough tens.
Regroup 1 hundred for 10 tens.

$$\overset{7}{8}\,\overset{11}{\cancel{2}}\,\overset{1}{3}$$
$$-2\,9\,4$$
$$9$$

Step 4. Subtract tens.

$$\overset{7}{\cancel{8}}\,\overset{11}{\cancel{2}}\,3$$
$$-2\,9\,4$$
$$2\,9$$

Step 5. Subtract hundreds.

$$\overset{7}{\cancel{8}}\,\overset{11}{\cancel{2}}\,3$$
$$-2\,9\,4$$
$$5\,2\,9$$

28

1.	385 200 − 162 223		2.	531 200 − 283 248
3.	617 200 − 356 261		4.	420 100 − 274 146
5.	569 200 − 372 197		6.	913 700 − 187 726
7.	$4.42 $0 − 3.65 $.77		8.	$12.86 $5 − 7.53 $5.33
9.	$46.32 $30 − 22.78 $23.54		10.	$58.10 $10 − 47.64 $10.46
11.	$42.22 $20 − 16.79 $25.43		12.	$34.23 $20 − 7.78 $26.45
13.	8263 5000 − 3288 4975		14.	5082 2000 − 2659 2423
15.	7938 4000 − 3814 4124		16.	8842 1000 − 7966 876
17.	5934 6000 − 359 5575		18.	2686 2000 − 1347 1339

Assignments

BASIC
page 28 exercises 1−18
page 29 exercises 19−38
Basic Worksheet 6

AVERAGE
page 28 exercises 1−18
page 29 exercises 19−41
Enrichment Worksheet 6

ENRICHED
page 28 exercises 1−18
page 29 exercises 19−41
Enrichment Worksheet 6

EXTRA PRACTICE
page 378 set 19

Sometimes you have to regroup more than once before you can subtract.

Step 1. Not enough ones. No tens. Regroup 1 hundred for 10 tens.

$$\overset{5}{\cancel{6}}\,0\,2$$
$$-3\,5\,7$$

Step 2. Regroup 1 ten for 10 ones.

$$\overset{5}{\cancel{6}}\overset{9}{\cancel{0}}\,2$$
$$-3\,5\,7$$

Step 3. Subtract.

$$\overset{5}{\cancel{6}}\overset{9}{\cancel{0}}\overset{}{1}2$$
$$-3\,5\,7$$
$$2\,4\,5$$

Subtract.

19. 503 −265 238	**20.** 702 −384 318	**21.** 804 −796 8	**22.** 200 −35 165	**23.** 400 −138 262	**24.** 800 −463 337
25. 7021 −1673 5348	**26.** 8003 −5236 2767	**27.** 8013 −5278 2735	**28.** 3107 −1288 1819	**29.** 8000 −2134 5866	**30.** 4000 −3906 94
31. 5821 −2774 3047	**32.** 5963 −4877 1086	**33.** 5062 −3748 1314	**34.** 3051 −1773 1278	**35.** 6000 −4193 1807	**36.** 2800 −766 2034

 To find a difference like this, I decrease each number by 1. The difference is the same and there is no regrouping.

$$9000 \longrightarrow 8999$$
$$-4763 \longrightarrow -4762$$

Use the shortcut to find the differences.

37. 800 −274 526	**38.** 7000 −2975 4025	**39.** 10000 −7358 2642	**40.** 23000 −18654 4346	**41.** 36000 −17368 18,632

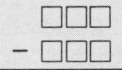

What is the sum of the first two odd numbers? $1 + 3 = ?$ 4

What is the sum of the first three odd numbers? $1 + 3 + 5 = ?$ 9

What is the sum of the first four odd numbers? $1 + 3 + 5 + 7 = ?$ 16

Guess: What is the sum of the first hundred odd numbers? 10,000

Check your guess.

29

Follow-up Activities

Reinforcement The following game may be used to provide further practice with the subtraction algorithm. Write the ten digits 0−9 on cards and have students draw a table like this:

☐☐☐
−☐☐☐

As you draw and replace the cards, have students fill in their tables with the digits. When all 6 cells have been filled in, have students subtract the "bottom number" from the "top number." The player getting the least difference wins the game. If a player's "top number" is less than his "bottom number" he will not be able to do the subtraction unless he works in the set of integers. Consequently, you may want the players to agree beforehand that if this should happen, the player would be disqualified for that game.

Enrichment Point out to students that if they add the numbers along each row, column, or diagonal in this square they will get the same sum. This is called a *magic square*.

4	9	2
3	5	7
8	1	6

Have students copy and complete these magic squares. Perhaps some students would like to make a report on magic squares. Answers are given in red.

23	28	21
22	24	26
27	20	25

115	120	113
114	116	118
119	112	117

CALCULATOR ACTIVITY
Have two students write down 20 numbers of their choice, between 1 and 100, on one sheet of paper. Name a target number. Each student tries to pick from the list two numbers whose difference is close to the target number. Each student uses the calculator to subtract the numbers to see how close they came. The student getting closer to the target number wins a point. First student to get 10 points is the winner.

To practice addition and subtraction of
large whole numbers.
To solve word problems dealing with
mathematics and world geography.

Suggested Lesson Plan

Introduction Review the meaning of
the grouping symbols, or parentheses,
for exercises 25–34. Ask students to
find the value of $24 - (3 \times 4)$. You are
looking for the answer 12. Any students
who get 84 have ignored the grouping
symbol and subtracted before
multiplying. Remind students that
grouping symbols are punctuation for
mathematical sentences as commas are
for English sentences. They are used to
insure that we understand the meaning.
The grouping symbols tell us to do the
operation inside them before doing other
operations.

Introduce page 31 by asking if
anyone in class has been to Great
Britain or if their parents have lived in
Great Britain. Point out that these
questions deal with populations and
areas of countries within Great Britain.

Using the pages Assign exercises
1–40 and 1–3 on page 31. Correct page
30 carefully and make note of students
who are missing these types of
problems.

Practice exercises

Add.

| 1. | 529 +788 | 1317 | 2. | 356 +429 | 785 | 3. | 752 +386 | 1138 | 4. | 714 +299 | 1013 | 5. | 637 +540 | 1177 |

Remember that you can add numbers in any order. Look for sums of 10.

| 6. | 38 9 72 +41 | 160 | 7. | 52 96 44 18 +53 | 263 | 8. | 328 252 767 +833 | 2180 | 9. | 5937 2615 7875 +1483 | 17,910 |

Subtract.

| 10. | 758 –294 | 464 | 11. | 936 –314 | 622 | 12. | 529 –286 | 243 | 13. | 415 –379 | 36 | 14. | 603 –258 | 345 |

| 15. | 502 –359 | 143 | 16. | 700 –675 | 25 | 17. | 3002 –1758 | 1244 | 18. | 9000 –2654 | 6346 | 19. | 18132 –7964 | 10,168 |

| 20. | 32109 –14836 | 17,273 | 21. | 52374 –35695 | 16,679 | 22. | 81034 –7526 | 73,508 | 23. | 493000 –158271 | 334,729 | 24. | 638002 –59708 | 578,294 |

Compute. Remember to work inside the grouping symbols first.

25. $(78 + 52) - 29$ 101
26. $78 + (52 - 29)$ 101
27. $(358 - 156) - 78$ 124
28. $358 - (156 - 78)$ 280
29. $(900 - 532) + 53$ 421
30. $900 - (532 + 53)$ 315
31. $(98 + 36) - (70 + 19)$ 45
32. $(163 - 129) + (800 - 593)$ 241
33. $(6381 - 592) + (753 + 96)$ 6638
34. $(3974 + 2831) - (3000 - 714)$ 4519
35. $(4983 + 627) - (40 - 8)$ 5578
36. $(295 + 6041) - (985 - 26)$ 5377
37. $(2539 - 109) + (863 - 92)$ 3201
38. $(4409 - 1283) + (62 - 19)$ 3169
39. $(7513 - 4998) - (253 + 1097)$ 1165
40. $(610 + 5347) - (1983 - 625)$ 4599

30

Assignments

BASIC
page 30   exercises 1–30
page 31   exercises 1–3
Basic Worksheet 6

AVERAGE
page 30   exercises 1–35
page 31   exercises 1–3
Enrichment Worksheet 6

ENRICHED
page 30   exercises 1–40
page 31   exercises 1–3
Enrichment Worksheet 6

REVIEW PRACTICE
page 377   set 17

Mathematics and world geography

Great Britain

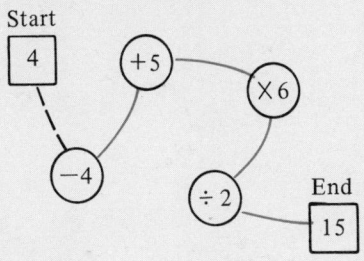

1. The United Kingdom includes Great Britain (England, Wales, Scotland) and Northern Ireland.

   a. What is the population of Great Britain? **53,811,000**

   b. What is the land area of Great Britain? **229,879 square km**

   c. How much larger in area is England than Scotland? **51,596 square km**

   d. How many fewer people live in Wales than in Scotland? **2,493,000**

2. Oxford University is the oldest university in England. Records show that lectures were given at Oxford as early as 1117. How many years was that before Columbus came to America? **375**

3. The largest cathedral of the Church of England is St. Paul's Cathedral in London. It was built between the years 1675 and 1710. How long did it take to build? **35 years**

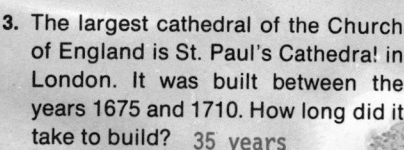

Country	Land area (square kilometers)	Population (recent census)
England	130,357	45,870,000
Wales	20,761	2,724,000
Scotland	78,761	5,217,000
Northern Ireland	14,118	1,534,000

31

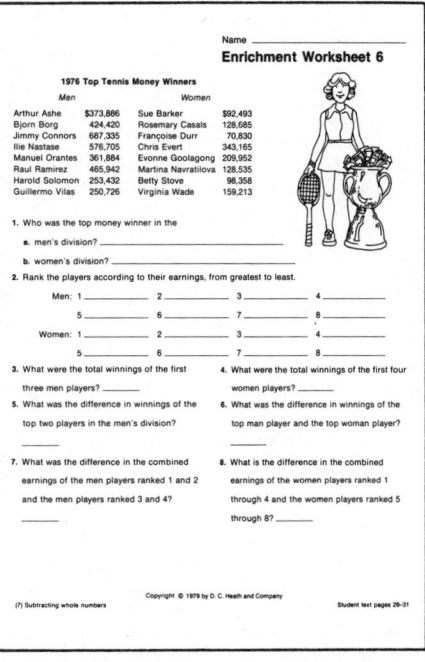

Follow-up Activities

Reinforcement Sit down with any student who misses more than 8 problems on page 30 and try to determine the student's particular difficulty. Try to prescribe activities that will overcome these deficiencies, such as basic-facts drill for those who are missing basic facts, etc. It would be well to try to get the parents of these students to help the student with some type of remedial program.

Enrichment Have students generate questions about your geographical region similar to the questions on page 31. By referring to a road atlas, they can formulate questions about the population of large cities or towns in the area. Post the better sets of these problems on the mathematics bulletin board.

EXCURSION
Copy, and finish drawing the path.

Start
4 ⋯ −4 → +5 → ×6 → ÷2 → End 15

Suggested Lesson Plan

Introduction   This lesson should be a review for all students, although you may find that some students have difficulty. Try to work with these students on an individual basis while the others work independently on the problems in the lesson.

Using the pages   Use the exposition on page 32 and the three steps to discuss the multiplication algorithm. Put the example on the board and show each step while calling on pupils. Try two or three more examples, recording the work while students explain. Encourage students to estimate by rounding and multiplying before working the example.

Assign exercises 1—34 for written work.

Multiplying by a 1-digit number

This skier is practicing for a downhill race. During practice one day she skied a 783-meter run 8 times. To find how many meters she skied that day, we can multiply.

Step 1.   Multiply ones and regroup.

$$\begin{array}{r} \overset{2}{783} \\ \times\,8 \\ \hline 4 \end{array}$$

Step 2.   Multiply tens and add. Then regroup.

$$\begin{array}{r} \overset{62}{783} \\ \times\,8 \\ \hline 64 \end{array}$$

Step 3.   Multiply hundreds and add.

$$\begin{array}{r} \overset{62}{783} \\ \times\,8 \\ \hline 6\,264 \end{array}$$

The answer is reasonable because 783×8 is about 800×8, or 6400.

32

Assignments

BASIC
page 32 Discuss
page 33 exercises 1—20
Basic Worksheet 7

AVERAGE
page 32 Discuss
page 33 exercises 1—33
Enrichment Worksheet 7

ENRICHED
page 32 Discuss
page 33 exercises 1—34, excursion
Enrichment Worksheet 7

EXTRA PRACTICE
page 378 set 20

EXERCISES

First estimate the product. Then multiply.

1. 78 · 320
$$\begin{array}{r} 78 \\ \times 4 \\ \hline 312 \end{array}$$

2. 59 · 360
$$\begin{array}{r} 59 \\ \times 6 \\ \hline 354 \end{array}$$

3. 73 · 560
$$\begin{array}{r} 73 \\ \times 8 \\ \hline 584 \end{array}$$

4. 85 · 450
$$\begin{array}{r} 85 \\ \times 5 \\ \hline 425 \end{array}$$

5. 94 · 630
$$\begin{array}{r} 94 \\ \times 7 \\ \hline 658 \end{array}$$

6. 292 · 1500
$$\begin{array}{r} 292 \\ \times 5 \\ \hline 1460 \end{array}$$

7. 311 · 2100
$$\begin{array}{r} 311 \\ \times 7 \\ \hline 2177 \end{array}$$

8. 529 · 4500
$$\begin{array}{r} 529 \\ \times 9 \\ \hline 4761 \end{array}$$

9. 614 · 4800
$$\begin{array}{r} 614 \\ \times 8 \\ \hline 4912 \end{array}$$

10. 673 · 4200
$$\begin{array}{r} 673 \\ \times 6 \\ \hline 4038 \end{array}$$

Multiply.

11. $\begin{array}{r} \$5.96 \\ \times 4 \\ \hline \$23.84 \end{array}$

12. $\begin{array}{r} \$7.84 \\ \times 3 \\ \hline \$23.52 \end{array}$

13. $\begin{array}{r} \$9.21 \\ \times 8 \\ \hline \$73.68 \end{array}$

14. $\begin{array}{r} \$7.56 \\ \times 6 \\ \hline \$45.36 \end{array}$

15. $\begin{array}{r} \$7.92 \\ \times 7 \\ \hline \$55.44 \end{array}$

16. $\begin{array}{r} 3821 \\ \times 5 \\ \hline 19,105 \end{array}$

17. $\begin{array}{r} 7456 \\ \times 3 \\ \hline 22,368 \end{array}$

18. $\begin{array}{r} 9378 \\ \times 6 \\ \hline 56,268 \end{array}$

19. $\begin{array}{r} 2916 \\ \times 4 \\ \hline 11,664 \end{array}$

20. $\begin{array}{r} 5304 \\ \times 2 \\ \hline 10,608 \end{array}$

21. $\begin{array}{r} 82771 \\ \times 8 \\ \hline 662,168 \end{array}$

22. $\begin{array}{r} 65382 \\ \times 7 \\ \hline 457,674 \end{array}$

23. $\begin{array}{r} 59307 \\ \times 6 \\ \hline 355,842 \end{array}$

24. $\begin{array}{r} 68259 \\ \times 9 \\ \hline 614,331 \end{array}$

25. $\begin{array}{r} 73006 \\ \times 5 \\ \hline 365,030 \end{array}$

26. 563 × 3   1689

27. 958 × 6   5748

28. 1814 × 7   12,698

29. 3254 × 5   16,270

30. 61078 × 4   244,312

31. 93865 × 9   844,785

Solve.

32. A one-day chair lift ticket costs $12.75. How much would it cost for 3 days? $38.25

33. There are two downhill runs. One is 783 meters and the other is 1002 meters. How much longer is the second run?   219 m

34. One day Beth skied the longer downhill run (see exercise 33) 6 times. How many meters was that?   6012

Excursion ■O■O■O■O■O■O■O■O■O■O■O■

You can use your fingers to multiply by 9. Here is how to find 8 × 9.

Hold your hands in front of you with your fingers extended. Since you are multiplying by 8, fold down the 8th finger from the left. The picture shows how you can see the product, 72.

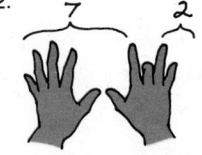

Try this with 3 × 9, 7 × 9, etc.

33

Reinforcement Prepare a display as shown below for the overhead projector.

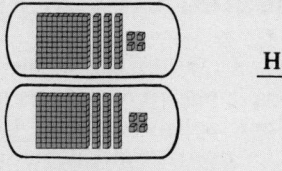 

Have students copy the table and record in the top row the number of ones, the number of bars of ten, and the number of squares of one hundred in each of the sets. Point out that the total number of unit squares can be determined by multiplying in columns. Have them complete their tables like this:

H	T	O
1	3	4
	×	2
2	6	8

Give other appropriate problems.

Enrichment Have students copy and complete the following multiplication boxes. The answers are given in red.

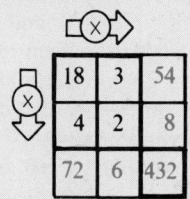

18	3	54
4	2	8
72	6	432

30	8	240
6	1	6
180	8	1440

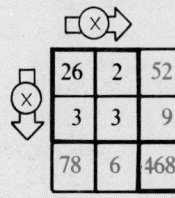

26	2	52
3	3	9
78	6	468

CALCULATOR ACTIVITY

Have pairs of students play "Target Multiplication." Each pair of students writes down 20 numbers on a sheet of paper and places the paper in front of them. As you give "target" numbers, each student selects two numbers whose product is close to the target number. Have the students then multiply the numbers on their calculator. The one who is closer wins a point. First student to get 10 points wins.

(core) Lesson 8   33

Basic Worksheet 7

Name _____

Step 1. Multiply and regroup.

Step 2. Multiply, add, and regroup.

Step 3. Multiply and add.

Multiply.

1. $\begin{array}{r} 234 \\ \times 5 \\ \hline 1170 \end{array}$

2. $\begin{array}{r} 453 \\ \times 4 \end{array}$

3. $\begin{array}{r} 212 \\ \times 6 \end{array}$

4. $\begin{array}{r} 310 \\ \times 4 \end{array}$

5. $\begin{array}{r} 502 \\ \times 7 \end{array}$

6. $\begin{array}{r} 934 \\ \times 5 \end{array}$

7. $\begin{array}{r} 821 \\ \times 6 \end{array}$

8. $\begin{array}{r} 752 \\ \times 5 \end{array}$

9. $\begin{array}{r} 695 \\ \times 6 \end{array}$

10. $\begin{array}{r} 457 \\ \times 7 \end{array}$

11. $\begin{array}{r} 628 \\ \times 4 \end{array}$

12. $\begin{array}{r} 742 \\ \times 5 \end{array}$

13. $\begin{array}{r} 539 \\ \times 6 \end{array}$

14. $\begin{array}{r} 603 \\ \times 8 \end{array}$

15. $\begin{array}{r} 902 \\ \times 5 \end{array}$

16. $\begin{array}{r} 821 \\ \times 7 \end{array}$

17. $\begin{array}{r} 493 \\ \times 5 \end{array}$

18. $\begin{array}{r} 291 \\ \times 4 \end{array}$

19. $\begin{array}{r} 758 \\ \times 3 \end{array}$

20. $\begin{array}{r} 962 \\ \times 9 \end{array}$

21. $\begin{array}{r} 5214 \\ \times 4 \end{array}$

22. $\begin{array}{r} 3872 \\ \times 2 \end{array}$

23. $\begin{array}{r} 9516 \\ \times 7 \end{array}$

24. $\begin{array}{r} 3054 \\ \times 3 \end{array}$

25. $\begin{array}{r} 6741 \\ \times 6 \end{array}$

26. $\begin{array}{r} 3162 \\ \times 8 \end{array}$

27. $\begin{array}{r} 5348 \\ \times 3 \end{array}$

28. $\begin{array}{r} 2976 \\ \times 2 \end{array}$

29. $\begin{array}{r} 8207 \\ \times 8 \end{array}$

30. $\begin{array}{r} 5396 \\ \times 7 \end{array}$

31. $\begin{array}{r} 6421 \\ \times 9 \end{array}$

32. $\begin{array}{r} 7003 \\ \times 4 \end{array}$

33. $\begin{array}{r} 8216 \\ \times 8 \end{array}$

34. $\begin{array}{r} 5147 \\ \times 2 \end{array}$

35. $\begin{array}{r} 8359 \\ \times 9 \end{array}$

(7) Multiplying by a 1-digit number

Copyright © 1979 by D. C. Heath and Company

Student text pages 32, 33

Enrichment Worksheet 7

Name _____

What do you call a purple monkey?

To find the answer:
1. Multiply.
2. Cross out each box below that contains an answer.
3. Read the answer using the letters in the remaining boxes.

1. $\begin{array}{r} 56 \\ \times 5 \\ \hline 280 \end{array}$

2. $\begin{array}{r} 76 \\ \times 7 \end{array}$

3. $\begin{array}{r} 90 \\ \times 4 \end{array}$

4. $\begin{array}{r} 86 \\ \times 9 \end{array}$

5. $\begin{array}{r} 91 \\ \times 8 \end{array}$

6. $\begin{array}{r} 378 \\ \times 4 \end{array}$

7. $\begin{array}{r} 253 \\ \times 4 \end{array}$

8. $\begin{array}{r} 301 \\ \times 6 \end{array}$

9. $\begin{array}{r} 821 \\ \times 5 \end{array}$

10. $\begin{array}{r} 728 \\ \times 8 \end{array}$

11. $\begin{array}{r} 3914 \\ \times 4 \end{array}$

12. $\begin{array}{r} 2965 \\ \times 3 \end{array}$

13. $\begin{array}{r} 5021 \\ \times 8 \end{array}$

14. $\begin{array}{r} 7371 \\ \times 5 \end{array}$

15. $\begin{array}{r} 529\epsilon \\ \times 3 \end{array}$

16. $\begin{array}{r} 8374 \\ \times 9 \end{array}$

17. $\begin{array}{r} 9006 \\ \times 7 \end{array}$

18. $\begin{array}{r} 5718 \\ \times 4 \end{array}$

19. $\begin{array}{r} 4295 \\ \times 8 \end{array}$

20. $\begin{array}{r} 3679 \\ \times 6 \end{array}$

B 40168	A 523	K 5824	E 34360	A 480	R 776	280	A 63402	M 1806
N 22872	E 1512	W 75366	P 4015	E 1608	T 532	O 15656	R 1012	A 360	A 63042
G 36855	S 728	U 22074	L 774	A 17790	E 1521	A 15888	I 1606	T 4105	A 22704

(7) Multiplying by a 1-digit number

Copyright © 1979 by D. C. Heath and Company

Student text pages 32, 33

STUDENT OBJECTIVE
To multiply any whole number by
multiples of 10, 100, and 1000.

Suggested Lesson Plan

Introduction Write 3 sets of numbers
on the board, one set of numbers less
than 10, one set between 10 and 100,
and one set greater than 100. Starting
with the numbers less than 10, ask
students for the product of a number
and 10. Record the multiplication
sentence on the board, $6 \times 10 = 60$.
Move to the second set and ask for
products of several numbers and 10.
Then move to the third set and have
students give products of several
numbers and 10. Students should be
ready to express the generalization "add
a zero to multiply by 10."

Continue by having students express
the generalizations about multiplying by
100 and 1000. At the conclusion of this
development, have students identify
these products as multiples of 10, 100,
and 1000.

Now using multiples of 10 as
multipliers, ask students to find the
product of a multiple of 10 and a
two-digit number. Have them record
their work on scratch paper while you
show the work on the board. Follow this
with finding several products of numbers
multiplied by multiples of 100 and 1000.
Leave the work on the board, for you
will refer to it during the discussion of
the exposition on the text page.

Using the pages Have students open
their books to page 34. Use the
exposition to point out that multiplying
by a multiple of 10, 100, or 1000 can be
done using a shortcut. Refer back to the
work on the board and show that, by
thinking of the multiple of 10 as a
number times 10, they can multiply by
the number first and then just add a
zero. The thought process is very much
like that used at the beginning of the
lesson to find multiples of 10, 100, and
1000. Summarize the development in the
lesson by showing how this relationship
can be justified by the associative
property. Write the expression of the
associative property and the vertical
algorithm on the board and then show
the matching parts as in the exposition
on page 34.

Have students write the products
for exercises 1–9 on scratch paper.
Give them a few minutes to complete
their work and then read the answers.
For those who were sucessful, assign

exercises 10–42 for written work. Work
individually with any students having
difficulty.

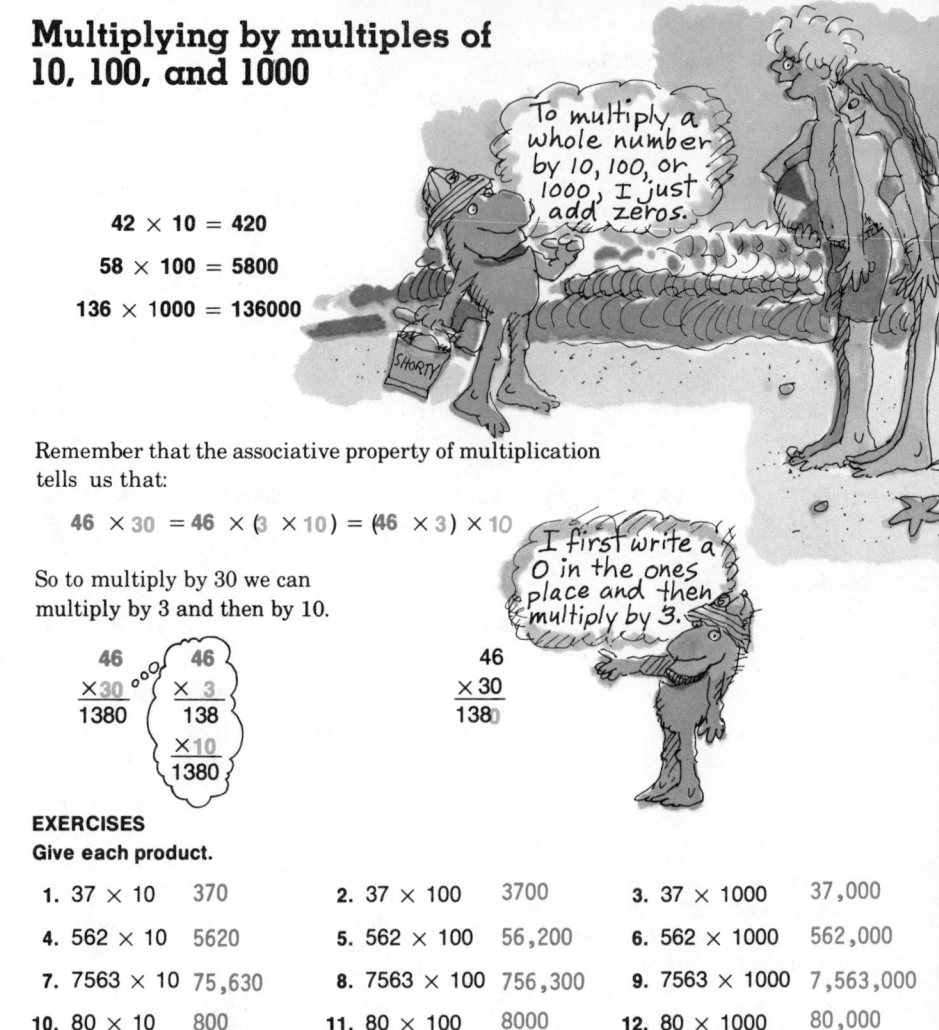

Multiplying by multiples of 10, 100, and 1000

$42 \times 10 = 420$

$58 \times 100 = 5800$

$136 \times 1000 = 136000$

Remember that the associative property of multiplication
tells us that:

$$46 \times 30 = 46 \times (3 \times 10) = (46 \times 3) \times 10$$

So to multiply by 30 we can
multiply by 3 and then by 10.

$$\begin{array}{r} 46 \\ \times 30 \\ \hline 1380 \end{array} \qquad \begin{array}{r} 46 \\ \times 3 \\ \hline 138 \\ \times 10 \\ \hline 1380 \end{array} \qquad \begin{array}{r} 46 \\ \times 30 \\ \hline 138 \end{array}$$

EXERCISES
Give each product.

1. 37×10 370
2. 37×100 3700
3. 37×1000 37,000

4. 562×10 5620
5. 562×100 56,200
6. 562×1000 562,000

7. 7563×10 75,630
8. 7563×100 756,300
9. 7563×1000 7,563,000

10. 80×10 800
11. 80×100 8000
12. 80×1000 80,000

13. 700×10 7000
14. 700×100 70,000
15. 700×1000 700,000

16. 1000×10 10,000
17. 1000×100 100,000
18. 1000×1000 1,000,000

34

Assignments

BASIC
page 34   exercises 1–18
page 35   exercises 19–39,
    Keeping Skills Sharp
Basic Worksheet 8

AVERAGE
page 34   exercises 1–18
page 35   exercises 19–40,
    Keeping Skills Sharp
Enrichment Worksheet 8

ENRICHED
page 34   exercises 1–18
page 35   exercises 19–42,
    Keeping Skills Sharp
Enrichment Worksheet 8

EXTRA PRACTICE
page 378   set 21

Multiply.

19. 57 × 20	20. 57 × 200	21. 57 × 2000	22. 570 × 200
23. 638 × 30	24. 638 × 300	25. 638 × 3000	26. 63800 × 30
27. 598 × 80	28. 473 × 50	29. 675 × 60	30. 341 × 90
31. 462 × 300	32. 296 × 500	33. 800 × 400	34. 300 × 700
35. 5673 × 3000	36. 9846 × 700	37. 5034 × 8000	38. 7735 × 9000

Complete the table.

39.	Minutes	15	38	75	120	135	212
	Seconds						

Solve.

40. A marathon (a foot race of just over 42 kilometers) has been run in 2 hours and 9 minutes. How many minutes is that?

41. The speed of sound in air at sea level at 0°C is about 332 meters per second. How far will sound travel in 30 seconds?

42. The speed of light is about 299,793 kilometers per second. How far does light travel in a minute?

Keeping Skills Sharp

Add.

1. 78
+ 29
107

2. 356
+ 75
431

3. 298
+ 574
872

4. 893
+ 277
1170

5. 3654
+ 2985
6639

6. 4736
+ 999
5735

7. 98
26
+59
183

8. 375
192
+468
1035

9. 26
35
44
+29
134

10. 529
638
466
+583
2216

35

Follow-up Activities

Reinforcement Have students do the Keeping Skills Sharp. After finishing the examples, they should correct their work with the answers provided.

Enrichment Organize students in pairs. Using newspaper ads, students take turns with one selecting an item and the other telling the price of 10 such items and 100 such items.

EXCURSION

Use these four numerals:

$$1, 2, 3, 4$$

and these symbols:

$$+, -, \times, \div$$
$$(\quad)$$

to write an expression for each of the numbers 1 through 10.

The numerals must all be used once and the symbols may be used as needed.

Example. $(4 \div 2 - 1) \times 3 = 3$

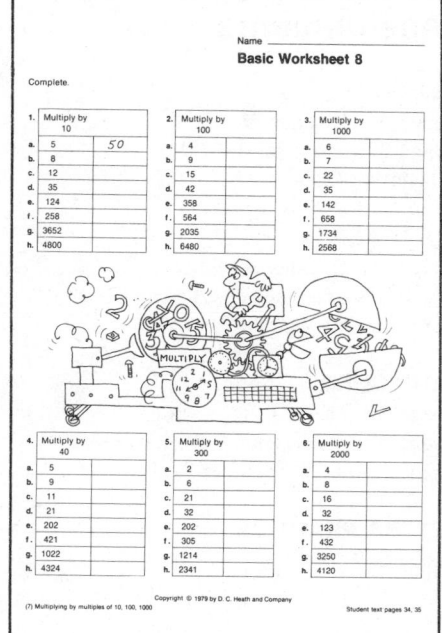

STUDENT OBJECTIVE

To multiply any whole number by a 2-digit number.

Suggested Lesson Plan

Introduction Review the work on pages 34 and 35 by having students multiply by multiples of 10 and 100.

Using the pages Use the situation on page 36 to generate interest in finding the product of 184 and 12. Multiplying by a 2-digit number should be a review for most students, but many will not have a high degree of accuracy. Put the example on the board and work through the algorithm one step at a time. As you record each partial product, show the factors beside the product. After you have completed the work, write the expression using the distributive property over the example. Circle matching product expressions in the sentence and the algorithm.

Present an additional problem by asking how far the car would travel in 18 hours at that same rate. Have students find the product on their paper while you move around the room observing their work. Note those students who are having difficulty, and give them individual help as the others proceed with their written work.

Assign some or all of exercises 1−29, depending on the time available. Daily practice on a few problems provides better maintenance of a skill than one large dose of practice.

In a 24-hour race a car averaged 184 kilometers per hour for the first 12 hours. We can multiply 184×12 to find how many kilometers the car traveled in 12 hours.

Remember that the distributive property tells us that:

$$184 \times 12 = 184 \times (2 + 10) = (184 \times 2) + (184 \times 10)$$

So to multiply by 12 we can multiply by 2, multiply by 10, and add.

Step 1. Multiply 184 by 2 to find how far the car traveled in 2 hours.

$$\begin{array}{r} 184 \\ \times\ 12 \\ \hline 368 \end{array} \longleftarrow 184 \times 2$$

Step 2. Multiply 184 by 10 to find how far the car traveled in 10 hours.

$$\begin{array}{r} 184 \\ \times\ 12 \\ \hline 368 \\ 1840 \end{array} \longleftarrow 184 \times 10$$

Step 3. Add to find how many kilometers the car traveled in 12 hours.

$$\begin{array}{r} 184 \\ \times\ 12 \\ \hline 368 \\ 184 \\ \hline 2208 \end{array} \longleftarrow 184 \times 12$$

36

Assignments

BASIC
page 36 Discuss
page 37 exercises 1−28
Basic Worksheet 9

AVERAGE
page 36 Discuss
page 37 exercises 1−29
Enrichment Worksheet 9

ENRICHED
page 36 Discuss
page 37 exercises 1−29, Excursion
Enrichment Worksheet 9

EXTRA PRACTICE
page 379 set 22

EXERCISES
Multiply.

1. 58 × 12 696	**2.** 65 × 46 2990	**3.** 74 × 33 2442	**4.** 92 × 69 6348	**5.** 89 × 52 4628
6. 156 × 54 8424	**7.** 474 × 53 25,122	**8.** 238 × 75 17,850	**9.** 506 × 24 12,144	**10.** 821 × 86 70,606
11. 734 × 49 35,966	**12.** 593 × 77 45,661	**13.** 658 × 92 60,536	**14.** 291 × 37 10,767	**15.** 756 × 54 40,824
16. 3214 × 68 218,552	**17.** 5978 × 86 514,108	**18.** 6359 × 75 476,925	**19.** 4618 × 34 157,012	**20.** 3921 × 93 364,653
21. 53826 × 38 2,045,388	**22.** 75346 × 46 3,465,916	**23.** 93580 × 68 6,363,440	**24.** 296374 × 89 26,377,286	**25.** 729108 × 27 19,685,916

Solve.

26. The winning car in the 24-hour race averaged 197 kilometers per hour. How far did the car go? 4728 km

27. One car averaged 192 kilometers per hour during the first 18 hours and 186 kilometers per hour during the last 6 hours. How far did the car go in the race? 4572 km

28. During the first half of the 24-hour race a car traveled 2172 kilometers. During the second half it averaged 178 kilometers per hour. How far did it travel? 4308 km

29. The car that came in last traveled 4399 kilometers. How much farther did the winning car travel? (See exercise 26.) 329 km

Excursion ◼◻◼◻◼◻◼◻◼◻◼◻◼◻

Finger Multiplication

You can use your fingers to find the product of 9 and a two-digit number *if* the tens digit of the two-digit number is less than the ones digit.

Example. 9 × 27

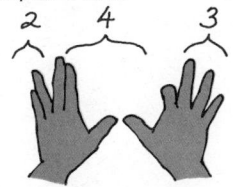

Make a space after the second finger from the left. Put down the seventh finger from the left. Read the answer: 243. Try this method with other problems. Check.

37

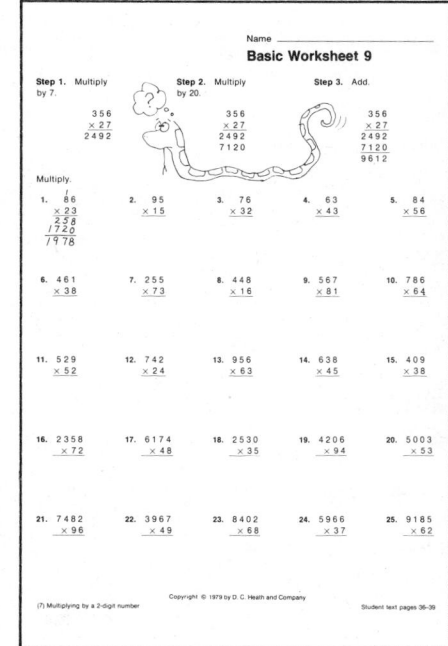

Follow-up Activities

Reinforcement You may wish to follow up the lesson by having students complete the following multiplication tables. Have them look for a shortcut for filling in the bottom cell of each column. (The product is the sum of the two products in the upper two cells, a consequence of the distributive property.)

×	21	32	26	38
6	126	192	156	228
20	420	640	520	760
26	546	832	676	988

×				
5	1180	1290	173.0	465.05
40	9440	10320	1384.0	3720.40
45	10620	11610	1557.0	4185.45

Enrichment Have students complete these missing-digit problems.

```
  3 □□          349
× □ 7         × 27
  2 4 □ 3       2443
  □□ 8          698
  □□ 2 3        9423
```

```
  □□ 8          518
×  4 □        × 46
  □□ 0 8       3108
  2 0 □ 2       2072
  2 □ 8 2 8     23828
```

CALCULATOR ACTIVITY
Without looking at their answers, students try to (1) pick the largest product in the first row of exercises on page 37, (2) pick the smallest product in the first row, etc.

After picking products, students take turns using a calculator to see whether they made the correct choice.

(core) Lesson 10 37

Suggested Lesson Plan

Introduction Review multiplication by
a 2-digit number before introducing this
lesson. Write these problems on the
board and have students work them
while you watch:

248	682	891
×24	×57	×36
(5952)	(38874)	(32076)

Any student who misses two of the
three should continue practice on
problems on page 37.

Using the pages Write the problem
presented on page 38 on the board, and
as students orally describe the work,
record each step on the board. After the
work is completed, point out that the
initial zero in the partial product
obtained when multiplying by a number
of tens can be omitted. Likewise the
zeros that are a result of multiplying by
a number of hundreds can be omitted in
the algorithm.

Caution students that if they use the
shortcut and omit the zeros, they must
be especially careful to align each
product below the digit by which they
are multiplying.

Ask students to work the two
additional examples at their seats. Have
a student describe the work while you
record it on the board. If any students
get the wrong answer, call on them to
identify the source of their error.

Assign some of exercises 1–34 and
the word problems for written work.
Plan to use those exercises not assigned
on another day.

Multiplying by a 3-digit number

Study these shortcuts for multiplying by a 3-digit number.

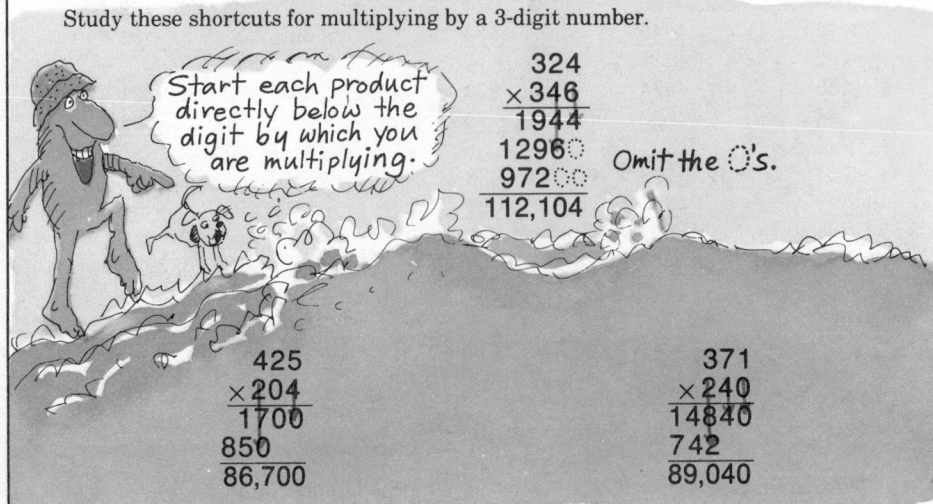

If you always write each product directly below the digit by
which you are multiplying, you will make few mistakes.

EXERCISES
Multiply.

1. 753	**2.** 821	**3.** 742	**4.** 658	**5.** 291
×162	×143	×234	×255	×368
121,986	117,403	173,628	167,790	107,088
6. 362	**7.** 455	**8.** 258	**9.** 615	**10.** 727
×248	×937	×342	×839	×189
89,776	426,335	88,236	515,985	137,403
11. 1538	**12.** 1965	**13.** 2742	**14.** 3953	**15.** 5829
×429	×364	×295	×338	×426
659,802	715,260	808,890	1,336,114	2,483,154

38

Assignments

BASIC
page 38 exercises 1–15
page 39 exercises 16–36
Basic Worksheet 9

AVERAGE
page 38 exercises 1–15
page 39 exercises 16–38
Enrichment Worksheet 9

ENRICHED
page 38 exercises 1–15
page 39 exercises 16–40
Enrichment Worksheet 9

EXTRA PRACTICE
page 379 set 23

Multiply.

16. 523 × 306 3138 1569 160,038	17. 421 × 603 253,863	18. 592 × 402 237,984	19. 603 × 501 302,103	20. 304 × 606 184,224
25. 3614 × 403 1,456,442	21. 571 × 630 359,730	22. 473 × 220 104,060	23. 217 × 300 65,100	24. 546 × 207 113,022
30. 5246 × 293 1,537,078	26. 2983 × 258 769,614	27. 7521 × 560 4,211,760	28. 6438 × 352 2,266,176	29. 2059 × 803 1,653,377
	31. 3958 × 405 1,602,990	32. 7042 × 200 1,408,400	33. 5063 × 540 2,734,020	34. 9384 × 398 3,734,832

Solve.

35. There were five hundred twelve tickets sold for a city baseball tournament. Each ticket sold for $1.25. What was the total in ticket sales? $640

36. The food committee for a club picnic bought 7 kilograms of hot dogs for $1.89 a kilogram and 10 dozen buns for $.59 a dozen. How much were these two items? $19.13

37. Marcia bought 12 golf balls for 75¢ each. She gave the clerk a ten-dollar bill. How much change should she have received? $1

38. In Campbell Junior High there are 27 more girls than boys. What is the total enrollment, if there are 342 girls?   657

Find the end number.

39. Start 378 ×138 +429 −548 End ? 110,818

40. 378 Start ×138 +429 −548 End ? 52,045

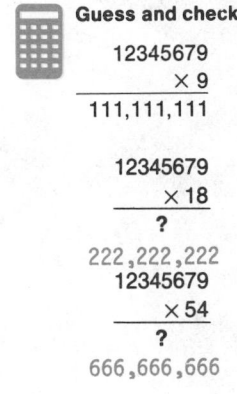

Guess and check!

```
  12345679
×        9
111,111,111

  12345679
×       18
        ?
222,222,222
  12345679
×       54
        ?
666,666,666
```

39

Follow-up Activities

Reinforcement Provide extra practice by having students complete this table. Students may realize that the products in a column are the partial products of the number in the bottom row.

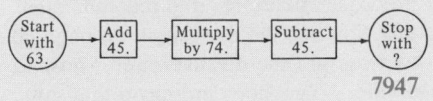

	24	36	48	86
7	168	252	336	602
20	480	720	960	1720
300	7200	10800	14400	25800
327	7848	11772	15696	28122

Enrichment You may wish to have more able students create a problem-solving situation for the following flow chart.

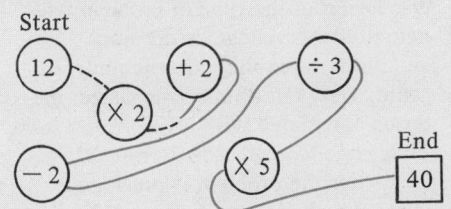

Start with 63. → Add 45. → Multiply by 74. → Subtract 45. → Stop with ?   7947

If time permits, have students write additional flow charts, exchange them, and write a problem for the flow chart they get.

EXCURSION

Copy, and finish drawing the path to get the ending number.

Start
12 +2 ÷3
×2
−2 ×5 End 40

Answer may vary.

(core) Lesson 11 39

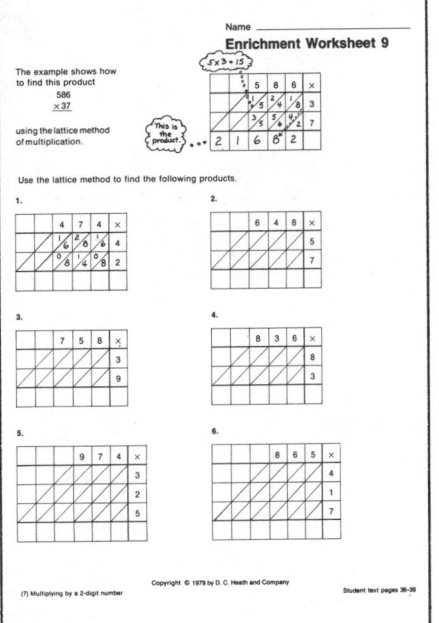

Basic Worksheet 9

Name _____

Step 1. Multiply by 7.
```
  356
× 27
2492
```
Step 2. Multiply by 20.
```
  356
× 27
2492
7120
```
Step 3. Add.
```
  356
× 27
2492
7120
9612
```

Multiply.

1. 86
× 23
258
1720
1978   2. 95
× 15   3. 76
× 32   4. 63
× 43   5. 84
× 56

6. 461
× 38   7. 255
× 73   8. 448
× 16   9. 567
× 81   10. 786
× 64

11. 529
× 52   12. 742
× 24   13. 956
× 63   14. 638
× 45   15. 409
× 38

16. 2358
× 72   17. 6174
× 48   18. 2530
× 35   19. 4206
× 94   20. 5003
× 53

21. 7482
× 96   22. 3967
× 49   23. 8402
× 68   24. 5966
× 37   25. 9185
× 62

Copyright © 1979 by D. C. Heath and Company

(7) Multiplying by a 2-digit number   Student text pages 36-39

Enrichment Worksheet 9

Name _____

The example shows how to find this product
```
  586
× 37
```
using the lattice method of multiplication.

This is the product … 2 1 6 8 2

Use the lattice method to find the following products.

1.   2.   3.   4.   5.   6.

Copyright © 1979 by D. C. Heath and Company

(7) Multiplying by a 2-digit number   Student text pages 36-39

STUDENT OBJECTIVE
To divide a whole number by a 1-digit number.

VOCABULARY
dividend, divisor, quotient, remainder

Suggested Lesson Plan

Introduction For certain students, the actual manipulation of place-value sticks for the division process may be helpful. On the other hand, all of your students have encountered the division algorithm before and most will be capable of dividing after a little review. The students who have had difficulty before will probably be more willing to listen to a direct "show and tell" lesson than one based on the "rationale" of the division process. Therefore, it is recommended that you use the exposition on page 40 to structure the discussion on "how to divide." This does not mean that you should avoid altogether the logic and reasoning behind the division algorithm. The extent and depth of your discussion should be based on your students' ability and their willingness to listen.

Using the pages Use the situation on page 40 to arouse interest in finding the answer to a division problem. A discussion of the type of problem will help students recognize division situations when they are encountered again. Use, but do not emphasize, the terms associated with division—*divisor*, *dividend*, *quotient*, and *remainder*.

After the problem is presented, write the division expression 113 ÷ 3 on the board. Next, show the algorithm form 3)113 so that students will realize that in the first expression the divisor follows the division sign ÷ . Ask a student to describe the steps in the division process while you record the work on the board.

The students should do the work for exercise 1 on their papers while you start the work on the board. Ask for a volunteer to complete the work as the students finish. Move around the room, noting how they are doing. Assign a subset of exercises 1–50 depending on the time available. Repeated practice on a few problems at a time is more beneficial than a large dose at one time. Also assign the word problems, exercises 51–54, for written work.

Carol, Joan, and Susan were given a box containing 113 records for working at a neighbor's garage sale. To find how many records each should get we can divide:

$$113 \div 3$$

Step 1. Not enough hundreds. Think about regrouping 1 hundred for 10 tens.

$$3\overline{)113}$$

Step 2. Divide tens. Subtract.

$$\begin{array}{r} 3 \\ 3\overline{)113} \\ \underline{-9} \\ 2 \end{array}$$

Step 3. Regroup and divide ones.

$$\begin{array}{r} 37 \text{ R2} \\ 3\overline{)113} \\ \underline{-9} \\ 23 \\ \underline{-21} \\ 2 \end{array}$$

The remainder is 2.

Each girl would get 37 records. They would have to decide who would get the remaining 2 records.

40

Assignments

BASIC
page 40 Discuss
page 41 exercises 1–50
Basic Worksheet 10

AVERAGE
page 40 Discuss
page 41 exercises 1–52
Enrichment Worksheet 10

ENRICHED
page 40 Discuss
page 41 exercises 1–54
Enrichment Worksheet 10

REVIEW PRACTICE
page 379 set 24

EXERCISES

Divide.

1. $\overset{123}{2)246}$	2. $\overset{68\ R1}{2)137}$	3. $\overset{19\ R1}{3)58}$	4. $\overset{16}{4)64}$	5. $\overset{19}{5)95}$
6. $\overset{43\ R1}{8)345}$	7. $\overset{206\ R2}{4)826}$	8. $\overset{52\ R3}{7)367}$	9. $\overset{97\ R2}{9)875}$	10. $\overset{16\ R2}{9)146}$
11. $\overset{155\ R5}{6)935}$	12. $\overset{67}{2)134}$	13. $\overset{76\ R2}{7)534}$	14. $\overset{189\ R2}{5)947}$	15. $\overset{272}{3)816}$
16. $\overset{\$0.71}{8)\$5.68}$	17. $\overset{\$0.55}{7)\$3.85}$	18. $\overset{\$1.59}{6)\$9.54}$	19. $\overset{\$0.23}{9)\$2.07}$	20. $\overset{\$1.46}{4)\$5.84}$
21. $\overset{1973}{2)3946}$	22. $\overset{1021\ R3}{5)5108}$	23. $\overset{1247\ R1}{3)3742}$	24. $\overset{2982\ R1}{2)5965}$	25. $\overset{540\ R2}{7)3782}$
26. $\overset{1304\ R2}{3)3914}$	27. $\overset{1419\ R2}{4)5678}$	28. $\overset{678\ R3}{6)4071}$	29. $\overset{762\ R1}{4)3049}$	30. $\overset{1155\ R6}{8)9246}$
31. $\overset{1000\ R3}{7)7003}$	32. $\overset{1302}{4)5208}$	33. $\overset{1543\ R2}{3)4631}$	34. $\overset{267}{9)2403}$	35. $\overset{191\ R3}{6)1149}$
36. $\overset{6320\ R4}{5)31604}$	37. $\overset{39,125\ R1}{2)78251}$	38. $\overset{7856\ R3}{5)39283}$	39. $\overset{9461\ R3}{8)75691}$	40. $\overset{8029\ R6}{8)64238}$
41. $\overset{15,029\ R3}{6)90177}$	42. $\overset{10,300\ R4}{7)72104}$	43. $\overset{9004\ R1}{7)63029}$	44. $\overset{24,526\ R2}{4)98106}$	45. $\overset{25,078\ R2}{3)75236}$
46. $\overset{64,817}{2)129634}$	47. $\overset{158,476\ R1}{5)792381}$	48. $\overset{76,787\ R2}{9)691085}$	49. $\overset{66,269\ R1}{6)397615}$	50. $\overset{29,315\ R7}{9)263842}$

Solve.

51. 25 comic books in each box
13 boxes
How many comic books?   325

52. Sold a radio for $7.50
Was given $20
How much change? $12.50

53. 3-day garage sale
Took in $382.11
What was the daily average? $127.37

54. Sold 2 bicycles for $12 each
Sold 3 bicycles for $19 each
What was the average price? $16.20

 Use all of these digits to make an 8-digit number.

1, 2, 3, 4, 5, 6, 7, 8

Divide your number by 9.
Did you get a whole-number quotient?   yes
Rearrange the digits in as many ways as you can.
Divide each number by 9. Do you ever get a
remainder?   no

$$72{,}538{,}146 \div 9$$

41

Follow-up Activities

Reinforcement You may wish to follow up the lesson by having some students do additional work at the concrete level. Use cutouts from tagboard to make the following display.

Write the division problem: $3)\overline{445}$ on the chalkboard. Have a student go to the chalkboard and "divide" the hundreds. Keep the record at the chalkboard by writing this:

$$\begin{array}{r} 1 \\ 3\overline{)445} \\ -3 \\ \hline 1 \end{array}$$

Have another student come to the chalkboard and cut the remaining hundred square into 10 bars of ten. Show this regrouping in the record by "bringing down the 4." Continue calling students to the chalkboard to work with the cutouts until they have been "divided up" and the division record is completed.

Enrichment You may need to explain briefly the word *average* to students. After doing so, have each student take a sample of 6 to 8 seventh-graders and find their heights. Then have them compute the average height. Of course, the average height would be determined by dividing the sum of the heights by the number of students in the sample.

EXCURSION
Humphrey had one nickel, one dime, one quarter, one half-dollar, and one silver dollar. After he lost one coin, he had seven times as much money as his sister. Which coin did he lose?

The half-dollar. After he lost the coin, he had either $1.85, $1.80, $1.65, $1.40, or $.90; only $1.40 is divisible by 7.

Basic Worksheet 10 and *Enrichment Worksheet 10*

Name _____
Basic Worksheet 10

Step 1. Not enough hundreds. Regroup. Think about 39 tens.

Step 2. Divide tens, subtract, and regroup.

Step 3. Divide ones, subtract, and write the remainder.

$$6)\overline{394}$$

$$\overset{6}{6)\overline{394}} \\ -36 \\ \overline{\ \ 34}$$

$$\overset{65\ R4}{6)\overline{394}} \\ -36 \\ \overline{\ \ 34} \\ -30 \\ \overline{\ \ \ 4}$$

Divide.

1. $4)\overline{753}$ 2. $5)\overline{927}$ 3. $8)\overline{832}$ 4. $3)\overline{516}$

5. $9)\overline{307}$ 6. $6)\overline{425}$ 7. $4)\overline{932}$ 8. $7)\overline{855}$

9. $7)\overline{931}$ 10. $2)\overline{6285}$ 11. $9)\overline{4291}$ 12. $6)\overline{7836}$

13. $8)\overline{5274}$ 14. $6)\overline{9583}$ 15. $3)\overline{6205}$ 16. $8)\overline{5116}$

Copyright © 1979 by D. C. Heath and Company

(7) Dividing by a 1-digit number   Student text pages 40, 41

Name _____
Enrichment Worksheet 10

Show how all the given digits can be used to make the equation true. There may be more than one way to complete some equations.

1. $5\ |\ 6\ |\ 8\ |\ -\ |\ 4\ |\ = 1292$
2. $\square\square - \square + \square = 32$
3. $\square\square \times \square\square + \square = 3302$
4. $\square\square \times \square - \square = 4879$

5. $\square\square\square - \square\square\square = 372$
6. $\square\square\square\square - \square + \square = 1641$
7. $\square\square\square \times \square - \square\square = 4757$
8. $\square\square \times \square\square + \square = 2657$

9. $\square\square\square + \square\square\square = 345$
10. $\square\square\square - \square + \square = 2607$
11. $\square\square - \square\square + \square = 33$
12. $\square\square\square \times \square - \square\square = 914$

Copyright © 1979 by D. C. Heath and Company

(7) Dividing by a 1-digit number   Student text pages 40-41

Suggested Lesson Plan

Introduction Plan to work individually with those students who had difficulty dividing by one-digit numbers. As you present and review the division algorithm with the other students, work on improving their skills by focusing on estimating, checking partial quotients, etc.

Using the pages Go over the exposition on page 42. Put the example on the board and explain the thought process and the recorded work step-by-step.

Remind students that the algorithm for two-digit divisors is exactly the same as for one-digit divisors. The only new difficulty is that we do not have the multiplication facts for two-digit numbers committed to memory. If some students have difficulty estimating and finding the correct trial quotient, they can make a list of the multiplication facts for the divisor and refer to these while dividing.

Write two or three division examples on the board. While students work on them, move around the room and observe their work. Work individually with students having difficulty.

Assign a subset of exercises 1–30 and the word problems 31–33 for written work.

Plan to assign a few of the remaining exercises every other day over the next few weeks to try to build good retention of the division algorithm.

Dividing by a 2-digit number

Dividing by a two-digit number is usually more difficult than dividing by a one-digit number because we have not memorized the multiplication facts for most two-digit numbers. This means that we have to estimate the digits in the quotient. Study this example.

Step 1. No thousands or hundreds in the quotient. The first digit will be in the tens place.

$$\underset{XX}{57\overline{)2056}}$$

Step 2. 57 is near 60. Since we know the multiplication facts for 60, we think about dividing by 60.

$$60 \quad 57\overline{)2056}^{3}$$

Step 3. The guess is 3. Multiply 57 by 3.

$$\begin{array}{r} 3 \\ 57\overline{)2056} \\ -171 \\ \hline 34 \end{array} \text{ It works!}$$

Step 4. Guess the next digit.

$$60 \quad \begin{array}{r} 3 \\ 57\overline{)2056} \\ -171 \\ \hline 346 \end{array}$$

Step 5. The guess is 5. Multiply 57 by 5.

$$\begin{array}{r} 35 \\ 57\overline{)2056} \\ -171 \\ \hline 346 \\ -285 \\ \hline 61 \end{array} \text{ Too big!}$$

Step 6. Since 5 is too small, try 6.

$$\begin{array}{r} 36 \text{ R4} \\ 57\overline{)2056} \\ -171 \\ \hline 346 \\ -342 \\ \hline 4 \end{array} \text{ It works!}$$

Assignments

BASIC
page 42 Discuss
page 43 exercises 1–30,
  Keeping Skills Sharp
Basic Worksheet 11

AVERAGE
page 42 Discuss
page 43 exercises 1–32,
  Keeping Skills Sharp
Enrichment Worksheet 11

ENRICHED
page 42 Discuss
page 43 exercises 1–33,
  Keeping Skills Sharp
Enrichment Worksheet 11

EXTRA PRACTICE
page 379 set 25

EXERCISES

Divide.

1. 18)593   32 R17
2. 24)842   35 R2
3. 31)900   29 R1
4. 25)675   27
5. 32)942   29 R14
6. 48)876   18 R12
7. 38)965   25 R15
8. 11)527   47 R10
9. 41)993   24 R9
10. 52)1404   27
11. 68)2584   38
12. 72)2088   29
13. 41)3157   77
14. 77)2464   32
15. 92)4324   47
16. 79)6080   76 R76
17. 28)4044   144 R12
18. 81)4536   56
19. 49)1773   36 R9
20. 52)3860   74 R12
21. 51)1836   36
22. 74)1998   27
23. 89)4162   46 R68
24. 35)1113   31 R28
25. 22)9460   430
26. 45)1281   28 R21
27. 36)1492   41 R16
28. 71)365986   5154 R52
29. 82)274164   3343 R38
30. 39)500813   12,841 R14

Solve.

31. Four backpackers agreed to divide 68 kilograms of supplies evenly. How much should each backpacker carry?   17 kg

32. If a large pizza costs $4.75 and a pitcher of root beer costs $1.25, how much do 3 pizzas and 2 pitchers of root beer cost? $16.75

33. Karl earned $4.95, $5.74, and $3.88 on the three days he worked. He needs $20 to buy a football. How much more does he need to earn? $5.43

Keeping Skills Sharp

Subtract.

1.   275 − 188 = 87
2.   352 − 167 = 185
3.   4203 − 1735 = 2468
4.   6000 − 2044 = 3956
5.   6523 − 1741 = 4782
6.   3998 − 1689 = 2309
7.   40305 − 16758 = 23,547
8.   50100 − 9837 = 40,263
9.   80000 − 17735 = 62,265
10.   703004 − 216558 = 486,446

43

Follow-up Activities

Reinforcement Prepare a worksheet of four division examples. Vertical lines drawn between digits will encourage straight alignment of the work. Have students list the multiplication facts of the divisor before they start dividing.

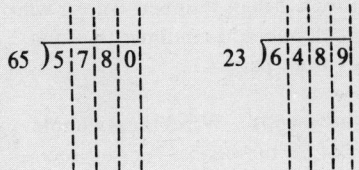

Design these problems with easier divisors; that is, the ones digit should be less than 6 to help build confidence before increasing the difficulty of the problems.

Enrichment Have students copy and complete the following missing-digit exercises.

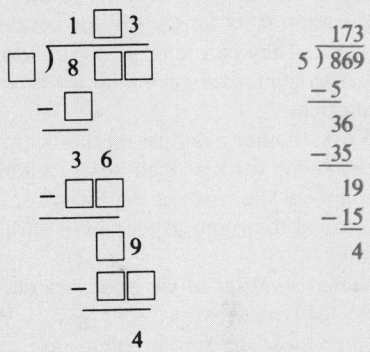

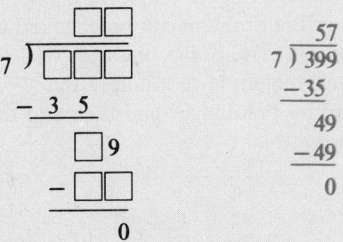

CALCULATOR ACTIVITY
Organize students in pairs with one calculator. Practice estimation skills by having students pick the division example that has the smallest quotient in the first row on page 43. After they make a choice, they use the calculator to divide to see who won. Play continues for each row.

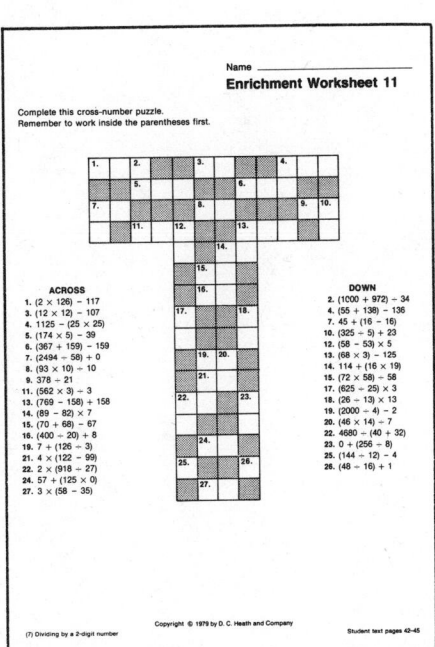

Suggested Lesson Plan

Introduction Assign this lesson only to those students who were successful with division by a 2-digit number. Those who had difficulty should continue to work exercises from page 43.

Using the pages Write the example on page 44 on the board. As you record the work on the board, use the text exposition to identify and explain each step in the algorithm. Focus attention on the method of estimating to arrive at a trial quotient. Explain that some estimates will be wrong, and that students need to learn to check the result of subtracting each time before bringing the next digit down.

If individual students are having difficulty, encourage them to write the multiplication facts for the divisor beside their work. They can refer to these facts rather than continually estimate for each trial quotient.

Work another example on the board while students work at their seats. After you complete the work at the board, walk around the room to help individual students.

Assign a subset of the exercises on page 45 for written work.

Since these division problems are very difficult and checking is a long process, have calculators available so that when a student completes a problem, the problem can be checked on a calculator. Of course, the best way to check a problem is to multiply the quotient by the divisor and then add the remainder.

Dividing by a 3-digit number

$$328\overline{)89356}$$

Step 1. Divide and subtract.

$$328\overline{)89356}$$
$$\underline{-656}$$
$$237$$
quotient: 2

Step 2. Regroup.

$$328\overline{)89356}$$
$$\underline{-656}$$
$$2375$$
quotient: 2

Step 3. Divide and subtract.

$$328\overline{)89356}$$
$$\underline{-656}$$
$$2375$$
$$\underline{-2296}$$
$$79$$
quotient: 27

Step 4. Regroup.

$$328\overline{)89356}$$
$$\underline{-656}$$
$$2375$$
$$\underline{-2296}$$
$$796$$
quotient: 27

Step 5. Divide and subtract.

$$328\overline{)89356}$$
$$\underline{-656}$$
$$2375$$
$$\underline{-2296}$$
$$796$$
$$\underline{-656}$$
$$140$$
quotient: 272 R140

44

Assignments

EXERCISES

Divide.

1. 112)35274 **314 R106**
2. 208)69782 **335 R102**
3. 115)59386 **516 R46**
4. 234)74261 **317 R83**

5. 326)37821 **116 R5**
6. 402)59784 **148 R288**
7. 453)60715 **134 R13**
8. 526)52830 **100 R230**

9. 704)42065 **59 R529**
10. 628)32978 **52 R322**
11. 750)74216 **98 R716**
12. 378)93852 **248 R108**

13. 288)756031 **2625 R31**
14. 813)258921 **318 R387**
15. 529)653184 **1234 R398**
16. 478)953165 **1994 R33**

17. 937)742167 **729 R63**
18. 653)406314 **622 R148**
19. 892)556395 **623 R679**
20. 960)814638 **848 R558**

Solve.

21. 74 weeks
How many days? **518**

22. 595 days
How many weeks? **85**

23. 38 days
How many hours? **912**

24. 888 eggs
How many dozen? **74**

25. 768 months
How many years? **64**

26. 2700 minutes
How many hours? **45**

27. 11,680 days
How many years? **32**
[Use 365 days
for 1 year.]

28. 15 years
How many days? **5475**

29. 5424 inches
How many feet? **452**

30. 2238 feet
How many yards? **746**

31. 492 feet
How many inches? **5904**

32. 2844 inches
How many yards? **79**

33. 591 pounds
How many ounces? **9456**

34. 52 yards
How many inches? **1872**

35. 864 ounces
How many pounds? **54**

36. 123 tons
How many pounds? **246,000**

45

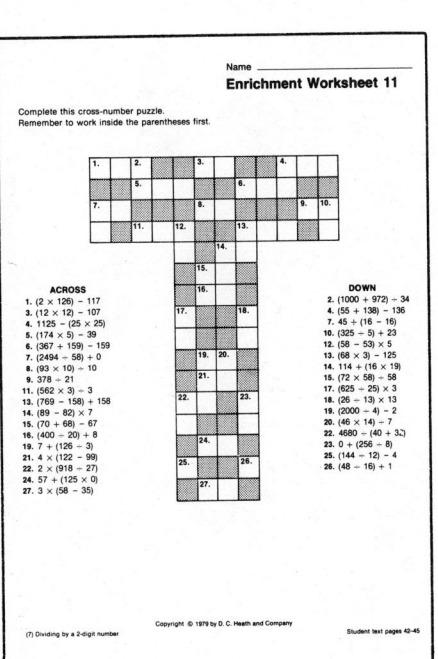

Follow-up Activities

Reinforcement The following game provides further practice with the long division algorithm. Write the ten digits 0 through 9 on index cards. Have students draw a table like this:

Select a card and have students copy the digit in any one of the cells in their tables. Replace the card and select a second card. Instruct students to copy the digit in any one of the 5 remaining cells. Continue in this way until all the cells have been filled. Have each student do his division. Declare the player with the greatest quotient the winner. Check the "winner's" work with all participants by copying and working it at the chalkboard. Of course, this gives you an opportunity to review the division algorithm.

Enrichment You may wish to have some students take a traffic survey and count the people that are riding in each vehicle. Have students compute the average number of people riding in each car of their survey. Ask them to round their quotients to the nearest tenth.

EXCURSION

Imagine having one of each of these weights and a balance;

| 1 gram | 2 grams | 4 grams | 8 grams | 16 grams |

What weights would you use to balance a 6-gram weight? A 9-gram weight? A 21-gram weight?

2 g, 4 g; 1 g, 8 g; 1 g, 4 g, 16 g

To use properties of addition and
multiplication to simplify
computations.
To solve word problems dealing with
mathematics in careers.

Suggested Lesson Plan

Introduction Review the addition and
multplication properties with your
students. Ask for examples of each
property.

Using the pages Do the exercises on
page 46 orally. Students should not use
paper and pencil. Call on one student for
the answer, another student to name the
property that can be used to make the
problem easy, and another student to
describe the steps used in solving the
problem.

Assign page 47, Mathematics in
Careers, to be completed in class. Be
prepared to help the poor readers with
the problems.

Properties of addition and multiplication

In this lesson we will review some properties of addition and
multiplication. Remembering the properties can sometimes
help with computing.

ADDITION	MULTIPLICATION
The Adding 0 Property The sum of any number and 0 is the number. $358 + 0 = 358$	**The Multiplying by 1 Property** The product of any number and 1 is the number. $594 \times 1 = 594$
The Commutative Property of Addition Changing the order of the addends does not change the sum. $267 + 139 = 139 + 267$	**The Commutative Property of Multiplication** Changing the order of the factors does not change the product. $68 \times 57 = 57 \times 68$
The Associative Property of Addition Changing the grouping of the addends does not change the sum. $(18 + 37) + 13 = 18 + (37 + 13)$	**The Associative Property of Multiplication** Changing the grouping of the factors does not change the product. $(28 \times 4) \times 25 = 28 \times (4 \times 25)$

The Distributive Property

$$19 \times (8 + 2) = (19 \times 8) + (19 \times 2)$$

EXERCISES

See if you can compute each answer in your head by using
one of the properties above.

$128 + (75 + 25)$

1. $(128 + 75) + 25$ 228
2. $(225 + 185) + 15$ 425
3. $(23 \times 4) \times 25$ 2300 $23 \times (4 \times 25)$

4. $(627 + 45) + 55$ 727
5. $(47 \times 5) \times 20$ 4700
6. $(245 \times 250) \times 4$ 245,000

7. $(13 \times 6) + (13 \times 4)$ 130
8. $(23 \times 3) + (23 \times 7)$ 230
9. $(52 \times 60) + (52 \times 40)$ 5200

46

Assignments

BASIC
page 46 exercises 1−9
page 47 exercises 1−2
Basic Worksheet 12

AVERAGE
page 46 exercises 1−9
page 47 exercises 1−3
Enrichment Worksheet 12

ENRICHED
page 46 exercises 1−9
page 47 exercises 1−3
Enrichment Worksheet 12

REVIEW PRACTICE
page 378 set 18

Mathematics in careers

Oceanographers are scientists who study the ocean. They study the physical and chemical properties of the ocean, as well as all forms of life in the ocean.

1. **a.** Which ocean is the largest?
   b. Which ocean is the smallest?
   c. How much larger is the Pacific Ocean than the Atlantic Ocean?
   d. What is the total area of the oceans?
   e. The total area of the earth's surface is 509,917,870 square kilometers. How much of the earth's surface area is not ocean?

2. The deepest known spot in the Pacific Ocean is Challenger Deep. It is 11,033 meters below the surface. The deepest known spot in the Atlantic Ocean is in the Puerto Rico Trench, 8648 meters below the surface. How much deeper is Challenger Deep?

3. The highest mountain in the world is Mount Everest, which is 8848 meters high. If Mount Everest were put into Challenger Deep, how far below the surface of the water would the top of Mount Everest be?

Areas of Oceans	
Ocean	Area (in square kilometers)
Pacific	165,200,000
Atlantic	81,662,000
Indian	73,441,700
Antarctic	13,000,000
Arctic	14,090,000

47

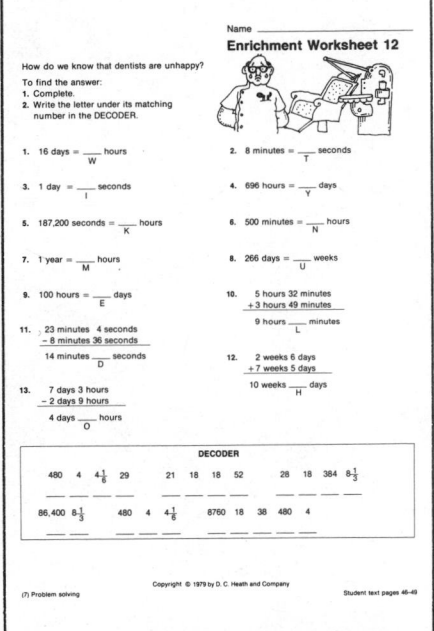

Follow-up Activities

Reinforcement Correct sections of the practice exercises. Examine individual exercises with those students who did not do well to try to identify their particular difficulty. Refer back to the exercises in related lessons for additional practice. Try to provide individual help for these students to remedy their particular weaknesses.

Enrichment Refer students to sources of additional information on oceanography and have them make up some interesting problems. Post the better problems on the mathematics bulletin board.

EXCURSION
Suppose that you have these weights and a balance:

1 gram   5 grams   25 grams

What would you use to balance a 12-gram object? A 37-gram object? A 49-gram object?

1 g, 1 g, 5 g, 5 g; 1 g, 1 g, 5 g, 5 g, 25 g;

1 g, 1 g, 1 g, 1 g, 5 g, 5 1g, 5 g, 5 g, 25 g

Answers.

1. a. Pacific
   b. Antarctic
   c. 83,538,000 square km
   d. 347,393,700 square km
   e. 162,524,170 square km

2. 2385 m

3. 2185 m

Suggested Lesson Plan

Introduction See if any of your students are interested in birds and bird watching. Ask whether students know how far birds migrate, and how scientists who study birds are able to find out how far birds migrate. (by banding)

Using the pages With this discussion to arouse interest, have students work exercises 1–6. If they have difficulty deciding which operation to use, tell them to think about a similar problem with small, convenient numbers. After they decide on the operation and with what numbers, they can do the same with the larger numbers.

Problem solving

These steps can help you solve word problems.

1. Read the problem and find the question.
2. What are the facts?
3. Decide what to do.
4. Answer the question.
5. Estimate! Does your answer seem right?

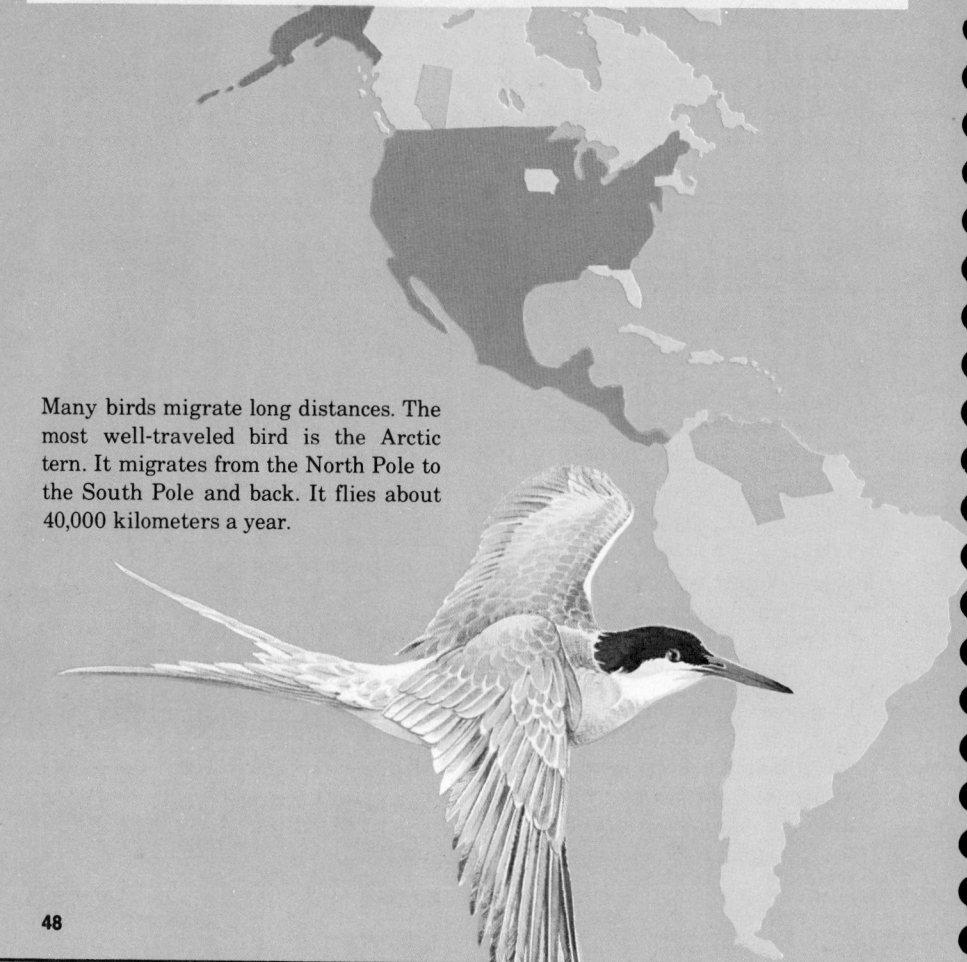

Many birds migrate long distances. The most well-traveled bird is the Arctic tern. It migrates from the North Pole to the South Pole and back. It flies about 40,000 kilometers a year.

48

For developing other higher level problem-solving skills see Creative Problem Solving Activities on pages 461-477.

Assignments

BASIC
page 48 Discuss
page 49 exercises 1–4
Basic Worksheet 12

AVERAGE
page 48 Discuss
page 49 exercises 1–6
Enrichment Worksheet 12

ENRICHED
page 48 Discuss
page 49 exercises 1–6
Enrichment Worksheet 12

REVIEW PRACTICE
page 378 set 19

EXTRA PROBLEM SOLVING
pages 398–399 set 1

Golden plover

Robin

Lesser yellowlegs

Blue-wing teal

Blackpolled warbler

Gray-cheeked thrush

1. A blue-wing teal that was banded (a ring put around its leg) in northern Alberta, Canada, was seen in Venezuela exactly 30 days later. If this distance is about 6100 kilometers, how many kilometers per day were averaged?   about 203

2. A lesser yellowlegs flew from Cape Cod, Massachusetts, to the French West Indies in 6 days. It averaged 509 kilometers per day. How far did it fly?   3054 km

3. The gray-cheeked thrush flies from northern Florida to northwest Alaska, a distance of 6500 kilometers. It averages about 210 kilometers per day. How long does it take to migrate the 6500 kilometers?   about 31 days

4. Robins have been known to fly from Iowa to Alaska, a distance of about 4800 kilometers, in 78 days. How many kilometers do they average each day?   about 62

5. Golden plovers hold the nonstop record. They fly from northeast Canada to South America nonstop, a distance of 3800 kilometers. If they fly 190 kilometers per day, how many days do they fly without stopping?   20

6. The blackpolled warbler migrates from Florida to western Alaska in the spring. It averages 56 kilometers per day for the first 29 days and then 320 kilometers per day for the next 15 days. How far is that?   6424 km

49

Follow-up Activities

Reinforcement Use the results of the practice exercises on page 46 to discover those students who need more developmental help or additional practice. Have these students work directly on basic skills, for progress in other areas is very much dependent upon mastery of basic skills in addition, subtraction, multiplication, and division.

Enrichment Have students copy and complete this missing-digit problem.

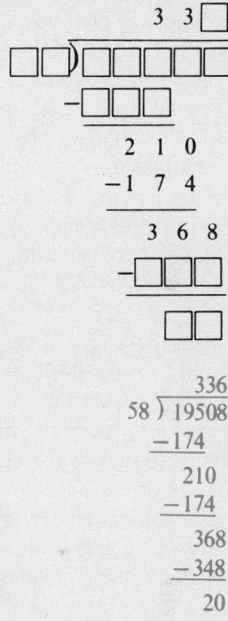

$$\begin{array}{r} 33\square \\ \square\square\,)\,\overline{\square\square\square\square\square} \\ -\underline{\square\square\square} \\ 210 \\ -174 \\ \hline 368 \\ -\underline{\square\square\square} \\ \hline \square\square \end{array}$$

$$\begin{array}{r} 336 \\ 58\,)\,\overline{19508} \\ -\underline{174} \\ 210 \\ -\underline{174} \\ 368 \\ -\underline{348} \\ \hline 20 \end{array}$$

Ask students to create other missing-digit problems for their classmates to complete.

CALCULATOR ACTIVITY
Play Target Multiplication. Students play in pairs. One student picks a target area, two numbers that differ by 20, say 80−100. The other student enters a number less than the target area. Then proceeding in turn, each student multiplies the number in the calculator by a number of his or her choice, trying to get the product in the target area. If one student misses the target, the other student multiplies that product to try to hit the target area.

STUDENT OBJECTIVES
To review the concepts introduced in Chapter 1.
To apply arithmetic skills in a real-life situation.

Suggested Lesson Plan

Introduction No pre-text activity is necessary for page 50 as this is a checkup for the chapter. However, it may be valuable to review briefly the lessons in the chapter so that students are reminded of the content over which they will be tested.

This Checkup will give you data about how well individual students have mastered the skills of the chapter. The Chapter Review on page 52 is provided for those students who need more specific individual help.

Page 51 is an activity that students will enjoy. Review briefly how to find an average before students begin the project.

Using the pages Assign all the exercises on page 50. As students complete the page they can work on the activity on page 51; or perhaps there are some games or activities in the chapter which they have not played and would like to. Assign a student leader to each game or activity. As pupils want to play, they can go to the assigned leader for the game rules and partners for the game.

Read aloud. [pages 18–19]

1. 5,265,328
2. 7,007,007,007
3. 81,081,273,006

Write the standard numeral. [pages 18–19]

4. seventeen million 17,000,000
5. two hundred billion
    200,000,000,000
6. eight trillion, eighteen billion, eighty thousand 8,018,000,080,000

Round. [pages 22–23]

7. 7583 to the nearest hundred. 7600
8. 23,488 to the nearest thousand.
    23,000
9. 47,500 to the nearest thousand 48,000
10. 8,754,321 to the nearest hundred thousand. 8,800,000

Add. [pages 26–27]

11. 578	12. 9835	13. 293	14. 36748
+ 466	+ 2768	476	867
1044	12,603	+ 351	+ 9988
		1120	47,603

Subtract. [pages 28–29]

15. 8321	16. 702	17. 5000	18. 603508
− 5673	− 427	− 2354	− 168739
2648	275	2646	434,769

Multiply. [pages 32–39]

19. 2783	20. 53	21. 482	22. 568
× 6	× 26	× 321	× 306
16,698	1378	154,722	173,808

Divide. [pages 40–45]

23. 9)4763 529 R2
24. 8)6449 806 R1
25. 38)58361 1535 R31
26. 405)19360 47 R325

Solve. [pages 48–49]

27. Eighteen busloads of 56 students each went to see their football team play in the championship game. Two hundred seventy-four students did not go. How many students in all? 1282

28. Joan bought 3 shirts for $7 each and a sweater for $9.95. How much change did she get from $40? $9.05

50

Assignments

BASIC
page 50 exercises 1 − 28
page 51 Project

AVERAGE
page 50 exercises 1 − 28
page 51 Project

ENRICHED
page 50 exercises 1 − 28
page 51 Project

Project

1. Find out how many minutes a day each of your classmates listens to the radio. (These data could be listed on the chalkboard.)

2. Compute the average number of minutes listened. Give your answer to the nearest whole number.

3. How many classmates listen

   a. more than the average?
   b. less than the average?
   c. twice as much as the average?
   d. half as much as the average?

4. Make a bar graph like the one shown here.

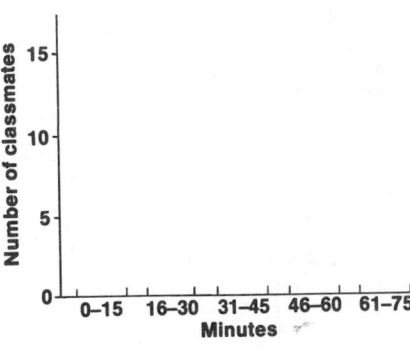

Time spent listening to radio each day

51

You may wish to assign some of the Creative Problem Solving Activities (pages 461–477) at this time.

Follow-up Activities

Reinforcement Correct all the items in the Chapter Checkup. Any student who misses six or more or any more than three problems in a row needs additional help. It is important for each student to achieve some degree of proficiency in the basic skills covered. At this point, students who are still having difficulty with these skills need concentrated individual help.

Enrichment Assign pupils to the games and activities that have been played throughout the chapter. Each student leader is responsible for teaching the game or activity to interested students and for supervising the play.

CALCULATOR ACTIVITY
Make one student responsible for the calculators and the calculator activities. The calculator student is in charge of keeping track of the calculators, for explaining the activities, and supervising the play.

STUDENT OBJECTIVE
To review or extend the skills and
concepts taught in Chapter 1.

Suggested Lesson Plan

Introduction After checking the
Chapter Checkup you will know which
students need additional reinforcement
and which students will be able to go
ahead with the Challenge activity. Get
the better students started on page 53
first as the students who are having
difficulty will need more of your time.

The students who need more review
should go back and correct their errors
on the Chapter Checkup. You may want
to go over those questions orally if this
group is small enough. Carefully probe
to determine which concepts and skills
the students have not mastered and
work individually to correct these
deficiencies.

Using the pages After the identified
students have corrected the Chapter
Checkup, they should answer questions
1–34 on page 52. After they complete
these questions, read the answers and let
the students correct their own papers.
Give them an opportunity to ask
questions about those exercises they
missed.

Assign page 53 to the students who
did well on the Chapter Checkup. You
might let pairs of students work
together, sharing their ideas and helping
each other.

CHAPTER REVIEW

Round to the nearest thousand.

thousands place

$63,672 \Rightarrow 64,000$

This digit is 5 or greater.

$$\begin{array}{r} {}^{1\ 1}\\ 358 \\ +267 \\ \hline 625 \end{array}$$

$$\begin{array}{r} {}^{2\ 9}\\ \cancel{3}\cancel{0}2 \\ -177 \\ \hline 125 \end{array}$$

$$\begin{array}{r} 321 \\ \times 34 \\ \hline 1284 \leftarrow 4 \times 321 \\ 963 \leftarrow 30 \times 321 \\ \hline 10,914 \end{array}$$

$$\begin{array}{r} 40 73\ R29 \\ 39\overline{)2876} \\ -273 \\ \hline 146 \\ -117 \\ \hline 29 \end{array}$$

Round to the nearest hundred.

1. 673   700
2. 650   700
3. 89,341   89,300

Round to the nearest thousand.

4. 7388   7000
5. 2500   3000
6. 67,832   68,000

Add.

7.	8.	9.	10.
563	463	5864	87351
+288	+297	+2995	+25489
851	760	8859	112,840

11.	12.	13.	14.
29	463	589	2975
37	297	678	467
+56	+341	+838	5986
122	1101	2105	+321
			9749

Subtract.

15.	16.	17.	18.
526	732	6731	56342
−238	−581	−2951	−8756
288	151	3780	47,586

19.	20.	21.	22.
904	5000	65002	30204
−656	−276	−14975	−16578
248	4724	50,027	13,626

Multiply.

23.	24.	25.
475	36	57
×8	×43	×65
3800	1548	3705

26.	27.	28.
394	592	548
×62	×326	×602
24,428	192,992	329,896

Divide.

29. 8)5287   660 R7
30. 7)4921   703
31. 23)5261   228 R17
32. 53)16165   305
33. 148)16673   112 R97
34. 321)26543   82 R221

52

Assignments

BASIC
page 52   exercises 1–34

AVERAGE
page 52   exercises 1–34

ENRICHED
page 53   exercises 1–17

Our place-value system for writing numerals is based on the number 10. We can, if we wish, use other whole numbers as bases for place-value systems. Here is the way to use 5 as a base.

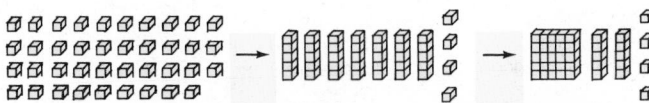

Group single blocks into groups of five blocks.

Put the bars of 5 into groups of 5 bars.

There are 124_{five} blocks. (Read as "one two four base five.")

How many blocks in all? Write a base 5 numeral.

1. 24_{five}
2. 41_{five}
3. 20_{five}
4. 132_{five}

Copy and complete this table.

		5.	6.	7.	8.	9.	10.	11.	12.	13.
Base 10	3	5	7	10	15	19	24	25	23	57
Base 5	3_{five}	?	?	?	?	?	?	?	?	?

10_* 12_* 20_* 30_* 34_* 44_* 100_* 43_* 212_*

*All answers have subscript five.

Use a base five numeral to give

Answers vary.

14. the number of people in your family.

15. your age in years.

16. the number of students in your class.

17. the number of states in the United States. 200_{five}

Form W

| | a | b | c | d | | a | b | c | d | | a | b | c | d | | a | b | c | d | | a | b | c | d | | a | b | c |
14
34
14
4
30
15
31

STUDENT OBJECTIVES

To practice skills learned previously.
To practice using a standardized test format.

Suggested Lesson Plan

Introduction (answer sheet duplicated from page 448) Explain to students that a test of this type will occur at the end of each chapter. Its purpose is to review all the material they have studied so far and to give them a chance to get used to taking standardized tests. Explain that these are called *multiple-choice* questions since there are 4 possible answers given. Instruct students how to use the answer sheets.

Have students answer the questions. Give students approximately 15 minutes for the test so that they get used to watching their time.

This Major Checkup reviews the concepts taught in the first chapter and it can be used to determine if more review and reteaching is necessary.

The table below correlates the test items and the student text pages. Assign review exercises as indicated by the Major Checkup results.

Test Item	Text Pages	Test Item	Text Pages
1	18–19	7	28–29
2	18–19	8	28–29
3	22–23	9	36–37
4	22–23	10	38–39
5	26–27	11	42–43
6	26–27	12	42–43

Chapter 1 Posttest

A chapter posttest is given full size in this teacher's edition at the end of each chapter. You may reproduce the posttests or you may purchase them as duplicating masters in either of the two booklets entitled TESTS and PERSONALIZED LEARNING PACKET.

If you are providing individualized instruction, enter the posttest scores on the Record and Assignment Chart (see page 33d) and assign reteaching assignments for objectives with unsatisfactory posttest scores.

If you are maintaining class-paced instructions, you can provide reteaching assignments for objectives with unsatisfactory posttest scores by reviewing the relevant student pages (indicated on the posttest) and using the Reinforcement activities suggested in the teacher's commentary for those pages.

MAJOR CHECKUP
Standardized Format

Choose the correct letter.

1. The standard numeral for four billion, twenty five thousand is

- a. 4,025,000
- (b.) 4,000,025,000
- c. 4,000,000,025,000
- d. none of these

2. Write in words. 7,000,000,000,000

- a. seven million
- b. seven quintillion
- c. seven billion
- (d.) none of these

3. Round 48,377 to the nearest thousand.

- (a.) 48,000
- b. 50,000
- c. 49,000
- d. none of these

4. Round 29,950 to the nearest hundred.

- a. 29,900
- b. 29,800
- (c.) 30,000
- d. none of these

5. Add.

5673
+4899

- a. 1572
- b. 10,562
- (c.) 10,572
- d. none of these

6. Add.

632
577
+298

- (a.) 1507
- b. 1497
- c. 1407
- d. none of these

7. Subtract.

5297
−3898

- a. 2399
- (b.) 1399
- c. 1409
- d. none of these

8. Subtract.

6000
−3956

- a. 3044
- b. 3043
- (c.) 2044
- d. none of these

9. Multiply.

37
×26

- (a.) 962
- b. 296
- c. 926
- d. none of these

10. Multiply.

372
×305

- a. 13,020
- b. 2976
- (c.) 113,460
- d. none of these

11. Divide.

25)4036

- (a.) 161 R11
- b. 160 R36
- c. 275
- d. none of these

12. Divide.

37)7548

- a. 240
- b. 24
- (c.) 204
- d. none of these

54

You can also assign Extra Practice Exercises and Basic Worksheets as indicated below.

Objectives	Extra Practice Sets	Pages	Basic Worksheets
1-1	14–15	377	1–2
1-2	16	377	3
1-3	18	378	5
1-4	19	378	6
1-5	20–23	378–379	7–9
1-6	24–26	379	10–11
1-7			12

Answers for Chapter 1 Posttest
1. 15,700 2. 42,000,000
3. 3,000,664,000 4. seven thousand two hundred thirty-four 5. five hundred million 6. nine billion three hundred forty-seven 7. 28,600 8. 8650
9. 58,000 10. 48,000,000 11. 85
12. 1635 13. 58,254 14. 204 15. 1565
16. 37 17. 324 18. 66,637 19. 43,354
20. 34,508 21. 4496 22. 2520 23. 4731
24. 355,069 25. 2,541,645 26. 171
27. 77 R1 28. 53 29. 763 R28
30. 73 R19 31. $415 32. $237

Chapter 1 Posttest

Name _____

Date _____

Write in standard numerals. [Obj. 1-1, pages 18–19]

1. fifteen thousand seven hundred _____

2. forty-two million _____

3. three billion, six hundred sixty-four thousand _____

Write in words.

4. 7234 _____

5. 500,000,000 _____

6. 9,000,000,347 _____

Round [Obj. 1-2, pages 20–23]

7. 28,592 to the nearest hundred. _____

8. 8653 to the nearest ten. _____

9. 57,500 to the nearest thousand. _____

10. 48,499,999 to the nearest million. _____

Add. [Obj. 1-3, pages 26–27, 30]

11.
```
  57
+ 28
```

12.
```
  849
+ 786
```

13.
```
  48,376
+  9,878
```

14.
```
  58
  87
+ 59
```

15.
```
  583
  297
+ 685
```

Subtract. [Obj. 1-4, pages 28–30]

16.
```
  94
- 57
```

17.
```
  802
- 478
```

18.
```
  95,413
- 28,776
```

19.
```
  49,321
-  5,967
```

20.
```
  70,000
- 35,492
```

Multiply. [Obj. 1-5, pages 32–39, 46]

21.
```
  562
×   8
```

22.
```
  504
×   5
```

23.
```
   57
×  83
```

24.
```
  2483
×  143
```

25.
```
  4215
×  603
```

Divide. [Obj. 1-6, pages 40–46]

26. $3\overline{)513}$

27. $5\overline{)386}$

28. $27\overline{)1431}$

29. $46\overline{)35126}$

30. $421\overline{)30752}$

Solve. [Obj. 1-7, pages 31, 47–49]

31. Karen saved $3400. Then she bought a used car for $2985. How much did she have left? _____

32. Bill bought skis for $125, boots for $98, and ski poles for $14. How much did he spend? _____

54a

NOTES

54b

Chapter 2
Decimals—Addition and Subtraction

Pages 55—80

Learning Objectives

After completing this chapter, all students should be able to do the following:

2-1 Write decimals in word and standard forms.

2-2 Determine which of two decimals is greater.

2-3 Round decimals.

2-4 Add and subtract decimals.

2-5 Show how to estimate sums and differences of decimals.

2-6 Solve word problems that involve addition and subtraction of decimals.

Decimals are introduced by extending the concept of place value. Students learn to read, write, compare, and round decimals. Then the addition and subtraction algorithms are reviewed and practiced. As usual, students are also given much practice in solving story problems.

Mathematics

Decimal Notation. A physical model can help us understand our place-value system, especially in writing decimal fractions. Suppose that we have learned the numbers 0-10 and wish to report the number of blocks shown here.

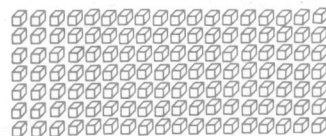

First, by counting to ten over and over, we can group the blocks by tens.

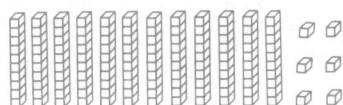

Next, by counting to ten again, we group ten bars of ten together.

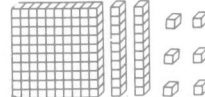

Now with the very simple language available to us we can report the number of blocks as 1 group of ten tens, 2 groups of ten, and 6 single blocks. This is a clumsy way of writing, however, so we use a table as a more efficient way.

Ten tens	Tens	Ones
1	2	6

Still in search of efficiency in writing we realize that if we *remember* the values of the columns or places, we can omit the table and merely write the digits:

1 2 6

Obviously, we name larger and larger whole numbers in the same way: by counting to ten as often as necessary and extending the place-value table as far to the left as necessary.

We can use the same physical model to explore how to extend the place-value notation to the right. We divide a unit block into ten equally large parts. Each part is a tenth of a unit. Then each tenth part can be divided into ten parts—ten tenths, or hundredths. This can be reported as often as desired.

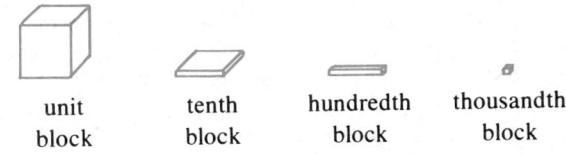

| unit block | tenth block | hundredth block | thousandth block |

We can report the number of blocks here on a place-value table.

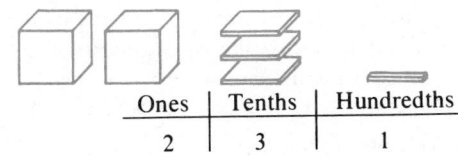

Ones	Tenths	Hundredths
2	3	1

As in the case of whole numbers, we can omit the table itself if we merely remember the values of the places. However, merely erasing the table is not enough. Confusion would result because we are accustomed to having the rightmost digit name the ones. For example, these would appear the same if the tables were erased.

Tens	Ones
4	6

Ones	Tenths
4	6

In order to clear up this confusion, we use a decimal point to show which digit is in the ones place when it is not the rightmost digit.

Ones	Tenths	Hundredths	
2	3	1	= 2.31

This *whole* place-value system is called a **decimal** system because it is based on the number ten. However, common usage of the word *decimal* now usually suggests numbers that are not whole numbers.

Adding and subtracting. Because the same place-value system is used for both whole numbers and decimals, the addition and subtraction algorithms for decimals are the same as those for whole numbers.

Teaching the Chapter

You may find that using a physical model of the decimal place-value system will help your students understand the system. Many seventh-grade students have matured to what Piaget calls the *stage of formal operations*, but others are still in the *stage of concrete operations*. These latter students do not learn abstract concepts well through verbal exposition alone. They need concrete representations of the concept.

Place-value blocks can be used nicely even to represent the cutting of a unit block into tenths and hundredths. Since the unit block and a cube of one thousand have the same shape, students can actually use the cube of one thousand as the unit block when they are ready to begin the work on page 56. Then the square of one hundred becomes a tenth block and the bar of ten becomes a hundredth block. If you are using sticks such as ice-cream-bar sticks, you can actually cut individual sticks into tenth parts and perhaps even hundredth parts. For another model that works quite well, cut out squares, strips of ten squares, and squares of one hundred squares from sheets of graph paper. If this model is used you can, when you are ready to begin work with tenths and hundredths, use the large squares as units, the strips of ten as tenths, and the small squares as hundredths. You *could* try cutting the original unit square into tenths as suggested for sticks, but the pieces are very small and difficult to manipulate.

It is important for students to get the idea that a place-value table is infintely long and that when we are operating with decimal numerals, we do exactly the same things no matter where on the table we are looking. For example, if we wished to round to the place indicated by the arrow, we would do exactly the same thing regardless of whether the place is the millions place, the hundreds place, or the thousandths place.

$$...3\ 7\ 5\ 4\ 1\ ...$$
$$\uparrow$$

Similarly, when we add or subtract, the mechanics are the same regardless of the values of the places.

$$
\begin{array}{r}
...4\ 7\ 1\ ....\\
+\ ...3\ 9\ 6\ ....\\
\hline
\end{array}
$$

It is necessary, of course, for digits with the same place value to be "lined up." This is also true for multiplication and division.

Vocabulary

centimeter
decimal
decimal point
decimeter
estimate
hundredth
meter
millimeter
millionth
tenth
thousandth

Materials

place-value blocks
hand calculators
meter sticks
centimeter rulers
dollars, dimes, pennies (real or play)

Chapter Tests

For discussion of how to use the chapter tests, please see page 17c.

Answers for Chapter 2 Pretest

1. 0.04 **2.** 5.7 **3.** 0.247 **4.** nine tenths **5.** twenty-seven and three tenths **6.** four and fifty-seven thousandths **7.** > **8.** < **9.** > **10.** > **11.** 4 **12.** 5.7 **13.** 16.60 **14.** 0.3 **15.** 9.69 **16.** 1.73 **17.** 3.407 **18.** 8.801 **19.** 11.33 **20.** 4.884 **21.** 5 + 3 = 8 **22.** 7 − 6 = 1 **23.** 12.5 km **24.** 1.8 km **25.** 57.2 km **26.** 15.7 m

Chapter 2 Pretest

Name _____

Date _____

Number right

0	1	2	3	4	5	6

Write as decimals. [Obj. 2-1, pages 56–61]

1. four hundredths _____

2. five and seven tenths _____

3. two hundred forty-seven thousandths _____

Write in words.

4. 0.9 _____

5. 27.3 _____

6. 4.057 _____

0	1	2	3	4

< or >? Write the correct sign. [Obj. 2-2, pages 62–63]

7. 3 ◯ 0.8

8. 0.03 ◯ 0.3

9. 0.5 ◯ 0.499

10. 23.65 ◯ 23.56

Round [Obj. 2-3, pages 64–65]

0	1	2	3	4

11. 3.521 to the nearest one. _____

12. 5.742 to the nearest tenth. _____

13. 16.598 to the nearest hundredth. _____

14. 0.25 to the nearest tenth. _____

Add or subtract. Watch the signs. [Obj. 2-4, pages 66–69]

0-2	3	4	5	6

15. 5.71
  + 3.98

16. 5.71
  − 3.98

17. 4.003
  − 0.596

18. 7.924
  + 0.877

19. 2.63 + 8.7 = _____

20. 5.31 − 0.426 = _____

Show how you estimate sums and differences. [Obj. 2-5, pages 70–71]

0	1	2

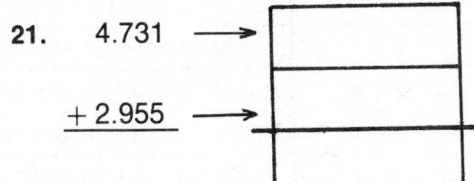

21. 4.731 ⟶

  + 2.955 ⟶

22. 7.031 ⟶

  − 5.966 ⟶

0	1	2	3	4

Solve. [Obj. 2-6, pages 72–75]

23. Jane ran 5.8 kilometers one day and 6.7 kilometers the next day. How far did she run

in all? _____

24. Walt ran 6.3 kilometers one day and 4.5 kilometers the next day. How much farther

did he run the first day? _____

25. Bob rode his bicycle 28.6 kilometers to his grandmother's house and then rode back

home. How far did he ride? _____

26. Mary cut a 2.3-meter long piece of wallpaper from an 18-meter long roll. How

much paper was left on the roll? _____

Chapter 2
Record and Assignment Chart

Name _____

Pretest Date _____   Posttest Date _____

Objectives

		Pretest Score Mark number correct	Posttest Score Mark number correct
2-1	Write decimals in words or as standard numerals.	0-1 | 2 | 3 | 4 ‖ 5 | 6	0-1 | 2 | 3 | 4 ‖ 5 | 6
2-2	Determine which of two decimals is greater.	0 | 1 | 2 | 3 ‖ 4	0 | 1 | 2 | 3 ‖ 4
2-3	Round decimals.	0 | 1 | 2 ‖ 3 | 4	0 | 1 | 2 ‖ 3 | 4
2-4	Add and subtract any decimals.	0-1 | 2 | 3 | 4 ‖ 5 | 6	0-1 | 2 | 3 | 4 ‖ 5 | 6
2-5	Show how to estimate sums and differences of decimals.	0 | 1 ‖ 2	0 | 1 ‖ 2
2-6	Solve word problems that involve addition and subtraction of decimals.	0 | 1 | 2 | 3 ‖ 4	0 | 1 | 2 | 3 ‖ 4

Unsatisfactory Score ‖ Satisfactory Score (Pretest)   Unsatisfactory Score ‖ Satisfactory Score (Posttest)

TEACHING ASSIGNMENTS*

	Student Page	Basic Assignment	Average Assignment	Enriched Assignment	Problem Solving	RETEACHING ASSIGNMENTS†
2-1	56, 57	1–33	1–35, EW 13	1–37, EW 13		page 380 Set 27, BW 13
	58, 59	1–44	1–44, EW 14	1–52, EW 14		page 380 Set 28, BW 14
2-1	60	1–25	1–25, EW 14	1–25, EW 14		BW 14
	61	1–4	1–7	1–7		BW 14
2-2	62, 63	1–24	1–24, EW 15	1–24, EW 15	25, 26, 27, 28, 29, 30	page 380, Set 29, BW 15
2-3	64, 65	1–39	1–42, EW 16	1–42, EW 16		page 380 Set 30, BW 16
2-4	66, 67	1–37	1–37, EW 17	1–37, EW 17	38, 39, 40	page 380 Set 31, BW 17
	68, 69	1–30	1–30, EW 18	1–30, EW 18	31, 32, 33, 34	page 381 Set 32, BW 18
2-5	70	1–20	1–32, EW 18	1–32, EW 18		page 381 Set 33, BW 18
	71		Skill Game			
2-4 2-6	72, 73	all	all, EW 19	all, EW 19		BW 19
2-6	74, 75	1–6	1–8, EW 19	1–8, EW 19		BW 19
	76		Chapter Checkup			
	77		Project			
	78		Chapter Review			
	79		Chapter Challenge			
	80		Major Checkup			

*Check assignments for objectives with unsatisfactory pretest scores.
†Check assignments for objectives with unsatisfactory posttest scores.

BW = Basic Worksheet
EW = Enrichment Worksheet

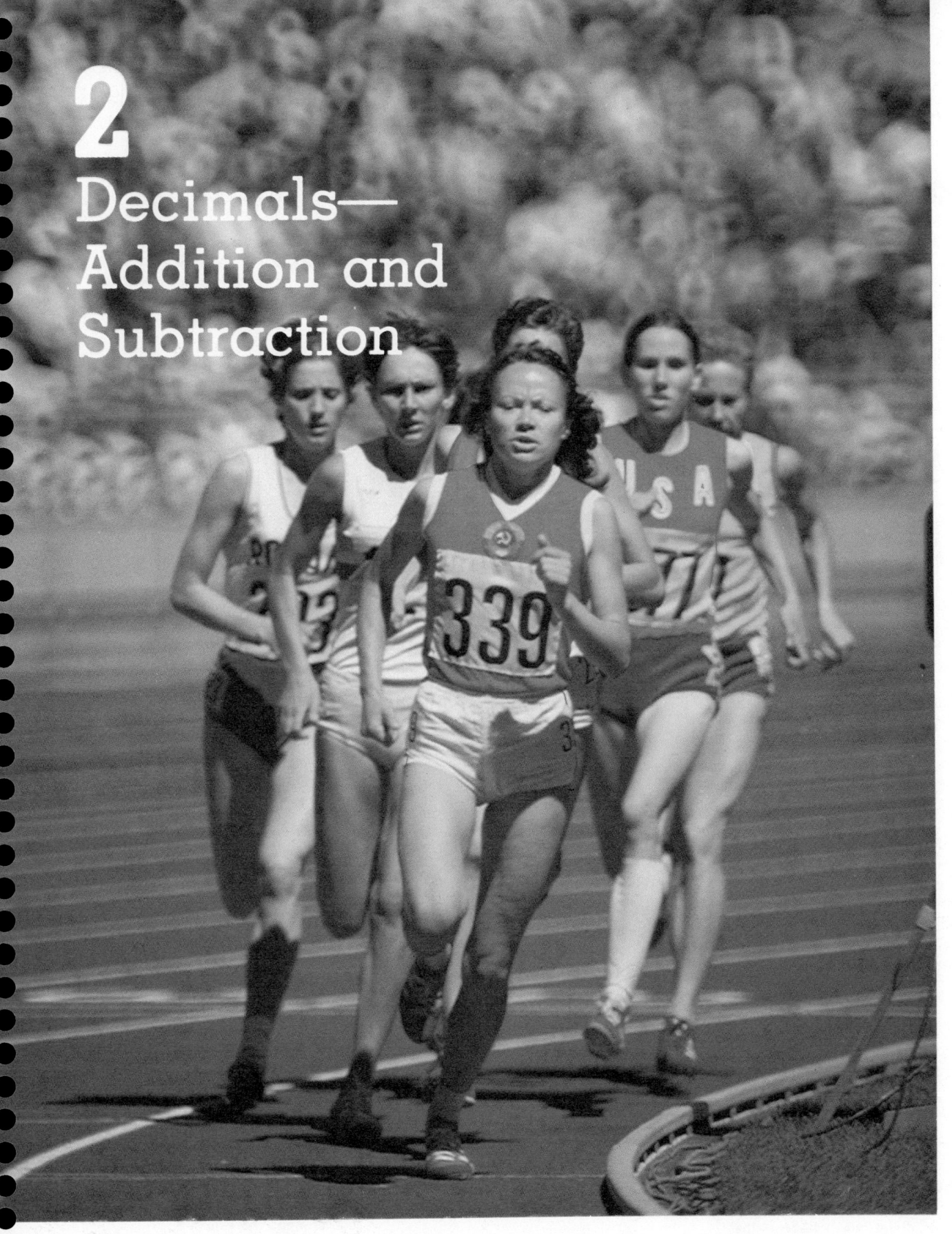

2 Decimals— Addition and Subtraction

VOCABULARY
decimal, tenth, hundredth

Suggested Lesson Plan

Introduction Begin this lesson by writing a 3-place number on the board and asking students what each digit names. As the students answer with the names of the places (ones, tens, hundreds) fill in a place-value chart around the number.

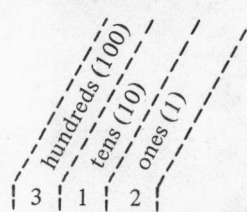

Ask students for the relationship between a place and the next place to the right. (The place on the right is always $\frac{1}{10}$ of the value of the place on the left.) Verify this relationship by pointing out that $\frac{1}{10}$ of 100 is 10, and $\frac{1}{10}$ of 10 is 1.

Point out to students that we can expand the place-value table by continuing this system to the right.

Since $\frac{1}{10}$ of 1 is $\frac{1}{10}$, the value of the place immediately to the right of the ones place is the $\frac{1}{10}$s place, or tenths place. Ask what $\frac{1}{10}$ of $\frac{1}{10}$ is. ($\frac{1}{100}$) Therefore, the place immediately to the right of the tenths place is $\frac{1}{100}$s, or hundredths. Students will know (but re-emphasize it anyway) that the decimal point separates the ones place from the tenths place. Continue to fill in the place-value chart, showing the place values for tenths and hundredths.

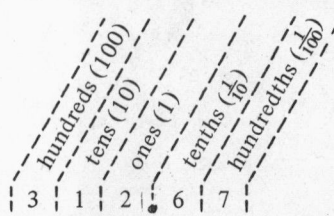

Using the pages Use the exposition on page 56 to summarize the introduction. Point out to students that the decimal point is read "and." Thus, 12.68 is read "twelve and sixty-eight hundredths."

We have adopted the convention of using a zero before the decimal point for

Tenths and hundredths

Decimal fractions (or just **decimals**) are written using our place-value system. In this system the value of each place is one tenth the value of the place to its left. To

 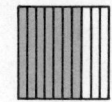

The standard numeral is written like this:
1.7

It is read as "one and seven tenths."

A decimal point separates the ones place and the tenths place.

Study this example.

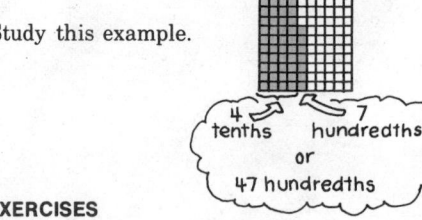

EXERCISES
Read aloud.

1. 0.3　　2. 0.03　　3. 0.9　　4. 0.09　　5. 0.27　　6. 0.58　　7. 0.30

8. 2.6　　9. 3.06　　10. 5.36　　11. 4.67　　12. 24.35　　13. 67.08　　14. 235.43

Give the standard numeral.

15. eight tenths 0.8　　16. eight hundredths 0.08　　17. eight hundred 800

18. two and three tenths 2.3　　19. six and five hundredths 6.05　　20. fourteen and fourteen hundredths 14.14

56

write decimals we extend the place-value system to the right of the ones place. The digits in this table show how many unit squares are shaded.

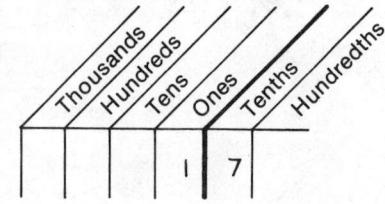

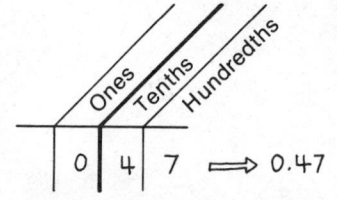

Read as "forty-seven hundredths."

numbers less than 1. In such numbers as .25, the decimal point may be overlooked. Therefore, we write it as 0.25.

Have students take turns reading the decimals for exercises 1−14 aloud. Assign exercises 15−37 for written work.

Assignments

BASIC
page 56 exercises 1−20
page 57 exercises 21−33
Basic Worksheet 13

AVERAGE
page 56 exercises 1−20
page 57 exercises 21−35
Enrichment Worksheet 13

ENRICHED
page 56 exercises 1−20
page 57 exercises 21−37
Enrichment Worksheet 13

EXTRA PRACTICE
page 380 set 27

21. two hundred three   203
22. two hundred and three tenths
                                      200.3
23. five and six hundredths   5.06
24. five hundred six
                506
25. ten and three tenths   10.3
26. one hundred and three tenths
                            100.3

How many unit squares are shaded?

27.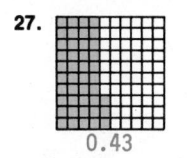
0.43

28.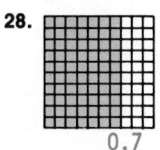
0.7

29.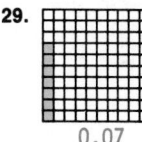
0.07

30.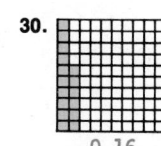
0.16

31.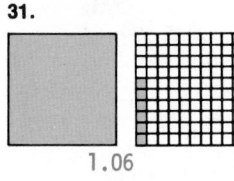
1.06

32.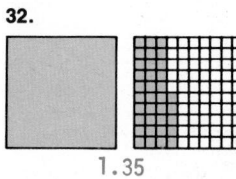
1.35

33.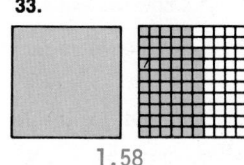
1.58

Copy the numeral and place a decimal so that the statement makes sense.

34.

In a bicycle race I averaged
2675 kilometers per hour.
26.75

35.

It is 258° Celsius today.
25.8

36. I weigh 4825 kilograms.
48.25

37. For lunch I ate 25 hamburgers.
2.5

57

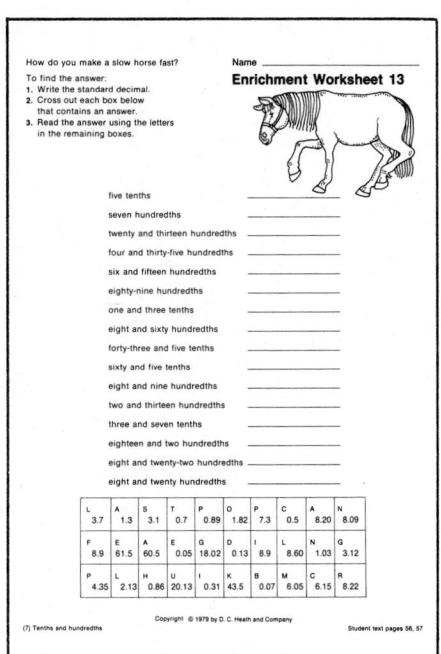

STUDENT OBJECTIVE
To read and write decimals showing up
   to millionths.

VOCABULARY
millionth, thousandth

Suggested Lesson Plan

Introduction   Redraw the place-value
chart that was drawn for the previous
lesson. Ask students for the values of
the places extending to the right of the
decimal point. Fill in these names on the
chart. Extend the chart to the millionths
place.

Using the pages   Ask a student to
read the number in the place-value chart
on page 58. If he or she has difficulty,
refer to the instructions below the chart:
First read the whole number part; say
"and" for the decimal point; read the
decimal part of the numeral as if it were
a whole number; and then say the name
of the place of the last digit.

   Write several numerals in the
place-value chart on the board and have
students take turns reading them aloud.
Next, write several numerals on the
board away from the chart and have
students take turns reading them aloud.
Listen carefully for the use of the
"and," which is important for the
discrimination between whole numbers
and decimals.

   Have students take turns reading
exercises 1–20 aloud. Assign exercises
21–52 for written work.

More about decimals

The place value system can be extended as far as needed in
both directions.

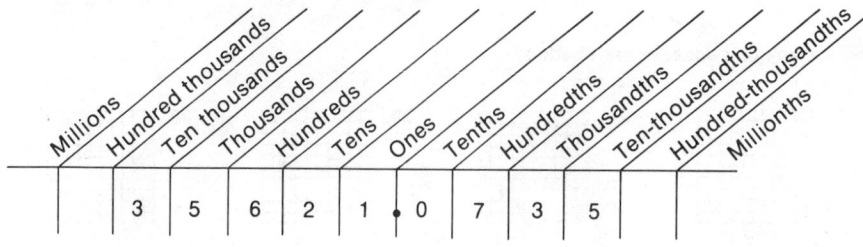

						•				
	3	5	6	2	1	•	0	7	3	5

Here is how to read a decimal.

1. Read the whole-number part. ——————→ thirty-five thousand six hundred twenty-
one

2. Say "and" for the decimal point. ——————→ and

3. Read the fraction part as if it were a ——→ seven hundred thirty-five ten-
whole number. Then say the name   thousandths
of the place of the last digit.

EXAMPLES.

47.00005   forty-seven and five hundred-thousandths

200.376   two hundred and three hundred seventy-six thousandths

I just say two hundred point three seven six.

EXERCISES
Read aloud in two ways.

1. 0.008	**2.** 0.0008	**3.** 0.00008	**4.** 0.000008	**5.** 0.035
6. 0.0035	**7.** 0.0352	**8.** 0.165	**9.** 0.2734	**10.** 0.00231
11. 6.007	**12.** 0.603	**13.** 600.003	**14.** 0.827	**15.** 800.027
16. 627.0627	**17.** 43.1675	**18.** 5000.0005	**19.** 67.359	**20.** 45.0036

58

Assignments

BASIC
page 58   exercises 1–20
page 59   exercises 21–44,
   Keeping Skills Sharp
Basic Worksheet 14

AVERAGE
page 58   exercises 1–20
page 59   exercises 21–44,
   Keeping Skills Sharp
Enrichment Worksheet 14

ENRICHED
page 58   exercises 1–20
page 59   exercises 21–52,
   Keeping Skills Sharp
Enrichment Worksheet 14

EXTRA PRACTICE
page 380   set 28

Write the standard numerals.

21. eight thousand 8000
22. eight thousandths 0.008
23. nine hundredths 0.09
24. nine hundred 900
25. twenty-four thousandths 0.024
26. twenty-four hundredths 0.24
27. eighty-seven ten thousandths 0.0087
28. nine hundred twenty-six millionths 0.000926
29. six hundred three thousandths 0.603
30. six hundred and three thousandths 600.003
31. five hundred forty thousandths 0.540
32. five hundred and forty thousandths 500.040
33. eight point six five four 8.654
34. two hundred point zero zero three 200.003

Look for a pattern.
Give the next three numbers.

35. 0.4, 0.5, 0.6, . . .
   0.7, 0.8, 0.9
36. 1.2, 1.3, 1.4, . . .
   1.5, 1.6, 1.7
37. 7.8, 7.9, 8.0, . . .
   8.1, 8.2, 8.3
38. 5.6, 5.7, 5.8, . . .
   5.9, 6.0, 6.1
39. 0.02, 0.03, 0.04, . . .
   0.05, 0.06, 0.07
40. 0.27, 0.28, 0.29, . . .
   0.30, 0.31, 0.32
41. 0.003, 0.004, 0.005, . . .
   0.006, 0.007, 0.008
42. 0.057, 0.058, 0.059, . . .
   0.060, 0.061, 0.062
43. 4.143, 4.144, . . .
   4.145, 4.146, 4.147
44. 6.056, 6.057, . . .
   6.058, 6.059, 6.060

Give a number that is between the two numbers. Answers vary.

45. 59.8, 60.0 59.9
46. 0.32, 0.34 0.33
47. 5.6, 5.7 5.65
48. 7.53, 7.54 7.535
49. 9.00, 9.01 9.005
50. 0.305, 0.306 0.3055
51. 2, 2.1 2.05
52. 3.99, 4 3.995

Keeping Skills Sharp

Multiply.

1. 92
  ×13
  1196

2. 46
  ×25
  1150

3. 87
  ×52
  4524

4. 126
  ×12
  1512

5. 628
  ×16
  10,048

6. 521
  ×28
  14,588

7. 468
  ×50
  23,400

8. 906
  ×49
  44,394

9. 3718
  ×74
  275,132

10. 4926
  ×38
  187,188

11. 2837
  ×242
  686,554

12. 5673
  ×804
  4,561,092

59

Follow-up Activities

Reinforcement The following game may be used to provide students with further experiences with place value and decimals. You will need the ten digits on index cards as shown:

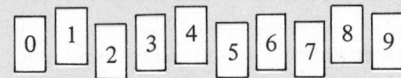

Have each student draw this table on paper:

Mix up the index cards and draw one. Instruct the students to write the digit on the card drawn in any one of the seven boxes. Replace the card and continue drawing until all seven boxes have been filled in. Declare the player who "built" the greatest number the winner. Let the winner draw the cards for the next game. Keep a tally of how many games each student wins. For each game, write the greatest number on the chalkboard and have all students read the decimal in two ways.

Enrichment The game above would also be appropriate for more able students. You may wish better students to use a table like this:

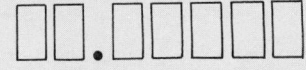

CALCULATOR ACTIVITY
Use the activity described on page 57.

Exercises 1–4, sum .008888
Exercises 5–8, sum .2387
Exercises 9–12, sum 6.88571
Exercises 13–16, sum 2027.9197
Exercises 17–20, sum 5155.5306

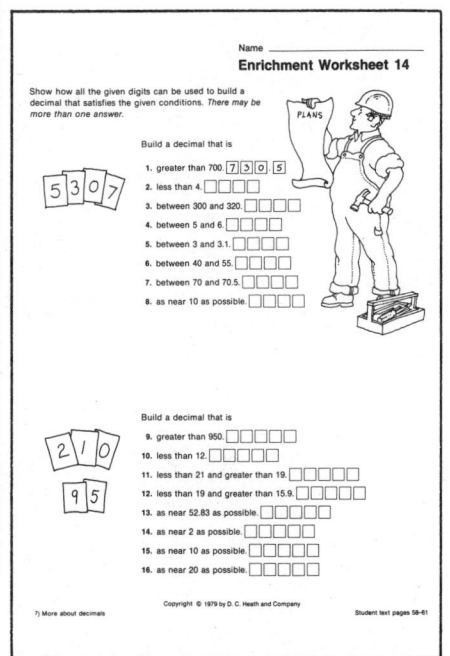

STUDENT OBJECTIVE
To use decimal notation with the metric system.

VOCABULARY
decimeter, meter, centimeter, millimeter

Suggested Lesson Plan

Introduction (meter stick, centimeter rulers) Copy the chart of metric equivalents on page 60 on the board. Try to have some sort of linear metric measuring device (meter stick, centimeter ruler, etc.) for every two students.

Hold up a meter stick and show the actual units when you read aloud the metric equivalents. As students complete the linear equivalents in exercises 1–18, try to get them to visualize the lengths rather than to try to follow a general rule, or algorithm.

Using the pages Let students work in pairs. As one student writes down the linear statement for an exercise, the other shows the actual length being considered. Students should take turns figuring out the equivalence and measuring the lengths.

Have the students continue to work in pairs on page 61. They should read through the facts together and discuss the information.

Practice exercises

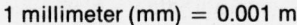

> 1 decimeter (dm) = 0.1 meter (m)
> 1 centimeter (cm) = 0.01 m
> 1 millimeter (mm) = 0.001 m

Complete.

1. 2 dm = ___?___ m   0.2
2. 2 cm = ___?___ m   0.02
3. 2 mm = ___?___ m   0.002

4. 8 dm = ___?___ m   0.8
5. 8 cm = ___?___ m   0.08
6. 8 mm = ___?___ m   0.008

7. 10 dm = ___?___ m   1
8. 10 cm = ___?___ m   0.1
9. 10 mm = ___?___ m   0.01

10. 27 dm = ___?___ m   2.7
11. 27 cm = ___?___ m   0.27
12. 27 mm = ___?___ m   0.027

13. 100 dm = ___?___ m   10
14. 100 cm = ___?___ m   1
15. 100 mm = ___?___ m   0.1

16. 375 dm = ___?___ m   37.5
17. 57 cm = ___?___ m   0.57
18. 148 mm = ___?___ m   0.148

This number is between 6 and 7 million. It can be written like this.

millions
↓
6,800,000 → 6.8 million

How many millions?

19. 8,200,000   8.2
20. 5,700,000   5.7
21. 12,800,000   12.8
22. 45,600,000   45.6
23. 68,750,000   68.75

Change to standard numerals.

24.
PUEBLO SUN
WORLD POPULATION REACHES 2.4 BILLION!
POWER BLACKOUTS BLAMED BY PSYCHIATRIST
2,400,000,000

25.
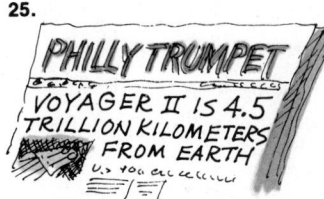
PHILLY TRUMPET
VOYAGER II IS 4.5 TRILLION KILOMETERS FROM EARTH
4,500,000,000,000

Assignments

BASIC
page 60 exercises 1–25
page 61 exercises 1–4
Basic Worksheet 14

AVERAGE
page 60 exercises 1–25
page 61 exercises 1–7
Enrichment Worksheet 14

ENRICHED
page 60 exercises 1–25
page 61 exercises 1–7
Enrichment Worksheet 14

REVIEW PRACTICE
page 377 set 14

Mathematics and science

Read these facts about the earth.

1. Some geologists estimate that the earth is about 4.5 billion years old.

2. a. The earth spins like a top, causing night and day. A point on the equator spins at a rate of about 1600 kilometers per hour.

   b. The earth also revolves around the sun, causing years. It revolves once around the sun in 365 days, 6 hours 9 minutes and 9.54 seconds. It travels around the sun at an average rate of about 107,200 kilometers per hour.

3. a. About 148,225,000 square kilometers of the earth's surface is land.

   b. About 361,847,000 square kilometers of the earth's surface is water.

4. The distance around the earth at the equator is about 40,076 kilometers.

5. The mass of the earth is about 5.52 times as much as the mass of the same volume of water.

6. About 0.67 of the earth is made up of silicon dioxide (SiO_2).

7. The earth is 0.00000037 times as far from the sun as it is from the next nearest star.

61

Follow-up Activities

Reinforcement Provide a piece of brown paper about 3 meters long and a meter stick for each pair of students. Have them draw a line of the given length for each exercise (exercises 1–18, page 60) and then measure each line with the meter stick. (Tell them to omit exercises 13 and 16.) They are to label each line with the measurement given and with the equivalent name. Post the better papers on the wall for future reference to metric units.

Enrichment Use the information on page 61 to encourage students to find out other facts about the earth. Have students use the facts in comparison with known quantities to prepare an illustration for the mathematics bulletin board.

EXCURSION

One of the largest numbers that has been given a special name is 10^{100}. It is called the *googol*. To write it in standard form you would write "1" followed by some zeros. How many zeros? 100

Here is a much larger number: $10^{(10^{100})}$. It is called the *googolplex*. How would you write it in standard form? 1 followed by 10^{100} zeros. How long do you think it would take you to write it? See *The World of Mathematics*, by James R. Newman (Simon and Schuster, 1956), pages 2007–2010. Read about these numbers and report to the class.

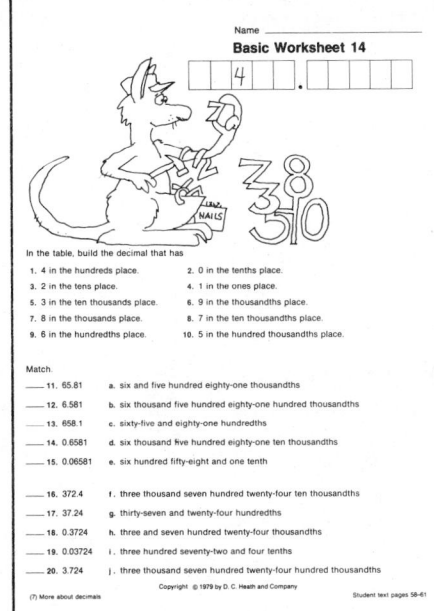

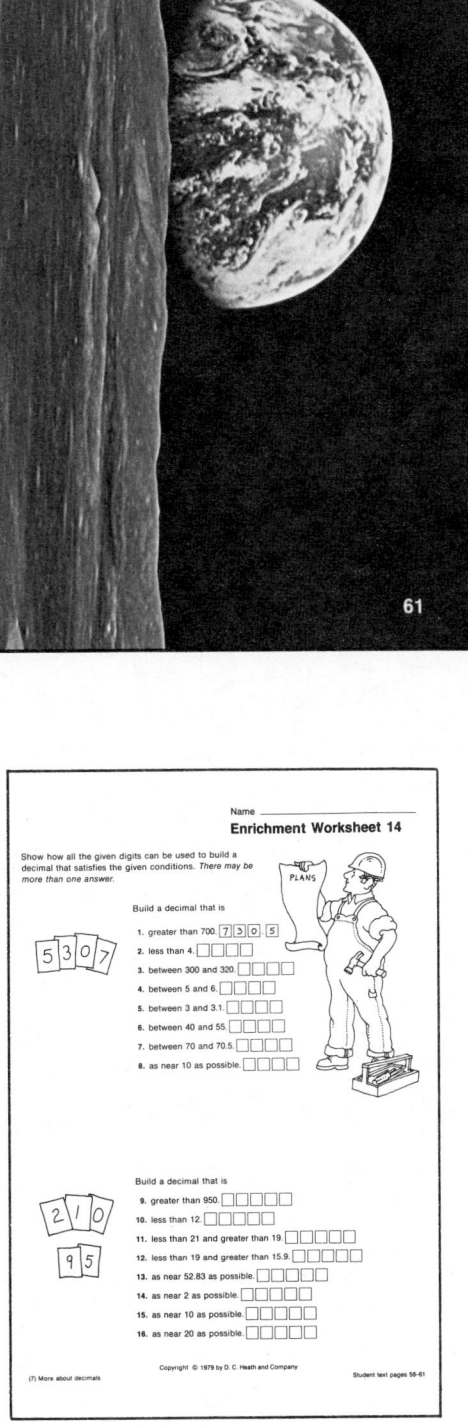

To compare decimals.
To order decimals by size.

Suggested Lesson Plan

Introduction Introduce the lesson with a discussion of batting averages and how they are computed. A batting average is the decimal found by dividing the number of hits by the number of times at bat. (Some of the times at bat, such as walks, sacrifice plays, etc., do not count.)

Try to obtain a list of the current batting averages and discuss the comparison of the averages.

Using the pages Refer to the National League Batting Champs Chart. Have a student compare two averages and tell which is larger. Frequently a student will be able to identify the larger decimal, but will not be able to verbalize his or her method.

Of course the process is almost like that used with whole numbers, except that with decimals, more digits do not make a greater number. The best way to compare decimals is to start at the decimal point and compare digit by digit.

Pick out other players from the chart and have students compare their batting averages. Finally, ask them to name the players, starting with the highest average, in order.

Assign exercises 1–24 for written work. Remind students that the narrow end of the comparison sign points to the smaller number.

Assign 25–30 for written work also.

Comparing and ordering decimals

Some National League Batting Champs			
Year	Player	Team	Ave.
1970	Rico Carty	Atlanta	.366
1971	Joe Torre	St. Louis	.363
1972	Billy Williams	Chicago	.333
1973	Pete Rose	Cincinnati	.338
1974	Ralph Garr	Atlanta	.353
1975	Bill Madlock	Chicago	.354

To compare the batting averages of Rico Carty and Joe Torre, we compare decimals. We can compare these decimals by comparing the digits that are in the same places.

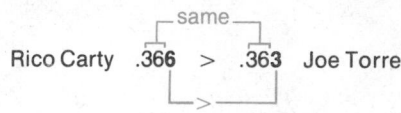

Rico Carty .366 > .363 Joe Torre

Rico Carty had a greater batting average.

Another example.

52.08 > 06.74

Since I know 52 is greater than 6, I don't have to compare digits in this example.

62

Assignments

BASIC
page 62 Discuss
page 63 exercises 1–28
Basic Worksheet 15

AVERAGE
page 62 Discuss
page 63 exercises 1–29
Enrichment Worksheet 15

ENRICHED
page 62 Discuss
page 63 exercises 1–30
Enrichment Worksheet 15

EXTRA PRACTICE
page 380 set 29

< or >?

1. 0.2 ● 0.3
2. 0.06 ● 0.05
3. 0.009 ● 0.008
4. 0.2 ● 0.02
5. 0.004 ● 0.03
6. 0.1 ● 0.08
7. 0.006 ● 0.2
8. 0.3 ● 0.004
9. 0.82 ● 0.85
10. 0.74 ● 0.71
11. 5.38 ● 5.83
12. 6.75 ● 6.57
13. 38.21 ● 38.54
14. 71.69 ● 71.7
15. 5.936 ● 59.36
16. 782.76 ● 780.99
17. 83.5 ● 8.76
18. 0.759 ● 1
19. 2 ● 1.899
20. 7.564 ● 7.099
21. 8.63 ● 16.58
22. 47.02 ● 9.385
23. 7.216 ● 72.16
24. 53.06 ● 5.899

25. Arrange the six batting averages given on page 62 in order from highest to lowest.

26. In one World Series, Lou Brock's batting average was .414 and pitcher Bob Gibson's batting average was .091. Who had the higher average?

Team Pitching	Earned-run Averages
Boston	3.99
New York	3.29
Kansas City	3.49
Chicago	3.94
California	3.89
Minnesota	4.05
Detroit	4.29
Oakland	3.29
Cleveland	3.84
Baltimore	3.17
Texas	3.90
Milwaukee	4.34

27. Which team had the lowest earned-run average? Baltimore

28. Which team had the highest earned-run average? Milwaukee

29. Which had the lower earned-run average, Detroit or Milwaukee? Detroit

30. List the teams in order from lowest to highest earned-run average.
Baltimore, New York and Oakland, Kansas City, Cleveland, California, Texas, Chicago, Boston, Minnesota, Detroit, Milwaukee

63

Follow-up Activities

Reinforcement Further experiences with comparing decimals can be had by playing the following game. Write 40 different decimal fractions between 0 and 10 on index cards. For example:

.01   .1   .132   .26   1.07   1.89

Thoroughly shuffle the cards and place the deck face down. Divide the students into two well-balanced teams. Have a player from each team go to the chalkboard and draw a card. Ask them to write their decimals on the chalkboard and decide which is greater. The player getting the greater number earns a point for his team. The team earning the greater number of points wins the game.

Enrichment Have students play the game described above but encourage them to work with three-place and four-place decimals. For a slight variation they may wish to play that the smaller number earns a point.

CALCULATOR ACTIVITY
See if you can get a few students interested in the statistics associated with baseball. Have them follow the daily reports and compute new averages based upon each game's result. If another sport is popular at the time, get students to compute statistics associated with it. Have students prepare a bulletin board showing the different statistics used to evaluate performances.

Name _____
Basic Worksheet 15

First circle the greater numbers. Then connect the dots of greater numbers in the order given below.

1. (0.6) 0.06
2. 0.5 (0.51)
3. 0.7 0.69
4. 0.003 0.02
5. 2.16 2.25
6. 3.43 3.34
7. 0.64 0.59
8. 0.09 0.9
9. 1 0.9
10. 3.99 4
11. 82.5 82.45
12. 0.6 1.5
13. 0.279 0.297
14. 1.348 1.384
15. 12.90 13.89
16. 28.201 28.21
17. 53.86 538.5
18. 74.91 749.0
19. 2.683 0.2688
20. 9.517 95.07

(7) Comparing decimals   Copyright © 1979 by D. C. Heath and Company   Student text pages 62, 63

What state
is called the Volunteer State,
has the mockingbird as state bird, and
had Davy Crockett as a U.S. congressman?

To find the answer:
1. Circle the greatest number in each group.
2. Cross out each box below that contains a greatest number.
3. Read the answer using the letters in the remaining boxes.

Name _____
Enrichment Worksheet 15

1.0096	1.057	1.0069	0.43	0.456	0.46
58.3	58.15	58.06	3.286	3.296	3.269
15.309	15.298	15.289	8.17	7.39	7.99
154.89	153.9	154.9	25.81	25.76	25.79
0.829	0.836	0.863	5.347	5.437	5.473
0.598	5.76	0.599	0.9256	0.9258	0.0959
183.52	183.169	183.196	17.05	17.049	17.051
34.092	34.075	34.29	6.008	6.2	6.19
5.008	5.08	5.799	2.059	2.006	2.061

A 6.2	T 1.0069	L 5.76	E 15.298	E 5.473	A 0.836	A 0.863
R 17.051	O 0.46	N 34.092	B 1.057	E 3.286	L 0.9258	25.81
A 183.52	S 0.599	N 3.296	M 5.437	E 58.3	H 17.049	34.29
R 15.309	G 5.799	E 2.059	A 8.17	A 154.9	2.061	

(7) Comparing decimals   Copyright © 1979 by D. C. Heath and Company   Student text pages 62, 63

Suggested Lesson Plan

Introduction Give students some review exercises dealing with rounding whole numbers. Next, write on the board:

6.43

Ask students to give the two "neighboring" whole numbers. (6 and 7) Ask what number is midway between 6 and 7. (6.5) Is 6.43 nearer to 6 or to 7? (6) Tell students that if we use the nearest whole number instead of the true value, we are *rounding* to the nearest whole number. Point out that we can do exactly the same thing mechanically. We can look at the digit in the tenths place. If it is less than 5 (this makes the number nearer to 6) drop all digits to the right of the ones place. If the tenths digit is 5 or greater, change the 6 to 7 and drop all digits to the right. The pattern is similar when we round to the tenths place, the hundredths place, and so on. Ask students to tell why we can just drop the digits to the right when we round to the nearest one or tenth but have to change digits to zeros when we round to the nearest ten or hundred.

Do several examples with your students.

Using the pages Use the exposition on page 64 to summarize the introduction. Call on students to explain both ways of rounding—on the number line or mechanically by looking at the digits. Students may use either method.

Assign exercises 1–42 for written work.

Rounding

Round decimals just as you would round whole numbers. You can think about the number line. For example, suppose that you want to round 12.73 to the nearest whole number. Think about where 12.73 is located on the number line.

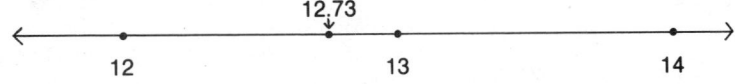

It is nearer 13. So, 12.73 rounded to the nearest whole number (or nearest one) is 13.

Here is a rounding shortcut.

Round to the nearest one.

Round to the nearest hundredth.

EXERCISES

Round to the nearest one.

1. 3.4 3   2. 3.7 4   3. 15.1 15   4. 15.9 16   5. 2.26 2   6. 2.96 3

7. $13.48   8. $27.51   9. $124.50
   $13 $28 $125

Round to the nearest tenth.

10. 0.73 0.7   11. 0.77 0.8   12. 8.94 8.9   13. 8.96 9.0   14. 12.411   15. 27.501
                                                                    12.4   27.5

16. $7.38   17. $19.41   18. $142.67
    $7.4 $19.4 $142.7

64

Assignments

BASIC
page 64 exercises 1–18
page 65 exercises 19–39
Basic Worksheet 16

AVERAGE
page 64 exercises 1–18
page 65 exercises 19–42
Enrichment Worksheet 16

ENRICHED
page 64 exercises 1–18
page 65 exercises 19–42, Excursion
Enrichment Worksheet 16

EXTRA PRACTICE
page 380 set 30

Round to the nearest hundredth.

19. 4.673	**20.** 21.987	**21.** 5.635	**22.** 4.8133	**23.** 2.7758	**24.** 16.296
4.67	21.99	5.64	4.81	2.78	16.30
25. 0.078	**26.** 0.0977	**27.** 19.999			
0.08	0.10	20.00			

Round to the nearest thousandth.

28. 2.8359	**29.** 5.7461	**30.** 8.4965	**31.** 0.8295	**32.** 3.6182	**33.** 14.7293
2.836	5.746	8.497	0.830	3.618	14.729
34. 6.0996	**35.** 7.7598	**36.** 4.2996			
6.100	7.760	4.300			

The speed record for a bicycle is 204.734
kilometers per hour. (A lead car had a mounted
wind shield to break the wind.) Round the number
to the nearest

37. hundredth 204.73

38. whole number 205

39. tenth 204.7

A world speed record for a skateboard was 86.886
kilometers per hour. Round to the nearest

40. tenth 86.9

41. hundredth 86.89

42. whole number 87

Excursion ▨◙▨◙▨◙▨◙▨◙▨◙▨◙▨◙▨◙▨◙▨◙▨◙
Look up the winning speed records for the Indianapolis
500. In what way have the speeds changed? Make a line
graph to show what you found.

65

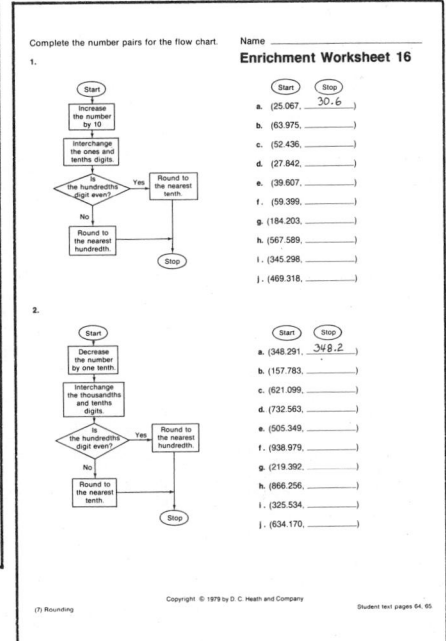

Suggested Lesson Plan

Introduction Quickly write three whole numbers on the board and have a student come to the board and find their sum. Pick numbers that have a different number of digits and do not write them in position for adding. Call attention to the student's arrangement of the numbers starting from the right so that ones are added to ones, tens are added to tens, etc. Point out that we do the same thing when adding decimals except that we line up the decimal points.

Using the pages Use the exposition on page 66 to review addition, noting that we add decimals just as we add whole numbers. Discuss each step, noting how the work is recorded.

Assign exercises 1–40 for written work. Observe students when they encounter exercise 6. In this case, although they can add, many will be more comfortable if they write a 0 below the 7 before adding.

Assign the Keeping Skills Sharp to all students.

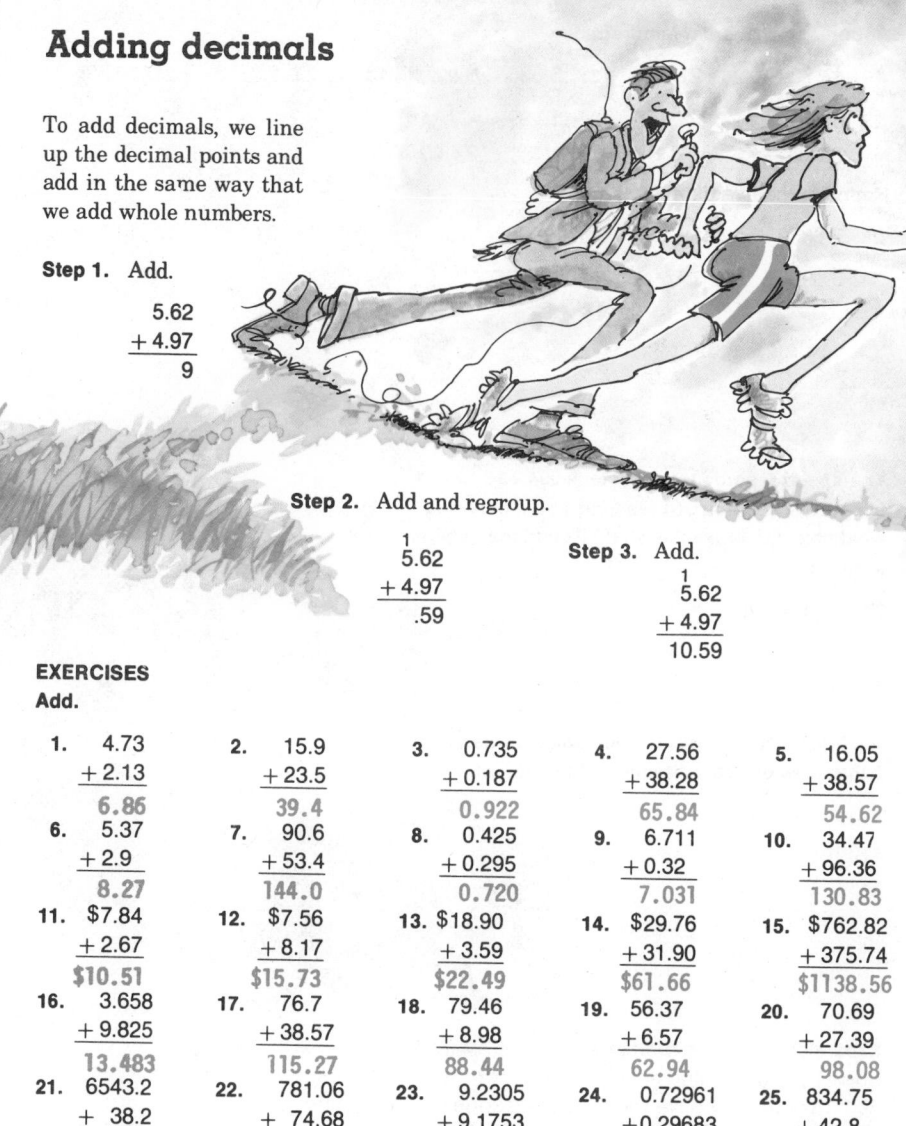

Adding decimals

To add decimals, we line up the decimal points and add in the same way that we add whole numbers.

Step 1. Add.

$$\begin{array}{r} 5.62 \\ + 4.97 \\ \hline 9 \end{array}$$

Step 2. Add and regroup.

$$\begin{array}{r} {}^{1} \\ 5.62 \\ + 4.97 \\ \hline .59 \end{array}$$

Step 3. Add.

$$\begin{array}{r} {}^{1} \\ 5.62 \\ + 4.97 \\ \hline 10.59 \end{array}$$

EXERCISES
Add.

1. $\begin{array}{r}4.73\\+2.13\\\hline 6.85\end{array}$	2. $\begin{array}{r}15.9\\+23.5\\\hline 39.4\end{array}$	3. $\begin{array}{r}0.735\\+0.187\\\hline 0.922\end{array}$	4. $\begin{array}{r}27.56\\+38.28\\\hline 65.84\end{array}$	5. $\begin{array}{r}16.05\\+38.57\\\hline 54.62\end{array}$
6. $\begin{array}{r}5.37\\+2.9\\\hline 8.27\end{array}$	7. $\begin{array}{r}90.6\\+53.4\\\hline 144.0\end{array}$	8. $\begin{array}{r}0.425\\+0.295\\\hline 0.720\end{array}$	9. $\begin{array}{r}6.711\\+0.32\\\hline 7.031\end{array}$	10. $\begin{array}{r}34.47\\+96.36\\\hline 130.83\end{array}$
11. $\begin{array}{r}\$7.84\\+2.67\\\hline \$10.51\end{array}$	12. $\begin{array}{r}\$7.56\\+8.17\\\hline \$15.73\end{array}$	13. $\begin{array}{r}\$18.90\\+3.59\\\hline \$22.49\end{array}$	14. $\begin{array}{r}\$29.76\\+31.90\\\hline \$61.66\end{array}$	15. $\begin{array}{r}\$762.82\\+375.74\\\hline \$1138.56\end{array}$
16. $\begin{array}{r}3.658\\+9.825\\\hline 13.483\end{array}$	17. $\begin{array}{r}76.7\\+38.57\\\hline 115.27\end{array}$	18. $\begin{array}{r}79.46\\+8.98\\\hline 88.44\end{array}$	19. $\begin{array}{r}56.37\\+6.57\\\hline 62.94\end{array}$	20. $\begin{array}{r}70.69\\+27.39\\\hline 98.08\end{array}$
21. $\begin{array}{r}6543.2\\+38.2\\\hline 6581.4\end{array}$	22. $\begin{array}{r}781.06\\+74.68\\\hline 855.74\end{array}$	23. $\begin{array}{r}9.2305\\+9.1753\\\hline 18.4058\end{array}$	24. $\begin{array}{r}0.72961\\+0.29683\\\hline 1.02644\end{array}$	25. $\begin{array}{r}834.75\\+42.8\\\hline 877.55\end{array}$

66

Assignments

BASIC
page 66 exercises 1–25
page 67 exercises 26–38,
   Keeping Skills Sharp
Basic Worksheet 17

AVERAGE
page 66 exercises 1–25
page 67 exercises 26–40,
   Keeping Skills Sharp
Enrichment Worksheet 17

ENRICHED
page 66 exercises 1–25
page 67 exercises 26–40, Excursion
Enrichment Worksheet 17

EXTRA PRACTICE
page 380 set 31

Add.

26. $0.02 + 31.4$
    31.42

27. $3.6 + 0.94$
    4.54

28. $48 + 5.06$
    53.06

29. $25.8 + 3.79$
    29.59

30. $226.4 + 15.84$
    242.24

31. $119.6 + 289$
    408.6

32. $39.54 + 7.621$
    47.161

33. $4.328 + 0.7493$
    5.0773

34. $0.593 + 16.48$
    17.073

35. $0.0295 + 0.0088$
    0.0383

36. $3.526 + 48.79$
    52.316

37. $5483 + 23.77$
    5506.77

Solve.

38. To practice for the cross-country team, Carol ran 4.5 km each morning and 6.8 km each evening. How far did she run each day?   11.3 km

39. At the beginning of the sixth grade, Bill weighed 38 kg. During the next year he gained 3.9 kg. How much did he weigh then?   41.9 kg

40. The four sections of a bike trail measure 8.9 km, 7.8 km, 9.0 km, and 8.7 km. What is the total distance?   34.4 km

Excursion ■□■□■□■□■□■
In a magic square, the sum of the numbers in each row, column, and diagonal is the same. Copy and complete this magic square.

5.8	5.1	5.6
5.3	5.5	5.7
5.4	5.9	5.2

Divide.

1. $8\overline{)592}$ 74
2. $6\overline{)6832}$ 1138 R4
3. $4\overline{)7906}$ 1976 R2
4. $9\overline{)8396}$ 932 R8
5. $15\overline{)945}$ 63
6. $23\overline{)966}$ 42
7. $35\overline{)2874}$ 82 R4
8. $52\overline{)1930}$ 37 R6
9. $47\overline{)3555}$ 75 R30
10. $68\overline{)9180}$ 135
11. $92\overline{)18960}$ 206 R8
12. $70\overline{)19618}$ 280 R18
13. $83\overline{)35279}$ 425 R4
14. $66\overline{)25028}$ 379 R14
15. $157\overline{)63825}$ 406 R83
16. $243\overline{)43016}$ 177 R5

67

Follow-up Activities

Reinforcement Some students may need additional work at the concrete level. If so, display the following collection of money:

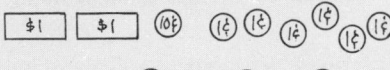
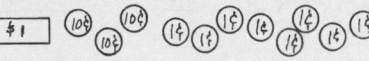

Then write this on the chalkboard:

$$2.16$$
$$+1.38$$

Push together the 14 pennies and then trade 10 pennies for 1 dime. Keep a record of what was done on the chalkboard by showing the regrouping like this:

```
   1
 2.16
+1.38
    4
```

Continue to add in columns, keeping a record of each step:

```
   1
 2.16
+1.38
 3.54
```

Enrichment The following game may be used to provide further experiences with adding decimals. Write the ten digits 0 through 9 on index cards. Have each student prepare a table like this:

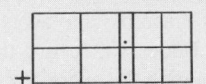

Draw a card and have each student write that digit in any one of the 8 boxes on his table. Replace the cards and continue to draw cards until all 8 boxes have been filled in. Ask students to add the two numbers in their table. Declare as winner the player who got the greatest sum. Later, you may wish to play having the least sum win.

EXCURSION
How many times will the minute hand pass the hour hand between 6 A.M. and 6 P.M.?   11 times

---

Basic Worksheet 17

Name _____

Step 1. Add.

```
  3 6.9 4
+ 2 7.3 5
        9
```

Step 2. Add and regroup.

```
  3 6.9 4
+ 2 7.3 5
     .2 9
```

Step 3. Add and regroup.

```
    1
  3 6.9 4
+ 2 7.3 5
    4.2 9
```

Step 4. Add.

```
    1 1
  3 6.9 4
+ 2 7.3 5
  6 4.2 9
```

Add.

1. $8.93 + 2.79$ 11.72
2. $57.6 + 68.9$
3. $5.74 + 0.38$
4. $0.933 + 0.256$
5. $9.34 + 25.9$

6. $6.94 + 7.28$
7. $5.36 + 0.59$
8. $29.5 + 74.8$
9. $2.25 + 4.79$
10. $0.186 + 0.359$

11. $41.68 + 37.95$
12. $2.764 + 9.283$
13. $785.6 + 297.4$
14. $31.76 + 85.34$
15. $8.625 + 5.943$

16. $36.82 + 5.93$
17. $759.2 + 88.8$
18. $3.784 + 0.916$
19. $59.38 + 2.57$
20. $629.4 + 57.8$

21. $5.21 + 3.68 + 4.25$
22. $95.6 + 38.4 + 21.7$
23. $0.394 + 0.682 + 0.756$
24. $7.46 + 3.91 + 6.5$
25. $0.538 + 0.27 + 0.594$

26. $25.1 + 38.4 + 59.2 + 1.65$
27. $5.93 + 8.2 + 7.61 + 4.5$
28. $0.963 + 0.178 + 0.42 + 0.56$
29. $2.341 + 7.158 + 4.25 + 3.68$
30. $71.35 + 20.06 + 5.80 + 39.4$

(7) Adding decimals

Copyright © 1979 by D. C. Heath and Company

Student text pages 66, 67

Enrichment Worksheet 17

Name _____

Complete the number pairs for the flow chart.

1. Start → Add 8.364 → Round to nearest hundredth → Is the digit in the hundredths place even? → Yes → Add 6.84 → Stop; No → Add 4.59 → Stop

   a. (5.356, ___20.56___)
   b. (9.748, _____)
   c. (3.559, _____)
   d. (6.778, _____)
   e. (1.390, _____)
   f. (8.479, _____)
   g. (2.635, _____)
   h. (9.587, _____)
   i. (5.923, _____)
   j. (7.426, _____)

2. Start → Round to the nearest hundredth → Add 7.99 → Is the digit in the hundredths place even? → Yes → Add 4.53 → Stop; No → Add 9.08 → Stop

   a. (3.846, ___16.37___)
   b. (9.537, _____)
   c. (8.359, _____)
   d. (7.064, _____)
   e. (4.659, _____)
   f. (5.328, _____)
   g. (2.444, _____)
   h. (1.963, _____)
   i. (3.098, _____)
   j. (9.369, _____)

(7) Adding decimals

Copyright © 1979 by D. C. Heath and Company

Student text pages 66, 67

Suggested Lesson Plan

Introduction Write this example on the board.

$$\begin{array}{r} 3.04 \\ -1.56 \\ \hline \end{array}$$

Ask students how they would represent 3.04 if one large square represented 1. They should say 3 large squares and 4 hundredths of one square. Draw this model on the board beside 3.04.

3.04

To represent the subtraction of 1.56, we can take away 1.56 squares from the number represented. Of course, to do this, we must trade pieces so that there are more tenths and hundredths. Ask a student what must be traded in order to take away 1.56. You are looking for the student to trade 1 square for 10 tenths and then 1 tenth for 10 hundredths. Represent these trades on the board.

$$\begin{array}{r} 2 \;\overset{9}{\cancel{10}}\; 14 \\ 3.\cancel{0}\cancel{4} \\ -1.56 \\ \hline \end{array}$$

After writing this regrouping on the board, ask a student to come to the board and erase or take away 1.56. As the student does so, record the answer.

Summarize the work for this problem by repeating the renaming that is done in the algorithm. Emphasize that the work is the same as when subtracting whole numbers.

Using the pages Use the situation on page 68 to generate interest in the chart. The different amounts of yearly precipitation are to be compared. Ask how the average yearly precipitation can be found from the chart. Have one row of students find the average yearly precipitation for Birmingham and another row do the same for Honolulu. Elicit from students that to compare these amounts we subtract the smaller amount from the larger.

Use the worked example in the book to focus attention on the regrouping process.

Have students work some other examples on scratch paper while you observe. Note any students having difficulty and plan to work individually with them.

Assign exercises 1–34 for written work. Point out to students that they will have to refer back to the table for information for problems 31–34.

Subtracting decimals

Average Monthly Precipitation
(in centimeters)

City	Jan.	Feb.	Mar.	Apr.	May	June	July	Aug.	Sept.	Oct.	Nov.	Dec.
Birmingham, Ala.	12.7	13.5	15.3	11.4	8.6	10.2	13.2	12.4	8.5	7.6	8.9	12.7
Chicago, Ill.	4.8	4.1	6.9	7.6	9.4	10.4	8.6	8.1	6.9	7.1	5.6	4.8
Honolulu, Ha.	9.7	8.4	7.4	3.3	2.5	0.8	1.0	2.3	2.5	4.6	5.6	7.6
Little Rock, Ark.	13.2	10.9	12.2	12.4	13.5	9.1	8.4	7.1	8.1	7.4	10.4	10.4
Miami, Fla.	5.1	4.8	5.8	9.9	16.3	18.8	17.3	17.8	24.1	20.8	7.1	4.3
New York, N.Y.	8.4	7.1	10.2	8.6	9.4	8.4	9.4	11.2	9.9	7.8	8.6	8.4

The average yearly precipitation in Birmingham is 135 centimeters and in Honolulu it is 55.7 centimeters. We subtract to find the difference.

Step 1. Line up the decimal points. Since 135 = 135.0, write a zero in the tenths place.

$$\begin{array}{r} 135.0 \\ -55.7 \\ \hline \end{array}$$

Step 2. Regroup.

$$\begin{array}{r} \overset{0\;12\;14}{\cancel{135}.0} \\ -55.7 \\ \hline \end{array}$$

Step 3. Subtract.

$$\begin{array}{r} \overset{0\;12\;14}{\cancel{135}.0} \\ -55.7 \\ \hline 79.3 \end{array}$$

The average precipitation is 79.3 centimeters more in Birmingham.

68

Assignments

BASIC
page 68 Discuss
page 69 exercises 1–32
Basic Worksheet 18

AVERAGE
page 68 Discuss
page 69 exercises 1–34
Enrichment Worksheet 18

ENRICHED
page 68 Discuss
page 69 exercises 1–34
Enrichment Worksheet 18

EXTRA PRACTICE
page 381 set 32

EXERCISES
Subtract.

1. 59.6
   − 13.5
   46.1

2. 8.42
   − 0.26
   8.16

3. 72.6
   − 7.8
   64.8

4. 9.68
   − 3.14
   6.54

5. 85.3
   − 28.9
   56.4

6. 0.314
   − 0.109
   0.205

7. 60.2
   − 28.9
   31.3

8. 5.19
   − 3.74
   1.45

9. 0.302
   − 0.195
   0.107

10. 9.64
   − 3.98
   5.66

11. 5.918
   − 0.265
   5.653

12. 72.95
   − 3.98
   68.97

13. 0.7426
   − 0.4285
   0.3141

14. 86.52
   − 32.97
   53.55

15. 646.4
   − 289.6
   356.8

16. 61.83
   − 59.34
   2.49

17. 6.882
   − 2.817
   4.065

18. 6.752
   − 0.395
   6.351

19. 93.71
   − 0.78
   92.93

20. 87.25
   − 3.95
   83.30

21. 70.2 − 26.14   **44.06**

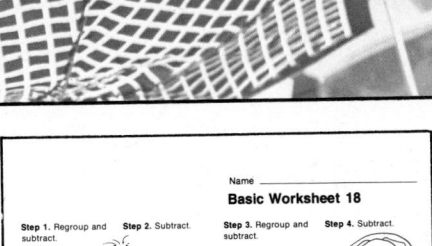

22. 581.68 − 59.38   **522.3**

23. 74.729 − 27.351   **47.378**

24. 723.16 − 56.87   **666.29**

25. 95.305 − 4.26   **91.045**

26. 16.3 − 5.491   **10.809**

27. 28.9 − 16.03   **12.87**

28. 90.06 − 5.178   **84.882**

29. 263.3 − 59.648   **203.652**

30. 520.4 − 9.871   **510.529**

Solve. Use the chart on the previous page.

31. What is the yearly precipitation in Chicago?   **84.3 cm**

32. Which city gets more precipitation in a year, Chicago or Honolulu?   **Chicago**

33. How much precipitation does New York get during the first half of the year? During the second half? How much   **52.1 cm, 55.3 cm** more during the second half?   **3.2 cm**

34. Which city gets more precipitation in a year, Little Rock **Miami** or Miami? How much more?   **29.0 cm**

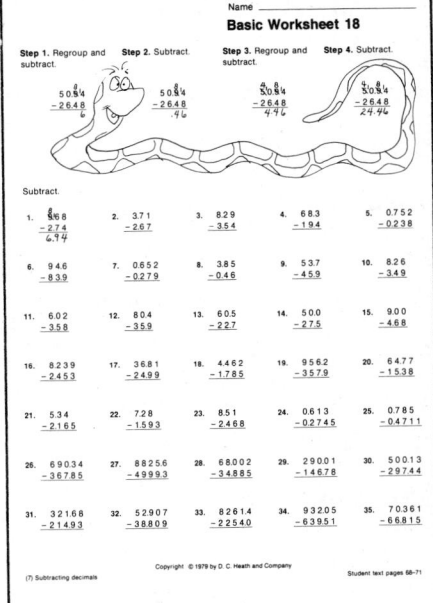

69

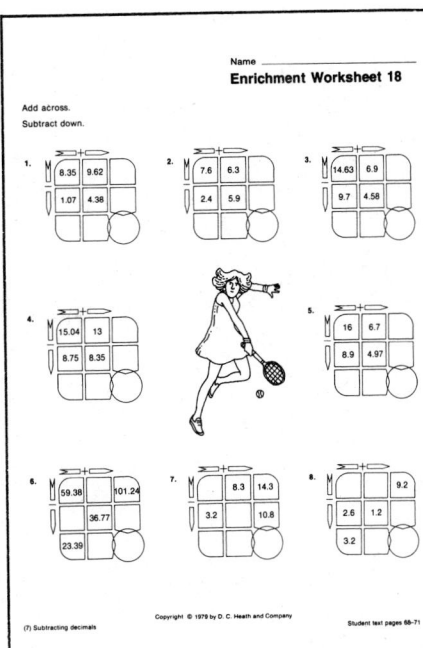

Follow-up Activities

Reinforcement   To provide more experiences with adding and subtracting decimals, you may wish to give students addition boxes like the following. Answers are given in red.

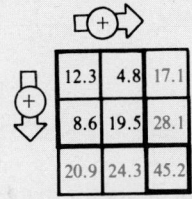

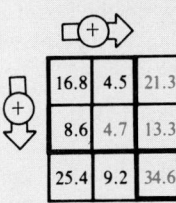

Notice that in the first exercise all cells can be filled in by merely adding. In the second exercise there are some missing addends.

Enrichment   Have students work through this flow chart to find the number they end with.

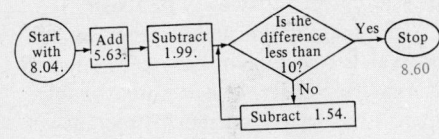

Give students some other starting numbers for the flow chart.

EXCURSION

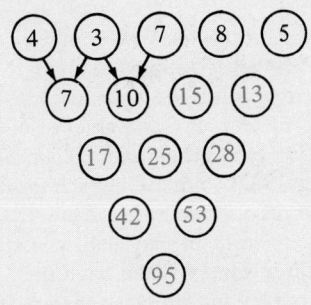

1. Copy the figure and fill in the circles with the correct numbers.

2. Try to guess the number in the bottom circle.

3. Repeat, using other numbers in the top circles. Can you make a rule?

(core) Lesson 26   69

To estimate before computing with decimals to see if your answer is reasonable.

To play a game to encourage estimating, adding, and subtracting decimals and to provide intuitive experiences with probability.

VOCABULARY
estimate

Suggested Lesson Plan

Introduction Write the multiplication equation below on the board and ask students, "Who can tell me whether this equation is true or false?"

$$3.897 \times 4.133 = 161.06301$$

Someone should volunteer that the equation is false. Ask how he or she knew. The answer should be that since both factors are near 4, the product should be near 16. Point out that this student estimated by rounding each factor to the nearest whole number and then multiplying. Ask students, "If the digits in the product are correct and just the decimal point has been placed wrong, where should it go?" (After the 6. The correct answer is 16.106301.)

Estimating will tell whether an answer is reasonable, but not whether it is exactly correct. If it is unreasonable, then it is surely incorrect. If the answer is reasonable, we don't know for sure whether it is correct or not until we compute.

Using the pages Go over the examples on page 70 with your students. Have them round to the nearest whole number and give an estimate for each example.

Assign exercises 1–32 for written work. Rather than have them start on the written work, organize the class into groups of four. Provide a set of digit cards for each group and explain how to play the Skill Game. Get each group started playing, and after 2 practice games, have them play until one student wins three games. Then have the winners play for the class championship. You can change the target number for the championship round.

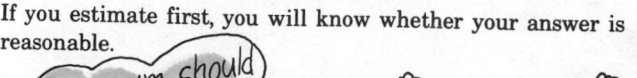

Estimating sums and differences

If you estimate first, you will know whether your answer is reasonable.

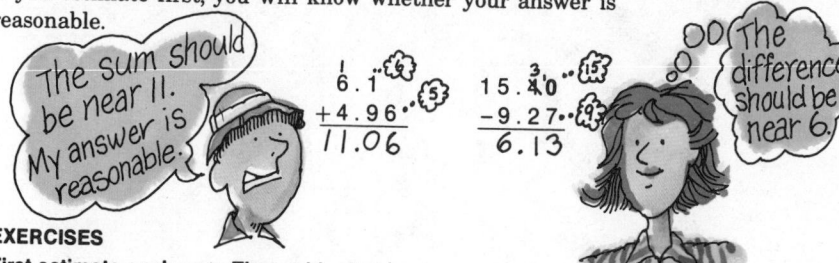

The sum should be near 11. My answer is reasonable.

$$\begin{array}{r} 6.1 \\ +4.96 \\ \hline 11.06 \end{array}$$

$$\begin{array}{r} 15.40 \\ -9.27 \\ \hline 6.13 \end{array}$$

The difference should be near 6.

EXERCISES

First estimate each sum. Then add. Estimates may vary.

1.	3.55 +2.5	7	**2.**	72.6 +39.4	110	**3.**	0.23 +4.583	5	**4.**	5.41 +23.8	29	**5.**	18.917 +9.6	29

1. 3.55
+2.5
6.05   7

2. 72.6
+39.4
112.0   110

3. 0.23
+4.583
4.813   5

4. 5.41
+23.8
29.21   29

5. 18.917
+9.6
28.517   29

6. 9.66
+3.15
12.81   13

7. 81.4
+0.56
81.96   81

8. 4.307
+0.853
5.160   5

9. 9.85
+15
24.85   25

10. 6.73
+2.496
9.226   9

First estimate each difference. Then subtract.

11. 5.37
−3.85
1.52   1

12. 29.4
−0.6
28.8   28

13. 2.18
−1.4
0.78   1

14. 3.92
−2.18
1.74   2

15. 62.5
−36.974
25.526   26

16. 7.21
−2.943
4.267   4

17. 74
−6.951
67.049   67

18. 5.84
−0.39
5.45   6

19. 3.43
−2.583
0.847   0

20. 6.89
−2.948
3.942   4

First estimate. Then compute.

21. 5.9 + 38.74 44.64   45

22. 63.5 − 29 34.5   35

23. 85 − 3.645 81.355   81

24. (2.8 + 3) − 1.64 4.16   4

25. (5.84 − 2.6) + 0.59 3.83   4

26. (7.4 − 2.34) − 2 3.06   3

27. (9.6 + 7.8) − 6.4 11   12

28. 9.6 + (7.8 − 6.4) 11   11

29. (15.2 − 9.48) − 4.6 1.12   1

30. 15.2 − (9.48 − 4.6) 10.32   11

31. (47.6 − 3.82) + 15.79 59.57   60

32. 47.6 − (3.82 + 15.79) 27.99   28

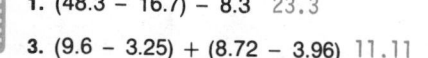

1. (48.3 − 16.7) − 8.3 23.3

2. 48.3 − (16.7 − 8.3) 39.9

3. (9.6 − 3.25) + (8.72 − 3.96) 11.11

4 (18.2 + 4.6) − (9.21 + 8.55) 5.04

70

Assignments

BASIC
page 70   exercises 1–20
page 71   game
Basic Worksheet 18

AVERAGE
page 70   exercises 1–32
page 71   game
Enrichment Worksheet 18

ENRICHED
Page 70   exercises 1–32
page 71   game
Enrichment Worksheet 18

EXTRA PRACTICE
page 381   set 33

Skill Game

Tell which is closer to the target number, 50.

1. a. 5|2 + 7|6 − 8|4 → 50 ✓
   b. 7|8 + 4|5 − 5|6 → 50

2. c. 9|3 + 4|0 − 6|8 → 50 ✓
   d. 7|8 + 6|9 − 4|0 → 50

Play the game.

1. Make a table like this.

   □□ + □□ − □□ → 50

2. A game leader will mix up these digit cards. The leader draws a card, replaces it, and continues until 6 cards have been drawn.

   0 1 2 3 4 5 6 7 8 9

3. As each card is drawn write the digit somewhere in your table.

4. Place a decimal point any place you wish in each pair of digits.
   For example:

   John's table:

   6|0, + ,4|7 − 6,|3 → 50

   Karen's table:

   4|6, + 3,|6 − ,0|7 → 50

5. The player closest to the target number, 50, wins the game. Who came closer, John or Karen? **Karen**

71

Follow-up Activities

Reinforcement You can simplify the game somewhat by arranging the numbers in position and fixing the decimal points in the problems. Have those students who need practice in addition and subtraction with decimals write the digits in this arrangement.

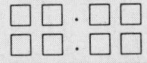

Target number 20 → _____

Enrichment Additional options can be introduced to the game to make it more challenging. Give students the option of picking the target number before each round. Also, let them connect the numbers with operations of their choice.

EXCURSION
There are 7 small triangles in the bottom row. How many small triangles are in the figure? 16

How many small triangles would there be if there were another row at the bottom of the figure? Can you find a rule?   25

n^2, where n is the number of rows.

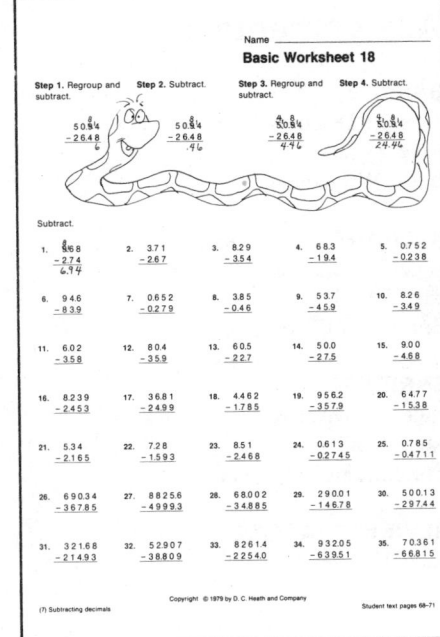

To observe and work with a common
application of mathematics.
To learn the rudiments of payroll
deductions.

Suggested Lesson Plan

Introduction Ask students whether
they or their older sisters and brothers
have jobs. If they do, ask whether they
ever hear complaints about the
deductions—"the more you earn, the
more the government takes,"etc.
Discuss these common attitudes before
introducing the charts on pages 72 and
73 which deal with deductions from
payroll checks due to federal income tax
and social security. Explain that income
tax withholding is a way of prepaying
income tax so that the total amount is
spread throughout the year, and that
social security withholding is a
percentage of the amount of money
earned up to a certain limit. Point out
that everyone who earns money should
expect to be required to pay some
amount of income tax and a certain
amount of social security tax, although
there are limitations and exceptions.

Using the pages Read and discuss the
material and the photograph on page 72
with the students. Go over the tables to
be sure they understand how they
should be used. Notice that the table on
page 72 gives income tax withholding for
salaries ranging from $200 to $300 in two
parts, one for married persons and one
for single persons. The three-columned
table on page 73 gives the social security
tax to be withheld for salaries between
$199.50 and $301.50.

Go over the first example. That is,
explain how the income tax, social
security, total tax, and, finally, the
take-home pay are found for A. Chaney,
a single employee (noted by an asterisk).

Have the students complete the
exercises on their own once they have
indicated that they understand the
tables.

Mathematics in careers

Many businesses have employees known
as *payroll clerks*, who compute and pay
the salary of each employee. After computing an employee's salary, the payroll
clerk deducts some money for federal income tax and social security. (Some employees may choose to have more money
deducted from their salary for such
things as savings bonds, group medical
insurance, group life insurance, etc.)

The following tables show the
amounts to be deducted for federal income tax and social security.

Federal Income Tax Withholding (Weekly Payroll)

Not Married				Married						
Weekly salary		Number of exemptions		Weekly salary		Number of exemptions				
At least	But less than	0	1	At least	But less than	0	1	2	3	4
$200	$210	$33.10	$29.60	$200	$210	$24.70	$22.10	$19.50	$16.90	$14.30
210	220	35.50	32.00	210	220	26.50	23.90	21.30	18.70	16.10
220	230	38.10	34.40	220	230	28.40	25.70	23.10	20.50	17.90
230	240	40.90	36.80	230	240	30.60	27.50	24.90	22.30	19.70
240	250	43.70	39.60	240	250	32.80	29.60	26.70	24.10	21.50
250	260	46.50	42.40	250	260	35.00	31.80	28.60	25.90	23.30
260	270	49.30	45.20	260	270	37.20	34.00	30.80	27.70	25.10
270	280	52.10	48.00	270	280	39.40	36.20	33.00	29.80	26.90
280	290	54.90	50.80	280	290	41.80	38.40	35.20	32.00	28.90
290	300	57.70	53.60	290	300	44.30	40.70	37.40	34.20	31.10

72

Assignments

BASIC
page 72 Discuss
page 73 all
Basic Worksheet 19

AVERAGE
page 72 Discuss
page 73 all
Enrichment Worksheet 19

ENRICHED
page 72 Discuss
page 73 all
Enrichment Worksheet 19

REVIEW PRACTICE
page 377 set 16

Social Security Tax Withholding (Weekly Payroll)

At least	But less than	Tax withheld	At least	But less than	Tax withheld	At least	But less than	Tax withheld
$199.50	$201.50	$11.73	$233.50	$235.50	$13.72	$267.50	$269.50	$15.71
201.50	203.50	11.85	235.50	237.50	13.84	269.50	271.50	15.82
203.50	205.50	11.96	237.50	239.50	13.95	271.50	273.50	15.94
205.50	207.50	12.08	239.50	241.50	14.07	273.50	275.50	16.06
207.50	209.50	12.20	241.50	243.50	14.19	275.50	277.50	16.18
209.50	211.50	12.31	243.50	245.50	14.30	277.50	279.50	16.29
211.50	213.50	12.43	245.50	247.50	14.42	279.50	281.50	16.41
213.50	215.50	12.55	247.50	249.50	14.54	281.50	283.50	16.53
215.50	217.50	12.67	249.50	251.50	14.65	283.50	285.50	16.64
217.50	219.50	12.78	251.50	253.50	14.77	285.50	287.50	16.76
219.50	221.50	12.90	253.50	255.50	14.89	287.50	289.50	16.88
221.50	223.50	13.02	255.50	257.50	15.01	289.50	291.50	16.99
223.50	225.50	13.13	257.50	259.50	15.12	291.50	293.50	17.11
225.50	227.50	13.25	259.50	261.50	15.24	293.50	295.50	17.23
227.50	229.50	13.37	261.50	263.50	15.36	295.50	297.50	17.35
229.50	231.50	13.48	263.50	265.50	15.47	297.50	299.50	17.46
231.50	233.50	13.60	265.50	267.50	15.59	299.50	301.50	17.58

EXERCISES

Copy and complete this table.

Employee	Number of exemptions	Weekly salary	Payroll deductions Income tax	Payroll deductions Social security	Payroll deductions Total	Take-home pay
*Chaney, A.	1	$222	$34.40	$13.02	$47.42	$174.58
Dyer, M.	3	261	$27.70	$15.24	$42.94	$218.06
Felker, R.	0	224	$28.40	$13.13	$41.53	$182.47
Klick, J.	2	253	$28.60	$14.77	$43.37	$209.63
*Lingol, P.	1	280	$50.80	$16.41	$67.21	$212.79
Murphy, P.	3	272	$29.80	$15.94	$45.74	$226.26
*Skoczen, L.	1	218	$32.00	$12.78	$44.78	$173.22
Ward, F.	4	295	$31.10	$17.23	$48.33	$246.67

*Single employee

73

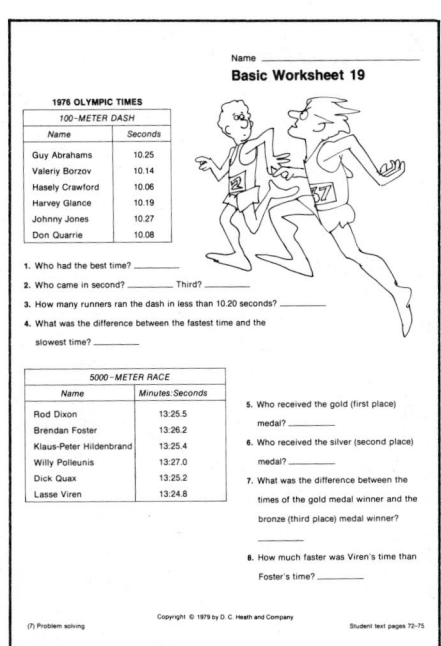

Follow-up Activities

Reinforcement Provide students with a "help wanted" section from a local newspaper. Circle the job descriptions where a salary is given. Ask students to compute the yearly salary when a weekly or monthly salary is given. Have students compute the monthly salary when the yearly salary is given.

Enrichment You may want to expand the activity with more able students. After the yearly salary is determined, have students compute the amount of withholding for federal income tax and social security.

EXCURSION

Can you complete this magic square so that all 8 of the sums shown are 15? Use only the digits 1 through 9.

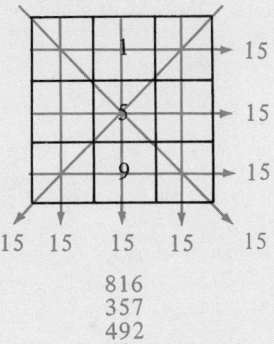

816
357
492

Can you make another magic square?

Suggested Lesson Plan

Introduction Use the situation of drag racing to generate interest in the problems presented.

Using the pages Quickly present the information on page 74. Allow a few minutes for students to read the information. Call attention to the notation that is used to give the time and speed of a car.

Assign exercises 1–8 for written work. If you have identified the poor readers, you may want to put them in a special group and read through the problems aloud. Use this method to discuss several aspects of problem solving such as identifying what is asked, whether there is extra information, etc.

Problem solving

Drag racing began in the early 1950's. The car that travels 440 yards in the shortest time wins the race.

Generally two decimals are used to show how a dragster performed. They are written like this:

8.72/162.54

The first number tells the number of seconds that it took to travel the distance. It is sometimes called the *elapsed time*. The second number tells the speed (in miles per hour) of the dragster when the car reached the finish line. This speed is sometimes called the *terminal speed*.

Here are the results of a certain class of racers.

Car	Driver	Time/Speed
Comet	Pride	8.71/164.38
Early Finish	Brent	8.68/165.93
Good Bye	Goza	8.64/170.08
Lightning II	Evans	8.67/167.43
Power Plus	Jennings	8.73/160.42
Smokie	Murphy	8.72/161.57

74

Assignments

BASIC
page 74 Discuss
page 75 exercises 1–6
Basic Worksheet 19

AVERAGE
page 74 Discuss
page 75 exercises 1–8
Enrichment Worksheet 19

ENRICHED
page 74 Discuss
page 75 exercises 1–8, Excursion
Enrichment Worksheet 19

REVIEW PRACTICE
page 377 set 17

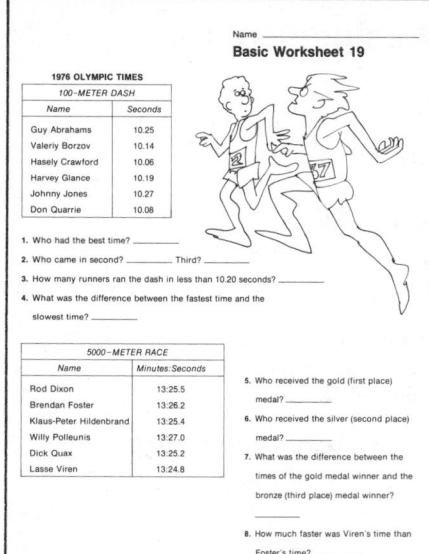

1. How many cars finished the race in less than 8.70 seconds? 3

2. How many cars had a terminal speed that was more than 164.5 miles per hour? 3

3. Which car won the class? Good Bye

4. What was the terminal speed of the winning car? 170.08 mi per h

5. What was the elapsed time of the car that placed last? 8.73 s

6. Find the difference of the elapsed times of the first- and last-place cars. 0.09 s

7. What was the difference of the terminal speeds of the first- and second-place cars? 2.65 mi per h

8. What was the difference of the terminal speeds of the second- and third-place cars? 1.5 mi per h

EXCURSION ▨▧▨▧▨▧▨▧▨▧▨▧▨▧

A frog fell to the bottom of a well that was 3 meters deep. During the first hour, the frog climbed up 17 centimeters and then slid back 10 centimeters. At this rate, how long did it take the frog to climb out of the well? 42 h

75

Follow-up Activities

Reinforcement Assign these students in pairs. Let them discuss the information in the table on page 74 with each other and each write a word problem. They then exchange problems and solve.

Enrichment Organize four students to develop a way to measure the speed of a car that has been timed over a certain distance. For example, have the students measure off approximately ¼ of a mile on an open stretch of road. After timing a car over this distance, have students determine the speed in miles per hour of the car.

$$t = \text{time in seconds}; \quad \text{speed} = \frac{3600}{4t}$$

CALCULATOR ACTIVITY

Students can use the following calculator code to change the kilometers/h to miles/h.

k = kilometer per hour,

k ÷ 1.609 =

Have students convert the speeds given on page 74 to miles per hour.

164.41
165.97
170.12
167.46
160.45
161.60

Name _____
Basic Worksheet 19

1976 OLYMPIC TIMES

100-METER DASH

Name	Seconds
Guy Abrahams	10.25
Valeriy Borzov	10.14
Hasely Crawford	10.06
Harvey Glance	10.19
Johnny Jones	10.27
Don Quarrie	10.08

1. Who had the best time? _____
2. Who came in second? _____ Third? _____
3. How many runners ran the dash in less than 10.20 seconds? _____
4. What was the difference between the fastest time and the slowest time? _____

5000 - METER RACE

Name	Minutes:Seconds
Rod Dixon	13:25.5
Brendan Foster	13:26.2
Klaus-Peter Hildenbrand	13:25.4
Willy Polleunis	13:27.0
Dick Quax	13:25.2
Lasse Viren	13:24.8

5. Who received the gold (first place) medal? _____
6. Who received the silver (second place) medal? _____
7. What was the difference between the times of the gold medal winner and the bronze (third place) medal winner? _____
8. How much faster was Viren's time than Foster's time? _____

(7) Problem solving

Copyright © 1979 by D. C. Heath and Company

Student text pages 72-75

Name _____
SPEED RECORDS-AIRPLANES **Enrichment Worksheet 19**

Year	Pilot	Country	Speed (km/h)
1906	Santos-Dumont	France	41.29
1912	Vedrines	France	174.06
1922	Mitchell	U.S.	358.76
1932	Doolittle	U.S.	473.66
1933	J. Wedell	U.S.	490.71
1939	F. Wedell	Germany	754.97
1945	Wilson	Great Britain	*975.46
1948	Johnson	U.S.	*1079.61
1951	Bridgeman	U.S.	*1239.61
1953	Yeager	U.S.	*2574.40

*Jet powered

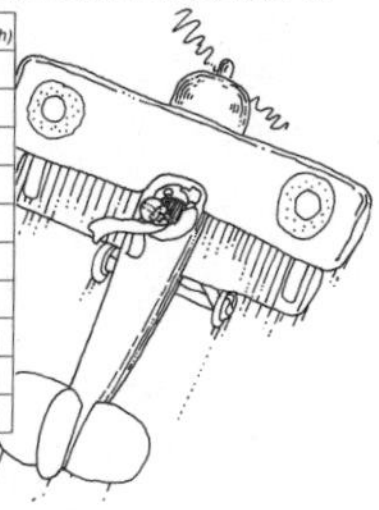

1. Who was the first pilot to fly faster than
   a. 300 km per hour? _____ b. 100 km per hour? _____
2. Who had the fastest speed for a propeller-driven airplane? _____
3. What was the difference in speeds of the fastest propeller-driven airplane and the slowest jet-powered airplane? _____
4. a. What was the record speed in 1933? _____
   b. By how much was the record speed increased during the next 20 years? _____
5. By how much was the record speed improved from 1906 to 1939? _____
6. How much faster would Doolittle have to have flown to fly as fast as J. Wedell? _____
7. Which pilots of propeller-driven airplanes broke the speed record by more than 100 km per hour? _____
8. Which pilot's speed record was 605.95 km per hour faster than Doolittle's speed record? _____

(7) Problem solving

Copyright © 1979 by D. C. Heath and Company

Student text pages 72-75

STUDENT OBJECTIVE

To review the concepts and skills introduced in Chapter 2.

Suggested Lesson Plan

Introduction No pre-text activity is necessary for page 76 as this is a checkup for the chapter. However, it may be valuable to review briefly the lessons in the chapter so that students are reminded of the content over which they will be tested.

This checkup will provide you with data about how individual students have mastered the skills of the chapter. The Chapter Review of page 78 is provided for those students who need more specific individual help.

Page 77 is an activity that students will enjoy doing as a project. Let all the students participate so that you will only have to collect the data once. After the data is collected, let each student make his or her own graph to portray the information. Paste the better graphs on the mathematics bulletin board.

Using the pages Assign all of the exercises on page 76. As students complete the page, they can work on the activity on page 77; or perhaps there are some games or activities in the chapter which they have not played and would like to. Assign a student leader to each game or activity. As pupils want to play, they can go to the assigned pupil for the game rules and partners for the game.

Read. [pages 56–59]

1. 0.3　　2. 0.03　　3. 0.003　　4. 7.6　　5. 93.17　　6. 8.1358

Give the standard numeral. [pages 56–59]

7. two and six tenths　2.6

8. six and three hundredths　6.03

9. forty-two thousandths　0.042

10. two hundred six thousandths　0.206

11. two hundred and six thousandths　200.006

12. five hundred four ten thousandths　0.0504

< or >? [pages 62–63]

13. 0.03 ● 0.004　>　14. 73.2 ● 73.4　<　15. 2.999 ● 3　<　16. 5.7346 ● 5.3382

Round 15.6599 to the nearest [pages 64–65]

17. tenth　15.7　18. one　16　19. hundredth　15.66　20. thousandth　15.660

Add. [pages 66–67, 70–71]

| 21. | 5.7
+ 3.8
9.5 | 22. | 3.98
+ 0.47
4.45 | 23. | 2.08
+ 5.26
7.34 | 24. 3.48 + 1.962　5.442
25. 25.37 + 0.4876　25.8576 |

Subtract. [pages 68–71]

| 26. | 7.4
− 3.8
3.6 | 27. | 5.93
− 2.86
3.07 | 28. | 30.2
− 19.5
10.7 | 29. 4.32 − 1.837　2.483
30. 25 − 2.68　22.32 |

Solve. [pages 74–75]

31.  wt 0.74 kg price $2.53　wt 0.83 kg price $2.79

a. What is the total cost?　$5.32
b. What is the total weight?　1.57 kg

32. Gibson City　28.4 km　Short Pump　33.7 km

How far apart are the two towns?　62.1 km

76

Assignments

BASIC
page 76　exercises 1 − 32
page 77　Project

AVERAGE
page 76　exercises 1 − 32
page 77　Project

ENRICHED
page 76　exercises 1 − 32
page 77　Project

EXTRA PROBLEM SOLVING
pages 400–401 set 2

Project

Think about standing under a basketball net and jumping straight up as high as you can. The distance that you could jump beyond your normal reach is your vertical jump. First guess what it would be. Then follow these steps to measure it.

1. Blacken the end of a middle finger with a pencil. While standing *flat-footed*, mark as high as you can reach on a paper strip that is taped to the wall. Measure the height of your mark to the nearest centimeter. Convert the height to meters.

2. From a standing position, jump to see how high you can mark on the same paper. Measure the distance to the nearest centimeter and convert it to meters.

3. Subtract to find your vertical jump in meters.

4. **a.** When all your classmates have measured their vertical jumps, list them on the chalkboard. Show the results on a graph like this:

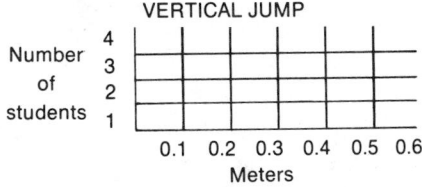

b. List some facts shown by your graph.

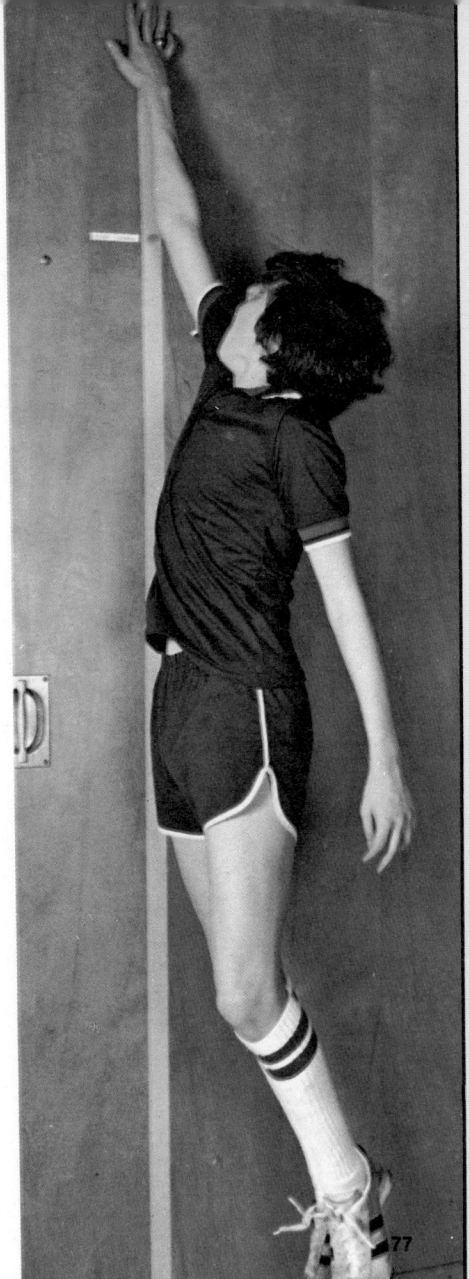

You may wish to assign some of the Creative Problem Solving Activities (pages 461-477) at this time.

You may wish to assign some of the Creative Problem Solving Activities (pages 461-477) at this time.

Follow-up Activities

Reinforcement Correct all the items in the Chapter Checkup. Any student who missed six or more, or any more than three problems in a row, needs additional help. It is important for each student to achieve some degree of proficiency in the basic skills covered. At this point, students who are still having difficulty with these skills need concentrated individual help.

Enrichment Assign these pupils to the games and activities that have been played throughout the chapter. Each student leader is responsible for teaching the game or activity to those interested students and for supervising the play.

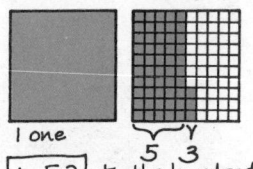

STUDENT OBJECTIVE

To review or extend the skills and concepts taught in Chapter 2.

Suggested Lesson Plan

Introduction After checking the Chapter Checkup you will know which students need additional reinforcement and which students will be able to go ahead with the Challenge activity. Get the better students started on page 79 first as the students who are having difficulty will need more of your time.

The students who need more review should go back and correct their errors on the Chapter Checkup. You may want to go over those questions orally if this group is small enough. Carefully probe to determine which concepts and skills the students have not mastered and work individually to correct these deficiencies.

Using the pages After the identified students have corrected the Chapter Checkup, they should answer questions 1–29. After they complete these questions, read the answers and let the students correct their own papers. Give them an opportunity to ask questions about the exercises they missed.

Assign page 79 to the students who did well on the Chapter Checkup. Have them work independently and instruct them not to tell when they find the answer.

I one

5 3

| 1.53 | tenths hundredths

1.037   thousandths place

↓ ↓ ↓ ↘ thirty-seven
one and thousandths

Round to the nearest 1.

ones place
↓
43.6
↑
5 or greater
44

1
4.6
+3.7
8.3

5 9
6.0̶3̶
-2.87
3.16

How many unit squares are shaded?

1. 1.27   2. 0.68   3. 0.99

Read.

4. 0.6   5. 0.08   6. 7.124

7. 6.057   8. 38.64   9. 29.4321

Round to the nearest 1.

10. 26.3 26   11. 38.9 39   12. 47.5 48

13. 6.09 6   14. 12.499 12 15. 117.511
                                    118

Round to the nearest 0.1.

16. 0.67 0.7   17. 0.61 0.6   18. 0.65 0.7

19. 13.341 13.3 20. 28.784 28.8 21. 31.976
                                        32.0

Add.

22.   5.9   23.   6.57   24. 5.25 + 0.776
    + 8.7   + 3.88   6.026
     14.6   10.45   25. 0.843 + 27.9
                                    28.743

Subtract.

26.   8.77   27. 0.608   28. 36.05 − 2.166
    − 3.98   − 0.419   32.894
     4.79   0.189   29. 14.035 − 6.27
                                     7.765

78

Assignments

BASIC
page 78 exercises 1–29

AVERAGE
page 78 exercises 1–29

ENRICHED
page 79 all

CHAPTER CHALLENGE

Code

A	C	E	I	L	N	P	S	T	W	Y
6.7	3.8	0.42	1.67	3.24	0.087	0.001	5.2	0.33	6.23	4.51

Where does a 200-kilogram gorilla sleep?

six and seven tenths — A

eighty-seven thousandths — N

four and fifty-one hundredths — Y

$0.94 + 5.8 - 5.07$ — I

$9.03 - 5.7 - 3$ — T

$100 - 99.999$ — P

$0.25 + 2.99$ — L

$10 - (3.9 - 0.6)$ — A

$12.5 - (5.9 + 2.8)$ — C

$0.12 + 0.3$ — E

0.5 greater than 5.73 — W

$95.47 - 1.8 - 86.97$ — A

$15 - (12.3 + 2.613)$ — N

$9.2 - (10 - 1.13)$ — T

0.083 less than 5.283 — S

79

Follow-up Activities

Reinforcement The reinforcement at this point should be individual help focused on the basic skills of addition, subtraction, multiplication, and division of whole numbers. It is important that students reach minimum levels in these basic skills before continuing on in mathematics.

Enrichment Pair these students with students who are having difficulty with basic skills. Give them several problems of the appropriate skill and have the student who needs help explain his or her work to the more able student.

STUDENT OBJECTIVES

To practice skills learned previously.
To practice using a standardized-test format.

Suggested Lesson Plan

Using the pages The Major Checkup at the end of each chapter of this textbook is given in standardized-test format. The answer sheet on page 448 is the type used with many standardized tests. You may duplicate it for use with the Major Checkups.

Pass out the answer sheets and be sure students understand how to use them. Allow a specified time, perhaps twenty minutes, to complete the checkup. Assign the exercises and use the results to determine what review is needed.

The table below correlates the test items and the student text pages. Assign review exercises as indicated by the Major Checkup results.

Test Item	Text Pages	Test Item	Text Pages
1	20–21	7	40–41
2	22–23	8	58–59
3	26–27	9	64–65
4	28–29	10	66–67
5	32–33	11	66–67
6	36–37	12	68–69

Chapter 2 Posttest

See page 54 for a full discussion of how to use the posttest. The table below suggests Extra Practice exercises and Basic Worksheets for those students who need further practice or reteaching.

Objectives	Extra Practice Sets	Pages	Basic Worksheets
2-1	27–28	380	13–14
2-2	29	380	15
2-3	30	380	16
2-4	31–32	380–381	17–18
2-5	33	381	
2-6			19

Choose the correct letter.

1. The standard numeral for three hundred million forty-two is

a. 342,000,000
b. 300,000,042
c. 3,000,042
d. none of these

2. Round 783,499 to the nearest thousand.

a. 783,000
b. 784,000
c. 780,000
d. none of these

3. Add.

2965
+4763

a. 6628
b. 7628
c. 7728
d. none of these

4. Subtract.

6003
−4297

a. 1706
b. 2706
c. 2816
d. none of these

5. Multiply.

6703
×5

a. 45,515
b. 33,515
c. 3365
d. none of these

6. Multiply.

47
×28

a. 1216
b. 470
c. 1316
d. none of these

7. Divide.

6)3716

a. 619 R2
b. 620 R6
c. 618
d. none of these

8. The standard numeral for two hundred and nine thousandths is

a. 200.009
b. 0.209
c. 0.0209
d. none of these

9. Round 67.751 to the nearest one.

a. 67
b. 67.8
c. 68
d. none of these

10. Add.

4.37
+2.69

a. 6.06
b. 0.0706
c. 7.06
d. none of these

11. Add.

3.98 + 42.7

a. 46.68
b. 82.5
c. 8.25
d. none of these

12. Subtract.

5.007
−0.389

a. 5.718
b. 5.382
c. 4.618
d. none of these

80

Answers for Chapter 2 Posttest
1. 0.05 2. 6.4 3. 0.436 4. three tenths
5. forty-three and five tenths 6. six and forty-one thousands 7. > 8. > 9. <
10. > 11. 7 12. 7.9 13. 24.40 14. 0.4
15. 12.59 16. 4.05 17. 5.507 18. 6.614
19. 14.16 20. 6.053 21. 6 + 7 = 13
22. 6 − 4 = 2 23. 0.3 km 24. 16.2 km
25. 6296 m 26. 5.7 m

Chapter 2 Posttest

Name _____

Date _____

Write as decimals. [Obj. 2-1, pages 56–61]

1. five hundredths _____   **2.** six and four tenths _____

3. four hundred thirty-six thousandths _____

Write in words.

4. 0.3 _____   **5.** 43.5 _____

6. 6.041 _____

| 0 | 1 | 2 | 3 | 4 |

< or >? Write the correct sign. [Obj. 2-2, pages 62–63]

7. 4 ◯ 0.6   **8.** 0.5 ◯ 0.05   **9.** 0.398 ◯ 0.5   **10.** 42.75 ◯ 42.57

| 0 | 1 | 2 | 3 | 4 |

Round. [Obj. 2-3, pages 64–65]

11. 6.533 to the nearest one. _____   **12.** 7.891 to the nearest tenth. _____
13. 24.397 to the nearest hundredth. _____   **14.** 0.35 to the nearest tenth. _____

| 0-2 | 3 | 4 | 5 | 6 |

Add or subtract. Watch the signs. [Obj. 2-4, pages 66–69]

15. 8.32
      + 4.27

16. 8.32
      − 4.27

17. 6.005
      − 0.498

18. 5.831
      + 0.783

19. 4.76 + 9.4 = _____   **20.** 6.41 − 0.357 = _____

Show how you estimate sums and differences. [Obj. 2-5, pages 70–71]

| 0 | 1 | 2 |

21. 5.821 ⟶
      + 6.955 ⟶

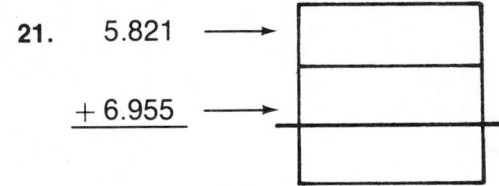

22. 6.042 ⟶
      − 3.877 ⟶

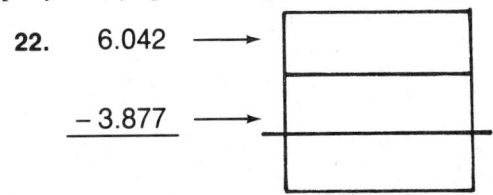

| 0 | 1 | 2 | 3 | 4 |

Solve. [Obj. 2-6, pages 72–75]

23. Jim swam 4.2 kilometers in the morning and 3.9 kilometers in the afternoon. How much farther did he swim in the morn-

ing? _____

24. Carol skied 9.7 kilometers one day and 6.5 kilometers the next day. How far did she ski

in all? _____

25. Jenny climbed 3,148 meters to the top of a mountain and then she climbed back down.

How far did she travel? _____

26. A 6.3-meter long piece of string was cut from a 12-meter long roll of string. How

much string was left on the roll? _____

Chapter 3
Decimals—Multiplication and Division

Pages 81–104

Learning Objectives

After completing this chapter, all students should be able to do the following:

3-1 Multiply any two decimals.

3-2 Divide any two decimals.

3-3 Solve word problems that involve multiplication or division of decimals.

The multiplication and division algorithms are carefully developed. Estimation is used to show students that the algorithms "make sense." Much practice is provided. Once again students are provided with many opportunities to develop problem-solving skills.

Mathematics

The algorithms for multiplying and dividing decimals are, of course, fundamentally the same as those for multiplying and dividing whole numbers. The only difference involves placing the decimal points. The rules for placing the decimal points can be explained in several ways. For example, fractions can be used.

Multiplication

$$0.3 \times 0.2 = \frac{3}{10} \times \frac{2}{10} = \frac{6}{100} = 0.06$$

Division

$$3.27\overline{)43.2} = \frac{43.2}{3.27} = \frac{43.2 \times 100}{3.27 \times 100}$$

$$= \frac{4320}{327} = 327.\overline{)4320.}$$

Another kind of explanation involves the use of a physical place-value model.

The fractions explanation is not very satisfying for most seventh-grade students because it is quite abstract and involves a concept (fractions) that they don't clearly understand. The physical model is quite complex and not well accepted by teachers. Therefore, we have chosen to use a more "common sense" approach, involving estimation. For example, to compute the product of 2.7 and 3.2, you can first multiply just as you would with whole numbers because these algorithms depended only on place-value concepts and various principles of operations and numbers, all of which are involved in decimal multiplication.

$$\begin{array}{r} 2.7 \\ \times 3.2 \\ \hline 5\ 4 \\ 81 \\ \hline 86\ 4 \end{array}$$

Next you round the factors to the nearest whole number and estimate the product.

$$3 \times 3 = 9$$

Then you place the decimal point in the product so that the product is as near to the estimated product, 9, as possible.

$$\begin{array}{r} 2.7 \\ \times 3.2 \\ \hline 5\ 4 \\ 81 \\ \hline 8.64 \end{array}$$

Many such examples can be used to develop a trust in the usual rule for placing the decimal points in products.

Similar work will develop a trust in the division algorithm.

Teaching the Chapter

All the computational algorithms tend to force students to "take numbers apart" and concentrate on those parts rather than considering the numbers as a whole. For example, when doing the multiplication problem below, we first think about multiplying 6 by 7 and then multiplying 2 by 7, etc.

$$\begin{array}{r} 42.6 \\ \times 3.27 \end{array}$$

Estimating is one way of forcing students to consider the number rather than its parts—to help develop "number sense." Be sure to do many kinds of estimating activities with your students.

Here is a game that we have used with some success to encourage students to estimate. Make cards like these:

$$\boxed{\begin{array}{r} 4.2 \\ \times 3.9 \end{array}} \qquad \boxed{\begin{array}{r} 5.77 \\ \times 2.93 \end{array}}$$

Flash these cards one at a time to the class, holding each card up for just a short time (perhaps 5 seconds). Students may do whatever computations they wish (or can) in the short time available to them, but it is unlikely that they can actually compute the true products. They are to write down a number that is as near to the product as they can get. Later, when you have finished showing the cards, you will award points to students according to how close to the actual products they were. For example, you might award 2 points for being within 2 of the actual product and 1 point for being within 3 of the product. The student with the greatest number of points is the winner. In order to win, students must be good estimators.

Notice that you will have to adjust the limits for awarding points according to the numbers that you use in the problems. In the problems above, students can be expected to be within 2 of the real products, but for a problem such as 278.3 × 597.5 they should only be expected to be within 20,000.

Continue to use the problem-solving activities described for Chapter 1.

Vocabulary

There is no new vocabulary in this chapter.

Materials

hand calculators
digit cards
dollars, dimes, pennies (real or play)
a deck of playing cards
centimeter rulers
paper clips
small scale
old long-playing records

Chapter Tests

For a discussion of how to use the chapter tests, please see page 17c.

Answers for Chapter 3 Pretest

1. 345.6   2. 0.2202   3. 11.88   4. 7.0977   5. 0.00006   6. 680
7. 43.3   8. 11.9   9. 0.9   10. 4.6   11. 21   12. $1.91
13. $6.96   14. 12.65 kg

Chapter 3 Pretest

Name _____

Date _____

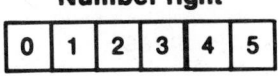
Multiply. [Obj. 3-1, pages 82–84, 86–87, 98–99]

1. 43.2
    × 8

2. 7.34
    × 0.03

3. 4.4
    × 2.7

4. 1.77
    × 4.01

5. 0.003
    × 0.02

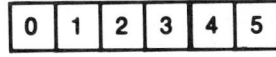

Divide. Round the quotient to the nearest tenth.
[Obj. 3-2, pages 90–93, 96–99]

6. 0.1)‾68‾

7. 0.05)‾2.165‾

8. 2.3)‾27.4‾

9. 0.74)‾0.68‾

10. 1.23)‾5.6‾

Solve. [Obj. 3-3, pages 88–89, 94–95]

11. Apples cost $.12 apiece. How many can you

    buy for $2.52? _____

12. 5 kilograms of meat cost $9.55. How much
    does the meat cost per kilogram?

    _____

13. 38.9 liters of gasoline were bought for 17.9¢
    per liter. How much did the gasoline

    cost? _____

14. Jim lost 2.3 kilograms of weight per month
    for 5.5 months. How much weight did he

    lose in all? _____

81c

Chapter 3
Record and Assignment Chart

Name _____

Pretest Date _____   Posttest Date _____

Objectives

Pretest Score
Mark number correct

Posttest Score
Mark number correct

| 3-1 | Multiply any two decimals. | 0 | 1 | 2 | 3 | 4 | 5 | | 0 | 1 | 2 | 3 | 4 | 5 |

| 3-2 | Divide any two decimals. | 0 | 1 | 2 | 3 | 4 | 5 | | 0 | 1 | 2 | 3 | 4 | 5 |

| 3-3 | Solve word problems that involve multiplication and division of decimals. | 0 | 1 | 2 | 3 | 4 | | 0 | 1 | 2 | 3 | 4 |

Unsatisfactory Score | Satisfactory Score

Unsatisfactory Score | Satisfactory Score

TEACHING ASSIGNMENTS*

	Student Page	Basic Assignment	Average Assignment	Enriched Assignment	Problem Solving	RETEACHING ASSIGNMENTS†
3-1	82, 83	1–30	1–30, EW 20	1–30, EW 20	31, 32, 33, 34	page 381 Set 34, BW 20
	84	1–18	1–24, EW 20	1–30, EW 20		page 381 Set 35, BW 20
	85	1–2	1–4	1–4		BW 20
3-1	86, 87	1–40	1–40, EW 21	1–45, EW 21	46, 47	BW 21
3-3	88, 89	1–8	1–9, EW 21	1–10, EW 21		BW 21
3-2	90, 91	1–34	1–34, EW 22	1–34, EW 22	35, 36	page 382 Set 36, BW 22
	92, 93	1–28	3–34, EW 23	5–36, EW 23		BW 23
3-3	94, 95	1–8	1–10, EW 23	1–10, EW 23		BW 23
3-2	96, 97	1–31	1–31, EW 24	1–31, EW 24	32, 33, 34, 35, 36, 37	page 382 Set 37, BW 24
3-1	98	1–28	1–30, EW 24	1–30, EW 24		BW 24
3-2	99		Skill Game			
3-3	402-409		Extra Problem Solving, Sets 3-6			
	100		Chapter Checkup			
	101		Project			
	102	Chapter Review				
	103		Chapter Challenge			
	104		Major Checkup			

*Check assignments for objectives with unsatisfactory pretest scores.
†Check assignments for objectives with unsatisfactory posttest scores.

BW = Basic Worksheet
EW = Enrichment Worksheet

3 Decimals— Multiplication and Division

$\begin{array}{r} \$1.75 \\ \times \ 3.2 \text{ lb} \\ \hline \$5.60 \end{array}$

Suggested Lesson Plan

Introduction Write the example
603 × 48 on the board. Call on one
student to multiply at the board while
other students multiply on scratch paper
at their seats.

Using the pages Introduce the
situation on page 82 by discussing the
speed of go-carts.

Use this introduction to motivate
interest in finding the distance the
go-cart went. Ask students what
operation we should use to find the total
distance, given the average hourly speed
and the time. (Multiplication) If students
hesitate to name the operation, give
similar but simple examples which
students will recognize as multiplication
situations. (2 sandwiches at 60¢ each, 8
gallons at $1.00 a gallon, etc.) Use the
exposition on page 82 to develop the
idea of estimating before multiplying.
Ask students about how far the go-cart
went. Have them estimate by rounding
both numbers to the nearest whole
number and then multiplying.

Show the multiplication of the
decimals on the board while students
note the work on page 82. Emphasize
the three steps: multiply as whole
numbers, count the number of decimal
places, and count off the same number
of places in the product.

Write several more examples on the
board. Ask for an estimate of each
product before the multiplication is
done. Call on students to do the
exercises on the board while the other
students work at their seats.

Assign exercises 1–34 for written
work. As students begin work, circulate
around the room checking their work to
make sure they remember to put decimal
points in the products.

Multiplying decimals

The go-cart averaged 19.5 kilometers
per hour for 3.5 hours. We can multiply
to find out how far the go-cart went. To
estimate the product, we round each
number to the nearest whole number
and multiply.

$$
\begin{array}{r} 19.5 \\ \times\,3.5 \end{array}
\qquad
\begin{array}{r} 20 \\ \times\,4 \\ \hline 80 \end{array}
$$

The product should be about 80.

Here is how to find the product of two decimals.

Step 1. Multiply the
numbers as whole
numbers.

$$
\begin{array}{r} 19.5 \\ \times\,3.5 \\ \hline 97\,5 \\ 585 \\ \hline 682\,5 \end{array}
$$

Step 2. Count the
digits to the
right of the
decimal points.

$$
\begin{array}{rl} 19.5 & 1\ \text{digit} \\ \times\,3.5 & +1\ \text{digit} \\ \hline 97\,5 \\ 585 \\ \hline 682\,5 & 2\ \text{digits} \end{array}
$$

Step 3. Count off the
same number of
digits to place
the decimal point
in the product.

$$
\begin{array}{r} 19.5 \\ \times\,3.5 \\ \hline 97\,5 \\ 585 \\ \hline 68.2\,5 \end{array}
$$

The go-cart went 68.25 km.

EXERCISES
First estimate the product. Then multiply.

1. 3.9 _28_ × 6.8 26.52	**2.** 5.7 _12_ × 2.1 11.97	**3.** 6.3 _24_ × 3.9 24.57	**4.** 7.8 _16_ × 1.8 14.04	**5.** 7.2 _35_ × 5.2 37.44	**6.** 9.1 _72_ × 7.6 69.16
7. 5.26 _20_ × 4.2 22.092	**8.** 3.28 _12_ × 3.5 11.480	**9.** 7.42 _42_ × 6.1 45.262	**10.** 9.06 _63_ × 7.4 67.044	**11.** 7.52 _72_ × 8.9 66.928	**12.** 3.91 _20_ × 5.3 20.723

82

Assignments

BASIC
page 82 exercises 1–12
page 83 exercises 13–30
Basic Worksheet 20

AVERAGE
page 82 exercises 1–12
page 83 exercises 13–32
Enrichment Worksheet 20

ENRICHED
page 82 exercises 1–12
page 83 exercises 13–34, Excursion
Enrichment Worksheet 20

EXTRA PRACTICE
page 381 set 34

Multiply.

13.	6.7 × 0.42 2.814	14.	0.57 × 3.5 1.995	15.	0.29 × 0.64 0.1856	16.	79 × 6.3 497.7	17.	8.2 × 0.51 4.182	18.	65 × 0.39 25.35
19.	368 × 2.7 993.6	20.	5.04 × 32 161.28	21.	67.3 × 4.1 275.93	22.	5.82 × 0.73 4.2486	23.	6.42 × 8.1 52.002	24.	75.9 × 0.36 27.324
25.	7.52 × 1.24 9.3248	26.	9.38 × 1.03 9.6614	27.	26.1 × 2.41 62.901	28.	5.18 × 72.5 375.550	29.	93.6 × 29.3 2742.48	30.	8.53 × 6.78 57.8334

Solve.

31. A can of oil contains 0.96 liters of oil. How much oil do 5 cans contain? 4.8 L

32. One lap around a certain go-cart track is 1.2 kilometers. How far is 2.5 laps around the track? 3 km

33. The winning cart averaged 37.5 kilometers per hour. It took 1.6 hours to complete the race. How many kilometers long was the race? 60

34. In a 48.5-kilometer race, the winning cart averaged 32.4 kilometers per hour for the first 1.25 hours. Then it made a pit stop. How many kilometers did it have to go after the pit stop? 8

Excursion ■□■□■□■□■□■□■□■□■□■□■□■●■□■●■□

$(1 \times 9) + 2 = ?$ 11 Guess first.
$(12 \times 9) + 3 = ?$ 111 $(1234 \times 9) + 5 = ?$ 11,111
$(123 \times 9) + 4 = ?$ 1111 $(12345 \times 9) + 6 = ?$ 111,111

83

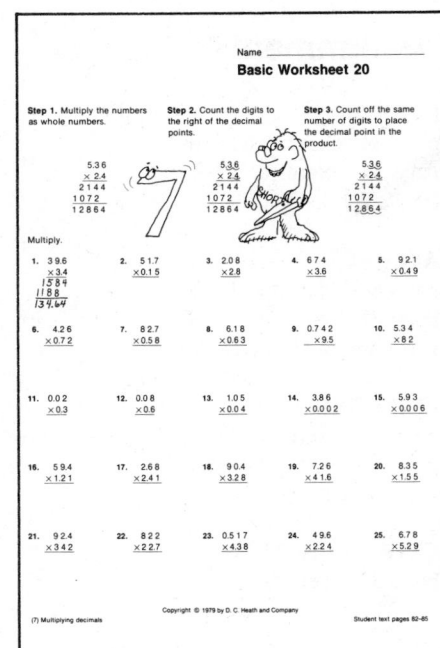

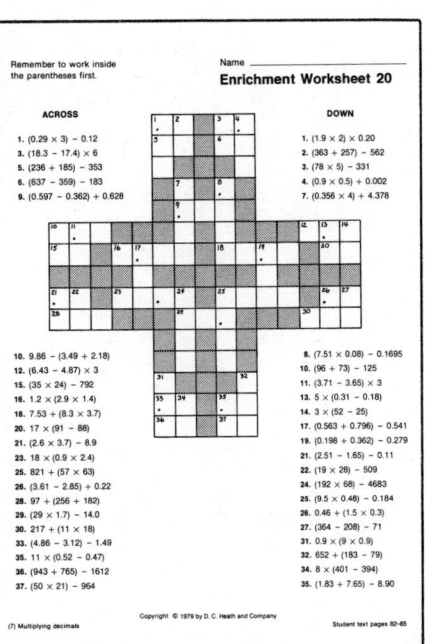

Follow-up Activities

Reinforcement The following game can be used to review and practice the multiplication algorithm. Write the ten digits 0−9 on index cards. Have students copy this table:

Draw a card and have each player copy the digit on the card in any one of the five cells in his table. Replace the card and draw a second digit, having each player copy it in any one of the four remaining cells. Continue drawing cards until all the cells have been filled in. Have each student multiply the two numbers in his table. Declare the player getting the greatest product the winner. *Note:* During the play of this game you can thoroughly review the multiplication algorithm. To do this, have all students help check the work of the player who claims to have the greatest product.

Enrichment You may wish to have more able students play the game described, using this table:

CALCULATOR ACTIVITY
Have students make tables for multiplication expressions as shown below. Duplicate the better ones and have students see how many products they can find.

Find .48

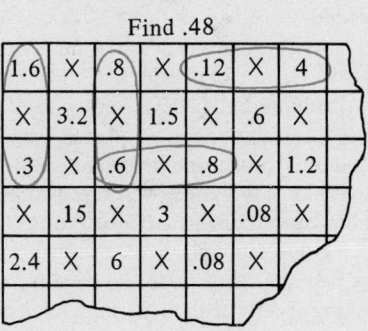

1.6	X	.8	X	.12	X	4
X	3.2	X	1.5	X	.6	X
.3	X	.6	X	.8	X	1.2
X	.15	X	3	X	.08	X
2.4	X	6	X	.08	X	

(core) Lesson 33 83

To add zeros to write decimals for
products.
To solve word problems dealing with
mathematics and geography.

Suggested Lesson Plan

Introduction Quickly review
multiplication of decimals by having
students find products for examples you
put on the board. After they "warm up"
on two or three problems, they can do
this sequence of exercises.

2.4	2.4	2.4	.24
×6	×.6	×.06	×.06
(14.4)	(1.44)	(.144)	(.0144)

As students pick up the sequence
(around the third example) they will
realize that they don't have to multiply
each time; instead they can just write
the product and place the decimal point.
At the same time, they should realize
that each example has one more decimal
place to point off than the previous
example. The dilemma occurs when the
last product has only three digits and
students must count off four places.
Some students will know what to do,
while others will stop. Try to wait until
they encounter the problem before
calling on a student for the answer.

Using the pages Use the examples on
page 84 to focus and restate the solution
to the problem encountered in the
introduction to the lesson. Of course,
when there are not enough digits for the
number of places needed in the product,
zeros can be added to the left so that
the decimal point can be correctly
placed.

Assign exercises 1−30 for written
work. Have calculators available, so that
as students finish they can try the
calculator excursion. You may want two
students to use one calculator. Working
together slows them down and forces
them to verbalize their discoveries.

Have students work exercises 1−4
on page 85. Introduce the page by
asking if any of their parents have been
to Australia.

Read through the problems with
those students who have reading
difficulties. Focus on reading slowly and
identifying the question asked.

Zeros in multiplication

Sometimes when you multiply decimals you must write extra
zeros in the product in order to get the decimal point in the
correct place. Study these examples.

$$\begin{matrix} 0.06 \\ \times 0.5 \\ \hline .030 \end{matrix} \Big\} 3$$
One zero had to be written
in the product so that
there are three digits to
the right of the decimal
point.

$$\begin{matrix} 0.32 \\ \times 0.03 \\ \hline .0096 \end{matrix} \Big\} 4$$
Two zeros had to be writ-
ten in the product.

EXERCISES
Multiply.

1.	0.02	2.	0.11	3.	2.1	4.	3.1	5.	0.67	6.	0.05
	×0.3		×0.5		×0.04		×0.12		×0.03		×0.4
	0.006		0.055		0.084		0.372		0.0201		0.020
7.	0.35	8.	0.35	9.	0.79	10.	0.35	11.	55.7	12.	5.76
	×3.6		×0.6		×0.08		×0.006		×0.38		×5.4
	1.260		0.210		0.0632		0.00210		21.166		31.104
13.	55.7	14.	5.7	15.	0.002	16.	0.006	17.	0.538	18.	58.9
	×2.31		×0.008		×0.13		×0.05		×12.7		×3.56
	128.667		0.0456		0.00026		0.00030		6.8326		209.684
19.	38.9	20.	7.56	21.	9.21	22.	0.704	23.	36.5	24.	0.825
	×2.84		×3.06		×71.4		×55.6		×1.83		×26.5
	110.476		23.1336		657.594		39.1424		66.795		21.8625
25.	3.78	26.	0.942	27.	68.3	28.	0.754	29.	3.82	30.	3.82
	×1.52		×3.75		×2.91		×0.169		×61.5		×19.6
	5.7456		3.53250		198.753		0.127426		234.930		74.872

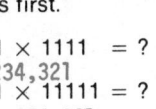

$1 \times 1 \quad = ? \; 1$ Guess first. $\qquad 9 \times 9 \quad = ? \, 81$ Guess first.

$11 \times 11 \; = ? \, 121 \quad 1111 \times 1111 \; = ? \qquad 99 \times 99 \; = ? \qquad 9999 \times 9999 \; = ?$
$\qquad\qquad\qquad\qquad 1,234,321 \qquad\qquad 9801 \qquad\qquad 99,980,001$

$111 \times 111 = ? \qquad 11111 \times 11111 = ? \qquad 999 \times 999 \; = ? \qquad 99999 \times 99999 \; = ?$
$\qquad 12,321 \qquad\qquad 123,454,321 \qquad\qquad 998,001 \qquad\qquad 9,999,800,001$

84

Assignments

BASIC
page 84 exercises 1−18
page 85 exercises 1−2
Basic Worksheet 20

AVERAGE
page 84 exercises 1−24
page 85 exercises 1−4
Enrichment Worksheet 20

ENRICHED
page 84 exercises 1−30
page 85 exercises 1−4
Enrichment Worksheet 20

EXTRA PRACTICE
page 381 set 35

Mathematics and world geography

Australia

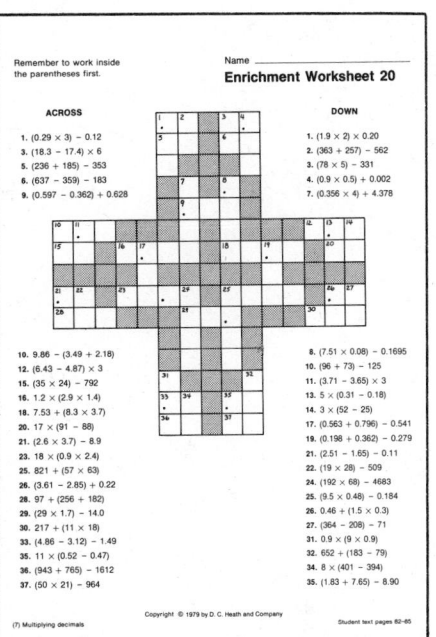

1. Australia was first settled by Europeans in 1788. How many years ago was that?

2. In the 15 years that followed World War II, more than 1,700,000 people emigrated to Australia. What was the yearly average? Round your answer to the nearest whole number.   113,333

3. Anthropologists believe that the first people to inhabit Australia (the Australian aborigines) came from Southeast Asia about 18,000 years ago. When Australia was first settled by Europeans, there were about 300,000 Australian aborigines. Today there are only about 40,000 pure-blooded aborigines. How much has their population decreased?   260,000

4. **a.** What is the total area of Australia?   7,686,850 square km
   b. What is the total population of Australia?   12,728,600

Australia States and Territories	Area (square kilometers)	Population
New South Wales	801,428	4,589,600
Victoria	227,619	3,496,200
Queensland	1,727,522	1,823,400
South Australia	984,377	1,172,800
Western Australia	2,527,621	1,027,400
Tasmania	68,332	389,900
Australian Capital Territory	2,432	143,800
Northern Territory	1,347,519	85,500

85

Follow-up Activities

Reinforcement You may wish to have students practice estimating products at this point. On index cards write some multiplication problems like these:

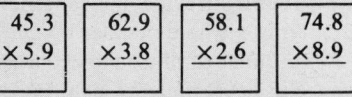

| 45.3 | 62.9 | 58.1 | 74.8 |
| ×5.9 | ×3.8 | ×2.6 | ×8.9 |

Have the students go to the chalkboard. Display a problem and allow the students 5 or 6 seconds to write an estimate of the product on the chalkboard. Have students compute the product to determine the accuracy of their estimates. Display another problem and continue the activity.

Enrichment The following game provides students with further estimating experiences. You will need to prepare on index cards some multiplication problems such as those shown above. Divide students into two well-balanced teams. Ask a member of each team to go to the chalkboard. Display a multiplication problem and inform the two players that they have 5 seconds to write their estimate of the product on the chalkboard. Next have them compute the product. The player whose estimate is closer earns a point for his team. Play continues until all players have had at least one chance to participate. The team earning the greater number of points wins the game.

CALCULATOR ACTIVITY
Without looking at their work, students should try to (1) pick the largest product in the first row of exercises on page 84, (2) pick the smallest product in the first row, etc.

After picking the products, students share using a calculator to see who made the correct choices.

Suggested Lesson Plan

Introduction Review the shortcut for
multiplying a whole number by 10, 100,
or 1000. Put several examples on the
board and have students give the
answers without actually multiplying.

67	384	6824	382
×10	×10	×100	×1000

Ask a student to state the rule that
he or she follows when doing
multiplication of this type. The student
should generalize something about
adding the same number of zeros as
there are in the multiplier.

Now ask for answers to several
examples involving decimals and a
multiplier of 10, 100, or 1000.

6.7	8.92	6.483	.0843
×10	×100	×100	×1000

Have a student express a rule for finding
these products. Expect the student to
make a statement very similar to the
rule for multiplying whole numbers by
10, 100, and 1000 except that he or she
should mention moving the decimal
point rather than adding zeros.

Using the pages Have students look
at the examples worked by Shortcut on
page 86. Have a student state the rule
given here for multiplying by 10, 100, or
1000. Note for students that when
multiplying by 10, 100, or 1000, the
product is always greater than the
number multiplied.

Continue the discussion to include
the examples which show multiplication
by .1, .01, and .001. Note that for these
examples the product is always less than
the number multiplied. After directing
the students' attention to the examples,
generalize the rule for multiplying by .1,
.01, and .001.

Have students write the products
for exercises 1–16 in class. Wait a few
minutes for them to complete the
exercises and then read the answers
aloud so they can correct their own
work. Those who get all 16 correct
should proceed with exercises 17–47 for
written work. Take a few minutes before
the end of the period and have all
students try the Keeping Skills Sharp.

Some multiplication shortcuts

When you multiply by 10, 100, or 1000, you get a product
that is greater than the number you multiplied.

Multiplying
by
10

$$
\begin{array}{r}
2.783 \\
\times\ 10 \\
\hline
27.830
\end{array}
$$

$2.783 \times 10 = 27.83$

Multiplying
by
100

$2.783 \times 100 = 278.3$

Multiplying
by
1000

$2.783 \times 1000 = 2783.$

To multiply by 10,
I move the decimal
point 1 place to
the right.
I move the decimal
point to the right
as many places as
there are
zeros.

When you multiply by 0.1, 0.01, or 0.001, you get a product
that is less than the number you multiplied.

Multiplying
by
0.1

$$
\begin{array}{r}
13.7 \\
\times 0.1 \\
\hline
1.37
\end{array}
$$

$13.7 \times 0.1 = 1.37$

Multiplying
by
0.01

$13.7 \times 0.01 = 0.137$

Multiplying
by
0.001

$13.7 \times 0.001 = 0.0137$

To multiply by
0.1, I move
the decimal
point 1 place
to the
left.

86

EXERCISES
Give each product.

1. 4.3×1
   4.3
2. 4.3×10
   43
3. 4.3×100
   430
4. 4.3×1000
   4300
5. 4.3×0.1
   0.43
6. 4.3×0.01
   0.043
7. 4.3×0.001
   0.0043
8. 4.3×0.0001
   0.00043

9. 28×1
   28
10. 28×0.1
    2.8
11. 28×0.01
    0.28
12. 28×0.001
    0.028
13. 28×10
    280
14. 28×100
    2800
15. 28×1000
    28,000
16. 28×10000
    280,000

17. 23.751×1
    23.751
18. 23.751×10
    237.51
19. 23.751×100
    2375.1
20. 23.751×1000
    23,751
21. 23.751×0.1
    2.3751
22. 23.751×0.01
    0.23751
23. 23.751×0.001
    0.023751
24. 23.751×0.0001
    0.0023751

Assignments

BASIC
page 86 exercises 1–24
page 87 exercises 25–40
    Keeping Skills Sharp
Basic Worksheet 21

AVERAGE
page 86 exercises 1–24
page 87 exercises 25–40
    Keeping Skills Sharp
Enrichment Worksheet 21

ENRICHED
page 86 exercises 1–24
page 87 exercises 25–47
    Keeping Skills Sharp
Enrichment Worksheet 21

REVIEW PRACTICE
page 378, set 21

Give each product.

25. 475.3×0.01
4.753
26. 621.5×10
6215
27. 53.87×100
5387

28. 6.28×0.01
0.0628
29. 0.5836×1000
583.6
30. 4725.6×0.001
4.7256

31. 6.7×0.001
0.0067
32. 6.7×1000
6700
33. 0.906×1000
906

Complete.

34. $6.3 \times \underline{\ ?\ } = 63$ 10
35. $6.3 \times \underline{\ ?\ } = 0.63$ 0.1

36. $7.25 \times \underline{\ ?\ } = 72.5$ 10
37. $7.25 \times \underline{\ ?\ } = 0.725$ 0.1

38. $526.3 \times \underline{\ ?\ } = 52.63$
0.1
39. $526.3 \times \underline{\ ?\ } = 5.263$
0.01

40. $0.84 \times \underline{\ ?\ } = 0.0084$
0.01
41. $0.673 \times \underline{\ ?\ } = 67.3$
100

42. $5683 \times \underline{\ ?\ } = 5.683$
0.001
43. $\underline{\ ?\ } \times 100 = 93.4$
0.934

44. $\underline{\ ?\ } \times 10 = 86.72$
8.672
45. $\underline{\ ?\ } \times 0.01 = 87.53$
8753

Solve.

46. 1 meter = 100 centimeters

Longest moustache
2.59 meters
How many centimeters?   259

47. 1 centimeter = 0.01 meter

Longest beard
533.4 centimeters
How many meters?   5.334

Follow-up Activities

Reinforcement   You may wish to provide further practice with multiplying by .1, .01, and .001 by having students copy and complete these multiplication tables.

×	.1
49	4.9
2.8	.28
.66	.066

×	.01
18	.18
5.6	.056
.81	.0081

×	.001
485	.485
41	.041
56.8	.0568

Review that multiplying by .1 moves the decimal point 1 place to the left, multiplying by .01 moves the decimal point 2 places to the left, and so on.

Enrichment   Have students make flow charts that include multiplication by .1, .01, and .001, and then determine the ending numbers.

CALCULATOR ACTIVITY

Have students write calculator codes for

(1) moving the decimal point 2 places to the right (number ⊠ 100 ▣)
(2) moving the decimal point 3 places to the left (number ⊠ .001 ▣)

Have students develop codes for additional rules.

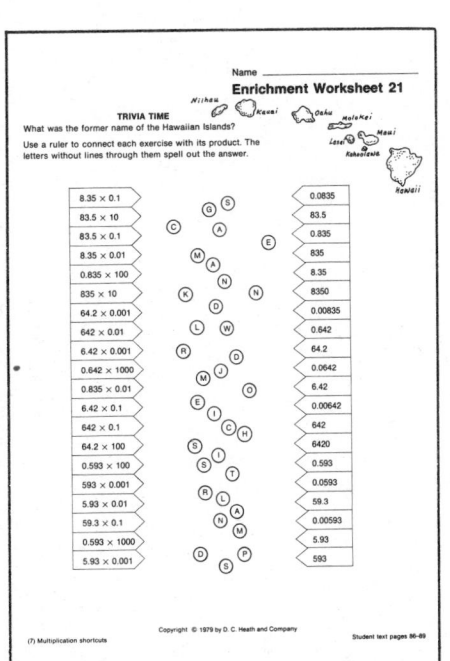

To solve word problems involving scale
  drawings.
To relate mathematics and science.

Suggested Lesson Plan

Introduction Find out whether any of
your students are interested in collecting
butterflies. If so, involve the interested
student(s) in the discussion about
butterflies. Refer students to an
encyclopedia or butterfly book, if any
are available, for pictures of other
butterflies.

  Point out that pictures are not
necessarily the actual sizes of the
butterflies. To find the actual size, one
must multiply by the decimal given.

  Quickly have students examine the
"ratio factors" and ask which pictures
are the actual size, which are greater,
and which are smaller than the actual
butterfly. All except the Buckeye and
the American Copper are smaller than
the actual size.

Using the pages Work through the
first example with all students, showing
them how to first measure the wingspan
of the butterfly and then multiply by the
decimal given to find the actual size.
Assign exercises 1−10 for written work.
Assist students with the measuring,
being sure they read the metric ruler
correctly. Point out that the small marks
on the ruler are tenths of a centimeter.

Problem solving

Scientists believe that there are about
100,000 different kinds of butterflies.
Since there are so many kinds, some different types are hard to tell apart. For
example, the Monarch and the Viceroy
look so much alike that birds can't tell
them apart. As soon as a young bird
learns that Monarchs taste bad, he re-
fuses to dine on either Monarchs or
Viceroys.

Notice that the pictures do not show actual size. You will need a centimeter
ruler for exercises 1 through 6. (If you
need to, trace the ruler on page 134.)

Monarch
For actual size, multiply
measurement by 1.2.

Viceroy
For actual size, multiply
measurement by 1.2.

**Measure to the nearest 0.1 centimeter and compute the wing-
span of each butterfly. Round each wingspan to the nearest 0.1 cm.**
Answers may vary slightly.

1. Monarch 10.0 cm
4. Buckeye 6.2 cm

2. Viceroy 7.1 cm
5. Mourning Cloak
          7.1 cm

3. Tiger Swallowtail
          10.1 cm
6. American Copper
          2.7 cm

88

Assignments

BASIC
page 88 exercises 1−6
page 89 exercises 7−8
Basic Worksheet 21

AVERAGE
page 88 exercises 1−6
page 89 exercises 7−9
Enrichment Worksheet 21

ENRICHED
page 88 exercises 1−6
page 89 exercises 7−10
Enrichment Worksheet 21

REVIEW PRACTICE
page 379 set 22

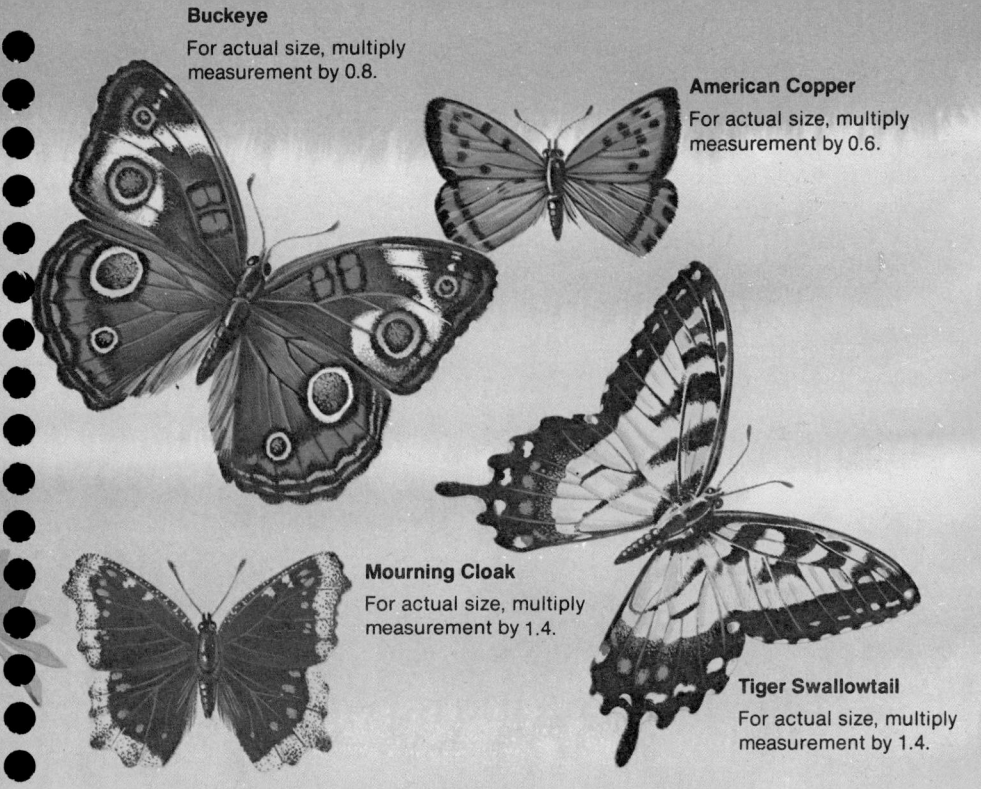

Buckeye
For actual size, multiply measurement by 0.8.

American Copper
For actual size, multiply measurement by 0.6.

Mourning Cloak
For actual size, multiply measurement by 1.4.

Tiger Swallowtail
For actual size, multiply measurement by 1.4.

7. How much greater is the wingspan of the Tiger Swallowtail than the wingspan of the Mourning Cloak? *Hint:* Use your answers to exercises 3 and 5. 3.0 cm

8. The smallest butterfly known is the Western Pygmy Blue. It has a wingspan of 1.4 cm. How much greater is the wingspan of the American Copper? 1.3 cm

9. The largest butterfly found in North America is the Giant Swallowtail. Its wingspan is 9.3 times as much as the Western Pygmy Blue. (See exercise 8.) What is the wingspan of the Giant Swallowtail? 13.0 cm

10. Which butterfly pictures are larger than full scale? How much greater are the wingspans in the picture than the actual wingspans?

Buckeye, 1.6 cm
American Copper, 1.8 cm

89

Follow-up Activities

Reinforcement Have students refer to an encyclopedia or science book and draw sketches of several butterflies at a scale of .75 and 1.3. To do so they must measure the full-size picture and then do the computation to know what size to make the drawing. Post the better drawings on the mathematics bulletin board.

Enrichment Have students make a scale drawing of the classroom and the location of major furniture. First they measure the dimensions of the classroom and decide on a scale, and then use the scale to make the drawing. Post the better efforts on the mathematics bulletin board.

EXCURSION
These are some of the symbols used to write Roman numerals:

I (one)   X (ten)
V (five)   L (fifty)

To name other numbers we combine the symbols above. Usually we add the values.

Example.
XXVI = 10 + 10 + 5 + 1 = 26

When a symbol for a smaller value is written to the left of a symbol for a greater value, we subtract the values.

Example.
XXIV = 10 + 10 + (5 − 1) = 24

Give each value.

1. VI	2. IV	3. XXI	4. XIX
5. LX	6. XL	7. LXVI	8. LXIV
6	4	21	19
60	40	66	64

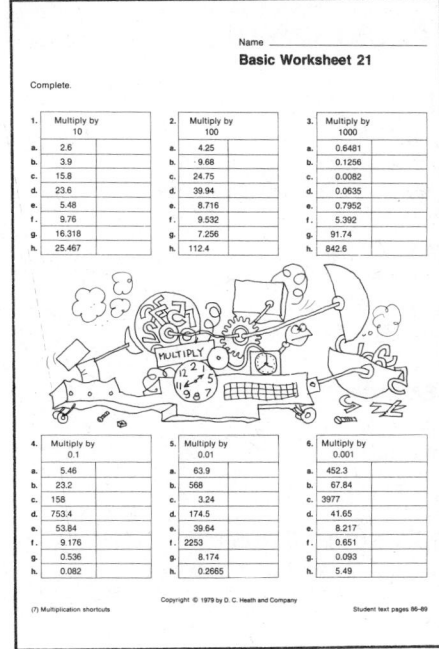

Name _____
Basic Worksheet 21

Complete.

1.	Multiply by 10		2.	Multiply by 100		3.	Multiply by 1000
a.	2.6		a.	4.25		a.	0.6481
b.	3.9		b.	9.68		b.	0.1256
c.	15.8		c.	24.75		c.	0.0082
d.	23.6		d.	39.94		d.	0.0635
e.	5.48		e.	8.716		e.	0.7952
f.	9.76		f.	9.532		f.	5.392
g.	16.318		g.	7.256		g.	91.74
h.	25.467		h.	112.4		h.	842.6

4.	Multiply by 0.1		5.	Multiply by 0.01		6.	Multiply by 0.001
a.	5.46		a.	63.9		a.	452.3
b.	23.2		b.	568		b.	67.84
c.	158		c.	3.24		c.	3977
d.	753.4		d.	174.5		d.	41.65
e.	53.84		e.	39.64		e.	8.217
f.	9.176		f.	2253		f.	0.651
g.	0.536		g.	8.174		g.	0.093
h.	0.082		h.	0.2665		h.	5.49

Copyright © 1979 by D. C. Heath and Company
(7) Multiplication shortcuts
Student text pages 86–89

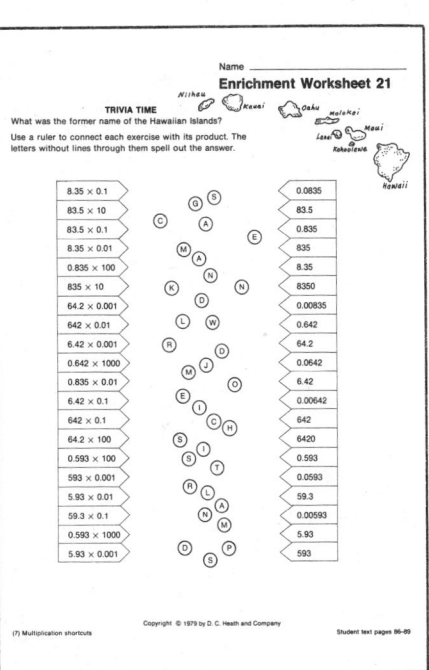

Name _____
Enrichment Worksheet 21

TRIVIA TIME
What was the former name of the Hawaiian Islands?
Use a ruler to connect each exercise with its product. The letters without lines through them spell out the answer.

8.35 × 0.1	0.0835
83.5 × 10	83.5
83.5 × 0.1	0.835
8.35 × 0.01	835
0.835 × 100	8.35
835 × 10	8350
64.2 × 0.001	0.00835
642 × 0.01	0.642
6.42 × 0.001	64.2
0.642 × 1000	0.0642
0.835 × 0.01	6.42
6.42 × 0.1	0.00642
642 × 0.1	642
64.2 × 100	6420
0.593 × 100	0.593
593 × 0.001	0.0593
59.3 × 0.01	59.3
59.3 × 0.1	0.00593
0.593 × 1000	5.93
5.93 × 0.001	593

Copyright © 1979 by D. C. Heath and Company
(7) Multiplication shortcuts
Student text pages 86–89

(core) Lesson 36   89

To divide a decimal by a whole number.

Suggested Lesson Plan

Introduction Write this division example on the board and ask a student to come to the board and do the work.

$$5\overline{)1255}$$

Ask whether they would do the problem 125.5 divided by 5 differently from the problem on the board. You may get the answer *yes* or *no*. If *yes*, ask how it would have been different. Some student may say that the answer would then be 25 with .5 left over. Lead students to see that they could complete the division by dividing the remaining .5 by 5 and recording the answer as a decimal. Of course, the purpose of the discussion is to point out to students that they divide decimals just as they divide whole numbers, except that they place a decimal point in the answer. Encourage students to estimate the answer before dividing, as estimating will remind them to place a decimal point in their answer.

Using the pages Use the exposition on page 90 to summarize the introduction. Write the examples on the board and record the work shown in the steps as students direct you in the division. Emphasize that, since we divide in place-value columns, the decimal point comes straight up to be placed in the quotient. It is a good plan for students to mark the decimal point for the quotient first, before dividing.

Assign some of the division exercises on page 91 for written work. Watch students as they work to be sure they are dividing correctly and placing the decimal point in the quotient. Assign exercises 35–36 for problem-solving practice.

Dividing a decimal by a whole number

Dividing a decimal by a whole number is like dividing a whole number by a whole number.

If you first estimate the quotient, you will know whether your answer is reasonable. Estimate the quotient by rounding to the nearest whole number.
Study these examples.

EXAMPLE 1.

$$2\overline{)10}$$

$$2\overline{)9.78}$$

Step 1. Divide ones.

$$\begin{array}{r} 4 \\ 2\overline{)9.78} \\ -8 \\ \hline 1 \end{array}$$

Step 2. Regroup.

$$\begin{array}{r} 4 \\ 2\overline{)9.78} \\ -8 \\ \hline 1\,7 \end{array}$$

Step 3. Divide tenths. Be sure to place the decimal point in the quotient.

$$\begin{array}{r} 4.8 \\ 2\overline{)9.78} \\ -8 \\ \hline 1\,7 \\ -1\,6 \\ \hline 1 \end{array}$$

Step 4. Regroup.

$$\begin{array}{r} 4.8 \\ 2\overline{)9.78} \\ -8 \\ \hline 1\,7 \\ -1\,6 \\ \hline 18 \end{array}$$

Step 5. Divide hundredths.

$$\begin{array}{r} 4.89 \\ 2\overline{)9.78} \\ -8 \\ \hline 1\,7 \\ -1\,6 \\ \hline 18 \\ -18 \\ \hline 0 \end{array}$$

Is the quotient near 5?

EXAMPLE 2.

$$\begin{array}{r} 1.48 \\ 53\overline{)78.44} \\ -53 \\ \hline 25\,4 \\ -21\,2 \\ \hline 4\,24 \\ -4\,24 \\ \hline 0 \end{array}$$

EXAMPLE 3.

$$\begin{array}{r} 0.75 \\ 4\overline{)3.00} \\ -2\,8 \\ \hline 20 \\ -20 \\ \hline 0 \end{array}$$

90

Assignments

BASIC
page 90 Discuss
page 91 exercises 1–34
Basic Worksheet 22

AVERAGE
page 90 Discuss
page 91 exercises 1–36
Enrichment Worksheet 22

ENRICHED
page 90 Discuss
page 91 exercises 1–36
Enrichment Worksheet 22

EXTRA PRACTICE
page 382 set 36

EXERCISES

Divide.

1. 5)8̄ = 1.6 2. 8)1̄ = 0.125 3. 4)1̄ = 0.25 4. 5)3̄ = 0.6 5. 4)30̄ = 7.5

6. 4)0.3̄ = 0.075 7. 8)30̄ = 3.75 8. 8)0.3̄ = 0.0375 9. 5)0.07̄ = 0.014 10. 2)0.5̄ = 0.25

11. 6)3.12̄ = 0.52 12. 3)0.72̄ = 0.24 13. 4)26.3̄ = 6.575 14. 9)0.459̄ = 0.051 15. 7)2.954̄ = 0.422

16. 8)4.368̄ = 0.546 17. 5)39.65̄ = 7.93 18. 9)4.815̄ = 0.535 19. 7)34.23̄ = 4.89 20. 6)537.6̄ = 89.6

21. 12)44.4̄ = 3.7 22. 18)651.6̄ = 36.2 23. 24)85.92̄ = 3.58 24. 37)239.39̄ = 6.47 25. 64)128.64̄ = 2.01

26. 47)143.82̄ = 3.06 27. 83)42.33̄ = 0.51 28. 91)278.46̄ = 3.06 29. 75)243̄ = 3.24 30. 86)3225̄ = 37.5

31. 123)801.96̄ = 6.52 32. 204)73.032̄ = 0.358 33. 418)685.52̄ = 1.64 34. 528)331.848̄ = 0.6285

Solve.

35. Four mountain climbers have to carry a total of 58.2 kilograms of supplies. How much should each climber carry if they divide the supplies evenly? 14.55 kg

36. The climbers began at an elevation of 1858.5 meters above sea level. Twelve hours later, they were at an elevation of 3172.5 meters.

   a. How many meters did they climb? 1314
   b. How many meters did they average each hour? 109.5

Divide 2 by 3.
Does your calculator round or just drop extra digits?

91

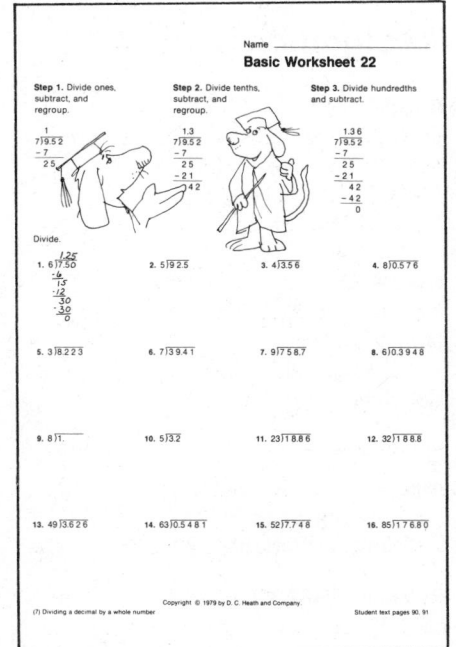

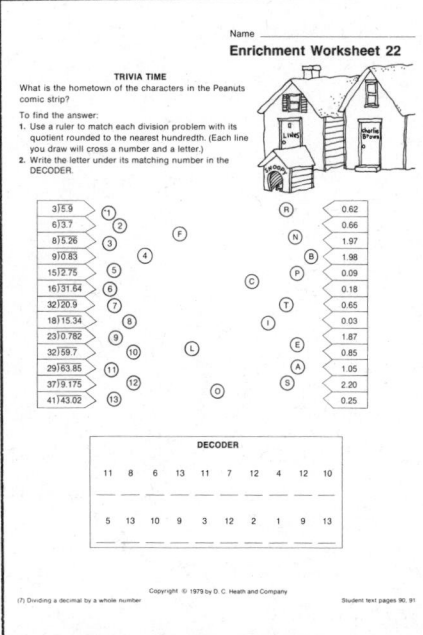

Follow-up Activities

Reinforcement Dividing a decimal by a whole number may be reviewed by working with a collection of dollars, dimes, and pennies. If real money is not available, use play money. Display 5 dollars, 3 dimes, and 7 pennies. Explain to students that the money is to be divided into 3 sets that are the same size. Go through the following steps with the students, making sure that the record is "brought up to date" at the conclusion of each step. The completed record should look like this:

dollars	dimes	pennies
ones	tenths	hundredths
1	7	9
3) 5	3	7
−3		
2	3	
−2	1	
	2	7
	−2	7
		0

Step 1. Put 1 dollar in each set. *Step 2.* Trade the 2 remaining dollars for 20 dimes. *Step 3.* Put 7 dimes in each set. *Step 4.* Trade 2 remaining dimes for 20 pennies. *Step 5.* Put 9 pennies in each set.

Enrichment Have students copy and complete the following missing-digit exercise.

```
  1 □ 3                173
□ )8 □ □            5 ) 869
 −□                   − 5
 3 6                    36
 −□□                  − 35
   □ 9                   19
  −□□                  − 15
     4                    4
```

EXCURSION

Can you place 6 counters on 6 different squares so that no two counters are in the same row, same column, or same diagonal?

If you place a
counter here,—
the Xs show
the squares that
you cannot use.

To estimate the quotient when dividing decimals.

To round the quotient when the division does not come out even.

Suggested Lesson Plan

Introduction Put the division example $43\overline{)825}$ on the board. Ask a student for an estimate before doing the division. After you get an estimate that the other students agree with, have the student explain how she found the estimate. (You hope that the student rounded both numbers and then divided "in her head." For this example, $40\overline{)800} = 20$.)

Ask a student to come to the board and actually carry out the division. As she divides she will find that she continues to have a remainder. When she finally stops dividing and looks to you for help, ask the others what to do when division does not come out even. Continue to ask questions until the students agree that one should continue to divide until there is one place more in the answer than is wanted. You then round the answer to the accuracy wanted. For example, for this problem if the answer is to be to the nearest tenth, the division should be carried out to hundredths and then rounded to tenths.

Using the pages Use the exposition on page 92 to summarize the lesson introduction. Use the example to focus on how to estimate and then carry out a division problem.

Work through exercises 1−7 in class orally. Have each student make an estimate and select a choice before telling the answers.

Assign exercises 8−22 for written work. Note that if the quotients do not come out even, the student should carry out the division to thousandths and then round the quotient to the nearest hundredth.

Assign the multiplication boxes to the better students, and the Keeping Skills Sharp to those who need maintenance on addition and subtraction of decimals.

More about division

Before dividing, we will use a shortcut for estimating the quotient. $39\overline{)9265.1}$

Step 1. Round the divisor to the nearest ten.

40

$39\overline{)9265.1}$

Step 2. Find the first digit of the quotient.

2

$39\overline{)9265.1}$

Step 3. Since the 2 is in the hundreds place, fill in two zeros.

200

$39\overline{)9265.1}$

Notice that the division will never come out evenly. In such cases we usually round the quotient.

$$
\begin{array}{r}
237.566 \\
39\overline{)9265.100} \\
-78 \\
146 \\
-117 \\
295 \\
-273 \\
22\,1 \\
-19\,5 \\
2\,60 \\
-2\,34 \\
260 \\
-234 \\
26 \\
\end{array}
$$

Rounded to the nearest hundredth → 237.57

The quotient is between 200 and 300.

Is the quotient between 200 and 300?

EXERCISES
Choose the quotient by estimating.

1. $38\overline{)2002.6}$
   a. 0.527
   b. 5.27
   c. 52.7
   d. 527

2. $42\overline{)153.3}$
   a. 0.365
   b. 3.65
   c. 36.5
   d. 365

3. $59\overline{)270.81}$
   a. 0.459
   b. 4.59
   c. 45.9
   d. 459

4. $96\overline{)195.84}$
   a. 0.204
   b. 2.04
   c. 20.4
   d. 204

92

Assignments

BASIC
page 92 exercises 1–4
page 93 exercises 5–28,
    Keeping Skills Sharp
Basic Worksheet 23

AVERAGE
page 92 exercises 3, 4
page 93 exercises 5–34,
    Keeping Skills Sharp
Enrichment Worksheet 23

ENRICHED
page 93 exercises 5–36,
    Keeping Skills Sharp
Enrichment Worksheet 23

REVIEW PRACTICE
page 379 set 24

5. $26\overline{)9.36}$
   a. 0.36
   b. 3.6
   c. 36
   d. 360

6. $42\overline{)2.184}$
   a. 0.052
   b. 0.52
   c. 5.2
   d. 52

7. $53\overline{)397.5}$
   a. 0.75
   b. 7.5
   c. 75
   d. 750

Divide. Round each quotient to the nearest hundredth.

8. $8\overline{)1}$ = 0.13
9. $6\overline{)1}$ = 0.17
10. $9\overline{)6}$ = 0.67
11. $3\overline{)22}$ = 7.33
12. $6\overline{)74}$ = 12.33
13. $8\overline{)35}$ = 4.38
14. $4\overline{)32.1}$ = 8.03
15. $9\overline{)4.38}$ = 0.49
16. $6\overline{)59.2}$ = 9.87
17. $6\overline{)5.97}$ = 1.00
18. $2\overline{)0.3956}$ = 0.20
19. $7\overline{)1.5931}$ = 0.23
20. $12\overline{)\$3.97}$ = $0.33
21. $16\overline{)\$5.63}$ = $0.35
22. $32\overline{)\$8.10}$ = $0.25
23. $27\overline{)\$.98}$ = $0.04
24. $23\overline{)\$6.04}$ = $.26
25. $48\overline{)\$5.21}$ = $0.11
26. $17\overline{)\$52.64}$ = $3.10
27. $25\overline{)\$42.34}$ = $1.69
28. $83\overline{)\$97.76}$ = $1.18
29. $105\overline{)59.6}$ = 0.57
30. $148\overline{)78.34}$ = 0.53
31. $179\overline{)9.706}$ = 0.05
32. $215\overline{)765.38}$ = 3.56
33. $308\overline{)96.748}$ = 0.31
34. $492\overline{)100.563}$ = 0.20

Multiply across and multiply down.

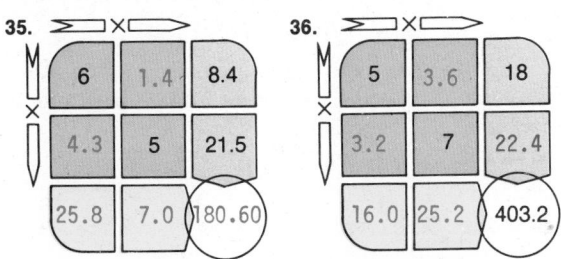

35.

	→×→	
6	1.4	8.4
4.3	5	21.5
25.8	7.0	180.60

36.

	→×→	
5	3.6	18
3.2	7	22.4
16.0	25.2	403.2

Follow-up Activities

Reinforcement Have students make choices for quotients for exercises 8–22 as shown for exercises 1–7. Then have these students work each other's problems, estimating, selecting the correct choice, and then dividing to check their estimates.

Enrichment Have students make additional boxes that require both multiplication and division. They should make the boxes challenging but also make sure they work. Save the better ones for extra practice.

CALCULATOR ACTIVITY
Students play in pairs. Each writes down 10 numbers between 0 and 100. These numbers are left in front of them as they play. One player selects a target number. Each player then selects two numbers (from his or her 10 numbers) whose quotient is close to the target number. The student closer to the target number wins one point. Play continues until one student wins 5 points.

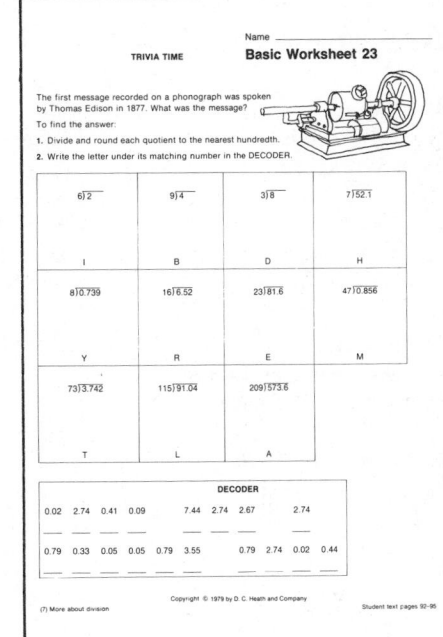

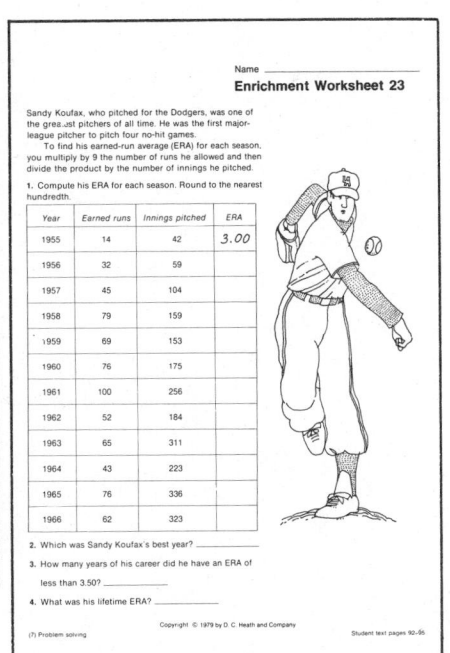

Suggested Lesson Plan

Introduction Ask students to name some uses of averages that they know of. They will probably suggest test-score averages for grading purposes, batting averages, weight of a football team, etc. Ask them how to find the average of 5 test scores of 18, 23, 16, 20, and 23. (20) Most students will know that they should add the scores and divide by the number of scores.

Using the pages Go over the exposition on page 94 to reinforce the introduction. Point out that the average may not come out even and then will be expressed as a decimal. For our purpose here, instruct students to divide to the hundredths place and then round to the nearest tenth.

Assign exercises 1–10 for written work. Be prepared to help the poor readers both in reading the questions and in reading the correct information from the chart. You may want to organize your poor readers in a small group and work through the problems together.

Problem solving

To find the average number of points that Beal scored during the first four games, we add the four numbers and divide by 4.

$$3 + 4 + 3 + 5 = 15$$

$$
\begin{array}{r}
3.75 \\
4\overline{)15.00} \\
-12 \\
\hline
3\,0 \\
-2\,8 \\
\hline
20 \\
-20 \\
\hline
0
\end{array}
$$

Rounded to the nearest tenth, her scoring average for the first four games was 3.8.

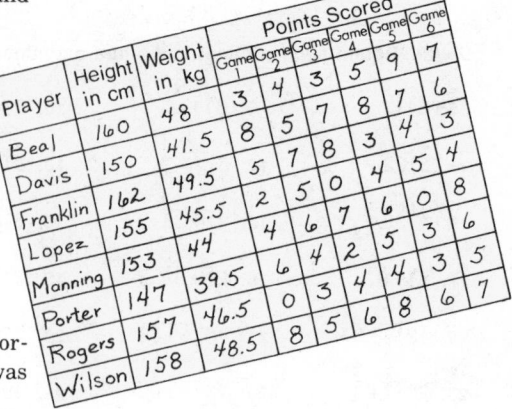

Player	Height in cm	Weight in kg	Game 1	Game 2	Game 3	Game 4	Game 5	Game 6
Beal	160	48	3	4	3	5	9	7
Davis	150	41.5	8	5	7	8	7	6
Franklin	162	49.5	5	7	3	4	3	
Lopez	155	45.5	2	5	0	4	5	4
Manning	153	44	4	6	7	6	0	8
Porter	147	39.5	6	4	2	5	3	6
Rogers	157	46.5	0	3	4	4	3	5
Wilson	158	48.5	8	5	6	8	6	7

EXERCISES

Round each decimal answer to the nearest tenth.

1. How many points did the team score in their first game? 36

2. How many more points did the team score in their sixth game than in their first game? 10

3. What is the average height of the team members? 155.3 cm

4. What is the average weight of the team members? 45.4 kg

5. How many points did Davis average during the first five games? 7

6. In which games did Franklin score below her average? games 4, 5, and 6

7. The player who holds the school scoring record (not a member of the present team) averaged 9.5 points per game for 12 games. How many points did she score? 114

8. Who had the greater scoring average, Wilson or Lopez? How much greater? Wilson, 3.4 points

9. What was the team's average score for the first three games? 37.3 points

10. What was the team's average score for the first six games? 39.7 points

94

Assignments

BASIC
page 94 exercises 1–8
Basic Worksheet 23

AVERAGE
page 94 exercises 1–10
Enrichment Worksheet 23

ENRICHED
page 94 exercises 1–10
Enrichment Worksheet 23

REVIEW PRACTICE
page 379 set 25

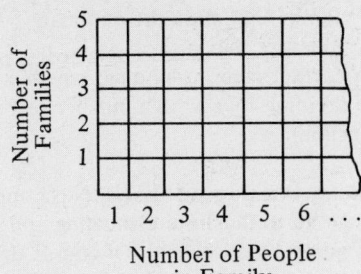

Follow-up Activities

Reinforcement Have students take a survey of other seventh-grade students, asking the number of people in the family. Ask them to show their findings on a bar graph like this:

Ask students some questions about their graphs. Finally, have them compute the average family size.

Enrichment You may wish to have some students take a survey of their classmates and determine how many minutes of television they watched during the preceding evening. Encourage students to show their findings on a bar graph. Have them compute the average time spent watching television.

CALCULATOR ACTIVITY

Finding averages is a good topic for practicing basic skills of addition and division, and it is also a good topic to illustrate how the calculator will greatly speed and simplify our computation in the real world. Look for examples of many large numbers to be averaged and have students use calculators to find these averages. For example, find the average price of a stock over a 30-day period, the average age of students in the class (express age as a decimal), etc.

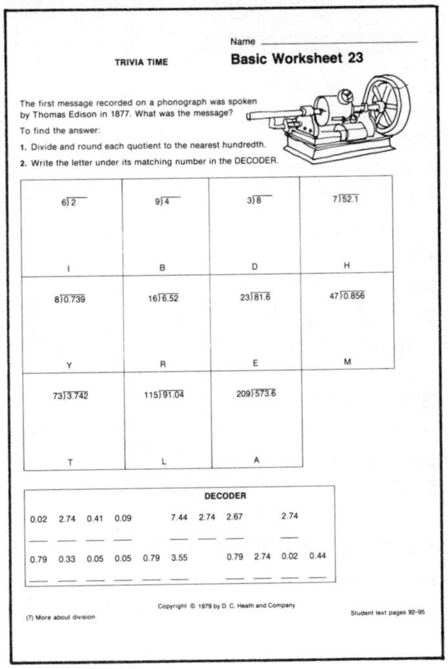

Name _____

TRIVIA TIME **Basic Worksheet 23**

The first message recorded on a phonograph was spoken by Thomas Edison in 1877. What was the message?
To find the answer:
1. Divide and round each quotient to the nearest hundredth.
2. Write the letter under its matching number in the DECODER.

$6\overline{)2}$	$9\overline{)4}$	$3\overline{)8}$	$7\overline{)52.1}$
I	B	D	H
$8\overline{)0.739}$	$16\overline{)6.52}$	$23\overline{)81.6}$	$47\overline{)0.856}$
Y	R	E	M
$73\overline{)3.742}$	$115\overline{)91.04}$	$209\overline{)573.8}$	
T	L	A	

DECODER
0.02 2.74 0.41 0.09   7.44 2.74 2.67   2.74
0.79 0.33 0.05 0.05 0.79 3.55   0.79 2.74 0.02 0.44

(7) More about division

Copyright © 1979 by D. C. Heath and Company Student text pages 92–95

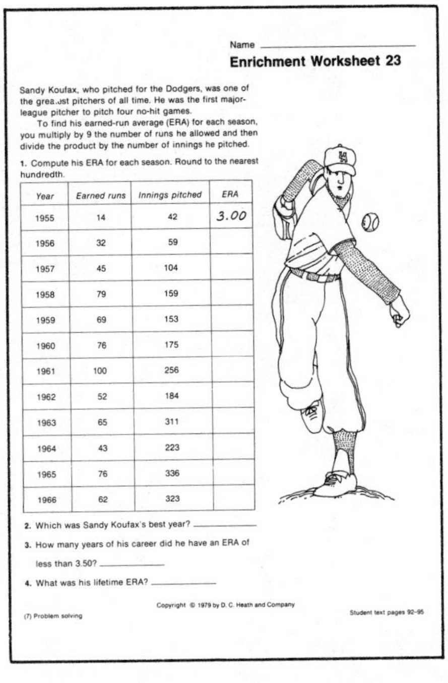

Name _____

Enrichment Worksheet 23

Sandy Koufax, who pitched for the Dodgers, was one of the greatest pitchers of all time. He was the first major-league pitcher to pitch four no-hit games.
To find his earned-run average (ERA) for each season, you multiply by 9 the number of runs he allowed and then divide the product by the number of innings he pitched.

1. Compute his ERA for each season. Round to the nearest hundredth.

Year	Earned runs	Innings pitched	ERA
1955	14	42	3.00
1956	32	59	
1957	45	104	
1958	79	159	
1959	69	153	
1960	76	175	
1961	100	256	
1962	52	184	
1963	65	311	
1964	43	223	
1965	76	336	
1966	62	323	

2. Which was Sandy Koufax's best year? _____

3. How many years of his career did he have an ERA of less than 3.50? _____

4. What was his lifetime ERA? _____

(7) Problem solving

Copyright © 1979 by D. C. Heath and Company Student text pages 92–95

Suggested Lesson Plan

Introduction Put 22)62.4 on the board and ask students the first thing to do in dividing. (Estimate the quotient) Emphasize that estimating is an important step in dividing, whether one is dividing by a whole number or by a decimal.

Using the pages Use the example on page 96 to illustrate estimating and then dividing by a decimal. Of course this first example illustrates placing the decimal point in the quotient by estimation.

Continue to use the exposition to develop the method of moving the decimal point in both the divisor and the dividend before dividing. This method can be justified mathematically by showing that multiplying the divisor and the dividend by the same number (not zero) does not change the quotient. Show several more examples on the board to be sure students accept this statement.

Take adequate time to clearly illustrate the mechanical way of moving the decimal points as shown at the bottom of page 96. This use of the little arrows is the commonly accepted notation for this shortcut, and shows exactly what has happened before the division is performed. Along with showing the arrows, be sure students locate the decimal point in the quotient when they divide.

Put several division examples on the board and have students just tell the numbers that would be involved in the division after the decimal points are moved. After they have done several examples, give them a problem such as 2.2)64. After they puzzle over this example, have a student explain (or you point out) that they have to add a zero to 64 in order to move the decimal point.

Assign some of examples 1−31 on page 97. Those examples not assigned can be used for maintenance or extra practice for students needing practice in long division.

Assign exercises 32−37 for problem-solving practice.

Dividing by a decimal

To divide by a decimal, we can first divide as if the divisor were a whole number. Then we can estimate to place the decimal in the quotient.

EXAMPLE. 1.2)74.76

Step 1. Divide 7476 by 12.

```
        6 23
1.2)74.76
   -72
     2 7
    -2 4
      36
     -36
       0
```

Step 2. Estimate the quotient. The quotient will be "near" 70.

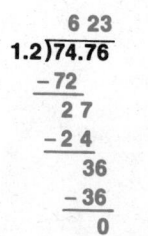
```
1.2)74.76
   70
  1)74.76
```

Step 3. Place the decimal point in the quotient.

```
        62.3
1.2)74.76
   -72
     2 7
    -2 4
      36
     -36
       0
```

If we multiply *both* the divisor and the dividend by the same nonzero number, the quotient remains the same.

```
    4                        4
3)12   Multiply    30)120
       by 10.
```

```
    17                       17
2)34   Multiply    200)3400
       by 100.
```

This fact gives us a shortcut for dividing by a decimal.

Step 1. Move both decimal points 1 place to the right. (Multiply by 10.)

```
1.2)74.7.6
```

Now we can divide by the whole number, 12.

Step 2. Divide.

```
        62.3
1.2)74.7.6
   -72
     2 7
    -2 4
      3 6
     -3 6
       0
```

96

Assignments

BASIC
page 96 Discuss
page 97 exercises 1−33
Basic Worksheet 24

AVERAGE
page 96 Discuss
page 97 exercises 1−35
Enrichment Worksheet 24

ENRICHED
page 96 Discuss
page 97 exercises 1−37
Enrichment Worksheet 24

EXTRA PRACTICE
page 382 set 37

EXERCISES

Divide.

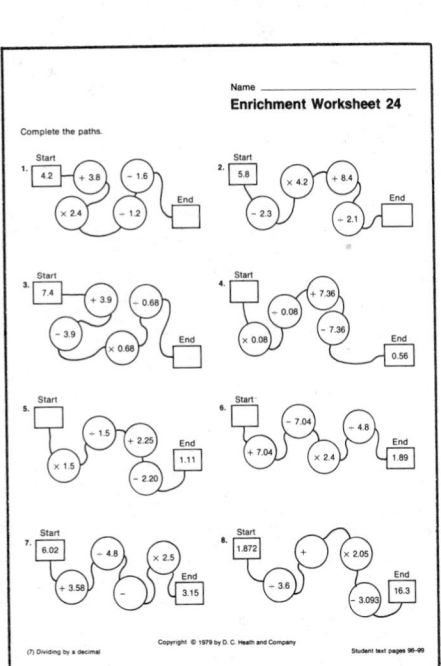

Need to Supply a Zero

1. $0.5\overline{)36.5}$ 73

2. $0.5\overline{)365}$ 730

3. $0.3\overline{)927}$ 3090

4. $0.02\overline{)0.642}$ 32.1

5. $0.07\overline{)0.91}$ 13

6. $0.04\overline{)13.20}$ 330

7. $0.003\overline{)0.1701}$ 56.7

8. $0.9\overline{)1.287}$ 1.43

9. $0.08\overline{)56}$ 700

10. $0.005\overline{)7.5}$ 1500

11. $3.5\overline{)1.05}$ 0.3

12. $5.2\overline{)19.24}$ 3.7

13. $6.3\overline{)3.654}$ 0.58

14. $0.28\overline{)20.16}$ 72

15. $0.31\overline{)0.0961}$ 0.31

16. $5.3\overline{)14.151}$ 2.67

17. $1.28\overline{)59.776}$ 46.7

18. $0.235\overline{)5.1324}$ 21.84

19. $46.2\overline{)1186.878}$ 25.69

Divide. Round each quotient to the nearest tenth.

20. $0.8\overline{)29.7}$ 37.1

21. $0.06\overline{)368}$ 6133.3

22. $0.14\overline{)5.297}$ 37.8

23. $2.6\overline{)7.438}$ 2.9

24. $7.5\overline{)62.91}$ 8.4

25. $3.9\overline{)7.503}$ 1.9

26. $0.78\overline{)68.2}$ 87.4

27. $1.23\overline{)49.37}$ 40.1

28. $4.56\overline{)68.214}$ 15.0

29. $0.387\overline{)5.2837}$ 13.7

30. $1.06\overline{)0.3577}$ 0.3

31. $98.7\overline{)62.357}$ 0.6

Solve.

32. How much will 2.4 kilograms of hamburger cost if 1 kilogram of hamburger is $3.20? $7.68

33. How many 0.25 kilogram servings can you get from 5.75 kilograms of hamburger?   23

34. How many 0.3-meter pieces can be cut from a 2.7-meter roll of ribbon?   9

35. If ribbon costs 78¢ a meter, how much will 3.8 meters of ribbon cost? Round your answer to the nearest cent. $2.96

36. On a trip, Ms. Miers bought 28 liters of gasoline for 26.9¢ per liter and 23.4 liters of gasoline for 25.9¢ per liter. How much did she spend for gasoline? Round each purchase to the nearest cent. $13.59

37. A customer bought a liter of oil for $.95. He gave the attendant a $10 bill. If gasoline sold for 27.5¢ a liter, how many liters of gasoline could he buy with the change? Round to the nearest tenth of a liter.   32.9

97

Follow-up Activities

Reinforcement Remind students that a missing factor can be found by dividing the product by the given factor. They will need to use that fact to complete the following multiplication boxes. Answers are in red.

⊗		
1.2	8	9.6
6	.8	4.8
7.2	6.4	46.08

⊗		
3.2	6	19.2
3	1.8	5.4
9.6	10.8	103.68

⊗		
5.4	3.2	17.28
6	4	24
32.4	12.8	414.72

Enrichment Have students take a survey and determine the average number of hours and minutes slept during a school night by their classmates.

EXCURSION
A man used 16 nails to put four shoes on a horse. He told the owner that he could pay either one dollar for each nail used or 1¢ for the first nail, 2¢ for the second nail, 4¢ for the third nail, 8¢ for the fourth nail, etc. Which way of paying is cheaper? How much cheaper?

first way, $311.68

STUDENT OBJECTIVES
To practice multiplication and division
   with decimals.
To play a math game using
   multiplication.

Suggested Lesson Plan

Using the pages Plan to give a short Inventory Test to identify students who are still having difficulty multiplying and dividing with decimals. Those who do well on the Inventory Test can go on to the Skill Game on page 99. Put a responsible student in charge of a team of 3 or 4 students. Let them figure out the rules and play the game independently.

Work individually with those students who did poorly on the Inventory Test. Have them work a problem on page 98. Check it and if it is wrong, go through the work with them to identify the error.

Work with these students for most of the period, but let them play the Skill Game on page 99 before the class ends so that they don't feel penalized or separated from the rest of the class.

Practice exercises

Multiply.

1. 3.84	2. 56.5	3. 81.3	4. 7.02	5. 51.8
×1.9	×5.3	×0.27	×5.8	×6.4
7.296	299.45	21.951	40.716	331.52
6. 5.36	7. 38.5	8. 4.93	9. 6.35	10. 71.5
×4.02	×5.63	×2.81	×34.6	×11.5
21.5472	216.755	13.8533	219.710	822.25

Divide. Round each quotient to the nearest hundredth.

11. 5.7)0.548   0.10   12. 0.68)4.82   7.09   13. 2.6)2.964   1.14   14. 0.53)0.8349   1.58   15. 4.8)0.7529   0.16

16. 0.26)75   288.46   17. 3.12)3.906   1.25   18. 4.08)52.831   12.95   19. 0.225)729.84   3243.73   20. 0.826)3.0715   3.72

Compute. [You should be able to do these problems without pencil and paper.]

21. (58.7 + 3.9) − 3.9   58.7   22. (358.62 − 16.94) + 16.94   358.62

23. (8.6 × 5.3) ÷ 5.3   8.6   24. (2.25 ÷ 0.15) × 0.15   2.25

25. (24.6 × 7.8) ÷ 24.6   7.8   26. (5.76 ÷ 0.18) × 0.18   5.76

27. (9.283 + 4.295) − 9.283   4.295   28. (3.719 × 1.065) ÷ 3.719   1.065

Find each end number.

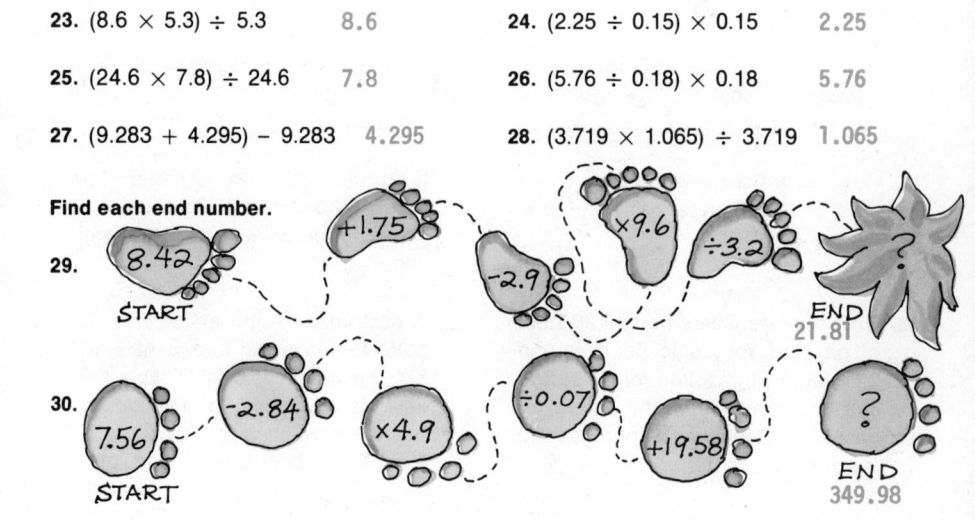

29. 8.42 START +1.75 −2.9 ×9.6 ÷3.2 END 21.81

30. 7.56 START −2.84 ×4.9 ÷0.07 +19.58 END 349.98

98

Assignments

BASIC
page 98 exercises 1−28
page 99 Game
Basic Worksheet 24

AVERAGE
page 98 exercises 1−30
page 99 Game
Enrichment Worksheet 24

ENRICHED
page 98 exercises 1−30
page 99 Game
Enrichment Worksheet 24

REVIEW PRACTICE
page 379 set 26

EXTRA PROBLEM SOLVING
pages 402−403 set 3

Skill Game

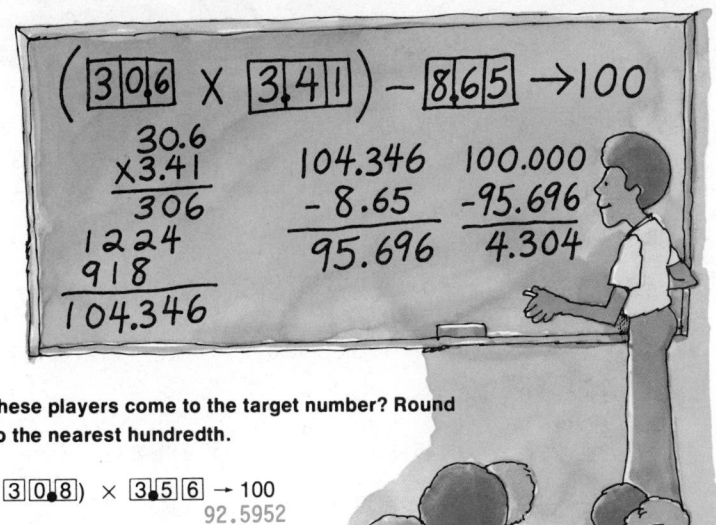

On the blackboard:

$(30.6 \times 3.41) - 8.65 \rightarrow 100$

$$\begin{array}{r} 30.6 \\ \times 3.41 \\ \hline 306 \\ 1224 \\ 918 \\ \hline 104.346 \end{array}$$

$$\begin{array}{r} 104.346 \\ - 8.65 \\ \hline 95.696 \end{array}$$

$$\begin{array}{r} 100.000 \\ - 95.696 \\ \hline 4.304 \end{array}$$

How close did these players come to the target number? Round each quotient to the nearest hundredth.

1. $(64.1 \div 30.8) \times 3.56 \rightarrow 100$
   92.5952

2. $(863 \times .160) - 45.3 \rightarrow 100$
   7.22

3. $(13.6 \times 5.03) \div .846 \rightarrow 100$
   19.14

4. $(53.6 + 13.0) - 6.84 \rightarrow 100$
   88.48

Play the game.

1. Choose a game leader. Make two cards for each of the digits 0 through 9.

2. Draw a table like this on your paper.

   $(\square\square\square \quad \square\square\square) \quad \square\square\square \rightarrow 100$

3. The game leader displays nine digit cards.

4. Each player has five minutes to fill in the digits in his or her table, write in any two operation signs $(+, -, \times, \div)$, and place three decimal points.

5. The player getting closest to the target number, 100, wins the game.

99

Name _____
Basic Worksheet 24

Step 1. So you can divide by a whole number, move both decimal points one place to the right.

Step 2. Divide.

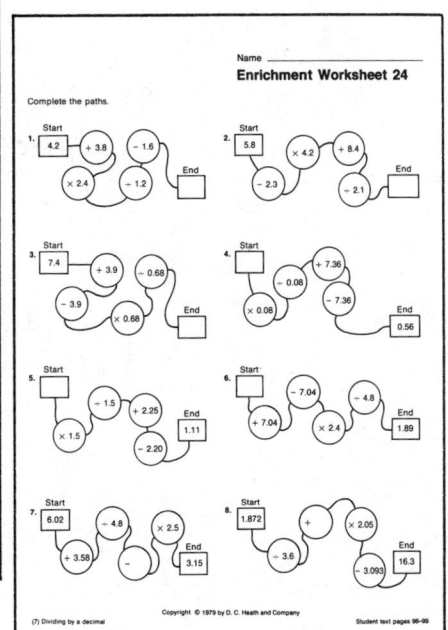

Name _____
Enrichment Worksheet 24

Complete the paths.

STUDENT OBJECTIVE
To review the concepts introduced in Chapter 3.

Suggested Lesson Plan

Introduction No pre-text activity is necessary for page 100 as it is a checkup for the chapter. However, it may be valuable to briefly review the lessons in the chapter so that students are reminded of the content over which they will be tested.

This checkup will provide you with data about how well individual students have mastered the skills of the chapter. The Chapter Review on page 102 is provided for those students who need more specific individual help.

Page 101 is an activity that students will enjoy. Assign the projects to pairs of students without further explanation. Make the materials available to them at different work stations and let them work independently to find the answers. Post the better answers on the mathematics bulletin board.

Material needed for projects:
Project 1: Ream of paper, centimeter ruler.
Project 2: Several boxes of paper clips and small scale such as a postage scale.
Project 3: Several long-playing records (ones you don't plan to play again).

Using the pages Assign all of the exercises on page 100. As students complete the page they can work on the projects on page 101.

Multiply. [pages 82–84, 98–99]

| 1. | 3.9 | 2. | 4.2 | 3. | 13.8 | 4. | 50.7 | 5. | 40.3 | 6. | 8.07 |

1. $\begin{array}{r} 3.9 \\ \times 0.5 \\ \hline 1.95 \end{array}$
2. $\begin{array}{r} 4.2 \\ \times 2.7 \\ \hline 11.34 \end{array}$
3. $\begin{array}{r} 13.8 \\ \times 3.8 \\ \hline 52.44 \end{array}$
4. $\begin{array}{r} 50.7 \\ \times 0.21 \\ \hline 10.647 \end{array}$
5. $\begin{array}{r} 40.3 \\ \times 31.4 \\ \hline 1265.42 \end{array}$
6. $\begin{array}{r} 8.07 \\ \times 1.04 \\ \hline 8.3928 \end{array}$

Multiply. [pages 86–87]

7. 5.8×10 58
8. 4.3×100 430
9. 0.5671×100 56.71
10. 3.2×0.1 0.32
11. 5.6×0.01 0.056
12. 3214.6×0.001 3.2146

Divide. [pages 90–93]

13. $3\overline{)13.68}$ 4.56
14. $5\overline{)3.9}$ 0.78
15. $9\overline{)3.483}$ 0.387
16. $10\overline{)67.34}$ 6.734
17. $21\overline{)37.8}$ 1.8
18. $82\overline{)323.08}$ 3.94
19. $134\overline{)3457.2}$ 25.8
20. $503\overline{)3274.53}$ 6.51

Divide. Round each quotient to the nearest hundredth. [pages 96–97]

21. $6\overline{)5.8}$ 0.97
22. $0.07\overline{)39.7}$ 567.14
23. $0.009\overline{)6.73}$ 747.78
24. $3.2\overline{)67.65}$ 21.14
25. $0.12\overline{)1.397}$ 11.64
26. $0.62\overline{)4.18}$ 6.74
27. $12.4\overline{)58.369}$ 4.71
28. $2.79\overline{)493.752}$ 176.97

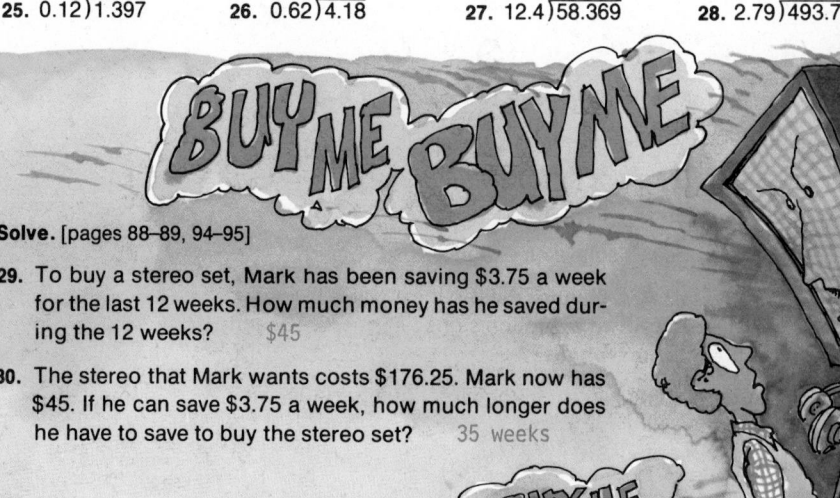

Solve. [pages 88–89, 94–95]

29. To buy a stereo set, Mark has been saving $3.75 a week for the last 12 weeks. How much money has he saved during the 12 weeks? $45

30. The stereo that Mark wants costs $176.25. Mark now has $45. If he can save $3.75 a week, how much longer does he have to save to buy the stereo set? 35 weeks

100

Assignments

BASIC
page 100 exercises 1–30
page 101 Project

AVERAGE
page 100 exercises 1–30
page 101 Project

ENRICHED
page 100 exercises 1–30
page 101 Project

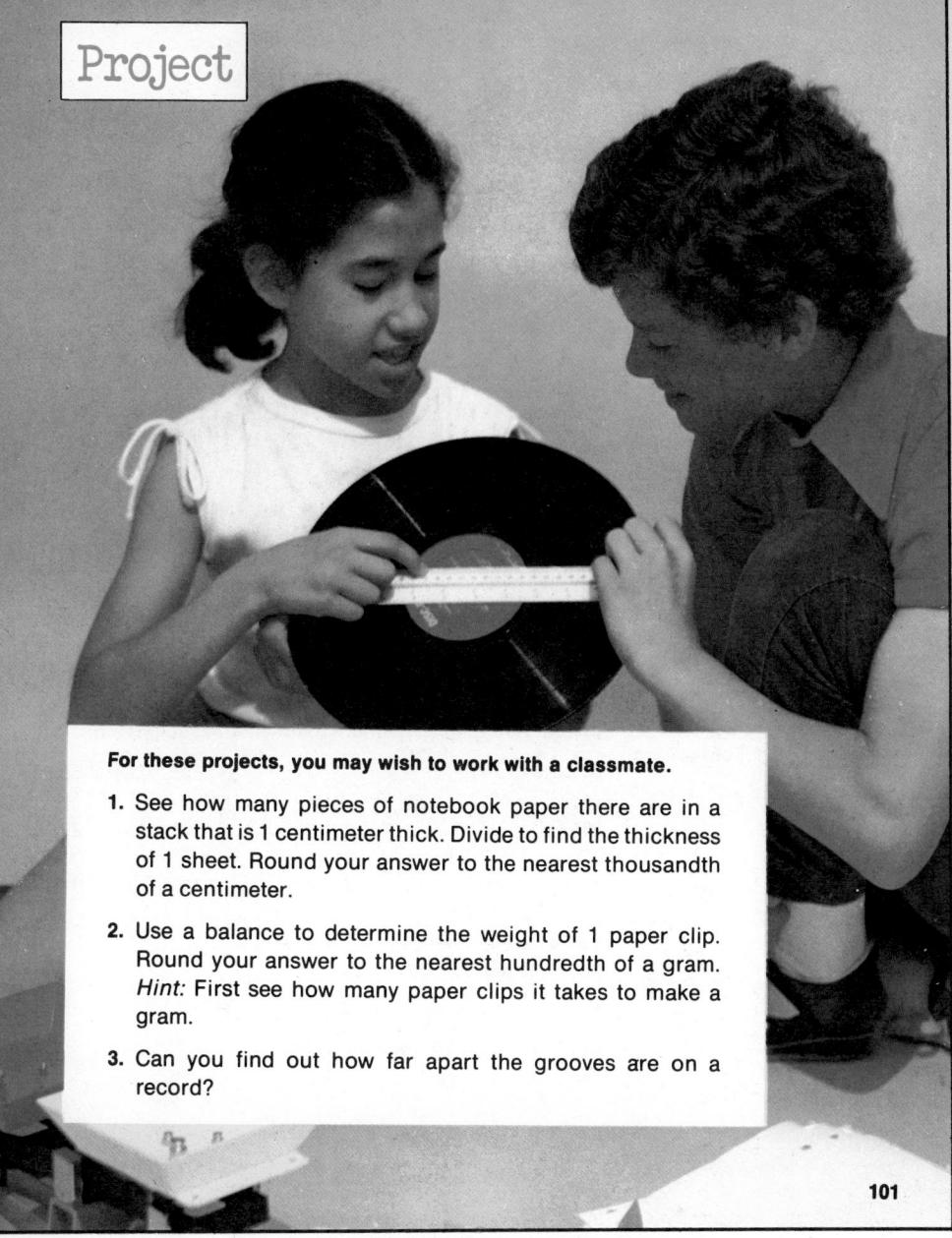

Project

For these projects, you may wish to work with a classmate.

1. See how many pieces of notebook paper there are in a stack that is 1 centimeter thick. Divide to find the thickness of 1 sheet. Round your answer to the nearest thousandth of a centimeter.

2. Use a balance to determine the weight of 1 paper clip. Round your answer to the nearest hundredth of a gram. *Hint:* First see how many paper clips it takes to make a gram.

3. Can you find out how far apart the grooves are on a record?

101

Follow-up Activities

Reinforcement Correct all of the items in the Chapter Checkup. Any student who misses six or more, or any more than three problems in a section, needs additional help. It is important for each student to achieve some degree of mastery of the basic skills covered. At this point, students who are still having difficulty with these skills need concentrated individual help.

Enrichment Assign these pupils to the games and activities that have been played out throughout the chapter. Assign a student leader to be responsible for teaching each game or activity to the interested students and to supervise the play.

CALCULATOR ACTIVITY
Assign one student to be in charge of the calculators and the calculator activities. The calculator student is responsible for keeping track of the calculators, for explaining the activities, and for supervising the play.

You may wish to assign some of the Creative Problem Solving Activities (pages 461-477) at this time.

Suggested Lesson Plan

Introduction After checking the Chapter Checkup you will know which students need additional reinforcement and which students will be able to go ahead with the Challenge activity. Get the better students started on page 103 first, as the students who are having difficulty will need more of your time.

The students who need more review should go back and correct their errors on the Chapter Checkup. You may want to go over the questions orally if this group is small enough. Carefully probe to determine which concepts and skills the students have not mastered and work individually to correct their deficiences.

Using the pages After the identified students have corrected the Chapter Checkup, they should answer questions 1—32 on page 102. After they complete these questions, read the answers and let the students correct their own papers. Give them an opportunity to ask questions about the exercises they missed.

Assign page 103 to those students who did well on the Chapter Checkup.

CHAPTER REVIEW

$$\begin{array}{r} 6.3 \\ \times 0.21 \\ \hline 63 \\ 126 \\ \hline 1.323 \end{array}$$ } 3 places

3 places

$3.75 \times 10 = 37.5$

$6.21 \times 0.01 = .0621$

$$\begin{array}{r} 8.81 \\ 3\overline{)26.43} \\ -24 \\ \hline 24 \\ -24 \\ \hline 3 \\ -3 \\ \hline 0 \end{array}$$

$$\begin{array}{r} 6.055 \\ 0.32\overline{)1.9376} \\ -192 \\ \hline 176 \\ -160 \\ \hline 160 \\ -160 \\ \hline 0 \end{array}$$

6, 4, 3, 8

$5.25 \rightarrow 5.3$

$$\begin{array}{r} 4\overline{)21.00} \\ -20 \\ \hline 10 \\ -8 \\ \hline 20 \\ -20 \\ \hline 0 \end{array}$$

6
4
3 } 4 numbers
+8
21

Multiply.

1. 2.7		**2.** 3.9		**3.** 0.57		**4.** 0.35	
×8		×0.6		×9		×0.7	
21.6		2.34		5.13		0.245	
5. 0.02		**6.** 6.7		**7.** 9.28		**8.** 5.47	
×0.3		×3.4		×3.6		×6.24	
0.006		22.78		33.408		34.1328	

Give each product.

9. 6.5×10 65   12.3   **10.** 1.23×10

11. 3.8×0.1 0.38   6.234   **12.** 623.4×0.01

13. 37.611×100 3761.1   480   **14.** 0.48×1000

Divide.

	4.65	0.48	35.7
15. $5\overline{)23.25}$		**16.** $3\overline{)1.44}$	**17.** $9\overline{)321.3}$
	0.071	0.62	0.0073
18. $6\overline{)0.426}$		**19.** $5\overline{)3.1}$	**20.** $8\overline{)0.0584}$
	0.23	0.128	0.018
21. $12\overline{)2.76}$		**22.** $25\overline{)3.2}$	**23.** $40\overline{)0.72}$

Divide. Round each quotient to the nearest hundredth.

24. $0.9\overline{)5.762}$ 6.40   116.98   **25.** $0.8\overline{)93.58}$

26. $0.05\overline{)3.711}$ 74.22   **27.** $2.5\overline{)7.12}$ 2.85

28. $0.19\overline{)46}$ 242.11   **29.** $8.1\overline{)0.731}$ 0.09

Compute the average.
Round to the nearest tenth.

30. 8, 8, 9, 5, 6, 3   **31.** 28, 31, 26, 25, 38   29.6

6.5

32. 126, 143, 182, 135   146.5

102

Assignments

BASIC
page 102   exercises 1—32

AVERAGE
page 102   exercises 1—32

ENRICHED
page 103   exercises 1—6

CHAPTER CHALLENGE

Complete.

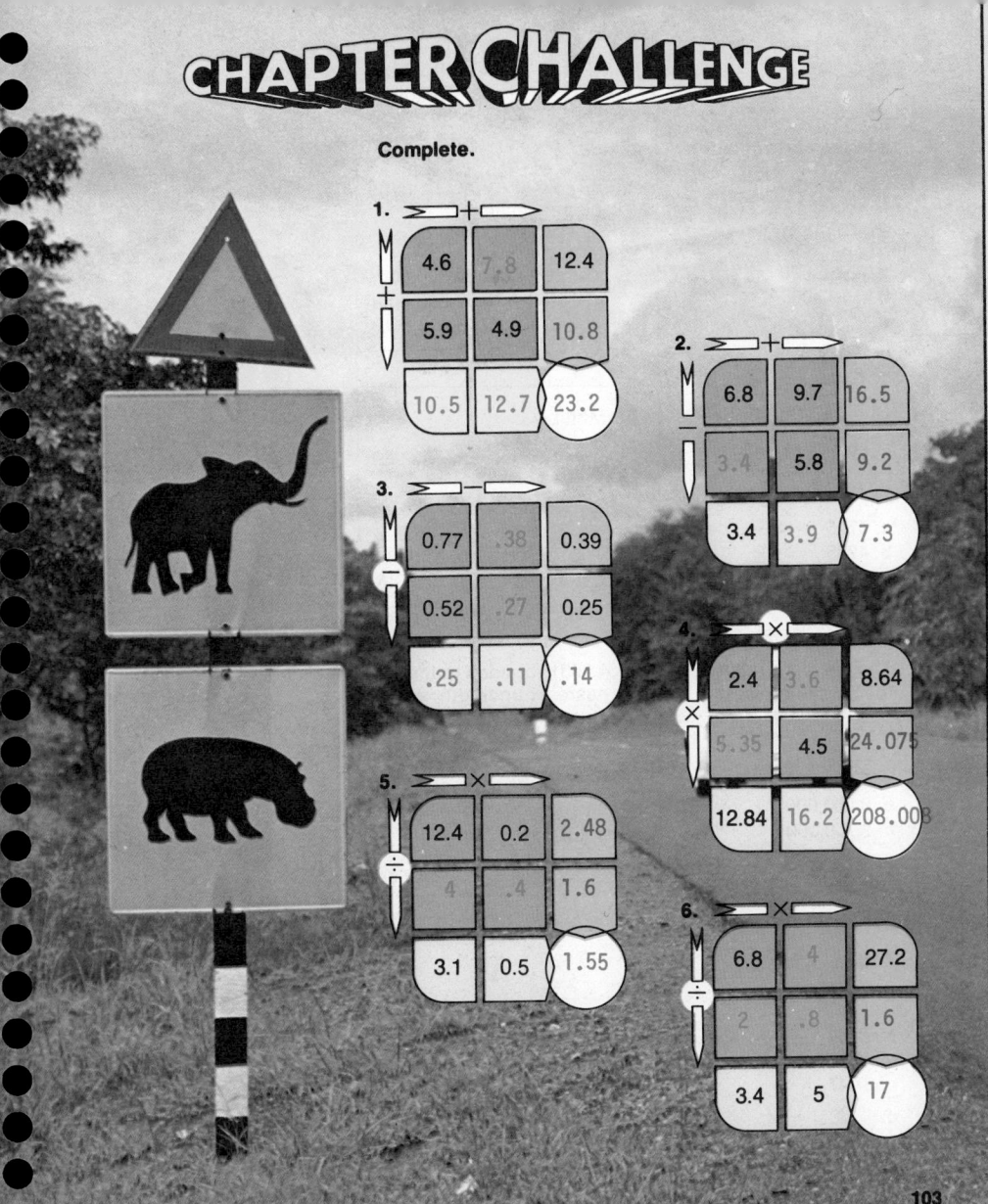

1.
4.6	7.8	12.4
5.9	4.9	10.8
10.5	12.7	23.2

2.
6.8	9.7	16.5
3.4	5.8	9.2
3.4	3.9	7.3

3.
0.77	.38	0.39
0.52	.27	0.25
.25	.11	.14

4.
2.4	3.6	8.64
5.35	4.5	24.075
12.84	16.2	208.008

5.
12.4	0.2	2.48
4	.4	1.6
3.1	0.5	1.55

6.
6.8	4	27.2
2	.8	1.6
3.4	5	17

103

Follow-up Activities

Reinforcement The reinforcement at this point should be individual help focused on multiplication and division of decimals.

Enrichment Pair these students with students who are having difficulty with basic skills. Give them several problems of the appropriate skill and have the student who needs help explain his or her work to the more able student.

MAJOR CHECKUP

STUDENT OBJECTIVES
To practice skills learned previously.
To practice using a standardized-test format.

Suggested Lesson Plan

Using the pages The Major Checkup at the end of each chapter of this textbook is given in standardized-test format. The answer sheet on page 448 is the type used with many standardized tests. You may duplicate it for use with the Major Checkups.

Pass out the answer sheets and be sure students understand how to use them. Allow a specified time, perhaps twenty minutes, to complete the checkup. Assign the exercises and use the results to determine what review is needed.

The table below correlates the test items and the student text pages. Assign review exercises as indicated by the Major Checkup results.

Test Item	Text Pages	Test Item	Text Pages
1	18–19	7	56–59
2	22–23	8	64–65
3	26–27	9	66–67
4	28–29	10	68–69
5	33–39	11	83–84
6	40–45	12	96–97

Chapter 3 Posttest

See page 54 for a full discussion of how to use the posttest. The table below suggests Extra Practice exercises and Basic Worksheets for those students who need further practice or reteaching.

Objectives	Extra Practice Sets	Pages	Basic Worksheets
3-1	34–35	381	20–21
3-2	36–37	382	22–24

Choose the correct letter.

1. The standard numeral for six million sixty thousand six is
   a. 6,066,000
   b. 6,060,006 ⬅
   c. 6,000,066
   d. none of these

2. 67,480,000 rounded to the nearest million is
   a. 60,000,000
   b. 67,000,000 ⬅
   c. 68,000,000
   d. none of these

3. Give the sum.
   56 + 381 + 9
   a. 446 ⬅
   b. 447
   c. 456
   d. none of these

4. Give the difference.
   5002 – 1327
   a. 4775
   b. 4785
   c. 3675 ⬅
   d. none of these

5. Multiply.
   324
   × 602
   a. 195,048 ⬅
   b. 20,088
   c. 196,148
   d. none of these

6. Divide.
   38)7752
   a. 204 ⬅
   b. 240
   c. 24
   d. none of these

7. The standard numeral for 3.7 million is
   a. 37,000,000
   b. 3,000,000.7
   c. 3,700,000 ⬅
   d. none of these

8. 4.2031 rounded to the nearest hundredth is
   a. 4.21
   b. 4.20 ⬅
   c. 4.203
   d. none of these

9. Add
   3.71 + 28.6
   a. 7.57
   b. 75.7
   c. 31.31
   d. none of these ⬅

10. Subtract.
    70.03 – 2.56
    a. 78.47
    b. 78.57
    c. 67.47 ⬅
    d. none of these

11. Multiply.
    0.32
    × 2.4
    a. 0.768 ⬅
    b. 7.68
    c. 76.8
    d. none of these

12. Divide.
    0.08)1.72
    a. 0.215
    b. 2.15
    c. 21.5 ⬅
    d. none of these

104

Answers for Chapter 3 Posttest
1. 37.17 2. 0.1868 3. 17.1 4. 8.0332
5. 0.00012 6. 720 7. 78.1 8. 15.2
9. 0.9 10. 4.7 11. $4.38 12. $2.25
13. 16.9¢ 14. 20.8 kg

Chapter 3 Posttest

Name _____

Date _____

Multiply. [Obj. 3-1, pages 82–84, 86–87, 98–99]

Number right

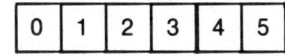

| 0 | 1 | 2 | 3 | 4 | 5 |

1. 53.1
    × 0.7

2. 4.67
    × 0.04

3. 3.8
    × 4.5

4. 2.66
    × 3.02

5. 0.004
    × 0.03

Divide. Round the quotient to the nearest tenth.
[Obj. 3-2, pages 90–93, 96–99]

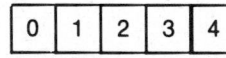

| 0 | 1 | 2 | 3 | 4 | 5 |

6. 0.1)‾72‾

7. 0.04)‾3.124‾

8. 3.6)‾54.8‾

9. 0.82)‾0.75‾

10. 1.42)‾6.7‾

Solve. [Obj. 3-3, pages 88–89, 94–95]

| 0 | 1 | 2 | 3 | 4 |

11. Apples cost $1.25 a dozen. How much will

    3.5 dozen apples cost? _____

12. 3 kilograms of meat cost $6.75. How much
    does the meat cost per kilogram?

    _____

13. 30 liters of gasoline cost $5.07. How much
    does one liter of gasoline cost?

    _____

14. Ken's calf gained 3.2 kilograms of weight
    per month for 6.5 months. How much

    weight did it gain in all? _____

NOTES

Chapter 4
Number Theory

Pages 105–132

Learning Objectives

After completing this chapter, all students should be able to do the following:

4-1 Tell whether one set is a subset of another set.

4-2 Give the intersection and the union of two sets.

4-3 Give the greatest common factor of two numbers.

4-4 Give the least common multiple of two numbers.

4-5 Substitute numbers into variable expressions and simplify.

4-6 Solve simple equations.

The concepts of subset, intersection, and union are reviewed and then used to develop the useful concepts of common factor, common multiple, and prime number. Then students learn what a variable is and how to substitute numbers for variables and simplify the resulting expressions. Finally, students are introduced to simple equation-solving techniques.

Mathematics

Subsets. One set concept that usually causes students difficulty is this: the empty set is a subset of every set. This difficulty is understandable because the logic of everyday discourse is not the same as formal logic. The usual definition of *subset* is this:

> A first set is a subset of a second set if and only if each member of the first set is a member of the second set.

Students argue that *since the empty set has no members* it cannot be a subset of another set. In the logic of everyday discourse the definition above requires a set to have members to be a subset. Now consider the following definition:

> A first set is a subset of a second set if and only if there is no member of the first set that is not also a member of the second set.

Students do not feel that this definition requires a set to have members in order to be a subset of another set. Therefore, when this definition is used students feel comfortable with the idea that the empty set is a subset of every set.

Of course, in formal logic, the two definitions are equivalent; "psychologically" they are not. We use the first definition because it is the one most commonly used, but suggest that if students have trouble, they be taught the second definition, too, and that the definitions are equivalent in formal logic.

Equation solving. Students are introduced to some of the equation-solving rules involving "doing the same thing to both sides." For example, to solve $y + 41 = 59$ for y, we subtract 41 from both sides:

$$y + 41 - 41 = 59 - 41$$
$$y = 18$$

You may wish to develop an intuitive approach to solving these types of problems by having the students consider what they must add to 41 to make 59.

Teaching the Chapter

The work in this chapter is quite simple. You may wish to provide opportunities for more able students to do more difficult work. For example, these students can be asked to solve fairly difficult equations such as

$$3(2a + 8) = 78$$

$$\frac{2(18 - 4b)}{7} = 4$$

Remember that students should solve these equations by using common sense rather than by applying the "do the same thing to both sides" rules. This is how a student might solve the first of those equations intuitively. She would first think: What do I multiply by 3 to get 78?

$$3(\; ? \;) = 78 \qquad 3(2a + 8) = 78$$

That is 26. What is in the parentheses must be 26.

$$2a + 8 = 26$$

Now she thinks: What do I add to 8 to get 26?

$$? + 8 = 26$$

That is 18, so

$$2a = 18$$

I know that 9 is the number that I multiply by 2 to get 18, so

$$a = 9$$

You may also let more able students make up very complex expressions with variables and grouping symbols and then substitute numbers for the variables and simplify.

Vocabulary

clock arithmetic
common factor
common multiple
composite number
element
empty set
even number
exponent
factor
greatest comon factor
intersection
least common multiple
multiples
odd number
power
prime factorization
prime number
rectangular number
scientific notation
set
simplify
solve
square number
subset
substitute
triangular number
union
variable

Symbols

{ }	set
∅	the empty set
U	union
∩	intersection

Materials

hand calculators

Chapter Tests

For a discussion of how to use the chapter tests, please see page 17c.

Answers for Chapter 4 Pretest

1. T **2.** F **3.** F **4.** T **5.** 3, 6 **6.** 1, 2, 3, 6 **7.** 1, 2, 3, 4, 5, 6, 7 **8.** 1, 2, 3, 4, 5, 6, 7, 8, 9, 10 **9.** 4 **10.** 8 **11.** 12 **12.** 45 **13.** 24 **14.** 36 **15.** 15 **16.** 16 **17.** 28 **18.** 3 **19.** 8 **20.** 4 **21.** 6 **22.** 32 **23.** 4 **24.** 94 **25.** 3 **26.** $5\frac{2}{3}$

Chapter 4 Pretest

Name _____

Date _____

True or false? [Obj. 4-1, pages 106–107]

1. B is a subset of A _____

2. C is a subset of B _____

3. A is a subset of C _____

4. C is a subset of A _____

0	1	2	3	4

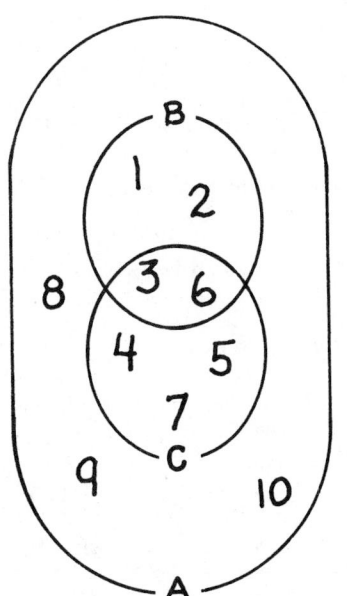

0	1	2	3	4

Write the elements. [Obj. 4-2, pages 108–109]

5. $B \cap C$ _____

6. $B \cap A$ _____

7. $C \cup B$ _____

8. $C \cup A$ _____

Give the greatest common factor. [Obj. 4-3, pages 110–111]

9. 20 and 24 _____

10. 48 and 56 _____

11. 36 and 24 _____

0	1	2	3

Give the least common multiple. [Obj. 4-4, pages 114–115]

12. 5 and 9 _____

13. 12 and 24 _____

14. 12 and 18 _____

0	1	2	3

Substitute and simplify. [Obj. 4-5, pages 118–119, 126–127]

15. $a \times b$_____

16. c^2 _____

17. $c \times (A + b)$_____

18. $(24 \div c) \div A$ _____

19. A^3 _____

20. $(a + b) \div A$_____

0-2	3	4	5	6

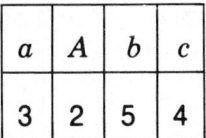

a	A	b	c
3	2	5	4

Solve. [Obj. 4-6, pages 120–121, 124–125]

21. $8a = 48$

22. $x + 15 = 47$

23. $7y = 28$

_____

_____

_____

24. $y - 41 = 53$

25. $3s = 9$

26. $3y = 17$

_____

_____

_____

0-2	3	4	5	6

Chapter 4
Record and Assignment Chart

Name _____

Pretest Date _____   Posttest Date _____

Objectives

		Pretest Score — Mark number correct	Posttest Score — Mark number correct
4-1	Tell if one set is a subset of another set.	0 1 2 ‖ 3 4	0 1 2 ‖ 3 4
4-2	Give the intersection and the union of two sets.	0 1 2 ‖ 3 4	0 1 2 ‖ 3 4
4-3	Give the greatest common factor of two numbers.	0 1 ‖ 2 3	0 1 ‖ 2 3
4-4	Give the least common multiple of two numbers.	0 1 ‖ 2 3	0 1 ‖ 2 3
4-5	Substitute numbers into variable expressions and simplify.	0-1 2 3 4 ‖ 5 6	0-1 2 3 4 ‖ 5 6
4-6	Solve simple equations.	0-1 2 3 4 ‖ 5 6	0-1 2 3 4 ‖ 5 6

Unsatisfactory Score | Satisfactory Score (Pretest)
Unsatisfactory Score | Satisfactory Score (Posttest)

TEACHING ASSIGNMENTS*

	Student Page	Basic Assignment	Average Assignment	Enriched Assignment	Problem Solving	RETEACHING ASSIGNMENTS †
4-1	106, 107	1–7	1–9, EW 25	1–9 EW 25		BW 25
4-2	108, 109	1–10	1–12, EW 26	1–13, EW 26		BW 26
4-3	110, 111	1–20	1–22, EW 27	1–25, EW 27		page 382 Set 38, BW 27
	112, 113	1–15	1–24, EW 28	1–24, EW 28		page 382 Set 39, BW 28
4-4	114, 115	1–29	1–33, EW 29	1–35, EW 29		page 382, Set 40, BW 29
	116	1–20	1–21, EW 30	1–22, EW 30		BW 30
	117	1–2	1–2	1–3		BW 30
4-5	118, 119	1–35	1–40, EW 31	1–46, EW 31		BW 31
	120, 121	1–20	1–30, EW 32	10–40, EW 32		page 383 Set 41, BW 32
4-6	122, 123	1–5	1–6, EW 32	1–6, EW 32		BW 32
	124, 125	1–33	1–35, EW 33	10–37, EW 33		page 383 Set 42, BW 33
	126	1–21	1–21, EW 34	1–21, EW 34		page 383 Set 43, BW 34
	127	1–8	1–10	1–12		BW 34
	128	Chapter Checkup				
	129	Project				
	130	Chapter Review				
	131	Chapter Challenge				
	132	Major Checkup				

* Check assignments for objectives with unsatisfactory pretest scores.
† Check assignments for objectives with unsatisfactory posttest scores.

BW = Basic Worksheet
EW = Enrichment Worksheet

4
Number
Theory

Suggested Lesson Plan

Introduction Tell students that a *set* is
a collection of *elements*. Hold up four or
five books. Tell students that these are
elements of a set of books—in fact,
these are the only elements of the
particular set that you have in mind.
Hold up one of the books and tell
students that it is an element of the set.
Ask how many elements there are in the
set. Write the words *set* and *element* on
the board. Name some other book that
is not in the set and ask whether it is an
element of the set. Ask students to name
all the elements of the set. Next, write
the set on the chalkboard using braces:

{——, ——, ——, ——, ——}

The names of the books go in the
blanks.

If you feel that your students
understand the idea of a set and its
elements, do not go on. However, if you
feel that they do not understand, give
examples of other sets in the
classroom—the set of brown-eyed boys,
the set of blonde girls, etc.

Using the pages Put the set of whole
numbers

$$W = \{0, 1, 2, 3, \ldots\}$$

on the chalkboard and explain what the
three dots mean. Ask the class to give
examples of other sets of numbers that
go on forever. (prime numbers, even
numbers, etc.)

Do exercises 1—5 as a class
activity. Then let the students work on
their own. Be available to answer
questions, but encourage students to try
to figure out the exercises themselves.
Most students should not find these
difficult once they get on the right track.

The whole numbers

In this chapter you will first work with the set of whole numbers.

$\{0, 1, 2, 3, \ldots\}$

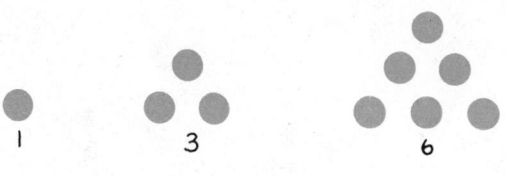

The 3 dots tell me that the numbers go on forever in the same manner.

The study of the whole numbers dates back to about 500 B.C.
At that time, the ancient Greeks began to explore and to
classify the whole numbers. In this lesson you will be asked to
take some of the same whole-number "journeys."

EXERCISES
Here are the first four triangular numbers.

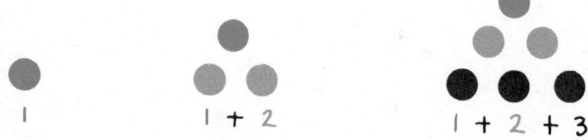

1   3   6   10

1. What is the fifth triangular number?   15
   The sixth triangular number? The seventh?   28
        21
2. Notice that each triangular number can be written as a
   sum.

   1   1 + 2   1 + 2 + 3

   Express the fourth triangular number as a sum.   1 + 2 + 3 + 4

3. Find the tenth triangular number by addition.   55
   Find the twentieth triangular number.   210

106

Assignments

Here are the first four square numbers.

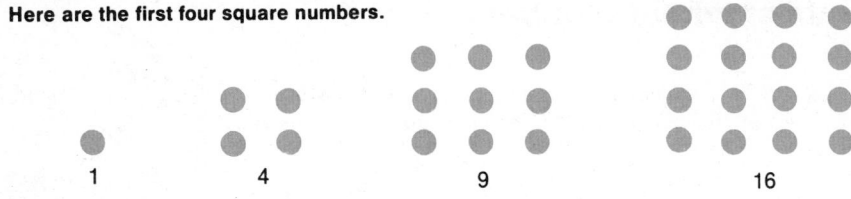

1 4 9 16

4. Give the next three square numbers.   25, 36, 49

Square numbers can also be written as a sum of odd numbers.
The set of odd numbers: {1, 3, 5, 7, 9, 11, . . .}

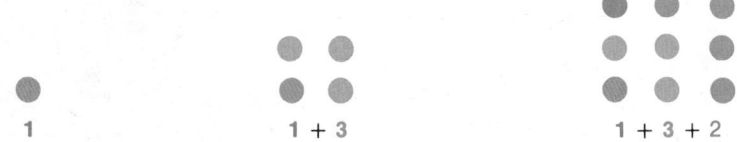

1   1 + 3   1 + 3 + 2

5. Write the next square number as a sum of odd numbers.   1 + 3 + 5 + 7

6. Find the eighth square number by addition.   64

7. Find the tenth square number by addition.   100

Here are the first four rectangular numbers. Notice that each
figure is one dot wider than it is high.

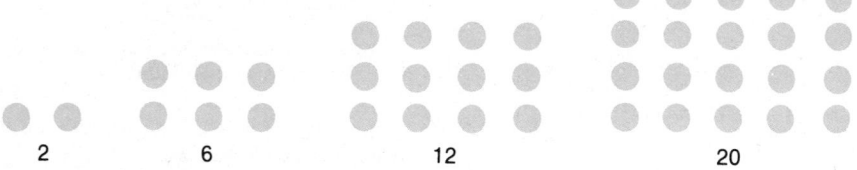

2   6   12   20

8. Find the next three rectangular numbers.   30, 42, 56

9. See if you can find a pattern for expressing the rectangular numbers as sums.
Find the tenth rectangular number by addition.   110

107

Follow-up Activities

Reinforcement You may wish to point out the set of all students in the class and have students identify the following:

1. The set of all students whose last names begin with *R*.
2. The set of all students whose first names begin with *J*.
3. The set of all students who wear glasses.
4. The set of all students who are wearing jeans.

Enrichment Ask students to find out about pentagonal numbers and report to the class. They might want to make a bulletin-board display of the various figurate numbers.

EXCURSION

1. What is the maximum number of pieces that can be obtained by slicing an orange with 1 cut?   2

2. What is the maximum number if 2 cuts are used?   4

3. What if 3 cuts are used?   8

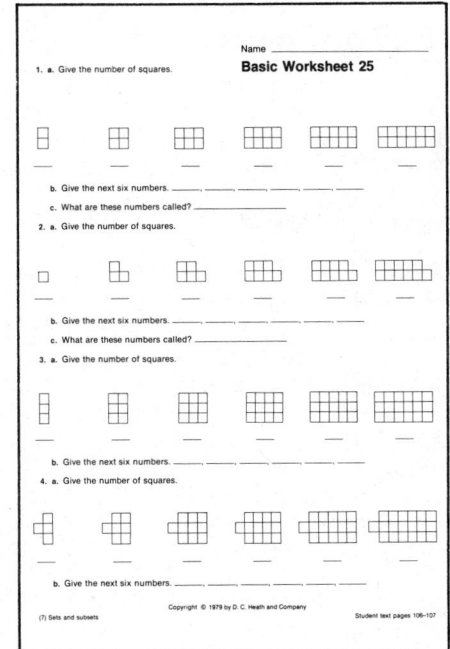

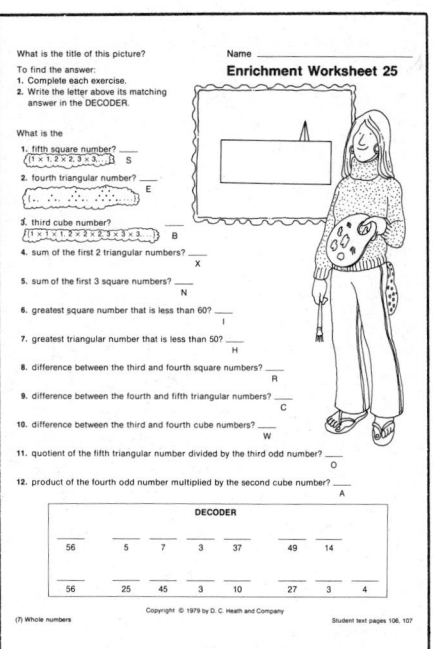

To determine whether a set is a subset of a second set.
To determine the members of the union of sets.
To determine the members of the intersection of sets.

VOCABULARY

empty set (∅), intersection (∩), subset, union (∪)

Suggested Lesson Plan

Introduction Your students will come with varying mathematical backgrounds, so for some the lesson will be a review and for others it will be new material.

Introduce the concept of subset. Tell students that you are thinking of two sets. One set contains John, Mary, William, and Sue. The other contains John and William. Be sure students note that all the elements of the second set are also elements of the first set. In such cases we say that the second set is a *subset* of the first set. Name other pairs of sets and have students determine whether one is a subset of the other. Write the word *subset* on the board.

Ask all of the students who have older brothers or sisters to stand. Tell students that you will call these students set *O*. Have them sit down and ask all students who have younger brothers or sisters to stand. Call this set *Y*. Ask all the students that were in both sets to stand; this is the set of students who have both older and younger siblings. Point out that this set of students is made up of those that were in both sets. This set is called the *intersection* of set *O* and set *Y*.

List the sets on the board and show the notation. For example:

O = {John, Amy, Bill, Jane, Doris}
Y = {Ann, Amy, Maria, Steve, Bill}
$O \cap Y$ = {Amy, Bill}

Now ask all the students who have *either* older or younger siblings to stand. Point out that this is the set of students who were in either set *O* or set *Y*. This set is called the *union* of set *O* and set *Y*. List the set on the board:

$O \cup Y$ = {John, Amy, Bill, Jane, Doris, Ann, Maria, Steve}

Using the pages Go over the exposition on page 108 to reinforce your introduction. Leave your examples and notation on the board.

Do exercises 1–5 with the class, and assign the rest for written work. If you wish, give a brief discussion of the empty set.

Have students complete the Keeping Skills Sharp during the class time.

Sets of whole numbers

Below are two sets of whole numbers. The elements of set *W* are the first 10 whole numbers. The elements of set *O* are the first 5 odd numbers.

$$W = \{0, 1, 2, 3, 4, 5, 6, 7, 8, 9\}$$
$$O = \{1, 3, 5, 7, 9\}$$

Since every element of set *O* is also an element of *W*, *O* is a **subset** of *W*. It is easy to see that *O* is a subset of *W* if we list the elements of each set inside loops like this:

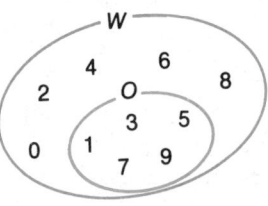

The elements of set *T* are the first 5 triangular numbers. The elements of set *E* are the first 6 even numbers.

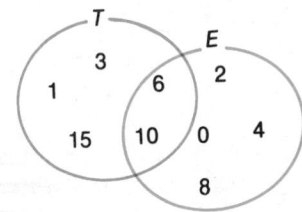

The **intersection** of sets *T* and *E* is the set of elements that are in both *T* and *E*.

We write: $T \cap E$ = {6, 10}

We read: *T* intersection *E* equals the set containing 6 and 10.

The **union** of sets *T* and *E* is the set of elements that are in *T* or in *E*, or in both.

We write: $T \cup E$ = {0, 1, 2, 3, 4, 6, 8, 10, 15}

We read: *T* union *E* equals the set containing 0, 1, 2, 3, 4, 6, 8, 10, and 15.

108

Answers for page 109.

9. $D \cap E$ = {0,12}
   $D \cup E$ = {0,2,3,4,5,6,8,9,10,12}
10. $R \cap S$ = {0,20}
    $R \cup S$ = {0,4,5,8,10,12,15,16,20}
11. $P \cap Q$ = {1,3,6}
    $P \cup Q$ = {1,2,3,4,5,6,10,15}
12. $Y \cap Z$ = ∅
    $Y \cup Z$ = {0,1,2,3,4,5,6,7,8,9,10}

Assignments

BASIC
page 108 Discuss
page 109 exercises 1–10, Keeping Skills Sharp
Basic Worksheet 26

AVERAGE
page 108 Discuss
page 109 exercises 1–12, Keeping Skills Sharp
Enrichment Worksheet 26

ENRICHED
page 108 Discuss
page 109 exercises 1–13, Keeping Skills Sharp
Enrichment Worksheet 26

REVIEW PRACTICE
page 380 set 28

EXERCISES
True or false?

1. The even numbers are a subset of the whole numbers. _true_

2. The whole numbers are a subset of the even numbers. _false_

3. The odd numbers are a subset of the even numbers. _false_

4. The triangular numbers are a subset of the odd numbers. _false_

Give the intersection and union.

$M \cap N = \{4\}$

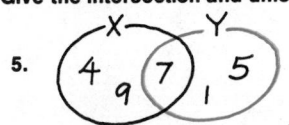

5.

$G \cap H = G$ $X \cap Y = \{7\}$
$G \cup H = H$ $X \cup Y = \{1,4,5,7,9\}$

6.

$M \cup N = \{2,3,4,6,7,9\}$

7.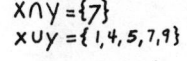

8.

$A \cap B = B$ $A \cup B = A$

9. D = {0,2,4,5,8,10,12}
   E = {0,3,6,9,12}

10. R = {0,5,10,15,20}
    S = {0,4,8,12,16,20}

11. P = {1,2,3,4,5,6}
    Q = {1,3,6,10,15}

12. Y = {0,2,4,6,8,10}
    Z = {1,3,5,7,9}

Hint: The empty set has no elements.
We write: $\varnothing$
We read: The empty set.

13. Try to find a quick way to find the sum of the first 50 odd numbers. 2500

$$1 = 1$$
$$1 + 3 = 4$$
$$1 + 3 + 5 = 9$$
$$1 + 3 + 5 + 7 = 16$$

Hint: What kind of number is each sum?

Keeping Skills Sharp

Round 793.576 to the nearest

1. hundred   800
2. tenth   793.6
3. hundredth 793.58
4. ten   790
5. one   794

Round 1509.7996 to the nearest

6. tenth   1509.8
7. one   1510
8. thousand   2000
9. hundred   1500
10. thousandth 1509.800

109

Follow-up Activities

Reinforcement You may wish to follow up the lesson with the following set game. Picture these sets on the chalkboard:

Divide the students into two teams, Team A and Team B. Have a player on Team A write a description of one of the elements on a slip of paper, for example, the large white circle. Have players on Team B ask questions until they determine the element. Here are some sample questions: Is it in the intersection of the two sets? Is it yellow? Is it a large figure? Each question must have a yes or no answer. Score a point for each question asked by a team. For example, if Team B asked five questions before they found out the element, Team B would get five points. The team getting the *fewer* points wins the game.

Enrichment Play the same game described above, using three sets. You may wish to restrict all questions to those involving intersections and unions.

EXCURSION

1. Get a sheet of notebook paper and fold it in half.

2. Fold it in half again.

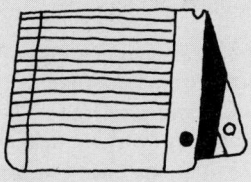

3. How many times do you think you can continue to fold the paper in half?

4. Check your guess.

5. Suppose that you started with a large sheet of newspaper. Guess how many folds you could make.

6. Check your guess.

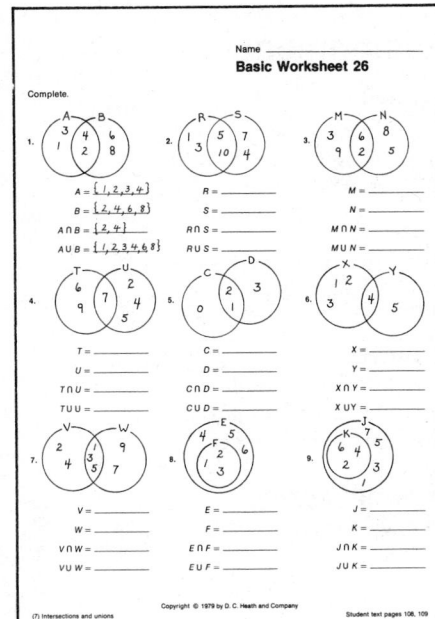

To identify factors of numbers.

To identify the common factors of two numbers.

To identify the greatest common factor (GCF) of two numbers.

To identify prime and composite numbers.

VOCABULARY

factor, common factor, greatest common factor (GCF), prime number, composite number

Suggested Lesson Plan

Introduction Remind students that 6 and 2 are *factors* of 12 because $2 \times 6 = 12$. Write 12 on the board and ask students for all the factors of 12. As they name the factors, write the factors beside the 12, using set notation. Ask if 5 is a factor of 12. (No, because there is no whole number that, multiplied by 5, gives 12.) Now ask students for all the factors of 18. As they are named, list them on the board using set notation.

12    $A = \{1, 2, 3, 4, 6, 12\}$

18    $B = \{1, 2, 3, 6, 9, 18\}$

$A \cap B = \{1, 2, 3, 6\}$

Now ask students for the intersection of set *A* and *B*. This is the set of common factors of 12 and 18. Ask students for the greatest number in this set. (6) This is called the *greatest common factor* (GCF) for 12 and 18.

Write other pairs of numbers on the board. For each, have students list (1) the set of factors for each number, (2) the set of common factors, and (3) the greatest common factor.

Using the pages Assign exercises 1–25 for written work. Let students review and think about prime and composite numbers by working through exercises 17–25. You may need to bring your poorer students together in a small group and work through the exercises together.

Factors

Both 2 and 4 are **factors**, or **divisors**, of 8. 3 is not a factor of 8 because there is no whole number that you can multiply by 3 to get 8.

The set of all factors of 8:

$X = \{1, 2, 4, 8\}$

The set of all factors of 12:

$Y = \{1, 2, 3, 4, 6, 12\}$

Notice that 1, 2, and 4 are in both sets of factors. They are **common factors** of 8 and 12.

The intersection of *X* and *Y* is the set of common factors of 8 and 12.

$X \cap Y = \{1, 2, 4\}$

The **greatest common factor** (GCF) of 8 and 12 is 4.

EXERCISES

Give the set of factors for each number.

1. 2   **2.** 9   **3.** 21   **4.** 36   **5.** 48   **6.** 50
{1, 2}   {1, 3, 9}   {1, 3, 7, 21}

4. {1,2,3,4,6,9,12,18,36}
5. {1,2,3,4,6,8,12,16,24,48}
6. {1,2,5,10,25,50}

Give the set of all common factors for each pair of numbers.

7. 6, 9   **8.** 12, 18   **9.** 15, 21   **10.** 36, 48   **11.** 8, 9   **12.** 24, 48
{1, 3}   {1, 2, 3, 6}   {1, 3}   {1,2,3,4,6,12} {1}

12. {1,2,3,4,6,8,12,24}

13. Give the GCF of each pair of numbers in exercises 7–12.   3, 6, 3, 12, 1, 24

14. Is it possible for two numbers to have no factors in common?   no

110

Assignments

BASIC

page 110 exercises 1–14
page 111 exercises 15–20
Basic Worksheet 27

AVERAGE

page 110 exercises 1–14
page 111 exercises 15–22
Enrichment Worksheet 27

ENRICHED

page 110 exercises 1–14
page 111 exercises 15–25
Enrichment Worksheet 27

EXTRA PRACTICE

page 382 set 38

Who am I?

15. I am a factor of every number. _1_

16. I am a common factor of every pair of numbers. _1_

17. Copy and complete. (You may wish to extend the table.)

Number	1	2	3	4	5	6	7	8	9	10
Factors	1	1, 2	1, 3	1,2,4	1,5	*	1,7	**	1,3,9	***
Number of factors	1	2	2	3	2	4	2	4	3	4

*1,2,3,6   **1,2,4,8   ***1,2,5,10

> Whole numbers with exactly 2 factors are called **prime numbers.**

> Whole numbers (other than 0) having more than 2 factors are called **composite numbers.**

18. Look at your completed table and give the first 4 prime numbers.
2,3,5,7

19. Give the first 12 prime numbers.
2,3,5,7,11,13,17,19,23,29,31,37

20. Give the first 12 composite numbers.
4,6,8,9,10,12,14,15,16,18,20,21

21. What is the smallest number that has exactly 3 factors?   4

22. What is the smallest number that has exactly 4 factors?   6

23. Give the greatest prime number that is less than 50.   47

24. Give the smallest composite number.   4

25. How many composite numbers are less than 50?   33

 Is 2311 a prime number?   yes

111

Reinforcement Have students copy and complete the following GCF table:

GCF	6	12	15	16	18	24	30	36
3	3	3	3	1	3	3	3	3
6	6	6	3	2	6	6	6	6
9	3	3	3	1	9	3	3	9
12	6	12	3	4	6	12	6	12
24	6	12	3	8	6	24	6	12

Enrichment Ask students to list the odd numbers from 7 through 49. Ask which numbers they listed can be expressed as the sum of three prime numbers. *Note:* The addends need not be different. Here are the first few:

$$7 = 2 + 2 + 3$$
$$9 = 3 + 3 + 3$$
$$11 = 3 + 3 + 5$$

Some students may wish to extend their lists.

CALCULATOR ACTIVITY
Have students devise a calculator sequence for finding out whether a large number is prime. (Divide by prime numbers starting with 2 and work toward the number looking for divisions without a remainder.)

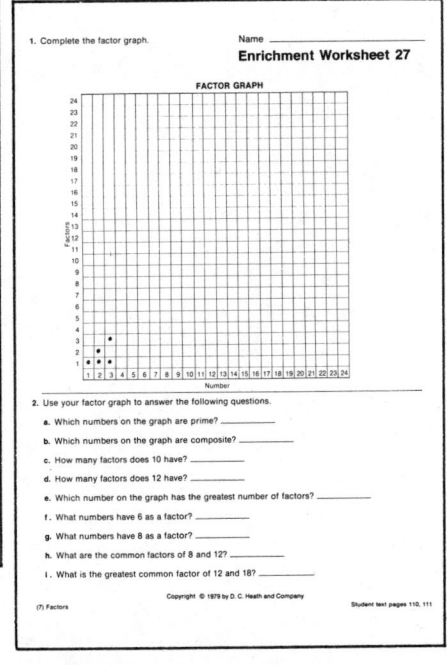

Basic Worksheet 27

Whole numbers with exactly two factors are called prime numbers.

Whole numbers (other than zero) with more than two factors are called composite numbers.

Complete this table.

	Whole number	Factors	Number of factors	Prime or composite?
1.	6	1,2,3,6	4	composite
2.	11			
3.	15			
4.	18			
5.	24			
6.	29			
7.	32			
8.	36			
9.	39			
10.	48			
11.	57			
12.	72			

Use your completed table to find the greatest common factor of each pair of numbers.

13. 6, 15 _____   14. 11, 15 _____   15. 15, 36 _____   16. 24, 32 _____

17. 36, 48 _____   18. 39, 57 _____   19. 6, 32 _____   20. 18, 24 _____

21. 18, 36 _____   22. 15, 18 _____   23. 32, 72 _____   24. 48, 72 _____

Enrichment Worksheet 27

1. Complete the factor graph.

FACTOR GRAPH

2. Use your factor graph to answer the following questions.

a. Which numbers on the graph are prime? _____

b. Which numbers on the graph are composite? _____

c. How many factors does 10 have? _____

d. How many factors does 12 have? _____

e. Which number on the graph has the greatest number of factors? _____

f. What numbers have 6 as a factor? _____

g. What numbers have 8 as a factor? _____

h. What are the common factors of 8 and 12? _____

i. What is the greatest common factor of 12 and 18? _____

(core) Lesson 47   111

To express any composite number as a product of prime numbers (prime factorization).

VOCABULARY
prime factorization

Suggested Lesson Plan

Introduction Write 36 on the board and ask a student to name two factors of 36. Show the two factors below the 36 and connect them with lines. Then

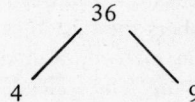

ask for pairs of factors for 4 and 9 (or the factors named). Continue until only prime factors remain. Tell students that this is called a *factor tree* and it gives you the prime factorization of a number.

Write several other numbers on the board and have students develop factor trees to find the prime factorization of the numbers. Point out that although students will have different factor trees since different factors will be chosen, the prime factorization of each number is unique.

Using the pages Assign exercises 1–24 for written work. Allow a few minutes at the end of the class for students to do the Keeping Skills Sharp. Correct the Keeping Skills Sharp in class and note any students who miss more than two.

Challenge students to do the Excursion.

Prime factorization

Every composite number can be factored into a product of prime numbers. Notice that the numbers in the bottom row of each **factor tree** are prime numbers.

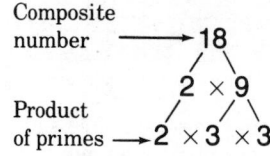

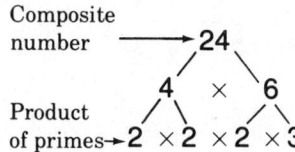

To express a composite number as a product of prime numbers is to give the **prime factorization** of the composite number.

prime factorization   prime factorization
18 = 2 × 3 × 3   24 = 2 × 2 × 2 × 3

Answers for page 113.

5. 2 x 3   6. 3 x 5   7. 3 x 7
8. 2 x 2 x 7   9. 2 x 2 x 2 x 2 x 2
10. 2 x 19   11. 2 x 3 x 7
12. 2 x 2 x 2 x 2 x 3   13. 2 x 5 x 5
14. 2 x 2 x 2 x 7
15. 2 x 2 x 2 x 2 x 2 x 2
16. 2 x 2 x 2 x 3 x 3
17. 2 x 2 x 2 x 2 x 5
18. 2 x 2 x 3 x 7
19. 2 x 2 x 2 x 2 x 2 x 3
20. 2 x 2 x 5 x 5
21. 2 x 2 x 2 x 2 x 7
22. 2 x 2 x 2 x 2 x 2 x 2 x 2
23. 2 x 2 x 3 x 11
24. 2 x 2 x 2 x 2 x 3 x 3

Assignments

BASIC
page 112 Discuss
page 113 exercises 1–15,
      Keeping Skills Sharp
Basic Worksheet 28

AVERAGE
page 112 Discuss
page 113 exercises 1–24,
      Keeping Skills Sharp
Enrichment Worksheet 28

ENRICHED
page 112 Discuss
page 113 exercises 1–24, Excursion
Enrichment Worksheet 28

EXTRA PRACTICE
page 382 set 39

EXERCISES

Copy and complete these factor trees.

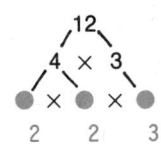

1.
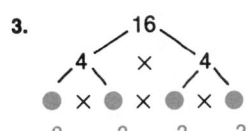

12
4 × 3
● × ● × ●
2   2   3

2.
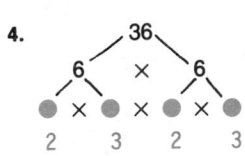

8
2 × 4
● × ● × ●
2   2   2

3.

16
4 × 4
● × ● × ● × ●
2   2   2   2

4.

36
6 × 6
● × ● × ● × ●
2   3   2   3

Give the prime factorization.

5. 6	**6.** 15	**7.** 21	**8.** 28
9. 32	**10.** 38	**11.** 42	**12.** 48
13. 50	**14.** 56	**15.** 64	**16.** 72
17. 80	**18.** 84	**19.** 96	**20.** 100
21. 112	**22.** 128	**23.** 132	**24.** 144

EXCURSION ●○●○●○●○●○●○●○●○●○●○●○●

Any even number greater than 2 can be expressed as a sum of two primes. (This was first proposed by a mathematician called Goldbach.)

$$4 = 2 + 2$$
$$6 = 3 + 3$$
$$8 = 3 + 5$$

Express other even numbers as the sum of two primes. 10 = 3 + 7, 12 = 5 + 7, 14 = 3 + 11, 16 = 3 + 13, 18 = 7 + 11, etc.

Keeping Skills Sharp

Give each sum or difference.

1. 3.86 + 2.59
   6.45
2. 7.09 − 3.14
   3.95
3. 2.678 + 3.259
   5.937
4. 9.1783 − 2.9999
   6.1784
5. 15.86 + 123.4
   139.26
6. 32.785 − 2.96
   29.825
7. 252 − 1.96
   250.04
8. 58.03 + 26.529
   84.559
9. 741.03 + 26.975
   768.005
10. 28.1 − 6.942
   21.158
11. 8.21 + 53.9
   62.11
12. 15.06 + 218.4
   233.46
13. 64.9 − 7.36
   57.54
14. 302.8 − 24.07
   278.73
15. 6.5 − 0.613
   5.887
16. 8.7 + 0.372
   9.072
17. 0.8 − 0.24
   0.56
18. 57 − 0.62
   56.38
19. 0.58 + 0.9
   1.48
20. 29 + 101.6
   130.6

113

Follow-up Activities

Reinforcement Have students work in pairs to make a chart for the numbers 1 to 100 showing either that the number is prime or the prime factorization of the number.

Enrichment Six is called a *perfect number* because all the factors of 6 (except 6) add up to the number. Have students find the next perfect number. (28)

EXCURSION

A closed network has no "loose ends."

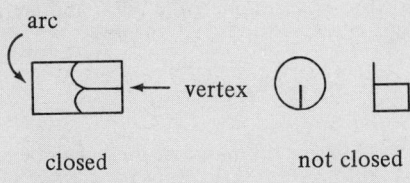

arc
← vertex

closed   not closed

A closed network is made up of *arcs*.

The point where two or more arcs meet is a *vertex*. This vertex has 4 "part arcs" meeting. Since 4 is an even number, we call the vertex an "even vertex."

This is an *odd vertex*. Why?

How many odd vertices and how many even vertices are there in each of these networks?

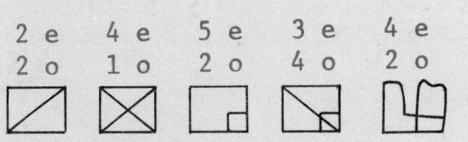

2 e	4 e	5 e	3 e	4 e
2 o	1 o	2 o	4 o	2 o

Draw other networks and give the number of odd vertices and even vertices.

Name _____
Basic Worksheet 28

Complete each factor tree. Do not use 1 as a factor. There is more than one way to complete each factor tree.

Name _____
Enrichment Worksheet 28

TRIVIA TIME
What are the names of Peter Rabbit's brothers and sisters?

(core) Lesson 48   **113**

STUDENT OBJECTIVES

To identify multiples of a number.

To identify common multiples of pairs of numbers.

To identify the least common multiple (LCM) of a pair of numbers.

VOCABULARY

multiples, common multiples, least common multiple, even numbers, odd numbers

Suggested Lesson Plan

Introduction Write this series of numbers on the board and ask students for the next number, the next, and so on.

0, 3, 6, 9, ____, ____, ____.

Ask for the name of these numbers. (multiples of 3) Ask similar questions for this sequence: 0, 5, 10, 15, ____, ____, ____. (multiples of 5) Ask students how this sequence is generated. (Multiply each whole number by 5) Point out that 0 is included in the set of multiples of a number.

Ask students for the multiples of 6. List them on the board. Ask for the multiples of 8 and list this set below the multiples of 6.

Multiples of 6 {0, 6, 12, 18, 24, 36, 42, . . .}

Multiples of 8 {0, 8, 16, 24, 32, 40, . . .}

Ask students to list the intersection of these two sets. {0, 24, 48, . . .}. Tell them that this set is called the *common multiples* of 6 and 8. This set is also the intersection of the sets of multiples of 6 and 8. Now ask for the least common multiple (not counting 0). (24) This is called the *least common multiple* or the *LCM.*

Using the pages Go over the exposition on page 114 to reinforce the introduction. Assign exercises 1–35 for written work.

Multiples

If you multiply the whole numbers by 3, you get the numbers shown in red. They are called **multiples of 3.**

Multiples of 3	0	1	2	3	4	5	6	7	8	9	10	11	12	13

Multiples of 4	0	1	2	3	4	5	6	7	8	9	10	11	12	13

The set of multiples of 3:

$A = \{0, 3, 6, 9, \ldots\}$

The set of multiples of 4:

$B = \{0, 4, 8, 12, \ldots\}$

The intersection of set A and set B is the set of **common multiples** of 3 and 4.

$A \cap B = \{0, 12, 24, \ldots\}$

The smallest common multiple, other than 0, is called the **least common multiple (LCM).** The least common multiple of 3 and 4 is 12.

EXERCISES

Give four multiples of each number.

1. 2 **2.** 3 **3.** 5 **4.** 7 **5.** 9 **6.** 12

0,2,4,6 0,3,6,9 0,5,10,15 0,7,14,21 0,9,18,27 0,12,24,36

Give two common multiples for each pair of numbers.

7. 2, 3 **8.** 3, 4 **9.** 2, 4 **10.** 5, 7 **11.** 10, 6 **12.** 3, 6

0,6 0,12 0,4 0,35 0,30 0,6

13. Give the LCM for each pair of numbers in exercises 7–12.

6 12 4 35 30 6

True or false?

14. Every number is a multiple of itself. true **15.** Every number is a factor of itself. true

16. 1 is a multiple of every number. false **17.** 1 is a factor of every number. true

114

Assignments

BASIC

page 114 exercises 1–17

page 115 exercises 18–29

Basic Worksheet 29

AVERAGE

page 114 exercises 1–17

page 115 exercises 18–33

Enrichment Worksheet 29

ENRICHED

page 114 exercises 13–17

page 115 exercises 18–35

Enrichment Worksheet 29

EXTRA PRACTICE

page 382 set 40

18. Every number is a multiple of 1. true

19. Every number is a factor of 1. false

20. 2 is a factor of 6. true

21. 6 is a multiple of 2. true

22. 5 is a factor of 10. true

23. 10 is a multiple of 5. true

24. 6 is a factor of 9. false

25. 9 is a multiple of 6. false

26. If a first number is a factor of a second number, then the second number is a multiple of the first number. true

Copy and complete.

27.
GCF
2
6 | 8
24
LCM

28.
GCF
3
6 | 9
18
LCM

29.
GCF
2
8 | 10
40
LCM

30.
GCF
6
12 | 18
36
LCM

31.
GCF
3
15 | 6
30
LCM

32.
GCF
8
24 | 16
48
LCM

33. In exercises 27–32, compare the product of the "green" numbers with the product of the "yellow" numbers. What did you find? They are the same.

34. Multiples of 2 are called **even numbers**. What can you say about the digit in the ones place of any even number? It is either 0, 2, 4, 6, or 8.

35. Whole numbers that are not even numbers are called **odd numbers**. What can you say about the digit in the ones place of any odd number? It is either 1, 3, 5, 7, or 9.

115

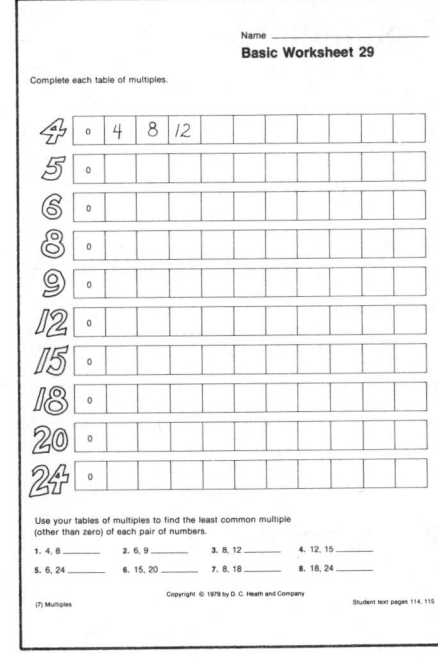
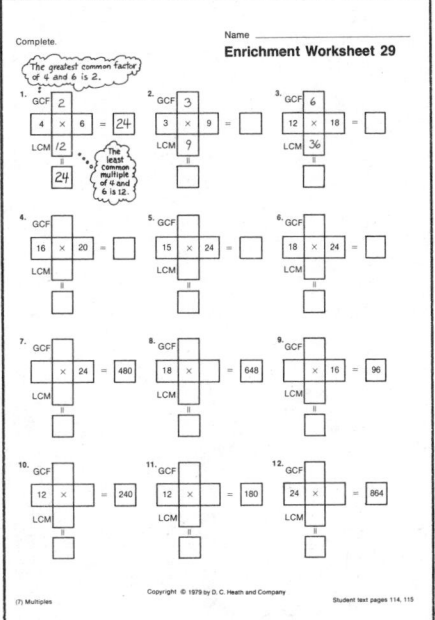

Follow-up Activities

Reinforcement Make a projectual for the overhead projector as shown.

0	1	2	3	4	5	6	7	8	9
10	11	12	13	14	15	16	17	18	19
20	21	22	23	24	25	26	27	28	29
30	31	32	33	34	. . . (Extend to 60.)				

Project it on the chalkboard. Ask a student to go to the chalkboard and mark off each multiple of 3 with a — . Then have another student go to the chalkboard and mark off each multiple of 5 with a / . Stress that the cells containing both — and / are those cells containing the common multiples of 3 and 5. Ask for the LCM of 3 and 5. Repeat the activity with other pairs of numbers.

Enrichment Prepare the following LCM table for students to complete. Ask them to look for patterns in their completed tables.

LCM	1	2	3	4	5	6	7	8	9
1	1	2	3	4	5	6	7	8	9
2	2	2	6	4	10	6	14	8	18
3	3	6	3	12	15	6	21	24	9
4	4	4	12	4	20	12	28	8	36
5	5	10	15	20	5	30	35	40	45
6	6	6	6	12	30	6	42	24	18
7	7	14	21	28	35	42	7	56	63
8	8	8	24	8	40	24	56	8	72
9	9	18	9	36	45	18	63	72	9

EXCURSION

Cross-number puzzle

¹2	²5
³8	1

Across

1. Has just 3 factors
3. Has just 5 factors

Down

1. Has just 6 factors
2. Has just 4 factors

(*Hint:* What kind of number has an odd number of factors?)

STUDENT OBJECTIVES
To use tests for divisibility by 2, 3, 4, and 5.
To solve word problems involving mathematics and careers.

Suggested Lesson Plan

Introduction Write these numbers on the board: 16, 48, 126, 348, 315, 879, and 1242. Ask which of the numbers are *divisible* by 2. Explain that *divisible* means that the remainder is zero when the number is divided by 2. Ask which numbers are divisible by 3. Let students identify the numbers without attempting to generalize the shortcuts for identifying the numbers. Continue by asking which are divisible by 4; by 5.

After the correct numbers have been identified, see if any students can express the shortcuts for testing for divisibility.

Using the pages Have students turn to page 116 for a formal description of the shortcuts for divisibility. Read through each description and write a few examples on the board to illustrate how to apply the shortcut. Assign exercises 1–22 for written work.

Pupils now turn to page 117 and discuss how fares for taxicabs are determined. Assign exercises 1–3, in which students determine total fares given the rules for the costs.

Divisibility

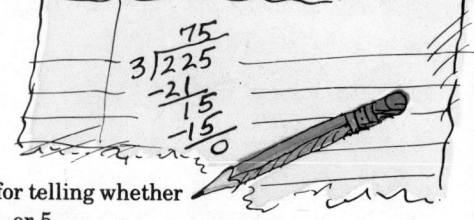

Since there is no remainder, we say that 225 is divisible by 3.

In this lesson you will learn some shortcuts for telling whether or not a whole number is divisible by 2, 3, 4, or 5.

A whole number is divisible by 2 if its last digit is divisible by 2. These numbers are divisible by 2:

7 5 3 **8**   2 9 6 **0**

A whole number is divisible by 3 if the sum of its digits is divisible by 3. These numbers are divisible by 3:

{1 + 3 + 2 + 6} {1 + 7 + 4 + 2 + 1}

1 3 2 6

A whole number is divisible by 4 if its last two digits are divisible by 4. These numbers are divisible by 4:

2 8   **3 6**

A whole number is divisible by 5 if its last digit is divisible by 5. These numbers are divisible by 5:

7 2 1 **0**   3 7 4 **5**

EXERCISES

Which of these numbers are divisible by 2? By 3? By 4? By 5?

5	2,3,4,5	3,5	2,4
2,3,4		2,3	2,4
2,3,5	2	3,5	2,5
2,4,5	2,4	2,3	2,4,5
3	5	2,4	2,3,4

21. See if you can find a rule for divisibility by 9. *Hint:* It is similar to the rule for divisibility by 3.

22. Can you find a rule for divisibility by 6?

116

Answers.

21. A whole number is divisible by 9 if the sum of its digits is divisible by 9.

22. A whole number is divisible by 6 if it is divisible by 2 and divisible by 3.

Assignments

BASIC
page 116 exercises 1–20
page 117 exercises 1–2
Basic Worksheet 30

AVERAGE
page 116 exercises 1–21
page 117 exercises 1–2
Enrichment Worksheet 30

ENRICHED
page 116 exercises 1–22
page 117 exercises 1–3
Enrichment Worksheet 30

REVIEW PRACTICE
page 380 set 30

Mathematics in careers

EXERCISES

1. In one city a taxi ride costs 25¢ for the first 0.1 kilometer and 10¢ for each additional 0.1 kilometer.

   a. How much is a 1-kilometer fare? $1.15
   b. How much is a 3.5-kilometer fare? $3.65
   c. How much is a 7-kilometer fare? $7.15

2. In another city a taxi ride costs 95¢ for the first 0.5 kilometer and 10¢ for each additional 0.1 kilometer. Compute the fare for

   a. 2.4 kilometers. $2.85
   b. 1.9 kilometers. $2.35
   c. 6.3 kilometers. $6.75

3. Suppose that a taxi ride costs 95¢ for the first 0.5 kilometer and 10¢ for each additional 0.1 kilometer. How far could a passenger ride for $4.25? 3.8 km

117

Follow-up Activities

Reinforcement Give students several large numbers and have them decide whether the numbers are divisible by 2, 3, 4, and 5.

Enrichment Students should examine divisibility rules for 6, 7, 9, 10, 11, 12, and 20, and try to devise shortcut rules that will work for these numbers. Give them time to report back to the class on any rules that appear to be actual shortcuts.

EXCURSION
What is the difference between the 1st and 2nd square numbers? The 2nd and 3rd? The 3rd and 4th? Can you give a rule?

3, 5, 7; $2n + 1$, where n^2 is the smaller square number.

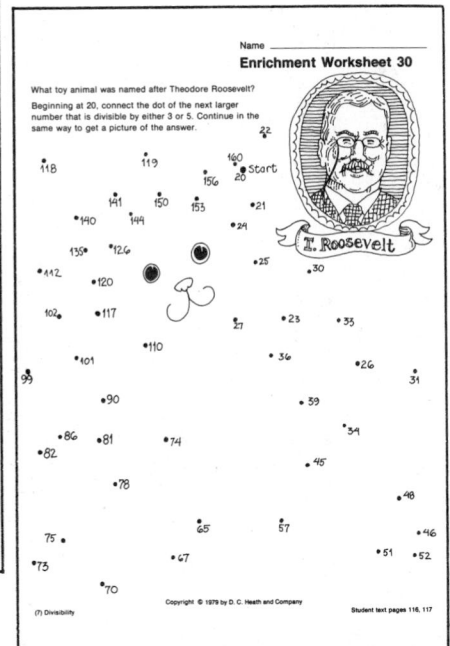

To replace variables with numbers.
To simplify expressions involving basic
operations.
To write expressions with variables for
English expressions.

VOCABULARY
variable, substitute, simplify

Suggested Lesson Plan

Introduction Write this expression on
the board:

$$7 + \square$$

Ask a student what number the whole
expression stands for if an 8 is written in
the box. (15) Repeat with several other
numbers. Tell students that the box is
called a *placeholder*, because it holds
the place for a number. Usually
mathematicians use letters of the
alphabet rather than boxes as
placeholders. These letters are called
variables, since they vary in value. Tell
students that the word that is used to
mean "replace the variable" is
"substitute." Write this expression on
the board:

$$3 \times b$$

Ask a student to go to the board and
substitute 7 for *b*. (3×7) Then ask him
to *simplify the expression*—that is, write
the simplest expression for the number.
(21)

Using the pages Go over the
exposition at the top of page 118 to give
students other examples. Assign the
exercises.
Exercises 31—46 are intended to
help students to begin to translate from
the English language to mathematical
expressions.

Variables

The letter *m* in the expression is a
variable.

If we **substitute** a 5 for *m*, we get the expression shown. After we substitute we
can **simplify** the expression. To simplify
the expression is to write the simplest
numeral for the number. When we simplify we get 12.

Study this example.

First, substitute for the variables. Then,
simplify the expression.

A	a	n
5	2	4

$$(A + a) - n$$

Substitute: $(5 + 2) - 4$
Simplify: 3

EXERCISES
Substitute and simplify.

b	B	C	g	r
2	0	6	7	3

1. $5 + C$ 11   2. $8 \times g$ 56   3. $C \times 4$ 24   4. $C \div 2$ 3   5. $B \times 10$ 0

6. $B + r$ 3   7. $C + g$ 13   8. $g + C$ 13   9. $r + g + C$ 16   10. $(C + g) - b$
                                                                              11

118

Substitute and simplify.

a	b	D	d	S	T
9	6	7	8	5	4

11. $a \times b$ 54   12. $D \times d$ 56   13. $3 \times S$ 15   14. $5 \times T$ 20   15. $b \times d$ 48

16. $d \times b$ 48   17. $a \times d$ 72   18. $D + d$ 15   19. $d + S$ 13   20. $13 - a$ 4

21. $17 - D$ 10   22. $12 - d$ 4   23. $b \times D$ 42   24. $2 \times S \times a$ 90   25. $(D + d) - a$ 6

26. Substitute your age in years for n and simplify.
    a. In 5 years I will be $n + 5$ years
    b. 6 years ago I was $n - 6$ years old.

27. Substitute your weight in kilograms for w and simplify.
    a. If I lose 4 kilograms, I will weigh $w - 4$ kilograms.
    b. If I gain 3 kilograms, I will weigh $w + 3$ kilograms.

Let h be your height in centimeters. Write an expression for a height that is

28. 5 centimeters less. $h - 5$

29. 8 centimeters more. $h + 8$

30. 2 times as much. $2 \times h$

Write an expression for

31. 4 more than a number n. $n + 4$ 32. 6 more than a number x. $x + 6$

33. 7 less than a number y. $y - 7$ 34. 12 less than a number y. $y - 12$

35. a number x increased by 3. $x + 3$ 36. a number y increased by 5. $y + 5$

37. a number r decreased by 1. $r - 1$ 38. a number z decreased by 3. $z - 3$

39. 5 times a number b. $5 \times b$ 40. 6 times a number x. $6 \times x$

41. the sum of a number m and 9. $m + 9$ 42. the product of 5 and a number y. $5 \times y$

43. 7 subtracted from a number c. $c - 7$ 44. a number a divided by 2. $a \div 2$

45. 6 divided by a number d. $6 \div d$ ★46. 3 less than 6 times a number m. $(6 \times m) - 3$

119

Follow-up Activities

Reinforcement At this time you may wish to introduce the headline activity, which relates an expression to a story. One version of the headline activity is to give an expression and ask students to create stories to go with the headline. Write this headline on the chalkboard:

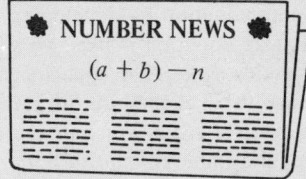

❀ NUMBER NEWS ❀

$(a + b) - n$

Ask students to create stories for the headline. Here are some sample stories:

1. I had a dollars and then earned b more dollars. I spent n dollars.
2. The first time Jerry carried the ball he gained a yards. The second time he carried the ball he gained b yards. On his next carry he lost n yards.

Enrichment Have students create some stories for this headline.

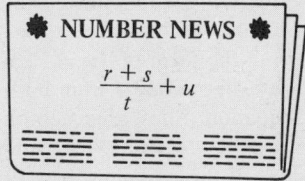

❀ NUMBER NEWS ❀

$\dfrac{r + s}{t} + u$

EXCURSION
On these maps two regions that share a boundary must have different colors. (Regions that touch only at a point may have the same color.)

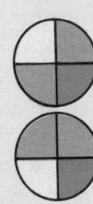

This map is colored correctly.

This map is not colored correctly.

What is the least number of colors needed to color these maps? 2, 3, 2, 3, 2

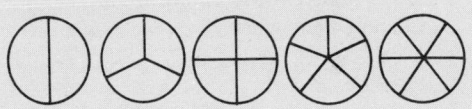

Can you make a rule about the number of colors needed for maps like these?

Even number of regions requires two colors, odd number of regions requires three colors.

Suggested Lesson Plan

Introduction Introduce the concept of solving an equation by developing the idea that an equation is like two weights on a balance scale. The equals sign says that these two weights are the same. As with a balance scale, you can add or subtract the same amount to both sides of the equation without destroying the equality.

Using the pages Have students turn to page 120 and use the pictures of the balance scale to develop the idea that an equation is like a balanced scale. Show that adding the same number to both sides does not destroy the balance and that subtracting from both sides does not destroy the balance.

Write the equation $n + 4 = 15$ on the board. Explain that in order to see what value for n would make the equation true, we have to get the equation in the form of "$n =$." We can do this by subtracting 4 from both sides of the equation. Show this step on the board: $n + 4 - 4 = 15 - 4$. Simplify both sides of the equation: $n = 11$.

Work through similar steps with the equation $n - 6 = 20$. Point out to students that since n has had 6 subtracted from it, we add 6 to both sides of the equation to *solve* the equation.

Write several more equations on the board and have students work at their desks while you solve them on the board.

Assign exercises 1–40. Be sure students show all their steps on their paper so that you can be sure they are thinking through the process rather than jumping to the solution.

Have students work the Keeping Skills Sharp at the end of the period. Correct their work.

Solving addition and subtraction equations

If we let n be the number of marbles in the box that is closed we get the equation

$$n + 3 = 11$$

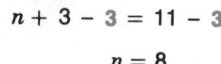

To **solve** the equation is to find the number that we can substitute for n to make the equation true.

To solve the equation we can subtract 3 from *both sides* and then simplify both sides.

To check the solution we substitute 8 for n in the first equation. Since the equation is true, it checks!

To solve this equation we can add 6 to *both sides* and then simplify both sides.

$$n + 3 = 11$$

$$n + 3 - 3 = 11 - 3$$
$$n = 8$$

Check: $8 + 3 = 11$

$$m - 6 = 17$$
$$m - 6 + 6 = 17 + 6$$
$$m = 23$$
Check: $23 - 6 = 17$

120

Assignments

BASIC
page 120 Discuss
page 121 exercises 1–20,
    Keeping Skills Sharp
Basic Worksheet 32

AVERAGE
page 120 Discuss
page 121 exercises 1–30,
    Keeping Skills Sharp
Enrichment Worksheet 32

ENRICHED
page 120 Discuss
page 121 exercises 10–40,
    Keeping Skills Sharp
Enrichment Worksheet 32

EXTRA PRACTICE
page 383 set 41

EXERCISES

Solve and check.

1. $n + 6 = 23$ $n = 17$
   Hint: Subtract 6 from both sides.

2. $8 + n = 37$ $n = 29$
   Hint: Subtract 8 from both sides.

3. $x + 7 = 19$ $x = 12$

4. $11 + n = 27$ $n = 16$

5. $10 + h = 38$ $h = 28$

6. $z + 19 = 29$ $z = 10$

7. $y + 18 = 46$ $y = 28$

8. $15 + t = 31$ $t = 16$

9. $17 + y = 35$ $y = 18$

10. $s + 23 = 29$ $s = 6$

11. $r + 37 = 43$ $r = 6$

12. $27 + w = 52$ $w = 25$

13. $42 + n = 73$ $n = 31$

14. $38 + k = 95$ $k = 57$

15. $14 + x = 29$ $x = 15$

16. $43 + y = 102$ $y = 59$

17. $n - 28 = 35$ $n = 63$
    Hint: Add 28 to both sides.

18. $k - 42 = 39$ $k = 81$
    Hint: Add 42 to both sides.

19. $a - 18 = 19$ $a = 37$

20. $h - 23 = 16$ $h = 39$

21. $e - 27 = 23$ $e = 50$

22. $r - 15 = 25$ $r = 40$

23. $k - 32 = 28$ $k = 60$

24. $b - 35 = 73$ $b = 108$

25. $d - 42 = 32$ $d = 74$

26. $g - 33 = 26$ $g = 59$

27. $x - 30 = 53$ $x = 83$

28. $s - 39 = 61$ $s = 100$

29. $f - 28 = 45$ $f = 73$

30. $c - 46 = 58$ $c = 104$

31. $y - 47 = 40$ $y = 87$

32. $j - 52 = 27$ $j = 79$

33. $x + 17 = 32$ $x = 15$

34. $a - 62 = 41$ $a = 103$

35. $n - 58 = 19$ $n = 77$

36. $x - 72 = 53$ $x = 125$

37. $a - 8 = 35$ $a = 43$

38. $r - 15 = 69$ $r = 84$

★ 39. $14 - a = 9$ $a = 5$

★ 40. $65 - x = 27$ $x = 38$

Multiply.

1.
$$\begin{array}{r} 3.8 \\ \times 1.6 \\ \hline 6.08 \end{array}$$

2.
$$\begin{array}{r} 27 \\ \times 2.3 \\ \hline 62.1 \end{array}$$

3.
$$\begin{array}{r} 38.2 \\ \times 3.8 \\ \hline 145.16 \end{array}$$

4.
$$\begin{array}{r} 6.75 \\ \times 0.14 \\ \hline 0.945 \end{array}$$

5.
$$\begin{array}{r} 396 \\ \times 0.25 \\ \hline 99 \end{array}$$

6.
$$\begin{array}{r} 7.53 \\ \times 3.8 \\ \hline 28.614 \end{array}$$

7.
$$\begin{array}{r} 0.8354 \\ \times 6.14 \\ \hline 5.129356 \end{array}$$

8.
$$\begin{array}{r} 25.35 \\ \times 1.05 \\ \hline 26.6175 \end{array}$$

9.
$$\begin{array}{r} 7.493 \\ \times 3.07 \\ \hline 23.00351 \end{array}$$

10.
$$\begin{array}{r} 0.0395 \\ \times 0.101 \\ \hline 0.0039895 \end{array}$$

121

Follow-up Activities

Reinforcement Have students write a story for the following headline:

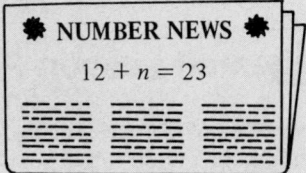

❋ **NUMBER NEWS** ❋
$12 + n = 23$

Here are some sample answers:

1. Janet hiked 12 miles the first day and n miles the second day. Altogether she hiked 23 miles.
2. Mr. Trotter had $23. He gave $12 to his son and kept $$n$.

Enrichment You may wish more able students to see how many equations they can write that have a particular solution. For example, you might have them write equations having the solution 4. Here are some examples:

1. $x + 9 = 13$
2. $48 \div 12 = n$
3. $2k + 6 = 14$

EXCURSION

What is the minimum number of colors needed to color each map? (See page 119.)

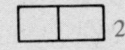 2

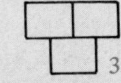 3

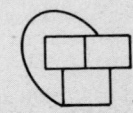 4

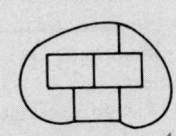 4

Can you find a map that needs 5 different colors?

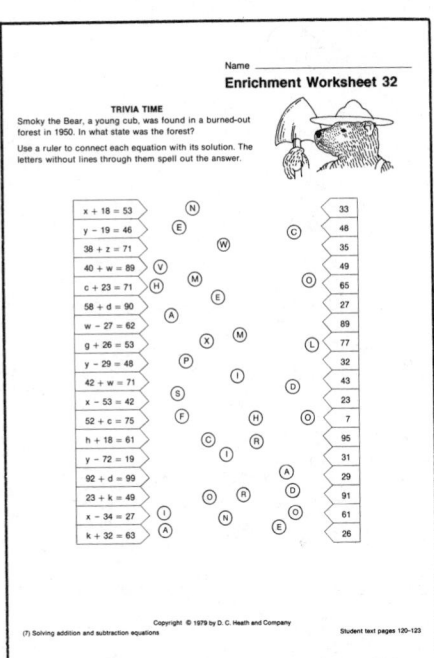

To write an equation for a word
problem.
To solve the equation to find the answer
to the word problem.

Suggested Lesson Plan

Introduction   While many of these
problems can be done with a simple
computation, the objective is to get
pupils to write an equation that
describes the relationship between the
quantities in the problem, and then to
solve the equation. Although students
may resist the writing of an equation for
problems they can already do, they need
to develop the skill because, when the
problem and the relationship become
more complex, the equation becomes an
important tool in problem solving.

Using the pages   Work through
example 1, following the steps
described. Be sure to point out to
students that the answer alone is not
acceptable. They must show an
equation, the solution to the equation,
and finally the labeled answer.

There are several correct equations
for each problem, but try to get students
to write the equation that expresses the
relationship or the action in the problem
rather than the operation needed to find
the answer. For example, both of the
equations $n + 8 = 23$ and $23 - 8 = n$
would find the answer for exercise 1,
but the first equation expresses the
relationship as it is presented in the
problem.

Assign exercises 2–6 for written
work. You may want to group your poor
readers and read through the problems
together.

Equations in problem solving

The pony express carried mail from St.
Joseph, Missouri, to Sacramento, California, a distance of 1966 miles. In 1860
this ad appeared in a newspaper:

WANTED - Young, skinny, wiry fellows
not over 18. Must be expert riders willing to risk death.

To solve each problem:

1. Write an equation.
2. Solve the equation.
3. Check the solution in the problem.

Equations may vary.

1. Two of the most famous men who
worked for the pony express were
James B. "Wild Bill" Hickok and William F. Cody, "Buffalo Bill." When
they were hired, Wild Bill Hickok was
23 years old. He was 8 years older
than Buffalo Bill. How old was Buffalo Bill?   15 years

Buffalo	Wild
Bill's	Bill's
age	age
↓	↓

Hint: $n + 8 = 23$

2. The pony express had a weight limit
of 125 pounds for their riders. Wild
Bill Hickok weighed about 33 pounds
more than the limit. How much did he
weigh?
$125 + 33 = n$, 158 pounds

122

3. At one time a total of 477 men worked
for the pony express. Of these, 79
were riders and the rest worked at
the relay stations. How many worked
at the relay stations?
$79 + n = 477$, 398

4. By Overland Mail, a letter from St.
Joseph, Missouri, to Sacramento
took 21 days. This was 9 days longer
than by pony express. How many
days did it take by pony express?
$n + 9 = 21$, 12

5. The distance between relay stations
was about 11 miles. After a rider
reached the first relay station, he still
had about 64 miles left to ride. About
how far did each rider ride?
$11 + 64 = n$, 75 miles

6. The record time of 185 hours was set
when the pony express carried Lin-
coln's inaugural address. It took 55
hours less than the first trip. How
long did it take to make the first trip?
$185 - 55 = n$, 240 hours

Assignments

BASIC
page 122 exercises 1–5
Basic Worksheet 32

AVERAGE
page 122 exercises 1–6
Enrichment Worksheet 32

ENRICHED
page 122 exercises 1–6
Enrichment Worksheet 32

REVIEW PRACTICE
page 381 set 32

BUFFALO BILL'S FIRST TRAIL,

OR

WILL CODY

THE

PONY EXPRESS RIDER

BY

NED BUNTLINE

123

Follow-up Activities

Reinforcement Have students look up the pony express in an encyclopedia and then write two new problems with the information they find.

Enrichment Students can use the *Guinness Book of World Records* to develop a series of word problems around a theme. Let students select their better problems and write them on a duplicating master. Run off copies and have students solve the problems for a written assignment.

EXCURSION

A tetromino is made of 4 squares joined along edges.

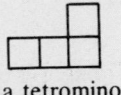

a tetromino

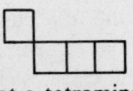

not a tetromino

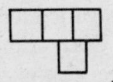

not a tetromino

These are the same tetromino because each can be cut out and fitted on the others.

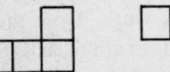 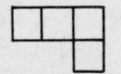 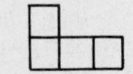

How many different tetrominos can you draw?

5

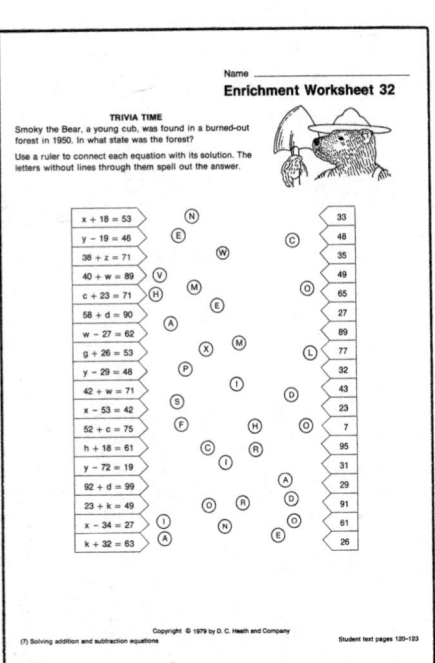

Name

Basic Worksheet 32

Example 1.

$n + 17 = 42$

$n + 17 - 17 = 42 - 17$ [Subtract 17]

$n = 25$ [Simplify]

Check: $25 + 17 = 42$

Example 2.

$n - 15 = 39$

$n - 15 + 15 = 39 + 15$ [Add 15]

$n = 54$ [Simplify]

Check: $54 - 15 = 39$

Solve and check.

1. $n + 19 = 37$
   $n + 19 - 19 = 37 - 19$
   $n = 18$
   Check: $18 + 19 = 37$

2. $n + 28 = 53$

3. $n + 31 = 49$

4. $n + 16 = 83$

5. $n + 52 = 97$

6. $n + 45 = 74$

7. $n - 15 = 21$

8. $n - 32 = 27$

9. $n - 53 = 45$

10. $n - 45 = 53$

11. $n - 39 = 67$

12. $n - 29 = 72$

13. $n + 53 = 105$

14. $n - 53 = 105$

15. $n + 42 = 112$

16. $n - 42 = 112$

17. $n + 82 = 127$

18. $n - 82 = 127$

Copyright © 1979 by D. C. Heath and Company

(7) Solving addition and subtraction equations

Student text pages 120–123

Name

Enrichment Worksheet 32

TRIVIA TIME

Smoky the Bear, a young cub, was found in a burned-out forest in 1950. In what state was the forest?

Use a ruler to connect each equation with its solution. The letters without lines through them spell out the answer.

$x + 18 = 53$		33
$y - 19 = 46$		48
$38 + z = 71$		35
$40 + w = 89$		49
$c + 23 = 71$		65
$58 + d = 90$		27
$w - 27 = 62$		89
$g + 26 = 53$		77
$y - 29 = 48$		32
$42 + w = 71$		43
$x - 53 = 42$		23
$52 + c = 75$		7
$h + 18 = 61$		95
$y - 72 = 19$		31
$92 + d = 99$		29
$23 + k = 49$		91
$x - 34 = 27$		61
$k + 32 = 63$		26

Copyright © 1979 by D. C. Heath and Company

(7) Solving addition and subtraction equations

Student text pages 120–123

(core) Lesson 53   123

Suggested Lesson Plan

Introduction Put the equation $4x = 20$ on the board. Be sure students realize that $4x$ means $4 \times x$. Ask students what the solution is. They will probably be able to tell you—5. Now put the equation $2x = 10$ on the board, and ask whether 5 is a solution of this equation also. (Yes) Ask what you did to the first equation to get the second. (Divided by 2) Point out that dividing both sides of the equation by the same number did not change the solution. Repeat with several other examples, multiplying and dividing both sides by the same number each time.

Using the pages Go over the exposition on page 124 carefully, emphasizing the importance of the check. Do some of exercises 1—6 on the board with the class, or have various students do so. Ask students to explain each step. Assign exercises 7—33 for written work. Correct the work in class if there is time. You may want to assign exercises 34—37 for homework.

Allow some time at the end of the class for students to take the Keeping Skills Sharp quiz. Correct the exercises as they complete their work. Note the students who miss four or more and plan to set up a regular maintenance program for these students.

Solving multiplication equations

Each box contains the same number of marbles. If we let n be the number of marbles in each box, we get the equation

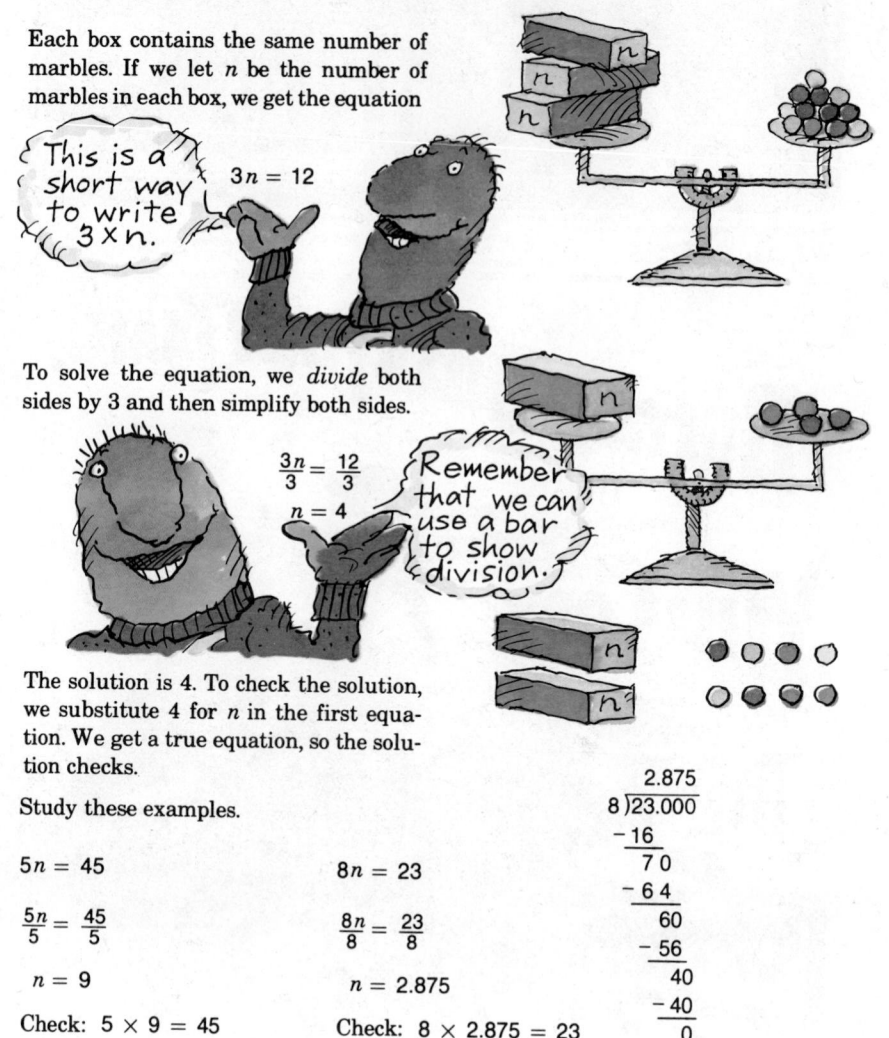

This is a short way to write $3 \times n$.

$3n = 12$

To solve the equation, we *divide* both sides by 3 and then simplify both sides.

$$\frac{3n}{3} = \frac{12}{3}$$
$$n = 4$$

Remember that we can use a bar to show division.

The solution is 4. To check the solution, we substitute 4 for n in the first equation. We get a true equation, so the solution checks.

Study these examples.

$5n = 45$

$$\frac{5n}{5} = \frac{45}{5}$$

$n = 9$

Check: $5 \times 9 = 45$

$8n = 23$

$$\frac{8n}{8} = \frac{23}{8}$$

$n = 2.875$

Check: $8 \times 2.875 = 23$

```
       2.875
   8 )23.000
     - 16
        7 0
       - 6 4
          60
         - 56
           40
          - 40
            0
```

124

Assignments

BASIC
page 124 Discuss
page 125 exercises 1—33,
       Keeping Skills Sharp
Basic Worksheet 33

AVERAGE
page 124 Discuss
page 125 exercises 1—35,
       Keeping Skills Sharp
Enrichment Worksheet 33

ENRICHED
page 124 Discuss
page 125 exercises 10—37,
       Keeping Skills Sharp
Enrichment Worksheet 33

EXTRA PRACTICE
page 383 set 42

EXERCISES

Solve and check.

1. $4n = 24$ 6
2. $5n = 30$ 6
3. $6n = 42$ 7
4. $3y = 21$ 7
5. $2n = 12$ 6
6. $8k = 88$ 11
7. $5z = 50$ 10
8. $7n = 70$ 10
9. $4x = 28$ 7
10. $8w = 120$ 15
11. $4j = 48$ 12
12. $9y = 108$ 12
13. $2n = 18$ 9
14. $6n = 72$ 12
15. $7n = 91$ 13
16. $3n = 51$ 17
17. $3x = 45$ 15
18. $6n = 120$ 20

Solve and check. Give the solution as a decimal.

19. $2j = 19$ 9.5
20. $8w = 20$ 2.5
21. $10c = 43$ 4.3
22. $8x = 44$ 5.5
23. $2k = 57$ 28.5
24. $4m = 49$ 12.25
25. $8t = 7$ 0.875
26. $4y = 9$ 2.25
27. $10r = 58$ 5.8
28. $20v = 58$ 2.9
29. $12s = 75$ 6.25
30. $25z = 140$ 5.6
31. $4n = 33$ 8.25
32. $8x = 3$ 0.375
33. $4w = 23$ 5.75

Find the number by writing and solving an equation. Check the solution in the problem.

I AM THINKING OF A NUMBER

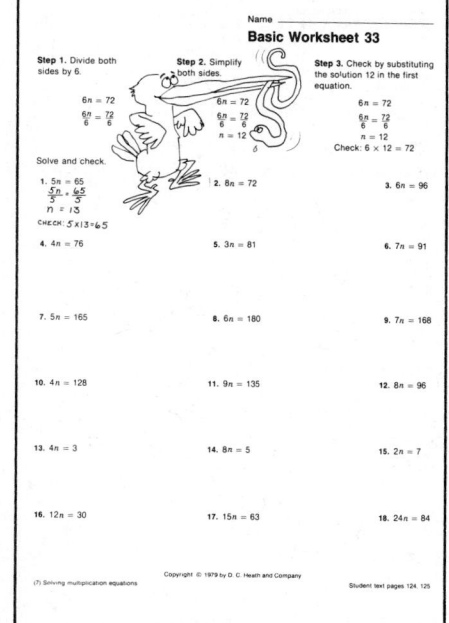

34. If I multiply it by 3, I get 42. 14
35. If I multiply it by 4, I get 39. 9.75
36. If I add 19 to it, I get 57. 38
37. If I subtract 37 from it, I get 74. 111

Keeping Skills Sharp

Divide.

1. $2.1\overline{)20.223}$ 9.63
2. $1.1\overline{)3.916}$ 3.56
3. $0.30\overline{)16.110}$ 53.7
4. $3.2\overline{)2.1312}$ 0.666
5. $50\overline{)458.50}$ 9.17
6. $6.3\overline{)505.89}$ 80.3
7. $5.8\overline{)25.346}$ 4.37
8. $0.62\overline{)14.88}$ 24
9. $36\overline{)26.568}$ 0.738
10. $0.046\overline{)3.1326}$ 68.1
11. $78.4\overline{)337.12}$ 4.3
12. $9.21\overline{)66.312}$ 7.2
13. $0.803\overline{)39.347}$ 49
14. $6.25\overline{)331.25}$ 53
15. $35.4\overline{)71.862}$ 2.03
16. $4.26\overline{)148.248}$ 34.8

125

Follow-up Activities

Reinforcement Ask students to make up a true equation. For example, $5 \times 4 = 20$. Then have them erase one of the numerals and replace it with a letter. For example, $5n = 20$. Next ask students to exchange papers and solve each other's equations.

Enrichment You may wish to follow up the lesson with this equation game. Divide students into two well-balanced teams. Ask each student to first write a true equation and then erase one of the numerals and replace it with a letter. (At this point each player should have an equation that has a solution.) Call a player from each team to the chalkboard. Have them exchange equations. The player who solves his equation first earns one point for his team. After all players have competed, the team with the greater number of points wins the game.

EXCURSION

Give the next number in each sequence by using the given rule.

Rule	Sequence
Add 7.	$1, 8, 15, 22, 29, 36, ?$ 43
Multiply by 2.	$1, 2, 4, 8, 16, 32, ?$ 64
Add 7, then multiply by 2.	$\{1 + 7 = 8, 8 \times 2 = 16\}$ $1, 16, 46, 106, 226, 466, ?$ 946
Multiply by 2, then add 7.	$\{1 \times 2 = 2, 2 + 7 = 9\}$ $1, 9, 25, 57, 121, 249, ?$ 505

Basic Worksheet 33

Name _____

Step 1. Divide both sides by 6.

$6n = 72$
$\frac{6n}{6} = \frac{72}{6}$

Step 2. Simplify both sides.

$6n = 72$
$\frac{6n}{6} = \frac{72}{6}$
$n = 12$

Step 3. Check by substituting the solution 12 in the first equation.

$6n = 72$
$\frac{6n}{6} = \frac{72}{6}$
$n = 12$
Check: $6 \times 12 = 72$

Solve and check.

1. $5n = 65$
$\frac{5n}{5} = \frac{65}{5}$
$n = 13$
CHECK: $5 \times 13 = 65$
2. $8n = 72$
3. $6n = 96$
4. $4n = 76$
5. $3n = 81$
6. $7n = 91$
7. $5n = 165$
8. $6n = 180$
9. $7n = 168$
10. $4n = 128$
11. $9n = 135$
12. $8n = 96$
13. $4n = 3$
14. $8n = 5$
15. $2n = 7$
16. $12n = 30$
17. $15n = 63$
18. $24n = 84$

(7) Solving multiplication equations Copyright © 1979 by D. C. Heath and Company Student text pages 124, 125

Enrichment Worksheet 33

The following examples show how to solve two-step equations.

Name _____

$5n + 7 = 22$
$5n + 7 - 7 = 22 - 7$
$5n = 15$
To get 5n as one side of the equation, subtract 7 from both sides.

$\frac{5n}{5} = \frac{15}{5}$
$n = 3$
Divide both sides by 5.

Check: $5(3) + 7 = 22$

$4n - 6 = 30$
$4n - 6 + 6 = 30 + 6$
$4n = 36$

$\frac{4n}{4} = \frac{36}{4}$
$n = 9$

Check: $4(9) - 6 = 30$

Solve and check.

1. $4n + 9 = 21$
2. $3n + 2 = 26$
3. $2n + 7 = 25$
4. $6n + 7 = 49$
5. $8n + 16 = 64$
6. $7n + 9 = 30$
7. $9n + 5 = 23$
8. $5n + 8 = 33$
9. $6n + 3 = 27$
10. $4n - 3 = 33$
11. $6n - 11 = 19$
12. $3n - 4 = 11$
13. $7n - 12 = 37$
14. $5n - 9 = 21$
15. $8n - 6 = 50$
16. $5n - 13 = 27$
17. $4n - 4 = 28$
18. $9n - 6 = 57$

(7) Solving multiplication equations Copyright © 1979 by D. C. Heath and Company Student text pages 124, 125

STUDENT OBJECTIVES
To name product expressions using exponents.
To write the standard numeral for an exponent name.
To solve word problems involving mathematics and science.

VOCABULARY
exponent, power, scientific notation

Suggested Lesson Plan

Introduction Tell students that most mathematicians are basically creative and hardworking as well as efficient. Being efficient, most of them don't like to write long, complex expressions over and over again when they can find a shorter way to do it. They invent shortcuts whenever they can. One shortcut is to omit multiplication signs whenever that omission will not be confusing. Show several such shortcuts as mn for $m \times n$; $m \cdot n$ for $m \times n$; $^3/_2$ for $2\overline{)3}$.

Another such shortcut is the use of exponents. Write this expression on the board, and ask a student for an expression that names the same thing: $3 \times 3 \times 3 \times 3$. Some student may remember exponents and suggest 3^4. If not, point out the shortcut. Notice that this notation is similar to writing 4×3 in place of $3 + 3 + 3 + 3$. Be sure that students do not confuse 3^4 with 4×3. Give other examples using exponents. Tell how to read expressions such as 3^4 and n^2.

Using the pages Use the exposition on page 126 to reinforce your introduction. Have students write answers for exercises 1–11. After completing those exercises, call on students to read their answers aloud. Assign exercises 12–21 for written work. Use the exposition on page 127 to introduce scientific notation, which uses exponents. Point out that scientific notation is a product of a number between 1 and 10 and a power of 10. The power of ten is written with an exponent. Assign exercises 1–12 for written work.

Exponents

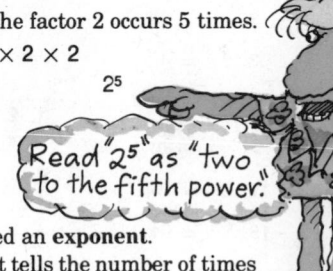

Notice that the factor 2 occurs 5 times.

$2 \times 2 \times 2 \times 2 \times 2$

2^5

Read "2^5" as "two to the fifth power."

Here is a short way to write the expression.

The 5 is called an **exponent**.
The exponent tells the number of times the base, 2, is used as a factor.

Other examples. $5 \times 5 = 5^2$ $6 \times 6 \times 6 = 6^3$

"five to the second power"   "six to the third power"
or "five squared"   or "six cubed"

EXERCISES
Write, using an exponent.

1. $2 \times 2 \times 2$ 2^3
2. 3×3 3^2
3. $4 \times 4 \times 4 \times 4 \times 4$ 4^5
4. $5 \times 5 \times 5$ 5^3
5. 6×6 6^2
6. $7 \times 7 \times 7$ 7^3
7. 10 10^1
8. 10×10 10^2
9. $10 \times 10 \times 10$ 10^3
10. $10 \times 10 \times 10 \times 10$ 10^4
11. $10 \times 10 \times 10 \times 10 \times 10$ 10^5

Give the standard numeral.

12. 2^4 16
13. 4^2 16
14. 3^2 9
15. 2^3 8
16. 5^4 625
17. 4^5 1024

Complete.

				18.	19.	20.
Power of 10	10^1	10^2	10^3	10^4	10^5	10^6
Standard numeral	10	100	1000	?	?	?
Number of 0s in standard numeral	1	2	3	?	?	?

21. In your complete table, compare the exponent of 10 with the number of 0s in the standard numeral. Are they the same? yes

$1^3 = ?$ 1
$1^3 + 2^3 = ?$ 9
$1^3 + 2^3 + 3^3 = ?$ 36

Guess first.
$1^3 + 2^3 + 3^3 + 4^3 = ?$ 100
$1^3 + 2^3 + 3^3 + 4^3 + 5^3 = ?$ 225

18. 10,000 4
19. 100,000 5
20. 1,000,000 6

126

Assignments

BASIC
page 126 exercises 1–21
page 127 exercises 1–8
Basic Worksheet 34

AVERAGE
page 126 exercises 1–21
page 127 exercises 1–10
Enrichment Worksheet 34

ENRICHED
page 126 exercises 1–21
page 127 exercises 1–12
Enrichment Worksheet 34

EXTRA PRACTICE
page 383 set 43

Mathematics and science

Scientists often write numbers in **scientific notation**. For example, the diameter of the sun, written in scientific notation, is

$$1.38 \times 10^6 \text{ kilometers}$$

A number in scientific notation is the product of a number between 1 and 10 and a power of 10. Here are some more examples of numbers written in scientific notation:

3.2×10^1 4.56×10^2 8×10^3 2.03×10^4

$(3.2 \times 10 = 32)$ $(4.56 \times 100 = 456)$ (8000) $(20,300)$

Notice that a whole-number exponent tells the number of places to the right the decimal point must be moved to express the number as a standard numeral.

EXERCISES
Give the standard numeral.

1. 3×10^3 2. 5.3×10^4 3. 6.04×10^5 4. 2.753×10^6

Express each of the following numbers in scientific notation.

5. 2600   6. 384,000   7. 5,930,000   8. 369,000,000,000

9. The sun is about 150,000,000 kilometers from the earth.

10. The sun is thought to be about 6,000,000,000 years old.

11. The mass of the sun is about 332,000 times greater than the mass of the earth.

12. The temperature at the center of the sun is about 20,000,000 degrees Celsius.

127

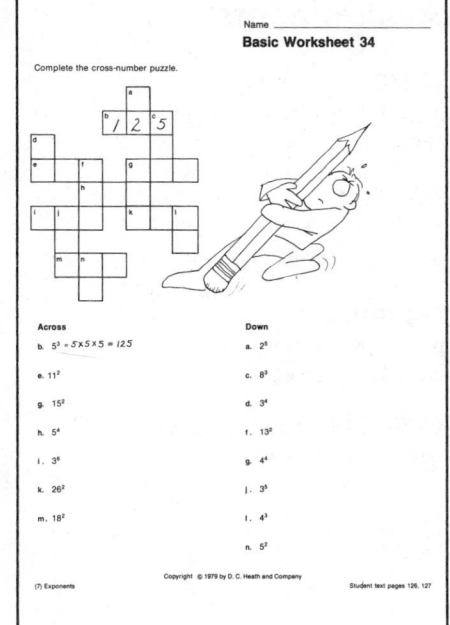

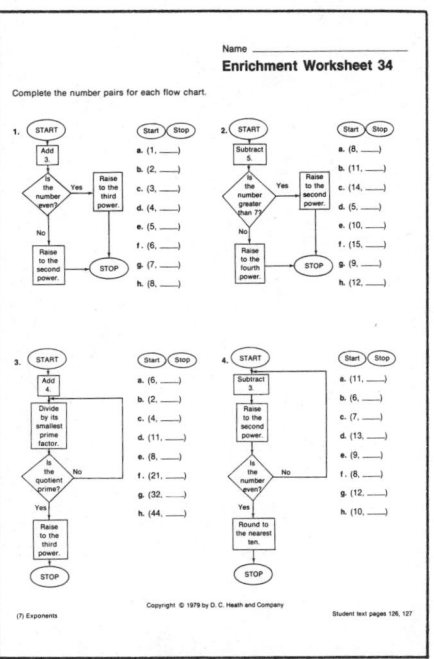

Follow-up Activities

Reinforcement You may wish to have students copy and complete the following table.

a	b	$(a + b)(a - b)$	$(a^2 - b^2)$
2	1	3	3
3	2	5	5
4	2	12	12
6	3	27	27
9	5	56	56
10	7	51	51

Have students compare the two numbers that they filled in in each row. You may wish to tell students that

$$(a + b)(a - b) = a^2 - b^2$$

no matter what numbers they pick.

Enrichment A famous mathematician named Fermat (1601−1665) once thought that the expression $2^{2^n} + 1$ would always give a prime number when whole numbers were substituted for n. Later it was shown that the expression would not always give a prime number. What numbers do you get when you substitute the following whole numbers for n? 0, 1, 2, 3, 4

3, 5, 17, 257, 65537

EXCURSION
Using only these weights:

3 grams   4 grams   5 grams

on a balance:

how could you get each of these amounts of sand in a single weighing?

1 gram, 2 grams, and 6 grams

$$\text{sand} + 3\,g = 4\,g;$$
$$\text{sand} + 3\,g = 5\,g;$$
$$\text{sand} + 3\,g = 4\,g + 5\,g$$

(core) Lesson 55   **127**

STUDENT OBJECTIVE

To review the concepts introduced in Chapter 4.

Suggested Lesson Plan

Introduction No pre-text activity is necessary for page 128 as this is a checkup for the chapter. However, it may be valuable to briefly review the lessons in the chapter so that students are reminded of the content over which they will be tested.

This Checkup will provide you with data about how individual students have mastered the skills of the chapter. The Chapter Review on page 130 is provided for those students who need more specific individual help.

Page 129 is a project that students can explore, working in pairs, to discover patterns in finding factors of composite numbers.

Using the pages Assign all of the exercises on page 128. As students complete the page they can work on the project on page 129.

True or false? [pages 106–109]

1. The whole numbers are a subset of the even numbers. **false**
2. The square numbers are a subset of the even numbers. **false**
3. A is a subset of B. **false**
4. $B = \{6, 7, 8, 9, 10\}$ **false**
5. $A \cap B = \{4, 5\}$ **true**
6. $A \cup B = \{1, 2, 3, 4, 5, 6, 7, 8, 9, 10\}$ **true**

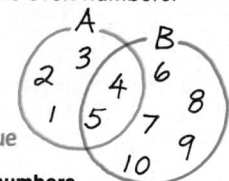

Give the greatest common factor of the two numbers.
[pages 110–111]

7. 12, 18   6   8. 8, 10   2   9. 6, 12   6   10. 14, 15   1

Give the prime factorization of each number. [pages 112–113]

11. 6   2x3
12. 18   2x3x3
13. 36   2x2x3x3
14. 42   2x3x7
15. 72   2x2x2x3x3
16. 156   2x2x3x13

Give the least common multiple of the two numbers.
[pages 114–115]

17. 3, 5   15   18. 4, 6   12   19. 5, 10   10   20. 8, 9   72

a	c	r	y
3	2	7	9

Substitute and simplify. [pages 118–119]

21. $a + 5$ 8   22. $9 - c$ 7   23. $15 - y$ 6   24. $r + 18$ 25
25. $r + c$ 9   26. $y - r$ 2   27. $20 - (a + y)$ 8   28. $5 \times (y - a)$ 30

Solve each equation. [pages 120–125]

29. $n + 18 = 21$ 3   30. $n - 6 = 19$ 25   31. $14 + n = 42$ 28
32. $3n = 21$ 7   33. $5n = 65$ 13   34. $13n = 78$ 6

Give the standard numeral. [pages 126–127]

35. 2^4 16   36. 4^2 16   37. 10^3 1000   38. 3^5 243   39. 10^4 10,000   40. 1^6 1

128

Assignments

BASIC
page 128 exercises 1–40
page 129 Project

AVERAGE
page 128 exercises 1–40
page 129 Project

ENRICHED
page 128 exercises 1–40
page 129 Project

EXTRA PROBLEM SOLVING
pages 404–405 set 4

Project

1. Make a dot diagram like the one shown above.

2. Find a way to use your dot diagram to find all factors of 6. 1,2,3,6
Of 12. 1,2,3,4,6,12

3. How can you use your dot diagram to find the GCF of 6 and
12? Look for the greatest factor with dots for numbers 6 and 12.

4. Use your diagram to find the first four multiples of 4. Of 6.
0,4,8,12 0,6,12,18

5. How can you use your dot diagram to find the LCM of 4
and 6? Look for the smallest number with dots for factors 4 and 6.

129

You may wish to assign some of the
Creative Problem Solving Activities
(pages 461-477) at this time.

Follow-up Activities

Reinforcement Correct all of the items
in the Chapter Checkup. Any student
who misses six or more or any more
than three problems in a section needs
additional help. It is important for each
student to achieve some degree of
familiarity with the concepts covered.
Although these are not considered basic
skills, being able to use mathematical
notation and the ability to solve
equations is necessary for success in
higher mathematics.

Enrichment Assign these pupils to the
games and activities that have been
played throughout the chapter. Assign a
student leader to be responsible for
teaching each game or activity to the
interested students and to supervise the
play.

CALCULATOR ACTIVITY
Assign one student to be responsible for
the calculators and the calculator
activities. The calculator student is
responsible for keeping track of the
calculators, for explaining the activities,
and for supervising the play.

STUDENT OBJECTIVE

To review or extend the skills and concepts taught in Chapter 4.

Suggested Lesson Plan

Introduction After checking the Chapter Checkup, you will know which students need additional reinforcement and which students will be able to go ahead with the Challenge activity. Get the better students started on page 131 first as the students who are having difficulty will need more of your time.

The students who need more review should go back and correct their errors on the Chapter Checkup. You may want to go over those questions orally if this group is small enough. Carefully probe to determine which concepts and skills the students have not mastered and work individually to correct their deficiencies.

Using the pages After the identified students have corrected the Chapter Checkup, they should answer questions 1–26 on page 130. Many of the concepts and notation of the chapter are summarized on page 130. Students may refer to this summary as they answer the questions.

After they complete these questions, read the answers and let the students correct their own papers. Give them an opportunity to ask questions about the exercises they missed.

Assign page 131 to those students who did well on the Chapter Checkup. You may let the students work in pairs on these exercises if that has worked well in the past.

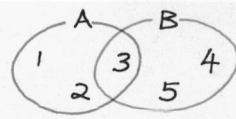

Intersection: $A \cap B = \{3\}$
Union: $A \cup B = \{1, 2, 3, 4, 5\}$

Factors of 8: {1, 2, 4, 8}
Factors of 12: {1, 2, 3, 4, 6, 12}
The greatest common factor is 4.

Whole numbers with exactly 2 factors are called **prime numbers**.

7: 1,7 is a prime number

Multiples of 6: {0, 6, 12, 18, ...}
Multiples of 9: {0, 9, 18, 27, ...}
The least common multiple (other than 0) is 18.

$n + 1 = 17$ $5n = 15$
$n + 1 - 1 = 17 - 1$ $\frac{5n}{5} = \frac{15}{5}$
$n = 16$ $n = 3$
Check: $16 + 1 = 17$ Check: $5 \times 3 = 15$

$2^3 = 2 \times 2 \times 2 = 8$

130

Give the intersection and the union.

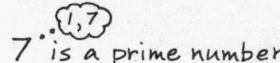

$R \cap S = \{6, 8\}$
$X \cap Y = Y$
$X \cup Y = X$

$R \cup S = \{2, 4, 6, 8, 10, 12, 14\}$

Give the greatest common factor (GCF).

3. 6   3   **4.** 12   4   **5.** 18   6   **6.** 27   9
   9   16   24   45

Which of these numbers are prime numbers?

7. 9   **8.** 11 ✓   **9.** 19 ✓   **10.** 27

11. 39   **12.** 43 ✓   **13.** 49   **14.** 51

Give the least common multiple (LCM).

15. 5   **16.** 8   **17.** 12   **18.** 15
    6   12   16   20
   30   24   48   60

Solve and check.

19. $n + 13 = 23$ 10   **20.** $n - 18 = 30$ 48

21. $9n = 27$ 3   **22.** $15n = 165$ 11

Give the standard numeral.

23. 3^2 **24.** 2^4 **25.** 10^2 **26.** 10^3
   9   16   100   1000

Assignments

BASIC
page 130 exercises 1–26

AVERAGE
page 130 exercises 1–26

ENRICHED
page 131 exercises 1–30

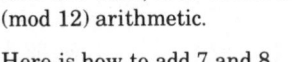
CHAPTER CHALLENGE

In this lesson you will work with an arithmetic that uses only the 12 numbers on a clock face. Since only 12 numbers are used, it is called a modulo 12 (mod 12) arithmetic.

Here is how to add 7 and 8.

Start at 7.   Move the hand 8 units *clockwise*.

$7 + 8 = 3 \pmod{12}$

Here is how to subtract 8 from 7.

Start at 7.   Move the hand 8 units *counterclockwise*.

$7 - 8 = 11 \pmod{12}$

EXERCISES

Add or subtract in mod 12. (*Hint:* Think about a clock as shown above.)

1. 6 + 6 12   2. 6 + 7 1   3. 9 + 5 2   4. 10 + 10 8   5. 11 + 9 8

6. 3 + 2 5   7. 11 + 10 9   8. 11 + 1 12   9. 3 + 12 3   10. 7 + 12 7

11. 9 + 12 9   12. 11 + 12 11   13. 3 − 5 10   14. 4 − 6 10   15. 7 − 9 10

16. 11 − 12 11   17. 8 − 3 5   18. 6 − 6 12   19. 10 − 10 12   20. 9 − 12 9

21. What number on the 12-hour clock acts just as 0 does in regular arithmetic? 12

To multiply in mod 12, we can think about adding in mod 12.

$$5 + 5 + 5 = 3 \pmod{12}$$

$$3 \times 5 = 3 \pmod{12}$$

Multiply in mod 12.

22. 2 × 6 12   23. 2 × 8 4   24. 2 × 3 6

25. 2 × 5 10   26. 3 × 4 12   27. 3 × 6 6

28. 4 × 3 12   29. 4 × 4 4   30. 5 × 3 3

131

13 a b c d 33 a b c d 13 a b c d 3 a b c d 29 a b c
14 34 a b c d 14 4 30 a b c
15 MAJOR CHECKUP Standardized Format 31
a b c a b c a b c

STUDENT OBJECTIVES

To practice skills learned previously.
To practice using a standardized-test format.

Suggested Lesson Plan

Using the pages The Major Checkup at the end of each chapter of this textbook is given in standardized-test format. The answer sheet on page 448 is the type used with many standardized tests. You may duplicate it for use with the Major Checkups.

Pass out the answer sheets and be sure students understand how to use them. Allow a specified time, perhaps twenty minutes, to complete the checkup. Assign the exercises and use the results to determine what review is needed.

The table below correlates the test items and the student text pages. Assign review exercises as indicated by the Major Checkup results.

Test Item	Text Pages	Test Item	Text Pages
1	22−23	7	66−67
2	26−27	8	68−69
3	28−29	9	84
4	36−37	10	96−97
5	42−43	11	114−115
6	58−59	12	110−111

Chapter 4 Posttest

See page 54 for a full discussion of how to use the posttest. The table below suggests Extra Practice exercises and Basic Worksheets for those students who need further practice or reteaching.

Objectives	Extra Practice Sets	Pages	Basic Worksheets
4-1			25
4-2			26
4-3	38−39	382	27−28
4-4	40	382	29
4-5			31
4-6	41−42	383	32−33

Answers for Chapter 4 Posttest

1. F 2. T 3. F 4. T 5. 5, 8 6. 1, 5, 7, 8 7. 1, 2, 3, 4, 5, 6, 7, 8, 9, 10 8. 1, 4, 5, 6, 7, 8 9. 6 10. 9 11. 12 12. 40 13. 20 14. 48 15. 8 16. 9 17. 27

18. 24 19. 125 20. $2\frac{2}{3}$ 21. 6 22. 31

23. 59 24. 6 25. 9 26. $7\frac{1}{3}$

Choose the correct letter.

1. 56,752 rounded to the nearest hundred is

    a. 56,700
    b. 56,800
    c. 57,000
    d. none of these

2. Add.

    624
    38
   +577

    a. 1238
    b. 1139
    c. 1239
    d. none of these

3. Subtract.

    6025
  −1773

    a. 4252
    b. 5252
    c. 5752
    d. none of these

4. Multiply.

    248
  × 72

    a. 18,836
    b. 17,836
    c. 18,856
    d. none of these

5. Divide.

    $43\overline{)8944}$

    a. 208
    b. 280
    c. 28
    d. none of these

6. The standard numeral for five hundred and six thousandths is

    a. 0.506
    b. 600.006
    c. 506,000
    d. none of these

7. Give the sum.

    6.7 + 0.488

    a. 0.555
    b. 7.188
    c. 55.5
    d. none of these

8. Give the difference.

    9.6 − 0.38

    a. 9.22
    b. 5.8
    c. .58
    d. none of these

9. Multiply.

    0.13
  ×0.04

    a. 0.52
    b. 0.052
    c. 0.0052
    d. none of these

10. Divide.

    $0.9\overline{)3.771}$

    a. 4.19
    b. 41.9
    c. 0.419
    d. none of these

11. The least common multiple of 4 and 6 is

    a. 12
    b. 24
    c. 2
    d. none of these

12. The greatest common factor of 8 and 12 is

    a. 24
    b. 4
    c. 1
    d. none of these

132

Chapter 4 Posttest

Date _____

True or false? [Obj. 4-1, pages 106–107]

1. A is a subset of B _____

2. B is a subset of C _____

3. C is a subset of A _____

4. A is a subset of C _____

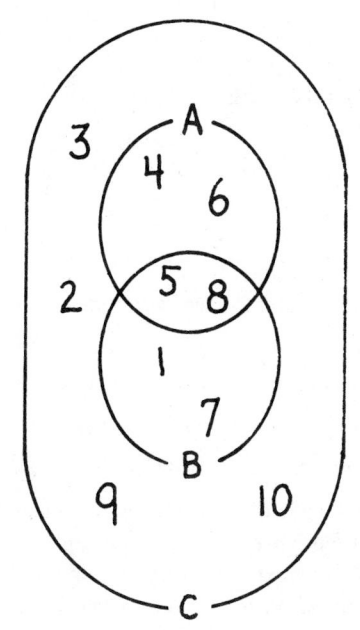

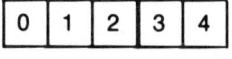

| 0 | 1 | 2 | 3 | 4 |

Write the elements. [Obj. 4-2, pages 108–109]

5. $A \cap B$ _____

6. $B \cap C$ _____

7. $C \cup B$ _____

8. $A \cup B$ _____

Give the greatest common factor. [Obj. 4-3, pages 110–111]

| 0 | 1 | 2 | 3 |

9. 18 and 24 _____   10. 45 and 54 _____   11. 48 and 36 _____

Give the least common multiple. [Obj. 4-4, pages 114–115]

| 0 | 1 | 2 | 3 |

12. 5 and 8 _____   13. 10 and 20 _____   14. 12 and 16 _____

Substitute and simplify. [Obj. 4-5, pages 118–119, 126–127]

| 0-2 | 3 | 4 | 5 | 6 |

15. $a \times b$ _____   16. c^2 _____

17. $c \times (A + b)$ _____   18. $(32 - A) - c$ _____

19. A^3 _____   20. $(a + b) \div c$ _____

a	A	b	c
2	5	4	3

| 0-2 | 3 | 4 | 5 | 6 |

Solve. [Obj. 4-6, pages 120–121, 124–125]

21. $7x = 42$ 22. $x + 12 = 43$ 23. $y - 17 = 42$

_____   _____   _____

24. $4a = 24$ 25. $6m = 54$ 26. $3y = 22$

_____   _____   _____

132a

Chapter 5
Measurement

Learning Objectives

After completing this chapter, all students should be able to do the following:

5-1 Measure lengths to the nearest millimeter.

5-2 Make conversions among metric units.

5-3 Compute perimeters and circumferences.

5-4 Compute areas.

5-5 Compute surface areas of prisms and cylinders.

5-6 Compute volumes of prisms and cylinders.

5-7 Make conversions among customary units.

Metric units for measuring length are introduced. Then students learn to compute the perimeter of a polygon and the circumference of a circle. Next, area formulas for parallelograms (including squares and other rectangles), triangles, and circles are developed. Then, students learn to compute surface areas and volumes of prisms and cylinders. Metric units of capacity and weight are introduced. Finally, customary units are reviewed.

Mathematics

Measurement. If we wish to make a record of a given length or to communicate about a given length, a primitive way would be to make a copy of the length, perhaps by cutting a string or stick to match. Besides involving problems of accuracy (the string stretching or the stick warping), this method is very cumbersome when a large number of records are to be stored or when the length to be copied is great (e.g., the circumference of the earth at the equator). A more sophisticated way is to compare the length in question with a selected length (unit). Then the length can be recorded or communicated orally: the object is 2 times as long as the unit or $1/_2$ as long as the unit. In order to facilitate the exchange of information, people agree to use the same units (e.g., centimeters, meters, inches, and feet).

Similar comments can be made for measuring areas and volumes.

Measurement systems. Various units are used to measure lengths. For example, in the customary system the inch is used for short lengths, the foot for somewhat longer lengths, the mile for very long lengths, etc. A collection of interrelated units that are often used together is called a system of measures. It may be a misnomer to call the customary system of measures a *system*. At least it is not what a rational person would create if he decided to create a system. The metric system is just such a system, however, for that is exactly how it came to be. In 1789 a committee of

five was appointed by the French government to decide upon the standards for a new system of measures. They chose as the standard unit of length one ten-millionth the distance from the equator to the North Pole. This was the standard meter.

In recent years the meter has been defined as 1,650,763.73 times the wave-length of orange light from krypton 86. All meter measures in the world, and many other units, including the United States yard, are related to these physical standards.

Here are the units for measuring length in the two systems:

METRIC SYSTEM

10 millimeters	=	1 centimeter
10 centimeters	=	1 decimeter
10 decimeters	=	1 meter
10 meters	=	1 dekameter
10 dekameters	=	1 hectometer
10 hectometers	=	1 kilometer

CUSTOMARY SYSTEM

12 inches	=	1 foot
3 feet	=	1 yard
1760 yards	=	1 mile

Because the metric sytem and the decimal place-value system are both based on ten, conversion from one unit to another in the metric system is merely a matter of shifting decimal places or points. In the customary system more difficult multiplications and divisions are required. It is easy to see why just about all countries of the world use metric units.

Measuring area. Measuring length is a matter of comparing the length to a unit length. The same is true of measuring area or volume or, for that matter, any magnitude. To measure the area of a given region, we compare the area of the region to that of a unit region. We can do that by covering the region to be measured with tiles whose areas are in the unit being used:

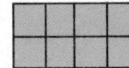

This, however, can be extremely tedious in all but the simplest cases. Also, the unit tiles may not fit well the region being measured, thus requiring much estimation and a high degree of error. For some simple figures (square, triangle, circle, etc.) mathematicians have discovered relationships between the area measures and some linear dimensions of the figures. These relationships are stated concisely in formulas. Therefore, measuring area in these simple cases is a matter of making some linear measurements and computing the area measure from the linear measures. For example, to find the area of a rectangle, we can measure the lengths of two adjacent sides (length and width) and multiply those lengths.

Computing with formulas. There are two common ways of handling the computation involved in finding, for example, area measures from length measures. One way is to work entirely with pure numbers (as opposed to denominate numbers). For example, to find the area of this rectangle using the formula $A = l \times w$, one would substitute the number of centimeters in the length for "l" and the number of centimeters in the width for "w" and then multiply. The product would indicate the number of square centimeters in the area.

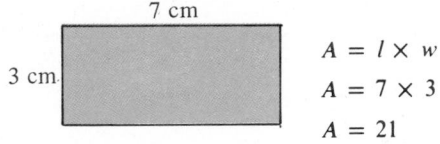

$$A = l \times w$$
$$A = 7 \times 3$$
$$A = 21$$

The area measure is 21 square centimeters.

Notice that one abstracts pure numbers from the real situation, operates with the numbers, and then translates the result back to the real situation. When using this method, the student must remember the units used to measure lengths, and he must also remember that the product indicates the number of square units in the area measure.

The second way of handling this situation is to actually compute with the denominate numbers. For the example above, one would substitute the measures of the length and width (not the number of units in the measure of the length and width) in the formula and multiply to get the area measure (not the number of square units in the area measure):

$$A = l \times w$$
$$A = 7 \text{ cm} \times 3 \text{ cm}$$
$$A = 21 \text{ cm}^2$$

The students must, of course, know that centimeters times centimeters gives square centimeters.

Teaching the Chapter

Measurement is a subject that cannot be learned passively. Students must actually make many measurements. As your students do the activities in the text and those suggested in the teacher's commentary, observe them closely to be sure that they use the measuring instruments correctly. Be sure, too, that when they measure long objects and have to use the ruler several times, end-to-end, they measure in a straight line.

Active involvement is particularly important when learning about longer units, such as the meter and the yard. Perhaps a child can become somewhat familiar with the centimeter merely by looking at a textbook, for a centimeter can be pictured. But the longer units cannot be pictured—at least not in standard-size textbooks. In order for students to learn more about a meter than the fact that it is 100 centimeters long, they must handle objects that are a meter long—objects such as meter sticks. They need to do much measuring with all the units. You should ask them, after they have had some experience measuring, to estimate some lengths and then to check their estimates by measuring.

One of the important outcomes of measuring activities is the realization that you need to pick units in a suitable way. It may be wise to use the centimeter as the unit for measuring the width of a page, but it would be silly to use it to measure the length of the corridor in the school.

Students may have had much experience with metric units in previous grades. If that is not the case for your students, you must give them such experience at the beginning of this chapter. The following are some activities to be used for that purpose.

Before spending much time learning about the interrelationships among metric units, students should develop a "feel" for the units. They should recognize lengths that are very near to 1 centimeter and to 1 meter, weights near 1 gram and 1 kilogram, and volumes near 1 liter. To do this, they should have experiences using these units. They should, for example, develop personal referents for the metric units mentioned above. They should find a fingernail or a finger joint that measures 1 centimeter. They could find that a slice of bread is about 1 centimeter thick. They can compare a meter stick with their arms and legs. This gives a body referent for the meter. They can find that a paper clip weighs about 1 gram and a nickel weighs about 5 grams. Similarly for the kilogram and the liter.

Another experience is to collect as many different lengths as possible that are about one centimeter—the thickness of a certain book or of a desk top, the width of a pen, etc. Similarly, they can find a collection of objects that are 1 meter long, weigh 1 kilogram, etc. Once students have these units well in mind, they can go on in the text to study the relationships among the units.

Vocabulary

area
base
bushel
circumference
cylinder
dekameter
diameter
gram
hectare
hectometer
kilogram
kilometer
liter
milligram
milliliter
peck
perimeter
pint
prism
quart
radius
rectangular prism
surface area
triangular prism
volume

Symbols

$\approx$	is approximately equal to
π	pi
in.^{2}	square inches
ft^2	square feet
yd^2	square yards
in.^{3}	cubic inches
ft^3	cubic feet
yd^3	cubic yards

Materials

meter sticks or metric rulers
geoboard or graph paper
overhead projector and acetate
blocks
cylindrical container (oatmeal box)
food boxes in different shapes
hand calculators
straws and pipe cleaners

Chapter Tests

For a discussion of how to use the chapter tests, please see page 17c.

Answers for Chapter 5 Pretest

1. 20 mm **2.** 45 mm **3.** 390 **4.** 0.039 **5.** 0.757 **6.** 5200
7. 0.4243 **8.** 3600 **9.** 3600 **10.** 0.5 **11.** 4.237 **12.** 28 cm
13. 38 cm **14.** 32 cm **15.** 37.68 cm **16.** 49 cm^2
17. 84 cm^2 **18.** 50 cm^2 **19.** 113.04 cm^2 **20.** 294 cm^2
21. 216 cm^2 **22.** 439.6 cm^2 **23.** 343 cm^3 **24.** 180 cm^3
25. 706.5 cm^3 **26.** 6 **27.** 2 **28.** 10,560 **29.** 64 **30.** 32
31. 6000 **32.** 688 **33.** 432 **34.** 54

Chapter 5 Pretest

Name _____

Date _____

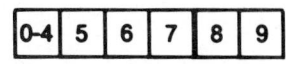

Measure each segment to the nearest millimeter. [Obj. 5-1, pages 134–135]

1. _____

2. _____

Complete. [Obj. 5-2, pages 134–137, 154–155]

| 0-4 | 5 | 6 | 7 | 8 | 9 |

3. 3.9 m = _____ cm

4. 3.9 cm = _____ m

5. 757 m = _____ km

6. 5.2 L = _____ mL

7. 424.3 mL = _____ L

8. 3.6 kg = _____ g

9. 3.6 g = _____ mg

10. 500 mg = _____ g

11. 4237 mm = _____ m

Compute each perimeter or circumference. Use 3.14 as an approximation for π. [Obj. 5-3, pages 138–139, 157]

| 0 | 1 | 2 | 3 | 4 |

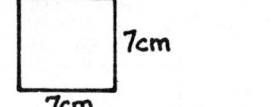

12.
7cm
7cm

13.
7cm
12 cm

14.
5cm 6cm
10cm

15.
12cm

_____   _____   _____   _____

Compute the areas of the figures in exercises 12-15. [Obj. 5-4, pages 140–144, 158–159]

| 0 | 1 | 2 | 3 | 4 |

16. A = _____

17. A = _____

18. A = _____

19. A = _____

Compute the surface area of each figure. Use 3.14 as an approximation for π. [Obj. 5-5, pages 146–149, 159]

| 0 | 1 | 2 | 3 |

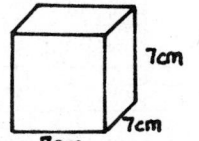

20.
7cm
7cm
7cm

21.
3cm
6cm
10cm

22.
5cm
9cm

_____   _____   _____

Compute the volumes of the figures in exercises 20-22. [Obj. 5-6, pages 150–153, 162–163]

| 0 | 1 | 2 | 3 |

23. V = _____

24. V = _____

25. V = _____

Complete. [Obj. 5-7, pages 156–157, 164–165]

| 0-2 | 3 | 4 | 5 | 6 | 7 | 8 | 9 |

26. 72 in. = _____ ft

27. 6 ft = _____ yd

28. 2 mi = _____ ft

29. 16 gal = _____ qt

30. 16 qt = _____ pt

31. 3 t = _____ lb

32. 43 lb = _____ oz

33. 36 ft = _____ in.

34. 18 yd = _____ ft

133d

Chapter 5
Record and Assignment Chart

Objectives

		Pretest Score Mark number correct	Posttest Score Mark number correct
5-1	Measure lengths to the nearest millimeter.	0 1 | 2	0 1 | 2
5-2	Make conversions among metric units.	0-4 5 6 7 | 8 9	0-4 5 6 7 | 8 9
5-3	Compute perimeters and circumferences.	0 1 2 | 3 4	0 1 2 | 3 4
5-4	Compute areas.	0 1 2 | 3 4	0 1 2 | 3 4
5-5	Compute surface areas of prisms and cylinders.	0 1 | 2 3	0 1 | 2 3
5-6	Compute volumes of prisms and cylinders.	0 1 | 2 3	0 1 | 2 3
5-7	Make conversions among customary units.	0-2 3 4 5 | 6 7 8 9	0-2 3 4 5 | 6 7 8 9

Unsatisfactory Score | Satisfactory Score   Unsatisfactory Score | Satisfactory Score

TEACHING ASSIGNMENTS*

	Student Page	Basic Assignment	Average Assignment	Enriched Assignment	Problem Solving	RETEACHING ASSIGNMENTS†
5-1	134, 135	1–20	1–24, EW 35	1–25, EW 35	21, 22, 23, 24	BW 35
5-2	136, 137	1–22	1–30, EW 35	1–32, EW 35		page 383 Set 44, BW 35
5-3	138, 139	1–8	1–8, EW 36	1–8, EW 36	9, 10	page 384 Set 45, BW 36
5-4	140, 141	1–9	1–9, EW 37	1–9, EW 37	10, 11, 12 13, 14	BW 37
	142, 143	1–12	1–12, EW 38	1–12, EW 38	13, 14, 15, 16	page 384 Set 46, BW 38
5-2 5-3 5-4	144	1–30	1–30, EW 38	1–30, EW 38	31, 32	BW 38
	145	1–12	1–14	1–15		BW 38
5-5	146, 147	1–9	1–9, EW 39	1–9, EW 39	10, 11, 12	BW 39
	148, 149	1–8	1–8, EW 39	1–8, EW 39	9, 10, 11, 12, 13	page 384 Set 47, BW 39
5-6	150, 151	1–6	1–6, EW 40	1–6, EW 40	7, 8, 9, 10	BW 40
	152, 153	1–6	1–6, EW 40	1–6, EW 40	7-12, 13, 14, 15	page 385 Set 48, BW 40
5-2	154, 155	1–25, 32–33	1–33, EW 41	1–33, EW 41		page 385 Set 49, BW 41
5-3 5-7	156, 157	1–37	1–37, EW 42	1–37, EW 42	38, 39	page 385 Set 50, BW 42
5-4 5-5	158, 159	1–18	1–20, EW 43	1–20, EW 43	21, 22	page 385 Set 51, BW 43
5-4	160, 161	1–4	1–5, EW 43	1–8, EW 43		BW 43
5-6	162, 163	1–11	1–11, EW 44	1–11, EW 44	12, 13, 14	page 386 Set 52, BW 44
5-7	164, 165	1–25	1–28, EW 45	1–28, EW 45	29, 30	page 386 Set 53, BW 45
	166	Chapter Checkup				
	167	Project				
	168	Chapter Review				
	169	Chapter Challenge				
	170	Major Checkup				

*Check assignments for objectives with unsatisfactory pretest scores.   BW = Basic Worksheet
†Check assignments for objectives with unsatisfactory posttest scores.   EW = Enrichment Worksheet

5
Measurement

STUDENT OBJECTIVES
To measure lengths in metric units.
To make conversions of linear measurements within the metric system.

VOCABULARY
meter (m), dekameter (dam), hectometer (hm), kilometer (km), decimeter (dm), centimeter (cm), millimeter (mm)

Suggested Lesson Plan

Introduction (meter sticks or metric rulers) Much of this work will be a review for your students, but actual measuring done with metric units is important so that students develop an intuitive "feel" for the length of the metric units.

Before you pass out meter sticks or metric rulers, ask your students to hold their hands about 1 meter apart. Walk around the room and measure the distances they have indicated. Let them adjust their hands so that they can "see" the length of a meter. Now ask them to show 1 decimeter. Since this is one tenth of a meter, or 10 centimeters, you can now distribute the meter sticks or metric rulers and let students indicate this length with the instruments.

Without using their measuring instrument, have them draw a segment on their paper 1 centimeter in length. After they have drawn the segment, have them measure it to see how close they were in their estimate. Continue the same activity for the millimeter.

Using the pages After the basic unit for length, the meter, and the three smaller units in the metric system have been introduced, the students should refer to the table of equivalent measures on page 134. The realization that these measures are related by 10s is the important concept in understanding the metric system. Point out the three units larger than the meter and estimate their lengths. The most important and most commonly used is, of course, the kilometer. Discuss things that are approximately 1 kilometer from the school. Estimate these lengths by thinking of a kilometer as approximately ½ a mile.

Use the exposition at the bottom of page 134 to point out to students the ease of reading measurements in different units. Since the units are based on 10, the conversion between units within the metric system involves only moving the decimal point. For example,

the segment pictured is 1 dm + 2 cm + 5 mm, or 12.5 cm. This is the same as 1.25 dm, or 125 mm.

Assign students to work in pairs to make the measurements for exercises 1–12. Each of them should draw the segments for exercises 13–25.

Measuring length

The basic unit for measuring length in the metric system is the **meter** (m). The dog is about 1 meter long. These units of length are used in the metric system:

1 kilometer (km) = 1000 meters	1 decimeter (dm) = 0.1 meter
1 hectometer (hm)* = 100 meters	1 centimeter (cm) = 0.01 meter
1 dekameter (dam)* = 10 meters	1 millimeter (mm) = 0.001 meter
1 meter (m) = 1 meter	

Notice that our metric system, like our place-value system, is based on the number 10. Because of this, decimals are used in writing metric measurements.

The length of the segment is 1 dm + 2 cm + 5 mm, or 12.5 cm. What is the length of the segment in mm?   125 mm

*These units are seldom used, but it is sometimes useful to know about them.

134

Assignments

BASIC
page 134 Discuss
page 135 exercises 1–20
Basic Worksheet 35

AVERAGE
page 134 Discuss
page 135 exercises 1–24
Enrichment Worksheet 35

ENRICHED
page 134 Discuss
page 135 exercises 1–25
Enrichment Worksheet 35

REVIEW PRACTICE
page 381 set 33

EXERCISES

Measure to the nearest centimeter.

1. your height   2. your waist measure

3. your arm span   4. your foot length

5. the width of your desk top

6. the length of a chalk eraser

7. the width of a book

8. the height of a table

9. Measure the width of a chalkboard to the nearest decimeter.

10. Measure the length of your classroom to the nearest meter.

11. Measure the width of a door to the nearest centimeter.

12. Measure the length of a straight pin to the nearest millimeter.

Get a ruler marked off in millimeters. Draw segments having these lengths.

13. 1 mm   14. 1 cm   15. 1 dm   16. 15 mm   17. 5.1 cm

18. 2.5 cm   19. 3.6 cm   20. 128 mm   21. 12.8 cm   22. 1.28 dm

23. Draw a segment that is 21 cm long.
   - a. How many mm long is it?   210
   - b. How many dm long is it?   2.1

24. On the chalkboard, draw a segment that is 1.23 m long.
   - a. How many dm long is it?   12.3
   - b. How many cm long is it?   123
   - c. How many mm long is it?   1230

25. On the chalkboard, draw a segment that is 425 mm long.
   - a. How many cm long is it?   42.5
   - b. How many dm long is it?   4.25
   - c. How many m long is it?   0.425

135

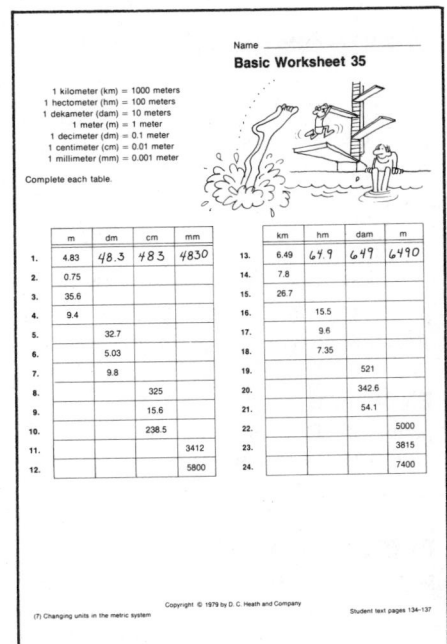
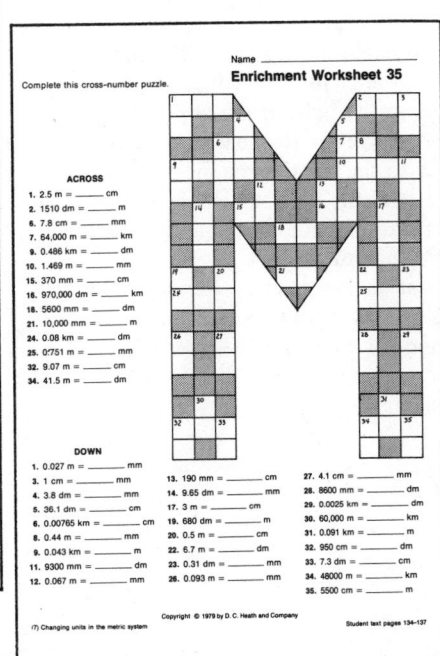

Suggested Lesson Plan

Introduction There are many different ways to teach changing units of measurement within the metric system. These ways vary from very mechanical methods to ones of comprehension and understanding. The approach taken with this lesson is first from the standpoint of thinking about the relationship of the units and thus multiplying by 10, 100, or 1000 (.1, .01, or .001), etc. The second half of the lesson introduces a shortcut method that students can learn and apply without having to completely think through the relationship between the units involved.

Begin the lesson by writing a number of measurements of length on the board and having students rename them with other units. Start with measurements of whole numbers of units and change to new units close to the unit used. For example, 12 m = ____ cm; 42 cm = ____ mm; 120 cm = ____ m. Develop this approach by having students first tell the relationship between the units, and then give the renamed measurement. For example, "12 m = ____ cm, there are 100 cm in 1 m, therefore, multiply 12 by 100, 12m = 1200 cm." Since decimals will naturally occur in changing units, gradually introduce some measurements with a decimal number of units, for example, 2.3 cm = ____ dam.

Using the pages Summarize your introduction by using the exposition on page 136. Notice that in example 2, since there is 0.001 km in a meter, we multiply by 0.001 to change m to km.

Move to the shortcut. Put the measurement chart shown below on the board and write several measurements in the chart.

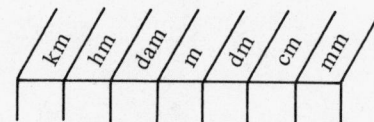

When you write the measurement in the chart, be sure the unit named in the measurement is in the ones place in relation to the decimal point in the measurement. The new measurement is simply read from the chart after the decimal point is moved so that the new unit is now in the ones place. In fact, you need not write the measurement in the chart. If you wish to change a measurement in meters to centimeters, look at the chart. The cm place is two places to the right of the m place, so simply move the decimal point two places to the right in the measurement. Have students copy the chart on their paper and practice changing units with several measurements.

Assign exercises 1−32 for written work. Be sure students use the chart method for exercises 5−28 or these exercises may be very difficult and confusing.

Changing units in the metric system

One advantage of the metric system is that we can change easily from one unit to another.

EXAMPLE 1. Change 4.372 m to cm.
There are 100 cm in a meter, so multiply by 100.
Notice that when you change to a smaller unit, you have a larger number.

$$4.372 \times 100 = 437.2$$
$$4.372 \text{ m} = 437.2 \text{ cm}$$

EXAMPLE 2. Change 392 m to km.
There is 0.001 km in a meter, so multiply by 0.001.
Notice that when you change to a larger unit, you have a smaller number.

$$392 \times 0.001 = 0.392$$
$$392 \text{ m} = 0.392 \text{ km}$$

Here is how I change 27.35m to decimeters.

Step 1. I think about the metric units matched with the digits. The unit used in the measurement (m) is matched to the digit in the ones place.

Step 2. Next I move the decimal point so that the new unit (dm) is in the ones place.

Step 3. Then I write the new unit, dm.

Here are two more examples.

Change 528.3 cm to meters.

Change 32.56 m to kilometers.

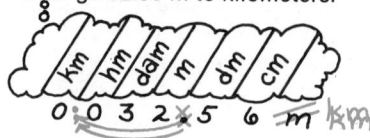

136

Assignments

BASIC
page 136 Discuss
page 137 exercises 1−22
Basic Worksheet 35

AVERAGE
page 136 Discuss
page 137 exercises 1−30
Enrichment Worksheet 35

ENRICHED
page 136 Discuss
page 137 exercises 1−32
Enrichment Worksheet 35

EXTRA PRACTICE
page 383 set 44

Copy and complete.

	mm	cm	dm	m	dam	hm	km
1.				100			
2.							8
3.			400				
4.	5348						

Complete.

5. 2 m = __?__ dm 20   6. 4 m = __?__ cm 400   7. 5 m = __?__ mm 5000

8. 1245 m = __?__ km 1.245   9. 1500 m = __?__ km 1.5   10. 354 m = __?__ km 0.354

11. 6.7 m = __?__ cm 670   12. 59.2 m = __?__ dm 592   13. 63.5 m = __?__ km 0.0635

14. 83 cm = __?__ m 0.83   15. 57.2 cm = __?__ mm 572   16. 63.8 cm = __?__ dm 6.38

17. 63 km = __?__ m 63,000   18. 58.9 dm = __?__ mm 5890   19. 173 mm = __?__ cm 17.3

20. 173 mm = __?__ dm 1.73   21. 173 mm = __?__ m 0.173   22. 675.41 mm = __?__ m 0.67541

23. 52.3 km = __?__ m 52,300   24. 52.3 mm = __?__ cm 5.23   25. 42.77 m = __?__ cm 4277

26. 42.77 cm = __?__ m 0.4277   27. 56.761 m = __?__ km 0.056761   28. 35.92 km = __?__ m 35,920

29. In the Olympic Games, one race is 10,000 m long. How many kilometers is that? 10

30. One Olympic swimming race is 1.5 km long. How many meters is that? 1500

31. At one time the world high-jump record was 2.27 m. How many centimeters is that? 227

32. At one time the world shot-put record was 21.60 m. How many millimeters is that? 21,600

137

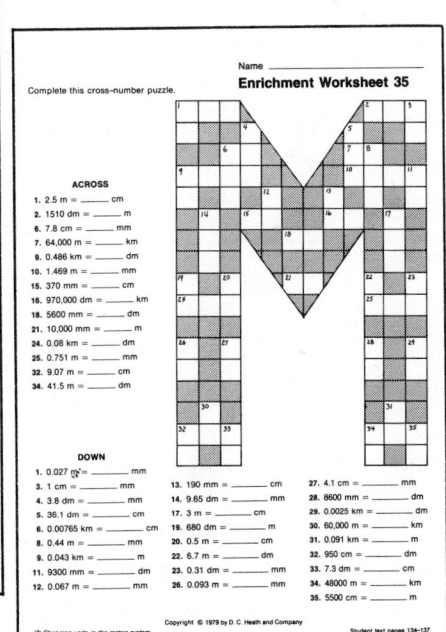

Suggested Lesson Plan

Introduction   Draw a polygon on the board. Define *perimeter* as the distance around the polygon. Then give a student a ruler and ask him to find the perimeter. He can, of course, measure each side and add the lengths. Then draw a circle on the board. Tell students that the distance around the circle is called the *circumference* instead of the perimeter. Ask a student to find the circumference. She should find that measuring the circumference directly is difficult, if not impossible. When we have a curved line to measure, it is usually best to measure it indirectly—that is, compute the length from some other direct measurements. We can do this with a circle. There is a relationship between the diameter of any circle and its circumference. The circumference is π times the diameter. π is a number that cannot be written exactly with fractions or decimals. It is near $3\frac{1}{7}$ and 3.14, so in our computations we can use those numbers as approximations for π. Write the formula on the board:

$$C = \pi d$$

Then write these formulas. Tell students that the "wavy equals sign" means *approximately equal to.*

$$C \approx 3.14d$$
$$C \approx 3\tfrac{1}{7}d$$

Using the pages   Go over the exposition on page 138. Assign the exercises.

Perimeter and circumference

The **perimeter** of a figure is the distance around the figure. Here are some examples.

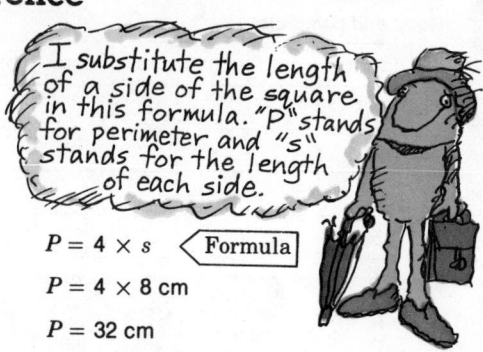

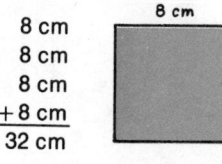

```
  8 cm
  8 cm
  8 cm
+ 8 cm
 32 cm
```

The perimeter is 32 cm.

$P = 4 \times s$ ◁ Formula
$P = 4 \times 8$ cm
$P = 32$ cm

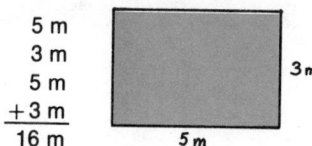

```
  5 m
  3 m
  5 m
+ 3 m
 16 m
```

The perimeter is 16 m.

$P = 2 \times l + 2 \times w$ ◁ Formula
$P = 2 \times 5\,\text{m} + 2 \times 3\,\text{m}$
$P = 10\,\text{m} + 6\,\text{m}$
$P = 16\,\text{m}$

The distance around a circle is called the **circumference**. The circumference of a circle (C) is equal to π (pi—a number slightly greater than 3) times the diameter (d). We'll use 3.14 as a decimal approximation for π.

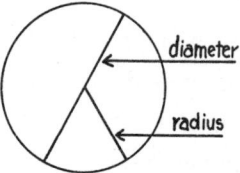

EXAMPLE.

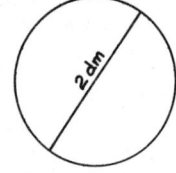

$C = \pi \times d$ ◁ Formula
$C \approx 3.14 \times 2$ dm
$C \approx 6.28$ dm

≈ is read "is approximately equal to."

138

Assignments

BASIC
page 138 Discuss
page 139 exercises 1−9,
      Keeping Skills Sharp
Basic Worksheet 36

AVERAGE
page 138 Discuss
page 139 exercises 1−10,
      Keeping Skills Sharp
Enrichment Worksheet 36

ENRICHED
page 138 Discuss
page 139 exercises 1−10,
      Keeping Skills Sharp
Enrichment Worksheet 36

EXTRA PRACTICE
page 384 set 45

EXERCISES

Give the perimeter of each figure.

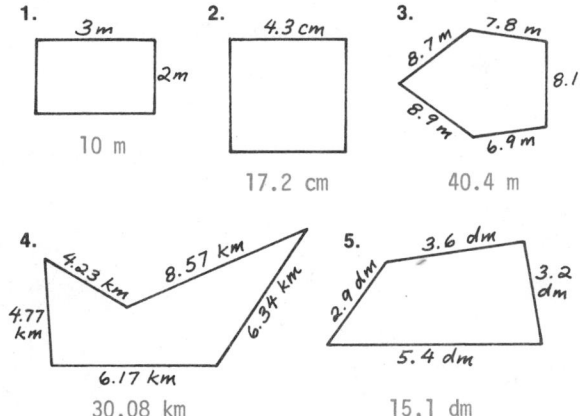

1. 3 m, 2 m, 10 m
2. 4.3 cm — 17.2 cm
3. 7.8 m, 8.7 m, 8.1 m, 8.9 m, 6.9 m — 40.4 m

4. 4.23 km, 8.57 km, 6.34 km, 4.77 km, 6.17 km — 30.08 km
5. 3.6 dm, 3.2 dm, 2.9 dm, 5.4 dm — 15.1 dm

Give the circumference of each circle.

6. 4.7 cm
7. 5.8 cm
8. 6.4 cm

Solve. 14.758 cm   18.212 cm   20.096 cm

9. Ceiling molding is needed for a rectangular room that measures 4.46 meters by 6.25 meters.

    a. How many meters of molding will be needed? Round your answer up to the nearest 0.5 meter.   21.5

    b. If molding is 37¢ a meter, how much will the molding for the ceiling cost? $7.96

10. The diameter of a certain bicycle wheel is 65 centimeters.

    a. How far does the bicycle travel when the wheel turns 1 revolution?   204.1 cm

    b. How many revolutions does the wheel make in a kilometer?   490.0

Give each sum.

1. 5.94 + 2.87   8.81
2. 3.056 + 2.785   5.841
3. 0.39 + 0.28 + 0.64   1.31
4. 5.6 + 7.9 + 3.8   17.3
5. 2.6 + 7.4 + 7.4   17.4
6. 9.8 + 3.62   13.42
7. 19 + 2.7   21.7
8. 3.8 + 0.24 + 0.9   4.94
9. 7.5 + 0.54 + 2   10.04
10. 4.8 + 0.006 + 2.53   7.336
11. 3.96 + 6.4   10.36
12. 18.5 + 0.68   19.18
13. 5.73 + 48.2   53.93
14. 6.4 + 0.86 + 27   34.26
15. 8.9 + 6.5 + 3.9   19.3
16. 0.204 + 3.1 + 17   20.304
17. 27.3 + 2.7 + 3.02   33.02
18. 16 + 1.6 + 0.16   17.76
19. 8.02 + 80.2 + 802   890.22
20. 7.93 + 79.3 + 0.793   88.023

Follow-up Activities

Reinforcement Have students do some more work with perimeter by having them find the perimeter of the following:

their classroom	a students's desk top
a table top	their basketball court
a teacher's desk top	their gym

In each case they will have to decide on an appropriate unit of measurement.

Enrichment Give each student a geoboard or some graph paper. Have them see how many figures they can construct that have a perimeter of 18 units. Use as the unit a side of one of the little squares on the graph paper or geoboard. Encourage students to keep a record of each figure. (This can be done by sketching the figure on graph paper if they are working with geoboards.) Here is an example:

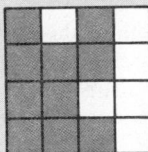

EXCURSION

Copy and finish drawing the dotted path to get the ending number.

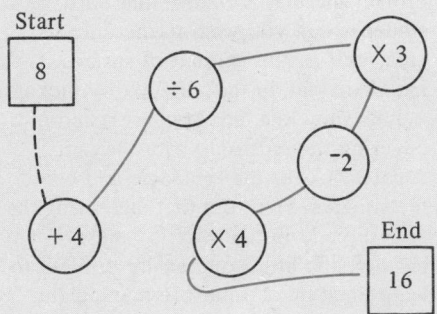

Answer may vary.

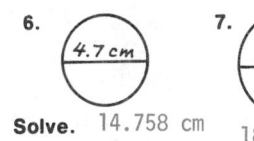
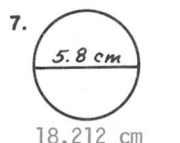
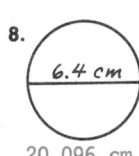
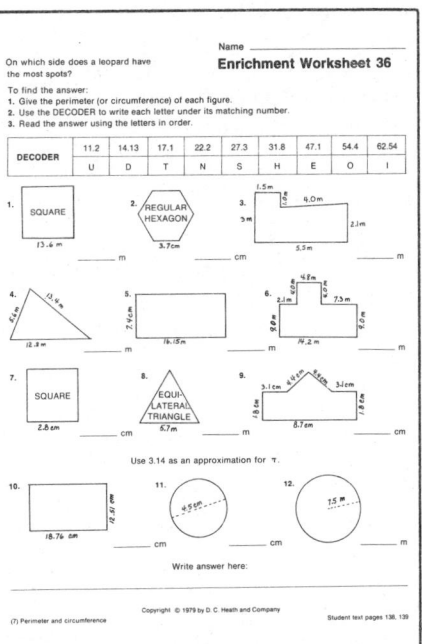

STUDENT OBJECTIVE
To compute the areas of squares, rectangles, and parallelograms.

VOCABULARY
area

Suggested Lesson Plan

Introduction (metric rulers) Before class, carefully draw a rectangle on a sheet of acetate for the overhead projector. Also cut out some small squares from a sheet of colored acetate. Be sure that the dimensions of the rectangle and the squares are such that the squares appear to fit the rectangle exactly. For example, 12 of the squares can fit the rectangle:

On another sheet of acetate draw a rectangle that the squares do not fit exactly. On a third sheet of acetate draw a grid of squares that are the same size as the small squares:

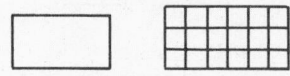

Project the first rectangle and tell students that you wish to measure its area, that is, the amount of surface it has. You can do that directly by picking a unit (show the small squares) and covering the rectangle with the unit squares. Cover the rectangle and count the squares. Point out that measuring the area directly in this way is "messy" because the little squares are difficult to keep lined up and hard to manipulate. An easier way would be to use a grid of squares. Show the grid. This is equivalent to using a ruler instead of many little unit sticks. Use the grid to measure the area of the rectangle.

Now repeat with the other rectangle. Students should see that it is difficult to count the part squares to find the area. Tell students that this is another case in which it is easier to measure the area indirectly. The grid does suggest a way of doing that. We can see that when the grid is placed on a rectangle (use the first rectangle) a shortcut for counting the squares is to multiply the number of rows of squares by the numbers of squares in each row.

This suggests that we can always measure the length and width directly and multiply to find the area.

Using the pages Go over the exposition, especially the formulas, on page 140. Assign the exercises.

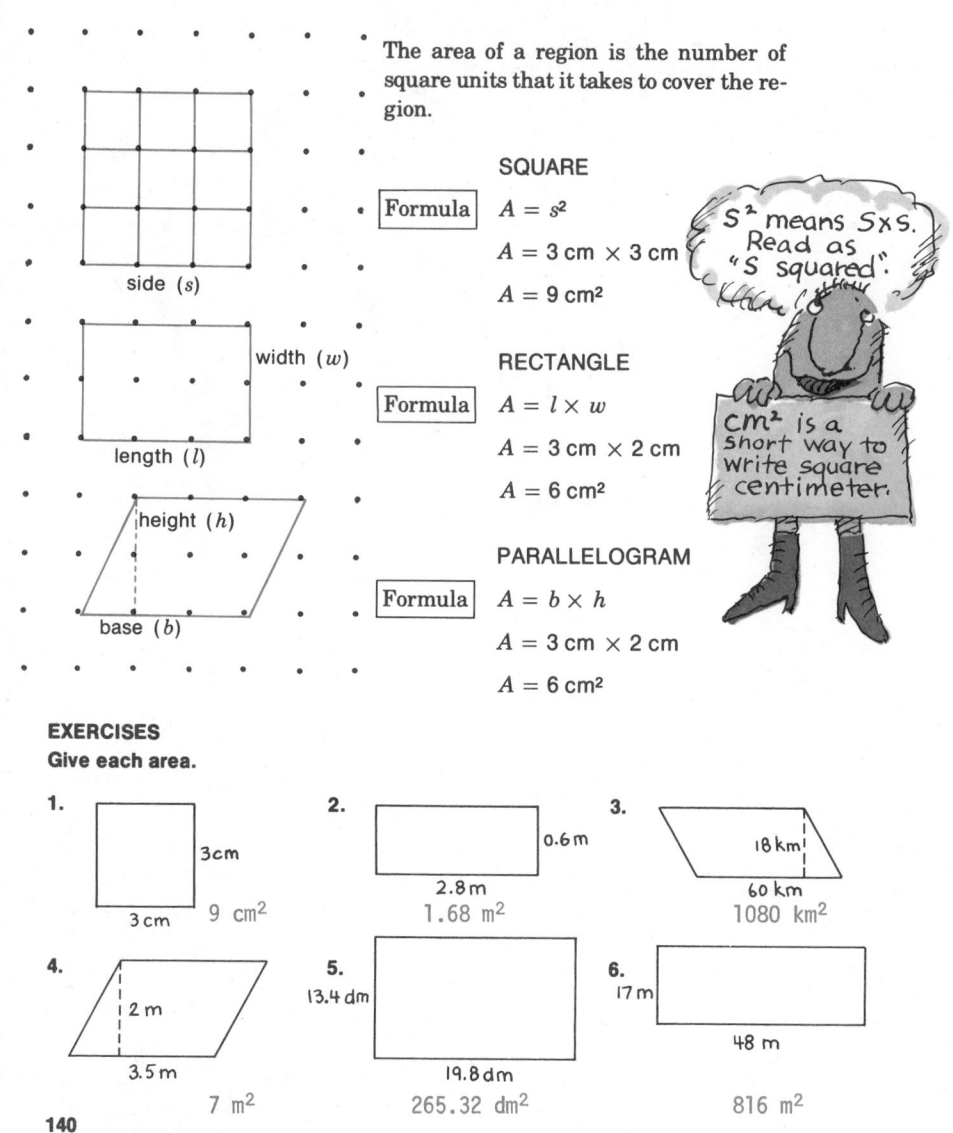

Area

The area of a region is the number of square units that it takes to cover the region.

SQUARE

Formula $A = s^2$
$A = 3 \text{ cm} \times 3 \text{ cm}$
$A = 9 \text{ cm}^2$

S^2 means $S \times S$. Read as "S squared".

cm^2 is a short way to write square centimeter.

RECTANGLE

Formula $A = l \times w$
$A = 3 \text{ cm} \times 2 \text{ cm}$
$A = 6 \text{ cm}^2$

PARALLELOGRAM

Formula $A = b \times h$
$A = 3 \text{ cm} \times 2 \text{ cm}$
$A = 6 \text{ cm}^2$

EXERCISES
Give each area.

1. 3 cm, 3 cm   9 cm²

2. 0.6 m, 2.8 m   1.68 m²

3. 18 km, 60 km   1080 km²

4. 2 m, 3.5 m   7 m²

5. 13.4 dm, 19.8 dm   265.32 dm²

6. 17 m, 48 m   816 m²

140

Assignments

BASIC
page 140 exercises 1—6
page 141 exercises 7—10
Basic Worksheet 37

AVERAGE
page 140 exercises 1—6
page 141 exercises 7—13
Enrichment Worksheet 37

ENRICHED
page 140 exercises 1—6
page 141 exercises 7—14
Enrichment Worksheet 37

REVIEW PRACTICE
page 381 set 34

First measure the dimensions to the nearest mm.
Then compute the area. Answers may vary slightly.

7.

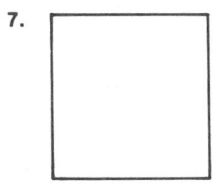

812 mm²

8.

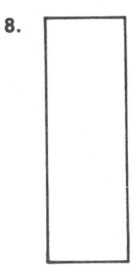

602 mm²

9.

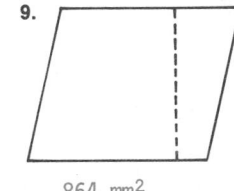

864 mm²

Solve.

10. Some carpet costs $11.50 per square meter. How much would the carpet cost for a rectangular room 4.1 meters by 6.8 meters? $320.62

11. A square lot measuring 25 meters on a side is to be seeded with grass seed. One kilogram of seed will cover 200 square meters. If grass seed costs $3.52 per kilogram, how much will it cost to seed the lot? $11

12. A floor tile 20 cm by 20 cm costs 38¢. How much would it cost to tile the floor of a 9-meter-by-5-meter recreation room? $427.50

13. Get a piece of graph paper. See how many different shapes you can draw that have the same area.

14. A carpet layer is to carpet two rectangular rooms, one 5 m by 8 m and another 3.1 m by 6 m. If he charges $1.80 per square meter, how much will he charge for the two rooms? $105.48

141

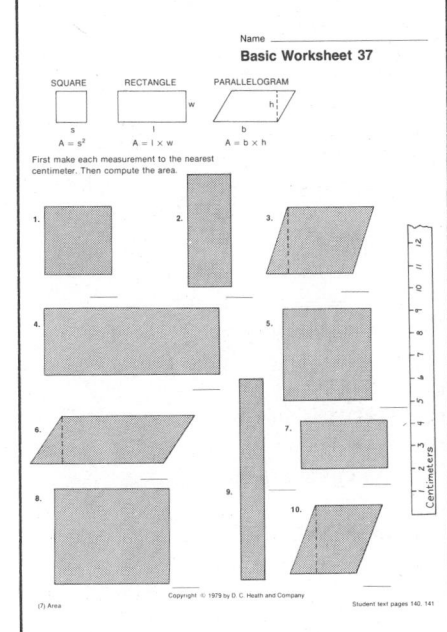

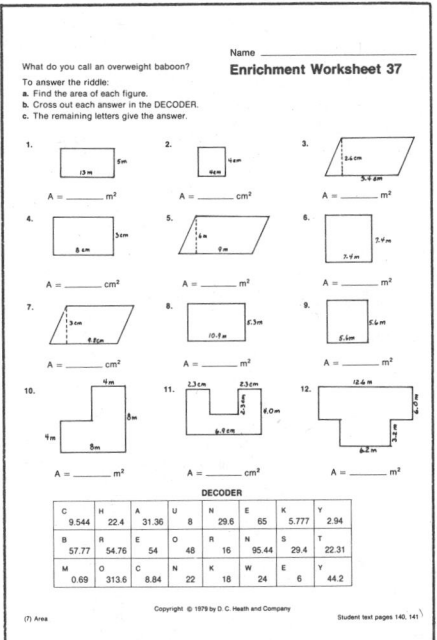

Follow-up Activities

Reinforcement You may wish to use the following activity to provide students with further experiences with area. Give each student a geoboard or some graph paper. Using one of the little squares as the unit, have students construct a square or a rectangle that has an area of 1 unit, a square or rectangle that has an area of 2 units, a square or a rectangle that has an area of 3 units, etc. Here are some examples:

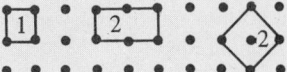

Enrichment The following activity is an extension of exercise 13 that provides students with further experiences with both perimeter and area. Give students a geoboard or some graph paper. Using a little square as the unit, have them "fence in" 16 squares. Emphasize that the area is 16 units. Next have them find the perimeter of the figure. Have them see if they can find different perimeters that "fence in" 16 units. After they have completed their investigations, stress that two figures may have the same area but different perimeters.

EXCURSION
A frog fell to the bottom of a 10-foot well. During the first hour the frog climbed up 7 inches and then slid back 4 inches. At that rate, how many hours did it take the frog to climb out of the well? Careful!!

39

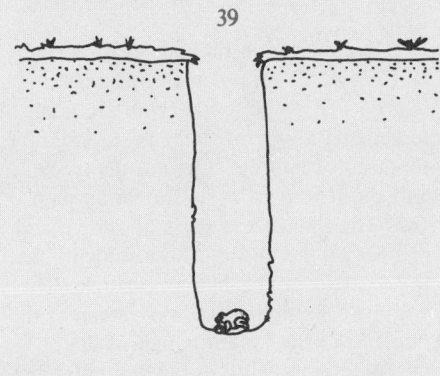

(core) Lesson 62 **141**

Suggested Lesson Plan

Introduction Use a cardboard triangle as a pattern and trace the triangle on the board. Tell students that you wish to find the area of the triangle. Tell them that you will consider the bottom side as the base and its distance from the opposite vertex as the height. Then turn the pattern around and trace again so that the triangles together make a parallelogram.

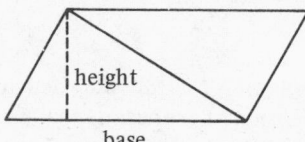

Ask students to identify the base and height of the parallelogram. (Same as the base and height of the triangle) Ask students to tell you the area of the parallelogram. (*bh*) Ask how the area of the triangle is related to the area of the parallelogram. (The area of the triangle is ¹/₂ of the area of the parallelogram.) This suggests that the area formula for a triangle is

$$A = \frac{1}{2} \text{ of } bh$$

(You may prefer to omit the word *of*. We have included it because we have not yet reviewed multiplication with fractions.)

Repeat with the trapezoid pattern. See the exposition at the top of page 142.

Draw a circle on a sheet of acetate and project it on a screen or on the board. Tell students that you are going to suggest a way of finding a formula for the area of a circle. Cut out the circle and cut it into parts as shown on page 142. Then place the parts as shown and project on the board. Show students that the figure is much like a rectangle. The width of the figure is *r*, the radius of the circle, and the length is half of the circumference. Half of the circumference is $\frac{1}{2} \pi d = \pi r$. If we multiply the base times the height, we get $r \pi r = \pi r^2$.

Using the pages Go over the exposition and then assign the exercises.

More about area

The area of the triangle is half the area of the parallelogram.

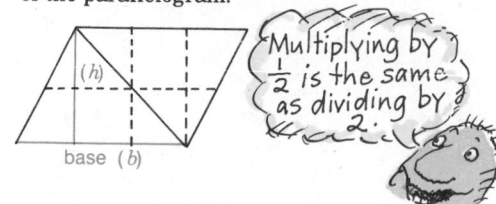

Formula

$A = \frac{1}{2} \times (b \times h)$

$A = \frac{1}{2} \times (3 \text{ cm} \times 2 \text{ cm})$

$A = \frac{1}{2} \times 6 \text{ cm}^2$

$A = 3 \text{ cm}^2$

The area of the trapezoid is half the area of the parallelogram.

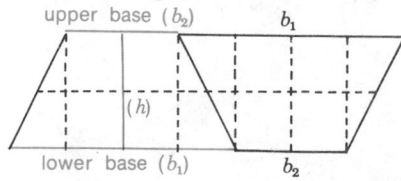

Formula

$A = \frac{1}{2} \times (b_1 + b_2) \times h$

$A = \frac{1}{2} \times (4 \text{ cm} + 2 \text{ cm}) \times 2 \text{ cm}$

$A = \frac{1}{2} \times 12 \text{ cm}^2$

$A = 6 \text{ cm}^2$

Notice that if you cut a circle into pieces as shown, the pieces will fit together to form a figure that looks like a rectangle. The length of the rectangle is $\frac{1}{2}$ the circumference ($\pi \times d$, or $\pi \times 2 \times r$) of the circle. The height of the rectangle is the radius *(r)* of the circle.

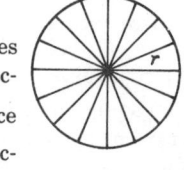

Formula

$A = \pi \times r \times r$, or
$A = \pi \times r^2$

r^2 means $r \times r$. Read as "r squared."

EXAMPLE. We will use 3.14 as an approximation for π when finding the area of a circle.

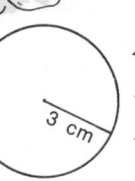

$A = \pi \times r^2$

$A = \pi \times (3 \text{ cm})^2$

$A = \pi \times 9 \text{ cm}^2$

$A \approx 28.26 \text{ cm}^2$

$$\begin{array}{r} 3.14 \\ \times 9 \\ \hline 28.26 \end{array}$$

142

Assignments

BASIC
page 142 Discuss
page 143 exercises 1−13
Basic Worksheet 38

AVERAGE
page 142 Discuss
page 143 exercises 1−15
Enrichment Worksheet 38

ENRICHED
page 142 Discuss
page 143 exercises 1−16
Enrichment Worksheet 38

EXTRA PRACTICE
page 384 set 46

EXERCISES

Give each area.

1.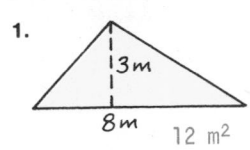
3m
8m
12 m²

2.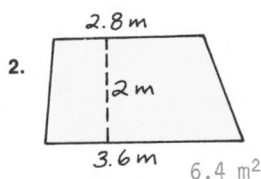
2.8 m
2m
3.6 m
6.4 m²

3.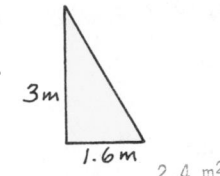
3m
1.6 m
2.4 m²

4.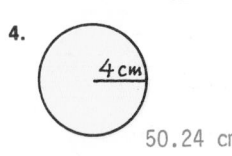
4 cm
50.24 cm²

5.
108 km
9156.24 km²

6.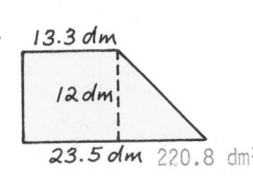
13.3 dm
12 dm
23.5 dm
220.8 dm²

7.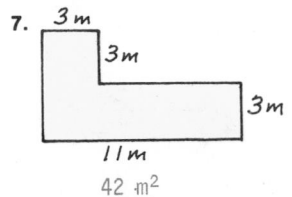
3 m
3m
3m
11m
42 m²

8.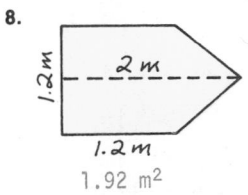
1.2 m
2 m
1.2 m
1.92 m²

9.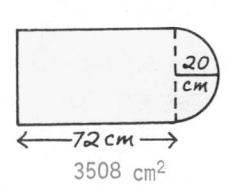
20 cm
72 cm
3508 cm²

First measure each dimension to the nearest mm. Then compute the area. Answers may vary slightly.

10.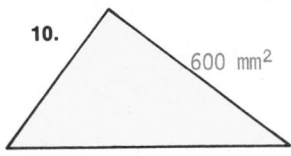
600 mm²

11.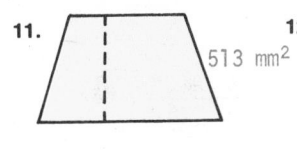
513 mm²

12.
452.16 mm²

Solve.

13. A triangular flower garden has a base of 42 decimeters and a height of 23 decimeters. What is its area?
483 dm²

14. A pizza house sells large pizzas (30 cm in diameter) for $4.80 and medium pizzas (15 cm in diameter) for $3.20. Which is the better buy?
a large pizza

15. A revolving lawn sprinkler sprays water a distance of 10 meters. How many square meters of lawn will it sprinkle without being moved?
314

16. A redwood deck in the shape of a trapezoid has a height of 4 meters and bases of 5 meters and 8.1 meters. If a liter of stain covers 7 square meters, will 4 liters be enough to stain the deck? yes

143

Follow-up Activities

Reinforcement Give students a geoboard or some graph paper. Have them construct and give the area of some figures they have studied.

A more challenging activity would be to have the students construct a square, a rectangle, a parallelogram, a triangle, and a trapezoid that all have the same area. Here is an example where each figure has an area of 16 square units.

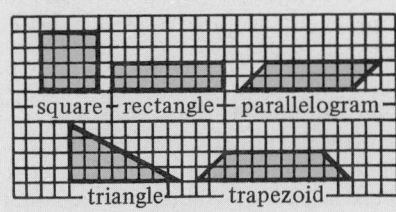

square — rectangle — parallelogram
triangle — trapezoid

Enrichment Have students cut from 1-inch graph paper a figure like the one on the left below. Point out that the area of the figure can be found by adding $3^2 + 4^2$. Have them cut along the dotted lines, getting five regions and put the pieces together to get a square that has an area of 5^2. Point out that $3^2 + 4^2 = 5^2$. This activity is an intuitive development of the Rule of Pythagoras.

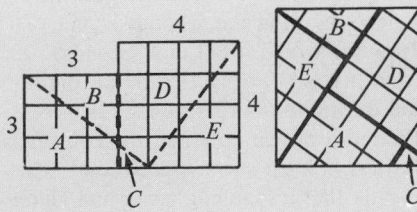

EXCURSION

The grid below shows the location of Juan's house and school. What's the shortest distance he can walk to get from his house to school?

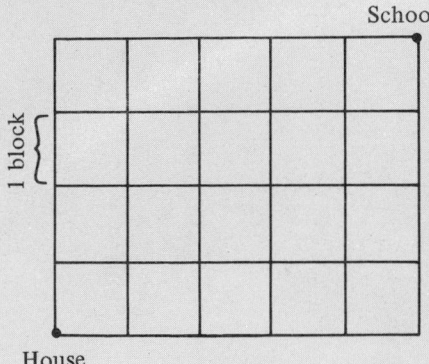

School
1 block
House
9 blocks

(core) Lesson 63   143

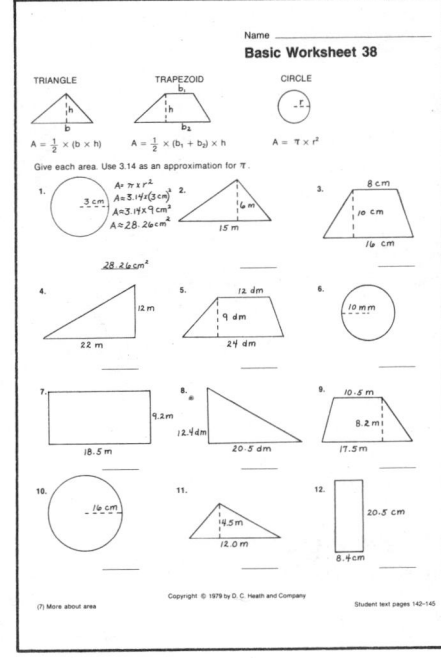
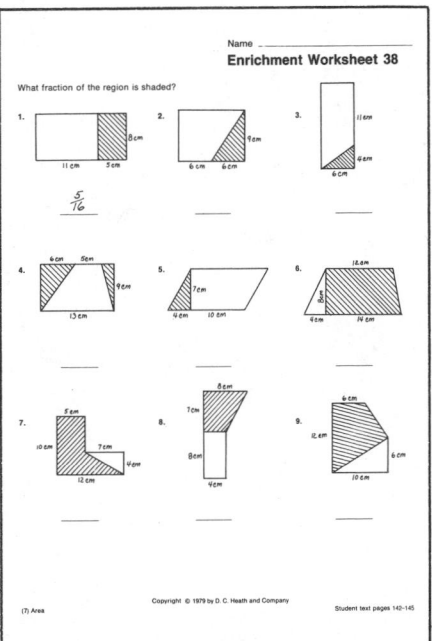

Suggested Lesson Plan

Introduction Before assigning page 144, quickly review the concepts and skills practiced. Go over using the "place-value" chart for renaming measurements within the metric system. Have students give you the formulas for the perimeter and area of the figures in exercises 22–27.

Using the pages Have students complete the practice exercises in class. You may want students to correct their papers in class as you read the answers so that they, and you, can react immediately to the results. Outline review of specific lessons for students who miss six or more of exercises 1–21, three or more of exercises 22–27.

Go over the exposition on page 145. Be sure students realize that the formula requires that the distance be in meters and the time in seconds. Ask students to compute the distance a body would fall in 1 second. ($d = 4.9t^2 = 4.9 \times 1^2 = 4.9$) How far would it fall in 2 seconds? ($d = 4.9 \times 2^2 = 19.6$) How far did it fall during the second second? (It fell 4.9 m in the first second and 19.6 m in the first two seconds. It must have fallen 14.7 m in the second second.) How far would it fall in 3 seconds? ($d = 4.9 \times 3^2 = 44.1$) How far did it fall during the third second? (24.5 m) Students should note that the body falls farther in each successive second. This means that it is falling faster and faster each second.

When students complete the exercises on page 144, let them go on to page 145.

Practice exercises

Complete.

1. 1 km = __?__ m   2. 3 km = __?__ m   3. 4.7 km = __?__ m
             1000   3000   4700

4. 1 m = __?__ cm   5. 23 m = __?__ cm   6. 2.91 m = __?__ cm
            100   2300   291

7. 1 m = __?__ mm   8. 2 m = __?__ mm   9. 4.1 m = __?__ mm
            1000   2000   4100

10. 1 cm = __?__ mm   11. 15 cm = __?__ mm   12. 3.21 cm = __?__ mm
            10   150   32.1

13. 10 mm = __?__ cm   14. 20 mm = __?__ cm   15. 14 mm = __?__ cm
            1   2   1.4

16. 4.2 mm = __?__ cm   17. 4.2 cm = __?__ mm   18. 523 cm = __?__ m
            0.42   42   5.23

19. 421 mm = __?__ m   20. 4210 mm = __?__ m   21. 456 m = __?__ km
            0.421   4.21   0.456

Give each perimeter (or circumference) and area.

22. 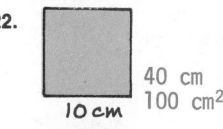 10 cm — 40 cm / 100 cm²

23. 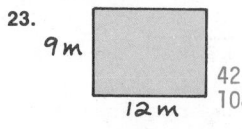 9 m, 12 m — 42 m / 108 m²

24. 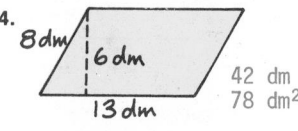 8 dm, 6 dm, 13 dm — 42 dm / 78 dm²

25. 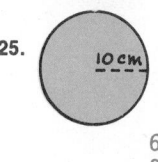 10 cm — 62.8 cm / 314 cm²

26. 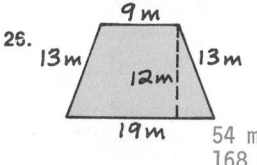 9 m, 13 m, 12 m, 13 m, 19 m — 54 m / 168 m²

27. 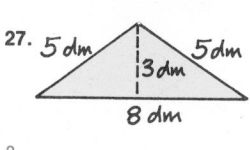 5 dm, 5 dm, 3 dm, 8 dm — 18 dm / 12 dm²

Tell whether the situation involves perimeter or area.

28. fencing a yard   29. cultivating a garden   30. carpeting a floor
    perimeter   area   area

Solve.

31. The area of a rectangular lot is 1229.1 m². What is its width if its length is 48.2 m?   25.5 m

★32. Eighty-three meters of fencing were used to fence in a square garden. What is the area of the garden?   430.5625 m²

Divide the area of the circle by the area of the square that it is in.

 12 cm   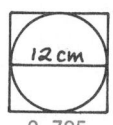 15 mm   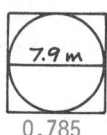 7.9 m

0.785   0.785   0.785

144

Assignments

BASIC

page 144 exercises 1–30
page 145 exercises 1–12
Basic Worksheet 38

AVERAGE

page 144 exercises 1–32
page 145 exercises 1–14
Enrichment Worksheet 38

ENRICHED

page 144 exercises 1–32
page 145 exercises 1–15
Enrichment Worksheet 38

REVIEW PRACTICE

page 381 set 35

Mathematics and science

The picture shows that an object was dropped (not thrown) from the top of a water tower. The distance in meters that a free-falling object drops is given by the formula:

$$d = 4.9 \times t^2$$

where t is the time in seconds. (The formula assumes that there is no air resistance.) Using the formula, we can find how far the object fell in the first 3 seconds.

$$d = 4.9 \times t^2$$
$$d = 4.9 \times 3^2 \quad (4.9 \times 9)$$
$$d = 44.1$$

So the object fell 44.1 meters in the first 3 seconds.

The velocity (speed) of a free-falling object increases as the object falls. We can find the velocity (V) after the object has been falling for a given time (t) by using this formula:

$V = 9.8\,t$ This formula gives the velocity in meters per second.

EXERCISES

How far would a free-falling object fall in each of these times?

1. 2 s	**2.** 4 s	**3.** 2.5 s	**4.** 5 s	**5.** 7.2 s	**6.** 0.5 minute
19.6 m	78.4 m	30.625 m	122.5 m	254.016 m	4410 m

What would be the velocity of a free-falling object at the end of each of these times?

7. 5 s	**8.** 3 s	**9.** 30 s	**10.** 6.5 s	**11.** 8.2 s	**12.** 16.4 s
49 m/s	29.4 m/s	294 m/s	63.7 m/s	80.36 m/s	160.72 m/s

Solve.

13. How long would it take a free-falling object to fall 490 meters?   10 s

14. How much would the velocity of a free-falling object increase between 3 seconds and 8 seconds?   49 m/s

★15. One kilometer an hour is about 0.28 meter per second. How far would a free-falling object have to fall to have a velocity of 10 kilometers an hour?   about 0.4 m

145

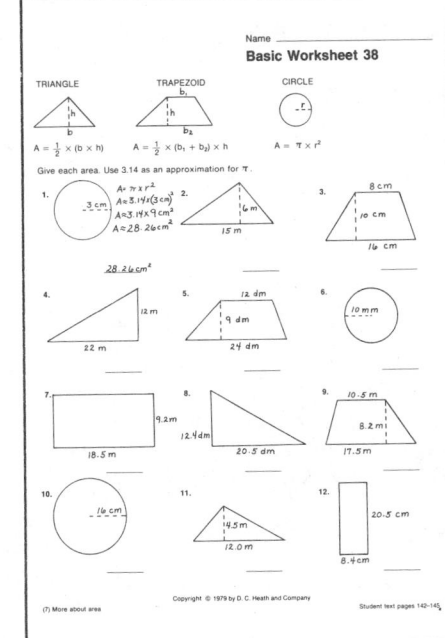

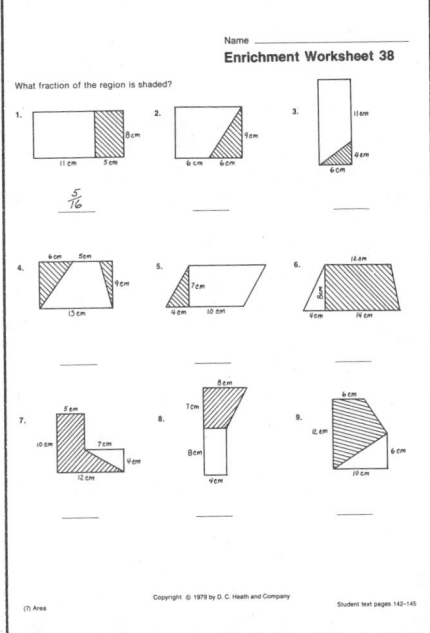

Follow-up Activities

Reinforcement At this point you may wish to use the following game to review and practice the computational skills that have been introduced thus far. Divide the students into two well-balanced teams. Have a player from one team go to the chalkboard and give a problem. Call on a volunteer from the other team to go to the chalkboard and work the problem. If her work is correct, her team is awarded 1 point. If her work is incorrect, the player who made up the problem may earn a point for his team by working the problem correctly. Next have a player from the other team make up a problem. Continue to play a game until all players have worked on a problem at the chalkboard. The team earning the greater number of points wins the game.

Enrichment Since more able students will probably give more challenging problems, the game above would also be appropriate for better students.

EXCURSION

Put the numbers 1, 2, 3, 4, 5, and 6 in the circles so that the sums along the sides of the triangle are all equal.

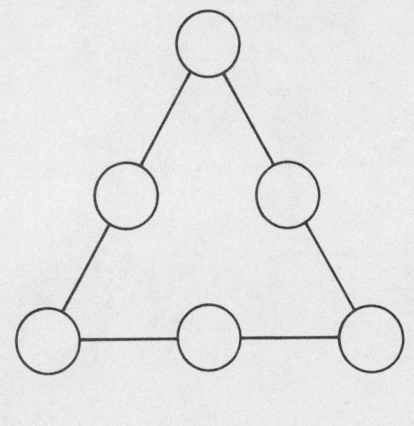

1	1
6 5	6 4
2 4 3	3 2 5
2	4
5 3	3 2
4 1 6	5 1 6

STUDENT OBJECTIVES
To recognize prisms.
To compute the surface areas of prisms.

VOCABULARY
prism, rectangular prism, triangular prism, base, surface area

Suggested Lesson Plan

Introduction Collect models of prisms to show your class. Wooden or plastic models made especially for mathematics classes would be best, but other objects will suffice. For example, books or bricks can be used to show what a rectangular prism is like. Use the models to show what a prism is—a three-dimensional figure that has two congruent faces called *bases* that are in parallel planes and lateral faces that are rectangular. It would be best to show prisms that are not perpendicular prisms first, because in a rectangular prism any pair of opposite faces can be considered to be the bases.

Using the pages Go over the exposition on page 146. Be sure that students understand that in a rectangular prism any pair of opposite faces can be called the bases.
   Assign the exercises.

Surface area of a prism

A **rectangular prism** has 6 faces.

A **triangular prism** has 5 faces.

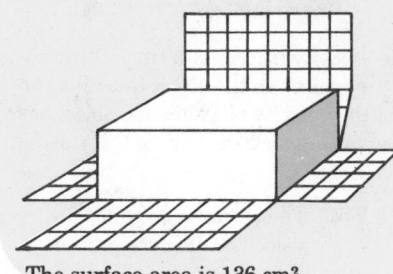

The **bases** of a prism are 2 faces that are the same size and shape and that are in parallel planes.

The **surface area** of a prism is the sum of the areas of all the faces.

The area of each face is:

top	--- 32 cm²
bottom	--- 32 cm²
right	--- 12 cm²
left	--- 12 cm²
front	--- 24 cm²
back	--- 24 cm²

The surface area is 136 cm².

EXERCISES
Give the surface area of each rectangular prism.

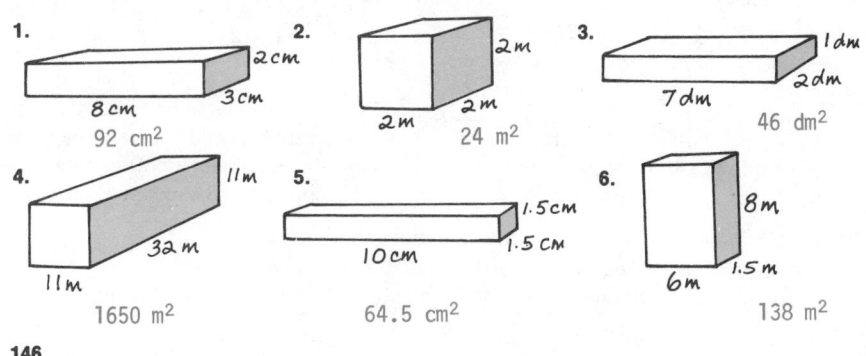

1. 8 cm, 3 cm, 2 cm
   92 cm²

2. 2 m, 2 m, 2 m
   24 m²

3. 7 dm, 2 dm, 1 dm
   46 dm²

4. 11 m, 11 m, 32 m
   1650 m²

5. 10 cm, 1.5 cm, 1.5 cm
   64.5 cm²

6. 6 m, 8 m, 1.5 m
   138 m²

146

Assignments

BASIC
page 146   exercises 1–6
page 147   exercises 7–9
Basic Worksheet 39

AVERAGE
page 146   exercises 1–6
page 147   exercises 7–12
Enrichment Worksheet 39

ENRICHED
page 146   exercises 1–6
page 147   exercises 7–12, Excursion
Enrichment Worksheet 39

REVIEW PRACTICE
page 382   set 36

Give the surface area of each triangular prism. Notice that each triangle is a right triangle (has a right angle).

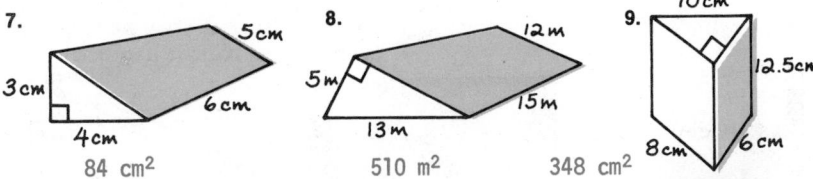

7.

3cm — 5cm — 6cm — 4cm

84 cm²

8.

12 m — 5 m — 13 m — 15 m

510 m²

9.

10cm — 12.5cm — 8cm — 6cm

348 cm²

Solve.

10. A rectangular box is to be gift-wrapped. One base of the box is a rectangle 18 cm by 24 cm. The height of the box is 14 cm. How much paper will it take to cover the box? **2040 cm²**

11. A wastebasket shaped like a rectangular prism is made of metal. The bottom is a 20-cm square and the height is 30 cm. How many square centimeters of metal did it take to make the basket? **2800 cm²**

12. Get a rectangular box. Measure each dimension to the nearest centimeter and compute the surface area.

EXCURSION ▨▨▨▨▨▨▨▨▨▨▨▨▨▨▨▨▨▨▨▨▨▨▨▨▨
The large block was made by stacking 27 white blocks together. All faces of the large block were then painted green.

How many small blocks have

0 green faces? **1** 1 green face? **6** 2 green faces? **12**
3 green faces? **8** 4 green faces? **0**

147

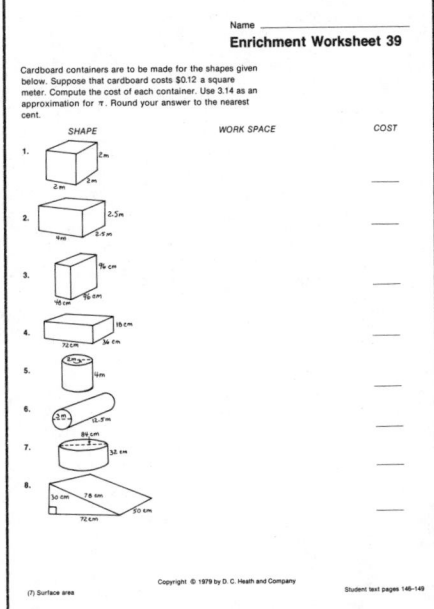

Follow-up Activities

Reinforcement You may wish to use the following activity to provide students with further experiences with surface area. Display 8 blocks. Arrange them in some manner and ask students to give the surface area of the arrangement. For example, this is a possible arrangement:

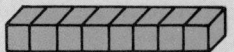

The surface area is 34 units. (The unit of area used is one face of a block.) Continue making arrangements and having students give the surface area for each arrangement. Emphasize that in each case they are working with the same number of blocks (same volume), but are getting different surface areas. Ask students how they would arrange the blocks to get the smallest surface area. (In the shape of a cube)

Enrichment Some students may wish to determine the surface area of their classroom.

EXCURSION
Here is part of a table.

1	2	3	4	5
6	7	8	9	10
11	12	13	14	15
16	17	18	19	20

This arrow means move 1 square to the right: →

This means move 1 square down: ↓

What do you think these arrows mean?

↘ ↑ ↗ ↘

You are given a starting number and some moves. What number do you end on?

1. 3 ↘   2. 9 →   3. 17 ↗   4. 20 ↓

5. 21 →→   6. 30 ↓←   7. 17 ↘↘

1. 9   2. 10   3. 13   4. 25

5. 23   6. 34   7. 29

Suggested Lesson Plan

Introduction Bring an oatmeal box (cylinder) to class. Preferably, the top of the box should not be cut completely free from the box. Show the box as an example of a cylinder. Call attention to the fact that a cylinder is very much like a prism. There are two bases that are congruent circles and that are in parallel planes. There is just one lateral face, however. Ask students to tell you how they would find the areas of the bases. ($A = \pi r^2$) Next, show them how to find the lateral area. Cut out the bottom of the box. Do not cut the bottom completely off. Next cut the lateral face straight from one base to the other. Carefully open and flatten the lateral face. Students should see that the lateral face flattens to a rectangle. Ask students to tell the height of the rectangle. (the height of the cylinder) What is the length of the rectangle? (the circumference of the base) The area is the height, h, times the length, πd. The surface area is the sum of the areas of the bases and the lateral area.

Using the pages Go over the exposition on page 148 for another example. Assign the exercises. If students have trouble with the word problems, they should try to draw pictures.

For exercise 13, have students draw a diagram of the area the goat can cover. Then they should divide that area into regions whose area they can find.

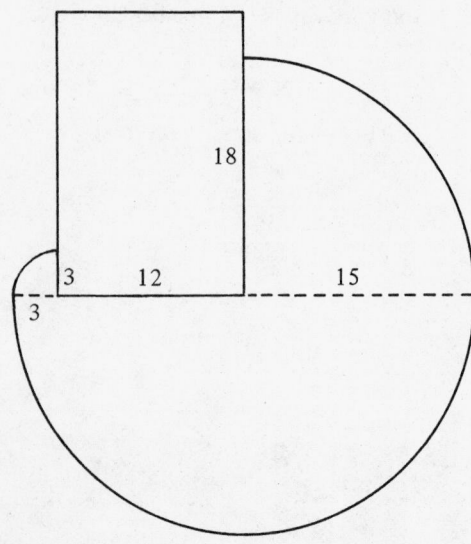

Surface area of a cylinder

Here is a cylinder:

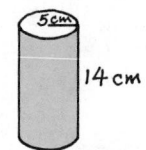

To find its surface area, we might think about cutting it apart like this:

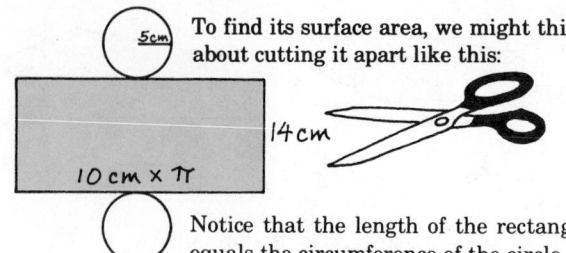

Notice that the length of the rectangle equals the circumference of the circle.

To find the surface area, we can add the areas of the circles and the area of the rectangle.

Area of Each Circle

$A = \pi \times r^2$

$A \approx 3.14 \times (5 \text{ cm})^2$

$A \approx 78.5 \text{ cm}^2$

So, the area of both circles is about 157 square centimeters.

Area of Rectangle

$A = l \times w$

$A = (10 \text{ cm} \times \pi) \times 14 \text{ cm}$

$A \approx (10 \text{ cm} \times 3.14) \times 14 \text{ cm}$

$A \approx 31.4 \text{ cm} \times 14 \text{ cm}$

$A \approx 439.6 \text{ cm}^2$

$$157 \text{ cm}^2 + 439.6 \text{ cm}^2 = 596.6 \text{ cm}^2$$

The surface area of the cylinder is about 596.6 cm².

EXERCISES

Give the surface area of each cylinder. Use 3.14 as an approximation for π.

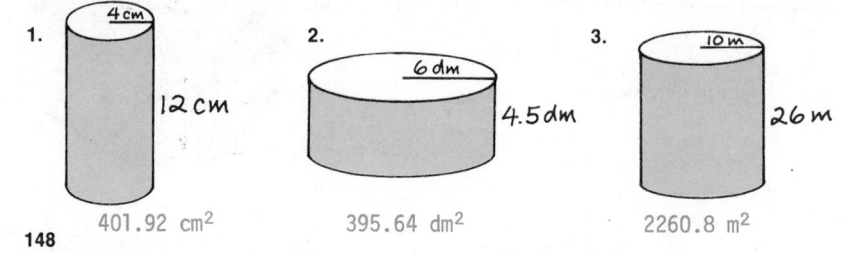

1. 4 cm, 12 cm — 401.92 cm²
2. 6 dm, 4.5 dm — 395.64 dm²
3. 10 m, 26 m — 2260.8 m²

148

Assignments

BASIC
page 148 exercises 1−3
page 149 exercises 4−10
Basic Worksheet 39

AVERAGE
page 148 exercises 1−3
page 149 exercises 4−13
Enrichment Worksheet 39

ENRICHED
page 148 exercises 1−3
page 149 exercises 4−13
Enrichment Worksheet 39

EXTRA PRACTICE
page 384 set 47

4.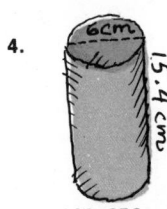
6cm
15.4 cm
346.656 cm²

5.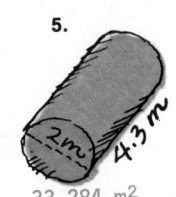
2m
4.3m
33.284 m²

6.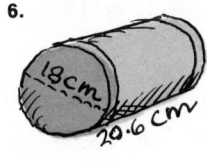
18cm
20.6 cm
1672.992 cm²

How much cardboard is in each cereal box? Use 3.14 as an approximation for π.

7.
PUFFO
Breakfast
CEREAL
2dm
0.6dm
1.4dm   9.68 dm²

8.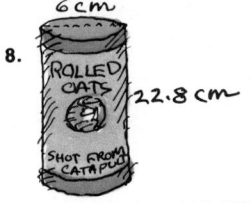
6cm
ROLLED
OATS
22.8cm
SHOT FROM A
CATAPULT
486.072 cm²

Solve.

9. A crepe-paper border is to be placed around some rectangular tables that measure 1 meter by 2 meters. How many meters of crepe paper will be needed for 7 tables?   42

10. A fence is to be built around a rectangular lot that is 22 m long and 13 m wide. If fencing costs $3.25 a meter, how much will it cost to fence the lot? $227.50

11. A triangular sail has a base of 5 meters and a height of 8 meters. How many square meters of sail is that?   20

12. A dog is leashed to a stake. If the leash is 4 meters long, how many square meters does the dog have to roam?   50.24

★**13.** A goat is tied to one corner of a barn by a 15-meter rope. The barn is 12 m wide by 18 m long. How much area does the goat have to roam?   536.94 m²

12m   18m   15m

How much must be shaved off the radius of a circular metal plate with a radius of 7.5 cm to get a circular plate with an area of 175 cm²?   about 0.035 cm

149

Follow-up Activities

Reinforcement Have students bring in food boxes that are shapes they have been studying. For example, cereal boxes are rectangular prisms, oatmeal boxes are cylinders, and there are some products packaged in triangular prisms. Students can arrange a display identifying these different shapes.

Enrichment Have students design some mobiles of figures they have studied, such as the square, rectangle, parallelogram, triangle, trapezoid, circle, rectangular prism, cube, triangular prism, and cylinder. To make a mobile that balances, students should start at the bottom and balance as they work up. Hang the completed mobiles in the classroom.

CALCULATOR ACTIVITY
Have students measure and then use calculators to determine the surface area of the models brought in.

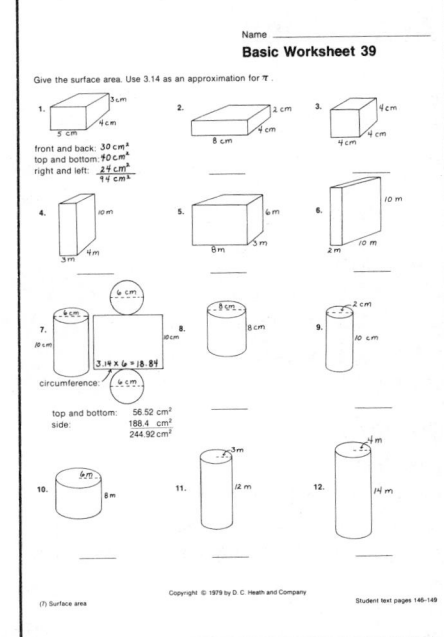

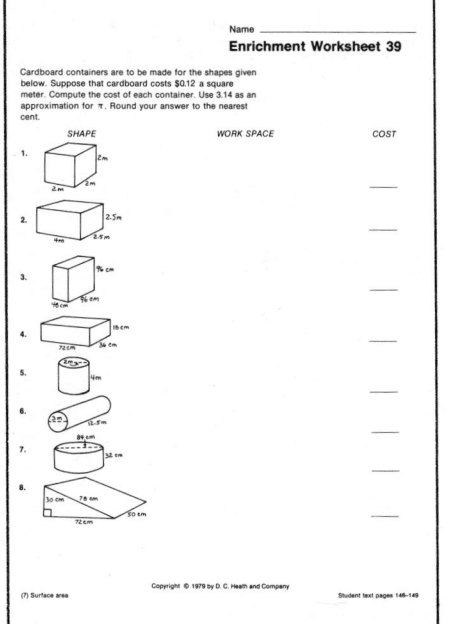

Suggested Lesson Plan

Introduction Before class build a 4-by-2-by-3 pile of cubical blocks. Then use thin cardboard to make an open-topped box that just fits around the pile of blocks.

Remind students that to measure length, we use a length as our unit and "pack" the length to be measured with copies of the unit length. The count of these units is the measure of the length. Similarly for area and angles. Now, to measure volume, we do a similar thing. We pick a volume as our unit. Show the cubical blocks. Now, to measure the volume of the box that you made, fill the box with the blocks. Count the blocks. That is the measure of the volume. Point out to students that we can have the same kinds of problems that we had with area. Usually the blocks won't fit so nicely into the box. Estimating is very difficult. So we use what we learned from filling the box to find a way of measuring indirectly—by computing. An easy way of counting the blocks in the sample box was to multiply 4 times 2 to find the number of blocks in one layer and then multiply that by 3 to find the total number of blocks. This suggests that we can always compute the volume of a rectangular solid by multiplying the length by the width by the height.

Using the pages Go over the exposition on page 150. Be sure students understand that in any prism we can find the number of blocks that there would be in one layer by finding the area of the base. In a prism all layers have the same number of blocks, so we can find the volume by multiplying the number of blocks in one layer by the number of layers—that is, by the height. Thus we get this general formula for the volume of a prism:

$$V = Bh$$

Assign exercises 1−10 for written work. Have students draw and label a prism for problems 7−10. They may not be skilled at drawing prisms, but a diagram should help them with the concepts involved.

Before the end of the class period have students work the Keeping Skills Sharp. Correct their work as they finish and note any students who miss more than three problems.

Volume of a prism

To find the volume of the box, we pick a unit 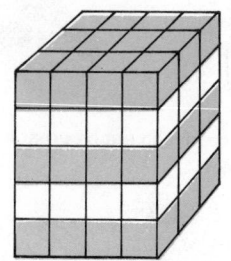, a cubic centimeter (cm³), and see how many cubes it takes to fill the box. There are 12 cm³ in each layer and there are 5 layers. So the volume is 60 cm³.

We can also find the volume by this formula.

$$V = l \times w \times h \quad \boxed{\text{Formula}}$$
$$V = 4\text{ cm} \times 3\text{ cm} \times 5\text{ cm}$$
$$V = 60\text{ cm}^3$$

Notice that the volume of a rectangular prism is equal to the area of a base times the height. So the volume can also be found by using the formula $V = B \times h$. (B stands for the area of a base.)

To find the volume of a triangular prism, multiply the area of a base (B) by the height (h).

$$V = B \times h \quad \boxed{\text{Formula}}$$
$$V = \frac{1}{2} \times (3\text{ cm} \times 4\text{ cm}) \times 7\text{ cm}$$

(6 square cm) $\quad V = 6\text{ cm}^2 \times 7\text{ cm}$

(42 cubic cm) $\quad V = 42\text{ cm}^3$

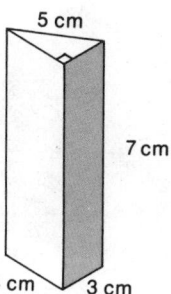

150

Assignments

BASIC
page 150 Discuss
page 151 exercises 1−6,
    Keeping Skills Sharp
Basic Worksheet 40

AVERAGE
page 150 Discuss
page 151 exercises 1−8,
    Keeping Skills Sharp
Enrichment Worksheet 40

ENRICHED
page 150 Discuss
page 151 exercises 1−10,
    Keeping Skills Sharp
Enrichment Worksheet 40

REVIEW PRACTICE
page 382 set 37

EXERCISES

Give each volume.

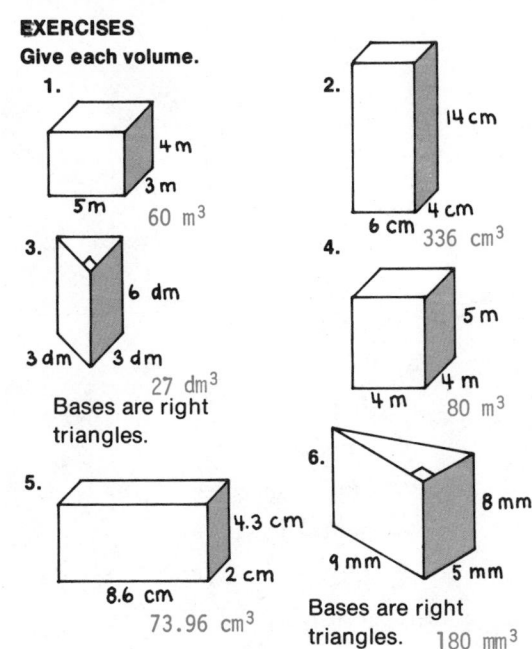

1. 4 m, 3 m, 5 m — 60 m³

2. 14 cm, 4 cm, 6 cm — 336 cm³

3. 6 dm, 3 dm, 3 dm — 27 dm³
Bases are right triangles.

4. 5 m, 4 m, 4 m — 80 m³

5. 4.3 cm, 2 cm, 8.6 cm — 73.96 cm³

6. 8 mm, 9 mm, 5 mm — 180 mm³
Bases are right triangles.

Solve.

7. A trench 0.6 meter wide, 1.2 meters deep, and 10 meters long was dug for a water main. How many cubic meters of earth were removed?   7.2

8. A box that is 8 centimeters wide, 12 centimeters long, and 4.5 centimeters high is to be filled with sand. How many cubic centimeters of sand are needed?   432

9. A rectangular form that measures 120 decimeters long, 50 centimeters wide, and 24 decimeters high is to be filled with concrete. If concrete costs $36 a cubic meter, what will be the total cost of the concrete? $518.40

10. Find the volume of your classroom in cubic meters. Make your measurements to the nearest 0.1 meter.

Keeping Skills Sharp

Multiply.

1. 4.5
   × 2.1
   —————
   9.45

2. 0.58
   × 5.2
   —————
   3.016

3. 7.4
   × 0.36
   —————
   2.664

4. 5.3
   × 2.9
   —————
   15.37

5. 6.7
   × 0.83
   —————
   5.561

6. 48
   × 3.4
   —————
   163.2

7. 0.94
   × 36
   —————
   33.84

8. 8.7
   × 4.5
   —————
   39.15

9. 2.86
   × 8.1
   —————
   23.166

10. 1.78
    × 8.3
    —————
    14.774

11. 8.96
    × 1.42
    —————
    12.7232

12. 79.5
    × 0.206
    —————
    16.377

151

Follow-up Activities

Reinforcement You may wish to use the following activity to provide students with further experiences with volume. Display a collection of rectangular boxes. Have students measure their dimensions to the nearest centimeter and record their measurements. Finally, have them compute the volume of each box. Be sure to emphasize that their computed volumes will be approximate.

Enrichment Give each student a piece of graph paper. Have the students cut and fold a rectangular prism having a surface area of 54 square units and the greatest possible volume. (Use the side of a small square as the unit.) Solution:

The volume is 27 cubic units.

CALCULATOR ACTIVITY
Have students measure all the models of prisms that they have brought in. Since many of the dimensions will not be "even" numbers, students can use a calculator to compute the volumes.

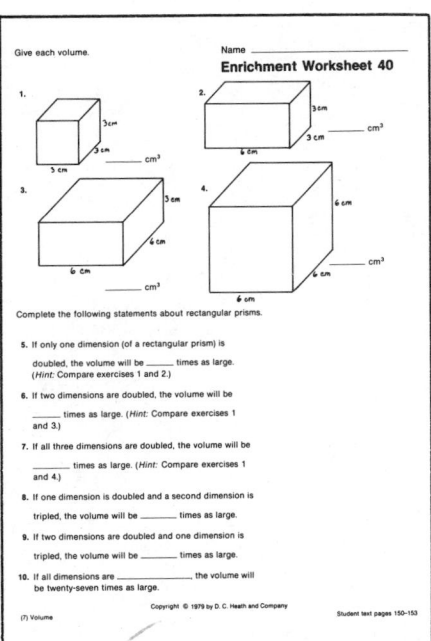

(core) Lesson 67   **151**

STUDENT OBJECTIVE
To find the volume of a cylinder.

Suggested Lesson Plan

Introduction Make a drawing of a prism on the board. Beside it make a drawing of a cylinder. Review the formula and the concept for finding the volume of a prism—that is, finding the area of the base and multiplying that by the height. Develop the idea that the volume of a cylinder can be found the same way.

Using the pages Since a cylinder is like a prism with a circular base, the same general formula for the volume will give the volume of a cylinder. Go over the exposition on page 152. Remind the students to use 3.14 as the value for π. Assign exercises 1–15 for written work. Be ready to assist individual students on the word problems. Encourage them to refer to the drawing or to make a diagram so they can see the relationship in the problems. Have calculators available for students to try the calculator problems.

Volume of a cylinder

Remember that you can find the volumes of prisms like these by multiplying the area of a base (B) by the height (h).

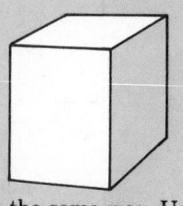 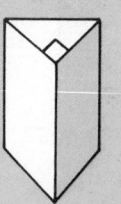

The volume of a cylinder can be found in the same way. Use 3.14 as an approximation for π.

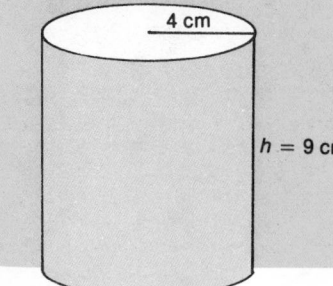

$$V = B \times h$$
$$V = (\pi \times r^2) \times h$$
$$V = (\pi \times 16 \text{ cm}^2) \times 9 \text{ cm}$$
$$V \approx (3.14 \times 16 \text{ cm}^2) \times 9 \text{ cm}$$
$$V \approx 50.24 \text{ cm}^2 \times 9 \text{ cm}$$
$$V \approx 452.16 \text{ cm}^3$$

EXERCISES

Give the volume of each cylinder. Use 3.14 as an approximation for π.

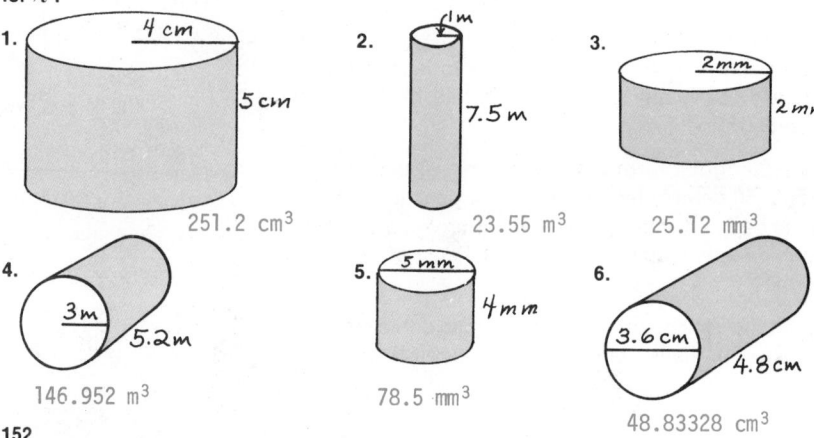

1. 4 cm, 5 cm — 251.2 cm³
2. 1 m, 7.5 m — 23.55 m³
3. 2 mm, 2 mm — 25.12 mm³
4. 3 m, 5.2 m — 146.952 m³
5. 5 mm, 4 mm — 78.5 mm³
6. 3.6 cm, 4.8 cm — 48.83328 cm³

152

Assignments

BASIC
page 152 exercises 1–6
page 153 exercises 7–12
Basic Worksheet 40

AVERAGE
page 152 exercises 1–6
page 153 exercises 7–14
Enrichment Worksheet 40

ENRICHED
page 152 exercises 1–6
page 153 exercises 7–15
Enrichment Worksheet 40

EXTRA PRACTICE
page 385 set 48

Solve. (Use 3.14 as an approximation for π.)

7. What is the volume of the can?

0.8635 cm³

8. How many cubic centimeters of water would this pipe hold?

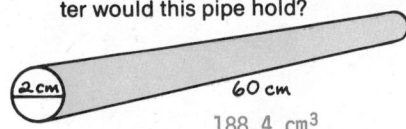

60 cm

188.4 cm³

9. How much metal would be needed to make a tin can having a radius of 6 cm and a height of 16 cm?
828.96 cm²

10. The volume of a tin can is 113.04 cubic cm. The radius of the can is 3 cm. What is its height?   4 cm

11. Two cylinders have a radius of 4 cm each. One cylinder is 3 cm high and the other is 6 cm high. What are the volumes?   150.72 cm³, 301.44 cm³

12. Two cylinders have a height of 8 cm each. One cylinder has a radius of 2 cm and the other has a radius of 4 cm. What are their volumes?
100.48 cm³, 401.92 cm³

13. A cylinder-shaped water tower has a radius of 4.2 m and a height of 24.5 m. How many cubic meters of water does it hold?
1357.0452

14. What is the volume of the largest cylinder contained in a 6-cm cube? *Hint:* First draw a picture.
169.56 cm³

15. Get some prisms and cylinders. Measure each dimension to the nearest centimeter and compute the volumes.

How many cm³ of metal are there in this block? (The hole goes all the way through.)   232

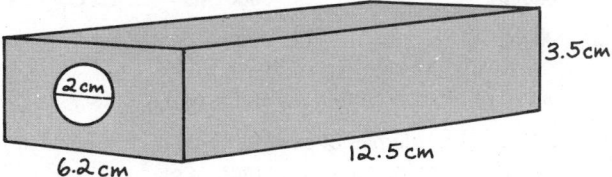

153

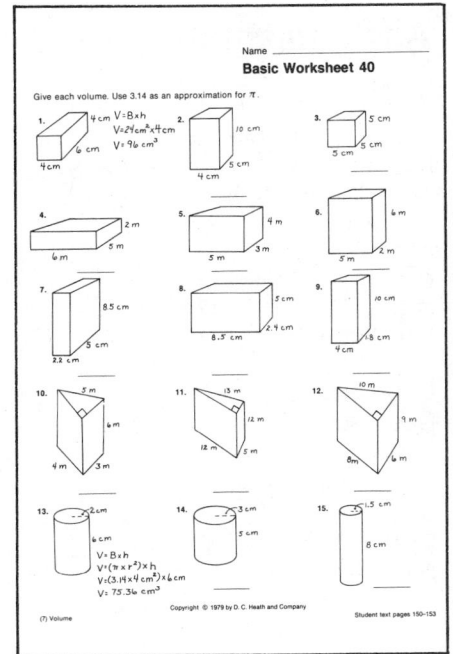

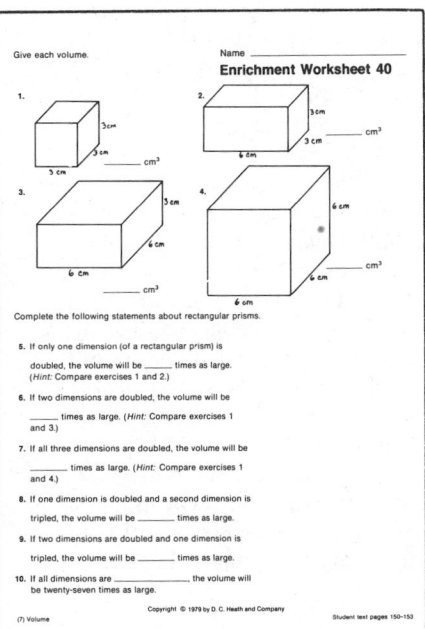

(core) Lesson 68   153

Follow-up Activities

Reinforcement You may wish to use this activity to do some more work with volume and to precede the next lesson, which deals with measuring capacity. Obtain some quart or gallon cans. (Paint cans would work nicely.) Have students measure the diameter and height of each can to the nearest centimeter. Ask them to compute the volume in cubic centimeters.

Enrichment Ask students if they can think of a way to determine the volume of some irregular solid, such as a rock. If a reasonable method is not suggested, you may wish to suggest the following method. Place a container inside a rectangular cake pan. Fill the container completely full with water. Slowly submerge the rock in the container. The volume of the rock is the same as the volume of water that overflows into the cake pan. Have students use such a technique to determine the volume of some irregularly shaped solids. You may wish to have them guess the volume before measuring it.

EXCURSION
Here is a table. (See page 147.)

1	2	3	4	5	6	7
8	9	10	11	12	13	14
15	16	17	18	19	20	21

Make up rules for the following moves on the table.

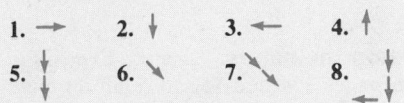

1. →   2. ↓   3. ←   4. ↑

5. ↓   6. ↘   7. ↘   8. ↓

1. add 1   **2.** add 7
3. subtract 1   **4.** subtract 7
5. add 14   **6.** add 8
7. add 16   **8.** add 13

(core) Lesson 68   **153**

STUDENT OBJECTIVES
To measure liquid volume with metric units.
To measure weight with metric units.

VOCABULARY
liter, milliliter, gram, milligram, kilogram

Suggested Lesson Plan

Introduction Explain to students that if a three-dimensional figure is a container, we often refer to its volume as its *capacity*. We can measure capacity or liquid volume with such units as cubic centimeters, cubic meters, or with metric units for measuring liquid volume such as liter, milliliter, etc. The prefixes for the units have the same meaning as the prefixes for similar linear units. Not all of the units with the special prefixes are normally used, so students should become more familiar with the common units—liter and milliliter.

For measuring weight, students should become familiar with the commonly used units—gram, milligram, and kilogram.

Students can change units within the metric system for liquid volume or weight by two different methods. They can use a "place-value" chart as they did for linear units or use the relationship between the units to change units. The latter method will probably be satisfactory since there are only two commonly used units for liquid volume and only three commonly used units for weight.

Using the pages Use the exposition on pages 154 and 155 to reinforce your introduction. Use the pictures to help the pupils develop mental images of the "size" of the units introduced. You may want to gather objects that can be referred to as close to the metric units in volume.

    1 liter—quart container
1 milliliter—1 cubic centimeter cube
          pencil eraser
    1 gram—weight of a paper clip
1 kilogram—weight of a textbook

Assign exercises 1—16 for the liquid volume exercises and exercises 17—33 for weight exercises. Try to observe as students work on the exercises and point out answers that are not reasonable.

NOTE: You should be aware that grams and kilograms are units of mass in the metric system. There is disagreement concerning the use of the words *weight*

and *weigh* in connection with these units. Scientists define weight as a force and do not allow the use of *weight* in reference to mass. Therefore, they disapprove of saying "My weight is 60 kilograms." Instead, they would say "My mass is 60 kilograms."

In nontechnical everyday use, however, the word *weight* usually refers to amount of substance, that is, mass. Thus both children and adults will frequently hear the words *weigh* and *weight* used in connection with milligrams, grams, kilograms, and tonnes. Although it will do no harm to point out to students that *weight* will take on a more precise meaning later as they study science, it would be inappropriate at this time to attempt to explain the distinction between mass (the amount of substance) and weight (the force of gravity upon this mass).

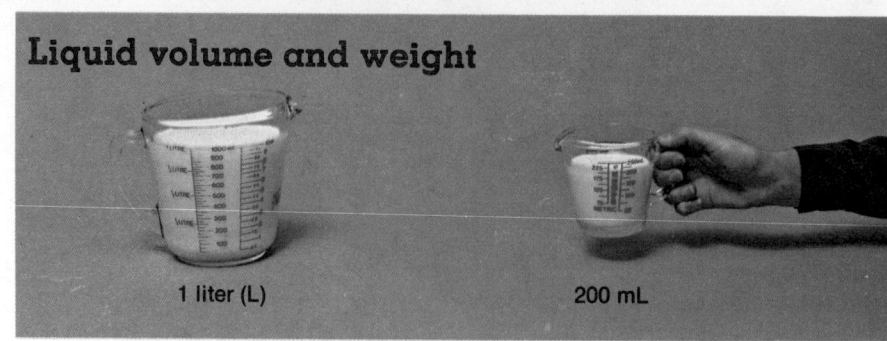

Liquid volume and weight

       1 liter (L)   200 mL

A unit for measuring liquid volume is the **liter (L)**. A liter is 1000 cubic centimeters.

The **milliliter (mL)** is used to measure small liquid volumes. A milliliter is 1 cubic centimeter.

$$1000 \text{ mL} = 1 \text{ L}$$

or $1 \text{ mL} = 0.001 \text{ L}$

EXERCISES
Choose the correct liquid volume.

1.
  a. 1.9 L ✓
  b. 1.9 mL

2.
  a. 355 L
  b. 355 mL ✓

Complete.

3. 1 L = __?__ mL *1000*
4. 2 L = __?__ mL *2000*
5. 1.5 L = __?__ mL *1500*

6. 1.3 L = __?__ mL *1300*
7. 0.258 L = __?__ mL *258*
8. 0.34 L = __?__ mL *340*

9. 1000 mL = __?__ L *1*
10. 3000 mL = __?__ L *3*
11. 1800 mL = __?__ L *1.8*

12. 900 mL = __?__ L *0.9*
13. 750 mL = __?__ L *0.75*
14. 124 mL = __?__ L *0.124*

15. Can you find a container that holds about 1 liter?

16. Estimate the volumes of several containers. Check your estimates by filling each container.

154

Assignments

BASIC
page 154 exercises 1—16
page 155 exercises 17—25, 32—33
Basic Worksheet 41

AVERAGE
page 154 exercises 1—16
page 155 exercises 17—33
Enrichment Worksheet 41

ENRICHED
page 154 exercises 1—16
page 155 exercises 17—33
Enrichment Worksheet 41

EXTRA PRACTICE
page 385 set 49

A unit for measuring weight is the
gram (g).

A smaller unit for measuring weight is
the **milligram (mg)**.

$$1000 \text{ mg} = 1 \text{ g}$$

or $1 \text{ mg} = 0.001 \text{ g}$

A larger unit for measuring weight is
the **kilogram (kg)**.

$$1 \text{ kg} = 1000 \text{ g}$$
or $1 \text{ g} = 0.001 \text{ kg}$

I kilogram

I gram

500 milligrams

EXERCISES
Choose the correct answer.

17. a. 5.5 mg
    b. 5.5 g ✓
    c. 5.5 kg

18. a. 400 mg ✓
    b. 400 g
    c. 400 kg

19. a. 1.8 mg
    b. 1.8 g
    c. 1.8 kg ✓

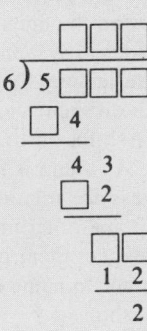

Complete.

20. 1 g = ___?___ mg 1000
21. 8 g = ___?___ mg 8000
22. 15 g = ___?___ mg 15,000
23. 2000 mg = ___?___ g 2
24. 1500 mg = ___?___ g 1.5
25. 800 mg = ___?___ g 0.8
26. 1 kg = ___?___ g 1000
27. 2.1 kg = ___?___ g 2100
28. 0.845 kg = ___?___ g 845
29. 3000 g = ___?___ kg 3
30. 2400 g = ___?___ kg 2.4
31. 560 g = ___?___ kg 0.56

32. Try to find an object that weighs about 1 kilogram.

33. Estimate the weights of some objects. Check your estimates by weighing each object.

155

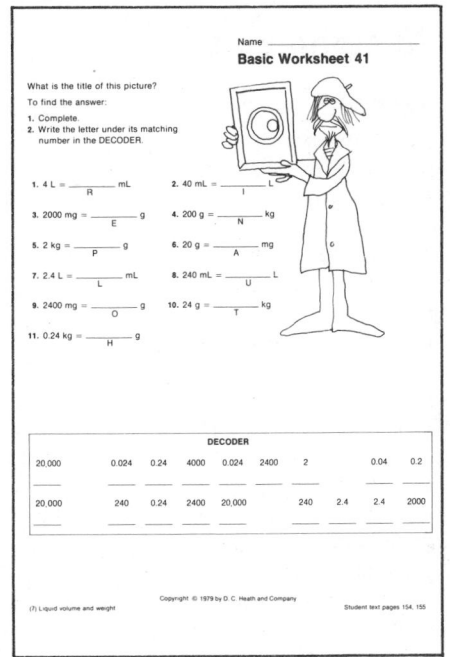
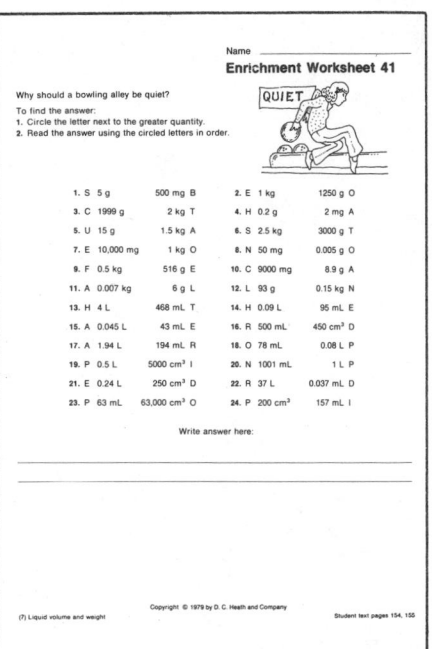
Follow-up Activities

Reinforcement Collect several containers. Have students estimate the volume of these containers. They can then check their estimates by filling the container with a dry material such as styrofoam beads, sawdust, etc. and measuring the amount in the container.

Enrichment Ask students to estimate and then measure the amount of water that would be lost from a leaking faucet if it leaked for 1 day; 1 week; 1 year. Have students measure the amount leaked in a short period of time and then compute to find the amount lost during a longer time period.

EXCURSION
Copy and fill in the missing digits.

```
        ☐☐☐
   6) 5 ☐☐☐
     ☐ 4
     4 3
     ☐ 2
       ☐☐
       1 2
        2
```

```
      972
   6) 5834
      54
      43
      42
      14
      12
       2
```

STUDENT OBJECTIVES
To measure lengths using customary units of measure.
To make conversions of units of length using customary units.

Suggested Lesson Plan

Introduction Although as adults, today's students will probably be using the metric system and measuring with metric units, there are and will continue to be many uses for customary units of measure in length, area, volume, liquid volume, and weight. Therefore, the next few lessons present the relationship between the units and present exercises dealing with measuring and converting units within the customary system. Students will be familiar with these units, but may need a review of the relationship between the units, especially as they use the metric system more.

Introduce the lessons by asking students to name different units for linear measure. Ask for customary units, not metric units. As a unit is named, ask students to express the relationship between that unit and other units already named. Do not expect them to be organized but rather to name many units and their relationships.

Using the pages Use the exposition on page 156 to organize the units and to simplify the relationships between the units. Of course, the units you want to emphasize are inch, foot, yard, and mile.

Work through the exercises showing the changing from one unit to another. Do not attempt to formalize the method of changing units. Have students recall the relationship between the units involved and use this to decide what operation to use.

You may want to encourage the technique of using a simpler problem to show how to do a harder problem. For example, if a student is stuck on changing 38 feet to inches, ask how many inches in 6 feet. Then ask, "How did you find that?" etc.

Quickly review the addition and subtraction of measurements with two units and show how the regrouping is done before students attempt exercises 16–31.

Assign exercises 1–39 for written work.

Length—customary units

Here are some customary units for measuring length.	12 inches (in. or ″) = 1 foot (ft)
	3 ft (′) = 1 yard (yd)
	1760 yd = 1 mile (mi)

These examples show how to change from one unit to another.

1. Change 2 miles to yards. There are 1760 yd in 1 mile.
   So, multiply 1760 by 2.

   1760
   ×2
   3520   2 mi = 3520 yd

2. Change 57 in. to feet and inches. There are 12 in. in 1 foot.
   So, divide 57 by 12.

   $$\begin{array}{r} 4 \\ 12\overline{)57} \\ -48 \\ \hline 9 \end{array}$$ 57 in. = 4 ft 9 in.

EXERCISES
Complete.

1. 9 ft = _?_ in. 108
2. 6 yd = _?_ ft 18
3. 6 yd = _?_ in. 216
4. 3 mi = _?_ yd 5280
5. 1 mi = _?_ ft 5280
6. 8 yd = _?_ in. 288
7. 108 in. = _?_ ft 9
8. 140 in. = _11_ ft _8_ in.
9. 48 ft = _?_ yd 16
10. 76 ft = _?_ yd _?_ ft 25 1
11. 92 in. = _?_ ft _?_ in. 7 8
12. 150 in. = _?_ ft _?_ in. 12 6
13. 2 ft 3 in. = _?_ in. 27
14. 5 yd 1 ft = _?_ ft 16
15. 2 yd 5 in. = _?_ in. 77

156

Assignments

BASIC
page 156 exercises 1–15
page 157 exercises 16–37
Basic Worksheet 42

AVERAGE
page 156 exercises 1–15
page 157 exercises 16–38
Enrichment Worksheet 42

ENRICHED
page 156 exercises 1–15
page 157 exercises 16–39
Enrichment Worksheet 42

EXTRA PRACTICE
page 385 set 50

Add. Regroup whenever possible.

Regroup 12 in. for 1 ft.

16.
  4 ft 9 in.
+ 2 ft 5 in.
  7 ft 2 in.

17.
  7 ft 8 in.
+ 3 ft 7 in.
  11 ft 3 in.

18.
  9 ft 6 in.
+ 5 ft 9 in.
  15 ft 3 in.

19.
  5 yd 2 ft
+ 2 yd 1 ft
  8 yd

20.
  3 yd 2 ft
+ 5 yd 2 ft
  9 yd 1 ft

21.
  4 yd 2 ft 8 in.
+ 3 yd 2 ft 2 in.
  8 yd 1 ft 10 in.

22.
  3 yd 1 ft 8 in.
+ 2 yd 2 ft 5 in.
  6 yd 1 ft 1 in.

23.
  2 yd 2 ft 7 in.
+ 1 yd 1 ft 6 in.
  4 yd 1 ft 1 in.

Subtract.

24.
  3 ft
− 1 ft 8 in.
  1 ft 4 in.

25.
  8 ft 5 in.
− 3 ft 9 in.
  4 ft 8 in.

26.
  7 ft 2 in.
− 4 ft 9 in.
  2 ft 5 in.

27.
  6 yd 2 ft
− 4 yd 1 ft
  2 yd 1 ft

28.
  8 yd 1 ft
− 3 yd 2 ft
  4 yd 2 ft

29.
  5 yd
− 2 yd 1 ft
  2 yd 2 ft

30.
  3 yd 2 ft 8 in.
− 1 yd 1 ft 9 in.
  2 yd 11 in.

31.
  11 yd 2 ft 4 in.
− 6 yd   8 in.
  5 yd 1 ft 8 in.

Give each perimeter.

32.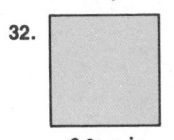
9 ft 6 in. 38 ft

33.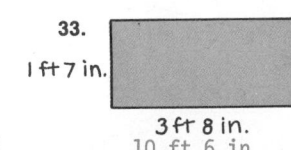
1 ft 7 in.
3 ft 8 in.
10 ft 6 in.

34.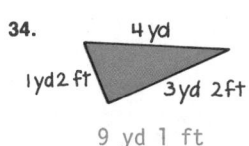
4 yd
1 yd 2 ft   3 yd 2 ft
9 yd 1 ft

Give the circumference. Use 3.14 as an approximation for π.

35.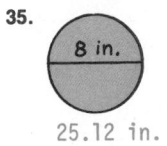
8 in.
25.12 in.

36.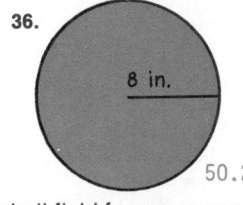
8 in.
50.24 in.

37.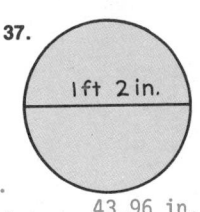
1 ft 2 in.
43.96 in.

Solve.

38. The base paths of a baseball field form a square. How far is it around the bases if the bases are 90 feet apart?   360 ft

39. Measure the length and width of a rectangular room to the nearest inch. Compute its perimeter.

157

Reinforcement Draw different geometric shapes on large cards. Provide students with rulers and have pairs of students measure to find the perimeter of the figure on a card. After they complete a card, have them exchange cards and check each other's work.

Enrichment Have pairs of students try to find a reasonable answer to the problem below. Have them explain their estimate and compare estimates with other students. "If all the paper your school uses in a year were put in a stack, how high would the stack be?" [possible solution: 5 sheets per pupil per day × 180 school days × 30 pupils per class × number of classes per school ÷ 200 (200 sheets per inch) = height of stack in inches]

EXCURSION
In a magic square the sum of the numbers in each row, column, and diagonal is the same. Copy and complete this magic square.

58	51	56
53	55	57
54	59	52

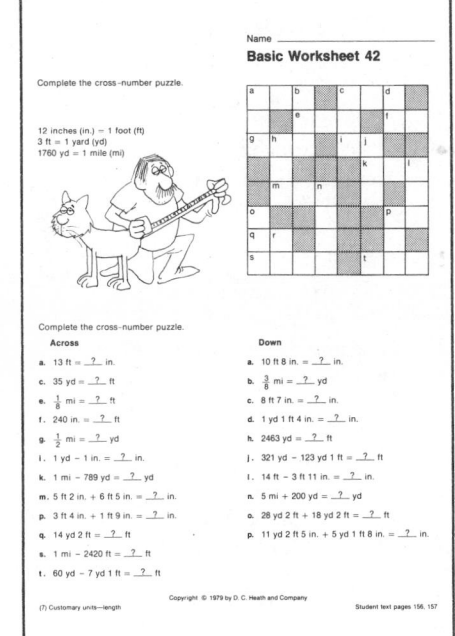

Basic Worksheet 42 and Enrichment Worksheet 42

STUDENT OBJECTIVE
To compute to find the area of
geometric figures using customary
units.

VOCABULARY
in.² (square inches), ft² (square feet), yd²
(square yards)

Suggested Lesson Plan

Introduction Since students have
found areas of figures using metric units,
finding area using customary units
should present very little difficulty.
Sometimes lengths are named with two
units, for example 3 feet 2 inches, and
these measurements must be changed to
a single unit before computing.

Using the pages Use the exposition
on page 158 to review finding areas and
to show the changing of a measurement
to a single unit before multiplying.
  Encourage students to make
diagrams for exercises 13—22. Show
them that for exercise 13, although 12
inches = 1 foot, this does not mean that
12 square inches = 1 square foot.
Explain to students that they will use
the answers for exercises 13—15 for
changing units in later exercises.
  Use the time at the end of the class
period for the Keeping Skills Sharp.

Area—customary units

When measurements are given in more than one unit, change
to a single unit before multiplying. Study this example.

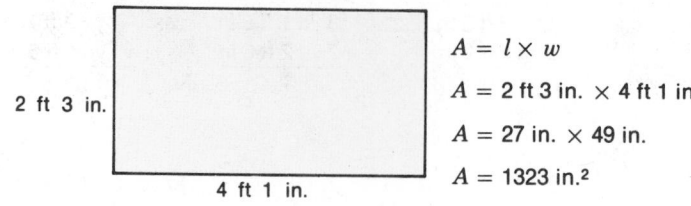

$A = l \times w$

$A = 2 \text{ ft } 3 \text{ in. } \times 4 \text{ ft } 1 \text{ in.}$

$A = 27 \text{ in. } \times 49 \text{ in.}$

$A = 1323 \text{ in.}^2$

EXERCISES
Give each area. Use 3.14 as an approximation for π.

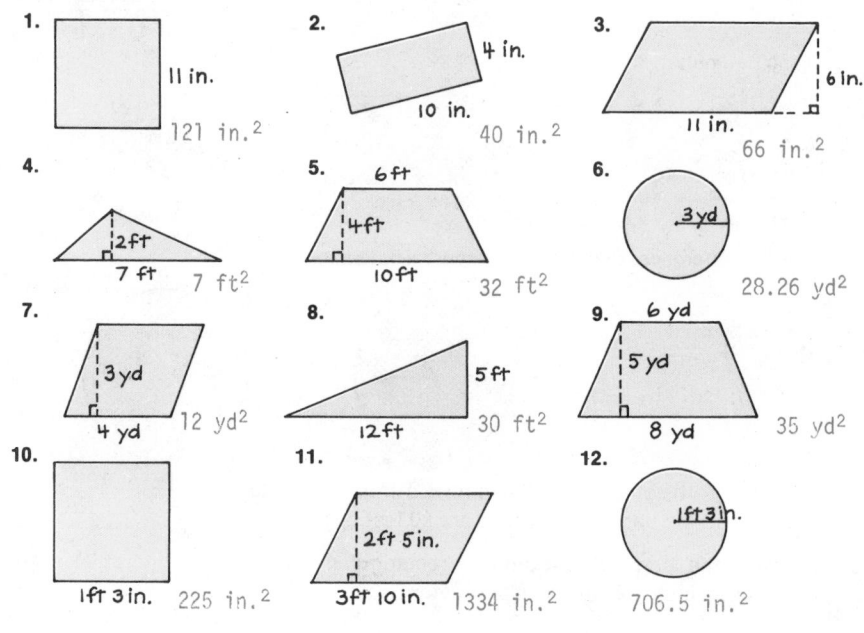

158

Assignments

BASIC
page 158 exercises 1—12
page 159 exercises 13—18,
    Keeping Skills Sharp
Basic Worksheet 43

AVERAGE
page 158 exercises 1—12
page 159 exercises 13—21,
    Keeping Skills Sharp
Enrichment Worksheet 43

ENRICHED
page 158 exercises 1—12
page 159 exercises 13—22,
    Keeping Skills Sharp
Enrichment Worksheet 43

EXTRA PRACTICE
page 385 set 51

13. How many square inches are in one square foot? **144**

14. How many square feet are in one square yard? **9**

15. How many square inches are in one square yard? **1296**

16. Measure the length and width of a rectangular room to the nearest foot. Compute the area. Change to square yards. (Round your answer to the nearest square yard.)

Give the surface area. Use 3.14 as an approximation for π.

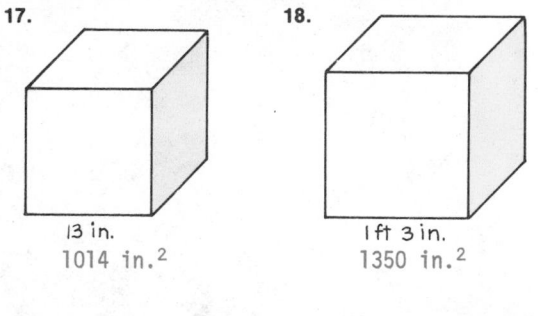

17.
13 in.
1014 in.²

18.
1 ft 3 in.
1350 in.²

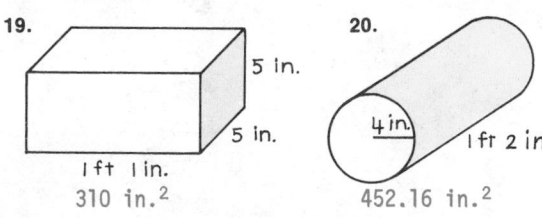

19.
5 in.
5 in.
1 ft 1 in.
310 in.²

20.
4 in.
1 ft 2 in.
452.16 in.²

Solve. Use 3.14 as an approximation for π.

21. What is the area in square feet of a circular garden with a diameter of 10 yards? **706.5**

22. How many square inches of cardboard are used to make a cereal box that is $2\frac{1}{2}$ in. thick, 10 in. wide, and 12 in. high and has an overlapping flap that measures 10 in. by $1\frac{1}{2}$ in.? **365**

Divide. Round each quotient to the nearest hundredth.

1. 1.2)3.482   **2.90**

2. 2.4)1.356   **0.57**

3. 0.31)0.9382   **3.03**

4. 0.43)0.3916   **0.91**

5. 0.83)0.1374   **0.17**

6. 0.57)3.056   **5.36**

7. 6.4)0.2973   **0.05**

8. 3.9)5.901   **1.51**

9. 7.8)2.643   **0.34**

10. 4.2)0.3967   **0.09**

11. 7.5)8.215   **1.10**

12. 8.2)37.19   **4.54**

13. 0.37)4.982   **13.46**

14. 0.74)63.74   **86.14**

15. 2.9)0.8762   **0.30**

16. 0.16)0.9027   **5.64**

159

Follow-up Activities

Reinforcement Use the cards for the Reinforcement, page 157, to have students measure and find the area in customary units. Continue to have them trade cards and verify each other's work.

Enrichment Students can use floor tiles as a unit to try to determine the area of the school, or a measurable part of it.

CALCULATOR ACTIVITY
After students determine the area of the school in floor-tile units, they should use the calculator to change the units to square feet.

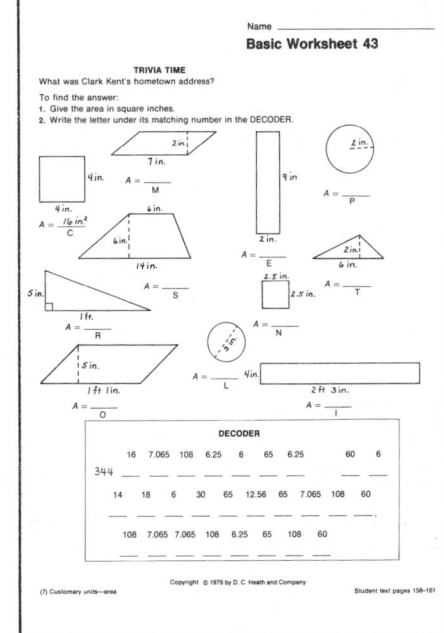

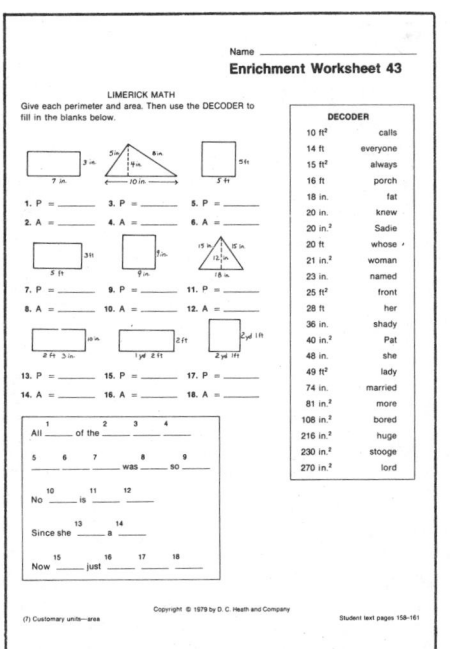

To solve problems relating to careers.
To find area of rectangular regions and
use this to determine the cost of
carpet.

Suggested Lesson Plan

Using the pages Go over the
exposition on page 160. You may wish
to obtain information similar to that
contained in the exercises from local
dealers or, better yet, let students obtain
that information. If you do get such
information, you may wish to use it in
place of the information given in the
exercises. Assign the exercises.

Mathematics in careers

Carpet layers generally are paid for each
square yard of carpet they lay. They
often charge extra for carpeting a small
room such as a bath or for carpeting
stairs.

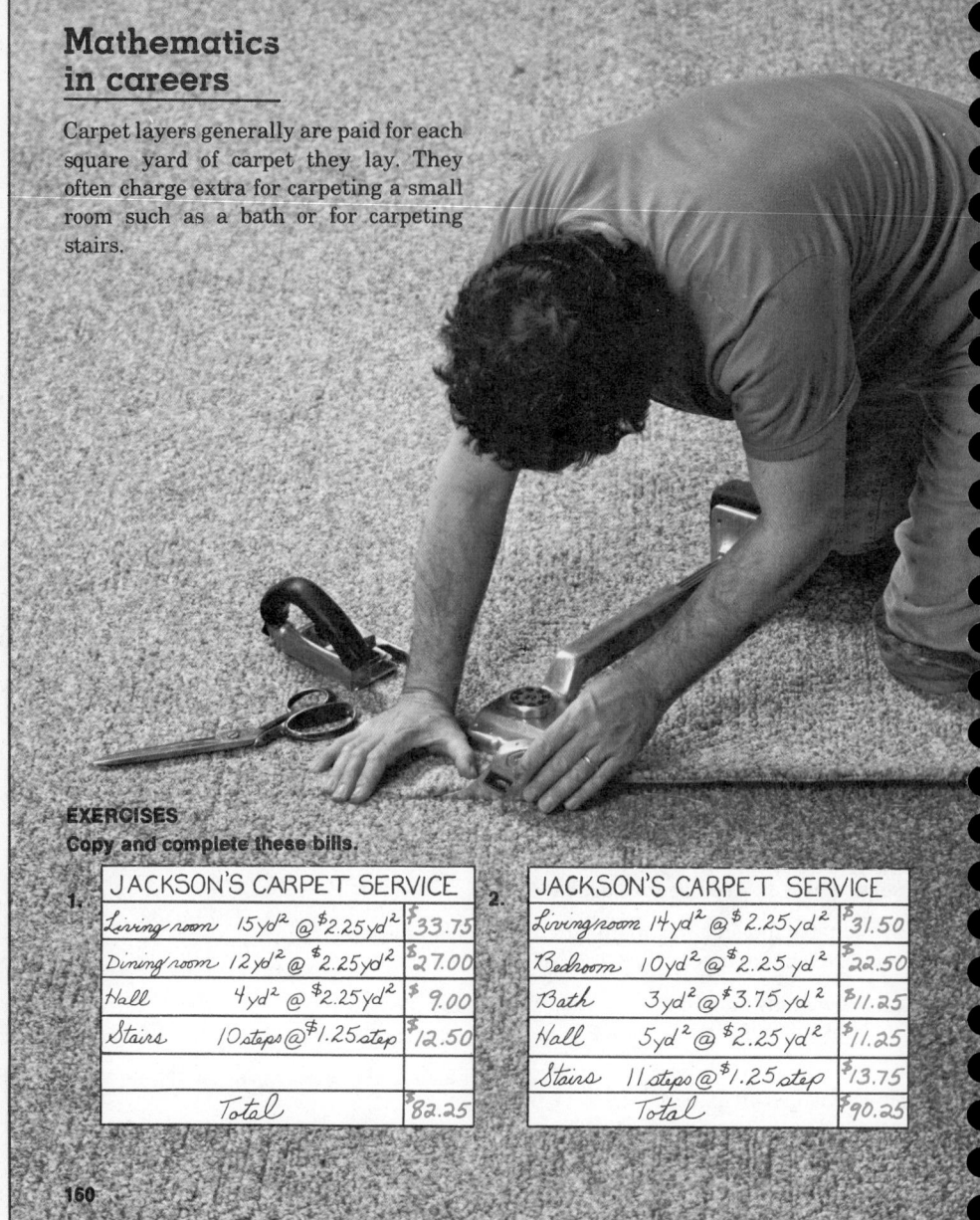

EXERCISES

Copy and complete these bills.

1.

JACKSON'S CARPET SERVICE		
Living room	15 yd² @ $2.25 yd²	$33.75
Dining room	12 yd² @ $2.25 yd²	$27.00
Hall	4 yd² @ $2.25 yd²	$9.00
Stairs	10 steps @ $1.25 step	$12.50
	Total	$82.25

2.

JACKSON'S CARPET SERVICE		
Living room	14 yd² @ $2.25 yd²	$31.50
Bedroom	10 yd² @ $2.25 yd²	$22.50
Bath	3 yd² @ $3.75 yd²	$11.25
Hall	5 yd² @ $2.25 yd²	$11.25
Stairs	11 steps @ $1.25 step	$13.75
	Total	$90.25

160

Assignments

BASIC
page 160 exercises 1−2
page 161 exercises 3−4
Basic Worksheet 43

AVERAGE
page 160 exercises 1−2
page 161 exercises 3−5
Enrichment Worksheet 43

ENRICHED
page 160 exercises 1−2
page 161 exercises 3−8
Enrichment Worksheet 43

REVIEW PRACTICE
page 380 set 30

Carpet layers have to compute area to determine the amount of carpet laid. (Since they charge by the square yard, each computed area must be in *square yards.*) The area of each "shaded room" shown below was computed and rounded up to the nearest square yard.

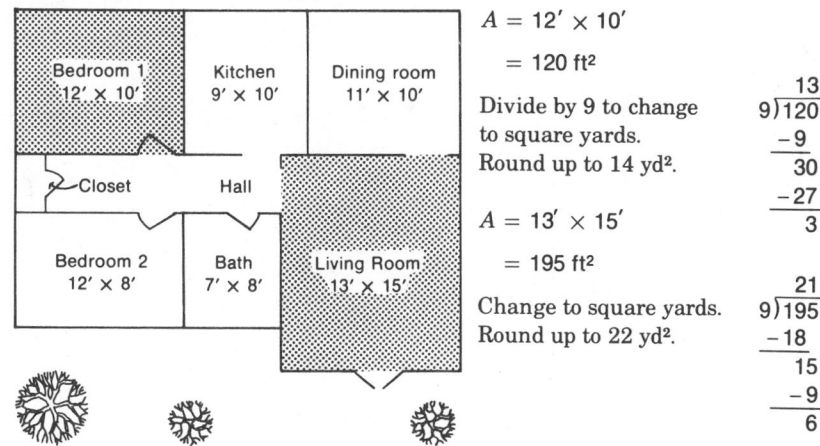

$A = 12' \times 10'$

$= 120 \text{ ft}^2$

Divide by 9 to change to square yards.
Round up to 14 yd².

$$\begin{array}{r} 13 \\ 9\overline{)120} \\ -9 \\ \hline 30 \\ -27 \\ \hline 3 \end{array}$$

$A = 13' \times 15'$

$= 195 \text{ ft}^2$

Change to square yards.
Round up to 22 yd².

$$\begin{array}{r} 21 \\ 9\overline{)195} \\ -18 \\ \hline 15 \\ -9 \\ \hline 6 \end{array}$$

Using the rate of $2.25 a square yard, compute the charge for laying the carpet in each of the following rooms. Round each area up to the nearest square yard.

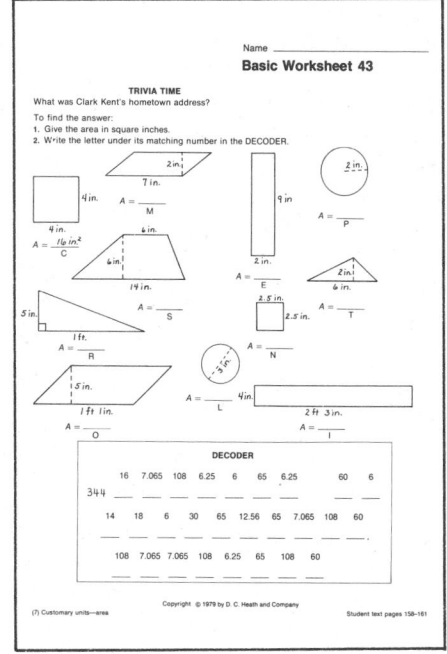

3. Living room 12' X 18'

   $54

4. Bedroom 12' X 13'

   $40.50

5. Bedroom 13' X 15'

   $49.50

6. Living room 11' X 20'

   $56.25

7. Dining room 12' X 11'

   $33.75

8. Kitchen

   $51.75

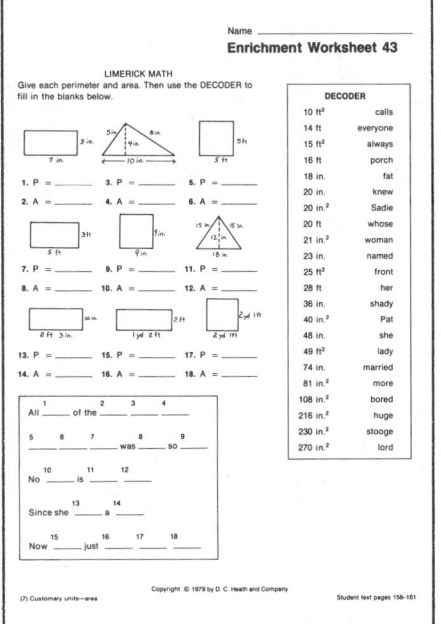

161

Reinforcement You may wish to provide students with further problem-solving experiences at this point. If so, have students write at least two stories for each of the following headlines:

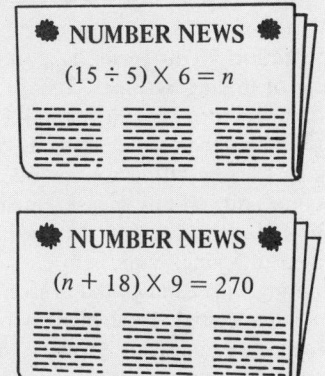

❋ NUMBER NEWS ❋
$(15 \div 5) \times 6 = n$

❋ NUMBER NEWS ❋
$(n + 18) \times 9 = 270$

Enrichment Have students create several stories for each of these headlines.

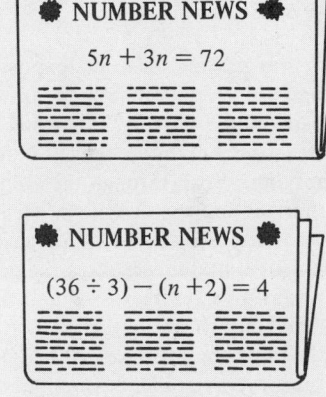

❋ NUMBER NEWS ❋
$5n + 3n = 72$

❋ NUMBER NEWS ❋
$(36 \div 3) - (n + 2) = 4$

If time permits, have students create additional headlines and stories.

Suggested Lesson Plan

Introduction This lesson is a good
review of finding volumes. Using
customary units, present several
additional problems that students must
solve. (1) Name all measurements with
the same unit. (If any measurement is a
compound measurement, it must be
changed to a single unit before
computing.) (2) Change the answer to
the unit requested. Equivalences
between cubic units are probably not
remembered, so students must either
figure out the relationship (144 in.² = 1
ft², etc.) and then convert or change all
the measurements before computing.
That is, if the answer is to be expressed
in square feet, the student can change all
the measurements to feet before
multiplying.

Using the pages Use the exposition
on page 162 to review finding volumes
of prisms and cylinders. Point out how
the measurements are changed before
multiplying. Work through the steps
together, noting the use of the formulas.
  Assign exercises 1–14 for written
work. Have students make a diagram to
help them for exercises 7–9 and then
point out that they use these
relationships for exercises 10 and 11.
  Observe as students work the word
problems and plan to help those who are
poor readers and those who are having
difficulty with the relationships between
cubic units.

Volume—customary units

Study these examples.

EXAMPLE 1.

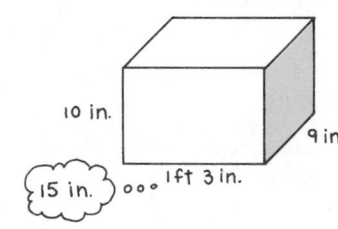

Remember that V stands for volume, B
stands for area of base, and h stands for
height.

$V = B \times h$

$V = (15 \text{ in.} \times 9 \text{ in.}) \times 10 \text{ in.}$

$V = 135 \text{ in.}^2 \times 10 \text{ in.}$

$V = 1350 \text{ in.}^3$

EXAMPLE 2.

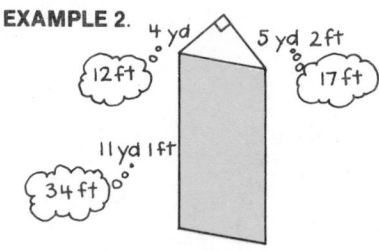

$V = B \times h$

$V = \frac{1}{2} \times (17 \text{ ft} \times 12 \text{ ft}) \times 34 \text{ ft}$

$V = \frac{1}{2} \times 204 \text{ ft}^2 \times 34 \text{ ft}$

$V = 102 \text{ ft}^2 \times 34 \text{ ft}$

$V = 3468 \text{ ft}^3$

EXAMPLE 3.
Use 3.14 for π.

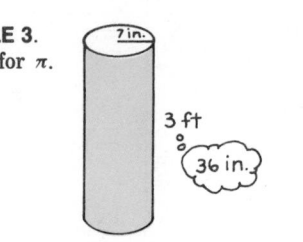

$V = B \times h$

$V = \pi \times (7 \text{ in.} \times 7 \text{ in.}) \times 36 \text{ in.}$

$V \approx 3.14 \times 49 \text{ in.}^2 \times 36 \text{ in.}$

$V \approx 153.86 \text{ in.}^2 \times 36 \text{ in.}$

$V \approx 5538.96 \text{ in.}^3$

162

Assignments

BASIC
page 162 Discuss
page 163 exercises 1–12
Basic Worksheet 44

AVERAGE
page 162 Discuss
page 163 exercises 1–13
Enrichment Worksheet 44

ENRICHED
page 162 Discuss
page 163 exercises 1–14
Enrichment Worksheet 44

EXTRA PRACTICE
page 386 set 52

EXERCISES

Give each volume.

1.
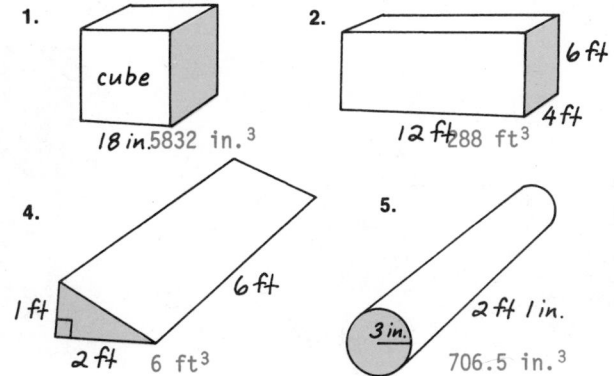
cube
18 in. 5832 in.³

2.
6 ft
4 ft
12 ft 288 ft³

3.
9 in.
2 ft 1 ft
2592 in.³

4.
6 ft
1 ft
2 ft
6 ft³

5.

3 in.
2 ft 1 in.
706.5 in.³

6. 2 yd 1 ft   1 yd 1 ft
3 yd
126 ft³

Complete.

7. 1 yd³ = __?__ ft³ 27

8. 1 ft³ = __?__ in.³ 1728

9. 1 yd³ = __?__ in.³
46,656

10. Convert your answer for exercise 2 to yd³.
Round to the nearest 0.1 yd³. 10.7 yd³

11. Convert your answer for exercise 3 to ft³.
Round to the nearest 0.1 ft³. 1.5 ft³

Solve.

about 4.9

12. Concrete is sold by the cubic yard.
How many cubic yards of concrete
are needed for a basement wall that
is 3 yd high, 10 yd long, and 0.25 yd
thick? 7.5

13. A concrete garage floor is 23 ft by 23
ft and 3 in. thick. How many cubic
yards of concrete were used?

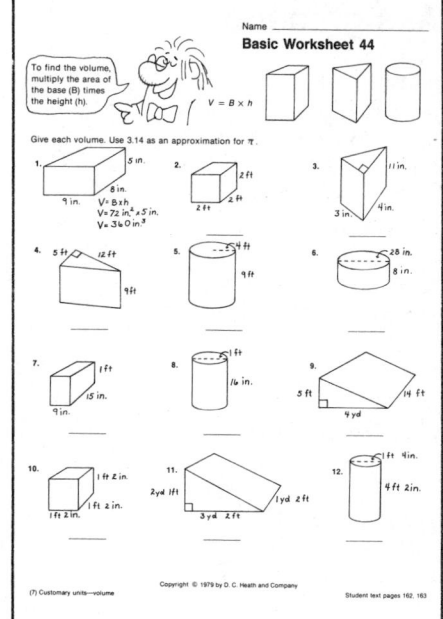

14. Measure the dimensions of a rectangular room (perhaps your
classroom) to the nearest ft. Compute the volume in ft³. Convert the
volume to yd³ and round to the
nearest 0.1 yd³.

163

163

Follow-up Activities

Reinforcement Have students
complete equivalence tables for
customary units for length, area, and
volume. Help students draw diagrams
for area and volume relationships. Post
the better charts on the mathematics
bulletin board.

Enrichment Have students use soda
straws and pipe cleaners to build two-
and three-dimensional figures. They
should tie tags to each shape giving the
name and appropriate measurements.

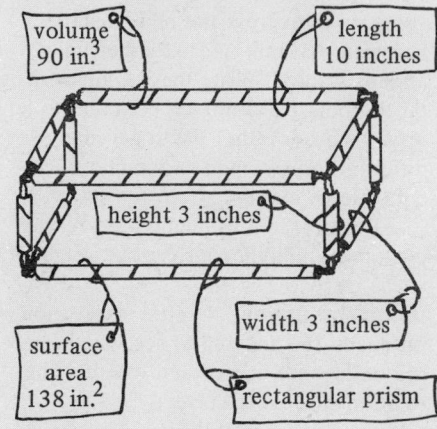

volume 90 in.³
length 10 inches
height 3 inches
width 3 inches
surface area 138 in.²
rectangular prism

Post or hang figures in the
mathematics interest area. Encourage
students to continue to add figures.

EXCURSION

How many different collections of coins
are there that have a value of 25¢? 13

Here is one such collection:

1 dime
2 nickels
5 pennies

Basic Worksheet 44

Name _____

To find the volume,
multiply the area of
the base (B) times
the height (h).

V = B × h

Give each volume. Use 3.14 as an approximation for π.

1. 5 in.
8 in.
3 in.
V = B × h
V = 72 in.² × 5 in.
V = 360 in.³

2. 2 ft
2 ft
2 ft

3. 11 in.
3 in.
4 in.

4. 5 ft
12 ft
9 ft

5. 3 ft
9 ft

6. 28 in.
8 in.

7. 1 ft
15 in.
9 in.

8. 16 in.

9. 5 ft
14 ft
4 yd

10. 1 ft 2 in.
1 ft 2 in.
1 ft 2 in.

11. 2 yd 1 ft
3 yd 2 ft
1 yd 2 ft

12. 4 in.
4 ft 2 in.

(7) Customary—volume
Copyright © 1979 by D. C. Heath and Company
Student text pages 162, 163

Enrichment Worksheet 44

Name _____

Give each volume. Use 3.14 as an approximation for π.

1. 1 ft 3 in.
1 ft 3 in.
1 ft 3 in.

2. 1 yd 1 ft
3 yd

3. 1 yd 1 ft
3 yd 1 ft
4 yd

4. 2 yd 1 ft
3 yd 1 ft
6 yd 2 ft

5. 1 yd 1 ft
4 yd 1 ft

6. 5 ft 10 in.
6 ft 3 in.

7. 2 ft 1 ft
3 ft
1 ft 6 in.
4 ft

8. 8 yd
5 yd
2 yd
1 ft 6 in.
2 yd 1 ft

9. 2 ft
2 ft
4 ft
5 ft 6 in.
6 ft

10. 4 yd

11. 2 yd
4 yd
8 yd 1 ft

12. 1 ft 6 in.
5 ft
3 ft 4 in.

(7) Customary units—volume
Copyright © 1979 by D. C. Heath and Company
Student text pages 162, 163

(core) Lesson 73   163

STUDENT OBJECTIVES
To make conversions among customary
    units for measuring liquid volume.
To make conversions among customary
    units for measuring weight.

VOCABULARY
bushel, peck, pint, quart

Suggested Lesson Plan

Introduction   Ask students to name
different (customary) units for measuring
liquid volume. As the units are named,
write them on the board and then ask
students to express the relationship
between that unit and the other units
already named. Write these equivalents
on the board. Do not expect them to be
organized but rather try to get many
different units named and many
equivalents expressed.

   Repeat the introduction above with
customary units for measuring weights.

Using the pages   Use the exposition
on pages 164 and 165 to see whether all
the units were named and whether the
relationships were correct. Use the
tables to organize the equivalents you
listed on the board.

   Point out the fact that there are
different units for liquid measure and dry
measure. Some of these units may not
have been named, so use this
opportunity to get these units listed.

   Assign exercises 1–30 for written
work. Point out the Excursion for those
students who want to think about it.

Liquid volume and weight— customary units

2 cups (c) = 1 pint (pt)

2 pints = 1 quart (qt)

2 quarts = 1 half-gallon

2 half-gallons = 1 gallon (gal)

EXERCISES
Complete.

1. 24 pt = __?__ qt   12
2. 8 c = __?__ pt   4
3. 4 qt = __?__ gal   1
4. 3 qt = __?__ c   12
5. 2 gal = __?__ qt   8
6. 6 pt = __?__ c   12
7. 1 gal = __?__ pt   8
8. 2 qt = __?__ half-gallon   1
9. 12 c = __?__ qt   3
10. 16 pt = __?__ qt   8
11. 2 qt = __?__ c   8
12. 3 gal = __?__ half-gallons   6
13. 3 pt 1 c = __?__ c   7
14. 3 gal 2 qt = __?__ qt   14
15. 8 qt 1 pt = __?__ pt   17

In the metric system, dry material such as grain is measured
with the same units used for liquids. In the customary system,
different units are used for dry measure.

| 2 pints (pt) = 1 quart (qt) |
| 8 quarts = 1 peck (pk) |
| 4 pecks = 1 bushel (bu) |

Complete.

16. 6 pt = __?__ qt   3
17. 16 qt = __?__ pk   2
18. 3 bu = __?__ pk   12
19. 5 pk = __?__ qt   40

Excursion ▪◘▪◘▪◘▪◘▪◘▪◘▪◘▪◘▪◘▪◘▪◘▪◘▪◘▪◘▪◘▪◘▪
                                    B   A
Suppose that you have a 3-qt container and a 5-qt container.
How could you use the containers to measure out 4 qt of water?

Answer.

Excursion

 I. Fill A. Fill B from A. Empty B.
    Empty A into B. Fill A. Fill B
    from A. Empty B.
II. Fill B. Fill A from B. Fill B.
    Fill A from B. Empty A. Empty B
    into A. Fill B. Empty B into A.

Assignments

BASIC
page 164 exercises 1–19
page 165 exercises 20–25
Basic Worksheet 45

AVERAGE
page 164 exercises 1–19
page 165 exercises 20–30
Enrichment Worksheet 45

ENRICHED
page 164 exercises 1–19, Excursion
page 165 exercises 20–30
Enrichment Worksheet 45

EXTRA PRACTICE
page 386 set 53

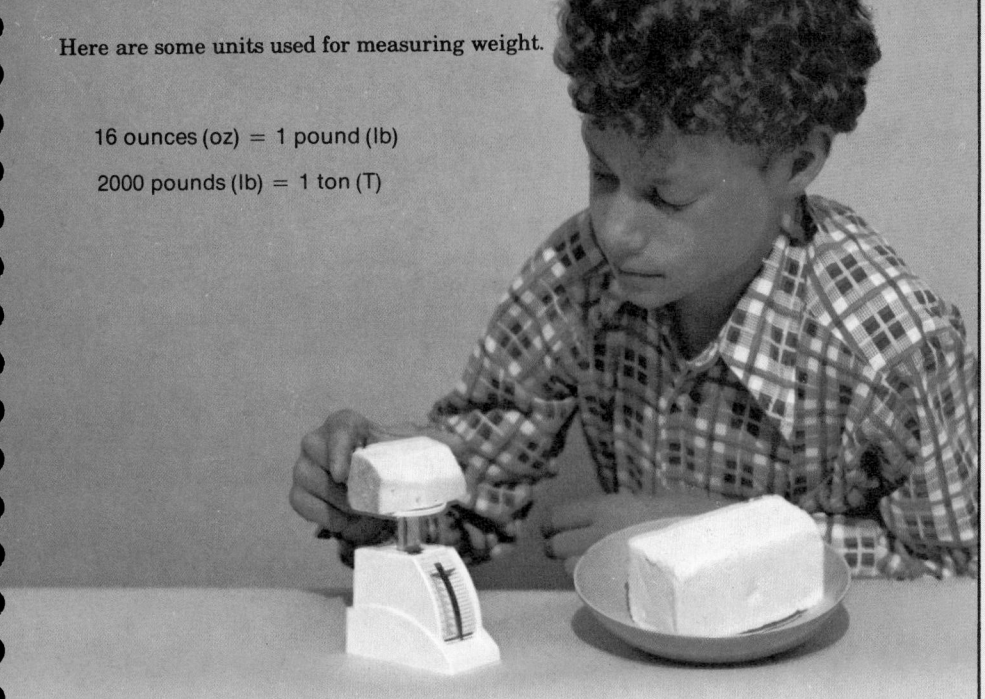

Here are some units used for measuring weight.

16 ounces (oz) = 1 pound (lb)

2000 pounds (lb) = 1 ton (T)

Complete.

20. 4 lb = ___?___ oz 64 **21.** 3 T = ___?___ lb 6000 **22.** 256 oz = ___?___ lb 16

23. 8000 lb = ___?___ T 4 **24.** 24 lb = ___?___ oz 384 **25.** 288 oz = ___?___ lb 18

26. 3 lb 6 oz = ___?___ oz 54 **27.** 4 lb 9 oz = ___?___ oz 73 **28.** 12 lb 3 oz = ___?___ oz
195

Solve.

29. A chili recipe calls for 2 lb of ground beef. If you had 1 lb 3 oz of ground beef, how much more would you need? 13 oz

30. A truck weighing 21,400 lb came to a bridge with this sign:

> **Closed to traffic**
> **over**
> **10 tons**

Should the truck cross the bridge?
no

165

Follow-up Activities

Reinforcement Have students make equivalence charts for liquid volume, dry volume, and weight. Post them on the mathematics bulletin board.

Enrichment Form two groups to debate the advantages and disadvantages of the use of the metric system and the use of customary units. Have the groups plan their debate and give each student a chance to discuss one particular aspect of either system.

EXCURSION
Study the number pairs to discover the rule. Then use the rule to find what goes in the circles.

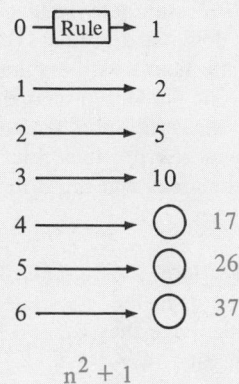

0 → Rule → 1

1 ———→ 2

2 ———→ 5

3 ———→ 10

4 ———→ ◯ 17

5 ———→ ◯ 26

6 ———→ ◯ 37

$n^2 + 1$

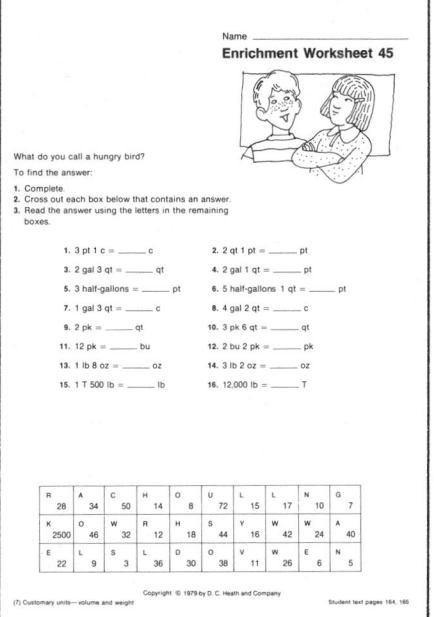

Basic Worksheet 45

Name _____

The state of Louisiana has three nicknames.
What are they?

Complete. Then use the DECODER to get the answer.

1. 2 pints = ____ cups
   G
2. 2 gallons = ____ quarts
   N
3. 24 quarts = ____ gallons
   I
4. 2 gallons = ____ pints
   P
5. 10 gallons = ____ half-gallons
   U
6. 6 cups = ____ pints
   O
7. 3 half-gallons = ____ pints
   L
8. 2 gallons = ____ cups
   R
9. 3 pounds = ____ ounces
   C
10. 80 ounces = ____ pounds
    S
11. 2 tons = ____ pounds
    A
12. 18,000 pounds = ____ tons
    E

DECODER

48	32	9	3	12	9
STATE

| 5 | 20 | 4 | 4000 | 32 |
STATE

| 16 | 9 | 12 | 6 | 48 | 4000 | 8 |
STATE

Copyright © 1979 by D. C. Heath and Company
(7) Customary units—liquid volume and weight   Student text pages 164, 165

Enrichment Worksheet 45

Name _____

What do you call a hungry bird?
To find the answer:
1. Complete.
2. Cross out each box below that contains an answer.
3. Read the answer using the letters in the remaining boxes.

1. 3 pt 1 c = ____ c
2. 2 qt 1 pt = ____ pt
3. 2 gal 3 qt = ____ qt
4. 2 gal 1 qt = ____ pt
5. 3 half-gallons = ____ pt
6. 5 half-gallons 1 qt = ____ pt
7. 1 gal 3 qt = ____ c
8. 4 gal 2 qt = ____ c
9. 2 pk = ____ qt
10. 3 pk 6 qt = ____ qt
11. 12 pk = ____ bu
12. 2 bu 2 pk = ____ pk
13. 1 lb 8 oz = ____ oz
14. 3 lb 2 oz = ____ oz
15. 1 T 500 lb = ____ lb
16. 12,000 lb = ____ T

R 28	A 34	C 50	H 14	O 8	U 72	L 15	L 17	N 10	G 7
K 2500	O 46	W 32	R 12	H 18	S 44	Y 16	W 42	A 24	A 40
E 22	L 9	S 3	L 36	D 30	O 38	V 11	W 26	E 6	N 5

Copyright © 1979 by D. C. Heath and Company
(7) Customary units—volume and weight   Student text pages 164, 165

STUDENT OBJECTIVE
To review the concepts and skills introduced in Chapter 5.

Suggested Lesson Plan

Introduction No pre-text activity is necessary for page 166 as this is a checkup for the chapter. However, it may be valuable to briefly review the lessons in the chapter so that students are reminded of the content over which they will be tested.

This checkup will provide you with data about how well individual students have mastered the skills of the chapter. The Chapter Review on page 168 is provided for those students who need more specific individual help.

Page 167 is an activity that students will enjoy doing as a project. Organize the class into teams with 4 students to a team. Put one student in charge. Have each team measure out a hectare on the school grounds. After they finish, compare the areas and see if they look equivalent.

Using the pages Assign all of the exercises on page 166. As students complete the page they can work on the activity on page 167.

Complete. [pages 134–137]

1. 30 mm = _?_ cm   3
2. 200 cm = _?_ m   2
3. 135 cm = _?_ dm   13.5
4. 68 cm = _?_ m   0.68
5. 2.1 km = _?_ m   2100
6. 82.4 mm = _?_ dm   0.824

Give the perimeter (or circumference) and the area. Use 3.14 as an approximation for π. [pages 138–143, 158–159]

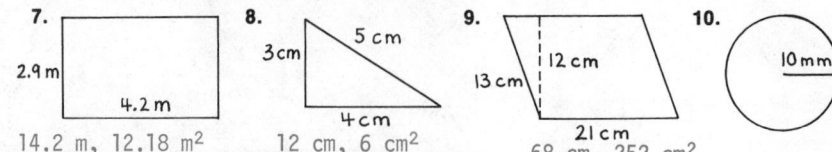

7. 14.2 m, 12.18 m²
8. 12 cm, 6 cm²
9. 68 cm, 252 cm²
10. 62.8 mm, 314 mm²

Give the surface area and the volume. Use 3.14 as an approximation for π. [pages 146–153, 159, 162–163]

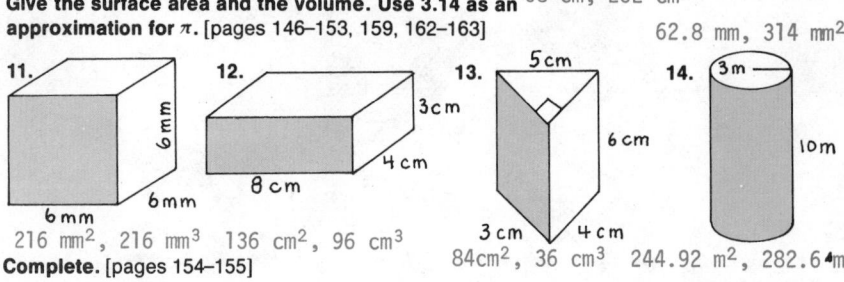

11. 216 mm², 216 mm³
12. 136 cm², 96 cm³
13. 84 cm², 36 cm³
14. 244.92 m², 282.64 m³

Complete. [pages 154–155]

15. 1 L = _?_ mL   1000
16. 2 L = _?_ mL   2000
17. 450 mL = _?_ L   0.45
18. 1 g = _?_ mg   1000
19. 560 g = _?_ kg   0.56
20. 0.73 kg = _?_ g   730

Complete. [pages 156–157]

21. 3 ft = _?_ in.   36
22. 7 yd = _?_ ft   21
23. 18 yd = _?_ in.   648
24. 58 in. = _?_ ft _?_ in.   4   10
25. 15 ft = _?_ yd _?_ ft   5   0
26. 2 mi = _?_ yd   3520

Complete. [pages 164–165]

27. 5 qt = _?_ pt   10
28. 4 gal = _?_ qt   16
29. 48 pt = _?_ gal   6
30. 2 T = _?_ lb   4000
31. 12 lb = _?_ oz   192
32. 56 oz = _?_ lb _?_ oz   3   8

166

Assignments

BASIC
page 166 exercises 1–32
page 167 Project

AVERAGE
page 166 exercises 1–32
page 167 Project

ENRICHED
page 166 exercises 1–32
page 167 Project

EXTRA PROBLEM SOLVING
pages 406–407 set 5

Project

A metric unit for measuring land area is the **hectare**. A square that is 100 meters on a side has an area of 1 hectare. The hectare is used to measure areas of such regions as parks and farms. Working in a group, lay out a hectare on your school grounds. Estimate the total area of your school grounds in hectares.

Answer these questions.

1. How many square meters are in a hectare?   10,000

2. How many hectares are in a square kilometer?   100

167

You may wish to assign some of the Creative Problem Solving Activities (pages 461-477) at this time.

Follow-up Activities

Reinforcement   Correct all of the items in the Chapter Checkup. Any student who missed six or more, or any more than three problems in a row, needs additional help. It is important for each student to achieve some degree of understanding of the units of measurement discussed in the chapter.

Enrichment   Assign these pupils to the games and activities that have been played throughout the chapter. Make a student leader responsible for teaching a game or activity to interested students and for supervising the play.

Suggested Lesson Plan

Using the pages After checking the Chapter Checkup you will know which students need additional reinforcement and which students will be able to go ahead with the Challenge Activity. Get the better students started on page 169 first as the students who are having difficulty will need more of your time.

The students who need more review should go back and correct their errors on the Chapter Checkup. You may want to go over those questions orally if this group is small enough. Carefully probe to determine which concepts and skills the students have not mastered and work individually to correct these deficiencies.

After the identified students have corrected the Chapter Checkup, they should answer questions 1–16. After they complete these questions, read the answers and let the students correct their own papers. Give them an opportunity to ask questions about those exercises they missed.

Assign page 169 to those students who did well on the Chapter Checkup. Have students work independently, reading the exposition and then trying the exercises. After students have completed the Chapter Challenge, you may want to discuss the concept of greatest possible error with all of the class.

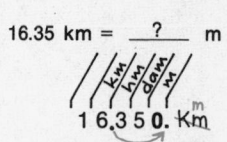

CHAPTER REVIEW

16.35 km = ___?___ m

km / hm / dam / m

1 6.3 5 0. km

Complete.

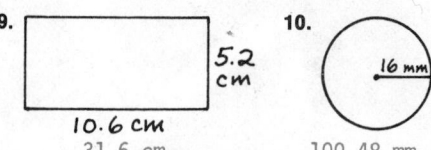

1. 723.1 m = ___?___ km   0.7231
2. 52.7 m = ___?___ cm   5270
3. 423 mm = ___?___ m   0.423
4. 53 cm = ___?___ m   0.53
5. 2.6 L = ___?___ mL   2600
6. 423.6 mg = ___?___ g   0.4236
7. 2.7 g = ___?___ kg   0.0027
8. 48.3m = ___?___ cm   4830

Perimeter of rectangle
$$P = 2 \times l + 2 \times w$$

Circumference of circle
$$C = \pi \times d$$

Give each perimeter. Use 3.14 for π.

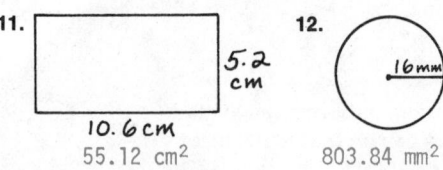

9.   5.2 cm   10.6 cm   31.6 cm
10.   16 mm   100.48 mm

Area of rectangle
$$A = l \times w$$

Area of circle
$$A = \pi \times r^2$$

Give each area. Use 3.14 for π.

11.   5.2 cm   10.6 cm   55.12 cm²
12.   16 mm   803.84 mm²

The surface area of a prism is the sum of the areas of the faces.

Give the surface area.

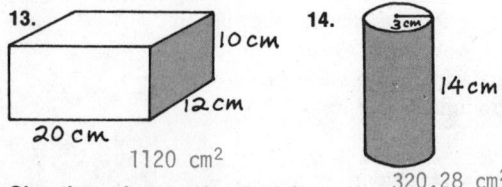

13.   10 cm   12 cm   20 cm   1120 cm²
14.   3 cm   14 cm   320.28 cm²

Volume of a prism or cylinder
$$V = B \times h$$
B is area of the base.

Give the volume. Use 3.14 for π.

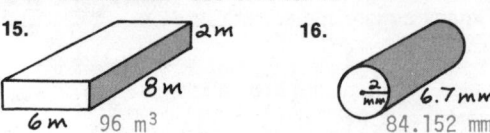

15.   2 m   8 m   6 m   96 m³
16.   2 mm   6.7 mm   84.152 mm³

168

Assignments

BASIC
page 168 exercises 1–16

AVERAGE
page 168 exercises 1–16

ENRICHED
page 169 exercises 1–9

CHAPTER CHALLENGE

Error of measurement

Suppose that you measured each of these segments to the nearest centimeter.

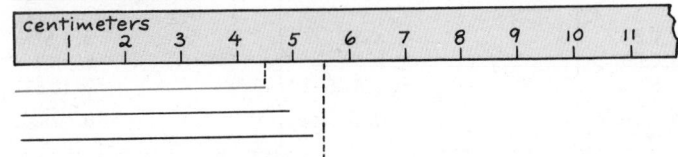

Each length would be recorded as 5 cm. In each case there is some error in the measurement—the difference between the true length and the recorded length. The **greatest possible error** (g.p.e.) occurs in the measurements of the blue segment and the red segment. The greatest possible error is always half of the unit used. In this case the g.p.e. is 0.5 cm.

If we use a smaller unit, we have less error.
Compare these two measurements.

Recorded measure   7 m
unit used: meter
  g.p.e.: 0.5 m

shortest possible true length: 6.5 m
longest possible true length: 7.5 m

Recorded measure   7.00 m
unit used: 0.01 m (1 cm)
  g.p.e.: 0.005 m (0.5 cm)

shortest possible true length: 6.995 m
longest possible true length: 7.005 m

EXERCISES

Give the g.p.e., the shortest possible true length, and the longest possible true length for each of these recorded measurements.

1. 15 m
2. 8 cm
3. 3.5 m
4. 20.45 m

5. 5.2 km
6. 6.0 om
7. 18.5 mm
8. 15.00 m

9. A measurement is given as 8 m ± 0.5 m.
The g.p.e. is 0.5 m.
  a. What is the shortest possible true length?   7.5 m
  b. What is the longest possible true length?   8.5 m

169

Follow-up Activities

Reinforcement The reinforcement at this point should be individual help focused on acquiring an intuitive understanding of the different units in the metric system and the customary units and the relationship between the units within either system. Students should have some general idea as to the size of a unit and the nature of what the unit is used to measure, such as length, area, weight, etc.

Enrichment Pair these students with students who are having difficulty with the units. The better student names a unit and the poorer student tells what is measured with the unit, gives an equivalent statement using the unit, and describes the approximate size of the unit.

	a b c d		a b c d		a b c d		a b c d		a b c
14		34		14		4		30	
	a b c d		a b c d						a b c
15								31	

STUDENT OBJECTIVES

To practice skills learned previously.
To practice using a standardized-test format.

Suggested Lesson Plan

Using the pages The Major Checkup at the end of each chapter of this textbook is given in standardized-test format. The answer sheet on page 448 is the type used with many standardized tests. You may duplicate it for use with the Major Checkups.

Pass out the answer sheets and be sure students understand how to use them. Allow a specified time, perhaps twenty minutes, to complete the checkup. Assign the exercises and use the results to determine what review is needed.

The table below correlates the test items and the student text pages. Assign review exercises as indicated by the Major Checkup results.

Test Item	Text Pages	Test Item	Text Pages
1	56–57	7	136–137
2	64–65	8	106–107
3	66–67	9	142–143
4	68–69	10	146–147
5	82–83	11	150–151
6	96–97	12	154–155

Chapter 5 Posttest

See page 54 for a full discussion of how to use the posttest. The table below suggests Extra Practice exercises and Basic Worksheets for those students who need further practice or reteaching.

Objectives	Extra Practice Sets	Pages	Basic Worksheets
5-2	44, 49	383, 385	35, 41
5-3	45	384	36
5-4	46, 51	384, 385	37–38, 43
5-5	47	384	39
5-6	48, 52	385, 386	40, 44
5-7	50, 53	385, 386	42, 45

MAJOR CHECKUP
Standardized Format

Choose the correct letter.

1. Give the standard numeral for fifty-seven tenths.

a. 0.57
b. 0.057
c. 57
d. none of these

2. Round 53.499 to the nearest whole number.

a. 53
b. 54
c. 53.5
d. none of these

3. Give the sum.

6.2 + 3.8 + 0.57

a. 1.57
b. 15.7
c. 10.57
d. none of these

4. Give the difference.

20.04 – 6.77

a. 13.27
b. 14.37
c. 23.27
d. none of these

5. Multiply.

2.48
×0.13

a. 3.2240
b. 0.3224
c. 32.2400
d. none of these

6. Divide.

0.08)3.216

a. 40.2
b. 4.02
c. 0.402
d. none of these

7. Change this measurement to meters.

324 mm

a. 324,000 m
b. 3.24 m
c. 0.324 m
d. none of these

8. Which of these is a subset of {1, 2, 3, 4}?

a. {1, 2, 3, 4, 5}
b. {0, 1, 2}
c. {3, 4}
d. none of these

9. Find the area.

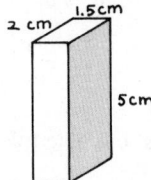

10 mm

a. 314 mm²
b. 314 mm³
c. 62.8 mm²
d. none of these

10. Give the surface area.

2 cm 1.5 cm
5 cm

a. 41 cm²
b. 15 cm²
c. 30 cm²
d. none of these

11. Find the volume.

8 m
8 m 8 m

a. 512 m
b. 512 m²
c. 512 m³
d. none of these

12. Which of these units is the basic unit of liquid volume in the metric system?

a. meter
b. liter
c. gram
d. none of these

170

Answers for Chapter 5 Posttest

1. 25 mm **2.** 48 mm **3.** 420 **4.** 0.042
5. 0.643 **6.** 7300 **7.** 0.4243 **8.** 5600
9. 3900 **10.** 0.75 **11.** 4.567 **12.** 24 cm
13. 40 cm **14.** 26 cm **15.** 62.8 cm
16. 36 cm² **17.** 96 cm² **18.** 30 cm²
19. 314 cm² **20.** 216 cm² **21.** 158 cm²
22. 408.2 cm² **23.** 216 cm³ **24.** 120 cm³
25. 628 cm³ **26.** 5 **27.** 3 **28.** 15,840
29. 48 **30.** 24 **31.** 8000 **32.** 816
33. 576 **34.** 72

Chapter 5 Posttest

Name _____

Date _____

Measure each segment to the nearest millimeter. [Obj. 5-1, pages 134–135]

1. _____

2. _____

Complete. [Obj. 5-2, pages 134–137, 154–155]

3. 4.2 m = _____ cm

4. 4.2 cm = _____ m

5. 643 m = _____ km

6. 7.3 L = _____ mL

7. 424.3 mL = _____ L

8. 5.6 kg = _____ g

9. 3.9 g = _____ mg

10. 750 mg = _____ g

11. 4567 mm = _____ m

Compute each perimeter or circumference. Use 3.14 as an approximation for π. [Obj. 5-3, pages 138–139, 157]

12. 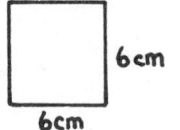 _____

13. 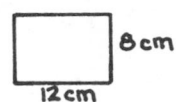 _____

14. 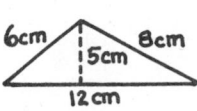 _____

15. 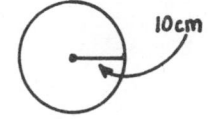 _____

Compute the areas of the figures in exercises 12-15. [Obj. 5-4, pages 140–144, 158–159]

16. A = _____

17. A = _____

18. A = _____

19. A = _____

Compute the surface area of each figure. Use 3.14 as an approximation for π. [Obj. 5-5, pages 146–149, 159]

20. 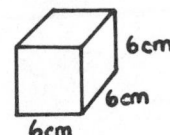 _____

21. 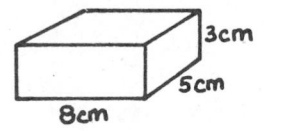 _____

22. 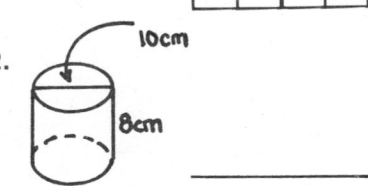 _____

Compute the volumes of the figures in exercises 20-22. [Obj. 5-6, pages 150–153, 162–163]

23. V = _____

24. V = _____

25. V = _____

Complete. [Obj. 5-7, pages 156–157, 164–165]

26. 60 in. = _____ ft

27. 9 ft _____ yd

28. 3 mi = _____ ft

29. 12 gal = _____ qt

30. 12 qt = _____ pt

31. 4 t = _____ lb

32. 51 lb = _____ oz

33. 48 ft = _____ in.

34. 24 yd = _____ ft

170a

Chapter 6
Fractions—Addition and Subtraction

Pages 171–200

Learning Objectives

After completing this chapter, all students should be able to do the following:

6-1   Reduce fractions to lowest terms.

6-2   Determine which of two fractions is greater.

6-3   Add and subtract fractions.

6-4   Change fractions to mixed numbers and vice versa.

6-5   Add mixed numbers.

6-6   Subtract mixed numbers.

6-7   Solve word problems that involve fractions.

Students are given a review of equivalent fractions and of reducing fractions to lowest terms. They learn to compare any two fractions by using equivalent fractions with the same denominators. Then addition and subtraction of fractions are treated carefully. Mixed numbers are introduced. Addition and subtraction of mixed numbers, especially when regrouping is required, are introduced. Emphasis is again given to applying the skills that are developed in real situations.

Mathematics

Equivalent fractions. The topic of equivalent fractions is an extremely important one and is treated in detail in Levels 4, 5, and 6. Equivalent fractions name the same number. For example, each of the fractions in this set of fractions refers to the same fractional number. All the fractions are equivalent.

$$\{\frac{1}{2}, \frac{2}{4}, \frac{3}{6}, \frac{4}{8}, \frac{5}{10}, \frac{6}{12}, \frac{7}{14}, \cdots\}$$

One can generate a different fraction equivalent to a given fraction by multiplying both numerator and denominator by the same number (not 0 or 1). This is a result of the multiplying by 1 property. For example:

$$\frac{1}{2} = \frac{1}{2} \times 1 = \frac{1}{2} \times \frac{3}{3} = \frac{1 \times 3}{2 \times 3} = \frac{3}{6}$$

Of course, unless students have learned how to multiply fractions, this explanation makes no sense. Since the concept of equivalent fractions is far too important to be delayed until after multiplication of fractions is taught, it is necessary to justify in some other way the method of generating equivalent fractions by multiplying both numerator and denominator by the same number. This can be done by appealing to a physical model. The picture on the left can be used to represent $1/2$, because $1/2$ of the square is shaded.

Now by drawing two horizontal lines, we triple (multiply by 3) the number of shaded parts and also triple the total number of parts. This is equivalent to multiplying both numerator and denominator by the same number:

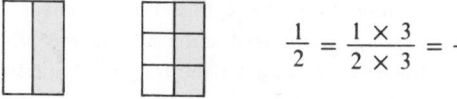

$$\frac{1}{2} = \frac{1 \times 3}{2 \times 3} = \frac{3}{6}$$

Since the same amount of the square is shaded, we know that $1/2 = 3/6$. A similar use of the model justifies reducing fractions by dividing both numerator and denominator by the same number.

The number-line model can also be used to show the same technique for generating equivalent fractions.

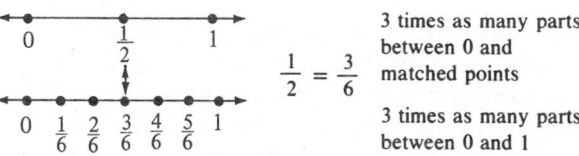

3 times as many parts between 0 and matched points

$$\frac{1}{2} = \frac{3}{6}$$

3 times as many parts between 0 and 1

Addition and subtraction. When we add or subtract, we are working with numbers and we may express those numbers in any way that makes the work easy. This is especially true when working with fractional numbers. For example, simplifying the sum or difference of two fractional numbers when the fractions used have the same denominator is very easy. One merely adds or subtracts the numerators and uses the same denominator:

$$\frac{2}{5} + \frac{1}{5} = \frac{3}{5} \qquad \frac{5}{7} - \frac{2}{7} = \frac{3}{7}$$

Since these tasks are so simple when the fractions have the same denominator, we take advantage of this fact when the given fractions have different denominators. Since we are adding the *numbers*, we can use any representation of the numbers that we wish. We merely change to equivalent fractions that do have the same denominator—we make a difficult task easy. For example, suppose the problem is to add $2/3$ and $1/2$. Since this is a problem about numbers, we are not restricted to using the numerals $2/3$ and $1/2$; we can use any numerals for the numbers we wish. The easy way is to pick fractions that have the same denominator. So we think about the equivalent fractions for each number:

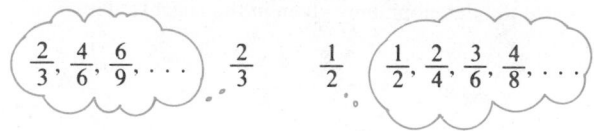

and pick fractions that have the same denominator:

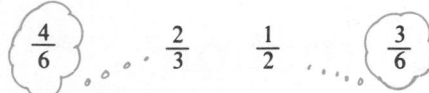

Now it is simple to express the sum by a fraction, $^7/_6$. It would be confusing to say that we can't add $^2/_3$ and $^1/_2$. We certainly can add these fractional numbers. Their sum is $^7/_6$. We change the names $^2/_3$ and $^1/_2$ to fractions with the same denominator in order to find a simple way of writing the sum.

Mixed numbers. A mixed number is a short way of writing the sum of a whole number and a fractional number that is less than 1, using a standard numeral for the whole number and a common fraction for the fractional number.

$$3 + \frac{1}{2} = 3\frac{1}{2}$$

Changing from a mixed number to an equivalent fraction is simply a matter of remembering that the mixed number represents a sum and applying the algorithm for adding with fractions.

$$3\frac{1}{2} = 3 + \frac{1}{2} = \frac{6}{2} + \frac{1}{2} = \frac{7}{2}$$

Changing from a fraction for a number greater than 1 to a mixed number involves thinking of the number in two parts; one part is the greatest whole number less than (or equal to) the given number, and the other part is a fractional number less than 1. This can be done by thinking about the whole numbers in terms of certain fractions, choosing the proper fraction, and then thinking of the second addend in the sum.

whole numbers: $\frac{5}{5}, \frac{10}{5}, \frac{15}{5}, \frac{20}{5}, \ldots$

$$\frac{17}{5} = \frac{15}{5} + \frac{2}{5} = 3 + \frac{2}{5} = 3\frac{2}{5}$$

An obvious shortcut that works for exactly the same reason is to divide the numerator by the denominator.

Teaching the Chapter

The concept of equivalent fractions is extremely important, and you should expect all students to be able to generate many fractions equivalent to a given fraction by multiplying both numerator and denominator by the same (nonzero) number. They should also be able to reduce any fractions to lowest terms.

Computation with fractions is one of those topics that becomes almost completely a matter of "symbol pushing" without understanding. We suggest that with less able students you use the developments given in the suggested lesson plans.

Vocabulary

denominator
equivalent fractions
fraction
fulcrum
greatest common divisor
greatest common factor
least common denominator
mixed number
numerator
reduce to lowest terms

Materials

hand calculators
meter stick or yardstick
pennies
digit cards
World Almanac or road atlas

Chapter Tests

For a discussion of how to use the chapter tests, please see page 17c.

Answers for Chapter 6 Pretest

1. $\frac{3}{4}$ 2. $\frac{3}{4}$ 3. $\frac{4}{5}$ 4. $\frac{5}{6}$ 5. $\frac{10}{11}$ 6. > 7. < 8. < 9. <

10. > 11. $\frac{3}{4}$ 12. $\frac{11}{12}$ 13. $\frac{9}{10}$ 14. $\frac{1}{4}$ 15. $\frac{1}{6}$ 16. $\frac{7}{20}$ 17. $\frac{7}{2}$

18. $\frac{7}{3}$ 19. $2\frac{3}{4}$ 20. $5\frac{1}{5}$ 21. $\frac{23}{5}$ 22. $9\frac{2}{4}$ 23. $7\frac{4}{7}$ 24. 8

25. $13\frac{5}{6}$ 26. $8\frac{1}{8}$ 27. $9\frac{7}{20}$ 28. $1\frac{3}{8}$ 29. $2\frac{3}{4}$ 30. $2\frac{1}{6}$

31. $1\frac{1}{2}$ 32. $2\frac{17}{20}$ 33. $1\frac{1}{6}$ ft 34. $25\frac{3}{8}$ in.

Chapter 6 Pretest

Name _____

Date _____

Reduce each fraction to lowest terms. [Obj. 6-1, pages 172–177]

Number right

0	1	2	3	4	5

1. $\frac{9}{12}$ _____

2. $\frac{18}{24}$ _____

3. $\frac{24}{30}$ _____

4. $\frac{45}{54}$ _____

5. $\frac{30}{33}$ _____

< or >? [Obj. 6-2, pages 178–179]

0	1	2	3	4	5

6. $\frac{1}{6}$ ◯ $\frac{1}{7}$ 7. $\frac{3}{8}$ ◯ $\frac{5}{8}$ 8. $\frac{7}{8}$ ◯ $\frac{8}{9}$ 9. $\frac{2}{5}$ ◯ $\frac{3}{7}$ 10. $\frac{3}{4}$ ◯ $\frac{5}{7}$

Add or subtract. [Obj. 6-3, pages 180–184]

0	1	2	3	4	5	6

11. $\frac{1}{4} + \frac{1}{2} =$ _____

12. $\frac{1}{6} + \frac{3}{4} =$ _____

13. $\frac{1}{2} + \frac{2}{5} =$ _____

14. $\frac{1}{2} - \frac{1}{4} =$ _____

15. $\frac{1}{2} - \frac{1}{3} =$ _____

16. $\frac{3}{5} - \frac{1}{4} =$ _____

Complete this table. [Obj. 6-4, pages 186–187]

0-2	3	4	5	6

Mixed Number	$3\frac{1}{2}$	$2\frac{1}{3}$	19.	20.	$4\frac{3}{5}$	22.
Fraction	17.	18.	$\frac{11}{4}$	$\frac{26}{5}$	21.	$\frac{38}{4}$

Add. [Obj. 6-5, pages 188–189, 192]

0	1	2	3	4	5

23. $3\frac{3}{7}$
    $+4\frac{1}{7}$

24. $5\frac{3}{8}$
    $+2\frac{5}{8}$

25. $6\frac{1}{3}$
    $+7\frac{1}{2}$

26. $2\frac{3}{8}$
    $+5\frac{3}{4}$

27. $6\frac{3}{5}$
    $+2\frac{3}{4}$

Subtract. [Obj. 6-6, pages 190–192]

0	1	2	3	4	5

28. $4\frac{7}{8}$
    $-3\frac{4}{8}$

29. $6\frac{3}{8}$
    $-3\frac{5}{8}$

30. $8\frac{2}{3}$
    $-6\frac{1}{2}$

31. $6\frac{1}{6}$
    $-4\frac{2}{3}$

32. $5\frac{3}{5}$
    $-2\frac{3}{4}$

Solve. [Obj. 6-7, pages 194–195]

0	1	2

33. Jim is $4\frac{1}{3}$ feet tall and John is $5\frac{1}{2}$ feet tall.

How much taller is John? _____

34. A metal rod $13\frac{3}{4}$ inches long is welded to the end of a rod that is $11\frac{5}{8}$ inches long. How long are the two rods together?

_____

Chapter 6
Record and Assignment Chart

Name _____

Objectives

		Pretest Score Mark number correct	Posttest Score Mark number correct
6-1	Reduce fractions to lowest terms.	0 1 2 3 4 5	0 1 2 3 4 5
6-2	Determine which of two fractions is greater.	0 1 2 3 4 5	0 1 2 3 4 5
6-3	Add and subtract fractions.	0 1 2 3 4 5 6	0 1 2 3 4 5 6
6-4	Change fractions to mixed numbers and vice versa.	0-1 2 3 4 5 6	0-1 2 3 4 5 6
6-5	Add mixed numbers.	0 1 2 3 4 5	0 1 2 3 4 5
6-6	Subtract mixed numbers.	0 1 2 3 4 5	0 1 2 3 4 5
6-7	Solve word problems that involve fractions.	0 1 2	0 1 2

Unsatisfactory Score | Satisfactory Score   Unsatisfactory Score | Satisfactory Score

TEACHING ASSIGNMENTS*

	Student Page	Basic Assignment	Average Assignment	Enriched Assignment	Problem Solving	RETEACHING ASSIGNMENTS†
	172, 173	1–25	1–30, EW 46	1–40, EW 46		BW 46
6-1	174, 175	1–40	1–40, EW 47	1–53, EW 47	54, 55, 56, 57	page 386 Set 54, BW 47
	176, 177	1–37	1–39, EW 47	7–41, EW 47		page 386 Set 55, BW 47
6-2	178, 179	1–35	1–40, EW 48	1–47, EW 48	48, 49, 50	page 386 Set 56, BW 48
6-3	180, 181	1–40	1–46, EW 49	1–46, EW 49	47, 48, 49, 50	page 387 Set 57, BW 49
	182, 183	1–47	1–47, EW 50	9–47, EW 50	48, 49, 50	page 387 Set 58, BW 50
6-3	184	1–48	1–48, EW 50	1–48, EW 50		BW 50
	185	1–2	1–3	1–4		BW 50
6-4	186, 187	1–45	1–51, EW 51	1–53, EW 51		page 387 Set 59, BW 51
6-5	188, 189	1–24	1–24, EW 52	1–24, EW 52	25, 26, 27, 28, 29, 30	page 388 Set 60, BW 52
6-6	190, 191	1–24	1–24, EW 53	1–24, 28–30, EW 53	25, 26, 27	page 388 Set 61, BW 53
6-5 6-6	192	1–40	1–40, EW 54	1–40, EW 54		BW 54
	193	1–4	1–6	1–8		BW 54
6-7	194, 195	1–8	1–10, EW 54	1–12, EW 54		BW 54
	196	Chapter Checkup				
	197	Project				
	198	Chapter Review				
	199	Chapter Challenge				
	200	Major Checkup				
	201, 202	Midyear Test				

*Check assignments for objectives with unsatisfactory pretest scores.
†Check assignments for objectives with unsatisfactory posttest scores.

BW = Basic Worksheet
EW = Enrichment Worksheet

6
Fractions—Addition and Subtraction

STUDENT OBJECTIVE
To write fractions that are equivalent to a given fraction.

VOCABULARY
equivalent fractions, fraction

Suggested Lesson Plan

Introduction Before starting this lesson, have students write down answers for Ready or Not? inventory test on page 172. This test covers some very basic concepts of fractions: identifying a fraction for part of a whole and identifying a fraction for part of a set. Correct these tests in class. Make note of any student who misses more than 2 questions. This test will determine whether there are weaknesses in the class in general or individual students who are missing some basic concepts for fractions.

Introduce the lesson by drawing these two models on the board:

 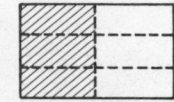

Ask what fraction is represented by the first model. ($\frac{1}{2}$) By the second model. (Students may say $\frac{1}{2}$ or $\frac{3}{6}$.) Point out that the same amount of each model is shaded, so $\frac{1}{2}$ and $\frac{3}{6}$ represent the same number; thus $\frac{1}{2}$ and $\frac{3}{6}$ are equivalent fractions. Write the expression on the board. Give one or two more examples of equivalent fractions.

Using the pages Continue the discussion by using the exposition on page 172 to show equivalent fractions on the number line. Have students draw a number line showing thirds on scratch paper, labeling the points above the number line. Then, keeping the same point for 1, have them divide the distance from 0 to 1 into sixths by locating points for $\frac{1}{6}$, $\frac{2}{6}$, $\frac{3}{6}$, $\frac{4}{6}$, and $\frac{5}{6}$. Of course, those points named with two names are examples of equivalent fractions.

Assign exercises 1−40 for written work. Tell students that drawing a number line will help them if they are not sure of any equivalent fractions.

READY OR NOT ?

What fraction of the region is colored?

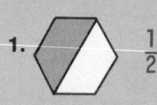 1. $\frac{1}{2}$

 2. $\frac{2}{3}$

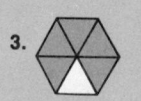 3. $\frac{5}{6}$

 4. $\frac{1}{3}$

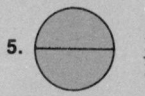 5. $\frac{2}{2}$

What fraction of the objects are colored?

6. ○ ● ● $\frac{2}{3}$

7. ○ ● ○ ● $\frac{2}{4}$

8. ○ ● ○ ○ ○ $\frac{1}{5}$

9. ● ● ● ● ● ○ ● ● $\frac{7}{8}$

10. ● ○ ● ○ ● $\frac{3}{5}$

172

Equivalent fractions

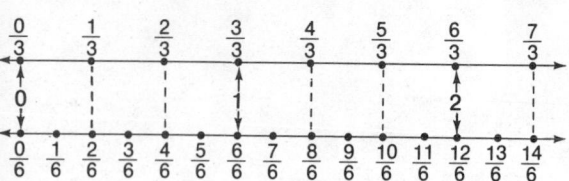

The fractions $\frac{2}{3}$ and $\frac{4}{6}$ name the same number. Fractions that name the same number are called **equivalent fractions**. We write $\frac{2}{3} = \frac{4}{6}$. What other equivalent fractions does the picture show?

EXERCISES
Give two equivalent fractions for each red point.   Answers vary.

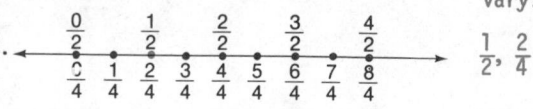

1. $\frac{1}{2}, \frac{2}{4}$

2. $\frac{2}{3}, \frac{4}{6}$

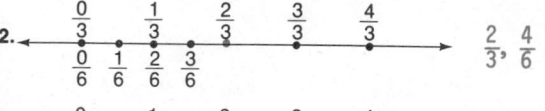

3. $\frac{4}{5}, \frac{8}{10}$

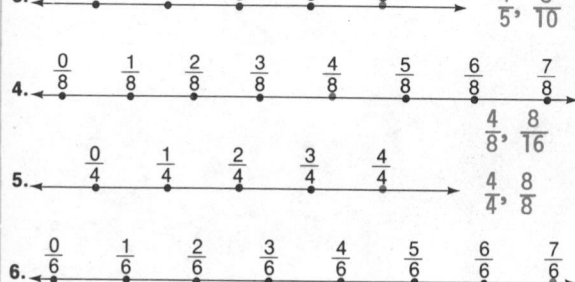

4. $\frac{4}{8}, \frac{8}{16}$

5. $\frac{4}{4}, \frac{8}{8}$

6. $\frac{7}{6}, \frac{14}{12}$

Assignments

BASIC
page 172 exercises 1−6
page 173 exercises 7−25
Basic Worksheet 46

AVERAGE
page 172 exercises 1−6
page 173 exercises 7−30
Enrichment Worksheet 46

ENRICHED
page 172 exercises 1−6
page 173 exercises 7−40
Enrichment Worksheet 46

REVIEW PRACTICE
page 382 set 39

Give two equivalent fractions for the part of the eggs that are

7. white $\frac{3}{12}$, $\frac{1}{4}$

8. brown $\frac{9}{12}$, $\frac{3}{4}$

9. in the carton $\frac{12}{12}$, $\frac{2}{2}$

10. broken $\frac{4}{12}$, $\frac{1}{3}$

11. not broken $\frac{8}{12}$, $\frac{2}{3}$

12. white and broken $\frac{2}{12}$, $\frac{1}{6}$

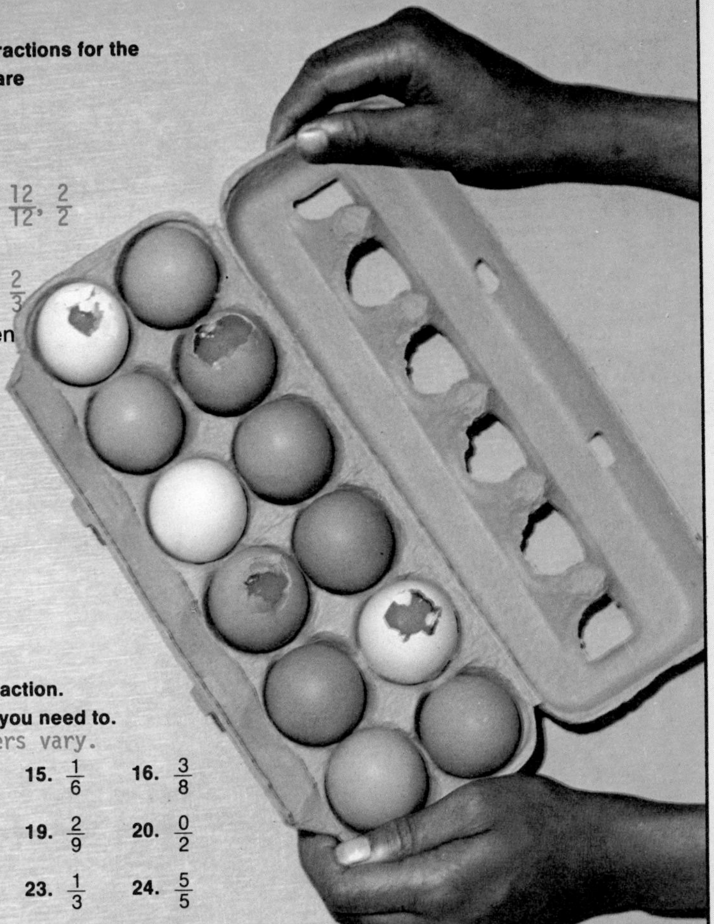

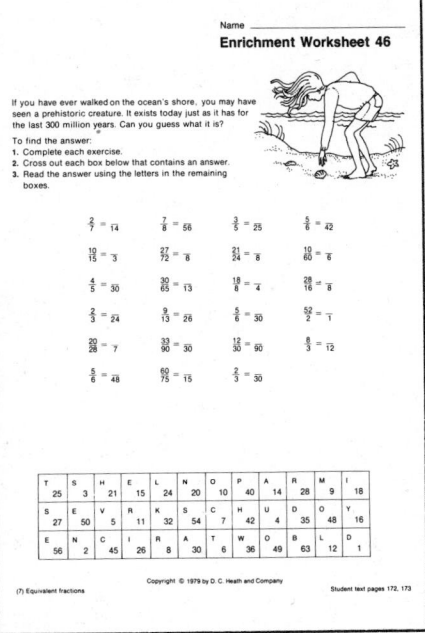

**Give an equivalent fraction.
Use a number line if you need to.**
Answers vary.

13. $\frac{1}{2}$ 14. $\frac{2}{3}$ 15. $\frac{1}{6}$ 16. $\frac{3}{8}$

17. $\frac{3}{2}$ 18. $\frac{1}{7}$ 19. $\frac{2}{9}$ 20. $\frac{0}{2}$

21. $\frac{7}{8}$ 22. $\frac{5}{10}$ 23. $\frac{1}{3}$ 24. $\frac{5}{5}$

25. $\frac{3}{4}$ 26. $\frac{7}{2}$ 27. $\frac{4}{6}$ 28. $\frac{4}{4}$

29. $\frac{1}{8}$ 30. $\frac{1}{4}$ 31. $\frac{3}{9}$ ·32. $\frac{4}{12}$

33. $\frac{3}{3}$ 34. $\frac{6}{4}$ 35. $\frac{1}{5}$ 36. $\frac{5}{7}$

37. $\frac{5}{3}$ 38. $\frac{4}{3}$ 39. $\frac{6}{10}$ 40. $\frac{0}{4}$

173

Basic Worksheet 46

Enrichment Worksheet 46

Follow-up Activities

Reinforcement You may wish to follow up the lesson with this game. Divide the students into two well-balanced teams. On the chalkboard locate a fractional number on a number line. For example:

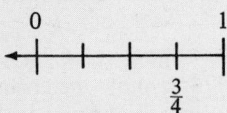

0   1

$\frac{3}{4}$

Call on a volunteer from one team to go to the chalkboard and write an equivalent fraction. If the player is correct, that team earns a point. List another fraction and call on a volunteer from the other team to go to the chalkboard and give an equivalent fraction. Play continues until all players have been to the chalkboard at least once. The team earning the greater total of points wins the game.

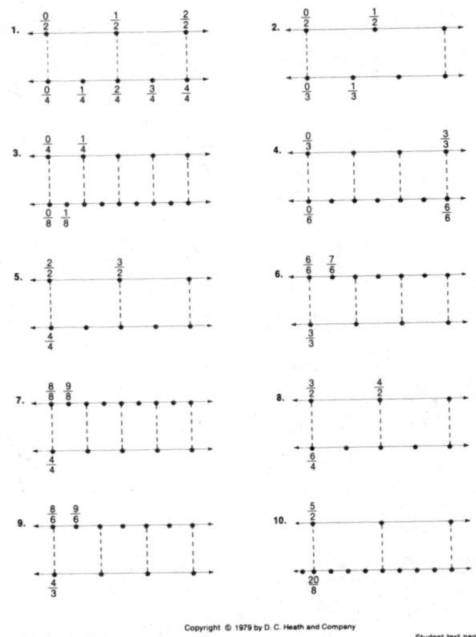

Enrichment Some students may wish to make a bulletin-board display of equivalent fractions on the number line. The display could look like this:

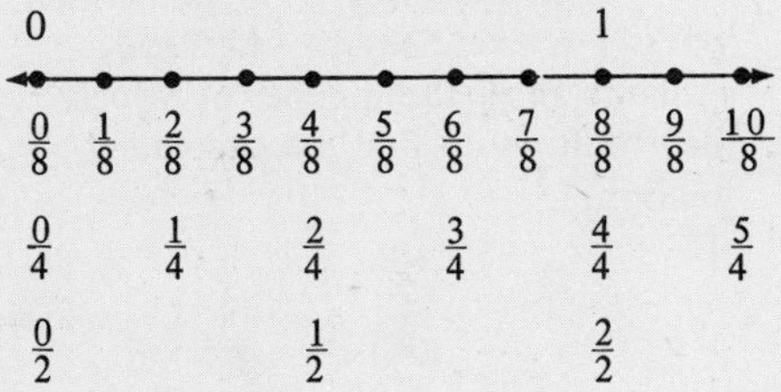

0   1

$\frac{0}{8}$ $\frac{1}{8}$ $\frac{2}{8}$ $\frac{3}{8}$ $\frac{4}{8}$ $\frac{5}{8}$ $\frac{6}{8}$ $\frac{7}{8}$ $\frac{8}{8}$ $\frac{9}{8}$ $\frac{10}{8}$

$\frac{0}{4}$ $\frac{1}{4}$ $\frac{2}{4}$ $\frac{3}{4}$ $\frac{4}{4}$ $\frac{5}{4}$

$\frac{0}{2}$ $\frac{1}{2}$ $\frac{2}{2}$

EXCURSION
Complete.

$66^2 =$ ___?___   4356

$666^2 =$ ___?___   443556

$6666^2 =$ ___?___   44435556

Look for a pattern.

Can you simplify the expression

$66666^2 =$ ___?___

without pencil or paper?

4444355556

STUDENT OBJECTIVE
To find fractions in higher terms that are equivalent to a given fraction.

VOCABULARY
numerator, denominator

Suggested Lesson Plan

Using the pages Use the exposition on page 174 to show the arithmetic that students use to find equivalent fractions. From the pictures, students should realize that ¾ and ⁶⁄₈ are equivalent fractions. Show the process of multiplying both the numerator and the denominator by 2 to find ⁶⁄₈. As you show the process, state the general rule written at the top of the page, noting that the number that you multiply by may be any number except 0.

Give several more examples on the board and let students find the equivalent fraction. For example, ²⁄₃ = /₉. Ask what number the denominator has been multiplied by. (3) Then ask what equivalent fraction is found by multiplying the numerator by the same number. (⁶⁄₉)

Assign exercises 1−57 for written work. For exercises 19−40, have students show the number by which they multiply to find the equivalent fraction.

More about equivalent fractions

Multiplying both numerator and denominator by the same nonzero number gives an equivalent fraction.

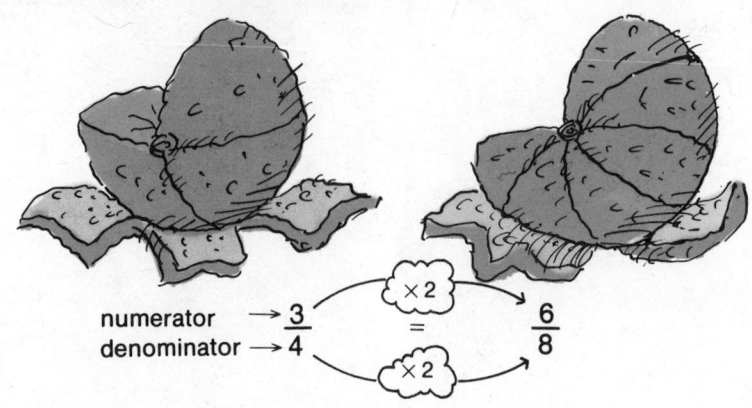

$$\text{numerator} \rightarrow \frac{3}{4} \quad \overset{\times 2}{\underset{\times 2}{=}} \quad \frac{6}{8}$$
$$\text{denominator} \rightarrow$$

$\frac{2}{3}$ is equivalent to how many twelfths?

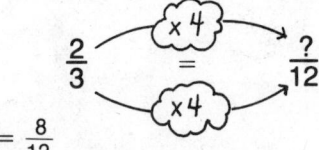

$$\frac{2}{3} \quad \overset{\times 4}{\underset{\times 4}{=}} \quad \frac{?}{12}$$

So, $\frac{2}{3} = \frac{8}{12}$

I would multiply 3 by 4 to get 12. So, I multiply 2 by 4 and get 8.

EXERCISES
Give an equivalent fraction. Answers vary.

1. $\frac{1}{3}$ 2. $\frac{1}{2}$ 3. $\frac{1}{4}$ 4. $\frac{3}{2}$ 5. $\frac{3}{4}$ 6. $\frac{1}{5}$

7. $\frac{0}{3}$ 8. $\frac{5}{2}$ 9. $\frac{3}{5}$ 10. $\frac{2}{3}$ 11. $\frac{5}{4}$ 12. $\frac{4}{3}$

13. $\frac{7}{8}$ 14. $\frac{5}{9}$ 15. $\frac{5}{6}$ 16. $\frac{2}{8}$ 17. $\frac{3}{8}$ 18. $\frac{8}{5}$

174

Assignments

BASIC
page 174   exercises 1−18
page 175   exercises 19−40, 54−55
Basic Worksheet 47

AVERAGE
page 174   exercises 1−18
page 175   exercises 19−40, 54−55
Enrichment Worksheet 47

ENRICHED
page 174   exercises 1−18
page 175   exercises 19−57
Enrichment Worksheet 47

EXTRA PRACTICE
page 386   set 54

Copy and complete.

19. $\frac{1}{2} = \frac{?}{8}$ 4
20. $\frac{2}{2} = \frac{?}{8}$ 8
21. $\frac{1}{5} = \frac{?}{20}$ 4
22. $\frac{3}{2} = \frac{?}{10}$ 15
23. $\frac{1}{4} = \frac{?}{16}$ 4

24. $\frac{2}{3} = \frac{?}{9}$ 6
25. $\frac{4}{3} = \frac{?}{12}$ 16
26. $\frac{1}{3} = \frac{?}{6}$ 2
27. $\frac{5}{2} = \frac{?}{10}$ 25
28. $\frac{1}{2} = \frac{?}{12}$ 6

29. $\frac{1}{3} = \frac{?}{12}$ 4
30. $\frac{8}{3} = \frac{?}{6}$ 16
31. $\frac{6}{6} = \frac{?}{2}$ 2
32. $\frac{2}{3} = \frac{?}{12}$ 8
33. $\frac{1}{6} = \frac{?}{18}$ 3

34. $\frac{3}{2} = \frac{?}{6}$ 9
35. $\frac{2}{3} = \frac{?}{6}$ 4
36. $\frac{1}{2} = \frac{?}{6}$ 3
37. $\frac{3}{3} = \frac{?}{9}$ 9
38. $\frac{1}{3} = \frac{?}{15}$ 5

39. $\frac{1}{2} = \frac{?}{10}$ 5
40. $\frac{0}{2} = \frac{?}{8}$ 0
41. $\frac{4}{3} = \frac{?}{6}$ 8
42. $\frac{1}{4} = \frac{?}{20}$ 5
43. $\frac{8}{7} = \frac{?}{14}$ 16

44. $\frac{5}{2} = \frac{?}{8}$ 20
45. $\frac{1}{3} = \frac{?}{9}$ 3
46. $\frac{1}{5} = \frac{?}{10}$ 2
47. $\frac{1}{4} = \frac{?}{8}$ 2
48. $\frac{1}{2} = \frac{?}{4}$ 2

49. $\frac{1}{4} = \frac{?}{12}$ 3
50. $\frac{3}{2} = \frac{?}{4}$ 6
51. $\frac{3}{3} = \frac{?}{6}$ 6
52. $\frac{1}{6} = \frac{?}{24}$ 4
53. $\frac{0}{2} = \frac{?}{6}$ 0

Solve.

54. Which is more, $\frac{5}{12}$ of the oranges or $\frac{7}{12}$ of the oranges? $\frac{7}{12}$

55. Which is less, $\frac{4}{6}$ of the oranges or $\frac{5}{6}$ of the oranges? $\frac{4}{6}$

56. Which is more, $\frac{1}{2}$ or $\frac{3}{4}$? $\frac{3}{4}$

57. Which is less, $\frac{5}{6}$ or $\frac{3}{4}$? $\frac{3}{4}$

175

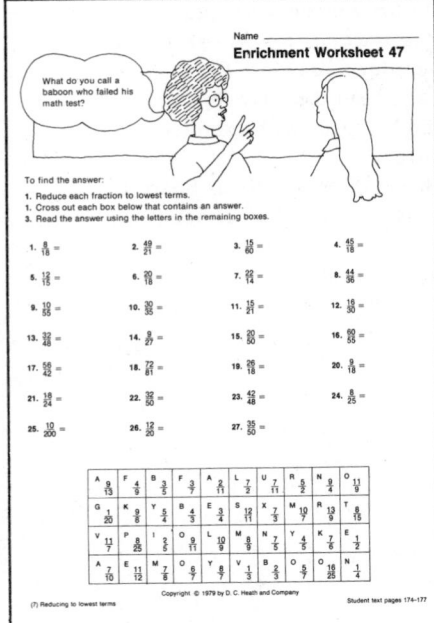

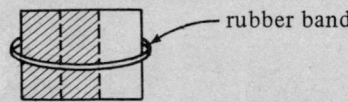
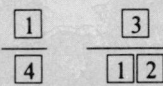
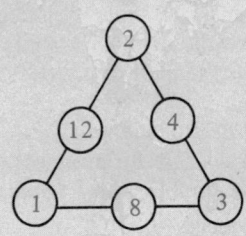

VOCABULARY
terms (of a fraction), greatest common factor, greatest common divisor

Suggested Lesson Plan

Introduction Write 12 and 16 on the board. Ask students to name all the numbers that will divide 12 evenly. As they name the divisors, list them under 12. Do the same for 16. Ask one student to come to the board and circle all these numbers that will divide both numbers. The work should look like this:

$$\overline{①\ ②\ 3\ ④\ 6\ \ 12}$$
$$12$$

$$\overline{①\ ②\ ④\ 8\ \ 16}$$
$$16$$

Explain that those numbers circled are called the *common divisors* of 12 and 16. Now ask students to name the greatest common divisor of 12 and 16. That, of course, is the greatest number circled, or 4. (It is also the greatest common factor of 12 and 16 but you should probably refer to divisors only or only to factors. Using both terms would just confuse students.)

List several more pairs of numbers on the board and have students find the greatest common divisor of each pair of numbers.

Using the pages Write the fraction $^6/_9$ on the board, and continuing the discussion of the introduction, ask a student for the greatest number that will divide both 6 and 9. After a student identifies 3 as the greatest common divisor, point out that if we divide both the numerator and denominator of $^6/_9$ by 3, the result is a fraction in lowest terms. A fraction in lowest terms has no common divisor greater than 1 for the numerator and denominator of the fraction.

Of course, students have encountered these terms and ideas before, so this lesson is really a review and summary of skills learned earlier. Students will understand what is meant by "lowest terms," but it does not hurt for you to formally define the term.

Call on students to give the greatest common divisors for exercises 1–12. If they have trouble with a fraction, go back to listing all the divisors of the

numerator and the denominator and then circling the greatest. Assign exercises 13–37 for written work. Have students find the fractions for 38–41 and submit answers for a drawing. Draw answer slips and read the answers aloud until you find a paper with exercises 38–41 all correct.

Assign Keeping Skills Sharp to students that have had difficulty with multiplication of whole numbers and multiplication of decimals.

Reducing a fraction to lowest terms

The numerator, 6, and the denominator, 9, are called the **terms** of the fraction.

$\frac{6}{9}$ are blue.

To reduce a fraction to lowest terms, divide both numerator and denominator by their greatest common factor (or divisor).

$\frac{2}{3}$ are blue.

If you reduce $\frac{4}{2}$ to lowest terms, you get $\frac{2}{1}$, or 2.

EXERCISES
Give the greatest common divisor of the numerator and denominator.

1. $\frac{2}{6}$ 2   2. $\frac{14}{6}$ 2   3. $\frac{10}{5}$ 5   4. $\frac{6}{6}$ 6   5. $\frac{6}{8}$ 2   6. $\frac{12}{4}$ 4

7. $\frac{18}{15}$ 3   8. $\frac{9}{12}$ 3   9. $\frac{6}{4}$ 2   10. $\frac{3}{9}$ 3   11. $\frac{4}{16}$ 4   12. $\frac{12}{18}$ 6

176

Assignments

BASIC
page 176 exercises 1–12
page 177 exercises 13–37,
    Keeping Skills Sharp
Basic Worksheet 47

AVERAGE
page 176 exercises 1–12
page 177 exercises 13–39,
    Keeping Skills Sharp
Enrichment Worksheet 47

ENRICHED
page 176 exercises 7–12
page 177 exercises 13–41,
    Keeping Skills Sharp
Enrichment Worksheet 47

EXTRA PRACTICE
page 386 set 55

Reduce each fraction to lowest terms.

13. $\frac{5}{5}$ 1   14. $\frac{6}{9}$ $\frac{2}{3}$ 15. $\frac{6}{12}$ $\frac{1}{2}$ 16. $\frac{2}{4}$ $\frac{1}{2}$ 17. $\frac{10}{8}$ $\frac{5}{4}$

18. $\frac{10}{12}$ $\frac{5}{6}$ 19. $\frac{4}{16}$ $\frac{1}{4}$ 20. $\frac{2}{8}$ $\frac{1}{4}$ 21. $\frac{2}{6}$ $\frac{1}{3}$ 22. $\frac{6}{10}$ $\frac{3}{5}$

23. $\frac{15}{18}$ $\frac{5}{6}$ 24. $\frac{6}{4}$ $\frac{3}{2}$ 25. $\frac{3}{9}$ $\frac{1}{3}$ 26. $\frac{15}{10}$ $\frac{3}{2}$ 27. $\frac{3}{6}$ $\frac{1}{2}$

28. $\frac{5}{15}$ $\frac{1}{3}$ 29. $\frac{4}{6}$ $\frac{2}{3}$ 30. $\frac{3}{12}$ $\frac{1}{4}$ 31. $\frac{4}{8}$ $\frac{1}{2}$ 32. $\frac{18}{15}$ $\frac{6}{5}$

33. $\frac{9}{6}$ $\frac{3}{2}$ 34. $\frac{0}{4}$ 0   35. $\frac{4}{12}$ $\frac{1}{3}$ 36. $\frac{16}{32}$ $\frac{1}{2}$ 37. $\frac{10}{15}$ $\frac{2}{3}$

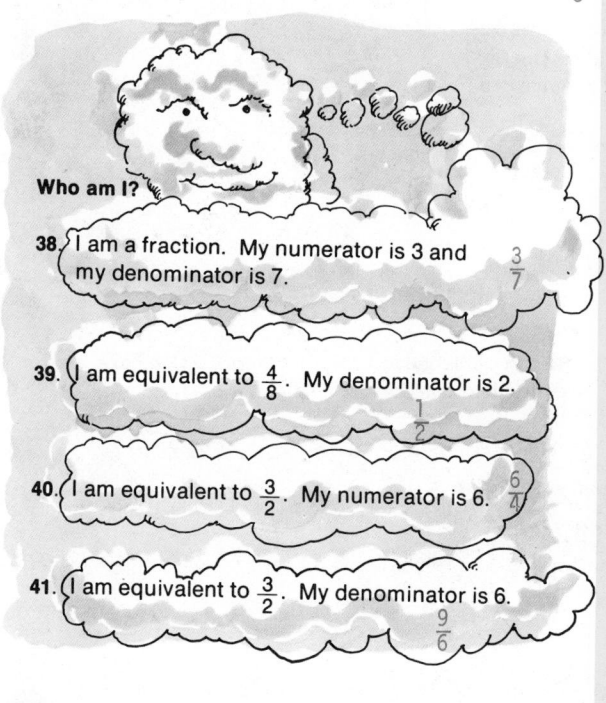

Who am I?

38. I am a fraction. My numerator is 3 and my denominator is 7. $\frac{3}{7}$

39. I am equivalent to $\frac{4}{8}$. My denominator is 2. $\frac{1}{2}$

40. I am equivalent to $\frac{3}{2}$. My numerator is 6. $\frac{6}{4}$

41. I am equivalent to $\frac{3}{2}$. My denominator is 6. $\frac{9}{6}$

Reduce to lowest terms. $\frac{9702}{14553}$ $\frac{2}{3}$

177

Follow-up Activities

Reinforcement Give pairs of numbers and have students list the sets of divisors for each number and then the greatest common divisor for the pair.

Enrichment Have students write new "Who am I?" questions about fractions and decimals. You can let them expand to more than just fractions—for example, any famous number such as "CB language for 'I received your message'" (10-4). Post several of these questions each day and run a contest to see who can name each number.

EXCURSION
Copy and finish drawing the dotted path to get the ending number.

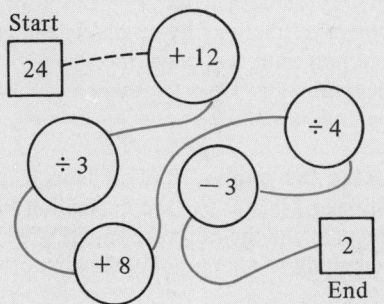

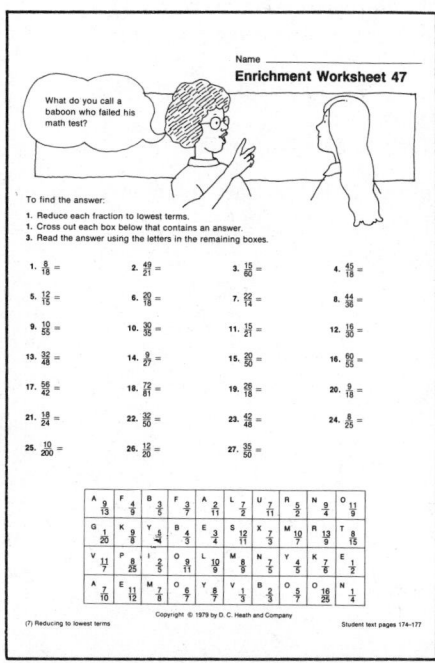

STUDENT OBJECTIVE
To compare two fractions.

Suggested Lesson Plan

Introduction There are a number of situations in which students will need to compare fractions. You will illustrate two ways of comparing. Introduce the lesson by writing two fractions, say $^3/_5$ and $^1/_2$, on the board and asking students which is larger. If they have an answer, which is probably a guess, ask how they know. One way to tell which of two fractions is larger is to locate both on a number line. The fraction to the right of the other one is the greater fraction. Draw a number line that shows both halves and fifths and locate $^3/_5$ and $^1/_2$. Now have a student tell which is larger.

Tell students that they can also compare fractions by renaming each fraction until they have the same denominator. Then the numerators can be compared.

Using the pages Tell students to turn to page 178 and use the exposition to develop the method of comparing by renaming to a common denominator.

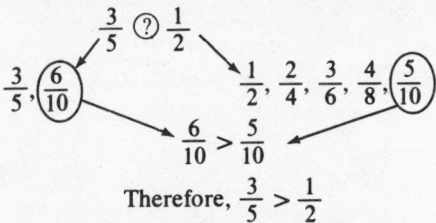

Therefore, $\frac{3}{5} > \frac{1}{2}$

Put two more fractions on the board and have students compare them by finding equivalent fractions until both fractions are named with the same denominator.

Use the shortcut, illustrated at the bottom of page 178—identify the least common denominator first and then rename the fractions just once before comparing. Some students may not be ready for this method until they are comfortable with the first method. Let students use any method they prefer to compare fractions for the written work.

Assign exercises 1–50 for written work. For exercises 11–22, students are only to find the least common denominator which, of course, is the least common multiple of the denominators. One formal method is to take the larger denominator and list its multiples until you find a number that the other denominator will divide

---

Comparing fractions

Some students decided to build a birdhouse for a shop project. To build the birdhouse, they had to compare fractions. They found fractions with the same denominator easy to compare. For example:

$$\frac{1}{8} < \frac{3}{8}$$

To compare fractions with different denominators, we find equivalent fractions that have the same (common) denominator.

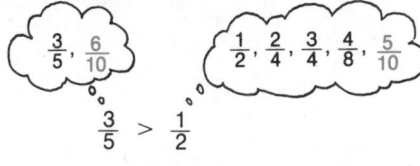

$$\frac{3}{5} > \frac{1}{2}$$

Here is a shortcut.

Step 1. Find the least common denominator.

Step 2. Change to equivalent fractions.

Step 3. Compare.

$$\frac{15}{6} \bullet \bullet \frac{5}{2} > \frac{7}{3} \bullet \bullet \frac{14}{6}$$

The least common multiple of the denominators is the least common denominator.

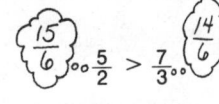

EXERCISES
< or >?

1. $\frac{4}{6}$ ● $\frac{5}{6}$ <
2. $\frac{3}{8}$ ● $\frac{3}{10}$ >
3. $\frac{9}{4}$ ● $\frac{7}{4}$ >
4. $\frac{5}{7}$ ● $\frac{2}{7}$ >
5. $\frac{5}{9}$ ● $\frac{4}{9}$ >

6. $\frac{2}{2}$ ● $\frac{3}{2}$ <
7. $\frac{5}{3}$ ● $\frac{4}{3}$ >
8. $\frac{7}{5}$ ● $\frac{7}{6}$ >
9. $\frac{7}{8}$ ● $\frac{5}{8}$ >
10. $\frac{0}{8}$ ● $\frac{1}{8}$ <

178

---

evenly; that number is the least common denominator. Show this method on the board before assigning exercises 11–22.

For example, for denominators 3 and 5:

5, 10, 15, . . .

3 divides 15 evenly

Therefore, 15 is the least common denominator of $^5/_3$ and $^8/_5$.

Assignments

BASIC
page 178 exercises 1–10
page 179 exercises 11–35, 48–49
Basic Worksheet 48

AVERAGE
page 178 exercises 1–10
page 179 exercises 11–40, 48–49
Enrichment Worksheet 48

ENRICHED
page 178 exercises 1–10
page 179 exercises 11–50
Enrichment Worksheet 48

EXTRA PRACTICE
page 386 set 56

Give the least common denominator.

11. $\frac{1}{2}, \frac{1}{3}$ 6   12. $\frac{2}{3}, \frac{3}{4}$ 12   13. $\frac{5}{2}, \frac{8}{5}$ 10   14. $\frac{4}{3}, \frac{6}{5}$ 15   15. $\frac{3}{4}, \frac{5}{6}$ 12   16. $\frac{7}{6}, \frac{11}{9}$ 18

17. $\frac{7}{5}, \frac{8}{7}$ 35   18. $\frac{2}{3}, \frac{5}{8}$ 24   19. $\frac{5}{6}, \frac{7}{8}$ 24   20. $\frac{5}{12}, \frac{1}{3}$ 12   21. $\frac{7}{9}, \frac{4}{8}$ 72   22. $\frac{5}{6}, \frac{2}{1}$ 6

<, = , or >? *Hint: Find the least common denominator.*

$\left(\dfrac{2}{3}, \dfrac{4}{6}\right)$ $\left(\dfrac{1}{4}, \dfrac{2}{8}\right)$ $\left(\dfrac{2}{3}, \dfrac{4}{6}, \dfrac{6}{9}\right)$ $\left(\dfrac{1}{3}, \dfrac{2}{6}, \cdots \dfrac{7}{21}\right)$ $\left(\dfrac{2}{7}, \dfrac{4}{14}, \dfrac{6}{21}\right)$

23. $\frac{2}{3}$ ● $\frac{5}{6}$ (<)   24. $\frac{1}{4}$ ● $\frac{3}{8}$ (<)   25. $\frac{2}{3}$ ● $\frac{5}{9}$ (>)   26. $\frac{1}{3}$ ● $\frac{2}{7}$ (>)   27. $\frac{3}{2}$ ● $\frac{5}{3}$ (<)

28. $\frac{3}{8}$ ● $\frac{1}{2}$ (<)   29. $\frac{1}{3}$ ● $\frac{3}{10}$ (>)   30. $\frac{1}{2}$ ● $\frac{5}{8}$ (<)   31. $\frac{1}{6}$ ● $\frac{1}{8}$ (>)   32. $\frac{5}{2}$ ● $\frac{5}{3}$ (>)

33. $\frac{2}{9}$ ● $\frac{1}{3}$ (<)   34. $\frac{2}{5}$ ● $\frac{3}{8}$ (>)   35. $\frac{6}{8}$ ● $\frac{3}{4}$ (=)   36. $\frac{3}{5}$ ● $\frac{1}{2}$ (>)   37. $\frac{0}{3}$ ● $\frac{0}{6}$ (=)

38. $\frac{15}{12}$ ● $\frac{5}{4}$ (=)   39. $\frac{3}{10}$ ● $\frac{1}{4}$ (>)   40. $\frac{1}{5}$ ● $\frac{1}{4}$ (<)   41. $\frac{4}{4}$ ● $\frac{2}{2}$ (=)   42. $\frac{5}{6}$ ● $\frac{7}{8}$ (<)

43. $\frac{7}{8}$ ● $\frac{3}{5}$ (>)   44. $\frac{4}{3}$ ● $\frac{3}{4}$ (>)   45. $\frac{5}{9}$ ● $\frac{7}{12}$ (<)   46. $\frac{9}{16}$ ● $\frac{5}{8}$ (<)   47. $\frac{7}{5}$ ● $\frac{9}{7}$ (>)

Solve.

48. Will a $\frac{3}{4}$-inch nail go through a $\frac{1}{2}$-inch-thick board?   yes

49. The small hole for the perch stick had to be $\frac{1}{4}$ inch in diameter. Would a $\frac{3}{8}$-inch drill bit be too large or too small?   too large

50. The hole for the birds to enter had to be $\frac{7}{8}$ inch or larger. Would a $\frac{13}{16}$-inch drill bit make a large enough hole?   no

179

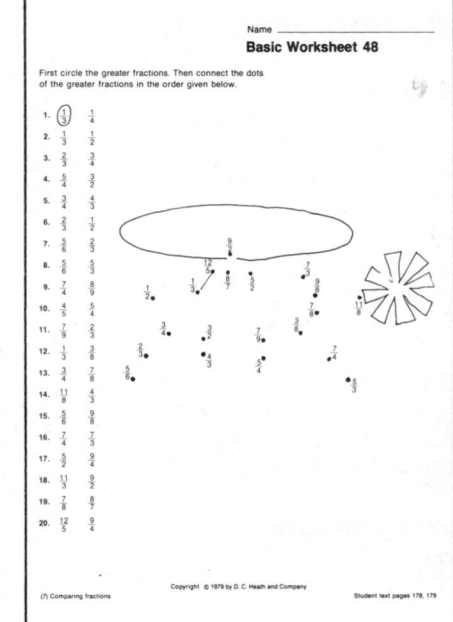

Follow-up Activities

Reinforcement At this point you may wish to have students make some equivalent fraction "strips" for the bulletin board. The strips can help students who have difficulty finding two equivalent fractions having like denominators. They will need to find two equivalent fractions with like denominator when comparing, adding, or subtracting fractional numbers. Equivalent fraction strips can be made from a strip of adding machine paper. Here is an example:

$\frac{1}{2}$	$\frac{2}{4}$	$\frac{3}{6}$	$\frac{4}{8}$	$\frac{5}{10}$	$\frac{6}{12}$	$\frac{7}{14}$

$\frac{8}{16}$	$\frac{9}{18}$	$\frac{10}{20}$	$\frac{11}{22}$	$\frac{12}{24}$	$\frac{13}{26}$	$\frac{14}{28}$

Enrichment This game provides further practice comparing fractional numbers. Have each pair of students make a deck of about 30 fraction cards of which no two fractions are equivalent. Have each pair of students shuffle their deck and place it face down between them. Each player then draws a card. The player getting the greater fractional number wins both cards. After all the cards have been drawn, the player having more cards wins the game.

CALCULATOR ACTIVITY
Students can compare fractions using a calculator by finding the decimal equivalent for each fraction, by dividing, and then comparing the decimals. For example, to compare $^7/_5$ and $^8/_7$:

$$7 \div 5 = 1.4$$
$$8 \div 7 = 1.428$$

$\dfrac{8}{7}$ is larger.

Have pairs of students use a calculator to compare the fractions in exercises 33–47.

Suggested Lesson Plan

Introduction Quickly review addition of fractions having the same denominator by using the following example. Draw a rectangle on the board and divide it into 8 equal parts. Shade 3 of the parts. Ask what fraction is represented. ($^3/_8$) Crosshatch 4 more of the parts and ask what fraction is represented on the cross-hatching. ($^4/_8$) Ask for an addition sentence suggested by the picture. ($^3/_8 + {}^4/_8 = {}^7/_8$) Point out that students could have found the sum of $^3/_8 + {}^4/_8$ by adding the numerators. Write $^3/_5 + {}^4/_5 =$ ____. Ask them what this sum is. ($^7/_5$) Do several more equations until all students are completely reminded how to find the sum.

Write the example $^1/_3 + {}^3/_4$ on the board without special comment. Ask students for the sum. Either expect someone to say $^4/_7$ or expect a student to say you cannot add these the same way as the others. Ask why and continue to probe with leading questions until students volunteer that since they do not have the same denominator, one or both have to be renamed so that they will have the same denominator; then they can be added. Ask students to suggest a common denominator and to rename the fractions. Write the equivalent fractions in an addition sentence below the original sentence.

$$\frac{\frac{1}{3}}{\frac{4}{12}} + \frac{\frac{3}{4}}{\frac{9}{12}} = \frac{13}{12}$$

Using the pages Use the exposition on page 180 to summarize your introduction. Point out that when renaming fractions to add, we try to rename them with the least common denominator—that is, the least number that both original denominators will divide.

Put an example such as $^3/_4 + {}^3/_4 =$ ____ on the board and after having a student tell the sum, $^6/_4$, point out that this is not in lowest terms. This sum should be reduced to $^3/_2$. Remind students that an answer can be left in "improper form," that is with the

numerator larger than the denominator, but that it should be reduced to lowest terms.

Assign exercises 1–8 and check answers immediately. Assign exercises 9, 10, 29, and 30 to be done first while you observe. Encourage students to use a horizontal form for exercises 9–28 and a vertical form for exercises 29–46.

Assign exercises 11–28, 31–46, and 47–50 for written work.

Adding fractions

To add two fractions having the same denominator, add the numerators and use the common denominator.

$$\frac{7}{8} + \frac{3}{8} = \frac{10}{8}$$
$$= \frac{5}{4} \quad \text{lowest terms}$$

When the fractions have different denominators, you must change to equivalent fractions with common denominators.

Step 1. Find the least common denominator.

$$\frac{2}{5} + \frac{5}{3} = \frac{}{15} + \frac{}{15}$$

Step 2. Change to equivalent fractions.

$$\frac{2}{5} + \frac{5}{3} = \frac{6}{15} + \frac{25}{15}$$

Step 3. Add.

$$\frac{2}{5} + \frac{5}{3} = \frac{6}{15} + \frac{25}{15}$$
$$= \frac{31}{15}$$

EXERCISES
Add. Reduce fractions to lowest terms.

1. $\frac{1}{3} + \frac{1}{3}$ $\frac{2}{3}$
2. $\frac{3}{8} + \frac{1}{8}$ $\frac{1}{2}$
3. $\frac{1}{6} + \frac{1}{6}$ $\frac{1}{3}$
4. $\frac{5}{6} + \frac{5}{6}$ $\frac{5}{3}$
5. $\frac{3}{8} + \frac{3}{8}$ $\frac{3}{4}$
6. $\frac{5}{9} + \frac{2}{9}$ $\frac{7}{9}$
7. $\frac{3}{10} + \frac{1}{10}$ $\frac{2}{5}$
8. $\frac{2}{7} + \frac{2}{7}$ $\frac{4}{7}$

180

Assignments

BASIC
page 180   exercises 1–8
page 181   exercises 9–40
Basic Worksheet 49

AVERAGE
page 180   exercises 1–8
page 181   exercises 9–48
Enrichment Worksheet 49

ENRICHED
page 180   exercises 1–8
page 181   exercises 9–50
Enrichment Worksheet 49

EXTRA PRACTICE
page 387   set 57

Add. Reduce answers to lowest terms. *Hint:* First find the least common denominator.

(thought bubble: $\frac{2}{2}$)

9. $\frac{1}{2} + \frac{5}{6}$ $\frac{4}{3}$
10. $\frac{1}{4} + \frac{1}{2}$ $\frac{3}{4}$
11. $\frac{1}{2} + \frac{3}{4}$ $\frac{5}{4}$
12. $1 + \frac{3}{2}$ $\frac{5}{2}$

13. $\frac{1}{2} + \frac{1}{6}$ $\frac{2}{3}$
14. $\frac{1}{4} + \frac{1}{3}$ $\frac{7}{12}$
15. $\frac{5}{6} + \frac{1}{8}$ $\frac{23}{24}$
16. $\frac{3}{8} + \frac{2}{5}$ $\frac{31}{40}$

17. $\frac{2}{3} + \frac{1}{2}$ $\frac{7}{6}$
18. $\frac{2}{3} + 3$ $\frac{11}{3}$
19. $\frac{1}{6} + \frac{1}{5}$ $\frac{11}{30}$
20. $\frac{1}{6} + \frac{3}{4}$ $\frac{11}{12}$

21. $\frac{0}{4} + \frac{3}{2}$ $\frac{3}{2}$
22. $\frac{1}{15} + \frac{2}{5}$ $\frac{7}{15}$
23. $\frac{3}{5} + \frac{1}{10}$ $\frac{7}{10}$
24. $\frac{2}{3} + \frac{1}{9}$ $\frac{7}{9}$

25. $\frac{1}{10} + \frac{2}{3}$ $\frac{23}{30}$
26. $2 + \frac{1}{4}$ $\frac{9}{4}$
27. $\frac{2}{2} + \frac{3}{8}$ $\frac{11}{8}$
28. $\frac{3}{10} + \frac{3}{4}$ $\frac{21}{20}$

Add. Give answers in lowest terms.

29. $\frac{3}{5}$ $+ \frac{1}{6}$ $\frac{23}{30}$
30. $\frac{1}{4}$ $+ \frac{1}{8}$ $\frac{3}{8}$
31. $\frac{3}{4}$ $+ \frac{3}{8}$ $\frac{9}{8}$
32. $\frac{0}{6}$ $+ \frac{2}{3}$ $\frac{2}{3}$
33. $\frac{5}{9}$ $+ \frac{1}{3}$ $\frac{8}{9}$
34. $\frac{3}{5}$ $+ \frac{5}{3}$ $\frac{34}{15}$

35. $\frac{7}{8}$ $+ \frac{1}{4}$ $\frac{9}{8}$
36. $\frac{3}{3}$ $+ \frac{1}{2}$ $\frac{3}{2}$
37. $\frac{5}{7}$ $+ \frac{2}{3}$ $\frac{29}{21}$
38. $\frac{5}{6}$ $+ \frac{2}{3}$ $\frac{3}{2}$
39. $\frac{5}{9}$ $+ \frac{2}{3}$ $\frac{11}{9}$
40. $\frac{5}{6}$ $+ \frac{1}{4}$ $\frac{13}{12}$

41. $\frac{1}{4}$ $+ \frac{5}{9}$ $\frac{29}{36}$
42. $\frac{3}{8}$ $+ \frac{1}{6}$ $\frac{13}{24}$
43. $\frac{2}{3}$ $+ \frac{3}{2}$ $\frac{13}{6}$
44. $\frac{5}{12}$ $+ \frac{1}{3}$ $\frac{3}{4}$
45. $\frac{7}{8}$ $+ \frac{3}{4}$ $\frac{13}{8}$
46. $\frac{3}{4}$ $+ \frac{7}{12}$ $\frac{4}{3}$

Solve.

47. John found $\frac{1}{2}$ pound of mushrooms in the morning and $\frac{1}{4}$ pound in the afternoon. How much did he find in all? $\frac{3}{4}$ pound

48. Terry used $\frac{2}{3}$ cup of sugar in one recipe and $\frac{3}{4}$ cup in another. How much sugar did he use? $\frac{17}{12}$ cup

49. Mary typed for $\frac{2}{5}$ of an hour before school and $\frac{3}{4}$ of an hour after school. How long did she type in all? $\frac{23}{20}$ of an hour

50. Jerry read $\frac{1}{3}$ of a book on Monday and $\frac{1}{4}$ of the book on Tuesday. What fraction of the book did he read during the two days? $\frac{7}{12}$

181

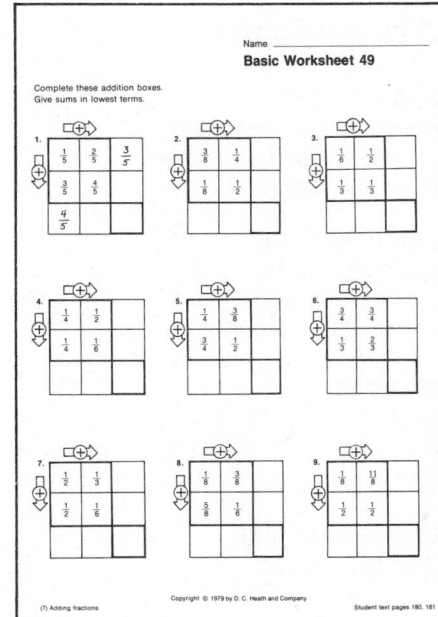

Follow-up Activities

Reinforcement The following activity provides students with further experiences adding fractional numbers. Prepare some equivalent-fraction strips as shown below for the overhead projector.

$\frac{1}{2}$	$\frac{2}{4}$	$\frac{3}{6}$	$\frac{4}{8}$	$\frac{5}{10}$	$\frac{6}{18}$
$\frac{1}{3}$	$\frac{2}{6}$	$\frac{3}{9}$	$\frac{4}{12}$	$\frac{5}{15}$	$\frac{6}{18}$

etc.

Project fraction strips on the screen and write an addition equation on the chalkboard like this:

$$\frac{1}{2} + \frac{1}{3} = \square$$

Instruct students to look at the fraction strips for $\frac{1}{2}$ and $\frac{1}{3}$ and find fractions with the same denominator. Ask for the sum and complete the equation. Continue the activity with other appropriate examples.

Enrichment Have students copy and complete the following addition boxes:

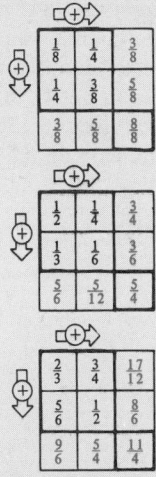

CALCULATOR ACTIVITY

Show students how fractions can be added with a calculator. The basic algorithm is to change each fraction to a decimal and then add decimals. Calculation may vary somewhat, but basically they should use some form of this calculator code:

$$\frac{1}{12} + \frac{3}{4} = \underline{(0.83)}$$

Code: 1 ÷ 12 = *

　　Write down or enter in memory

　　3 ÷ 4 = + * =

Suggested Lesson Plan

Introduction Quickly review and have students explain what they do to add fractions having the same denominator and what they do to add fractions having different denominators.

Put several subtraction examples on the board, starting with an example in which the fractions have the same denominator. After a student has found the difference, present a subtraction example in which the fractions have different denominators. The transfer from addition to subtraction should not be difficult and you should get a complete explanation of the algorithm.

Using the pages Use the examples on page 182 to summarize the discussion. Have students do examples 16—35 in horizontal form and exercises 36—47 in vertical form. Remind them to check their answer after subtracting to see if it can be reduced to lower terms.

Assign exercises 1—15 to be done in class immediately while you observe. Correct them after about 3 minutes. Expect students to get 13 of 15 correct. Then assign exercises 16—50 for written work. Have students do the Excursion for extra credit.

Subtracting fractions

To subtract fractions having the same denominator, subtract the numerators and use the common denominator.

$$\frac{3}{4} - \frac{1}{4} = \frac{2}{4}$$
$$= \frac{1}{2}$$

Reduced to lowest terms.

When the two denominators are different, find the least common denominator and change to equivalent fractions.

$$\frac{1}{2} - \frac{1}{3} = \frac{3}{6} - \frac{2}{6}$$
$$= \frac{1}{6}$$

EXERCISES

Subtract. Reduce answers to lowest terms.

1. $\frac{5}{8} - \frac{1}{8}$ $\frac{1}{2}$
2. $\frac{7}{6} - \frac{5}{6}$ $\frac{1}{3}$
3. $\frac{1}{3} - \frac{1}{3}$ 0
4. $\frac{7}{5} - \frac{2}{5}$ 1
5. $\frac{6}{7} - \frac{1}{7}$ $\frac{5}{7}$

6. $\frac{4}{3} - \frac{3}{3}$ $\frac{1}{3}$
7. $\frac{4}{8} - \frac{1}{8}$ $\frac{3}{8}$
8. $\frac{2}{5} - \frac{1}{5}$ $\frac{1}{5}$
9. $\frac{5}{9} - \frac{4}{9}$ $\frac{1}{9}$
10. $\frac{5}{4} - \frac{2}{4}$ $\frac{3}{4}$

11. $\frac{7}{5} - \frac{4}{5}$ $\frac{3}{5}$
12. $\frac{7}{9} - \frac{1}{9}$ $\frac{2}{3}$
13. $\frac{7}{8} - \frac{0}{8}$ $\frac{7}{8}$
14. $\frac{5}{3} - \frac{1}{3}$ $\frac{4}{3}$
15. $\frac{7}{4} - \frac{4}{4}$ $\frac{3}{4}$

182

Assignments

BASIC
page 182 exercises 1—15
page 183 exercises 16—48
Basic Worksheet 50

AVERAGE
page 182 exercises 1—15
page 183 exercises 16—50
Enrichment Worksheet 50

ENRICHED
page 182 exercises 9—15
page 183 exercises 16—50, Excursion
Enrichment Worksheet 50

EXTRA PRACTICE
page 387 set 58

Subtract. Reduce answers to lowest terms. *Hint:* First find the least common denominator.

16. $\frac{1}{3} - \frac{2}{9}$ $\frac{1}{9}$ 17. $\frac{5}{6} - \frac{5}{9}$ $\frac{5}{18}$ 18. $\frac{5}{7} - \frac{1}{3}$ $\frac{8}{21}$ 19. $2 - \frac{1}{4}$ $\frac{7}{4}$ 20. $\frac{2}{3} - \frac{1}{6}$ $\frac{1}{2}$

21. $\frac{5}{3} - \frac{6}{5}$ $\frac{7}{15}$ 22. $\frac{7}{6} - \frac{2}{3}$ $\frac{1}{2}$ 23. $\frac{5}{4} - \frac{2}{3}$ $\frac{7}{12}$ 24. $\frac{3}{4} - \frac{1}{3}$ $\frac{5}{12}$ 25. $\frac{5}{6} - \frac{1}{3}$ $\frac{1}{2}$

26. $\frac{3}{4} - \frac{2}{3}$ $\frac{1}{12}$ 27. $\frac{3}{4} - \frac{5}{8}$ $\frac{1}{8}$ 28. $\frac{3}{8} - \frac{1}{4}$ $\frac{1}{8}$ 29. $\frac{1}{2} - \frac{1}{6}$ $\frac{1}{3}$ 30. $1 - \frac{1}{2}$ $\frac{1}{2}$

31. $\frac{4}{5} - \frac{2}{3}$ $\frac{2}{15}$ 32. $\frac{3}{4} - \frac{1}{2}$ $\frac{1}{4}$ 33. $3 - \frac{3}{4}$ $\frac{9}{4}$ 34. $\frac{1}{2} - \frac{0}{8}$ $\frac{1}{2}$ 35. $\frac{5}{4} - \frac{2}{4}$ $\frac{1}{4}$

Subtract. Give answers in lowest terms.

36. $\frac{8}{9}$ $- \frac{3}{4}$ $\frac{5}{36}$
37. $\frac{3}{4}$ $- \frac{5}{8}$ $\frac{1}{8}$
38. $\frac{3}{4}$ $- \frac{3}{10}$ $\frac{9}{20}$
39. $\frac{3}{4}$ $- \frac{1}{6}$ $\frac{7}{12}$
40. $\frac{2}{5}$ $- \frac{3}{8}$ $\frac{1}{40}$
41. $\frac{5}{6}$ $- \frac{3}{8}$ $\frac{11}{24}$

42. $\frac{9}{5}$ $- \frac{2}{3}$ $\frac{17}{15}$
43. $\frac{5}{9}$ $- \frac{1}{2}$ $\frac{1}{18}$
44. $\frac{2}{3}$ $- \frac{1}{4}$ $\frac{5}{12}$
45. $\frac{5}{4}$ $- \frac{5}{8}$ $\frac{5}{8}$
46. $\frac{5}{6}$ $- \frac{0}{4}$ $\frac{5}{6}$
47. $\frac{9}{4}$ $- \frac{3}{2}$ $\frac{3}{4}$

Solve.

48. Had $\frac{3}{4}$ cup of flour. Used $\frac{2}{3}$ cup. How much was left? $\frac{1}{12}$ cup

49. Need $\frac{3}{2}$ cups of sugar. Have $\frac{3}{4}$ cup. How much more sugar is needed? $\frac{3}{4}$ cup

50. Should bake $\frac{1}{2}$ hour. Have baked $\frac{1}{4}$ hour. How much longer to bake? $\frac{1}{4}$ hour

Excursion ■●■

Complete this magic square.

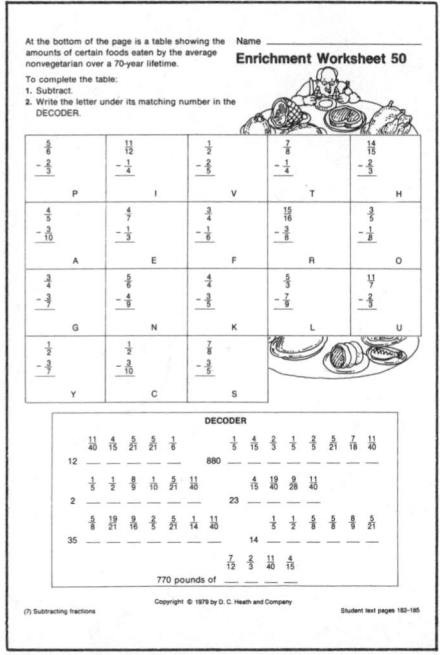

$\frac{2}{3}$	$\frac{1}{12}$	$\frac{1}{2}$
	$\frac{5}{12}$	$\frac{7}{12}$
$\frac{1}{3}$	$\frac{3}{4}$	$\frac{1}{6}$

183

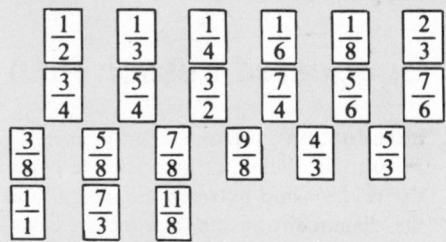
(core) Lesson 83   **183**

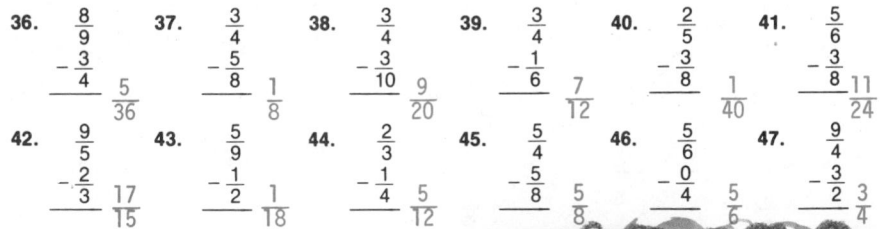

To practice addition and subtraction of fractions.
To solve word problems dealing with mathematics and science.

VOCABULARY
fulcrum

Suggested Lesson Plan

Introduction (meter sticks; pennies)
For the Mathematics and Science page, the relationship between the weight and the distance from the fulcrum is easily demonstrated with materials. Using a meter stick or a yardstick, a fulcrum, and pennies, the relationship can be made obvious through experimentation.

The relationship can be expressed as $W_1 \times D_1 = W_2 \times D_2$. This is an inverse relationship. If one side is held constant and W_2 is decreased, then D_2 must be increased to maintain the balance.

Using the pages Assign all the odd-numbered exercises on page 184. If any student misses more than 6 of the 24 exercises, go over the missed exercises and have that student work the even-numbered exercises.

Demonstrate the balance using the materials suggested. If you can find enough material, set up several stations at which students can work with the materials to verify the relationship. If you have work stations, demonstrate the experiment to students first and give 4 or 5 specific problems for them to work at the station. Then have students work exercises 1—4 for written work.

Practice exercises

Give each sum in lowest terms.

1. $\frac{1}{2} + \frac{2}{3} = \frac{7}{6}$
2. $\frac{1}{3} + \frac{1}{2} = \frac{5}{6}$
3. $\frac{5}{3} + \frac{5}{4} = \frac{35}{12}$
4. $\frac{2}{3} + \frac{5}{9} = \frac{11}{9}$
5. $\frac{2}{3} + \frac{3}{2} = \frac{13}{6}$
6. $\frac{1}{3} + \frac{3}{5} = \frac{14}{15}$

7. $\frac{5}{8} + \frac{1}{4} = \frac{7}{8}$
8. $\frac{0}{2} + \frac{3}{8} = \frac{3}{8}$
9. $\frac{2}{3} + \frac{3}{4} = \frac{17}{12}$
10. $\frac{6}{5} + \frac{3}{10} = \frac{3}{2}$
11. $\frac{5}{6} + \frac{1}{2} = \frac{4}{3}$
12. $\frac{3}{4} + \frac{1}{8} = \frac{7}{8}$

13. $\frac{1}{4} + \frac{3}{8} = \frac{5}{8}$
14. $\frac{4}{4} + \frac{3}{3} = 2$
15. $\frac{1}{4} + \frac{1}{2} = \frac{3}{4}$
16. $\frac{1}{3} + \frac{7}{8} = \frac{29}{24}$
17. $\frac{1}{5} + \frac{3}{7} = \frac{22}{35}$
18. $\frac{1}{4} + \frac{5}{12} = \frac{2}{3}$

19. $\frac{1}{2} + \frac{5}{8} = \frac{9}{8}$
20. $\frac{7}{10} + \frac{5}{6} = \frac{23}{15}$
21. $\frac{4}{4} + \frac{7}{15} = \frac{22}{15}$
22. $\frac{4}{5} + \frac{2}{3} = \frac{22}{15}$
23. $\frac{1}{3} + \frac{3}{4} = \frac{13}{12}$
24. $\frac{2}{3} + \frac{3}{8} = \frac{25}{24}$

Give each difference in lowest terms.

25. $\frac{1}{2} - \frac{1}{4} = \frac{1}{4}$
26. $\frac{7}{8} - \frac{3}{4} = \frac{1}{8}$
27. $\frac{3}{4} - \frac{5}{8} = \frac{1}{8}$
28. $\frac{1}{2} - \frac{1}{3} = \frac{1}{6}$
29. $\frac{5}{6} - \frac{2}{3} = \frac{1}{6}$
30. $\frac{7}{2} - 2 = \frac{3}{2}$

31. $\frac{3}{10} - \frac{1}{5} = \frac{1}{10}$
32. $\frac{3}{4} - \frac{3}{8} = \frac{3}{8}$
33. $\frac{3}{4} - \frac{1}{4} = \frac{1}{2}$
34. $\frac{7}{9} - \frac{0}{2} = \frac{7}{9}$
35. $\frac{1}{2} - \frac{3}{8} = \frac{1}{8}$
36. $\frac{7}{4} - 1 = \frac{3}{4}$

37. $\frac{2}{3} - \frac{3}{8} = \frac{7}{24}$
38. $1 - \frac{2}{3} = \frac{1}{3}$
39. $2 - \frac{5}{4} = \frac{3}{4}$
40. $\frac{5}{8} - \frac{5}{8} = 0$
41. $\frac{5}{9} - \frac{1}{3} = \frac{2}{9}$
42. $\frac{5}{4} - \frac{5}{8} = \frac{5}{8}$

43. $\frac{2}{3} - \frac{1}{3} = \frac{1}{3}$
44. $\frac{1}{2} - \frac{4}{9} = \frac{1}{18}$
45. $\frac{3}{4} - \frac{1}{2} = \frac{1}{4}$
46. $\frac{2}{3} - \frac{1}{4} = \frac{5}{12}$
47. $\frac{8}{9} - \frac{3}{4} = \frac{5}{36}$
48. $\frac{3}{4} - \frac{2}{3} = \frac{1}{12}$

184

Assignments

BASIC
pge 184 exercises 1—48
page 185 exercises 1—2
Basic Worksheet 50

AVERAGE
page 184 exercises 1—48
page 185 exercises 1—3
Enrichment Worksheet 50

ENRICHED
page 184 exercises 1—48
page 185 exercises 1—4
Enrichment Worksheet 50

REVIEW PRACTICE
page 382 set 40

Mathematics and science

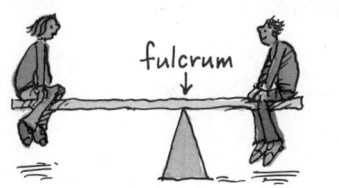

fulcrum

Notice that the boy and the girl are in balance.
When they are in balance, these products are equal:

$$\begin{array}{ccccccc} \text{boy's} & \times & \text{his distance} & = & \text{girl's} & \times & \text{her distance} \\ \text{weight} & & \text{from fulcrum} & & \text{weight} & & \text{from fulcrum} \end{array}$$

Problem: The boy weighs 60 kg and is seated 2 m from the
fulcrum.
How much does the girl weigh if she is seated 3
m from the fulcrum?

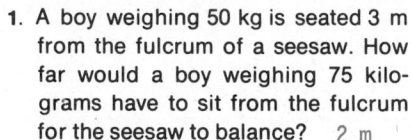

Solution:
$$60 \times 2 = w \times 3$$
$$120 = w \times 3$$
$$40 = w$$

What do you multiply by 3 to get 120?

I DUNNO— WHAT?

Answer: 40 kg

EXERCISES
Solve. You may first want to picture each problem.

1. A boy weighing 50 kg is seated 3 m from the fulcrum of a seesaw. How far would a boy weighing 75 kilograms have to sit from the fulcrum for the seesaw to balance? **2 m**

2. A mechanic wants to lift a 160-kg engine by using a steel bar that is 5 m long. If the fulcrum is located 1 m from the engine, how much must the mechanic weigh to lift the engine? **40 kg**

3. A girl weighing 40 kg is seated 1.5 m from the fulcrum of a seesaw. When another girl is seated 2 m from the fulcrum, the seesaw is in balance. How much does the other girl weigh? **30 kg**

★ 4. A man weighing 80 kg wants to lift a rock that weighs 400 kg. If he places the fulcrum 2 m from the rock, how long a lever does he need to lift the rock? **12 m**

185

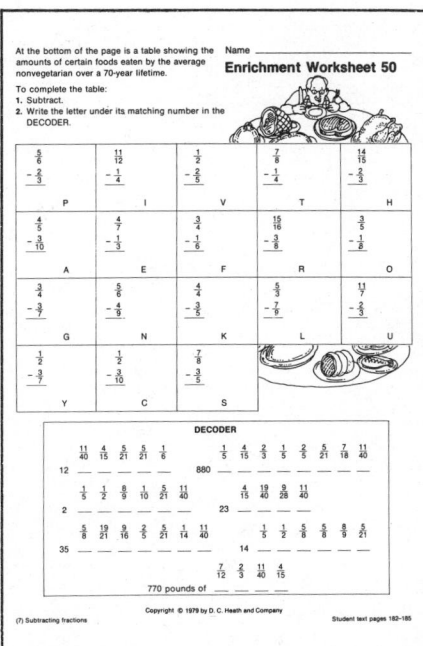

Follow-up Activities

Reinforcement Students work in pairs. Give each pair of students a deck of digit cards. As one student draws a card, both students place the digit in one position in the sentence below to get the largest sum. Each digit card is replaced and a second card is drawn. Continue until 4 cards have been drawn.

$$\frac{\square}{\square} + \frac{\square}{\square} = \underline{\quad}$$

Each student then finds his or her sum. The winner gets the difference between his or her score and the other player's score. First player to get 1 wins.

Enrichment Have students look for other examples of uses of the lever illustrated on page 185. Have them give values for weights and forces associated with the use. Example:

Crowbar

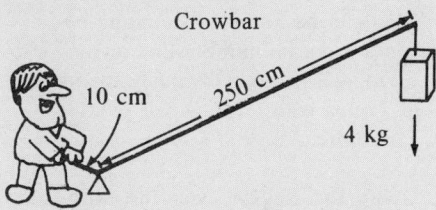

10 cm   250 cm   4 kg

Post the good examples on the mathematics bulletin board.

EXCURSION
Who am I?

I am less than 50. If you divide me by 5, you get a remainder of 2. If you divide me by 9, you get a remainder of 1.

37

STUDENT OBJECTIVES

To name points on the number line for mixed numbers.
To rename mixed numbers and fractions.

VOCABULARY

mixed number

Suggested Lesson Plan

Introduction Draw a number line showing halves. Draw a segment above the number line that is $6\frac{1}{2}$ units long. Ask a student to tell how long the segment is. He will almost certainly use a mixed number. Ask another student to give another name for the segment. Lead up to this answer by writing $\frac{2}{2}$ over each unit of the six units. Now ask how many halves in the segment. (13). Therefore, another name for the segment is $\frac{13}{2}$.

Now put a fraction such as $\frac{13}{4}$ on the board and ask for another name. One way to find this is to find the greatest whole number less than $\frac{13}{4}$. This can be found by counting by fourths on the number line or by dividing 13 by 4. Obviously the answer is 3 ones with 1 fourth left over. Therefore, $\frac{13}{4} = 3\frac{1}{4}$.

Using the pages Use the exposition on page 186 to summarize your introduction. Go over each skill and draw attention to the thought bubbles and the shortcuts. Be sure students know the skills they are practicing and that they see them as "inverse" skills.

Assign exercises 1–51 for written work. Have students work exercises 52–53 for extra credit.

Assign the Keeping Skills Sharp section for all students.

Mixed numbers

fraction $\longrightarrow \dfrac{5}{2} = 2\dfrac{1}{2} \longleftarrow$ mixed number

Changing a Mixed Number to a Fraction

mixed number $\qquad$ fraction

$5\dfrac{3}{4} = 5 + \dfrac{3}{4} = \dfrac{20}{4} + \dfrac{3}{4} = \dfrac{23}{4}$

Changing a Fraction to a Mixed Number

fraction (whole number) mixed number

$\dfrac{17}{3} = \dfrac{15}{3} + \dfrac{2}{3} = 5 + \dfrac{2}{3} = 5\dfrac{2}{3}$

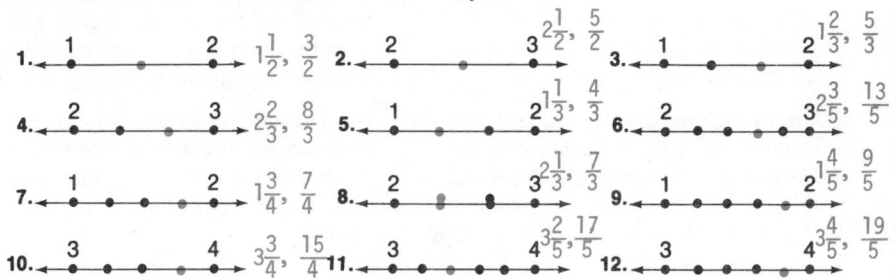

I multiply 4 and 5 to get the number of fourths in 5. Then I add 3 to get how many fourths in all.

$5\dfrac{3}{4} = \dfrac{23}{4}$ $(4 \times 5) + 3$

I divide 17 by 3 to get the whole number part. The remainder tells how many thirds in the fraction part.

$$\begin{array}{r} 5 \\ 3\overline{)17} \\ -15 \\ \hline 2 \end{array}$$

$\dfrac{17}{3} = 5\dfrac{2}{3}$

EXERCISES

Give a mixed number and a fraction for each red point.

1. (number line 1 to 2) $1\dfrac{1}{2}, \dfrac{3}{2}$ 2. (number line 2 to 3) $2\dfrac{1}{2}, \dfrac{5}{2}$ 3. (number line 1 to 2) $2\dfrac{2}{3}, \dfrac{5}{3}$

4. (number line 2 to 3) $2\dfrac{2}{3}, \dfrac{8}{3}$ 5. (number line 1 to 2) $2\dfrac{1}{3}, \dfrac{4}{3}$ 6. (number line 2 to 3) $3\dfrac{2}{5}, \dfrac{13}{5}$

7. (number line 1 to 2) $1\dfrac{3}{4}, \dfrac{7}{4}$ 8. (number line 2 to 3) $3\dfrac{1}{3}, \dfrac{7}{3}$ 9. (number line 1 to 2) $2\dfrac{1}{5}, \dfrac{9}{5}$

10. (number line 3 to 4) $3\dfrac{3}{4}, \dfrac{15}{4}$ 11. (number line 3 to 4) $4\dfrac{2}{5}, \dfrac{17}{5}$ 12. (number line 3 to 4) $4\dfrac{3}{5}, \dfrac{19}{5}$

186

Assignments

BASIC
page 186 exercises 1–12
page 187 exercises 13–45, Keeping Skills Sharp
Basic Worksheet 51

AVERAGE
page 186 exercises 1–12
page 187 exercises 13–51, Keeping Skills Sharp
Enrichment Worksheet 51

ENRICHED
page 186 exercises 1–12
page 187 exercises 13–53, Excursion
Enrichment Worksheet 51

EXTRA PRACTICE
page 387 set 59

Change each mixed number to a fraction.

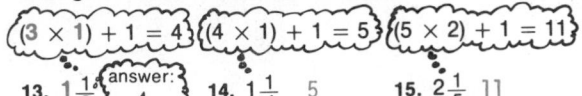

$(3 \times 1) + 1 = 4$ $(4 \times 1) + 1 = 5$ $(5 \times 2) + 1 = 11$

13. $1\frac{1}{3}$ answer: $\frac{4}{3}$ 14. $1\frac{1}{4}$ $\frac{5}{4}$ 15. $2\frac{1}{5}$ $\frac{11}{5}$

16. $1\frac{3}{4}$ $\frac{7}{4}$ 17. $2\frac{3}{5}$ $\frac{13}{5}$ 18. $2\frac{2}{5}$ $\frac{12}{5}$

19. $4\frac{3}{5}$ $\frac{23}{5}$ 20. $4\frac{3}{10}$ $\frac{43}{10}$ 21. $3\frac{1}{3}$ $\frac{10}{3}$

22. $3\frac{1}{4}$ $\frac{13}{4}$ 23. $2\frac{3}{8}$ $\frac{19}{8}$ 24. $5\frac{1}{5}$ $\frac{26}{5}$ 25. $6\frac{2}{3}$ $\frac{20}{3}$ 26. $1\frac{7}{8}$ $\frac{15}{8}$

27. $6\frac{3}{4}$ $\frac{27}{4}$ 28. $2\frac{5}{6}$ $\frac{17}{6}$ 29. $3\frac{5}{8}$ $\frac{29}{8}$ 30. $2\frac{4}{9}$ $\frac{22}{9}$ 31. $4\frac{3}{5}$ $\frac{23}{5}$

Change each fraction to a whole number or a mixed number.

32. $\frac{5}{3}$ $1\frac{2}{3}$ 33. $\frac{7}{2}$ $3\frac{1}{2}$ 34. $\frac{5}{4}$ $1\frac{1}{4}$ 35. $\frac{5}{2}$ $2\frac{1}{2}$ 36. $\frac{11}{4}$ $2\frac{3}{4}$

37. $\frac{9}{8}$ $1\frac{1}{8}$ 38. $\frac{6}{6}$ 1 39. $\frac{9}{5}$ $1\frac{4}{5}$ 40. $\frac{15}{5}$ 3 41. $\frac{7}{6}$ $1\frac{1}{6}$

42. $\frac{9}{4}$ $2\frac{1}{4}$ 43. $\frac{11}{8}$ $1\frac{3}{8}$ 44. $\frac{7}{3}$ $2\frac{1}{3}$ 45. $\frac{9}{2}$ $4\frac{1}{2}$ 46. $\frac{8}{3}$ $2\frac{2}{3}$

47. $\frac{25}{6}$ $4\frac{1}{6}$ 48. $\frac{21}{3}$ 7 49. $\frac{10}{2}$ 5 50. $\frac{10}{3}$ $3\frac{1}{3}$ 51. $\frac{0}{3}$ 0

Who am I?

52. I am a fraction equivalent to $3\frac{1}{2}$. My denominator is 4.
$\frac{14}{4}$

53. I am a fraction equivalent to $2\frac{3}{5}$. I am in lowest terms.
$\frac{13}{5}$

Excursion ■□●□●□●□●□●□●□●□●□●□●□●□●□●□●□●□●

Using four 4s, write expressions for the numbers 1 through 8. Here are the first two:

$\frac{44}{44} = 1$ $\frac{4 \times 4 + 4}{4} = 5$

$\frac{4}{4} + \frac{4}{4} = 2$ $4 + \frac{4 + 4}{4} = 6$

$\frac{4 + 4 + 4}{4} = 3$ $4 + 4 - \frac{4}{4} = 7$

$\frac{4 - 4}{4} + 4 = 4$ $4 + 4 + 4 - 4 = 8$

Divide.

1. $3\overline{)15.9}$ 5.3
2. $6\overline{)15.6}$ 2.6
3. $2\overline{)15.6}$ 7.8
4. $9\overline{)85.5}$ 9.5
5. $6\overline{)2.28}$ 0.38
6. $5\overline{)2.35}$ 0.47
7. $5\overline{)6.75}$ 1.35
8. $3\overline{)85.2}$ 28.4
9. $4\overline{)0.824}$ 0.206
10. $7\overline{)46.9}$ 6.7
11. $3\overline{)8.91}$ 2.97
12. $4\overline{)3.44}$ 0.86
13. $4\overline{)146.8}$ 36.7
14. $3\overline{)17.82}$ 5.94
15. $2\overline{)1.472}$ 0.736
16. $9\overline{)874.8}$ 97.2

187

Follow-up Activities

Reinforcement You may wish to follow up the lesson by having students do the following measurement activities. Give each student a 12-inch ruler that is graduated in $\frac{1}{8}$ inches. Have students draw segments of these lengths:

$1\frac{1}{2}$ in., $3\frac{1}{4}$ in., $2\frac{5}{8}$ in.,

$3\frac{7}{8}$ in., $1\frac{3}{4}$ in., etc.

Have each student measure his or her height, round it to the nearest inch, and use a mixed number to express the height in feet. For example, if a student got a measurement of $53\frac{1}{4}$ inches, she would round the measurement to 53 inches and then convert to feet, that is, $4\frac{5}{12}$ feet.

Enrichment You may wish to have some students find out how mixed numbers are used in stock quotations. Ask them to find out how to read the stock quotations and share their findings with other class members.

EXCURSION

Get a geoboard or some dot paper. How many squares of different sizes can you get on a 4-by-4 geoboard if the vertices are at the pegs?   5

Example. A square of area 2 square units.

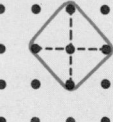

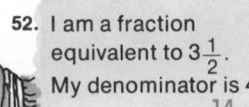

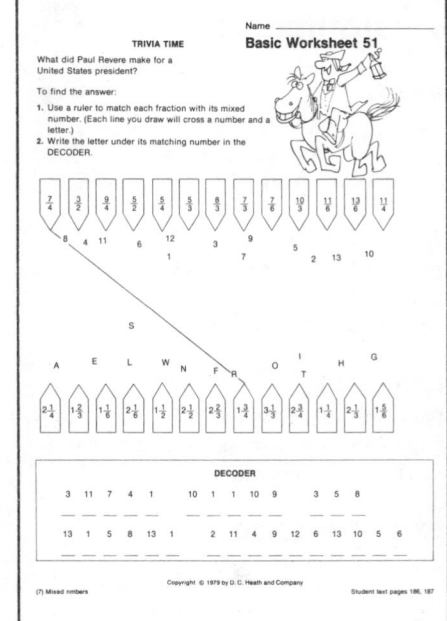

Suggested Lesson Plan

Introduction Draw these squares on the board and shade them as shown:

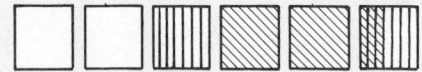

Ask students how many squares are shaded one way and how many are shaded the other way. ($2^2/_7$ and $2^3/_7$) How many squares are shaded in all? ($4^5/_7$) Ask for an addition equation for this problem. ($2^3/_7 + 2^2/_7 = 4^5/_7$) When using the picture, students probably counted the number of seventh-squares that were shaded and the number of single squares that were shaded. This suggests that we can find the sum by just looking at the numerals and then adding the fraction parts and adding the whole-number parts. That is, we can add in columns.

Next write this problem on the board and ask students to add in columns. They will probably write the sum as shown.

$$3\frac{3}{8}$$
$$+4\frac{6}{8}$$
$$\overline{7\frac{9}{8}}$$

Remind students of some basic rules that we have for writing numerals. For example, when we add these two numbers:

$$47$$
$$+26$$

we do not write 13 in the ones place. We have a rule for place-value notation that tells us that we don't write more than one digit in a column. In the addition problem we must regroup. Similarly, we have a rule for mixed numerals that tells us that the fraction part must stand for a number less than 1. In the addition problem above, the sum in the "fraction column" is greater than 1. Therefore we must regroup. Since $9/_8 = 1^1/_8$, the sum is properly written as:

$$3\frac{3}{8}$$
$$+4\frac{6}{8}$$
$$\overline{7\frac{9}{8} = 8\frac{1}{8}}$$

188 Lesson 86 (core)

Adding mixed numbers

Here is how to find the sum of two mixed numbers.

EXAMPLE 1.

Step 1. Add fractions.

Step 2. Add whole numbers.

$$2\frac{2}{5}$$
$$+1\frac{1}{5}$$
$$\overline{3\frac{3}{5}}$$

EXAMPLE 2.

Step 1. Write fractions with a common denominator.

Step 2. Add fractions.

Step 3. Add whole numbers.

$$3\frac{2}{3} = 3\frac{8}{12}$$
$$+5\frac{1}{4} = +5\frac{3}{12}$$
$$\overline{8\frac{11}{12}}$$

EXAMPLE 3.

Step 1. Write fractions with a common denominator.

Step 2. Add fractions.

Step 3. Add whole numbers.

Step 4. Regroup so that the fraction is less than 1.

$$7\frac{2}{3} = 7\frac{4}{6}$$
$$+4\frac{1}{2} = +4\frac{3}{6}$$
$$\overline{11\frac{7}{6} = 12\frac{1}{6}}$$

You can regroup as you do with whole numbers.

EXERCISES

Add. Remember to give the fraction part in lowest terms.

1. $3\frac{1}{4}$ $+4\frac{1}{4}$ $7\frac{1}{2}$
2. $8\frac{1}{7}$ $+3\frac{4}{7}$ $11\frac{5}{7}$
3. $5\frac{1}{2}$ $+6\frac{1}{2}$ 12
4. $9\frac{3}{8}$ $+6\frac{1}{8}$ $15\frac{1}{2}$
5. $10\frac{1}{6}$ $+6\frac{5}{6}$ 17
6. $8\frac{3}{8}$ $+7\frac{3}{8}$ $15\frac{3}{4}$

7. $4\frac{1}{4}$ $+3\frac{1}{2}$ $7\frac{3}{4}$
8. $3\frac{5}{6}$ $+3\frac{1}{3}$ $7\frac{1}{6}$
9. $12\frac{1}{3}$ $+5\frac{2}{3}$ 18
10. $6\frac{1}{2}$ $+7\frac{2}{3}$ $14\frac{1}{6}$
11. $6\frac{3}{4}$ $+8\frac{1}{8}$ $14\frac{7}{8}$
12. $13\frac{2}{5}$ $+6$ $19\frac{2}{5}$

188

Using the pages Go over the three examples to reinforce the introduction. Emphasize the steps students do as the problems become more complex. Relate the algorithm back to the addition of whole numbers as you work through the examples.

Assign exercises 1–30 for written work. Let students who have the time and interest work on the Excursion.

Assignments

BASIC
page 188 exercises 1–12
page 189 exercises 13–26
Basic Worksheet 52

AVERAGE
page 188 exercises 1–12
page 189 exercises 13–30
Enrichment Worksheet 52

ENRICHED
page 188 exercises 1–12
page 189 exercises 13–30, Excursion
Enrichment Worksheet 52

EXTRA PRACTICE
page 388 set 60

13. $6\frac{1}{2}$
$+4\frac{5}{6}$ = $11\frac{1}{3}$

14. $4\frac{5}{8}$
$+3\frac{1}{2}$ = $8\frac{1}{8}$

15. $2\frac{1}{2}$
$+\frac{5}{8}$ = $3\frac{1}{8}$

16. $16\frac{3}{7}$
$+4\frac{1}{3}$ = $20\frac{16}{21}$

17. $12\frac{3}{4}$
$+5\frac{3}{8}$ = $18\frac{1}{8}$

18. $17\frac{2}{5}$
$+11\frac{3}{4}$ = $29\frac{3}{20}$

19. $15\frac{3}{5}$
$+8\frac{1}{2}$ = $24\frac{1}{10}$

20. $12\frac{2}{3}$
$+11\frac{3}{4}$ = $24\frac{5}{12}$

21. $16\frac{5}{8}$
$+13\frac{2}{3}$ = $30\frac{7}{24}$

22. $23\frac{4}{5}$
$+14$ = $37\frac{4}{5}$

23. $20\frac{5}{8}$
$+6\frac{5}{6}$ = $27\frac{11}{24}$

24. $24\frac{3}{4}$
$+19\frac{5}{8}$ = $44\frac{3}{8}$

RIBBON 48¢ a yard

Solve.

25. Mushrooms cost $2.40 per pound. How much will $1\frac{1}{2}$ pounds cost? $3.60

26. Ribbon is 48¢ a yard. How much will $6\frac{2}{3}$ yards cost? $3.20

27. Jerry baby-sat $2\frac{1}{2}$ hours one evening and $1\frac{3}{4}$ hours the next evening. How many hours did he baby-sit in all? $4\frac{1}{4}$

28. The rainfall in May was $4\frac{3}{4}$ inches and in June it was $5\frac{1}{4}$ inches. What was the total rainfall for the two months? 10 in.

29. Mary baked $2\frac{3}{4}$ dozen chocolate cookies and $3\frac{1}{3}$ dozen peanut butter cookies. How many dozen cookies did she bake? How many cookies did she bake? $6\frac{1}{12}$, 73

30. During the first 3 days of a trip the Hunt family drove $5\frac{1}{2}$, $6\frac{3}{4}$, and $4\frac{1}{3}$ hours. How many hours did they drive during the 3 days? $16\frac{7}{12}$

Excursion ●■●■●■●■●■●■●■●■●■●■●■●■●■●■●■●■●

Ancient Egyptians expressed fractional numbers as a sum of unit fractions with *different* denominators. Here are some examples:

$$\frac{2}{5} = \frac{1}{3} + \frac{1}{15}$$
$$\frac{3}{5} = \frac{1}{3} + \frac{1}{15} + \frac{1}{5} \text{ or } \frac{1}{2} + \frac{1}{10}$$

How might they have expressed these fractions?

$$\frac{2}{7}, \frac{3}{7}, \frac{4}{9}, \frac{5}{9}$$

$$\frac{2}{7} = \frac{1}{4} + \frac{1}{28}$$
$$\frac{3}{7} = \frac{1}{7} + \frac{1}{4} + \frac{1}{28}$$
$$\frac{4}{9} = \frac{1}{3} + \frac{1}{9}$$
$$\frac{5}{9} = \frac{1}{2} + \frac{1}{18}$$

189

Basic Worksheet 52

Name _____

Step 1. Change to a common denominator.

$\begin{array}{r}4\frac{2}{3} = 4\frac{8}{12}\\ +3\frac{3}{4} = 3\frac{9}{12}\end{array}$

Step 2. Add fractions.

$\begin{array}{r}4\frac{2}{3} = 4\frac{8}{12}\\ +3\frac{3}{4} = 3\frac{9}{12}\\ \hline \frac{17}{12}\end{array}$

Step 3. Regroup.

$\begin{array}{r}4\frac{2}{3} = 4\frac{8}{12}\\ +3\frac{3}{4} = 3\frac{9}{12}\\ \hline 1\frac{5}{12}\end{array}$

Step 4. Add whole numbers.

$\begin{array}{r}4\frac{2}{3} = 4\frac{8}{12}\\ +3\frac{3}{4} = 3\frac{9}{12}\\ \hline 8\frac{5}{12}\end{array}$

Add. Give fractions in lowest terms.

1. $6\frac{3}{6} = 6\frac{4}{6}$
$+5\frac{1}{3} = 5\frac{2}{6}$
$= 12\frac{1}{6}$

2. $4\frac{1}{2}$
$+3\frac{3}{8}$

3. $5\frac{5}{6}$
$+4\frac{2}{3}$

4. $4\frac{3}{4}$
$+6\frac{1}{2}$

5. $7\frac{1}{2}$
$+5\frac{1}{4}$

6. $6\frac{2}{3}$
$+1\frac{5}{6}$

7. $5\frac{4}{5}$
$+5\frac{1}{2}$

8. $4\frac{3}{8}$
$+8\frac{5}{6}$

9. $9\frac{3}{4}$
$+6\frac{5}{8}$

10. $8\frac{1}{2}$
$+7\frac{3}{4}$

11. $6\frac{1}{8}$
$+8\frac{1}{2}$

12. $6\frac{2}{3}$
$+6\frac{1}{4}$

13. $18\frac{2}{5}$
$+5\frac{3}{4}$

14. $14\frac{7}{9}$
$+8\frac{2}{3}$

15. $23\frac{2}{3}$
$+9\frac{1}{4}$

16. $26\frac{1}{2}$
$+8\frac{4}{5}$

17. $21\frac{1}{3}$
$+11\frac{3}{2}$

18. $26\frac{5}{8}$
$+19\frac{3}{4}$

19. $25\frac{5}{9}$
$+18\frac{5}{6}$

20. $29\frac{2}{3}$
$+13\frac{5}{6}$

21. $28\frac{2}{3}$
$+16\frac{5}{9}$

22. $36\frac{1}{2}$
$+25\frac{5}{6}$

23. $19\frac{2}{3}$
$+37$

24. $42\frac{2}{3}$
$+18\frac{4}{5}$

(7) Adding mixed numbers   Copyright © 1979 by D. C. Heath and Company   Student text pages 188, 189

Enrichment Worksheet 52

Name _____

TRIVIA TIME

In 1935 Carl C. Magee invented something that you have seen in practically every city you have visited. What did he invent, and in what city was it first used?

To find the answers:
1. Add.
2. Write the letter under its matching number in the DECODER.

$7\frac{3}{8}$ $+\frac{5}{8}$	$1\frac{3}{10}$ $+4\frac{7}{10}$	$6\frac{4}{5}$ $+2\frac{2}{5}$	$2\frac{4}{9}$ $+3\frac{2}{3}$
C	Y	P	E
$3\frac{4}{5}$ $+4\frac{4}{9}$	$5\frac{7}{9}$ $+3\frac{5}{9}$	$4\frac{7}{10}$ $+2\frac{9}{10}$	$7\frac{5}{8}$ $+\frac{5}{6}$
R	I	G	H
$8\frac{3}{5}$ $+3\frac{7}{10}$	$6\frac{7}{8}$ $+6\frac{7}{16}$	$5\frac{3}{4}$ $+9\frac{3}{8}$	$16\frac{2}{5}$ $+7\frac{5}{8}$
A	N	M	T
$4\frac{1}{3}$ $+12\frac{4}{5}$	$15\frac{1}{2}$ $+12\frac{7}{10}$	$18\frac{2}{5}$ $+4\frac{7}{12}$	
K	L	O	

DECODER

$24\frac{7}{24}$ $8\frac{1}{3}$ $6\frac{1}{3}$ 9 $12\frac{3}{5}$ $8\frac{7}{8}$ $17\frac{2}{5}$ $9\frac{1}{3}$ $13\frac{5}{8}$ $7\frac{3}{5}$ $15\frac{2}{3}$ $6\frac{1}{3}$ $24\frac{7}{24}$ $6\frac{1}{3}$ $7\frac{2}{5}$

$23\frac{1}{4}$ $17\frac{2}{5}$ $28\frac{1}{5}$ $12\frac{3}{5}$ $8\frac{1}{3}$ $23\frac{1}{4}$ $15\frac{2}{3}$ $12\frac{3}{5}$ 8 $9\frac{1}{3}$ $24\frac{7}{24}$ 6

(7) Adding mixed numbers   Copyright © 1979 by D. C. Heath and Company   Student text pages 188, 189

Follow-up Activities

Reinforcement You may wish some students to have additional practice adding mixed numerals. The following addition boxes provide an interesting format. Answers are shown in red.

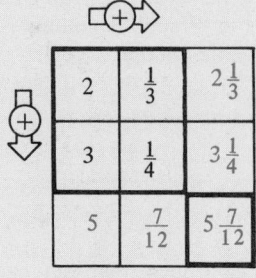

2	$\frac{1}{3}$	$2\frac{1}{3}$
3	$\frac{1}{4}$	$3\frac{1}{4}$
5	$\frac{7}{12}$	$5\frac{7}{12}$

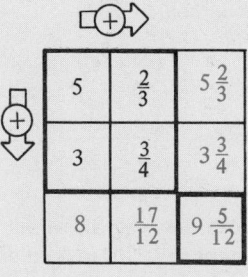

5	$\frac{2}{3}$	$5\frac{2}{3}$
3	$\frac{3}{4}$	$3\frac{3}{4}$
8	$\frac{17}{12}$	$9\frac{5}{12}$

Enrichment Have students measure the length and width of their classroom to the nearest inch. Have them use a mixed numeral to express each dimension in feet. For example, the width might be $26\frac{2}{3}$ feet. Have them add to determine the perimeter of the classroom.

EXCURSION

Copy and fill in the missing digits.

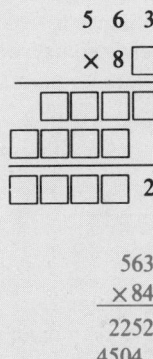

$$\begin{array}{r} 5\ 6\ 3 \\ \times\ 8\ \square \\ \hline \square\square\square\square \\ \square\square\square\square \\ \hline \square\square\square\ 2 \end{array}$$

$$\begin{array}{r} 563 \\ \times 84 \\ \hline 2252 \\ 4504 \\ \hline 47292 \end{array}$$

(core) Lesson 86   **189**

Suggested Lesson Plan

Introduction Use this addition example to remind students that when they added in mixed numeral form, they could add first in the "fractions column" and then in the whole-number column:

$$4\frac{5}{9}$$
$$+3\frac{3}{9}$$
$$\overline{7\frac{8}{9}}$$

Next remind them that they can also subtract in columns.

$$4\frac{5}{9}$$
$$-3\frac{3}{9}$$
$$\overline{1\frac{2}{9}}$$

Sometimes, just as with whole numbers, they cannot subtract in a column. For example:

$$5\frac{3}{7}$$
$$-1\frac{5}{7}$$

Ask students to tell what they did when they couldn't subtract in a column when working with whole numbers. (They regrouped.) For whole numbers, of course, the regrouping was always based on 10, but now the regrouping depends on the denominator of the fraction. In our example we change 5 to $4 + \frac{7}{7}$, so the "top" number becomes $4^{10}/_7$. Now we subtract.

$$5\frac{3}{7} = 4\frac{10}{7}$$
$$-1\frac{5}{7} = -1\frac{5}{7}$$
$$\overline{3\frac{5}{7}}$$

Repeat with other examples. Concentrate on the regrouping.

Using the pages Go over the three examples on page 190. Once more, concentrate on the regrouping and the steps to be followed. Assign the exercises. Circulate around the room, helping students on an individual basis.

You may have success in asking students who are having difficulty with the algorithm to invent their own way of doing subtraction. You may find that this technique works not only this time, but also whenever students seem to

reject the textbook methods.

Assist students who are poor readers with the word problems. For exercises 28 – 30, remind students that perimeter is the distance around.

Assign the Keeping Skills Sharp on an individual basis.

Subtracting mixed numbers

Here is how to find the difference of two mixed numbers.

EXAMPLE 1.

Step 1. Subtract fractional numbers.

Step 2. Subtract whole numbers.

$$3\frac{5}{7}$$
$$-1\frac{2}{7}$$
$$\overline{2\frac{3}{7}}$$

EXAMPLE 2.

Step 1. Write fractions with a common denominator.

Step 2. Subtract fractional numbers.

Step 3. Subtract whole numbers.

$$5\frac{2}{3} = 5\frac{4}{6}$$
$$-2\frac{1}{2} = -2\frac{3}{6}$$
$$\overline{3\frac{1}{6}}$$

Sometimes you will need to regroup before subtracting the fractions.

EXAMPLE 3.

Step 1. Not enough fifths. Regroup 1 into $\frac{5}{5}$.

Step 2. Subtract.

$$9\frac{2}{5} = 8\frac{7}{5}$$
$$-6\frac{3}{5} = -6\frac{3}{5}$$
$$\overline{2\frac{4}{5}}$$

You can show regrouping as you did with whole numbers.

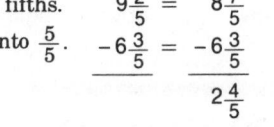

$$9\frac{2}{5}\,^{8\ 7}$$
$$-6\frac{3}{5}$$
$$\overline{2\frac{4}{5}}$$

EXERCISES

Subtract. Remember to give the fraction part in lowest terms.

1. $8\frac{3}{4}$ $-2\frac{1}{4}$ $\overline{6\frac{1}{2}}$

2. $9\frac{7}{8}$ $-3\frac{3}{8}$ $\overline{6\frac{1}{2}}$

3. $6\frac{1}{2}$ $-3\frac{1}{6}$ $\overline{3\frac{1}{3}}$

4. $15\frac{3}{4}$ $-8\frac{3}{8}$ $\overline{7\frac{3}{8}}$

5. $8\frac{5}{9}$ $-1\frac{1}{3}$ $\overline{7\frac{2}{9}}$

6. $15\frac{5}{7}$ $-9\frac{1}{7}$ $\overline{6\frac{4}{7}}$

7. $11\frac{3}{4}$ $-2\frac{1}{3}$ $\overline{9\frac{5}{12}}$

8. $9 = \left(8\frac{5}{5}\right)$ $-1\frac{3}{5}$ $\overline{7\frac{2}{5}}$

9. 12 $-3\frac{1}{4}$ $\overline{8\frac{3}{4}}$

10. 6 $-2\frac{5}{8}$ $\overline{3\frac{3}{8}}$

11. 8 $-3\frac{2}{3}$ $\overline{4\frac{1}{3}}$

12. $11\frac{6}{7}$ $-7\frac{1}{2}$ $\overline{4\frac{5}{14}}$

190

Assignments

BASIC
page 190 exercises 1 – 12
page 191 exercises 13 – 25,
   Keeping Skills Sharp
Basic Worksheet 53

AVERAGE
page 190 exercises 1 – 12
page 191 exercises 13 – 26,
   Keeping Skills Sharp
Enrichment Worksheet 53

ENRICHED
page 190 exercises 1 – 12
page 191 exercises 13 – 30,
   Keeping Skills Sharp
Enrichment Worksheet 53

EXTRA PRACTICE
page 388 set 61

13. $8\frac{5}{6}$
$-2\frac{1}{6}$
$6\frac{2}{3}$

14. $6\frac{1}{4}$
$-5\frac{3}{4}$
$\frac{1}{2}$

15. $16\frac{3}{8}$
$-5\frac{5}{8}$
$10\frac{3}{4}$

16. $12\frac{3}{4}$
-10
$2\frac{3}{4}$

17. $6\frac{3}{8}$
$-2\frac{3}{4}$
$3\frac{5}{8}$

18. $18\frac{3}{8}$
$-2\frac{3}{4}$
$15\frac{5}{8}$

19. $9\frac{2}{5}$
$-6\frac{1}{2}$
$2\frac{9}{10}$

20. $24\frac{1}{3}$
$-18\frac{1}{2}$
$5\frac{5}{6}$

21. 16
$-5\frac{7}{8}$
$10\frac{1}{8}$

22. $26\frac{7}{8}$
$-4\frac{3}{4}$
$22\frac{1}{8}$

23. 18
$-9\frac{1}{2}$
$8\frac{1}{2}$

24. $23\frac{3}{8}$
-12
$11\frac{3}{8}$

Solve.

25. One week Alvin watched TV for $6\frac{1}{4}$ hours and Beth watched TV for $3\frac{3}{4}$ hours. How many more hours did Alvin watch TV? $2\frac{1}{2}$

26. John long-jumped $16\frac{1}{4}$ feet and Kevin long-jumped $14\frac{2}{3}$ feet. How many feet farther did John jump? $1\frac{7}{12}$

27. Susan had $78\frac{1}{2}$ feet of kite string. She gave $18\frac{3}{4}$ feet of it to a friend. How many feet of string did she have left? $59\frac{3}{4}$

Give the perimeter of each figure.

28.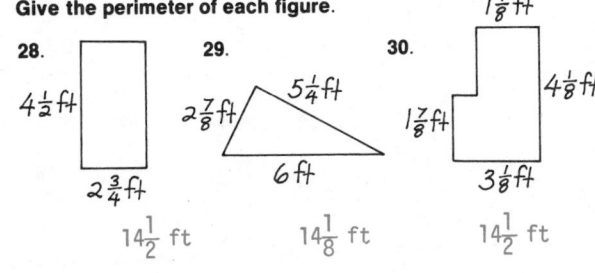

$4\frac{1}{2}$ ft

$2\frac{3}{4}$ ft

$14\frac{1}{2}$ ft

29. $2\frac{7}{8}$ ft $5\frac{1}{4}$ ft 6 ft $14\frac{1}{8}$ ft

30. $1\frac{7}{8}$ ft $4\frac{1}{8}$ ft $1\frac{7}{8}$ ft $3\frac{1}{8}$ ft $14\frac{1}{2}$ ft

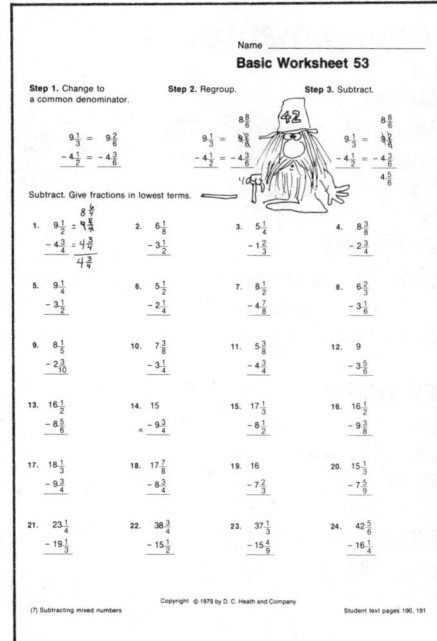

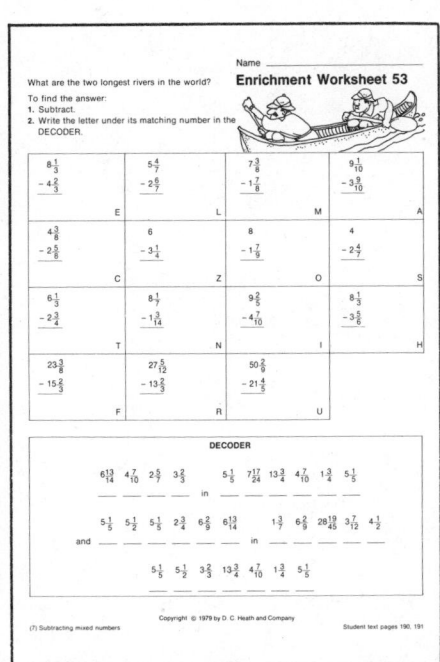

Divide.

1. $0.47\overline{)39.01}$ 83

2. $59\overline{)42.48}$ 0.72

3. $3.8\overline{)237.12}$ 62.4

4. $2.6\overline{)15.938}$ 6.13

5. $0.52\overline{)37.856}$ 72.8

6. $4.1\overline{)21.894}$ 5.34

7. $0.73\overline{)22.338}$ 30.6

8. $8.9\overline{)814.35}$ 91.5

9. $6.5\overline{)21.645}$ 3.33

10. $4.4\overline{)36.3}$ 8.25

11. $0.27\overline{)25.974}$ 96.2

12. $0.64\overline{)3.6544}$ 5.71

13. $113\overline{)20.679}$ 0.183

14. $22.6\overline{)117.972}$ 5.22

15. $0.438\overline{)0.279882}$ 0.639

191

Follow-up Activities

Reinforcement This lesson may be followed up by having students copy and complete the following addition boxes. (They require subtraction.)

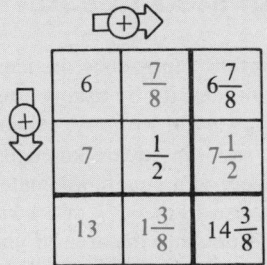

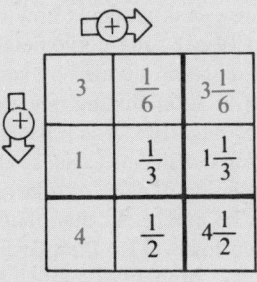

Enrichment Sketch the following on the chalkboard.

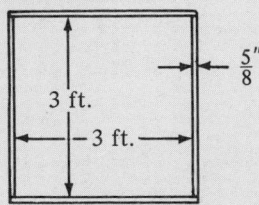

Explain that the sketch shows the top view of a box. The sides of the box form a square that is 3 feet on a side. Have students determine the lengths of the sides, if they are made from boards that are $5/8''$ thick.

EXCURSION

This method of multiplication was used in the Middle Ages. It was called the "grating" method.

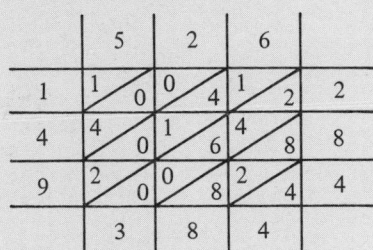

$526 \times 284 = 149{,}384$

Study the example to see how the method works. Use the grating method to find other products.

Suggested Lesson Plan

Introduction Introduce the idea of population density by asking students the area of the town (city, school district, state) in square kilometers. If the concept of a square kilometer is difficult, use 1 km = ½ mi., 1 km² = ¼ mi² for estimating the area of your region. Ask students for the population of the area. Ask students how to find the density per square kilometer for the area. (population divided by square kilometers) After finding this answer, introduce page 193, which deals with the population density of Canada. Of course, the population density of a large area is going to be much less than that of a populated town. Also the density of Canada will probably be much less than the area you have considered. You may want to develop the relationship between population, area, and density to help students with exercises 3–8.

population (p) $\quad d = \dfrac{p}{a} \quad a = \dfrac{p}{d}$

area (a)

density (d) $\qquad p = da$

Using the pages Assign a selection of the exercises on page 192. Use the unassigned exercises for additional work for those students whose success is less than 70% of the assigned exercises.

Assign exercises 1–8 on page 193. You may want to pair students to help each other on these problems.

Practice exercises

Add.

1. $5\frac{2}{3}$ $+7\frac{1}{3}$ = 13	2. 6 $+8\frac{3}{5}$ = $14\frac{3}{5}$	3. $7\frac{3}{4}$ $+9\frac{1}{4}$ = 17	4. $7\frac{1}{5}$ $+8\frac{1}{8}$ = $15\frac{13}{40}$	5. $8\frac{3}{4}$ $+8\frac{1}{8}$ = $16\frac{7}{8}$
6. $5\frac{5}{9}$ $+9\frac{1}{3}$ = $14\frac{8}{9}$	7. $8\frac{1}{8}$ $+9\frac{1}{4}$ = $17\frac{3}{8}$	8. $6\frac{5}{8}$ $+6$ = $12\frac{5}{8}$	9. $9\frac{1}{2}$ $+9\frac{1}{3}$ = $18\frac{5}{6}$	10. $8\frac{2}{3}$ $+5\frac{1}{4}$ = $13\frac{11}{12}$
11. $12\frac{7}{8}$ $+8\frac{1}{4}$ = $21\frac{1}{8}$	12. $13\frac{5}{8}$ $+5\frac{1}{2}$ = $19\frac{1}{8}$	13. $19\frac{3}{4}$ $+6\frac{2}{5}$ = $26\frac{3}{20}$	14. $17\frac{3}{4}$ $+3\frac{3}{8}$ = $21\frac{1}{8}$	15. $18\frac{5}{6}$ $+7\frac{1}{3}$ = $26\frac{1}{6}$
16. $12\frac{2}{3}$ $+10\frac{5}{9}$ = $23\frac{2}{9}$	17. $15\frac{3}{8}$ $+13\frac{7}{8}$ = $29\frac{1}{4}$	18. $23\frac{3}{4}$ $+15\frac{1}{2}$ = $39\frac{1}{4}$	19. $25\frac{5}{8}$ $+18\frac{3}{4}$ = $44\frac{3}{8}$	20. $30\frac{2}{3}$ $+12\frac{3}{4}$ = $43\frac{5}{12}$

Subtract.

21. $8\frac{4}{5}$ $-4\frac{1}{5}$ = $4\frac{3}{5}$	22. $9\frac{8}{9}$ $-3\frac{2}{9}$ = $6\frac{2}{3}$	23. $7\frac{2}{3}$ $-1\frac{1}{6}$ = $6\frac{1}{2}$	24. $9\frac{1}{2}$ $-\frac{1}{3}$ = $9\frac{1}{6}$	25. $7\frac{7}{8}$ $-2\frac{3}{4}$ = $5\frac{1}{8}$
26. $6\frac{9}{10}$ $-3\frac{2}{5}$ = $3\frac{1}{2}$	27. $5\frac{3}{4}$ $-2\frac{1}{3}$ = $3\frac{5}{12}$	28. $8\frac{5}{6}$ -3 = $5\frac{5}{6}$	29. $5\frac{3}{4}$ $-2\frac{5}{8}$ = $3\frac{1}{8}$	30. $9\frac{3}{5}$ -6 = $3\frac{3}{5}$
31. 11 $-4\frac{2}{3}$ = $6\frac{1}{3}$	32. 13 $-8\frac{1}{4}$ = $4\frac{3}{4}$	33. $12\frac{1}{4}$ $-3\frac{1}{8}$ = $9\frac{1}{8}$	34. $15\frac{1}{3}$ $-9\frac{1}{2}$ = $5\frac{5}{6}$	35. $18\frac{1}{8}$ $-9\frac{3}{4}$ = $8\frac{3}{8}$
36. $22\frac{1}{2}$ $-8\frac{3}{4}$ = $13\frac{3}{4}$	37. 24 $-9\frac{3}{5}$ = $14\frac{2}{5}$	38. $25\frac{1}{4}$ $-11\frac{2}{5}$ = $13\frac{17}{20}$	39. $29\frac{1}{3}$ $-16\frac{5}{6}$ = $12\frac{1}{2}$	40. 27 $-18\frac{7}{8}$ = $8\frac{1}{8}$

192

Assignments

BASIC
page 192 exercises 1–40
page 193 exercises 1–4
Basic Worksheet 54

AVERAGE
page 192 exercises 1–40
page 193 exercises 1–6
Enrichment Worksheet 54

ENRICHED
page 192 exercises 1–40
page 193 exercises 1–8
Enrichment Worksheet 54

REVIEW PRACTICE
page 383 set 41

Mathematics and world geography

Canada

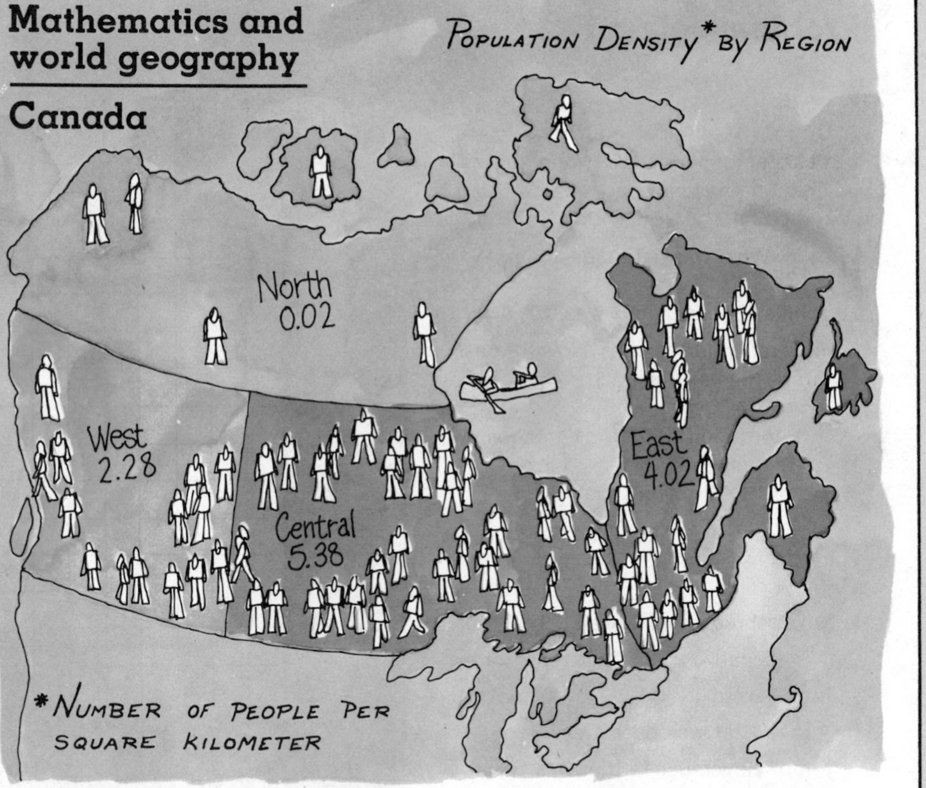

Population Density* by Region
North
0.02
West
2.28
Central
5.38
East
4.02
*Number of people per square kilometer

1. Which area has the greatest population density? Central

2. Which area has the least population density? North

3. The area of the East is 2,080,332 square kilometers. What is the population of the East? 8,362,935

4. The area of the North is 3,917,044 square kilometers. What is the population of the North? 78,341

5. The population of the West is 5,251,000. What is the area of the West? 2,303,070 square km

6. The population of the Central region is 9,357,000. What is the area of the Central region? 1,739,219 square km

7. What is the total population of Canada? (Use exercises 3–6.) 23,049,276

8. What is the total area of Canada? (Use exercises 3–6.) 10,039,665 square km

193

Follow-up Activities

Reinforcement Identify those students who are still having difficulty with the problems on page 192. Assign additional exercises and provide individual help. Consider using some of the other students in peer tutoring pairs to see if other students can inspire greater concentration and effort.

Enrichment Have students develop a population density map of your area to show towns, cities, and states. They can use different colors or cross-hatching to show density levels. Make the project a team or pair project and post the better maps on the mathematics bulletin board.

EXCURSION

Complete.

$(1 \times 9) + 2 = \underline{\ ?\ }$ 11

$(12 \times 9) + 3 = \underline{\ ?\ }$ 111

$(123 \times 9) + 4 = \underline{\ ?\ }$ 1111

$(1234 \times 9) + 5 = \underline{\ ?\ }$ 11,111

$(12345 \times 9) + 6 = \underline{\ ?\ }$ 111,111

Look for a pattern.

Can you simplify the expression

$$(12345678 \times 9) + 9$$

without pencil or paper? 111, 111, 111

Name ______________________

Basic Worksheet 54

Solve.

Problem	Work space	Answer
1. Beth is $63\frac{1}{4}$ inches tall. Her little brother is $54\frac{1}{2}$ inches tall. How much taller is Beth?		
2. Mr. Johnson bought $2\frac{3}{4}$ pounds of ground beef and a $3\frac{1}{2}$-pound beef roast. How many pounds of beef did he buy?		
3. A recipe calls for $1\frac{3}{4}$ cups of white sugar and $1\frac{1}{3}$ cups of brown sugar. How many cups of sugar does it call for?		
4. Ms. Harcourt bought $28\frac{1}{2}$ gallons of gasoline one week and $40\frac{9}{10}$ gallons the next week. How many gallons did she buy?		
5. A rectangular lot is $59\frac{1}{2}$ feet wide and $180\frac{1}{2}$ feet long. How many feet of fencing is needed to fence in the lot?		
6. One month it rained $6\frac{1}{10}$ inches, and the next month it rained $4\frac{1}{2}$ inches. How many more inches did it rain the first month?		
7. The perimeter of a triangle is $18\frac{1}{8}$ inches. Two of the sides measure $5\frac{3}{4}$ inches and $7\frac{5}{8}$ inches. What is the length of the other side?		
8. On Monday a certain stock was listed at $54\frac{1}{2}$ points. Tuesday it went down $2\frac{1}{4}$ points, Wednesday it gained $2\frac{1}{2}$ points, and Thursday it went down $1\frac{3}{4}$ points. What was the stock listed at on Friday morning?		

Copyright © 1979 by D. C. Heath and Company

(7) Problem solving

Student text pages 192–195

Name ______________________

Enrichment Worksheet 54

Complete.
Add across.
Subtract down.

1.

2	$\frac{3}{4}$	
1	$\frac{1}{2}$	

2.

3		$3\frac{5}{8}$
2		$2\frac{1}{4}$

3.

4		
	$\frac{1}{4}$	
3	$\frac{1}{12}$	

4.

$4\frac{1}{2}$	$2\frac{3}{4}$	
$2\frac{1}{4}$	$1\frac{5}{8}$	

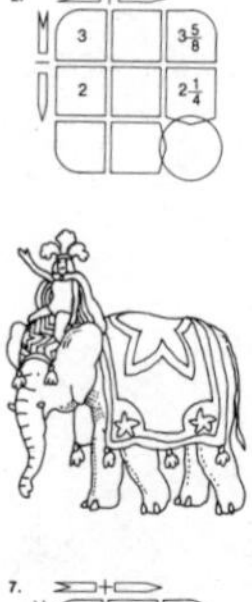

5.

$4\frac{2}{3}$	$2\frac{1}{2}$	
$2\frac{1}{4}$	$1\frac{1}{3}$	

6.

$5\frac{3}{4}$		$7\frac{1}{4}$
	$\frac{3}{4}$	$4\frac{1}{8}$

7.

$7\frac{1}{3}$		
	$2\frac{5}{8}$	
$4\frac{1}{2}$	$1\frac{1}{4}$	

8.

$8\frac{3}{4}$		$12\frac{5}{12}$
	$2\frac{5}{6}$	
		$8\frac{2}{3}$

Copyright © 1979 by D. C. Heath and Company

(7) Adding and subtracting mixed numbers

Student text pages 192–195

Suggested Lesson Plan

Introduction Use the situation
described to motivate computational
work with denominate numbers. These
numbers are usually the result of
measurements and sometimes have
different units of measure, like 3′ 2½″.
Start the lesson with the reading of
exercise 1 and ask a student to identify
the longest jump. You could motivate
addition of these numbers by asking how
far Jan jumped for all three jumps. This
addition would require regrouping of
inches to feet, and would be a good
lead-in to the regrouping required for
subtraction. Of course, the main
difficulty is for students to realize and
use the relationship 1 foot equals 12
inches rather than regrouping as with
whole numbers. This lesson is a good
way to focus on the regrouping skill in a
new context.

Using the pages Write the numbers
for exercise 2 on the board and call on
one of your better students to explain
the regrouping required while you record
the work on the board. Be sure to
emphasize the regrouping of feet to
inches.

Assign exercises 1–12 for written
work. Plan to assist your poor readers,
helping them read through the problems
to decide which operations to use and
with which numbers.

Problem solving

1. During a physical education class
   each student made 3 long jumps.
   The longest jump was recorded. Jan
   jumped 10′ $2\frac{1}{2}$″, 11′ $3\frac{1}{4}$″, and 10′
   $8\frac{1}{4}$″. What was her longest jump?

   $11'\ 3\frac{1}{4}''$

2. John's longest jump was 10′ $8\frac{1}{2}$″.
   How much farther was Jan's longest
   jump? (See exercise 1.) $6\frac{3}{4}''$

   Regrouped 1 foot for 12 inches.

   $$11'\,3\frac{1}{4}'' \;=\; 10'\,15\frac{1}{4}''$$
   $$-10'\,8\frac{1}{2}'' \;=\; -10'\ 8\frac{1}{2}''$$

   _____

3. Mike's three jumps were 11′ $1\frac{1}{2}$″, 10′
   $11\frac{3}{4}$″, and 11′ $1\frac{1}{2}$″. Terry's three
   jumps were 10′ $\frac{1}{2}$″, 11′ $\frac{3}{4}$″, and 11′
   $4\frac{1}{4}$″. What was each boy's longest
   jump? How much farther was Terry's
   longest jump?

4. Bill's shortest jump was 9′ $4\frac{1}{2}$″. His
   longest jump was 1′ $7\frac{3}{4}$″ longer than
   his shortest jump. How far was his
   longest jump? $11'\ \frac{1}{4}''$

3. Mike's: 11′ $1\frac{1}{2}''$

   Terry's: 11′ $4\frac{1}{4}''$

   $2\frac{3}{4}''$

194

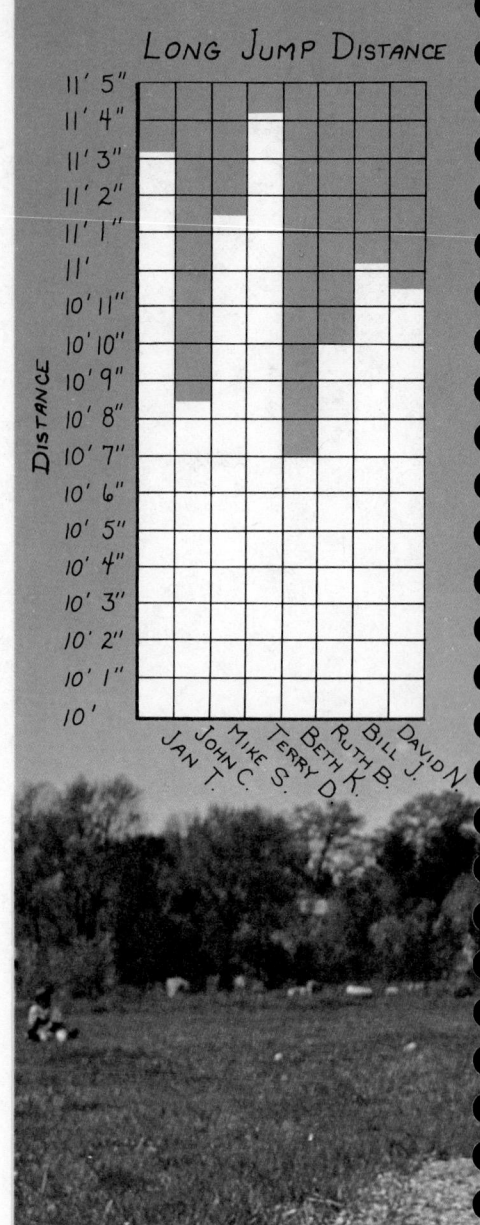

LONG JUMP DISTANCE

Assignments

BASIC
page 194 exercises 1–4
page 195 exercises 5–8
Basic Worksheet 54

AVERAGE
page 194 exercises 1–4
page 195 exercises 5–10
Enrichment Worksheet 54

ENRICHED
page 194 exercises 1–4
page 195 exercises 5–12
Enrichment Worksheet 54

REVIEW PRACTICE
page 383 set 43

Refer to the graph to answer the following questions.

5. What was the longest jump? 11' 4$\frac{1}{4}$"

6. Who had the shortest jump? Beth

7. How many jumped more than 11 ft? 4

8. How many jumped farther than Ruth? 5

9. How much farther did Bill jump than John? 3$\frac{3}{4}$"

10. Who jumped 2 in. farther than David? Mike

11. Who had the fifth longest jump? David

12. What was the difference between the longest and shortest jumps? 9$\frac{1}{4}$"

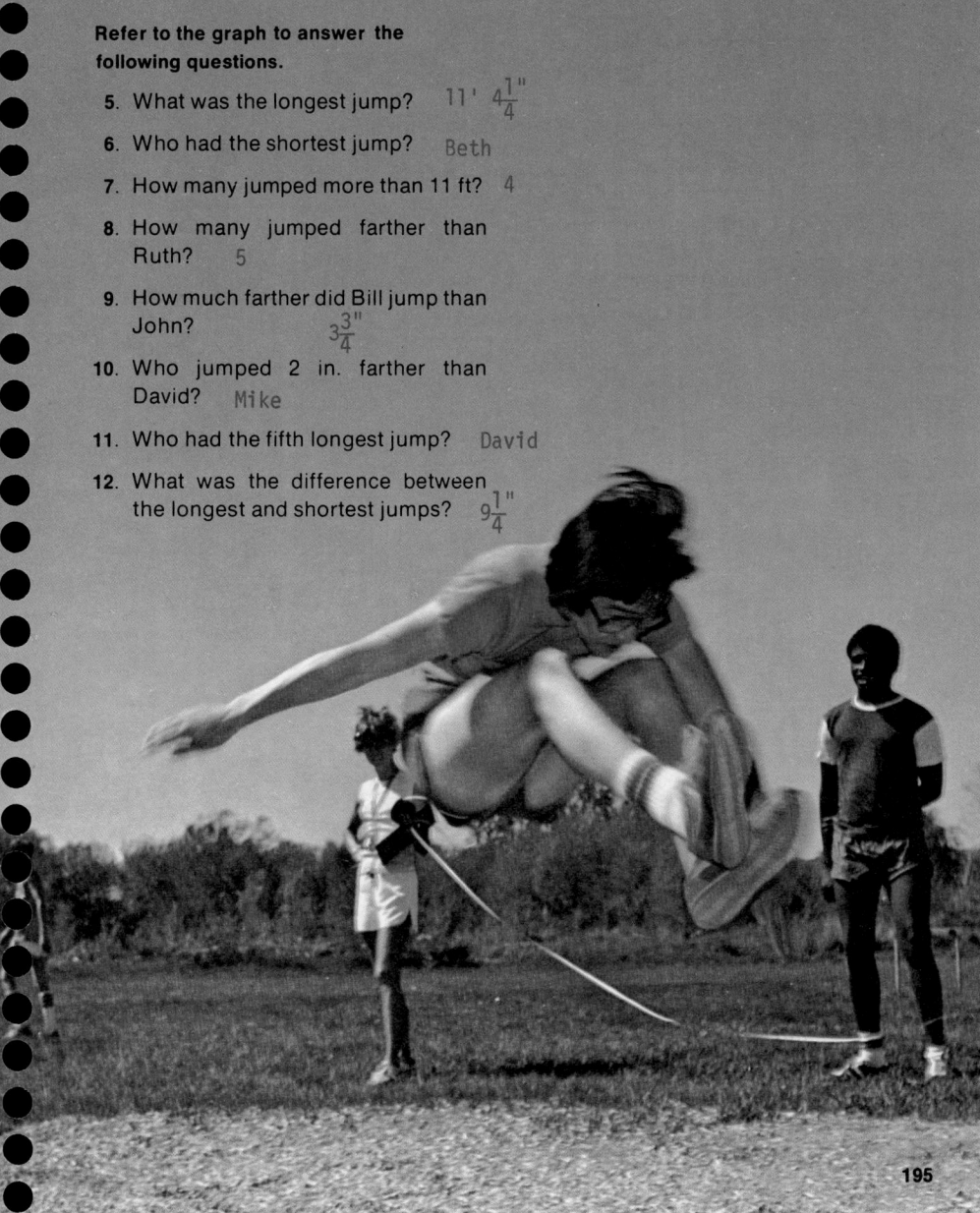

195

Follow-up Activities

Reinforcement For the subtractions for exercises 2−4, have students rename the distances jumped as mixed numbers of inches and then compute to find the answers. For example, 11' 3$\frac{1}{4}$" would be renamed as 135 $\frac{1}{4}$ inches.

Enrichment Have students find the winner (Jan, John, Mike, or Bill) if the contest is to jump the greatest distance in three jumps. Have them make a bar graph as on page 194 and see if there is a different winner.

CALCULATOR ACTIVITY
Using the World Almanac and a road atlas, students should show how far the winner of the most recent Indianapolis 500 race would have gone if he had started from your town or city and had driven at this winning average for 24 hours. Use the road atlas to show your location and the trip. Post the map on the mathematics bulletin board.

STUDENT OBJECTIVE
To review the concepts and skills introduced in Chapter 6.

Suggested Lesson Plan

Introduction No pre-text activity is necessary for page 196 as this is a checkup for the chapter. However, it may be valuable to briefly review the lessons in the chapter so that students are reminded of the content over which they will be tested.

This checkup will provide you with data about how well individual students have mastered the skills of the chapter. The Chapter Review on page 198 is provided for those students that need more specific individual help.

Page 197 is an activity that students will enjoy. Let all the students participate so that you will only have to collect the data once. After the data are collected, let each student make his or her own graph to portray the information. Post the better graphs on the mathematics bulletin board.

Using the pages Assign all the exercises on page 196. As students complete the page, they can work on the activity on page 197, or perhaps there are games or activities that some students have not played during the chapter which they would like to try. Assign a student leader to each game or activity and as pupils want to play, they can go to the assigned pupil for the game rule and partners for the game.

Give each sum in lowest terms. [pages 176–177, 180–181]

1. $\frac{1}{5} + \frac{3}{5}$ $\frac{4}{5}$
2. $\frac{1}{4} + \frac{1}{2}$ $\frac{3}{4}$
3. $\frac{3}{8} + \frac{1}{4}$ $\frac{5}{8}$
4. $\frac{1}{3} + \frac{1}{4}$ $\frac{7}{12}$

5. $\frac{3}{4} + \frac{2}{3}$ $\frac{17}{12}$
6. $\frac{7}{8} + \frac{5}{4}$ $\frac{17}{8}$
7. $\frac{5}{9} + \frac{2}{3}$ $\frac{11}{9}$
8. $\frac{0}{6} + \frac{3}{5}$ $\frac{3}{5}$

Give each difference in lowest terms. [pages 176–177, 182–184]

9. $\frac{5}{9} - \frac{2}{9}$ $\frac{1}{3}$
10. $\frac{7}{8} - \frac{3}{8}$ $\frac{1}{2}$
11. $\frac{5}{6} - \frac{1}{2}$ $\frac{1}{3}$
12. $\frac{3}{2} - \frac{3}{4}$ $\frac{3}{4}$

13. $\frac{5}{7} - \frac{0}{3}$ $\frac{5}{7}$
14. $\frac{1}{2} - \frac{1}{3}$ $\frac{1}{6}$
15. $\frac{3}{4} - \frac{2}{3}$ $\frac{1}{12}$
16. $\frac{5}{6} - \frac{5}{8}$ $\frac{5}{24}$

[pages 186–187]

Copy and complete. 17. 18. 19. 20. 21. 22. 23. 24. 25.

Fraction	$\frac{3}{2}$	$\frac{5}{3}$	$\frac{11}{4}$	$\frac{9}{5}$	$\frac{15}{6}$	$\frac{5}{2}$	$\frac{13}{4}$	$\frac{14}{3}$	$\frac{8}{5}$
Mixed number	$1\frac{1}{2}$	$1\frac{2}{3}$	$2\frac{3}{4}$	$1\frac{4}{5}$	$2\frac{3}{6}$	$2\frac{1}{2}$	$3\frac{1}{4}$	$4\frac{2}{3}$	$1\frac{3}{5}$

Add. [pages 188–189]

26. $3\frac{1}{5}$ $+ 2\frac{2}{5}$ $5\frac{3}{5}$
27. $5\frac{1}{4}$ $+ 2\frac{1}{2}$ $7\frac{3}{4}$
28. $6\frac{5}{8}$ $+ 3\frac{3}{4}$ $10\frac{3}{8}$
29. $9\frac{5}{8}$ $+ 4\frac{3}{8}$ 14
30. $6\frac{2}{5}$ $+ 3\frac{3}{4}$ $10\frac{3}{20}$
31. 8 $+ 5\frac{2}{7}$ $13\frac{2}{7}$

Subtract.

32. $8\frac{5}{9}$ $- 3\frac{4}{9}$ $5\frac{1}{9}$
33. $9\frac{3}{4}$ $- 2\frac{1}{2}$ $7\frac{1}{4}$
34. $8\frac{1}{2}$ $- 5\frac{1}{3}$ $3\frac{1}{6}$
35. $7\frac{1}{2}$ $- 1\frac{3}{4}$ $5\frac{3}{4}$
36. $7\frac{2}{3}$ $- 5\frac{5}{6}$ $1\frac{5}{6}$
37. 6 $- 3\frac{7}{8}$ $2\frac{1}{8}$

Solve. [pages 194–195]

38. A bread recipe calls for $\frac{3}{4}$ cup of white flour and $\frac{1}{2}$ cup of whole wheat flour. How much flour does the recipe call for? $1\frac{1}{4}$ cups

39. Alice had $\frac{5}{8}$ yard of ribbon. She used $\frac{1}{2}$ yard on a dress. What fraction of a yard did she have left? $\frac{1}{8}$

196

Assignments

BASIC
page 196 exercises 1–39
page 197 Project

AVERAGE
page 196 exercises 1–39
page 197 Project

ENRICHED
page 196 exercises 1–39
page 197 Project

EXTRA PROBLEM SOLVING
pages 408–409 set 6

Project

1. Have each of your classmates jump from a line, measure the length of the jump in centimeters, and record the distance.

2. Have each classmate divide the length of the jump by his or her height and find the quotient to the nearest tenth.

EXAMPLE.

$$\begin{array}{r} 1.17 \\ 152\overline{)178.00} \\ \underline{152} \\ 26\ 0 \\ \underline{15\ 2} \\ 10\ 80 \\ \underline{10\ 64} \\ 16 \end{array}$$

height → in cm ← length of jump in cm

3. Graph the results on a graph like this:

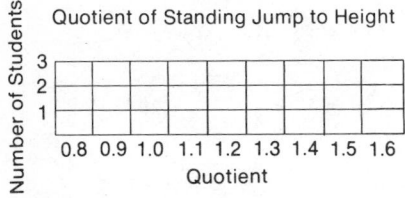

Quotient of Standing Jump to Height

Number of Students

3
2
1

0.8 0.9 1.0 1.1 1.2 1.3 1.4 1.5 1.6
Quotient

4. Repeat steps 1–3 for a running long jump.

You may wish to assign some of the Creative Problem Solving Activities (pages 461–477) at this time.

Follow-up Activities

Reinforcement Correct all of the items in the Chapter Checkup. Any student who missed 6 or more or any more than three problems in a row needs additional help. It is important for each student to achieve some degree of mastery of the basic skills covered. At this point, students who are still having difficulty with these skills need concentrated individual help.

Enrichment Assign these pupils to the games and activities that have been played throughout the chapter. Each student leader is responsible for teaching the game or activity to the interested students and for supervising the play.

STUDENT OBJECTIVE
To review or extend the skills and concepts taught in Chapter 6.

Suggested Lesson Plan

Introduction After correcting the Chapter Checkup you will know which students need additional reinforcement and which ones will be able to go ahead with the Challenge activity. Get the better students started on page 199 first, as the students who are having difficulty will need more of your time.

The students who need more review should go back and correct their errors on the Chapter Checkup. You may want to go over those questions orally if this group is small enough. Carefully probe to determine which concepts and skills the students have not mastered and work individually to correct their deficiencies.

Using the pages After the identified students have corrected the Chapter Checkup, they should answer questions 1–32. After they complete these questions, read the answers and let the students correct their own papers. Give them an opportunity to ask questions about those exercises they missed.

Assign page 199 to the students who did well on the Chapter Checkup. Have each student work independently. After they find all the numbers, they should have a magic square—that is, the sum of each row, column, and diagonal should be the same.

The least common multiple of two denominators is the least common denominator.

$$\frac{3}{4} + \frac{2}{3} = \frac{9}{12} + \frac{8}{12} = \frac{17}{12}$$

$$\frac{5}{3} - \frac{2}{5} = \frac{25}{15} - \frac{6}{15} = \frac{19}{15}$$

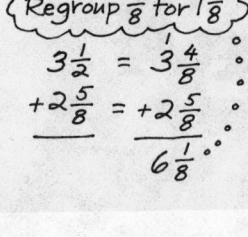

Regroup $\frac{9}{8}$ for $1\frac{1}{8}$

$$3\frac{1}{2} = 3\frac{4}{8}$$
$$+2\frac{5}{8} = +2\frac{5}{8}$$
$$\overline{6\frac{1}{8}}$$

Regroup 1 for $\frac{12}{12}$

$$6\frac{1}{3} = 6\frac{4}{12} = 5\frac{16}{12}$$
$$-2\frac{3}{4} = -2\frac{9}{12} = -2\frac{9}{12}$$
$$\overline{\phantom{-2\frac{9}{12}}3\frac{7}{12}}$$

Give the least common denominator.

1. $\frac{1}{3}, \frac{1}{4}$ 12   2. $\frac{2}{3}, \frac{1}{2}$ 6   3. $\frac{3}{8}, \frac{3}{4}$ 8   4. $\frac{2}{5}, \frac{1}{3}$ 15

5. $\frac{5}{6}, \frac{3}{8}$ 24   6. $\frac{4}{9}, \frac{2}{3}$ 9   7. $\frac{5}{2}, \frac{3}{5}$ 10   8. $\frac{7}{4}, \frac{5}{6}$ 12

Add. Reduce answers to lowest terms.

9. $\frac{2}{9} + \frac{3}{9}$ $\frac{5}{9}$ 10. $\frac{3}{8} + \frac{1}{8}$ $\frac{1}{2}$ 11. $\frac{3}{4} + \frac{1}{2}$ $\frac{5}{4}$

12. $\frac{5}{6} + \frac{1}{3}$ $\frac{7}{6}$ 13. $\frac{2}{3} + \frac{5}{4}$ $\frac{23}{12}$ 14. $\frac{7}{6} + \frac{5}{8}$ $\frac{43}{24}$

Subtract. Reduce answers to lowest terms.

15. $\frac{5}{6} - \frac{1}{6}$ $\frac{2}{3}$ 16. $\frac{1}{2} - \frac{1}{3}$ $\frac{1}{6}$ 17. $\frac{5}{8} - \frac{1}{4}$ $\frac{3}{8}$

18. $\frac{11}{12} - \frac{3}{4}$ $\frac{1}{6}$ 19. $\frac{5}{2} - \frac{5}{6}$ $\frac{5}{3}$ 20. $\frac{7}{3} - \frac{0}{5}$ $\frac{7}{3}$

Add.

21. $3\frac{1}{3}$ $+2\frac{1}{3}$ $5\frac{2}{3}$ 22. $4\frac{1}{4}$ $+3\frac{1}{2}$ $7\frac{3}{4}$ 23. $5\frac{1}{2}$ $+2\frac{1}{3}$ $7\frac{5}{6}$

24. $6\frac{1}{2}$ $+3\frac{5}{8}$ $10\frac{1}{8}$ 25. $4\frac{5}{6}$ $+2\frac{1}{3}$ $7\frac{1}{6}$ 26. $5\frac{3}{4}$ $+3\frac{2}{3}$ $9\frac{5}{12}$

Subtract.

27. $8\frac{5}{9}$ $-2\frac{1}{9}$ $6\frac{4}{9}$ 28. $7\frac{3}{4}$ $-3\frac{1}{4}$ $4\frac{1}{2}$ 29. $9\frac{5}{8}$ $-4\frac{1}{4}$ $5\frac{3}{8}$

30. $6\frac{1}{3}$ $-1\frac{1}{2}$ $4\frac{5}{6}$ 31. $8\frac{2}{3}$ $-2\frac{5}{6}$ $5\frac{5}{6}$ 32. $7\frac{1}{8}$ $-3\frac{5}{16}$ $3\frac{13}{16}$

198

Assignments

BASIC
page 198   exercises 1–32

AVERAGE
page 198   exercises 1–32

ENRICHED
page 199   exercises 1–3

CHAPTER CHALLENGE

1. Make a 4 × 4 square like the one shown.
2. Work the following exercises and replace each letter by its number.

a 3	b $1\frac{3}{8}$	c $1\frac{1}{4}$	d $2\frac{5}{8}$
e $1\frac{5}{8}$	f $2\frac{1}{4}$	g $2\frac{3}{8}$	h 2
i $2\frac{1}{8}$	j $1\frac{3}{4}$	k $1\frac{7}{8}$	l $2\frac{1}{2}$
m $1\frac{1}{2}$	n $2\frac{7}{8}$	o $2\frac{3}{4}$	p $1\frac{1}{8}$

Give

a. the greatest common factor of 15 and 18.

b. the sum of $\frac{5}{8}$ and $\frac{6}{8}$.

c. the sum of 1 and $\frac{1}{4}$.

d. the sum of $1\frac{1}{4}$ and $1\frac{3}{8}$.

e. the number that is $\frac{3}{8}$ less than 2.

f. the number that is $\frac{3}{4}$ less than 3.

g. the number that is $\frac{3}{8}$ greater than 2.

h. the only even prime number.

i. the number that is $1\frac{1}{2}$ greater than $\frac{5}{8}$.

j. the number that is $\frac{7}{12}$ greater than $1\frac{1}{6}$.

k. the difference of $3\frac{3}{8}$ and $1\frac{1}{2}$.

l. the difference of 3 and $\frac{1}{2}$.

m. the difference of $4\frac{5}{8}$ and $3\frac{1}{8}$.

n. the number that is $\frac{1}{2}$ greater than the sum of 1 and $1\frac{3}{8}$.

o. the number that is $\frac{1}{4}$ less than the difference of $5\frac{1}{8}$ and $2\frac{1}{8}$.

p. the number that is $\frac{3}{8}$ greater than the difference of 1 and $\frac{1}{4}$.

3. If you didn't make any mistakes, your completed square should be a magic square. That is, the sum of the numbers in each row, column, and diagonal should be the same. Check to see whether your square is magic.

199

a b c d | a b c d | a b c d | a b c d | a b c
14 | 34 | 14 | 4 | 30
a b c d | a b c d | a b c d | c d | a b c
15 | b c | 31

STUDENT OBJECTIVES

To practice skills learned previously.
To practice using a standardized-test format.

Suggested Lesson Plan

Using the pages The Major Checkup at the end of each chapter of this textbook is given in standardized-test format. The answer sheet on page 448 is the type used with many standardized tests. You may duplicate it for use with the Major Checkups.

Pass out the answer sheets and be sure students understand how to use them. Allow a specified time, perhaps twenty minutes, to complete the checkup. Assign the exercises and use the results to determine what review is needed.

The table below correlates the test items and the student text pages. Assign review exercises as indicated by the Major Checkup results.

Test Item	Text Pages	Test Item	Text Pages
1	22−23	7	138−139
2	44−45	8	142−143
3	66−67	9	146−147
4	68−69	10	152−153
5	82−83	11	110−111
6	96−97	12	110−111

Chapter 6 Posttest

See page 54 for a full discussion of how to use the posttest. The table below suggests Extra Practice exercises and Basic Worksheets for those students who need further practice or reteaching.

Objectives	Extra Practice Sets	Pages	Basic Worksheets
6-1	54−55	386	46−47
6-2	56	386	48
6-3	57−58	387	49−50
6-4	59	387	51
6-5	60	388	52
6-6	61	388	53
6-7			54

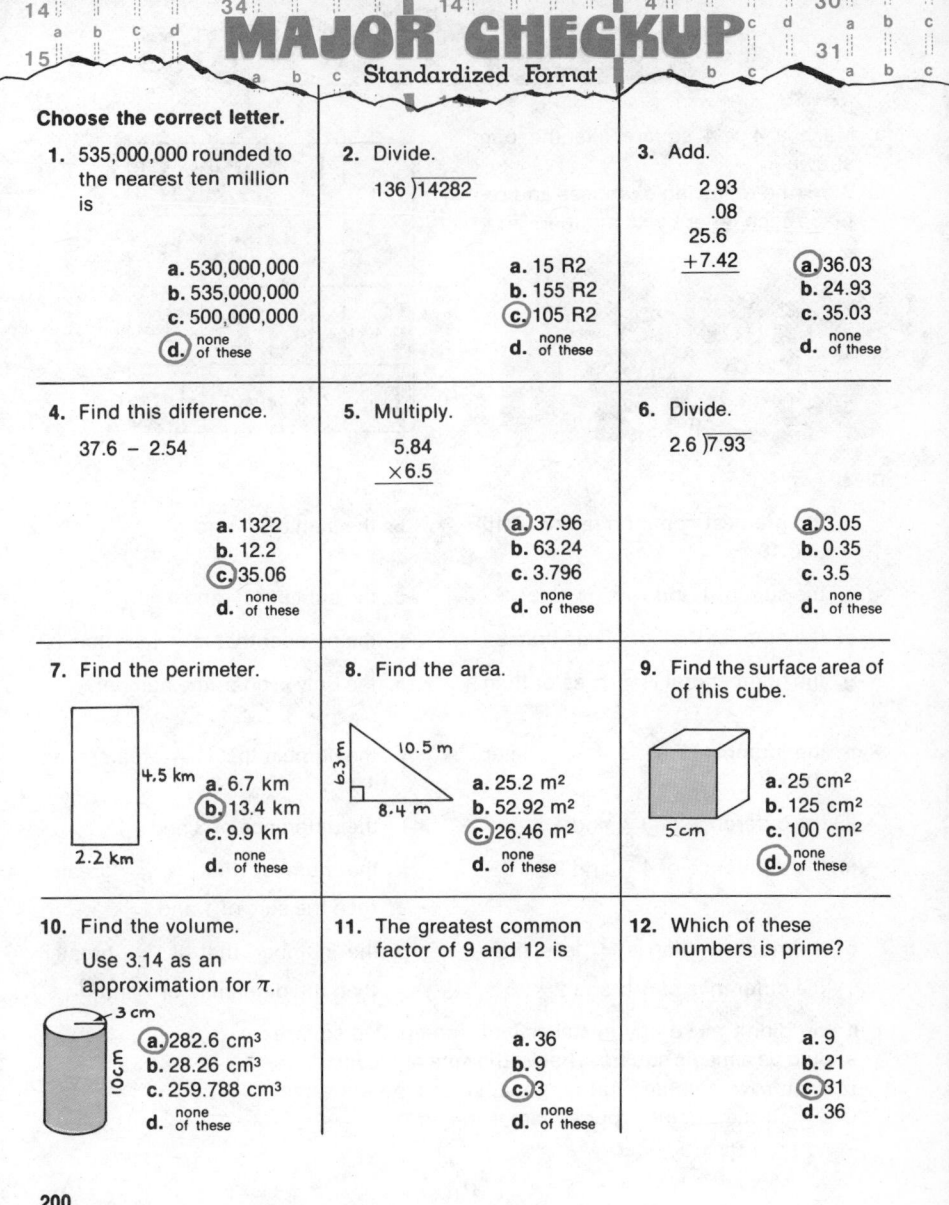

MAJOR CHECKUP
Standardized Format

Choose the correct letter.

1. 535,000,000 rounded to the nearest ten million is
a. 530,000,000
b. 535,000,000
c. 500,000,000
d. none of these

2. Divide.
$136\overline{)14282}$
a. 15 R2
b. 155 R2
c. 105 R2
d. none of these

3. Add.
2.93
.08
25.6
+7.42
a. 36.03
b. 24.93
c. 35.03
d. none of these

4. Find this difference.
37.6 − 2.54
a. 1322
b. 12.2
c. 35.06
d. none of these

5. Multiply.
5.84
×6.5
a. 37.96
b. 63.24
c. 3.796
d. none of these

6. Divide.
$2.6\overline{)7.93}$
a. 3.05
b. 0.35
c. 3.5
d. none of these

7. Find the perimeter.
4.5 km
2.2 km
a. 6.7 km
b. 13.4 km
c. 9.9 km
d. none of these

8. Find the area.
10.5 m
6.3 m
8.4 m
a. 25.2 m²
b. 52.92 m²
c. 26.46 m²
d. none of these

9. Find the surface area of this cube.
5 cm
a. 25 cm²
b. 125 cm²
c. 100 cm²
d. none of these

10. Find the volume.
Use 3.14 as an approximation for π.
3 cm
10 cm
a. 282.6 cm³
b. 28.26 cm³
c. 259.788 cm³
d. none of these

11. The greatest common factor of 9 and 12 is
a. 36
b. 9
c. 3
d. none of these

12. Which of these numbers is prime?
a. 9
b. 21
c. 31
d. 36

200

Answers for Chapter 6 Posttest

1. $\frac{2}{3}$ 2. $\frac{5}{6}$ 3. $\frac{4}{3}$ 4. $\frac{3}{4}$ 5. $\frac{13}{14}$ 6. >

7. < 8. < 9. > 10. < 11. $\frac{2}{3}$

12. $\frac{11}{18}$ 13. $\frac{11}{15}$ 14. $\frac{1}{3}$ 15. $\frac{1}{6}$ 16. $\frac{7}{20}$

17. $\frac{9}{2}$ 18. $\frac{11}{3}$ 19. $3\frac{3}{4}$ 20. $7\frac{3}{5}$ 21. $\frac{27}{5}$

22. $10\frac{3}{4}$ 23. $7\frac{5}{7}$ 24. 7 25. $10\frac{5}{6}$

26. $9\frac{1}{8}$ 27. $10\frac{3}{20}$ 28. $1\frac{5}{8}$ 29. $2\frac{1}{2}$

30. $4\frac{1}{6}$ 31. $1\frac{1}{2}$ 32. $4\frac{17}{20}$ 33. $1\frac{1}{6}$ lb

34. $28\frac{3}{8}$ in.

Chapter 6 Posttest

Name _____

Date _____

Number right

0	1	2	3	4	5

Reduce each fraction to lowest terms. [Obj. 6-1, pages 172–177]

1. $\frac{8}{12}$ _____ 2. $\frac{20}{24}$ _____ 3. $\frac{24}{18}$ _____ 4. $\frac{48}{64}$ _____ 5. $\frac{39}{42}$ _____

0	1	2	3	4	5

< or >? [Obj. 6-2, pages 178–179]

6. $\frac{1}{7}$ ◯ $\frac{1}{8}$ 7. $\frac{3}{7}$ ◯ $\frac{4}{7}$ 8. $\frac{5}{6}$ ◯ $\frac{7}{8}$ 9. $\frac{3}{5}$ ◯ $\frac{4}{7}$ 10. $\frac{1}{4}$ ◯ $\frac{2}{7}$

Add or subtract. [Obj. 6-3, pages 180–184]

0	1	2	3	4	5	6

11. $\frac{1}{2} + \frac{1}{6} =$ _____

12. $\frac{1}{6} + \frac{4}{9} =$ _____

13. $\frac{1}{3} + \frac{2}{5} =$ _____

14. $\frac{1}{2} - \frac{1}{6} =$ _____

15. $\frac{2}{3} - \frac{1}{2} =$ _____

16. $\frac{3}{5} - \frac{1}{4} =$ _____

Complete this table. [Obj. 6-4, pages 186–187]

0-2	3	4	5	6

Mixed Number	$4\frac{1}{2}$	$3\frac{2}{3}$	19.	20.	$5\frac{2}{5}$	22.
Fraction	17.	18.	$\frac{15}{4}$	$\frac{38}{5}$	21.	$\frac{43}{4}$

Add. [Obj. 6-5, pages 188–189, 192]

0	1	2	3	4	5

23. $3\frac{2}{7}$
    $+4\frac{3}{7}$

24. $5\frac{3}{8}$
    $+1\frac{5}{8}$

25. $8\frac{1}{3}$
    $+2\frac{1}{2}$

26. $5\frac{3}{8}$
    $+3\frac{3}{4}$

27. $7\frac{2}{5}$
    $+2\frac{3}{4}$

Subtract. [Obj. 6-6, pages 190–192]

0	1	2	3	4	5

28. $4\frac{7}{8}$
    $-3\frac{2}{8}$

29. $6\frac{1}{8}$
    $-3\frac{5}{8}$

30. $8\frac{2}{3}$
    $-4\frac{1}{2}$

31. $5\frac{1}{6}$
    $-3\frac{2}{3}$

32. $6\frac{3}{5}$
    $-1\frac{3}{4}$

Solve. [Obj. 6-7, pages 194–195]

0	1	2

33. One package weighs $5\frac{2}{3}$ pounds and another weighs $4\frac{1}{2}$ pounds. How much heavier is the first package? _____

34. A wooden rod $15\frac{1}{2}$ inches long is glued to the end of another rod that is $12\frac{7}{8}$ inches long. How long are they together?

_____

NOTES

200b

MIDYEAR TEST

Add or subtract.

1. 9461
    +3953
    13,414

2. 786
    237
    +89
    1112

3. 6248
    −2519
    3729

4. 7002
    −3594
    3408

Multiply or divide.

5. 596
    ×58
    34,568

6. 7218
    ×309
    2,230,362

7. $8\overline{)1624}$ 203

8. $94\overline{)36085}$ 383 R83

Round 563.8905 to the nearest

9. hundredth
    563.89

10. tenth
    563.9

11. one
    564

12. thousandth
    563.891

Add or subtract.

13. 2.9
    +5.78
    8.68

14. 8.846
    5.92
    +1.396
    16.162

15. 450.3
    −318.4
    131.9

16. 34
    −15.75
    18.25

Multiply or divide.

17. 9.84
    ×62
    610.08

18. 12.8
    ×10.3
    131.84

19. $5\overline{)3.965}$ 0.793

20. $1.25\overline{)43.285}$ 34.628

Solve.

21. What was Garcia's best time? 12.9 s

22. What is the difference between Northrup's best and worst times?   0.6 s

23. Find Jackson's average time. 13.4 s

24. Find the average time for the third dash. Give answer to the nearest 0.01 of a second.   13.35 s

Results of 50-Meter Dash			
Name	Time in Seconds of 3 Dashes		
	1st	2nd	3rd
Davis	12.5	13.0	12.8
Garcia	13.4	12.9	13.3
Howard	14.3	13.6	13.4
Jackson	13.5	13.6	13.1
Northrup	14.3	13.9	13.7
Trotter	13.6	14.2	13.8

Continued on the next page

Complete.

25. The greatest common factor of 18 and 24 is ___?___.   6

26. The prime factorization of 60 is ___?___.   2 x 2 x 3 x 5

27. The least common multiple of 6 and 9 is ___?___.   18

Solve each equation.

28. $n - 8 = 9$ n = 17

29. $n + 18 = 39$ n = 21

30. $25 + n = 25$
    n = 0

Complete.

31. 40 mm = ___?___ cm   4

32. 900 cm = ___?___ m   9

33. 3.6 km = ___?___ m   3600

34. 570 mm = ___?___ m   0.57

Give the perimeter (circumference).
Use 3.14 as an approximation for π.

35.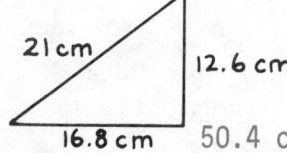
21 cm   12.6 cm   16.8 cm   50.4 cm

36.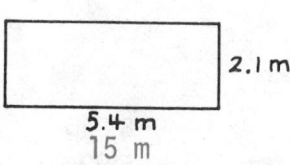
2.1 m   5.4 m   15 m

37.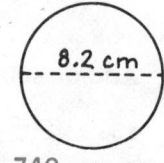
8.2 cm
25.748 cm or
25.7 cm

Give the area.
Use 3.14 as an approximation for π.

38.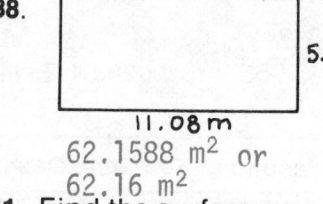
5.61 m   11.08 m
62.1588 m² or
62.16 m²

39.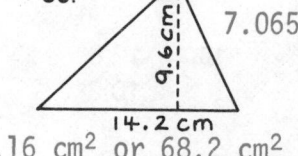
9.6 cm   14.2 cm
68.16 cm² or 68.2 cm²

40.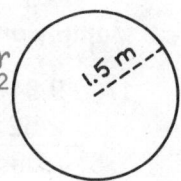
1.5 m
7.065 m² or
7.1 m²

41. Find the surface area.
103 cm²

42. Find the volume.
59.4 cm³

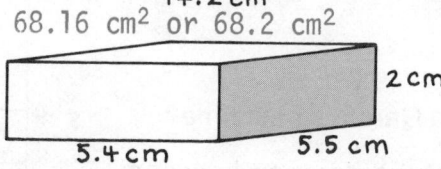
5.4 cm   5.5 cm   2 cm

Give each sum or difference in lowest terms.

43. $\frac{2}{5} + \frac{1}{5}$ $\frac{3}{5}$

44. $\frac{3}{4} + \frac{2}{3}$ $\frac{17}{12}$

45. $\frac{5}{8} - \frac{3}{8}$ $\frac{1}{4}$

46. $\frac{3}{2} - \frac{2}{3}$ $\frac{5}{6}$

47. $5\frac{1}{3}$
    $+ 2\frac{1}{2}$
    $7\frac{5}{6}$

48. $6\frac{3}{4}$
    $+ 4\frac{5}{8}$
    $11\frac{3}{8}$

49. $7\frac{1}{3}$
    $- 2\frac{3}{8}$
    $4\frac{23}{24}$

50. 9
    $- 4\frac{3}{5}$
    $4\frac{2}{5}$

Chapter 7
Fractions—Multiplication and Division

Pages 203–238

Learning Objectives

After completing this chapter, all students should be able to do the following:

7-1 Multiply any two fractions.

7-2 Divide any two fractions.

7-3 Change fractions to terminating decimals and vice versa.

7-4 Change fractions to repeating decimals and vice versa.

7-5 Multiply mixed numbers.

7-6 Divide mixed numbers.

7-7 Solve word problems that involve multiplication and division of mixed numbers.

Multiplication and division of fractions are explained in terms of concrete models. Then relationships between fractions and decimals are developed. Finally multiplication and division of mixed numbers are developed. Problem-solving practice is provided.

Mathematics

Multiplication. In the following discussion we use area units and length units. The area unit is always a unit square, and the length unit is the length of a side of that unit square.

unit square   length unit

If we wish to represent the product of a pair of numbers pictorially, we can use the area of a rectangular region. For example, if we wish to represent the product of 2 and 3, we can draw a rectangular region that is 2 units long and 3 units wide. The product is the number of unit squares in the area. This can be found by counting.

$$2 \times 3 = 6$$

We can follow a similar procedure with fractional numbers. For example, suppose that we wish to picture the product of $\frac{4}{5}$ and $\frac{2}{3}$. We could draw a rectangle that is $\frac{4}{5}$ unit long and $\frac{2}{3}$ unit wide.

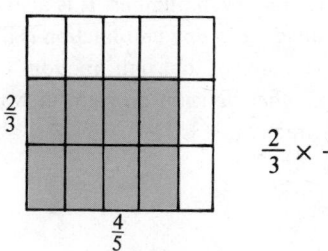

$$\frac{2}{3} \times \frac{4}{5}$$

To find the answer to the problem, we must find the area of the rectangle. This amounts to finding what fraction of the unit square is shaded. To do that, we count the number of shaded parts (8) and the total number of parts (15). The area of the shaded region is $\frac{8}{15}$ of a unit. This means that

$$\frac{2}{3} \times \frac{4}{5} = \frac{8}{15}$$

Notice that instead of counting the parts, we could have done two multiplications. To find the number of shaded parts, we could have multiplied 2 by 4 because there are 2 rows with 4 parts in each row. To find the total number of parts, we could have multiplied 3 by 5 because there are 3 rows with 5 parts in each row. That is, we could have multiplied the numerators to find the numerator of the product, and we could have multiplied the denominators to find the denominator of the product. Obviously, this will always be the case. This gives the usual multiplication algorithm—to multiply with fractions, multiply numerators and multiply denominators.

Division. Now consider this division problem:

$$6 \div 2 = ?$$

We can solve this problem by using physical objects. We can get 6 objects and divide them into groups of 2 objects each. The number of such groups is the answer to the problem.

$$6 \div 2 = 3$$

We can solve this division problem in a similar way.

$$6 \div \frac{1}{3} = ?$$

We can get 6 objects and divide them into groups of $\frac{1}{3}$ of an object each. The number of groups is the answer.

 $6 \div \frac{1}{3} = 18$

Notice that the quotient, 18, is 3 times the dividend. It is easy to see that whenever a given number is divided by $\frac{1}{3}$ the quotient is 3 times the given number. It is also easy to see that, in general, dividing by any unit fraction is like multiplying by the denominator of that unit fraction.

Now consider another division problem in which the divisor is not a unit fraction:

$$6 \div \frac{2}{3} = ?$$

Obviously, we can do this problem using physical objects, too. We can get 6 objects and divide them into groups of $\frac{2}{3}$ of an object. An easy way of doing that is to first divide

them into groups of $\frac{1}{3}$ objects, and then divide those into groups of 2 of the $\frac{1}{3}$ objects—that is, into groups of $\frac{2}{3}$ of an object each. The number of such groups is the answer to the division problem.

$6 \div \frac{2}{3} = 9$

Notice that the problem was done in two steps: first divide by $\frac{1}{3}$ and then divide that answer by 2:

$$6 \div \frac{2}{3} = (6 \div \frac{1}{3}) \div 2$$

Finally, notice that dividing by $\frac{1}{3}$ is like multiplying by 3, and dividing by 2 is like multiplying by $\frac{1}{2}$.

$$6 \div \frac{2}{3} = (6 \div \frac{1}{3}) \div 2 = (6 \times 3) \times \frac{1}{2} = 6 \times \frac{3}{2}$$

This is the usual division algorithm.

Decimals and fractions. Every number that can be named by a common fraction can also be named by either a terminating decimal (e.g., 0.25) or a repeating decimal (e.g., 0.33333 . . .). Changing a fraction to a decimal is a simple matter of dividing the numerator by the denominator. Changing a terminating decimal to a fraction is equally simple. Changing a repeating decimal to a fraction is somewhat more difficult. Here is an example of a technique that can be used. We change $0.\overline{37}$ to a fraction.

Let $n = 0.\overline{37}$

Then $100\,n = 37.\overline{37}$

(If the number of digits in the repetand (repeating part) had 1 digit, we would have multiplied by 10; for 3 digits—multiply by 1000; etc. This means that when we subtract, the repeating portion of the number drops out.)

Now we subtract the top equation from the bottom equation.

$$99\,n = 37$$
$$n = \frac{37}{99}$$

This technique is straightforward, but it leads students to what they consider to be a contradiction. They will, for example, find that $0.2\overline{9} = \frac{3}{10} = 0.3$. This equation is true, but students have difficulty accepting it.

Teaching the Chapter

It is important to use the text materials and the suggestions in the teacher's edition to help students develop an understanding of fractions. Students should come to rely on the algorithms, but they should realize that the algorithms express natural ways of carrying out operations.

If slower students have much difficulty in this chapter, you may wish not to demand mastery. Multiplication and division of fractions may be less valuable than most other topics.

Vocabulary

canceling
complex fraction
reciprocal
repeating decimal

Materials

spinner
recipes
hand calculators

Chapter Tests

For a discussion of how to use the chapter tests, please see page 17c.

Answers for Chapter 7 Pretest

1. $\frac{3}{10}$ 2. $\frac{1}{2}$ 3. $\frac{5}{16}$ 4. 1 5. $\frac{6}{35}$ 6. $\frac{15}{8}$ 7. 2 8. $\frac{5}{2}$ 9. 1
10. $\frac{21}{10}$ 11. 0.75 12. 0.625 13. 0.4 14. $\frac{3}{5}$ 15. $\frac{1}{4}$ 16. $\frac{3}{8}$
17. $0.\overline{6}$ 18. $\frac{1}{9}$ 19. $0.\overline{36}$ 20. $11\frac{1}{5}$ 21. $19\frac{1}{2}$ 22. $1\frac{3}{4}$
23. 15 24. $1\frac{5}{8}$ 25. $1\frac{1}{3}$ 26. 8 27. 3

Chapter 7 Pretest

Name _____

Date _____

Number right

| 0 | 1 | 2 | 3 | 4 | 5 |

Multiply. [Obj. 7-1, pages 204–209, 214, 216]

1. $\frac{2}{5} \times \frac{3}{4} =$ _____

2. $\frac{2}{3} \times \frac{3}{4} =$ _____

3. $\frac{3}{8} \times \frac{5}{6} =$ _____

4. $\frac{2}{3} \times \frac{3}{2} =$ _____

5. $\frac{3}{5} \times \frac{2}{7} =$ _____

| 0 | 1 | 2 | 3 | 4 | 5 |

Divide. [Obj. 7-2, pages 210–214, 217, 220–221]

6. $\frac{3}{4} \div \frac{2}{5} =$ _____

7. $\frac{4}{3} \div \frac{2}{3} =$ _____

8. $\frac{5}{6} \div \frac{1}{3} =$ _____

9. $\frac{3}{4} \div \frac{3}{4} =$ _____

10. $\frac{3}{5} \div \frac{2}{7} =$ _____

Complete this table. [Obj. 7-3, pages 222–223]

| 0 | 1 | 2 | 3 | 4 | 5 | 6 |

Fraction	$\frac{3}{4}$	$\frac{5}{8}$	$\frac{2}{5}$	**14.**	**15.**	**16.**
Decimal	**11.**	**12.**	**13.**	0.6	0.25	0.375

Complete this table. [Obj. 7-4, pages 224–225]

| 0 | 1 | 2 | 3 |

Fraction	$\frac{2}{3}$	**18.**	$\frac{4}{11}$
Repeating Decimal	**17.**	$0.\overline{1}$	**19.**

Multiply. [Obj. 7-5, pages 226–227]

| 0 | 1 | 2 | 3 |

20. $4\frac{1}{5} \times 2\frac{2}{3} =$ _____

21. $6 \times 3\frac{1}{4} =$ _____

22. $2\frac{1}{3} \times \frac{3}{4} =$ _____

Divide. [Obj. 7-6, pages 228–229]

| 0 | 1 | 2 | 3 |

23. $3 \div \frac{1}{5} =$ _____

24. $3\frac{1}{4} \div 2 =$ _____

25. $3\frac{2}{3} \div 2\frac{3}{4} =$ _____

| 0 | 1 | 2 |

Solve. [Obj. 7-7, pages 218–219, 231–233]

26. Two thirds of the students in a class of 24 students are girls. How many students in

    the class are boys? _____

27. How many ribbons $2\frac{1}{3}$ feet long can be cut from a piece of ribbon that is 7 feet

    long? _____

Chapter 7
Record and Assignment Chart

Name _____

Pretest Date _____   Posttest Date _____

Objectives

		Pretest Score Mark number correct	Posttest Score Mark number correct
7-1	Multiply any two fractions.	0 1 2 3 | 4 5	0 1 2 3 | 4 5
7-2	Divide any two fractions.	0 1 2 3 | 4 5	0 1 2 3 | 4 5
7-3	Change fractions to terminating decimals and vice versa.	0-1 2 3 4 | 5 6	0-1 2 3 4 | 5 6
7-4	Change fractions to repeating decimals and vice versa.	0 1 | 2 3	0 1 | 2 3
7-5	Multiply mixed numbers.	0 1 | 2 3	0 1 | 2 3
7-6	Divide mixed numbers.	0 1 | 2 3	0 1 | 2 3
7-7	Solve word problems that involve multiplication and division of mixed numbers.	0 1 | 2	0 1 | 2

Unsatisfactory Score | Satisfactory Score   Unsatisfactory Score | Satisfactory Score

TEACHING ASSIGNMENTS*

	Student Page	Basic Assignment	Average Assignment	Enriched Assignment	Problem Solving	RETEACHING ASSIGNMENTS†
7-1	204, 205	1–40	1–49, EW 55	1–8, 20–51, EW 55		page 389 Set 62, BW 55
	206, 207	1–28	1–28, EW 56	1–28, EW 56	29–34, 35, 36	page 389 Set 63, BW 56
7-1	208, 209	1–34	1–37, EW 57	1–39, EW 57		BW 57
	210, 211	1–51	1–53, EW 57	1–55, EW 57		page 389 Set 64, BW 57
7-2	212, 213	1–36	1–36, EW 58	1–36, EW 58	37, 38, 39, 40	page 389 Set 65, BW 58
7-1 7-2	214	1–48	1–48, EW 58	1–51, EW 58		BW 58
	215	1–4	1–4	1–4		BW 58
7-1 7-2	216, 217	1–34	1–34, EW 59	1–34, 38, EW 59	35, 36, 37	BW 59
7-2	218, 219	1–25	1–25, EW 60	1–25, EW 60	26, 27, 28, 29, 30, 31	BW 60
7-2	220, 221	1–30	1–30, EW 61	1–30, EW 61	31, 32, 33, 34	page 390 Set 66, BW 61
7-3	222, 223	1–39	1–45, EW 62	1–51, EW 62		page 390 Set 67, BW 62
7-4	224, 225	1–58	1–64, EW 62	1–68, EW 62		page 390 Set 68, BW 62
7-5	226, 227	1–24	1–24, EW 63	1–24, EW 63	25, 26, 27, 28	page 391 Set 69, BW 63
7-6	228, 229	1–24	1–24, EW 64	1–24, 27, EW 64	25, 26	page 391 Set 70, BW 64
7-1 7-2	230	Skill Game				
	231	1–4	1–6, EW 65	1–6, EW 65		BW 65
7-7	232, 233	1–11	1–11, EW 65	1–11, EW 65		BW 65
7-7	410-417	Extra Problem Solving, Sets 7-10				
	234	Chapter Checkup				
	235	Project				
	236	Chapter Review				
	237	Chapter Challenge				
	238	Major Checkup				

*Check assignments for objectives with unsatisfactory pretest scores.

†Check assignments for objectives with unsatisfactory posttest scores.

BW = Basic Worksheet

EW = Enrichment Worksheet

7 Fractions—Multiplication and Division

Suggested Lesson Plan

Introduction Without explanation, have students write the answers for the questions in the Ready or Not? Give them about five minutes to finish and then read the answers while students correct their papers. Quickly survey the results to see whether they understand the concept of a fraction representing part of the area of a rectangle.

Remind students how they can find the area of a rectangular region by multiplying length by width. Draw this picture and explain that the small squares are the area units.

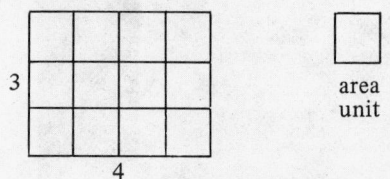

The area is 3 × 4 units, that is, 12 units. Next draw this picture. The whole square is the area unit.

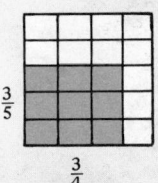

Ask students to find the length of the shaded region. ($3/5$) What is the width of the shaded region? ($3/4$) Remind students that the area is the length times the width, $3/5 \times 3/4$. Ask students to find the area of the shaded region by using the picture. They should be able to tell you that there are 20 parts in all and 9 of them are shaded, so the unit square is $9/20$ shaded. Point out that the picture shows that $3/5 \times 3/4 = 9/20$. Leave the equation on the board while you repeat the procedure with other multiplication problems. When you have several equations on the board, ask students if they see any relationships among the numbers in the equations. Most students will see that the numerator of the product is the product of the numerators of the factors and that the denominator of the product is the product of the denominators of the factors. Point out that the pictures you have been drawing show that we can multiply numerators and denominators. The shaded region is rectangular, and the numerators of the

fractions tell how many shaded parts are in a row and how many rows there are. The denominators tell how many small regions are in a row of the whole square and how many rows there are. Therefore the product of the numerators tells how many shaded parts there are, and the product of the denominators tells how many parts there are in all.

Using the pages Use the exposition on page 204 to reinforce your introduction. Assign the exercises. If students have trouble, be sure that they draw pictures similar to those in the exposition and those you drew on the board.

This is a unit square.

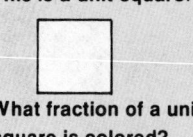

What fraction of a unit square is colored?

1. $\frac{2}{6}$

2. $\frac{6}{9}$

3. $\frac{6}{12}$

4. $\frac{6}{6}$

5. $\frac{7}{8}$

6. $\frac{8}{9}$

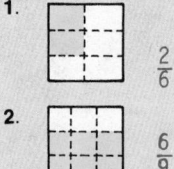
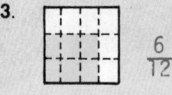
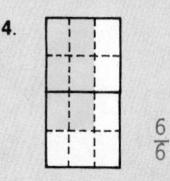
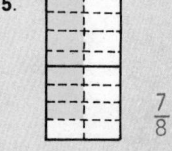
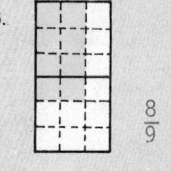

204

Multiplying fractions

We can multiply to find what part of the square is green.

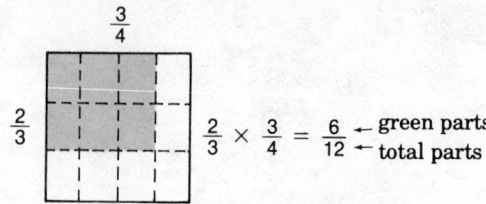

$\frac{2}{3} \times \frac{3}{4} = \frac{6}{12}$ ← green parts ← total parts

To multiply two fractions, multiply the numerators to get the numerator of the product, and multiply the denominators to get the denominator of the product.

EXERCISES

Multiply.

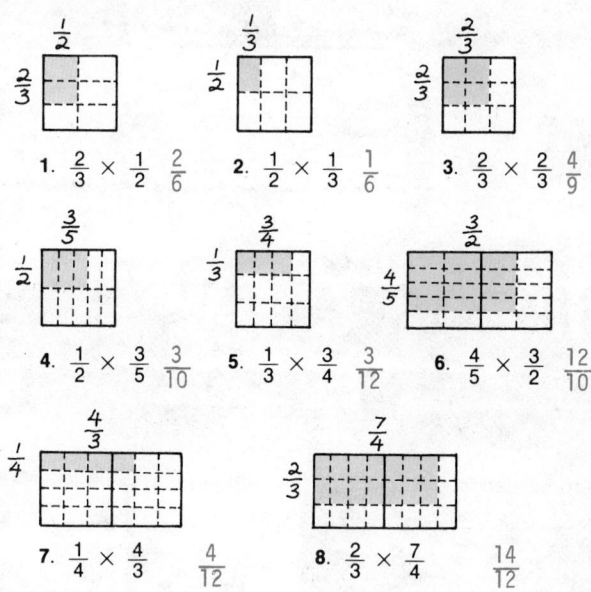

1. $\frac{2}{3} \times \frac{1}{2}$ $\frac{2}{6}$
2. $\frac{1}{2} \times \frac{1}{3}$ $\frac{1}{6}$
3. $\frac{2}{3} \times \frac{2}{3}$ $\frac{4}{9}$

4. $\frac{1}{2} \times \frac{3}{5}$ $\frac{3}{10}$
5. $\frac{1}{3} \times \frac{3}{4}$ $\frac{3}{12}$
6. $\frac{4}{5} \times \frac{3}{2}$ $\frac{12}{10}$

7. $\frac{1}{4} \times \frac{4}{3}$ $\frac{4}{12}$
8. $\frac{2}{3} \times \frac{7}{4}$ $\frac{14}{12}$

Assignments

BASIC
page 204 exercises 1–8
page 205 exercises 9–40
Basic Worksheet 55

AVERAGE
page 204 exercises 1–8
page 205 exercises 9–49
Enrichment Worksheet 55

ENRICHED
page 204 exercises 1–8
page 205 exercises 20–51
Enrichment Worksheet 55

EXTRA PRACTICE
page 389 set 62

Multiply. Reduce answers to lowest terms.

9. $\frac{1}{4} \times \frac{1}{5}$ $\frac{1}{20}$ 10. $\frac{7}{8} \times \frac{2}{3}$ $\frac{7}{12}$ 11. $\frac{1}{8} \times \frac{1}{7}$ $\frac{1}{56}$ 12. $\frac{3}{1} \times \frac{2}{3}$ 2

13. $\frac{3}{8} \times \frac{2}{3}$ $\frac{1}{4}$ 14. $\frac{8}{5} \times \frac{3}{4}$ $\frac{6}{5}$ 15. $\frac{3}{5} \times \frac{5}{3}$ 1   16. $\frac{0}{3} \times \frac{4}{5}$ 0

17. $\frac{3}{7} \times \frac{2}{3}$ $\frac{2}{7}$ 18. $4 \times \frac{5}{6}$ $\frac{10}{3}$ 19. $\frac{1}{2} \times \frac{3}{8}$ $\frac{3}{16}$ 20. $\frac{2}{3} \times \frac{3}{10}$ $\frac{1}{5}$

21. $\frac{7}{8} \times \frac{8}{7}$ 1   22. $\frac{4}{7} \times \frac{2}{5}$ $\frac{8}{35}$ 23. $\frac{3}{4} \times 5$ $\frac{15}{4}$ 24. $\frac{3}{2} \times \frac{5}{2}$ $\frac{15}{4}$

25. $\frac{3}{4} \times \frac{4}{3}$ 1   26. $\frac{3}{4} \times \frac{8}{7}$ $\frac{6}{7}$ 27. $\frac{5}{7} \times \frac{4}{6}$ $\frac{10}{21}$ 28. $\frac{3}{5} \times \frac{2}{2}$ $\frac{3}{5}$

29. $\frac{3}{5} \times \frac{1}{4}$ $\frac{3}{20}$ 30. $\frac{5}{2} \times \frac{2}{3}$ $\frac{5}{3}$ 31. $\frac{5}{9} \times \frac{3}{1}$ $\frac{5}{3}$ 32. $\frac{5}{9} \times \frac{3}{2}$ $\frac{5}{6}$

33. $\frac{3}{10} \times \frac{5}{6}$ $\frac{1}{4}$ 34. $\frac{4}{5} \times \frac{4}{5}$ $\frac{16}{25}$ 35. $5 \times \frac{2}{3}$ $\frac{10}{3}$ 36. $\frac{7}{8} \times 2$ $\frac{7}{4}$

37. $\frac{7}{4} \times 4$ 7   38. $\frac{2}{3} \times \frac{0}{3}$ 0   39. $\frac{0}{8} \times 5$ 0   40. $4 \times \frac{5}{4}$ 5

41. $3 \times \frac{4}{5}$ $\frac{12}{5}$ 42. $\frac{4}{5} \times \frac{3}{8}$ $\frac{3}{10}$ 43. $\frac{3}{8} \times \frac{5}{6}$ $\frac{5}{16}$ 44. $\frac{0}{5} \times \frac{1}{2}$ 0

45. $\frac{2}{3} \times \frac{3}{2}$ 1   46. $\frac{5}{12} \times \frac{3}{5}$ $\frac{1}{4}$ 47. $\frac{7}{5} \times \frac{5}{3}$ $\frac{7}{3}$ 48. $\frac{7}{10} \times 2$ $\frac{7}{5}$ $\frac{7}{25}$

Multiply across and multiply down. Give answers in lowest terms.

49. 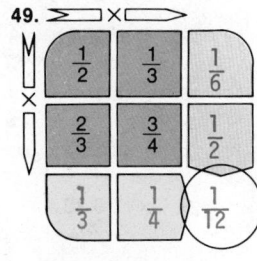   50. 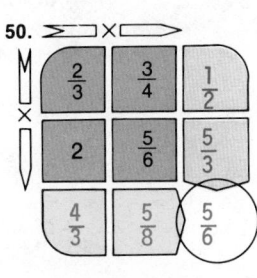   51.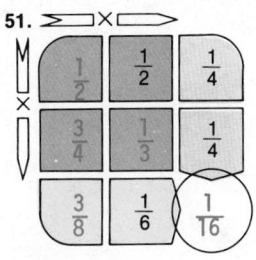

205

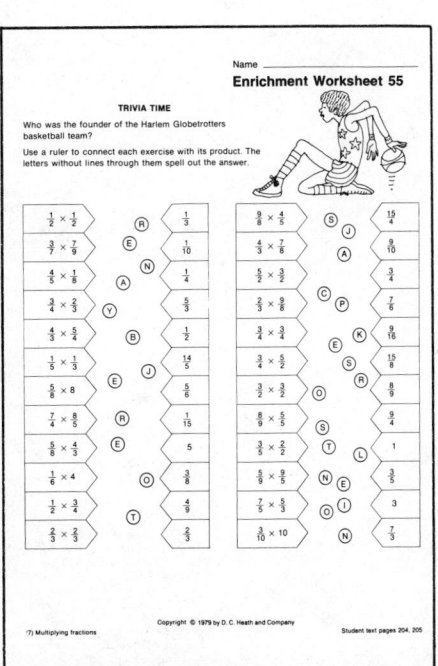

(7) Multiplying fractions   Copyright © 1979 by D. C. Heath and Company   Student text pages 204, 205

Reinforcement The following game may be used to provide further practice multiplying fractions. Write the digits 0 through 9 on cards. Ask students to copy this table:

As you pick the cards, have students write the digits in the boxes. After all the boxes have been filled in, have students multiply and reduce their answers to lowest terms. The player getting the greatest product wins the game. Later, they may wish to change the rules so that the least product wins.

Enrichment More able students may wish to play a game like the one above, except that the player with the product closest to 1 wins the game.

EXCURSION
Make a small dot any place on a piece of unlined paper.

Now on another piece of unlined paper make a dot in the *same* place. You may use a ruler, protractor, or compass. You cannot place one paper on top of the other except to check your work.

How many different ways can you find to do this?

To multiply a fraction and a whole number.
To solve word problems involving fractions and whole numbers.

Suggested Lesson Plan

Introduction   Quickly review the work of the previous lesson by writing several problems such as $\frac{3}{4} \times \frac{2}{3}$, $\frac{5}{6} \times \frac{1}{8}$, etc., on the board and having students find the products. After your students finish, read the answers and survey the class to see how they did. Summarize the work by generalizing that to multiply two fractions, they write the product of the numerators over the product of the denominators and then reduce if possible. Now present this problem on the board:

$$\frac{3}{4} \times 20 = ?$$

Elicit from pupils that they should regard 20 as $\frac{20}{1}$. Then the problem simply becomes finding the product of two fractions, $\frac{3}{4} \times \frac{20}{1}$. Present several similar examples until pupils are comfortable finding the products.

Using the pages   Use the exposition on page 206 to present two alternative ways to find the product of a fraction and a whole number.

First, point out that the word "of" can be thought of as meaning multiplication as used in this context. $\frac{3}{4}$ of 24 means $\frac{3}{4} \times 24$. Quickly review the method presented in the introduction: 24 means $\frac{24}{1}$, therefore $\frac{3}{4}$ of 24 is $\frac{3}{4} \times \frac{24}{1}$. Next use the exposition to develop a shortcut. Since $\frac{3}{4}$ of 24 is 3 times $\frac{1}{4}$ of 24, and $\frac{1}{4}$ of 24 is $24 \div 4$, $\frac{3}{4}$ of 24 can be found by finding $24 \div 4$ and then multiplying by 3.

Put several more examples on the board and have students find the products. Read the answers and if no one is having difficulty, assign exercises 1−36 for written work. Keep an eye on your poor readers and be ready to group them together if they have difficulty with exercises 29−36.

Fraction of a number

The Denim Den is having a sale on blue jeans. One style of jeans is regularly $24. To find the sale price, we take $\frac{3}{4}$ of $24.

$$\frac{3}{4} \text{ of } \$24 = \$18$$

To find $\frac{3}{4}$ of 24, I first divide 24 by 4 to find $\frac{1}{4}$ of 24. Then I multiply that by 3, getting 18.

SALE all jeans $\frac{3}{4}$ of Marked price

Finding a fraction of a number can be thought of as a multiplication problem.

$$\frac{3}{4} \text{ of } 24 = \frac{3}{4} \times 24$$
$$= \frac{72}{4}$$
$$= 18$$

EXERCISES
Compute.

1. $\frac{1}{2}$ of 18   9
2. $\frac{1}{3}$ of 21   7
3. $\frac{1}{5}$ of 60   12
4. $\frac{1}{4}$ of 20   5

5. $\frac{1}{8}$ of 32   4
6. $\frac{1}{6}$ of 54   9
7. $\frac{1}{3}$ of 18.3   6.1
8. $\frac{2}{3}$ of 3.18   2.12

9. $\frac{4}{9}$ of 38.7   17.2
10. $\frac{1}{4}$ of 264   66
11. $\frac{2}{4}$ of 264   132
12. $\frac{3}{4}$ of 264   198

13. $\frac{5}{8}$ of 24   15
14. $\frac{3}{8}$ of 16   6
15. $\frac{5}{4}$ of 100   125
16. $\frac{3}{2}$ of 140   210

17. $\frac{5}{6}$ of 30   25
18. $\frac{7}{8}$ of 56   49
19. $\frac{2}{3}$ of 36   24
20. $\frac{3}{2}$ of 36   54

21. $\frac{6}{5}$ of 40   48
22. $\frac{3}{10}$ of 54.6   16.38
23. $\frac{4}{5}$ of 3.75   3
24. $\frac{2}{2}$ of 9.38   9.38

206

Assignments

BASIC
page 206   exercises 1−24
page 207   exercises 25−30
Basic Worksheet 56

AVERAGE
page 206   exercises 1−24
page 207   exercises 25−32
Enrichment Worksheet 56

ENRICHED
page 206   exercises 1−24
page 207   exercises 25−36
Enrichment Worksheet 56

EXTRA PRACTICE
page 389   set 63

EXTRA PROBLEM SOLVING
pages 410−411   set 7

Here are some price tags from the Denim Den. Compute the sale prices. *Remember:* The sale price is $\frac{3}{4}$ of the regular price. Round each price to the nearest cent.

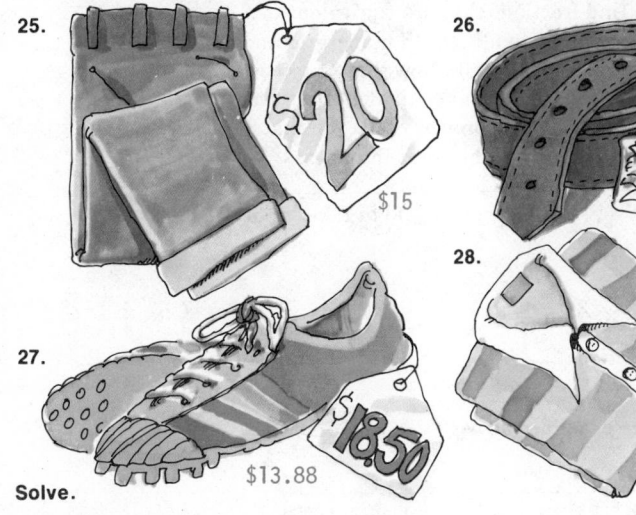

25. $15

26. $13.50

28. $12.56

27. $13.88

Solve.

29. Sarah wants to buy a new bicycle that cost $96.99. Her father will pay $\frac{1}{3}$ of the price. How much money will Sarah need for her share? $64.66

30. Joe can throw a football $\frac{2}{5}$ of the length of a football field (100 yards). How many yards can he throw a football? 40

31. A club wants to sell 120 tickets for a chili supper. They have sold $\frac{5}{6}$ of their tickets. How many tickets do they have left to sell? 20

32. To get to school, Alex ran $\frac{3}{8}$ of a mile. How many yards is that? 660

33. There are 464 students in a school. Five-eighths of them are girls. How many boys are in the school? 174

34. Mr. Adams earns $1120 per month. How much money would he save in a year if he saved $\frac{1}{8}$ of his earnings? $1680

35. A furlong, $\frac{1}{8}$ of a mile, is used for horse racing. How many yards long is a 7-furlong race? 1540

★ 36. Carol earns $1.75 per hour. She saves $\frac{5}{7}$ of that. How many hours must she work to save $25? 20

207

Follow-up Activities

Reinforcement Give students the problem, "How much would you pay for a coat that is on sale for $^3/_4$ of the regular price of $18.50?" Have pupils ask this question of several adults (not other teachers) and report back on the method used by adults and the answers. $13.88

Enrichment Give students number squares and have them develop problems as shown below. Put the better ones on duplicating masters and use them for extra practice.

Sample:

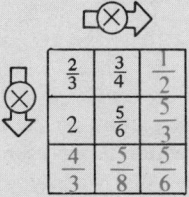

EXCURSION
Study the number pairs to discover the rule. Then use the rule to find what goes in the circles.

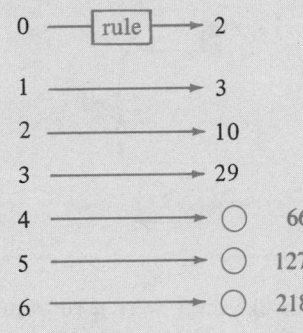

0 —— rule —— 2

1 ——————→ 3

2 ——————→ 10

3 ——————→ 29

4 ——————→ ○ 66

5 ——————→ ○ 127

6 ——————→ ○ 218

$n^3 + 2$

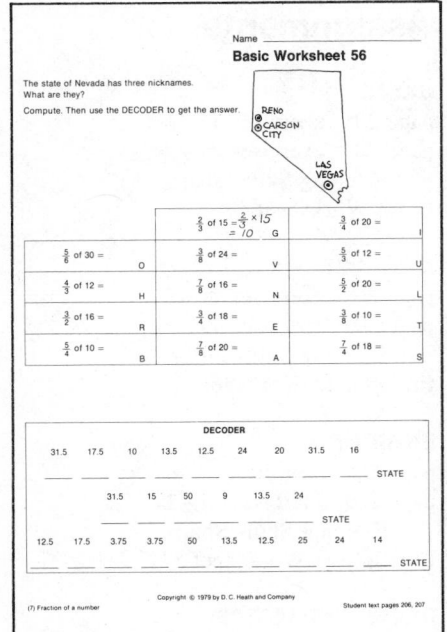

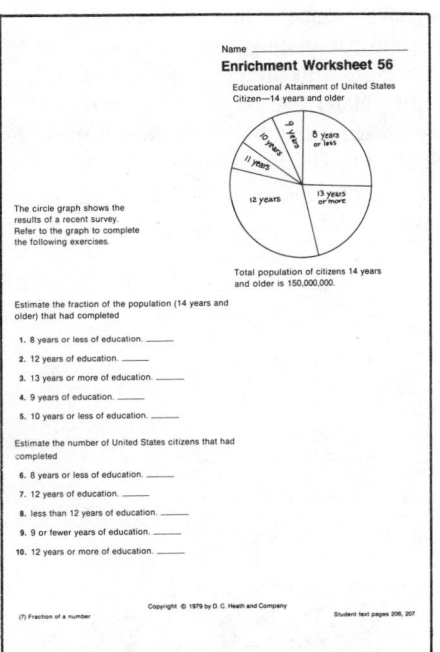

STUDENT OBJECTIVE
To use the multiplication algorithm to
find equivalent fractions.

Suggested Lesson Plan

Introduction On the chalkboard copy
the picture on the left and ask students
to give the fraction represented. (²/₃)
Then draw the horizontal line as

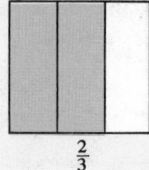 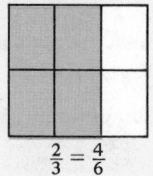

$$\frac{2}{3} \qquad \frac{2}{3} = \frac{4}{6}$$

shown in the picture on the right and
ask what fraction is represented now.
(⁴/₆) Point out that when you drew the
horizontal line, you doubled the total
number of parts and the number of
shaded parts. That is like multiplying
both numerator and denominator of the
first fraction by 2.

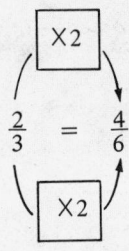

$$\frac{2}{3} = \frac{4}{6}$$

Pictures like these were used to justify
generating equivalent fractions by
multiplying the numerator and
denominator by the same number. Now
point out that multiplying both the
numerator and denominator by 2 is like
multiplying by ²/₂. But ²/₂ is just 1, and
multiplying by 1 does not change the
number. This is the multiplying by 1
property. This shows that both the
pictures and the multiplication algorithm
give us the same way of finding fractions
that are equivalent to a given fraction.

More about equivalent fractions

Earlier, you learned to find fractions that are equivalent to a
given fraction by multiplying or dividing both numerator and
denominator by the same number (not 0). Now that you know
how to multiply fractions, you can look at equivalent fractions
in another way. The multiplying by 1 property tells you that if
you multiply a number by 1, you get that same number.

You also know that $\frac{2}{2}$, $\frac{3}{3}$, $\frac{4}{4}$, etc., are all equal to 1. Let's put
these ideas together.

$$\frac{3}{4} = \frac{3}{4} \times 1 = \frac{3}{4} \times \frac{2}{2} = \frac{6}{8} \qquad \underbrace{\qquad}_{\text{equivalent fractions}} \qquad\qquad \frac{7}{3} = \frac{7}{3} \times 1 = \frac{7}{3} \times \frac{4}{4} = \frac{28}{12} \qquad \underbrace{\qquad}_{\text{equivalent fractions}}$$

Explain each step in the examples above.

Equivalent fractions →

X	$\frac{2}{2}$	$\frac{3}{3}$	$\frac{4}{4}$	$\frac{5}{5}$	$\frac{6}{6}$	$\frac{7}{7}$	$\frac{8}{8}$
$\frac{1}{2}$	$\frac{2}{4}$	$\frac{3}{6}$	$\frac{4}{8}$	$\frac{5}{10}$	$\frac{6}{12}$	$\frac{7}{14}$	$\frac{8}{16}$
$\frac{1}{3}$	$\frac{2}{6}$	$\frac{3}{9}$	$\frac{4}{12}$	$\frac{5}{15}$	$\frac{6}{18}$	$\frac{7}{21}$	$\frac{8}{24}$
$\frac{2}{3}$	$\frac{4}{6}$	$\frac{6}{9}$	$\frac{8}{12}$	$\frac{10}{15}$	$\frac{12}{18}$	$\frac{14}{21}$	$\frac{16}{24}$

EXERCISES

Multiply. Give each product in lowest terms.

1. $\frac{1}{4} \times \frac{2}{2}$ $\frac{1}{4}$
2. $\frac{2}{3} \times \frac{3}{3}$ $\frac{2}{3}$
3. $\frac{1}{3} \times \frac{5}{5}$ $\frac{1}{3}$
4. $\frac{3}{2} \times \frac{4}{4}$ $\frac{3}{2}$

5. $\frac{5}{2} \times \frac{6}{6}$ $\frac{5}{2}$
6. $\frac{1}{2} \times \frac{5}{5}$ $\frac{1}{2}$
7. $\frac{4}{3} \times \frac{8}{8}$ $\frac{4}{3}$
8. $\frac{5}{4} \times \frac{2}{2}$ $\frac{5}{4}$

9. $\frac{5}{3} \times \frac{3}{4}$ $\frac{5}{4}$
10. $\frac{3}{5} \times \frac{2}{3}$ $\frac{2}{5}$
11. $\frac{1}{5} \times \frac{4}{5}$ $\frac{4}{25}$
12. $\frac{4}{5} \times \frac{2}{3}$ $\frac{8}{15}$

13. $\frac{5}{6} \times \frac{4}{4}$ $\frac{5}{6}$
14. $\frac{1}{6} \times \frac{3}{5}$ $\frac{1}{10}$
15. $\frac{7}{2} \times \frac{2}{5}$ $\frac{7}{5}$
16. $\frac{7}{5} \times \frac{1}{6}$ $\frac{7}{30}$

208

Using the pages Let students read
the exposition on page 208 by
themselves. Assign the exercises. It is
important for students to feel very
comfortable with the idea that equivalent
fractions stand for the same number.
They must realize that even though they
multiplied to get greater numerators and
denominators, the number did not
change.

Assignments

BASIC
page 208 exercises 1–16
page 209 exercises 17–34,
  Keeping Skills Sharp
Basic Worksheet 57

AVERAGE
page 208 exercises 1–16
page 209 exercises 17–37,
  Keeping Skills Sharp
Enrichment Worksheet 57

ENRICHED
page 208 exercises 1–16
page 209 exercises 17–39,
  Keeping Skills Sharp
Enrichment Worksheet 57

REVIEW PRACTICE
page 383 set 44

Give each product in lowest terms.

17. $3 \times \frac{3}{4}$ $\frac{9}{4}$ 18. $\frac{1}{2} \times \frac{1}{3}$ $\frac{1}{6}$

19. $\frac{1}{3} \times 6$ 2 20. $4 \times \frac{3}{4}$ 3

21. $\frac{3}{8} \times \frac{4}{5}$ $\frac{3}{10}$ 22. $\frac{2}{3} \times \frac{3}{5}$ $\frac{2}{5}$

23. $\frac{7}{8} \times \frac{4}{3}$ $\frac{7}{6}$ 24. $\frac{5}{9} \times \frac{2}{2}$ $\frac{5}{9}$

25. $\frac{2}{2} \times 3$ 3 26. $\frac{1}{4} \times 7$ $\frac{7}{4}$

27. $\frac{5}{8} \times \frac{5}{8}$ $\frac{25}{64}$ 28. $\frac{5}{9} \times \frac{3}{5}$ $\frac{1}{3}$

29. $\frac{5}{8} \times \frac{3}{3}$ $\frac{5}{8}$ 30. $\frac{7}{2} \times \frac{4}{3}$ $\frac{14}{3}$

31. $\frac{6}{7} \times \frac{2}{3}$ $\frac{4}{7}$ 32. $\frac{5}{8} \times \frac{12}{5}$ $\frac{3}{2}$

33. $\frac{1}{2} \times 2$ 1 34. $\frac{3}{2} \times \frac{2}{3}$ 1

Give the sale price of each item.

SALE $\frac{2}{3}$ of marked price

35. 39¢

36. Eraser 10¢   26¢

37. Glue   48¢   32¢

38. 78¢   52¢

39. 45¢   30¢

15¢

Follow-up Activities

Reinforcement You may wish to extend the table on page 208. Copy the table and extend it downward, inserting the fractions $\frac{3}{4}$, $\frac{5}{2}$, $\frac{5}{3}$, $\frac{3}{8}$, and $\frac{7}{4}$.

Enrichment Discuss with students that 1 is the multiplicative identity. That is, if you pick a nonzero number and multiply it by 1, you get a product that is identical to the number you picked. Copy the following table on the chalkboard. Explain that the table shows some facts in "Martian mutiplication." Ask them to find the multiplicative identity. ($\mathcal{Z}$)

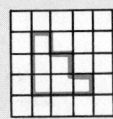

EXCURSION

This shape fences in 6 squares.

Get some graph paper and see how many other shapes you can draw that fence in 6 squares. Draw along the lines of the graph paper.

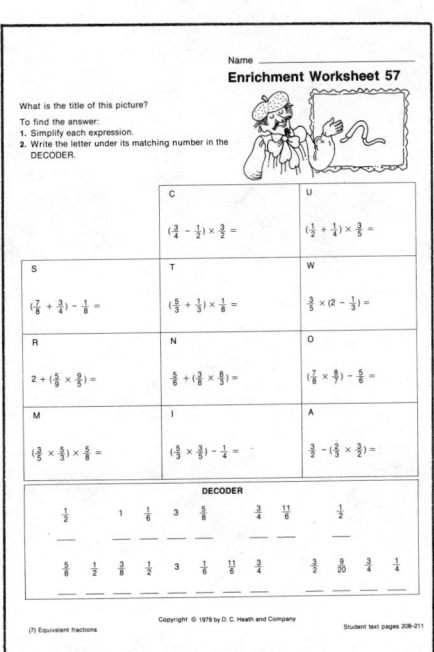

(core) Lesson 95   209

Suggested Lesson Plan

Introduction Write the number $^3/_7$ on the board and ask students to find the number that they can multiply $^3/_7$ by to get 1. If students have trouble with this idea, you can help them as follows. In order for the product to be 1, the numerator and the denominator must be the same. Also, the numerator must be a multiple of 3 and the denominator a multiple of 7. Since the numerator and denominator are the same, that number must be a common multiple of 3 and 7. Ask students to find a common multiple of 3 and 7. (21, 42, etc.) Suggest to students that they find a number that when multiplied by $^3/_7$ is $^{21}/_{21}$. The rest is easy. Repeat with other numbers.

Tell students that a pair of numbers whose product is 1 are called *reciprocals*. $^3/_7$ and $^7/_3$ are reciprocals. We also say that $^3/_7$ is the reciprocal of $^7/_3$ and vice versa. Give other examples. Be sure that students recognize that the form for writing the numbers is not important. For example, 4 and .25 are reciprocals. It is not necessary to write $^1/_4$ instead of .25.

Using the pages Let students read the exposition at the top of page 210 and do the exercises.

The exercises on page 211 are intended to begin a development of division with fractions. That development is completed in the next lesson.

Reciprocals

Two numbers are **reciprocals** if their product is 1. Since $\frac{2}{3} \times \frac{3}{2} = 1$, $\frac{2}{3}$ and $\frac{3}{2}$ are reciprocals.

For a fraction that is not 0, I find the reciprocal by "inverting" the fraction.

$\frac{3}{5} \diagdown \frac{5}{3}$

EXERCISES

Give the reciprocal of each number.

1. 3 $\frac{1}{3}$ 2. $\frac{1}{2}$ 2 3. $\frac{1}{9}$ 9 4. $\frac{5}{8}$ $\frac{8}{5}$ 5. $\frac{2}{3}$ $\frac{3}{2}$ 6. $\frac{6}{7}$ $\frac{7}{6}$ 7. $\frac{3}{5}$ $\frac{5}{3}$ 8. $\frac{2}{9}$ $\frac{9}{2}$

9. $\frac{3}{4}$ $\frac{4}{3}$ 10. $\frac{4}{3}$ $\frac{3}{4}$ 11. $\frac{11}{12}$ $\frac{12}{11}$ 12. 6 $\frac{1}{6}$ 13. $\frac{13}{2}$ $\frac{2}{13}$ 14. $\frac{15}{9}$ $\frac{9}{15}$ 15. 15 $\frac{1}{15}$ 16. 100 $\frac{1}{100}$

Who am I?

17. I do not have a reciprocal. 0 18. I am my own reciprocal. 1

Complete.

19. $\frac{2}{3} \times ? = 1$ $\frac{3}{2}$ 20. $? \times \frac{1}{2} = 1$ 2 21. $5 \times ? = 1$ $\frac{1}{5}$

22. $1 \times ? = 1$ 1 23. $\frac{3}{4} \times ? = 1$ $\frac{4}{3}$ 24. $? \times \frac{9}{5} = 1$ $\frac{5}{9}$

25. $? \times \frac{1}{3} = 1$ 3 26. $\frac{5}{8} \times ? = 1$ $\frac{8}{5}$ 27. $12 \times ? = 1$ $\frac{1}{12}$

28. $4 \times ? = 1$ $\frac{1}{4}$ 29. $16 \times ? = 1$ $\frac{1}{16}$ 30. $\frac{1}{18} \times ? = 1$ 18

31. $\frac{5}{9} \times ? = 1$ $\frac{9}{5}$ 32. $? \times \frac{7}{5} = 1$ $\frac{5}{7}$ 33. $? \times \frac{13}{4} = 1$ $\frac{4}{13}$

34. $\frac{2}{5} \times ? = 1$ $\frac{5}{2}$ 35. $? \times \frac{9}{2} = 1$ $\frac{2}{9}$ 36. $? \times \frac{7}{8} = 1$ $\frac{8}{7}$

37. $3 \times ? = 1$ $\frac{1}{3}$ 38. $? \times 10 = 1$ $\frac{1}{10}$ 39. $? \times \frac{3}{5} = 1$ $\frac{5}{3}$

40. $? \times 6 = 1$ $\frac{1}{6}$ 41. $? \times \frac{1}{6} = 1$ 6 42. $\frac{1}{8} \times ? = 1$ 8

43. $\frac{5}{6} \times ? = 1$ $\frac{6}{5}$ 44. $\frac{10}{9} \times ? = 1$ $\frac{9}{10}$ 45. $? \times \frac{10}{11} = 1$ $\frac{11}{10}$

210

Assignments

BASIC
page 210 exercises 1—45
page 211 exercises 46—51
Basic Worksheet 57

AVERAGE
page 210 exercises 1—45
page 211 exercises 46—53
Enrichment Worksheet 57

ENRICHED
page 210 exercises 1—45
page 211 exercises 46—55
Enrichment Worksheet 57

EXTRA PRACTICE
page 389 set 64

First complete. Then compare your answers in each exercise.

46.

a. How many $\frac{1}{2}$s in 3? 6

b. $3 \div \frac{1}{2} = ?$ 6

c. $3 \times 2 = ?$ 6

47.

a. How many $\frac{1}{3}$s in 2? 6

b. $2 \div \frac{1}{3} = ?$ 6

c. $2 \times 3 = ?$ 6

48.

a. How many $\frac{2}{3}$s in 2? 3

b. $2 \div \frac{2}{3} = ?$ 3

c. $2 \times \frac{3}{2} = ?$ 3

49.

a. How many $\frac{3}{4}$s in 3? 4

b. $3 \div \frac{3}{4} = ?$ 4

c. $3 \times \frac{4}{3} = ?.$ 4

50.

a. How many $\frac{2}{5}$s in $\frac{4}{5}$? 2

b. $\frac{4}{5} \div \frac{2}{5} = ?$ 2

c. $\frac{4}{5} \times \frac{5}{2} = ?$ 2

51.

a. How many $\frac{2}{3}$s in $\frac{8}{3}$? 4

b. $\frac{8}{3} \div \frac{2}{3} = ?$ 4

c. $\frac{8}{3} \times \frac{3}{2} = ?$ 4

Complete.

52. Look at exercise 48. Dividing by $\frac{2}{3}$ is the same as multiplying by ___?___. $\frac{3}{2}$

53. Look at exercise 49. Dividing by $\frac{3}{4}$ is the same as multiplying by ___?___. $\frac{4}{3}$

54. Look at exercise 50. Dividing by $\frac{2}{5}$ is the same as multiplying by the reciprocal of ___?___. $\frac{2}{5}$

55. Look at exercise 51. Dividing by $\frac{2}{3}$ is the same as multiplying by the reciprocal of ___?___. $\frac{2}{3}$

 What is the reciprocal of 0.125? Of 0.0125?
8   80

211

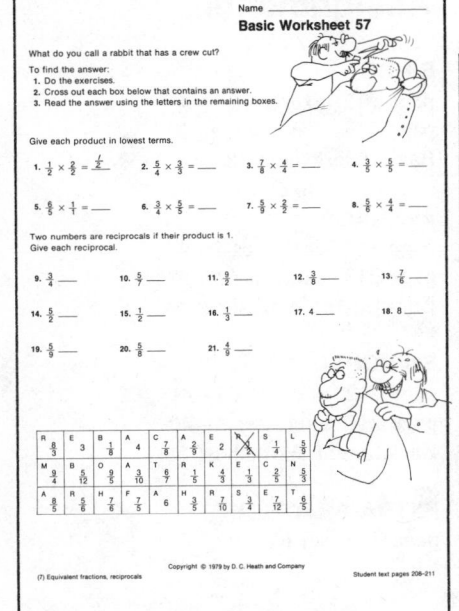

Follow-up Activities

Reinforcement   Review with students the fact that if the product of two numbers is 1, then each number is the reciprocal of the other. Have students copy and complete the following equations:

$$\frac{1}{3} \times \underline{\quad} = 1 \qquad 4 \times \underline{\quad} = 1$$

$$\frac{2}{3} \times \underline{\quad} = 1 \qquad \underline{\quad} \times \frac{3}{4} = 1$$

$$\underline{\quad} \times 6 = 1 \qquad \underline{\quad} \times \frac{3}{2} = 1$$

Have students study their completed equations to determine whether the following statements are true or false. The reciprocal of a number that is less than 1 is greater than 1. The reciprocal of a number greater than 1 is less than 1.

Enrichment   You may wish to have better students try to solve each of these puzzles:

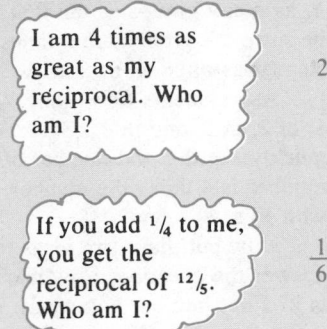

I am 4 times as great as my reciprocal. Who am I?   2

If you add ¼ to me, you get the reciprocal of ¹²/₅. Who am I? $\frac{1}{6}$

Encourage students to create similar puzzles for their classmates to solve.

EXCURSION

$$1^2 = 1$$
$$1^2 + 1^2 = 2$$
$$1^2 + 1^2 + 1^2 = 3$$
$$2^2 = 4$$
$$2^2 + 1^2 = 5$$

Continue writing numbers as the sum of not more than 4 square numbers.

$$2^2 + 1^2 + 1^2 = 6$$
$$2^2 + 1^2 + 1^2 + 1^2 = 7$$
$$2^2 + 2^2 = 8$$
$$3^2 = 9$$
$$\text{etc.}$$

Suggested Lesson Plan

Introduction Go over the exercises on page 211. Ask students to tell why there are half as many $\frac{2}{6}$'s in 1 as there are $\frac{1}{6}$'s in 1. ($\frac{2}{6}$ is twice as big as $\frac{1}{6}$.) Why are there $\frac{1}{3}$ as many $\frac{3}{6}$'s in 1 as there are $\frac{1}{6}$'s in 1? If students don't seem to have the concept that when you divide a quantity into groups that are twice as big as before there are $\frac{1}{2}$ as many groups as before, go back over the concept with whole numbers. For example, ask students how many groups there would be if they divided 24 counters into groups of 2. (12) How many groups if the groups were twice as big? (6; that is, $\frac{1}{2}$ as many groups as before.) Suppose that the 24 counters were divided into groups of 6. (4; that is, there would be $\frac{1}{3}$ as many groups as the first time because the groups are 3 times as big.) Repeat as often as necessary.

Ask students how many $\frac{1}{4}$'s are in 1, in 2, in 3, and in $\frac{3}{4}$. Students should quickly see that the number of $\frac{1}{4}$'s in a number is 4 times the number. Repeat with $\frac{1}{5}$'s, $\frac{1}{3}$'s, etc.

Now put these two ideas together to answer the question, How many $\frac{2}{3}$'s are in 2? First find out how many $\frac{1}{3}$'s are in 2. That is easy; there are 3×2, or 6, $\frac{1}{3}$'s in 2. A picture will help if necessary.

Now, how many $\frac{2}{3}$'s are in 2? Obviously, from what has been done before, there are $\frac{1}{2}$ as many $\frac{2}{3}$'s in 2 as there are $\frac{1}{3}$'s. There are $\frac{1}{2} \times 6$, or 3, $\frac{2}{3}$'s in 2. Again a picture may help. The loops show groups of $\frac{2}{3}$'s.

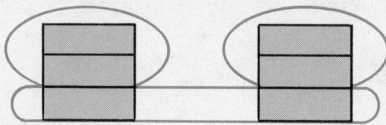

Repeat with other fractions if necessary.

Using the pages Go over the exposition on page 212 carefully. Be sure students understand that the explanation given on that page and in the introduction tells why we can find a quotient by multiplying by the reciprocal of the divisor. Assign the exercises.

Dividing by a fraction

Suppose that it takes $\frac{3}{4}$ of a pound of salt mixed with ice to freeze one container of ice cream. How many containers of ice cream can be frozen with 5 $\frac{1}{2}$-pound boxes of salt?

$$\frac{5}{2} \div \frac{3}{4} = ?$$

To solve this, you can think about cutting the boxes in half to get $\frac{1}{4}$-lb boxes and then grouping 3 of the $\frac{1}{4}$-lb boxes together.

There is enough salt to freeze $3\frac{1}{3}$, or $\frac{10}{3}$, containers of ice cream.

$$\frac{5}{2} \div \frac{3}{4} = \frac{10}{3}$$

To divide by a fraction, you can multiply by its reciprocal.

$$\frac{5}{2} \div \frac{3}{4} = \frac{5}{2} \times \frac{4}{3}$$
$$= \frac{20}{6}$$
$$= \frac{10}{3}$$

reciprocals

EXERCISES
Complete.

1. To divide by $\frac{3}{5}$, you can multiply by the reciprocal of __?__. $\frac{3}{5}$

2. Dividing by $\frac{4}{7}$ is the same as multiplying by the reciprocal of __?__. $\frac{4}{7}$

3. Dividing by $\frac{6}{5}$ is the same as multiplying by __?__. $\frac{5}{6}$

4. To divide by $\frac{5}{8}$, you can multiply by the reciprocal of __?__. $\frac{5}{8}$

212

Assignments

BASIC
page 212 exercises 1−4
page 213 exercises 5−37
Basic Worksheet 58

AVERAGE
page 212 exercises 1−4
page 213 exercises 5−39
Enrichment Worksheet 58

ENRICHED
page 212 exercises 1−4
page 213 exercises 5−40
Enrichment Worksheet 58

EXTRA PRACTICE
page 389 set 65

Divide. Give quotients in lowest terms.

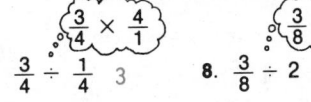

$\boxed{\frac{2}{3} \times \frac{1}{2}}$ $\boxed{\frac{3}{2} \times \frac{4}{1}}$ $\boxed{\frac{3}{4} \times \frac{4}{1}}$ $\boxed{\frac{3}{8} \times 2}$

5. $\frac{2}{3} \div 2$ $\frac{1}{3}$ 6. $\frac{3}{2} \div \frac{1}{4}$ 6   7. $\frac{3}{4} \div \frac{1}{4}$ 3   8. $\frac{3}{8} \div 2$ $\frac{3}{16}$

9. $\frac{3}{4} \div \frac{2}{3}$ $\frac{9}{8}$ 10. $\frac{5}{8} \div 3$ $\frac{5}{24}$ 11. $\frac{4}{5} \div \frac{2}{2}$ $\frac{4}{5}$ 12. $8 \div \frac{3}{5}$ $\frac{40}{3}$

13. $5 \div \frac{2}{5}$ $\frac{25}{2}$ 14. $\frac{5}{6} \div \frac{3}{8}$ $\frac{20}{9}$ 15. $\frac{3}{5} \div 4$ $\frac{3}{20}$ 16. $\frac{0}{4} \div \frac{1}{2}$ 0

17. $\frac{5}{9} \div \frac{1}{3}$ $\frac{5}{3}$ 18. $6 \div \frac{1}{2}$ 12   19. $\frac{6}{5} \div \frac{3}{3}$ $\frac{6}{5}$ 20. $\frac{7}{4} \div \frac{7}{4}$ 1

21. $\frac{3}{8} \div \frac{3}{4}$ $\frac{1}{2}$ 22. $\frac{3}{4} \div \frac{3}{8}$ 2   23. $\frac{5}{9} \div \frac{2}{3}$ $\frac{5}{6}$ 24. $\frac{2}{3} \div \frac{5}{9}$ $\frac{6}{5}$

25. $\frac{5}{6} \div \frac{2}{3}$ $\frac{5}{4}$ 26. $\frac{2}{3} \div \frac{5}{6}$ $\frac{4}{5}$ 27. $\frac{3}{8} \div \frac{3}{2}$ $\frac{1}{4}$ 28. $\frac{3}{?} \div \frac{3}{?}$ 4

29. $\frac{2}{5} \div \frac{1}{4}$ $\frac{8}{5}$ 30. $\frac{0}{5} \div \frac{5}{6}$ 0   31. $\frac{5}{9} \div \frac{4}{3}$ $\frac{5}{12}$ 32. $\frac{7}{8} \div \frac{5}{4}$ $\frac{7}{10}$

33. $\frac{5}{4} \div 3$ $\frac{5}{12}$ 34. $\frac{6}{5} \div \frac{1}{10}$ 12   35. $\frac{8}{3} \div \frac{4}{3}$ 2   36. $\frac{9}{2} \div \frac{3}{4}$ 6

Solve.
$5\frac{1}{2}$ tablespoons

37. How much vanilla is needed to make 2 gallons of ice cream?

38. The recipe calls for $2\frac{1}{2}$ ($\frac{5}{2}$) cups of sugar. How many gallons of ice cream can be made from $1\frac{1}{4}$ ($\frac{5}{4}$) cups of sugar? $\frac{1}{2}$
   Hint: $\frac{5}{4} \div \frac{5}{2}$

39. Suppose that you have $1\frac{1}{2}$ cups of heavy cream. How much more heavy cream do you need to make a full recipe? $1\frac{3}{4}$ cups

40. Suppose that you have $3\frac{1}{4}$ cups of sugar and want to make 2 gallons of ice cream. How much more sugar do you need? $1\frac{3}{4}$ cups

---

Vanilla Ice Cream
makes 1 gallon

4 eggs

$2\frac{1}{2}$ cups of sugar

$3\frac{1}{4}$ cups of heavy cream

$2\frac{3}{4}$ tablespoons of vanilla

$6\frac{1}{2}$ cups of whole milk

Beat eggs and sugar until thick. Blend in cream and vanilla. Add milk

213

Follow-up Activities

Reinforcement You may wish to follow up the lesson by having students complete a table like this:

Dividing		Multiplying	
$12 \div \frac{1}{8}$ = ☐ 96		12×8 = ☐ 96	
$12 \div \frac{1}{4}$ = ☐ 48		12×4 = ☐ 48	
$12 \div 2$ = ☐ 6		$12 \times \frac{1}{2}$ = ☐ 6	
$12 \div \frac{4}{3}$ = ☐ 9		$12 \times \frac{3}{4}$ = ☐ 9	

Enrichment Students can use division to complete the following multiplication boxes. Answers are given in red.

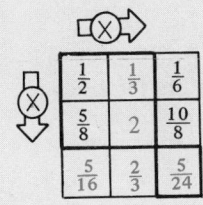
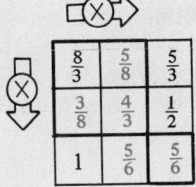

EXCURSION
Give the next number.

0, 1, 3, 7, 15, 31, ? 63

Multiply by 2, then add 1.

Fill 5-gal pail and use it to fill 3-gal pail; 2 gal remain. Fill 3-gal pail, pour into 5-gal pail, refill 3-gal pail and use it to fill 5-gal pail; 1 gal remains.

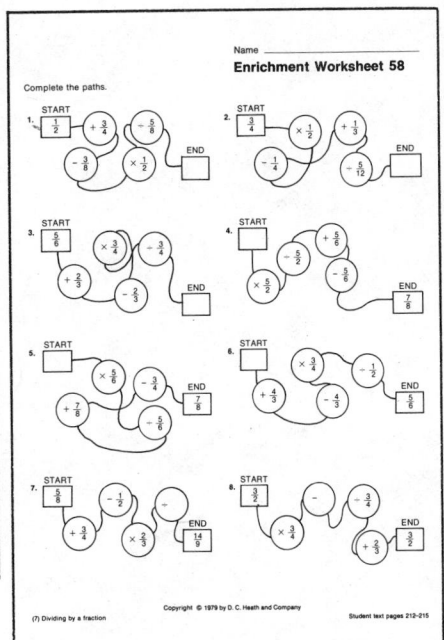

(core) Lesson 97 **213**

STUDENT OBJECTIVES
To practice the skills learned previously.
To solve word problems involving
mathematics and world geography.

Suggested Lesson Plan

Introduction Quickly review
multiplication of fractions by writing two
examples on the board and having
students find the products. Read the
answers and be prepared to assist any
student who missed these practice
exercises with the review. Do the same
with two division examples.

Introduce page 215 with a
discussion of Egypt and the wonder of
the pyramids. This page could spark
interest in further details and more
information could be obtained from
resources in the library.

Using the pages Assign exercises
1–48 on page 214 for practice. Assign
exercises 1–4 on page 215 for practice
in solving word problems.

Practice exercises

Give each product in lowest terms.

1. $\frac{2}{3} \times \frac{4}{4}$ $\frac{2}{3}$
2. $\frac{3}{10} \times \frac{2}{9}$ $\frac{1}{15}$
3. $\frac{2}{5} \times \frac{4}{7}$ $\frac{8}{35}$
4. $\frac{5}{8} \times \frac{0}{6}$ 0

5. $\frac{1}{8} \times \frac{1}{6}$ $\frac{1}{48}$
6. $\frac{1}{4} \times \frac{1}{2}$ $\frac{1}{8}$
7. $\frac{1}{2} \times \frac{5}{8}$ $\frac{5}{16}$
8. $\frac{4}{4} \times \frac{3}{8}$ $\frac{3}{8}$

9. $\frac{5}{3} \times \frac{2}{2}$ $\frac{5}{3}$
10. $\frac{5}{6} \times \frac{3}{10}$ $\frac{1}{4}$
11. $6 \times \frac{5}{12}$ $\frac{5}{2}$
12. $\frac{5}{3} \times 2$ $\frac{10}{3}$

13. $\frac{7}{9} \times \frac{3}{7}$ $\frac{1}{3}$
14. $2 \times \frac{3}{4}$ $\frac{3}{2}$
15. $\frac{1}{4} \times \frac{2}{2}$ $\frac{1}{4}$
16. $\frac{0}{3} \times \frac{5}{2}$ 0

17. $\frac{3}{8} \times 5$ $\frac{15}{8}$
18. $\frac{5}{8} \times \frac{8}{5}$ 1
19. $\frac{2}{2} \times \frac{3}{2}$ $\frac{3}{2}$
20. $\frac{7}{10} \times \frac{4}{3}$ $\frac{14}{15}$

21. $\frac{5}{6} \times \frac{0}{2}$ 0
22. $\frac{5}{12} \times \frac{3}{8}$ $\frac{5}{32}$
23. $\frac{5}{9} \times \frac{9}{5}$ 1
24. $5 \times \frac{2}{5}$ 2

Give each quotient in lowest terms.

25. $\frac{1}{2} \div \frac{1}{3}$ $\frac{3}{2}$
26. $\frac{1}{3} \div \frac{1}{2}$ $\frac{2}{3}$
27. $\frac{2}{3} \div \frac{2}{3}$ 1
28. $\frac{3}{4} \div \frac{1}{4}$ 3

29. $3 \div \frac{4}{5}$ $\frac{15}{4}$
30. $\frac{3}{4} \div \frac{2}{2}$ $\frac{3}{4}$
31. $\frac{7}{3} \div 2$ $\frac{7}{6}$
32. $\frac{1}{8} \div \frac{9}{5}$ $\frac{5}{72}$

33. $\frac{8}{5} \div \frac{5}{9}$ $\frac{72}{25}$
34. $\frac{0}{6} \div \frac{4}{3}$ 0
35. $\frac{4}{9} \div \frac{1}{3}$ $\frac{4}{3}$
36. $\frac{9}{2} \div \frac{5}{8}$ $\frac{36}{5}$

37. $\frac{8}{7} \div 4$ $\frac{2}{7}$
38. $\frac{1}{2} \div \frac{2}{3}$ $\frac{3}{4}$
39. $2 \div \frac{5}{6}$ $\frac{12}{5}$
40. $\frac{7}{2} \div 4$ $\frac{7}{8}$

41. $\frac{3}{4} \div \frac{1}{8}$ 6
42. $\frac{3}{15} \div \frac{5}{3}$ $\frac{3}{25}$
43. $\frac{5}{16} \div \frac{1}{2}$ $\frac{5}{8}$
44. $\frac{3}{2} \div \frac{3}{14}$ 7

45. $\frac{0}{3} \div \frac{5}{8}$ 0
46. $\frac{9}{5} \div \frac{3}{8}$ $\frac{24}{5}$
47. $\frac{1}{5} \div \frac{15}{4}$ $\frac{4}{75}$
48. $\frac{3}{4} \div \frac{3}{4}$ 1

Multiply across and multiply down. Give answers in lowest terms.

49.
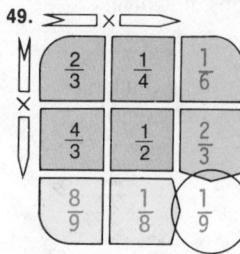

50.
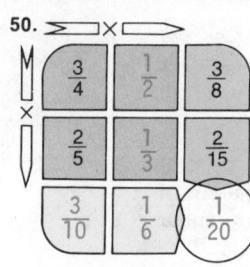

51.
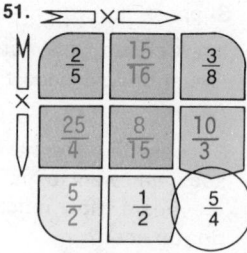

214

Assignments

BASIC
page 214 exercises 1–48
page 215 exercises 1–4
Basic Worksheet 58

AVERAGE
page 214 exercises 1–48
page 215 exercises 1–4
Enrichment Worksheet 58

ENRICHED
page 214 exercises 1–51
page 215 exercises 1–4
Enrichment Worksheet 58

REVIEW PRACTICE
page 384 set 45

Mathematics and world geography

Egypt

1. When the largest of the pyramids was completed, its base was a square about 234 meters on each side and its height was 147 meters. What was the volume of the pyramid? (The formula for the volume of a pyramid is $V = \frac{1}{3} Bh$, where B is the area of the base and h is the height of the pyramid.)   2,683,044 m³

2. For 30 years 100,000 men worked, first to build a roadway for transporting the stone, and then to build the Great Pyramid. If the men worked every day of every year, how many man-days of work did it take to complete the job? (Ignore leap years.)   1,095,000,000

3. Khufu, the Egyptian king buried in the Great Pyramid, reigned for about 23 years beginning in 2900 B.C. When did his reign end?   2877 B.C.

4. The circumference of the head of the Sphinx is about 22 meters. Assuming that the head is circular, what is its diameter?   about 7 m

215

Follow-up Activities

Reinforcement Have students use the information in exercise 1 on page 215 to lay out the base of a pyramid on the school grounds. (Estimate 1 meter as one step.) Have students relate the height of 147 meters to some building or object with which they are familiar.

Enrichment Have students research and find additional information on Egypt and the pyramids. Students should write problems similar to those on page 215. Select the better problems, put them on a duplicating master, and give them to the class for additional practice in solving word problems.

EXCURSION
Who am I? 36

> I am between 20 and 50.
>
> I am an even number.
>
> I have exactly 9 factors.

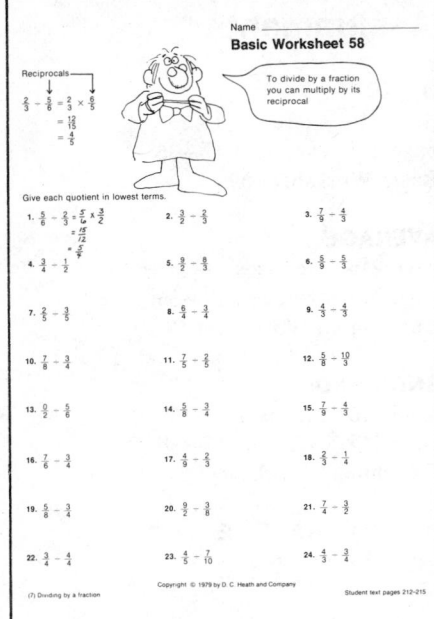

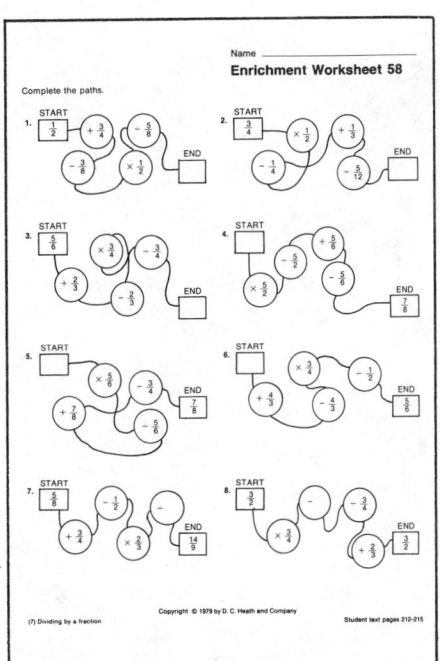

(core) Lesson 98 **215**

STUDENT OBJECTIVE
To use canceling in multiplication and
  division with fractions.

VOCABULARY
canceling

Suggested Lesson Plan

Introduction Write this multiplication problem on the board and ask students to give the product in lowest terms:

$$\frac{4}{9} \times \frac{3}{8}$$

Most students will multiply the numerators and then multiply the denominators to get $^{12}/_{72}$. Then they will look for common factors by which to divide both the numerator and the denominator. Then they will reduce the fraction to $^1/_6$. Now tell students that people who are skillful at multiplying with fractions divide through by common factors *before* they multiply because the factors are usually easier to recognize then. Use the example that is on the board. Point out that it is easy to see that 4 is a common factor of both the numerator and the denominator because 4 is a factor of both 4 and 8. Divide through by the common factor 4. Say, "4 divided by 4 is 1 and 8 divided by 4 is 2." As you talk, cancel as shown below:

$$\overset{1}{\cancel{\frac{4}{9}}} \times \frac{3}{\underset{2}{\cancel{8}}}$$

Repeat with the common factor 3.

$$\overset{1}{\underset{3}{\cancel{\frac{4}{9}}}} \times \overset{1}{\underset{2}{\cancel{\frac{3}{8}}}}$$

Then multiply to get $^1/_6$. Be sure students are aware that this is the same product that they got the long way.

Repeat with other examples. Students should realize that canceling *is* reducing to lowest terms.

Using the pages Go over the exposition on page 216 with your students. Also do a division example for them. Be sure to change the division problem to a multiplication problem *before* doing any canceling. Assign the exercises.

Near the end of the class period, have students work the Keeping Skills Sharp. Correct in class and make note of students needing review of fractions.

The cancellation shortcut

Here is a shortcut that can often be used when multiplying fractions. It gives the product in lowest terms. The shortcut, called **canceling**, is to divide both numerator and denominator by a common factor *before* doing the multiplication. Here is an example.

EXAMPLE.

$$\frac{3}{8} \times \frac{4}{3} = ?$$

Step 1. Divide by 3.

$$\overset{1}{\cancel{\frac{3}{8}}} \times \frac{4}{\cancel{3}} = ?$$

Step 2. Divide by 4.

$$\overset{1}{\cancel{\frac{3}{8}}}_{2} \times \frac{\cancel{4}}{\cancel{3}} = ?$$

Step 3. Multiply.

$$\overset{1}{\cancel{\frac{3}{8}}}_{2} \times \frac{\cancel{4}}{\cancel{3}} = \frac{1}{2}$$

The product is in lowest terms.

OTHER EXAMPLES.

Divide by 2.   Divide by 2.
Divide by 2.   Divide by 3.

$$\underset{2}{\cancel{\frac{\cancel{6}}{8}}} \times \frac{2}{5} = \frac{3}{10} \qquad \underset{4}{\cancel{\frac{9}{12}}} \times \frac{\overset{3}{\cancel{6}}}{8} = \frac{9}{16}$$

EXERCISES
Multiply.

1. $\frac{3}{5} \times \frac{10}{3}$ 2
2. $\frac{4}{7} \times \frac{14}{12}$ $\frac{2}{3}$
3. $\frac{5}{9} \times \frac{3}{15}$ $\frac{1}{9}$
4. $\frac{7}{5} \times \frac{6}{14}$ $\frac{3}{5}$

5. $\frac{6}{4} \times \frac{8}{9}$ $\frac{4}{3}$
6. $\frac{4}{9} \times \frac{18}{12}$ $\frac{2}{3}$
7. $8 \times \frac{1}{12}$ $\frac{2}{3}$
8. $\frac{16}{9} \times \frac{3}{20}$ $\frac{4}{15}$

9. $12 \times \frac{3}{16}$ $\frac{9}{4}$
10. $\frac{15}{21} \times \frac{14}{10}$ 1
11. $\frac{16}{24} \times \frac{18}{14}$ $\frac{6}{7}$
12. $\frac{15}{32} \times \frac{24}{20}$ $\frac{9}{16}$

13. $\frac{35}{8} \times \frac{12}{20}$ $\frac{21}{8}$
14. $\frac{16}{42} \times \frac{36}{24}$ $\frac{4}{7}$
15. $\frac{16}{7} \times 35$ 80
16. $\frac{45}{14} \times \frac{28}{35}$ $\frac{18}{7}$

216

Assignments

BASIC
page 216 exercises 1–16
page 217 exercises 17–36
Basic Worksheet 59

AVERAGE
page 216 exercises 1–16
page 217 exercises 17–36
Enrichment Worksheet 59

ENRICHED
page 216 exercises 1–16
page 217 exercises 17–38
Enrichment Worksheet 59

REVIEW PRACTICE
page 384 set 46

Divide. Example. $\frac{5}{6} \div \frac{2}{3} = \frac{5}{\cancel{6}_2} \times \frac{\cancel{3}}{2} = \frac{5}{4}$

17. $\frac{3}{8} \div \frac{5}{6}$ $\frac{9}{20}$ 18. $\frac{4}{7} \div \frac{2}{3}$ $\frac{6}{7}$ 19. $\frac{6}{9} \div \frac{1}{3}$ 2

20. $\frac{24}{36} \div 2$ $\frac{1}{3}$ 21. $\frac{16}{42} \div \frac{36}{24}$ $\frac{16}{63}$ 22. $\frac{45}{13} \div \frac{25}{26}$ $\frac{18}{5}$

23. $\frac{15}{17} \div \frac{15}{17}$ 1   24. $\frac{18}{24} \div \frac{3}{8}$ 2   25. $8 \div \frac{3}{2}$ $\frac{16}{3}$

26. $\frac{4}{5} \div 6$ $\frac{2}{15}$ 27. $5 \div \frac{10}{3}$ $\frac{3}{2}$ 28. $\frac{3}{4} \div 8$ $\frac{3}{32}$

29. $\frac{4}{5} \div \frac{5}{4}$ $\frac{16}{25}$ 30. $\frac{12}{5} \div \frac{4}{10}$ 6   31. $\frac{4}{5} \div \frac{8}{10}$ 1

32. $\frac{5}{9} \div \frac{15}{3}$ $\frac{1}{9}$ 33. $\frac{7}{8} \div \frac{21}{8}$ $\frac{1}{6}$ 34. $\frac{24}{25} \div \frac{16}{5}$ $\frac{3}{10}$

Solve.

35. There are 32 students in Bill's math class. One day $\frac{1}{8}$ of the students were absent. How many students were present?   28

36. Meg had $\frac{5}{6}$ of a yard of wire. She used $\frac{1}{2}$ of a yard to hang a picture. What fraction of a yard did she have left? $\frac{1}{3}$

★37. Jack earned $4.80. He saved $\frac{1}{3}$ of it and spent $\frac{1}{2}$ of the rest going to a movie. How much did the movie cost? $1.60

Follow the path to find the end number.

38.

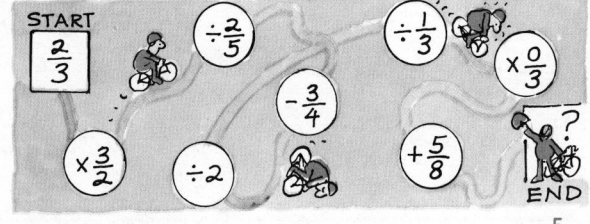

$\frac{5}{8}$

Change to a fraction.

1. $2\frac{1}{2}$ $\frac{5}{2}$ 2. $3\frac{1}{4}$ $\frac{13}{4}$

3. $4\frac{1}{4}$ $\frac{17}{4}$ 4. $5\frac{1}{3}$ $\frac{16}{3}$

5. $2\frac{2}{3}$ $\frac{8}{3}$ 6. $2\frac{5}{16}$ $\frac{37}{16}$

7. $3\frac{3}{4}$ $\frac{15}{4}$ 8. $4\frac{2}{5}$ $\frac{22}{5}$

9. $2\frac{5}{6}$ $\frac{17}{6}$ 10. $1\frac{7}{8}$ $\frac{15}{8}$

11. $3\frac{5}{9}$ $\frac{32}{9}$ 12. $2\frac{3}{8}$ $\frac{19}{8}$

13. $4\frac{3}{5}$ $\frac{23}{5}$ 14. $3\frac{7}{10}$ $\frac{37}{10}$

Change to a mixed number.

15. $\frac{7}{2}$ $3\frac{1}{2}$ 16. $\frac{10}{3}$ $3\frac{1}{3}$

17. $\frac{5}{4}$ $1\frac{1}{4}$ 18. $\frac{13}{5}$ $2\frac{3}{5}$

19. $\frac{13}{2}$ $6\frac{1}{2}$ 20. $\frac{7}{6}$ $1\frac{1}{6}$

21. $\frac{9}{4}$ $2\frac{1}{4}$ 22. $\frac{13}{3}$ $4\frac{1}{3}$

23. $\frac{17}{8}$ $2\frac{1}{8}$ 24. $\frac{23}{9}$ $2\frac{5}{9}$

25. $\frac{23}{10}$ $2\frac{3}{10}$ 26. $\frac{17}{5}$ $3\frac{2}{5}$

27. $\frac{13}{2}$ $6\frac{1}{2}$ 28. $\frac{11}{9}$ $1\frac{2}{9}$

217

Follow-up Activities

Reinforcement You may wish to have students copy and work through this path to determine the ending number. The answer is given in red.

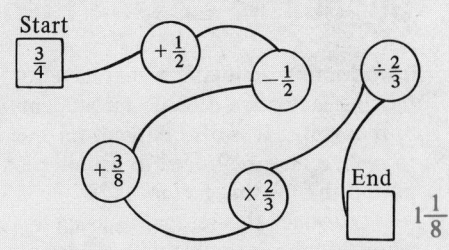

After students have completed the path, point out the inverse operations. Students who were aware of them probably saved some effort.

Enrichment Have the more able students work backwards through a path containing fractions to determine the starting number. This will necessitate thinking about inverse operations.

EXCURSION

Here is a table. (See pages 147 and 153.)

1	2	3	4	5	6	7	8
9	10	11	12	13	14	15	16
17	18	19	20	21	22	23	24

Show the moves for these rules.

1. $n \rightarrow n + 2$ 2. $g \rightarrow g + 7$

3. $r \rightarrow r + 8$ 4. $x \rightarrow x + 9$

5. $y \rightarrow y + 16$ 6. $y \rightarrow y + 24$

7. $y \rightarrow y + 25$ 8. $m \rightarrow m - 2$

Is there a move for the rule $n \rightarrow 2n$? Why or why not?

1. →→   2. ↙

3. ↓   4. ↘

5. ↓↓   6. ↓

7. ↓↓↓   8. ←

No, because moves vary with n.

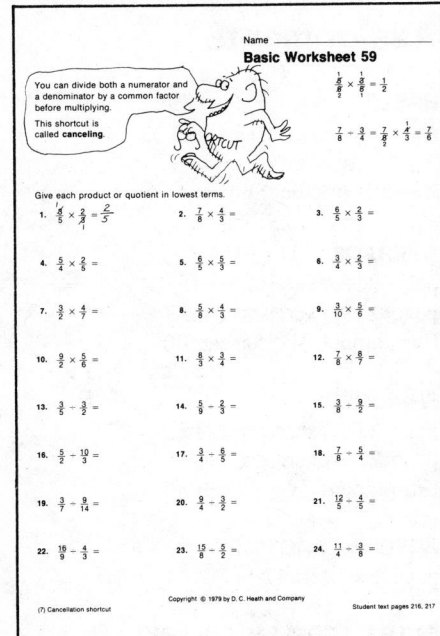

To recognize situations that require division.
To use division of fractions to solve word problems.

Suggested Lesson Plan

Introduction Situations that have a missing factor are difficult for students to recognize. It is also difficult for them to realize that they need to use division to find the missing factor.

Introduce this lesson by using a whole-number example with a missing factor, which requires division for the solution—for example, $6 \times \_\_ = 48$. Ask students to find the missing number. (8) Ask them what operation they used. (division) Point out to them that to find a missing factor they use division.

Using the pages Use the exposition on page 218 to present a situation similar to the introduction. For the equation $\frac{2}{3} \times \_\_ = 10$, what operation is used to find the missing factor? (division) The solution is found by solving the sentence $10 \div \frac{2}{3} = \_\_$. Work through the example, pointing out that they have to divide to find the missing factor. Assign exercises 1−24 for written work. Point out to students that the word problems on page 219 are also missing-factor problems. Students should write equations for the action in the problem and then solve the problem. For example, for exercise 26, they should write $\frac{3}{8} \times \_\_ = 483$. The answer is found by $483 \div \frac{3}{8}$. Help your poorer readers as they try the word problems. Assign the word problems for written work. Check.

Using division

$\frac{2}{3}$ of the nickels in a coin collection are buffalo nickels. If there are 10 buffalo nickels, how many nickels are there in all?

Equation:
$\frac{2}{3}$ of ? $= 10$

Solution:

The $\frac{2}{3}$ tells us to think about 2 out of 3 sets with the same number of nickels in each set.

The 10 tells us that there are 10 nickels equally divided between the 2 sets.

Since there are 5 nickels in each set, there are 15 nickels in all.

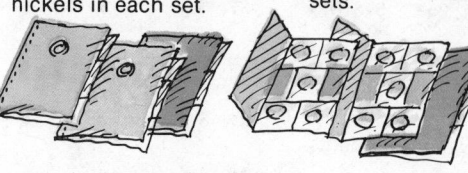

$\frac{2}{3}$ of ? $= 10$

$\frac{2}{3}$ of ? $= 10$

$\frac{2}{3}$ of **15** $= 10$

You can just divide to find the missing factor.

$10 \div \frac{2}{3} = 10 \times \frac{3}{2} = 15$

EXERCISES
Solve.

1. $\frac{1}{3}$ of ? $= 4$ 12
2. $\frac{1}{4}$ of ? $= 12$ 48
3. $\frac{1}{2}$ of ? $= 17$ 34

4. $\frac{2}{3}$ of ? $= 24$ 36
5. $\frac{3}{8}$ of ? $= 39$ 104
6. $\frac{5}{6}$ of ? $= 30$ 36

7. $\frac{4}{4}$ of ? $= 48$ 48
8. $\frac{3}{2}$ of ? $= 6.42$ 4.28
9. $\frac{2}{3}$ of ? $= 6.42$ 9.63

10. $\frac{5}{8}$ of ? $= 40$ 64
11. $\frac{4}{3}$ of ? $= 48$ 36
12. $\frac{3}{2}$ of ? $= 41.4$ 27.6

13. $\frac{1}{3}$ of ? $= 16.3$ 48.9
14. $\frac{5}{7}$ of ? $= 68.5$ 95.9
15. $\frac{5}{9}$ of ? $= 435$ 783

218

Assignments

BASIC
page 218 exercises 1−15
page 219 exercises 16−27
Basic Worksheet 60

AVERAGE
page 218 exercises 1-15
page 219 exercises 16−33
Enrichment Worksheet 60

ENRICHED
page 218 exercises 1-15
page 219 exercises 16−33
Enrichment Worksheet 60

REVIEW PRACTICE
page 384 set 47

EXTRA PROBLEM SOLVING
pages 412−413 set 8

16. $\frac{3}{5}$ of ? = 3111   5185   17. $\frac{2}{3}$ of ? = 42   63   18. $\frac{1}{2}$ of ? = 1.96
                                                                                           3.92

19. $\frac{9}{2}$ of ? = 603   134   20. $\frac{7}{8}$ of ? = 4.83   5.52   21. $\frac{2}{2}$ of ? = 12.6
                                                                                           12.6

22. $\frac{4}{3}$ of ? = 6.16   4.62   23. $\frac{3}{8}$ of ? = 91.2   243.2   24. $\frac{5}{3}$ of ? = 0.3815
                                                                                           0.2289

The sale price of each item is shown on the tag. Find the regular price of each item.

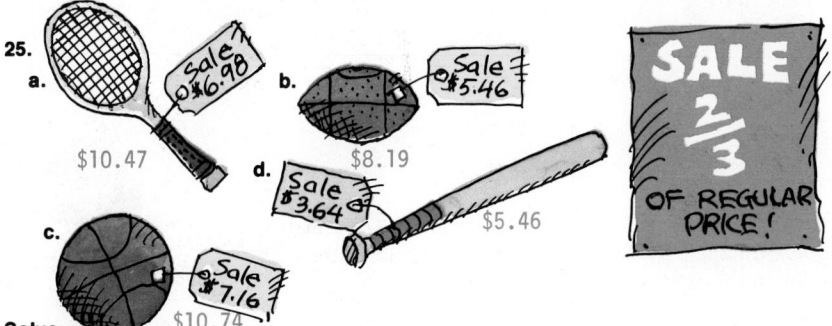

25.
a. Sale $6.98 $10.47
b. Sale $5.46 $8.19
d. Sale $3.64 $5.46
c. Sale $7.16 $10.74

SALE $\frac{2}{3}$ OF REGULAR PRICE!

Solve.

26. One day Mr. Allan drove 483 kilometers. This was $\frac{3}{8}$ of the total trip. How many kilometers was the total trip?   1288 km

27. Terry baked $\frac{2}{3}$ of a recipe of cookies. She baked 36 cookies. How many cookies would be in a full recipe?   54

28. A raincoat is on sale for $\frac{3}{4}$ of its regular price. What is the sale price if the regular price is $18.72? $14.04

29. A raincoat is on sale for $\frac{3}{4}$ of its regular price. What is the regular price if the sale price is $18.72? $24.96

30. In a physical education class, $\frac{2}{3}$ of the students passed a fitness test. If 46 passed, how many students took the test?   69

31. A drama class had to sell 424 tickets to the school play. By the end of the first week they had sold $\frac{5}{8}$ of the tickets. How many tickets had they sold?   265

32. Jerry spends $\frac{2}{3}$ of his weekly allowance for lunches. If he spends $3 a week for lunches, what is his weekly allowance? $4.50

33. On one math test, $\frac{3}{8}$ of the class got an A or a B. If 32 students took the test, how many got a grade below a B?   20

219

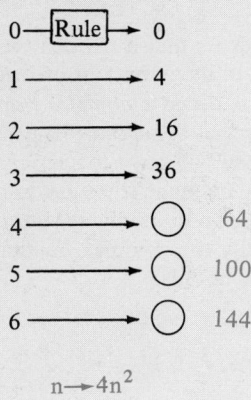
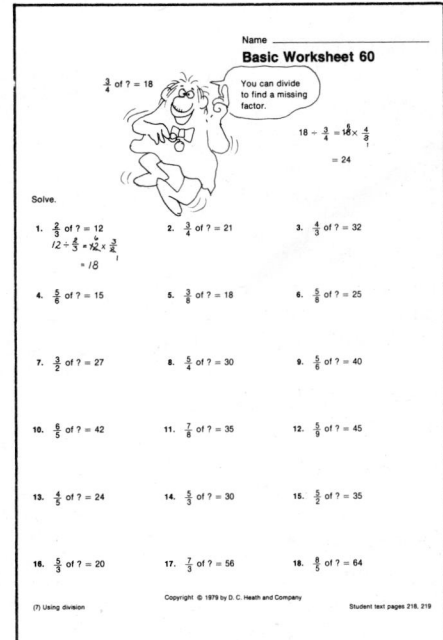

Name _____
Basic Worksheet 60

$\frac{3}{4}$ of ? = 18   You can divide to find a missing factor.

$18 \div \frac{3}{4} = 18 \times \frac{4}{3}$

$= 24$

Solve.

1. $\frac{2}{3}$ of ? = 12
$12 \div \frac{2}{3} = \frac{6}{12} \times \frac{3}{2}$
$= 18$

2. $\frac{3}{7}$ of ? = 21   3. $\frac{4}{3}$ of ? = 32

4. $\frac{5}{6}$ of ? = 15   5. $\frac{3}{5}$ of ? = 18   6. $\frac{5}{4}$ of ? = 25

7. $\frac{3}{2}$ of ? = 27   8. $\frac{5}{4}$ of ? = 30   9. $\frac{5}{6}$ of ? = 40

10. $\frac{5}{6}$ of ? = 42   11. $\frac{7}{6}$ of ? = 35   12. $\frac{5}{9}$ of ? = 45

13. $\frac{4}{5}$ of ? = 24   14. $\frac{5}{3}$ of ? = 30   15. $\frac{5}{2}$ of ? = 35

16. $\frac{5}{6}$ of ? = 20   17. $\frac{7}{4}$ of ? = 56   18. $\frac{8}{5}$ of ? = 64

(7) Using division   Copyright © 1979 by D. C. Heath and Company   Student text pages 218, 219

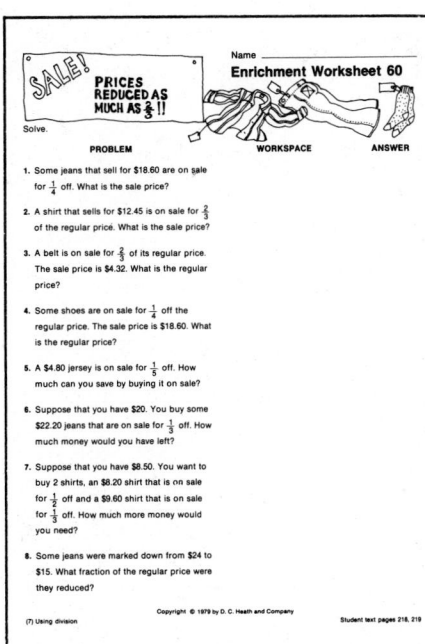

Name _____
Enrichment Worksheet 60

SALE! PRICES REDUCED AS MUCH AS $\frac{2}{3}$!!

Solve.

| PROBLEM | WORKSPACE | ANSWER |

1. Some jeans that sell for $18.60 are on sale for $\frac{1}{3}$ off. What is the sale price?

2. A shirt that sells for $12.45 is on sale for $\frac{2}{3}$ of the regular price. What is the sale price?

3. A belt is on sale for $\frac{2}{3}$ of its regular price. The sale price is $4.32. What is the regular price?

4. Some shoes are on sale for $\frac{1}{4}$ off the regular price. The sale price is $18.60. What is the regular price?

5. A $4.80 jersey is on sale for $\frac{1}{5}$ off. How much can you save by buying it on sale?

6. Suppose that you have $20. You buy some $22.20 jeans that are on sale for $\frac{1}{3}$ off. How much money would you have left?

7. Suppose that you have $8.50. You want to buy 2 shirts, an $8.20 shirt that is on sale for $\frac{1}{2}$ off and a $9.60 shirt that is on sale for $\frac{1}{3}$ off. How much more money would you need?

8. Some jeans were marked down from $24 to $15. What fraction of the regular price were they reduced?

(7) Using division   Copyright © 1979 by D. C. Heath and Company   Student text pages 218, 219

Suggested Lesson Plan

Introduction Ask students to suggest ways of writing the quotient of 2 by 3. They may suggest various ways, including decimals and percents, but be sure that the fraction $^2\!/_3$ is included. Remind students that we often indicate division by using a fraction. Then point out that sometimes the same thing is done with two fractions. That is, we sometimes write one fraction over another to indicate their quotient. Write this example on the board:

$$\frac{\frac{3}{5}}{\frac{1}{6}} \cdots \left(\frac{3}{5} \div \frac{1}{6} \right)$$

Tell students that a fraction that has a fraction in its numerator or denominator or both is called a *complex fraction*. Tell students that sometimes (usually on tests) they will have to simplify a complex fraction. It is easy to do so. All they have to do is divide. For example, to simplify the complex fraction above, they can do this:

$$\frac{\frac{3}{5}}{\frac{1}{6}} = \frac{3}{5} \div \frac{1}{6} = \frac{3}{5} \times \frac{6}{1} = \frac{18}{5}$$

Do other examples if necessary.

Using the pages Let students read the exposition on page 220 and then do the exercises. This topic is probably not especially important. If it is difficult for your students, you should feel free to go ahead without expecting mastery.

Complex fractions

We can think of the fraction bar as indicating division.

We can use a fraction to show the quotient of two fractions.

$$\frac{1}{2} = 1 \div 2$$

$$\frac{\frac{2}{3}}{\frac{3}{4}}$$

Such a fraction is called a **complex fraction**. To simplify a complex fraction, divide the fraction in the numerator by the fraction in the denominator.

$$\frac{\frac{2}{3}}{\frac{5}{6}} = \frac{2}{3} \div \frac{5}{6}$$

$$= \frac{2}{3} \times \frac{6}{5}$$

$$= \frac{4}{5}$$

EXERCISES
Simplify each complex fraction.

1. $\dfrac{\frac{1}{5}}{\frac{3}{4}}$ $\frac{4}{15}$
2. $\dfrac{\frac{7}{3}}{\frac{14}{9}}$ $\frac{3}{2}$
3. $\dfrac{\frac{5}{9}}{\frac{15}{6}}$ $\frac{2}{9}$
4. $\dfrac{\frac{6}{9}}{\frac{6}{12}}$ $\frac{4}{3}$
5. $\dfrac{\frac{5}{3}}{\frac{10}{6}}$ 1
6. $\dfrac{\frac{8}{5}}{\frac{10}{4}}$ $\frac{16}{25}$

7. $\dfrac{\frac{7}{5}}{\frac{14}{10}}$ 1
8. $\dfrac{\frac{3}{8}}{\frac{9}{4}}$ $\frac{1}{6}$
9. $\dfrac{\frac{5}{6}}{\frac{15}{9}}$ $\frac{1}{2}$
10. $\dfrac{\frac{15}{24}}{\frac{20}{12}}$ $\frac{3}{8}$
11. $\dfrac{\frac{9}{18}}{\frac{6}{15}}$ $\frac{5}{4}$
12. $\dfrac{\frac{7}{15}}{\frac{38}{10}}$ $\frac{7}{57}$

220

Assignments

BASIC
page 220 exercises 1−12
page 221 exercises 13−30
Basic Worksheet 61

AVERAGE
page 220 exercises 1−12
page 221 exercises 13−32
Enrichment Worksheet 61

ENRICHED
page 220 exercises 1−12
page 221 exercises 13−34
Enrichment Worksheet 61

EXTRA PRACTICE
page 390 set 66

Simplify.

$$5 \div \frac{2}{3}$$

13. $\dfrac{\frac{5}{3}}{\frac{3}{9}}$ 5

14. $\dfrac{\frac{7}{5}}{\frac{21}{10}}$ $\frac{2}{3}$

15. $\dfrac{\frac{5}{2}}{\frac{2}{3}}$ $\frac{15}{2}$

16. $\dfrac{\frac{3}{3}}{\frac{3}{4}}$ 4

17. $\dfrac{\frac{3}{8}}{9}$ $\frac{1}{24}$

18. $\dfrac{\frac{7}{8}}{\frac{4}{4}}$ $\frac{7}{8}$

19. $\dfrac{\frac{1}{2}}{\frac{3}{4}}$ $\frac{2}{3}$

20. $\dfrac{\frac{5}{8}}{\frac{5}{4}}$ $\frac{1}{2}$

21. $\dfrac{\frac{3}{5}}{\frac{6}{3}}$ $\frac{3}{10}$

22. $\dfrac{7}{\frac{3}{5}}$ $\frac{35}{3}$

23. $\dfrac{\frac{2}{3}}{\frac{4}{5}}$ $\frac{5}{6}$

24. $\dfrac{\frac{5}{12}}{\frac{10}{6}}$ $\frac{1}{4}$

25. $\dfrac{\frac{7}{5}}{3}$ $\frac{7}{15}$

26. $\dfrac{\frac{7}{8}}{\frac{3}{8}}$ $\frac{7}{3}$

27. $\dfrac{\frac{6}{3}}{\frac{3}{4}}$ 8

28. $\dfrac{\frac{8}{9}}{2}$ $\frac{4}{9}$

29. $\dfrac{\frac{5}{12}}{\frac{1}{6}}$ $\frac{5}{2}$

30. $\dfrac{\frac{0}{4}}{\frac{1}{2}}$ 0

Solve.

31. One week Mrs. Rogers bought 46.6 liters of gasoline for 27.9¢ per liter and 59.1 liters of gasoline for 26.9¢ per liter. How much did she spend in all? Round each sale to the nearest cent. $28.90

32. One week the daily high Celsius temperature readings were 27°, 31°, 30°, 26°, 32°, 29°, and 28°. Find the average daily high for the week.   29° C

33. Rachel wants to attend a summer camp that costs $370. Her parents have agreed to pay $\frac{3}{5}$ if she pays the rest. How much money will Rachel have to pay? $148

34. From the table, compute the average yearly precipitation in Atlanta.   119.8 cm

Average Monthly Precipitation, Atlanta, Georgia.

Month	Precipitation (cm)
January	11.2
February	11.4
March	13.7
April	11.4
May	8.1
June	9.7
July	11.9
August	9.1
September	8.4
October	6.1
November	7.6
December	11.2

221

Follow-up Activities

Reinforcement At this time you may wish to provide students with further problem-solving experiences. If so, have students create at least two stories for each of the following headlines:

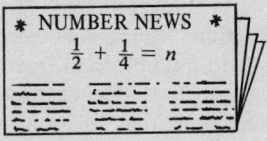

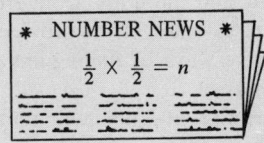

Enrichment Have your more able students create several headlines for each of the following headlines. Have them share their stories with other classmates.

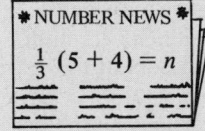

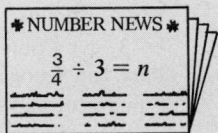

If time permits, have students make up other headlines to write stories for.

EXCURSION

Any even number greater than 2 can be expressed as a sum of two primes.

$$4 = 2 + 2$$
$$6 = 3 + 3$$
$$8 = 3 + 5$$

Express other even numbers as the sum of two primes.

$10 = 7 + 3$, $12 = 7 + 5$,
$14 = 3 + 11$, etc.

Suggested Lesson Plan

Introduction Being able to change decimals to fractions and fractions and mixed numbers to decimals are important skills that when mastered can greatly simplify computation with decimals and fractions. Converting numbers to other forms provides alternative ways of finding answers to problems.

Write several decimals on the board and ask students to write them as fractions. If the decimal shows tenths, then the denominator is 10; if it shows hundredths, then the denominator is 100, etc. The most difficult part of this procedure is reducing the fraction to lowest terms. Encourage students to do this as efficiently as possible, but if they have difficulty, have them divide by 2 or by 3 or by other small numbers until they can recognize divisors of the numerator and denominator.

Write several fractions on the board and reemphasize that a fraction also means division. Therefore, to change a fraction to a decimal, you must divide. Work through several examples. Be sure to avoid repeating decimals at this point; they are introduced in the next lesson.

Using the pages Use the exposition on page 222 to reinforce your introduction. Point out that a mixed number is changed to a decimal by writing the whole number as the whole number part of the decimal and then just changing the fraction part to a decimal. Assign exercises 1 – 12, 13 – 24, and 25 – 36. Discuss each set of exercises and the instructions. For exercises 25 – 36, point out that before the numbers can be compared, they must be changed to the same form. Then they are easily compared. Continue to stress that it is easier to compare decimals than fractions.

Assign exercises 37 – 51 for practice changing fractions to decimals. With the increasing emphasis on the metric system and the use of calculators, more of our computation will be done with decimals. Expect all students to know the decimal equivalents for halves, quarters, and eighths. Practice them on occasion so students will realize their importance.

222 Lesson 102 (core)

Fractions, mixed numbers, and decimals

Changing decimals to fractions
If you can *read* a decimal correctly, you can easily change a decimal to a fraction. Then you may have to reduce that fraction. Study these examples.

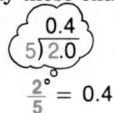

2 tenths
$$0.2 = \frac{2}{10}$$
$$= \frac{1}{5}$$

375 thousandths
$$0.375 = \frac{375}{1000}$$
$$= \frac{3}{8}$$

3 and 25 hundredths
$$3.25 = 3\frac{25}{100}$$
$$= 3\frac{1}{4}$$

Changing fractions to decimals
To change a fraction to a decimal, divide the numerator by the denominator. Study these examples.

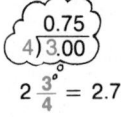

$$5\overline{)2.0} \quad 0.4$$
$$\frac{2}{5} = 0.4$$

$$4\overline{)3.00} \quad 0.75$$
$$2\frac{3}{4} = 2.75$$

EXERCISES
Change to a fraction or mixed number.

1. 0.3 $\frac{3}{10}$ 2. 0.5 $\frac{1}{2}$ 3. 0.8 $\frac{4}{5}$ 4. 0.25 $\frac{1}{4}$ 5. 0.64 $\frac{16}{25}$ 6. 0.80 $\frac{4}{5}$

7. 3.375 $3\frac{3}{8}$ 8. 3.1 $3\frac{1}{10}$ 9. 1.08 $1\frac{2}{25}$ 10. 2.16 $2\frac{4}{25}$ 11. 1.875 $1\frac{7}{8}$ 12. 3.48 $3\frac{12}{25}$

Change to a decimal.

13. $\frac{1}{2}$ 0.5   14. $\frac{7}{8}$ 0.875   15. $\frac{1}{4}$ 0.25   16. $\frac{1}{8}$ 0.125   17. $\frac{3}{8}$ 0.375   18. $1\frac{1}{2}$ 1.5

19. $1\frac{1}{4}$ 1.25   20. $\frac{3}{10}$ 0.3   21. $2\frac{1}{8}$ 2.125   22. $3\frac{1}{4}$ 3.25   23. $2\frac{3}{5}$ 2.6   24. $\frac{4}{5}$ 0.8

<, =, or >?

25. $\frac{1}{8}$ ● 0.12   >   26. $\frac{1}{5}$ ● 0.25   <   27. $\frac{4}{5}$ ● 0.75   >   28. $\frac{3}{8}$ ● 0.375   =

29. $\frac{3}{4}$ ● 0.8   <   30. $\frac{1}{4}$ ● 0.25   =   31. $\frac{3}{5}$ ● 0.5   >   32. $\frac{5}{8}$ ● 0.63   <

33. $1\frac{1}{2}$ ● 1.6   <   34. $1\frac{1}{4}$ ● 1.20   >   35. $3\frac{7}{8}$ ● 3.8   >   36. $4\frac{2}{5}$ ● 4.4   =

222

Assignments

BASIC
page 222 exercises 1 – 36
page 223 exercises 37 – 39,
    Keeping Skills Sharp
Basic Worksheet 62

AVERAGE
page 222 exercises 1 – 36
page 223 exercises 37 – 45,
    Keeping Skills Sharp
Enrichment Worksheet 62

ENRICHED
page 222 exercises 1 – 36
page 223 exercises 37 – 51,
    Keeping Skills Sharp
Enrichment Worksheet 62

EXTRA PRACTICE
page 390 set 67

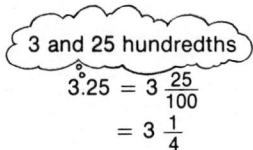

Copy and complete these tables.

37.

Fraction or Mixed Number	$\frac{1}{4}$	$\frac{2}{4}$	$\frac{3}{4}$	$\frac{4}{4}$	$1\frac{1}{4}$	$1\frac{2}{4}$
Decimal	0.25	0.5	0.75	1	1.25	1.5

38.

Fraction or Mixed Number	$\frac{1}{5}$	$\frac{2}{5}$	$\frac{3}{5}$	$\frac{4}{5}$	$\frac{5}{5}$	$1\frac{1}{5}$
Decimal	0.2	0.4	0.6	0.8	1	1.2

39.

Fraction or Mixed Number	$\frac{1}{8}$	$\frac{2}{8}$	$\frac{3}{8}$	$\frac{4}{8}$	$\frac{5}{8}$	$\frac{6}{8}$
Decimal	0.125	0.25	0.375	0.5	0.625	0.75

Many measurements in customary units are made in half-inches, quarter-inches, eighth-inches, sixteenth-inches, and thirty-second-inches. Often these measurements must be changed to decimals. Tables like this make that job easier.

Fraction	$\frac{1}{2}$	$\frac{1}{4}$	$\frac{1}{8}$	$\frac{1}{16}$	$\frac{1}{32}$
Decimal	0.5	0.25	0.125	0.0625	0.03125

Use the table to change to decimals.

40. $\frac{5}{16}$ 0.3125 **41.** $\frac{3}{32}$ 0.09375 **42.** $\frac{5}{8}$ 0.625 **43.** $\frac{4}{16}$ 0.25

44. $\frac{3}{8}$ 0.375 **45.** $\frac{3}{4}$ 0.75 **46.** $3\frac{7}{8}$ 3.875 **47.** $6\frac{1}{4}$ 6.25

48. $2\frac{5}{32}$ **49.** $7\frac{9}{16}$ **50.** $12\frac{5}{8}$ **51.** $16\frac{15}{16}$

2.15625   7.5625   12.625   16.9375

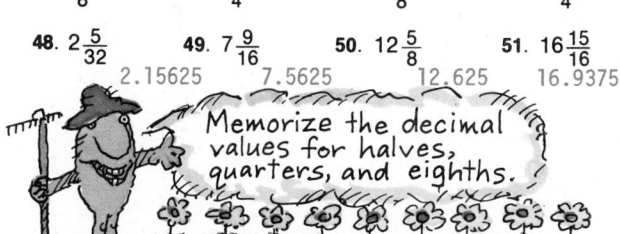

Memorize the decimal values for halves, quarters, and eighths.

Add. Reduce answers to lowest terms.

1. $\frac{4}{9} + \frac{1}{9}$ $\frac{5}{9}$

2. $\frac{3}{5} + \frac{2}{5}$ 1

3. $\frac{1}{2} + \frac{1}{4}$ $\frac{3}{4}$

4. $\frac{3}{8} + \frac{1}{4}$ $\frac{5}{8}$

5. $\frac{1}{2} + \frac{1}{3}$ $\frac{5}{6}$

6. $\frac{2}{3} + \frac{3}{4}$ $\frac{17}{12}$, $1\frac{5}{12}$

7. $\frac{5}{8} + \frac{2}{3}$ $\frac{31}{24}$, $1\frac{7}{24}$

8. $\frac{5}{9} + \frac{5}{6}$ $\frac{25}{18}$, $1\frac{7}{18}$

9. $\frac{0}{8} + \frac{3}{2}$ $\frac{3}{2}$, $1\frac{1}{2}$

10. $\frac{3}{2} + \frac{2}{3}$ $\frac{13}{6}$, $2\frac{1}{6}$

11. $\frac{4}{9} + \frac{1}{2}$ $\frac{17}{18}$

12. $\frac{1}{6} + \frac{3}{4}$ $\frac{11}{12}$

13. $\frac{2}{3} + \frac{3}{5}$ $\frac{19}{15}$, $1\frac{4}{15}$

14. $\frac{1}{2} + \frac{4}{5}$ $\frac{13}{10}$, $1\frac{3}{10}$

15. $\frac{3}{5} + \frac{1}{4}$ $\frac{17}{20}$

16. $\frac{8}{9} + \frac{2}{3}$ $\frac{14}{9}$, $1\frac{5}{9}$

223

Follow-up Activities

Reinforcement The following game may be used to provide further practice with changing fractions to decimals. Make a spinner like this:

Students play against each other. A player spins the spinner twice. The first number is the numerator; the second is the denominator. Each student names the fraction as a decimal. If either names the wrong decimal, the other player wins a point. If both name the decimal correctly, the student with the greater number wins a point. First player to 10 wins.

Enrichment Have students make a large chart showing decimal equivalents for the most used fractions. Post the completed chart on the mathematics bulletin board.

EXCURSION

There are 6 pairs of black socks and 6 pairs of red socks in a drawer. If you reach into the drawer when it is dark, how many socks must you take out to be sure of having 1 pair of matching socks?   3

Suppose there were also 6 pairs of white socks in the drawer. Then how many socks must you take out?   4

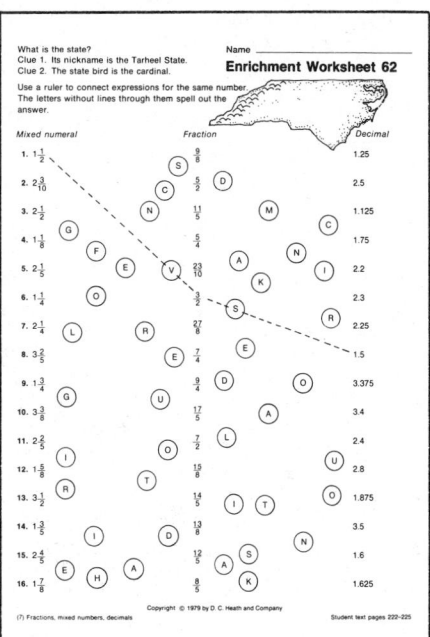

(core) Lesson 102   **223**

Suggested Lesson Plan

Introduction Ask students to explain how they would divide 2 candy bars equally among 3 people. (One way is to divide each candy bar into 3 equal pieces and give each person 1 piece from each bar, or 2 pieces in all.) Be sure that the technique above comes out in the discussion, even if you have to tell it yourself. The technique works any time you wish to divide n things equally into m groups. You can divide each thing into m parts and then put 1 part from each thing into a group. There would be n parts in each group. There would be n/m of the original things in each group. Give other examples to be sure that students understand that if 2 things are divided into 3 equal parts, each part is $^2/_3$ of the thing. If 3 objects are divided into 5 equally large groups, each group has $^3/_5$ of an object. Point out that $2 \div 3 = {}^2/_3$ and $3 \div 5 = {}^3/_5$. So, as they have done, to convert from a fraction to a decimal we can divide the numerator by the denominator.

Example. Change $\frac{1}{2}$ to a decimal

$$2)\overline{1.0}$$
$$\underline{1\ 0}$$

$$\frac{1}{2} = .5$$

Now have students change $^7/_{11}$ to a decimal.

$$11\ )\overline{7.0000}$$

.6363

$$\underline{-6\ 6}$$
$$40$$
$$\underline{-33}$$
$$70$$
$$\underline{-66}$$
$$40$$
$$\underline{-33}$$

It soon should be obvious that because the remainders repeat over and over, the quotient digits will also repeat over and over. The division will not "come out even."

Using the pages Use the examples on page 224 to reinforce the introduction. Using the examples that students have done, write on the board the four different ways of recording a repeating decimal. Assign exercises 1–24, 25–30, and 31–42. Be sure students understand the directions. Before students start on exercises 43–58, work exercise 43 together. Since $^1/_3$ is .333 . . . and the other number is just .3, $^1/_3$ is greater.

Repeating decimals

In these two examples, the division never ends!

$$\frac{2}{3} = ? \quad 3)\overline{2.00}$$

0.66

$$\underline{-1\ 8}$$
$$20$$
$$\underline{-18}$$
$$2$$

The 6 will keep repeating as long as you keep dividing.

The 36 will keep repeating as long as you keep dividing.

$$\frac{15}{11} = ?$$

$$11)\overline{15.00}$$

1.36

$$\underline{-11}$$
$$4\ 0$$
$$\underline{-3\ 3}$$
$$70$$
$$\underline{-66}$$
$$4$$

Such decimals are called **repeating** decimals.

There are four ways of writing a repeating decimal.

1. Write 3 dots after the decimal to show that it repeats.

   $$\frac{2}{3} = 0.66 \ldots \qquad \frac{15}{11} = 1.3636 \ldots$$

   This can be confusing because you can't be sure what part repeats.

2. Use a bar over the digits that repeat.

   $$\frac{2}{3} = 0.66 \ldots = 0.\overline{6} \qquad \frac{15}{11} = 1.3636 \ldots = 1.\overline{36}$$

3. Write the answer as a **mixed decimal**.

   mixed decimal

   $$\frac{2}{3} = 0.66\frac{2}{3} \qquad \text{Read this as "sixty-six and two-thirds hundredths."}$$

   This method is not used often, but it will be useful in your work with percents.

4. Round the decimal.

   $$\frac{2}{3} = 0.666 \ldots \approx 0.67 \qquad \frac{15}{11} = 1.3636 \ldots \approx 1.364$$

224

Have students change the fractions to decimals for exercises 59–68 before they compare them.

Assignments

BASIC
page 224 Discuss
page 225 exercises 1–58
Basic Worksheet 62

AVERAGE
page 224 Discuss
page 225 exercises 1–64
Enrichment Worksheet 62

ENRICHED
page 224 Discuss
page 225 exercises 1–68
Enrichment Worksheet 62

EXTRA PRACTICE
page 390 set 68

EXERCISES

Change to decimals. Use three dots to write repeating decimals.

1. $\frac{1}{3}$　　2. $\frac{2}{3}$　　3. $\frac{1}{9}$　　4. $\frac{2}{9}$　　5. $\frac{3}{9}$　　6. $\frac{4}{9}$

7. $\frac{5}{9}$　　8. $\frac{6}{9}$　　9. $\frac{7}{9}$　　10. $\frac{8}{9}$　　11. $\frac{1}{6}$　　12. $\frac{5}{6}$

13. $\frac{4}{3}$　　14. $\frac{10}{9}$　　15. $\frac{7}{6}$　　16. $\frac{1}{12}$　　17. $\frac{4}{12}$　　18. $\frac{5}{12}$

19. $\frac{1}{7}$　　20. $\frac{1}{13}$　　21. $\frac{2}{17}$　　22. $\frac{4}{15}$　　23. $\frac{10}{15}$　　24. $\frac{7}{17}$

Change to mixed decimals. Give answers in hundredths.

25. $\frac{1}{3}$ $0.33\frac{1}{3}$　26. $\frac{1}{8}$ $0.12\frac{1}{2}$　27. $\frac{5}{6}$ $0.83\frac{1}{3}$　28. $\frac{3}{8}$ $0.37\frac{1}{2}$　29. $\frac{1}{9}$ $0.11\frac{1}{9}$　30. $\frac{4}{9}$ $0.44\frac{4}{9}$

Change to decimals. Round to the nearest hundredth.

31. $\frac{1}{3}$ 0.33　32. $\frac{1}{6}$ 0.17　33. $\frac{5}{6}$ 0.83　34. $\frac{3}{8}$ 0.38　35. $\frac{7}{9}$ 0.78　36. $\frac{1}{9}$ 0.11

37. $\frac{1}{12}$ 0.08　38. $\frac{11}{12}$ 0.92　39. $1\frac{5}{8}$ 1.63　40. $\frac{13}{6}$ 2.17　41. $2\frac{5}{9}$ 2.56　42. $\frac{17}{7}$ 2.43

<, = , or >?

43. $\frac{1}{3}$ ● 0.3 　$>$　44. $\frac{1}{3}$ ● 0.33 　$>$　45. $\frac{1}{3}$ ● 0.333 　$>$　46. $\frac{1}{3}$ ● 0.3333 　$>$

47. $\frac{1}{3}$ ● $0.\overline{3}$ 　$=$　48. $\frac{2}{3}$ ● 0.6 　$>$　49. $\frac{2}{3}$ ● 0.66 　$>$　50. $\frac{2}{3}$ ● 0.67 　$<$

51. $\frac{2}{3}$ ● 0.666 　$>$　52. $\frac{2}{3}$ ● 0.6666 　$>$　53. $\frac{2}{3}$ ● $0.\overline{6}$ 　$=$　54. $\frac{1}{7}$ ● 0.1 　$>$

55. $\frac{1}{7}$ ● 0.14 　$>$　56. $\frac{1}{7}$ ● 0.143 　$<$　57. $\frac{1}{7}$ ● 0.1429 　$>$　58. $\frac{1}{7}$ ● 0.14285 　$>$

Changing fractions to decimals makes it easier to compare them.

Which number is greater?

59. $\frac{3}{8}$　$\frac{4}{7}$ ✓　60. $\frac{3}{5}$　$\frac{2}{3}$ ✓　61. $\frac{1}{3}$　$\frac{2}{5}$ ✓　62. $\frac{3}{4}$　$\frac{4}{5}$ ✓

63. $\frac{5}{6}$ ✓　$\frac{5}{8}$　64. $\frac{4}{5}$ ✓　$\frac{5}{7}$　65. $\frac{4}{5}$　$\frac{6}{7}$ ✓　66. $\frac{4}{9}$ ✓　$\frac{3}{8}$

 67. $\frac{57}{78}$ ✓　$\frac{45}{64}$　68. $\frac{105}{432}$　$\frac{293}{957}$ ✓

225

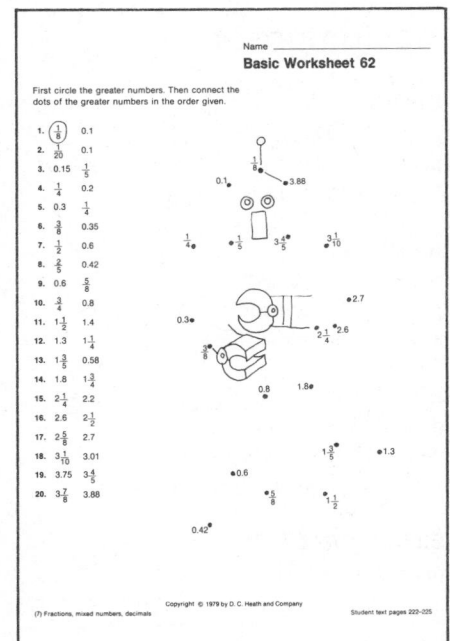

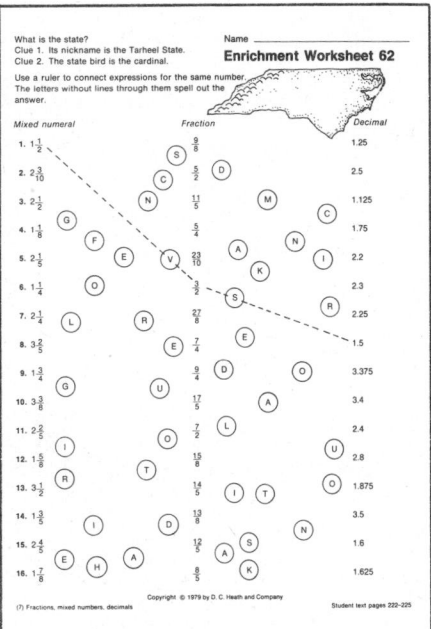

Reinforcement The following game may be used to provide further experience with changing decimals to percentages. Prepare a spinner like this:

The spinner is made by attaching a pointer (a bent paper clip) with a thumbtack. Divide the students into two teams. Spin the spinner two times. Use the first number on which the spinner stops as the numerator of a fraction and the second number as the denominator of the fraction. Have all students convert the fraction to a decimal. Award one point for every correct conversion. After playing the game several times, add the points of each team. The team with the greater sum wins the game.

Enrichment The digits that repeat in a repeating decimal are called the *repetend* of the repeating decimal. Encourage students to find fractions that are equivalent to repeating decimals that have a 1-digit repetend, a 2-digit repetend, a 3-digit repetend, etc.

EXCURSION

There are 6 pairs of black gloves and 6 pairs of red gloves in a drawer. If you reach into the drawer when it is dark, how many gloves must you take out to be sure of having 1 pair of matching gloves? 13

Suppose there were also 6 pairs of white gloves in the drawer. Then how many gloves must you take out? 19

Answers.

1. 0.33... 2. 0.66... 3. 0.11...
4. 0.22... 5. 0.33... 6. 0.44...
7. 0.55... 8. 0.66... 9. 0.77...
10. 0.88... 11. 0.166...
12. 0.833... 13. 1.33...
14. 1.11... 15. 1.166...
16. 0.0833... 17. 0.33...
18. 0.4166... 19. 0.142857...
20. 0.076923...
21. 0.1176470588235294...
22. 0.266...
23. 0.66...
24. 0.4117647058823529...

STUDENT OBJECTIVES
To multiply two mixed numbers.
To solve word problems.

Suggested Lesson Plan

Introduction Quickly review multiplying fractions by putting two examples on the board and having students find the products. Write a third example on the board, this time with one of the numbers a mixed number. As students encounter the problem, simply tell them to change the mixed number to a fraction and then multiply.

Using the pages Use the exposition on page 226 to follow your introduction. Use the example to discuss multiplication leaving the mixed number alone. This is usually easier if one of the numbers is a whole number and the mixed number is large.

Assign exercises 1–20, encouraging students to use either method discussed. Assign exercises 21–28. Be ready to help your poorer readers.

Multiplying mixed numbers

A custom T-shirt store charges $9\frac{1}{2}$¢ for each letter they put on a T-shirt. We can multiply to find how much these letters will cost:

SUPERMAN

To multiply, we first change the mixed number to a fraction.

$$8 \times 9\frac{1}{2} = \overset{4}{\cancel{8}} \times \frac{19}{\underset{1}{\cancel{2}}}$$
$$= 76$$

So, the letters will cost 76¢.

Here is another way to multiply $9\frac{1}{2}$ by 8.

Step 1. Multiply the fraction.

$$\begin{array}{r} 9\frac{1}{2} \\ \times 8 \\ \hline 4 \end{array}$$

Step 2. Multiply the whole number.

$$\begin{array}{r} 9\frac{1}{2} \\ \times 8 \\ \hline 4 \\ 72 \end{array}$$

Step 3. Add the products.

$$\begin{array}{r} 9\frac{1}{2} \\ \times 8 \\ \hline 4 \\ 72 \\ \hline 76 \end{array}$$

When multiplying two mixed numbers, it is easier to change them to fractions first. Before you multiply, estimate the product by rounding each factor to the nearest whole number.

$$\overset{1}{1\frac{1}{4}} \times \overset{3}{2\frac{2}{3}}$$

The product is about 3.

$$1\frac{1}{4} \times 2\frac{2}{3} = \frac{5}{\underset{1}{\cancel{4}}} \times \frac{\overset{2}{\cancel{8}}}{3}$$
$$= \frac{10}{3}$$
$$= 3\frac{1}{3}$$

226

Assignments

BASIC
page 226 Discuss
page 227 exercises 1–26
Basic Worksheet 63

AVERAGE
page 226 Discuss
page 227 exercises 1–28
Enrichment Worksheet 63

ENRICHED
page 226 Discuss
page 227 exercises 1–28
Enrichment Worksheet 63

EXTRA PRACTICE
page 391 set 69

EXERCISES

First estimate. Then multiply. Give answers as mixed or whole numbers.

1. $3\frac{3}{4} \times 1\frac{2}{3}$
2. $5\frac{3}{4} \times 2\frac{3}{4}$
3. $3 \times 4\frac{2}{3}$
4. $1\frac{5}{8} \times 3\frac{1}{3}$

5. $5\frac{1}{6} \times 8\frac{1}{5}$
6. $2\frac{1}{2} \times 2\frac{1}{2}$
7. $6\frac{2}{7} \times 4$
8. $9 \times 2\frac{1}{6}$

9. $7\frac{3}{4} \times 9$
10. $3\frac{3}{4} \times 5\frac{1}{6}$
11. $5\frac{3}{4} \times 2\frac{2}{3}$
12. $6\frac{1}{3} \times 4\frac{2}{5}$

13. $4\frac{3}{8} \times 2$
14. $5 \times 2\frac{5}{8}$
15. $3 \times 4\frac{2}{5}$
16. $6\frac{2}{3} \times 8$

17. $1\frac{2}{5} \times 2\frac{3}{8}$
18. $4 \times 4\frac{5}{6}$
19. $3\frac{2}{3} \times 5\frac{1}{2}$
20. $5\frac{3}{8} \times 7\frac{3}{4}$

Compute each total cost. Remember that the letters cost $9\frac{1}{2}$¢ each. Round each cost up to the nearest cent.

21.  95¢

22.  $1.52

23.  95¢

24.  $1.05

Solve.

25. Mrs. Albert plans to drive 55 miles per hour on a trip. At that rate, how far will she travel in $2\frac{3}{4}$ hours?

$151\frac{1}{4}$ miles

26. Howard jogs $3\frac{1}{3}$ miles each day. How many miles does he jog in a week?

$23\frac{1}{3}$

27. Connie works Saturday mornings for $1.75 an hour. One Saturday she worked from 9:00 A.M. to 11:45 A.M. How much did she earn that Saturday? Give answer to the nearest cent. $4.81

28. Bill works every day after school from 4:00 P.M. to 6:15 P.M., and from 10:30 to 3:30 on Saturdays. If he is paid $1.70 an hour, how much does he earn in a week? Give answer to the nearest cent. $27.63

227

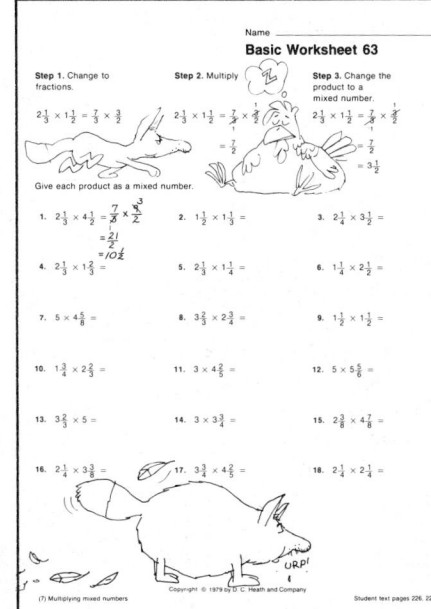

Follow-up Activities

Reinforcement The following activity provides a review of area and at the same time provides for further practice multiplying with mixed numbers. Briefly review area and the area formulas. Have students determine the area of each of the following regions.

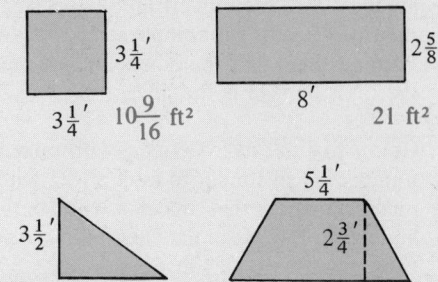

$3\frac{1}{4}'$ $3\frac{1}{4}'$ $10\frac{9}{16}$ ft²

$2\frac{5}{8}'$ $8'$ 21 ft²

$3\frac{1}{2}'$ $9\frac{5}{8}$ ft² $5\frac{1}{2}'$

$5\frac{1}{4}$ $2\frac{3}{4}'$ $7\frac{1}{2}'$ $17\frac{17}{32}$ ft²

Enrichment Provide a newspaper that contains a stock market report. You may have to explain briefly how the stock quotations are read. Have each student assume he owns:

48 shares of General Motors
27 shares of AT&T
19 shares of IBM
72 shares of TWA

Ask them to compute the current market value of their "holdings." Some students may wish to give a report about the stock market.

EXCURSION

Use only these numbers as addends:

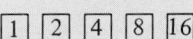

See how many whole numbers you can get by adding not more than four of the numbers. Here are the first few.

$$1 = 1$$
$$2 = 2$$
$$1 + 2 = 3$$
$$4 = 4$$
$$1 + 4 = 5$$
$$2 + 4 = 6$$
$$1 + 2 + 4 = 7$$

You can get numbers through 31.

(core) Lesson 104   **227**

STUDENT OBJECTIVES
To divide mixed numbers.
To solve word problems with mixed
numbers.

Suggested Lesson Plan

Introduction Quickly review division
of fractions. Put several examples on the
board and have students divide. Remind
students that they invert the divisor and
then proceed as in multiplication.
Remind them that the number following
the division sign is the divisor.

Using the pages Dividing with mixed
numbers is so similar to multiplying with
mixed numbers that students will need
almost no introduction. They follow the
same procedure as when multiplying
with mixed numbers—that is, change the
mixed numbers to fractions and then
divide as with fractions.

Use the exposition on page 228 to
introduce division of mixed numbers.
Without formal discussion, let the
students read page 228 and then start on
the exercises. Assign exercises 1–24 for
written work and exercises 25–26 for
word problems.

Assign the Keeping Skills Sharp at
the end of the class time, and allow
enough time for pupils to do the
exercises.

Dividing mixed numbers

Two girls hiked from Base Camp to
Clear Lake Camp in $2\frac{3}{4}$ hours. We can
divide to find how many miles they averaged each hour.

To divide mixed numbers, change each
mixed number to an equivalent fraction
and divide.

$$8\frac{1}{2} \div 2\frac{3}{4} = \frac{17}{2} \div \frac{11}{4}$$

$$= \frac{17}{{}_1 2} \times \frac{4^2}{11}$$

$$= \frac{34}{11} = 3\frac{1}{11}$$

They averaged $3\frac{1}{11}$ miles per hour.

We can estimate the quotient by rounding each mixed number to the nearest
whole number and dividing.

$$8\frac{1}{2} \div 2\frac{3}{4}$$

The quotient
should be about 3.

228

Assignments

BASIC
page 228 Discuss
page 229 exercises 1–24,
    Keeping Skills Sharp
Basic Worksheet 64

AVERAGE
page 228 Discuss
page 229 exercises 1–26,
    Keeping Skills Sharp
Enrichment Worksheet 64

ENRICHED
page 228 Discuss
page 229 exercises 1–27,
    Keeping Skills Sharp
Enrichment Worksheet 64

EXTRA PRACTICE
page 391 set 70

EXERCISES

First estimate the quotient. Then give the quotient as a mixed number or fraction.

1. $5\frac{1}{2} \div 1\frac{1}{3}$ 2. $3\frac{1}{4} \div 2$ 3. $4\frac{2}{3} \div 1\frac{1}{4}$

4. $6\frac{2}{3} \div 4\frac{1}{5}$ 5. $5 \div 2\frac{1}{3}$ 6. $5\frac{3}{8} \div 4\frac{4}{5}$

7. $8\frac{1}{5} \div 3\frac{3}{4}$ 8. $4\frac{1}{2} \div 2$ 9. $6\frac{1}{2} \div 2\frac{2}{3}$

10. $5\frac{1}{2} \div 2\frac{1}{4}$ 11. $1\frac{1}{3} \div 5$ 12. $5\frac{3}{8} \div 2\frac{1}{3}$

13. $1\frac{3}{4} \div 4\frac{1}{2}$ 14. $3\frac{1}{2} \div 1\frac{1}{8}$ 15. $6\frac{3}{4} \div 3$

16. $5\frac{2}{3} \div 1\frac{1}{4}$ 17. $2\frac{3}{8} \div 1\frac{1}{3}$ 18. $3\frac{1}{2} \div 2\frac{3}{4}$

19. $4 \div 1\frac{1}{9}$ 20. $5 \div 3\frac{5}{8}$ 21. $8\frac{3}{4} \div 3$

22. $6 \div 2\frac{3}{4}$ 23. $4\frac{1}{3} \div 2\frac{1}{2}$ 24. $2 \div 1\frac{1}{2}$

Solve.

25. Laura packed $4\frac{3}{4}$ pounds of food. If she rationed herself to $1\frac{1}{2}$ pounds per day, how many days of food did she pack?

26. Laura and Leslie rented a canoe at Clear Lake for $3\frac{1}{2}$ hours. How much did it cost if the canoe rented for $1.20 an hour?

Work through the path backwards to find the starting number.

27.

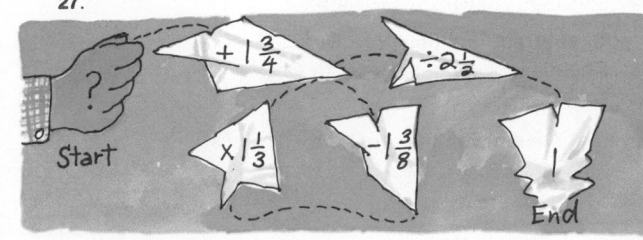

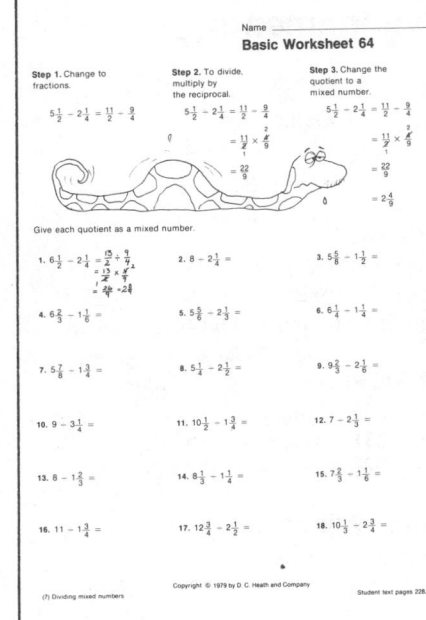

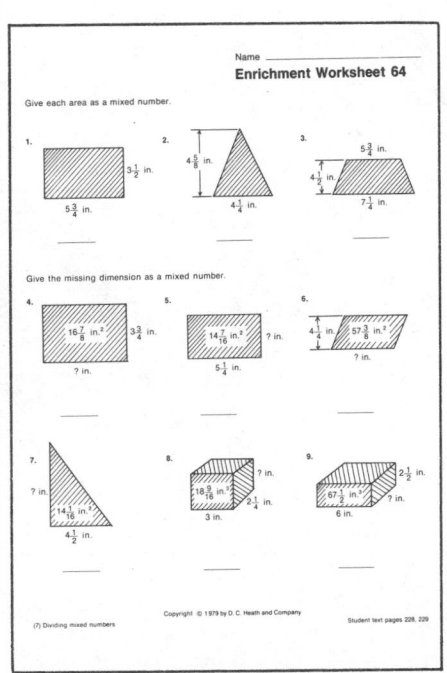

Keeping Skills Sharp

Add or subtract.

1. $4\frac{1}{3}$
   $+2\frac{1}{3}$
   ———
   6 2/3

2. $3\frac{1}{2}$
   $+1\frac{1}{4}$
   ———
   4 3/4

3. $5\frac{1}{2}$
   $+2$
   ———
   7 1/2

4. $2\frac{5}{8}$
   $+2\frac{1}{2}$
   ———
   5 1/8

5. $4\frac{2}{3}$
   $+3\frac{5}{6}$
   ———
   8 1/2

6. $2\frac{1}{6}$
   $+1\frac{5}{6}$
   ———
   4

7. $7\frac{2}{9}$
   $+4\frac{1}{6}$
   ———
   11 7/18

8. $5\frac{3}{8}$
   $-4\frac{2}{3}$
   ———
   17/24

9. $4\frac{5}{9}$
   $-2\frac{1}{9}$
   ———
   2 4/9

10. $3\frac{5}{8}$
   $-1\frac{1}{4}$
   ———
   2 3/8

11. $7\frac{1}{2}$
   $-4\frac{1}{3}$
   ———
   3 11/12

12. 6
   $-1\frac{1}{2}$
   ———
   4 1/2

13. $2\frac{3}{4}$
   $-1\frac{5}{6}$
   ———
   11/12

14. $7\frac{5}{9}$
   $-4\frac{1}{6}$
   ———
   3 7/18

229

Follow-up Activities

Reinforcement At this point you may wish to have students review and practice addition, subtraction, multiplication, and division with mixed numbers. To do this, have them work through the following path to find the ending number. The answer is in red.

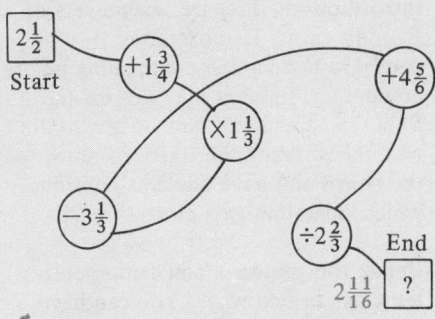

If time permits, have students create some paths of their own for their classmates to determine ending numbers for.

Enrichment Ask your more able students to determine the starting number by working through the path backwards. Notice that to do this they will need to think of inverse operations. For example, the end number was obtained by subtracting $2\frac{1}{2}$ from some number. So to find the number, we can add $2\frac{1}{2}$ to the end. Have students continue to work backwards through the path in this manner.

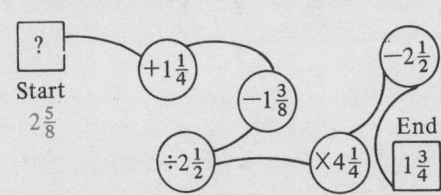

If time permits, have students create some paths of their own for their classmates to find the start or end numbers for.

EXCURSION
There are 6 McIntosh, 6 Delicious, and 6 Cortland apples mixed up in a box. How many apples must you take to be sure of getting at least 2 apples of the same kind? **4**

At least 3 apples of the same kind? **7**

STUDENT OBJECTIVES
To practice estimating and then adding,
   subtracting, multiplying and dividing
   fractions and mixed numbers.
To solve problems involving
   mathematics in careers.

Suggested Lesson Plan

Introduction Prepare several sets of
fraction cards. Use exercises 1–6 on
page 230 to encourage estimating before
computing. Explain the rules for the
Skill Game and call on students to draw
two cards. Write the fractions drawn on
the board and have students consider
which operation gets closest to 1.

Using the pages You can organize
the class in two ways. You can have
two teams and let individual members
take turns playing, or you can organize
several games with two players on a
side. This way each student is involved
and active during the play.

At various times, you can have
teams stop the game and work on the
word problems on page 231, or assign
the problems for written work.

Which is closer to 1?

1. a. $1\frac{3}{4} \div 1\frac{1}{4}$
   b. $1 - \frac{1}{6}$ ✓

2. a. $\frac{3}{8} + \frac{3}{4}$
   b. $\frac{3}{4} \times 1\frac{1}{3}$ ✓

3. a. $1\frac{5}{6} - \frac{7}{8}$ ✓
   b. $2\frac{1}{4} \div 1\frac{5}{6}$

4. a. $\frac{5}{8} + \frac{1}{3}$ ✓
   b. $1\frac{7}{8} - \frac{3}{4}$

5. a. $1\frac{5}{6} - \frac{5}{8}$
   b. $2 \div 1\frac{7}{8}$ ✓

6. a. $2\frac{1}{4} - 1$
   b. $1 \div \frac{7}{8}$ ✓

Play the game.

1. Make this set of cards.

| $\frac{1}{2}$ | $\frac{1}{3}$ | $\frac{1}{4}$ | $\frac{3}{4}$ | $\frac{3}{8}$ | $\frac{5}{8}$ | $\frac{7}{8}$ | $\frac{1}{6}$ | $\frac{5}{6}$ | 1 | $1\frac{1}{4}$ | $1\frac{1}{3}$ |

| $1\frac{1}{2}$ | $1\frac{3}{4}$ | $1\frac{3}{8}$ | $1\frac{5}{8}$ | $1\frac{7}{8}$ | $1\frac{1}{6}$ | $1\frac{5}{6}$ | 2 | $2\frac{1}{4}$ | $2\frac{1}{3}$ | $2\frac{1}{2}$ | $2\frac{3}{8}$ |

2. Divide the class into two teams.

3. Mix up the cards. A player from each team picks two cards.

4. Each player may either add, subtract, multiply, or divide
   the two numbers he picks. The player who gets closer to 1
   earns a point for his team.

5. After all players have played, the team with the greater total wins the game.

230

Assignments

BASIC
page 230 Game
page 231 exercises 1–4
Basic Worksheet 65

AVERAGE
page 230 Game
page 231 exercises 1–6
Enrichment Worksheet 65

ENRICHED
page 230 Game
page 231 exercises 1–6
Enrichment Worksheet 65

REVIEW PRACTICE
page 385 set 48

Mathematics in careers

Workers in a greenhouse must often use mathematics in their work. They follow recipes for mixing soil, apply fertilizers according to formulas, and compute costs, prices, and taxes.

Here is a recipe for potting soil.

2 parts loam

$1\frac{1}{2}$ parts peat moss

1 part coarse sand

1 lb of bone meal for each bushel of mixture

1. A worker mixing potting soil started with 4 bushels of loam. How much peat moss did he need? **3 bushels**

2. How much bone meal would be used in a mixture that started with 8 bushels of loam? **18 lb**

3. How much peat moss would be used with 3 bushels of sand? $4\frac{1}{2}$ **bushels**

4. How much loam would be used with 6 bushels of peat moss? **8 bushels**

5. A fertilizer marked 5-10-5 is $\frac{5}{100}$ nitrogen, $\frac{10}{100}$ phosphorus, and $\frac{5}{100}$ potash. How much nitrogen is in a 50-lb bag of the fertilizer? $2\frac{1}{2}$ **lb**

6. How much phosphorus is in a 25-lb bag of fertilizer marked 10-15-15? $3\frac{3}{4}$ **lb**

231

Follow-up Activities

Reinforcement As the teams play, see whether some students have difficulty deciding on the correct operation. Have these students compete against each other. Rather than try to force the estimation, have the students perform each operation with the numbers drawn and then select the result closest to 1—thus encouraging more computation, which is probably what these students need.

Enrichment Organize the class into two-person teams for the Skill Game. After everyone has played the game several times, conduct a tournament with the winning teams playing other winning teams until one team is declared the room champion.

EXCURSION

How would you stack these blocks in order to get the smallest surface area?

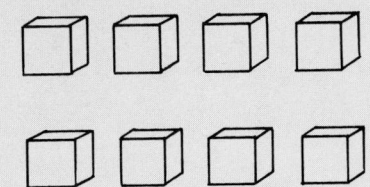

Form a cube.

STUDENT OBJECTIVE
To solve word problems involving
fractions and mixed numbers.

Suggested Lesson Plan

Introduction Use the theme of recipes
for large amounts of foods to start the
discussion to this lesson. You might
want to have a cook for the school lunch
program talk to the class and provide
recipes for additional problems.

Using the pages Review the recipes
on pages 232 and 233. Introduce
problems 1–5 by asking the students
what number they should multiply each
ingredient by to find the new amount.
Since they wish to make 10 dozen and
the recipe is for 4 dozen, each amount
should be multiplied by $^{10}\!/_4$, or $2^1\!/_2$.
Without further discussion, have
students work exercises 1–11 for
written work.

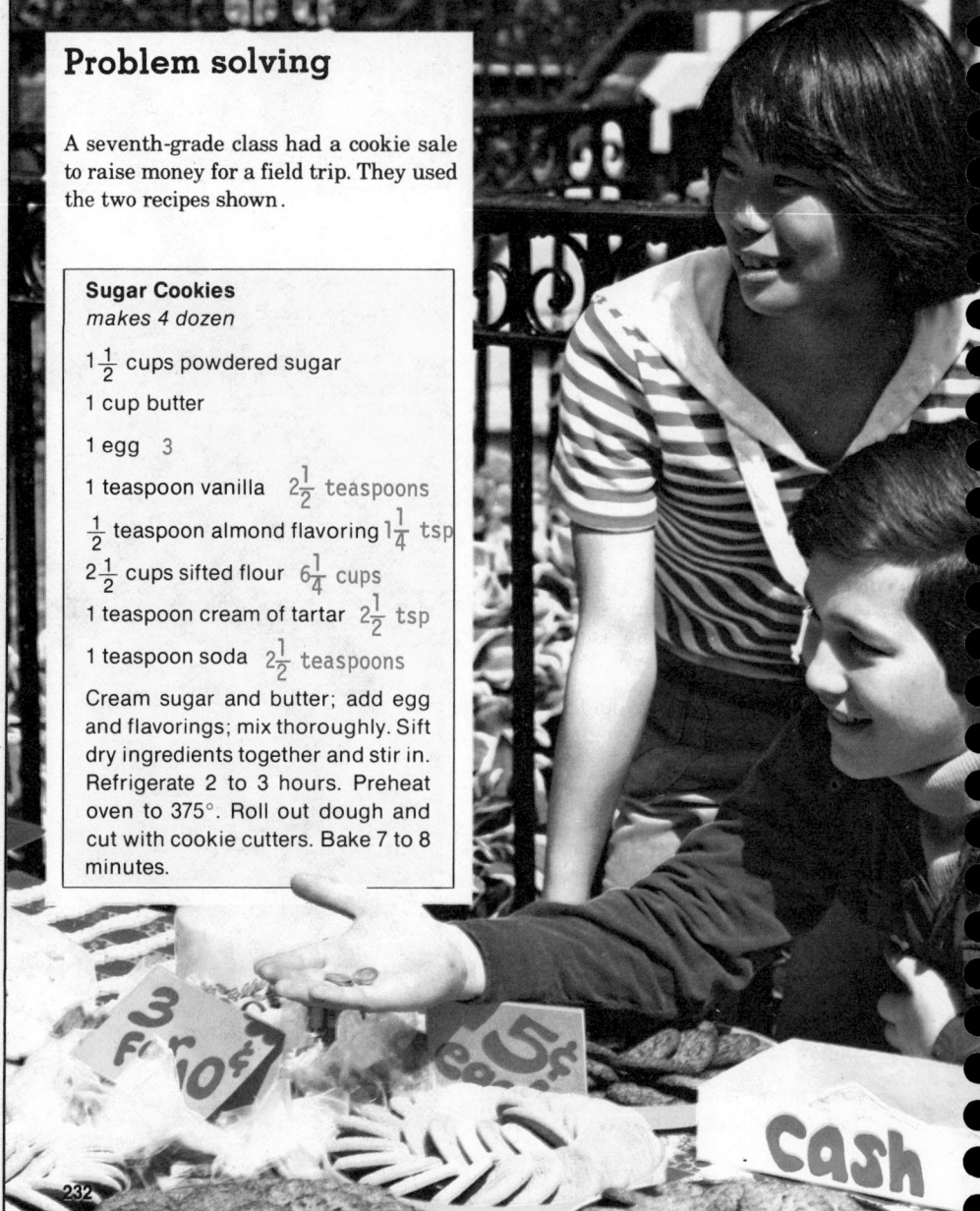

Problem solving

A seventh-grade class had a cookie sale
to raise money for a field trip. They used
the two recipes shown.

Sugar Cookies
makes 4 dozen

$1\frac{1}{2}$ cups powdered sugar

1 cup butter

1 egg   3

1 teaspoon vanilla $2\frac{1}{2}$ teaspoons

$\frac{1}{2}$ teaspoon almond flavoring $1\frac{1}{4}$ tsp

$2\frac{1}{2}$ cups sifted flour $6\frac{1}{4}$ cups

1 teaspoon cream of tartar $2\frac{1}{2}$ tsp

1 teaspoon soda $2\frac{1}{2}$ teaspoons

Cream sugar and butter; add egg
and flavorings; mix thoroughly. Sift
dry ingredients together and stir in.
Refrigerate 2 to 3 hours. Preheat
oven to 375°. Roll out dough and
cut with cookie cutters. Bake 7 to 8
minutes.

Assignments

BASIC
page 232 Discuss
page 233 exercises 1–11
Basic Worksheet 65

AVERAGE
page 232 Discuss
page 233 exercises 1–11
Enrichment Worksheet 65

ENRICHED
page 232 Discuss
page 233 exercises 1–11
Enrichment Worksheet 65

REVIEW PRACTICE
page 385 set 49

EXTRA PROBLEM SOLVING
pages 414–415 set 9

Nut 'n' Chip Cookies
makes 3 dozen

$1\frac{1}{2}$ cups whole-wheat flour

$\frac{1}{4}$ cup nonfat dry milk $\frac{5}{6}$ cup

$\frac{1}{2}$ teaspoon baking soda

$\frac{1}{2}$ teaspoon salt $1\frac{2}{3}$ teaspoons

4 tablespoons butter $13\frac{1}{3}$ tbsp

$\frac{3}{4}$ cup packed brown sugar $2\frac{1}{2}$ cups

2 eggs 7

2 tablespoons water $6\frac{2}{3}$ tbsp

$\frac{1}{2}$ teaspoon vanilla $1\frac{2}{3}$ tsp

1 cup semi-sweet chocolate chips

$\frac{1}{2}$ cup walnuts $1\frac{2}{3}$ cups $3\frac{1}{3}$ cups

$\frac{1}{4}$ cup pecans $\frac{5}{6}$ cup

Thoroughly mix flour, dry milk, soda, and salt. Cream together butter and brown sugar. Blend eggs, water, and vanilla. Add flour mixture and blend well. Stir in chocolate chips and nuts. Drop by teaspoons on a greased cookie sheet. Bake at 375° for 8 to 10 minutes.

A group of students made 10 dozen nut 'n' chip cookies.

1. How many recipes was 10 dozen cookies? $3\frac{1}{3}$

2. How much flour did they use? 5 cups

3. How much baking soda did they use? $1\frac{2}{3}$ teaspoons

4. How much of the other ingredients did they use? See left.

5. If they had 6 cups of brown sugar before baking the cookies, how much should they have had after baking the cookies? $3\frac{1}{2}$ cups

Another group of students made 10 dozen sugar cookies.

6. How many recipes was 10 dozen cookies? $2\frac{1}{2}$

7. How much powdered sugar did they use? $3\frac{3}{4}$ cups

8. How much butter did they use? $2\frac{1}{2}$ c

9. How much of the other ingredients did they use? See page 232.

10. How many sugar cookies can be made with $\frac{3}{4}$ cup of powdered sugar? 2 dozen

11. How many nut 'n' chip cookies can be made with 1 cup of whole-wheat flour? 2 dozen

233

Follow-up Activities

Reinforcement Each student should bring in a recipe. Have students determine how many people each recipe would serve, and then change the amounts of the ingredients to prepare enough for the class.

Enrichment Have each student bring in a recipe. Proceed as with the reinforcement activity, except this time ask for recipes that would serve the entire school. Tell the students to name the amounts needed with larger units.

EXCURSION
A balance has only two weights, 1 g and 4 g. In three weighings, split 180 g of cereal into two packages of 40 g and 140 g. **1.** Split the 180 g between the two pans of the balance. Each will hold 90 g. **2.** Split one 90-g batch into 45 g and 45 g, again using the balance without the weights. **3.** Remove 5 g from a 45-g batch by balancing against the two weights. Now you have 40 g for one package, and the rest of the cereal is 140 g for the second package.

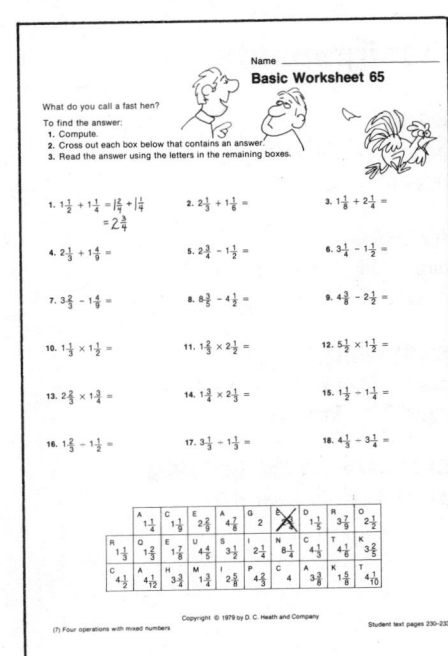

STUDENT OBJECTIVE
To review the concepts introduced in Chapter 7.

Suggested Lesson Plan

Introduction No pre-text activity is necessary for page 234 as this is a checkup for the chapter. However, it may be valuable to briefly review the lessons in the chapter so that students are reminded of the content over which they will be tested.

This Checkup will provide you with data about how well individual students have mastered the skills of the chapter. The Chapter Review on page 236 is provided for those students who need more specific individual help.

The project on page 235 can be assigned as an individual activity or you can have students work in teams to make a graph of their time and how they use it.

You may need to point out that students need to make a fraction for the time spent on any one activity, and then multiply this fraction by 360 to determine the number of degrees in the central angle of the circle graph.

Using the pages Assign all the exercises on page 234. As students complete the page they can work on the project on page 235.

Solve. [206–207, 218–219, 232–233]

1. $\frac{1}{2}$ of 16 = ? 8
2. $\frac{2}{3}$ of 81 = ? 54
3. $\frac{4}{3}$ of 132 = ? 176
4. $\frac{1}{3}$ of ? = 8 24
5. $\frac{5}{8}$ of ? = 65 104
6. $\frac{3}{2}$ of ? = 921 614

7. A record that regularly sells for $5.76 is on sale for $\frac{2}{3}$ of its regular price. What is the sale price? $3.84

8. A girls' club has raised $120 to buy books for the library. This is $\frac{4}{5}$ of the total money needed. How much is the total amount? $150

Give each product in lowest terms. [pages 204–205, 216]

9. $\frac{3}{4} \times \frac{1}{2}$ $\frac{3}{8}$
10. $\frac{2}{3} \times 2$ $\frac{4}{3}$
11. $\frac{7}{8} \times \frac{0}{3}$ 0
12. $\frac{5}{9} \times \frac{3}{4}$ $\frac{5}{12}$
13. $\frac{5}{8} \times \frac{8}{5}$ 1
14. $\frac{3}{2} \times \frac{5}{6}$ $\frac{5}{4}$
15. $9 \times \frac{4}{3}$ 12
16. $\frac{8}{3} \times \frac{3}{4}$ 2

Give each quotient in lowest terms. [pages 212–213, 217]

17. $\frac{3}{4} \div \frac{1}{4}$ 3
18. $3 \div \frac{2}{3}$ $\frac{9}{2}$
19. $\frac{4}{3} \div \frac{2}{5}$ $\frac{10}{3}$
20. $\frac{7}{8} \div \frac{3}{4}$ $\frac{7}{6}$
21. $\frac{5}{6} \div \frac{2}{3}$ $\frac{5}{4}$
22. $\frac{7}{8} \div \frac{3}{2}$ $\frac{7}{12}$
23. $\frac{5}{6} \div 4$ $\frac{5}{24}$
24. $\frac{9}{4} \div \frac{3}{8}$ 6

Copy and complete this table. Give fractions in lowest terms. [pages 222–225]

	25.	26.	27.	28.	29.	30.	31.	32.
Fraction	$\frac{6}{10}$	$\frac{27}{100}$	$\frac{1}{4}$	$\frac{3}{10}$	$\frac{17}{25}$	$\frac{3}{2}$	$\frac{5}{4}$	$\frac{2}{3}$
Decimal	0.6	0.27	0.25	0.3	0.68	1.5	.25	$0.66\frac{2}{3}$

Multiply. Give the product as a mixed or whole number. [pages 226–227]

33. $2\frac{1}{2} \times 3$ $7\frac{1}{2}$
34. $4 \times 2\frac{3}{4}$ 11
35. $1\frac{1}{2} \times 3\frac{3}{4}$ $5\frac{5}{8}$
36. $2\frac{5}{8} \times 3\frac{2}{3}$ $9\frac{5}{8}$

Divide. Give the quotient as a mixed number. [pages 228–229]

37. $8\frac{1}{2} \div 1\frac{3}{4}$ $4\frac{6}{7}$
38. $6\frac{2}{3} \div 2$ $3\frac{1}{3}$
39. $9\frac{1}{4} \div 2\frac{3}{8}$ $3\frac{17}{19}$
40. $10\frac{5}{6} \div 3\frac{2}{3}$ $2\frac{21}{22}$

234

Assignments

BASIC
page 234 exercises 1—40
page 235 Project

AVERAGE
page 234 exercises 1—40
page 235 Project

ENRICHED
page 234 exercises 1—40
page 235 Project

EXTRA PROBLEM SOLVING
pages 416–417 set 10

Project

1. List the following activities. For a typical school day, estimate the fraction of a whole day (24 hours) spent on each activity.

   a. sleeping
   b. eating
   c. going to and from school
   d. doing class work
   e. doing homework
   f. socializing
   g. watching television
   h. other

2. Show how you spend your time by making a circle graph.

   EXAMPLE.

   Suppose $\frac{5}{12}$ of the day is spent sleeping.

   $\frac{5}{12}$ of $360° = 150°$ ← angle shaded for sleeping

Sleeping

235

You may wish to assign some of the Creative Problem Solving Activities (pages 461-477) at this time.

Follow-up Activities

Reinforcement Correct the items in the Chapter Checkup. Any student who misses six or more, or any more than three problems in a section, needs additional help. It is important for each student to achieve some degree of mastery of the basic skills with fractions and mixed numbers. With the increasing use of decimals, it is probably even more important that students compute correctly with decimals.

Enrichment Assign these pupils to the games and activities that have been played throughout the chapter. Assign a student leader to be responsible for teaching each game or activity to the interested students and to supervise the play.

STUDENT OBJECTIVE
To review or extend the skills and concepts taught in Chapter 7.

Suggested Lesson Plan

Introduction After checking the Chapter Checkup you will know which students need additional reinforcement and which ones will be able to go ahead with the Challenge activity. Get the better students started on page 237 first, as the students who are having difficulty will need more of your time.

The students who need more review should go back and correct their errors on the Chapter Checkup. You may want to go over those questions orally if this group is small enough. Carefully probe to determine which concepts and skills the students have not mastered and work individually to correct their deficiencies.

Using the pages After the identified students have corrected the Chapter Checkup, they should answer questions 1–30 on page 236.

After they complete these questions, read the answers and let the students correct their own papers. Give them the opportunity to ask questions about the exercises they missed.

Assign page 237 to those students who did well on the Chapter Checkup. Students should work individually on these exercises.

To find a fraction of a quantity, divide by the denominator and multiply by the numerator.

$$\frac{2}{3} \text{ of } 36 = 24$$

$$\frac{3}{5} \times \frac{3}{2} = \frac{9}{10}$$

To divide, multiply by the reciprocal.

$$\frac{4}{3} \div \frac{2}{5} = \frac{4}{3} \times \frac{5}{2}$$
$$= \frac{20}{6}$$
$$= \frac{10}{3}$$

$$2\frac{1}{2} \times 3\frac{3}{4} = \frac{5}{2} \times \frac{15}{4}$$
$$= \frac{75}{8}$$
$$= 9\frac{3}{8}$$

$$8\frac{2}{3} \div 1\frac{3}{4} = \frac{26}{3} \div \frac{7}{4}$$
$$= \frac{26}{3} \times \frac{4}{7}$$
$$= \frac{104}{21}$$
$$= 4\frac{20}{21}$$

Complete.

1. $\frac{1}{4}$ of 20 = ?   5
2. $\frac{1}{3}$ of 24 = ?   8
3. $\frac{3}{4}$ of 36 = ?   27
4. $\frac{3}{2}$ of 18 = ?   27
5. $\frac{5}{8}$ of 40 = ?   25
6. $\frac{7}{3}$ of 42 = ?   98

Give each product in lowest terms.

7. $3 \times \frac{1}{2}$ $\frac{3}{2}$
8. $\frac{7}{8} \times \frac{2}{5}$ $\frac{7}{20}$
9. $\frac{2}{3} \times 4$ $\frac{8}{3}$
10. $\frac{3}{4} \times \frac{2}{3}$ $\frac{1}{2}$
11. $\frac{5}{6} \times \frac{6}{5}$ 1
12. $\frac{5}{9} \times \frac{3}{8}$ $\frac{5}{24}$

Give each quotient in lowest terms.

13. $\frac{5}{6} \div \frac{1}{2}$ $\frac{5}{3}$
14. $\frac{2}{3} \div 3$ $\frac{2}{9}$
15. $\frac{7}{8} \div \frac{3}{4}$ $\frac{7}{6}$
16. $\frac{5}{9} \div \frac{5}{3}$ $\frac{1}{3}$
17. $4 \div \frac{7}{8}$ $\frac{32}{7}$
18. $\frac{6}{5} \div \frac{5}{9}$ $\frac{54}{25}$

Give each product as a mixed or whole number.

19. $2\frac{1}{2} \times 6$ 15
20. $2\frac{1}{5} \times 3\frac{1}{4}$ $7\frac{3}{20}$
21. $8 \times 3\frac{2}{3}$ $29\frac{1}{3}$
22. $1\frac{1}{5} \times 5\frac{1}{2}$ $6\frac{3}{5}$
23. $9\frac{3}{4} \times 3\frac{1}{3}$ $32\frac{1}{2}$
24. $4\frac{3}{5} \times 2\frac{3}{8}$ $10\frac{37}{40}$

Give each quotient as a mixed number.

25. $9\frac{1}{2} \div 3$ $3\frac{1}{6}$
26. $8 \div 2\frac{1}{2}$ $3\frac{1}{5}$
27. $5\frac{1}{2} \div 1\frac{1}{4}$ $4\frac{2}{5}$
28. $6\frac{3}{5} \div 2\frac{1}{3}$ $2\frac{29}{35}$
29. $8\frac{3}{8} \div 1\frac{2}{3}$ $5\frac{1}{40}$
30. $6\frac{2}{3} \div 1\frac{2}{5}$ $4\frac{16}{21}$

236

Assignments

BASIC
page 236   exercises 1–30

AVERAGE
page 236   exercises 1–30

ENRICHED
page 237   exercises 1–12

CHAPTER CHALLENGE

You remember that multiplying a number by 1 does not change the number: $16 \times 1 = 16$, $\frac{4}{5} \times 1 = \frac{4}{5}$. You probably also remember that there are lots of ways to write 1: $\frac{2}{2}$, $\frac{8}{8}$, $\frac{65}{65}$, etc. Here are some other ways to write 1, which are different from the ways you already know:

$$\frac{1 \text{ ft}}{12 \text{ in.}} \qquad \frac{12 \text{ in.}}{1 \text{ ft}} \qquad \frac{1 \text{ yd}}{3 \text{ ft}} \qquad \frac{16 \text{ oz}}{1 \text{ lb}} \qquad \frac{2 \text{ c}}{1 \text{ pt}}$$

Fractions like these are called **conversion fractions**. They can be used to convert a measurement from one unit to another unit.

EXAMPLE 1. Convert 32 feet to inches.

Choose an appropriate conversion fraction.   Cancel units.   Multiply.

$$32 \text{ ft} \times \frac{12 \text{ in.}}{1 \text{ ft}} \quad = \quad 32 \cancel{\text{ ft}} \times \frac{12 \text{ in.}}{1 \cancel{\text{ ft}}} \quad = \quad 384 \text{ in.}$$

Choose a conversion fraction whose denominator is the unit you began with and whose numerator is the unit you wish to end with.

You may use more than one conversion fraction.

EXAMPLE 2. Convert 80,000 ounces to tons.

$$\overset{5}{\underset{1}{\cancel{\underset{5000}{\cancel{80,000}}}}} \text{ oz} \times \frac{1 \cancel{\text{ lb}}}{\underset{1}{\cancel{16 \text{ oz}}}} \times \frac{1 \text{ T}}{\underset{2}{\cancel{2000 \text{ lb}}}} = \frac{5}{2}\text{T} = 2\frac{1}{2}\text{T}$$

EXERCISES
Complete. Use conversion fractions.

1. 16 pt = $\underline{\ ?\ }$ gal   2   2. 16 gal = $\underline{\ ?\ }$ pt   128   3. 6 qt = $\underline{\ ?\ }$ c   24   4. 6 c = $\underline{\ ?\ }$ qt $1\frac{1}{2}$

5. 3 ft² = $\underline{\ ?\ }$ in.²   432   6. 6 ft² = $\underline{\ ?\ }$ yd² $\frac{2}{3}$ 7. 1 mi = $\underline{\ ?\ }$ in.   8. 2 yd³ = $\underline{\ ?\ }$ ft³

   ⏜ ft × ft ⏜   ⏜ in. × in. ⏜   63,360   54

9. 283 km = $\underline{\ ?\ }$ m   10. 283 m = $\underline{\ ?\ }$ km   11. 12 kg = $\underline{\ ?\ }$ mg   12. 12 mg = $\underline{\ ?\ }$ kg

   283,000   0.283   12,000,000   0.000012

237

STUDENT OBJECTIVES

To practice skills learned previously.
To practice using a standardized-test
format.

Suggested Lesson Plan

Using the pages The Major Checkup
at the end of each chapter of this textbook
is given in standardized-test format. The
answer sheet on page 448 is the type used
with many standardized tests. You may
duplicate it for use with the Major
Checkups.

Pass out the answer sheets and be
sure students understand how to use
them. Allow a specified time, perhaps
twenty minutes, to complete the
checkup. Assign the exercises and use
the results to determine what review is
needed.

The table below correlates the test
items and the student text pages. Assign
review exercises as indicated by the
Major Checkup results.

Test Item	Text Pages	Test Item	Text Pages
1	64–65	7	142–143
2	66–67	8	150–151
3	68–69	9	114–115
4	86–87	10	110–111
5	96–97	11	188–189
6	136–137	12	190–191

Chapter 7 Postest

See page 54 for a full discussion of how
to use the posttest. The table below
suggests Extra Practice exercises and
Basic Worksheets for those students
who need further practice or reteaching.

Objectives	Extra Practice Sets	Pages	Basic Worksheets
7-1	62–63	389	55–57
7-2	65–66	389–390	58–61
7-3	67	390	62
7-4	68	390	
7-5	69	391	63
7-6	70	391	64

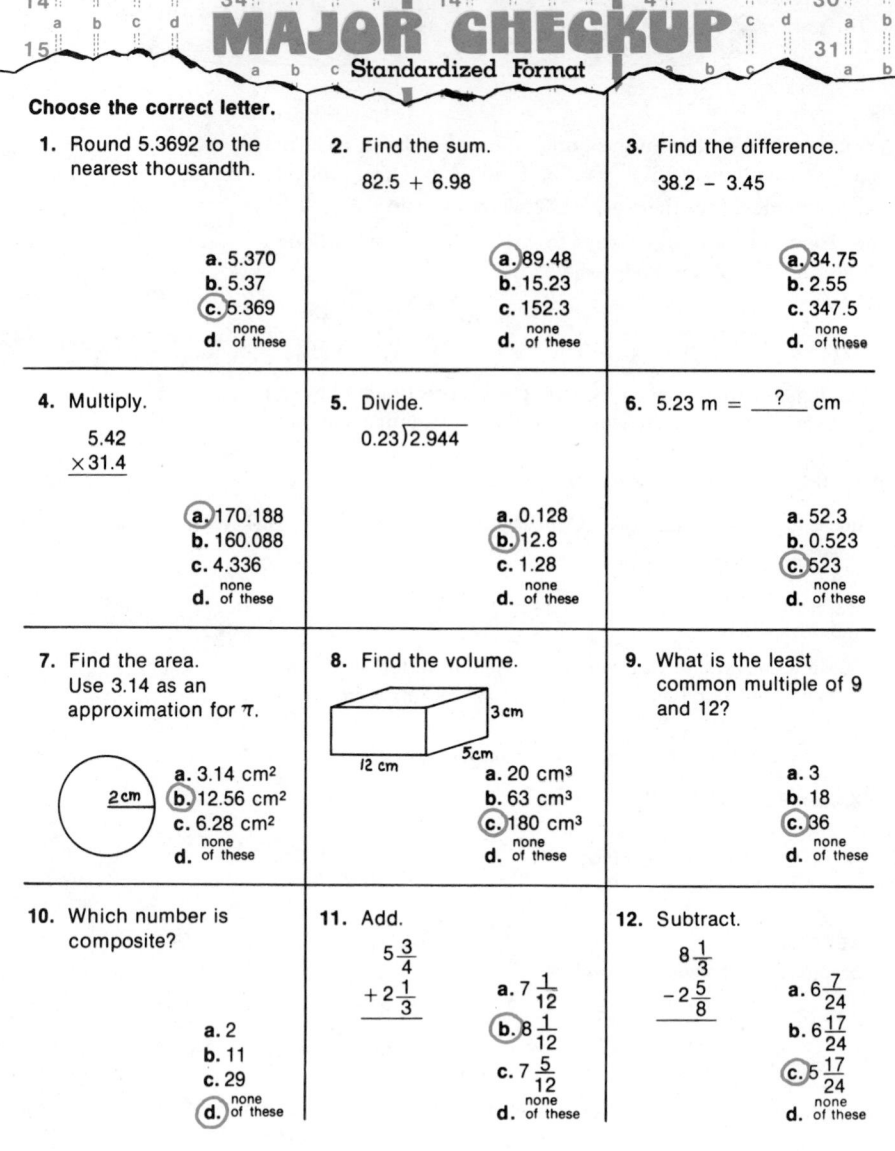

238 Lesson 110

Answers for Chapter 7 Posttest

1. $\frac{3}{10}$ 2. $\frac{1}{2}$ 3. $\frac{5}{16}$ 4. 1 5. $\frac{6}{35}$ 6. $\frac{8}{15}$
7. 2 8. $\frac{5}{2}$ 9. 1 10. $\frac{21}{8}$ 11. 0.25
12. 0.375 13. 0.8 14. $\frac{1}{2}$ 15. $\frac{3}{4}$ 16. $\frac{7}{8}$
17. $0.\overline{3}$ 18. $\frac{2}{9}$ 19. $0.8\overline{3}$ 20. $5\frac{1}{3}$
21. $15\frac{3}{4}$ 22. $2\frac{1}{2}$ 23. 16 24. $1\frac{5}{6}$
25. $1\frac{7}{32}$ 26. 6 27. 4

Chapter 7 Posttest

Name _____

Date _____

Multiply. [Obj. 7-1, pages 204–209, 214, 216]

1. $\frac{3}{4} \times \frac{2}{5} =$ _____

2. $\frac{3}{4} \times \frac{2}{3} =$ _____

3. $\frac{3}{8} \times \frac{5}{6} =$ _____

4. $\frac{3}{4} \times \frac{4}{3} =$ _____

5. $\frac{2}{7} \times \frac{3}{5} =$ _____

Divide. [Obj. 7-2, pages 210–214, 217, 220–221]

| 0 | 1 | 2 | 3 | 4 | 5 |

6. $\frac{2}{5} \div \frac{3}{4} =$ _____

7. $\frac{4}{5} \div \frac{2}{5} =$ _____

8. $\frac{5}{8} \div \frac{1}{4} =$ _____

9. $\frac{3}{5} \div \frac{3}{5} =$ _____

10. $\frac{3}{4} \div \frac{2}{7} =$ _____

Complete this table. [Obj. 7-3, pages 222–223]

| 0 | 1 | 2 | 3 | 4 | 5 | 6 |

Fraction	$\frac{1}{4}$	$\frac{3}{8}$	$\frac{4}{5}$	**14.**	**15.**	**16.**
Decimal	**11.**	**12.**	**13.**	0.5	0.75	0.875

Complete this table. [Obj. 7-4, pages 224–225]

| 0 | 1 | 2 | 3 |

Fraction	$\frac{1}{3}$	**18.**	$\frac{5}{6}$
Repeating Decimal	**17.**	$0.\overline{2}$	**19.**

Multiply. [Obj. 7-5, pages 226–227]

| 0 | 1 | 2 | 3 |

20. $3\frac{1}{5} \times 1\frac{2}{3} =$ _____

21. $7 \times 2\frac{1}{4} =$ _____

22. $3\frac{3}{4} \times \frac{2}{3} =$ _____

Divide. [Obj. 7-6, pages 228–229]

| 0 | 1 | 2 | 3 |

23. $4 \div \frac{1}{4} =$ _____

24. $3\frac{2}{3} \div 2 =$ _____

25. $3\frac{1}{4} \div 2\frac{2}{3} =$ _____

Solve. [Obj. 7-7, pages 218–219, 231–233]

| 0 | 1 | 2 |

26. Three fourths of the apples in a bag of 2 dozen apples are rotten. How many apples in the bag are not rotten? _____

27. How many pieces of rope $2\frac{1}{4}$-feet long can be cut from a piece of rope that is 9 feet long? _____

Chapter 8
Ratios and Percent

Pages 239–272

Learning Objectives

After completing this chapter, all students should be able to do the following:

8-1　Write the ratio of two quantities.

8-2　Solve proportions.

8-3　Make conversions among fractions, decimals, and percents.

8-4　Find what percent one number is of another.

8-5　Find a given percent of a number.

8-6　Find a number when a given percent of it is known.

8-7　Solve word problems that involve percents.

Ratio and proportion are reviewed, and proportions are solved. Then proportions are used to solve various real problems, particularly rate problems. Percent notation is then introduced and students learn the relationships among percents, fractions, and decimals. Then students learn to solve the three kinds of percent problems and to apply this ability to real problems.

Mathematics

Ratio and proportion. A ratio is the quotient of two quantities, usually stated as a pure number—that is, without a unit. For example, the ratio of the number of red dots to

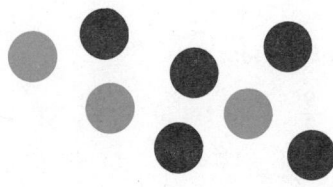

the number of black dots is $^3/_5$; or, for short, the ratio of red dots to black dots is $^3/_5$. Any fraction equivalent to $^3/_5$ can be used, or entirely different notations can be used:

$$3 \text{ to } 5 \qquad 3 : 5$$

Although this use of fractional notation may be new to students, the idea is not. They have on many occasions made statements like this: "In the example above, $^3/_8$ of the dots are red." This is equivalent to saying that the ratio of red dots to all the dots is 3 to 8.

A proportion is an equation both of whose members are ratios. In a proportion the product of the numerator of one ratio and the denominator of the other is equal to the product of the denominator of the first by the numerator of the second.

$$\frac{a}{b} = \frac{c}{d}$$
$$ad = bc$$

The fact that each proportion has a related multiplication equation gives a simple way of solving proportions—change to the related multiplication equation, which we already know how to solve:

$$\frac{5}{a} = \frac{7}{9}$$
$$7a = 45$$
$$a = 6\frac{3}{7}$$

Rates. A rate is the quotient of two quantities (usually unlike) and is generally stated as a denominate number, that is, with a unit. For example, 60 miles per hour (60 miles ÷ 1 hour) and 10¢ per apple (10 cents ÷ 1 apple) are rates. Rates are generally stated "per *unit* quantity." That is, we would generally not give a rate as "120 miles per 2 hours." Instead, we would say, "60 miles per [1] hour."

Percent problems. Once students can solve proportions, they are equipped to solve all percent problems of the form $a\%$ of $b = c$. That equation is equivalent to this proportion:

$$\frac{a}{100} = \frac{c}{b}$$

Therefore, all a student needs to do is substitute the proportion for the equation and solve by using the related multiplication equation.

$$a \times b = 100 \times c$$

Another equivalent equation is:

$$\frac{a \times b}{100} = c$$

Instead of substituting values for a, b, or c in the proportion, we could go straight to one of the other equations. This is commonly done.

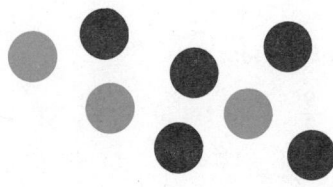

239a

Teaching the Chapter

This chapter is very important. The concepts developed here are widely used. Students should definitely learn to solve proportions and percent problems.

Many students find that solving word problems involving percents is very difficult. Here is a method that we have found works very well for most of the problems that students will have to solve. Consider this typical word problem:

> The enrollment of Robinson Junior High School is 900. One day 5% of the students are absent. How many students are absent?

Students should look for the *key sentence* in the problem. The key sentence is the one that has the same basic structure as this one: $a\%$ of $b = c$. In the problem above, the key sentence is "One day 5% of the students are absent." Now we eliminate unnecessary words from the sentence and substitute numerals or variables where possible.

~~One day~~ 5% of the students are absent.

| 5% of | 900 | = | x |

Now the rest is easy for most students who have learned the use of proportions as taught in this text.

Here is another example:

> John spent 15% of his weekly earnings for a radio. The radio cost $32.50. What are John's weekly earnings?

Key sentence:

~~John~~ spent 15% of his weekly earnings for a radio.

| 15% of | y | = | $32.50 |

Consider one more example:

> Karen spent $20 of the $80 she had saved. What percent of her savings did she spend?

Key sentence:

What percent of her savings did she spend?

| $x\%$ | of | $80 | = | $20 |

Once again, when a student has come this far, the rest is easy.

Vocabulary

cross products
percent
proportion
rate
ratio
scale drawing

Symbols

$a : b$ the ratio of a to b
$\%$ percent

Materials

sticks of varying length
hand calculators
digit cards
items from grocery store with price tags
maps of small areas
road maps
spring with different weights

Chapter Tests

For a discussion of how to use the chapter tests, please see page 17c.

Answers for Chapter 8 Pretest

1. $\frac{3}{4}$ 2. $\frac{4}{2}$ 3. $\frac{3}{9}$ 4. $\frac{9}{2}$ 5. 10 6. 20 7. $9\frac{1}{3}$ 8. $15\frac{3}{4}$
9. 0.72 10. 0.06 11. 32% 12. 6.2% 13. $\frac{1}{2}$ 14. $\frac{1}{3}$
15. 75% 16. $66\frac{2}{3}\%$ 17. 75 18. 125 19. $33\frac{1}{3}$ 20. 100
21. 17 22. 40 23. 15 24. 21 25. 6.08 26. 50 27. 76
28. 0.74 29. 20 30. 30 31. 48 32. 54 33. 8 34. 375
35. $71.25 36. 20%

Chapter 8 Pretest

Name _____

Date _____

Write the ratios. [Obj. 8-1, pages 240–241]

0	1	2	3	4

1. squares to circles _____

2. circles to triangles _____

3. shaded figures to all figures _____

4. all figures to triangles _____

0	1	2	3	4

Solve. [Obj. 8-2, pages 242–243, 250]

5. $\frac{2}{3} = \frac{a}{15}$ 6. $\frac{4}{5} = \frac{16}{b}$ 7. $\frac{3}{4} = \frac{7}{c}$ 8. $\frac{n}{9} = \frac{7}{4}$

_____   _____   _____   _____

0-3	4	5	6	7	8

Complete. [Obj. 8-3, pages 252–257]

Percent	72%	6%	**11.**	**12.**
Decimal	**9.**	**10.**	0.32	0.062

Percent	50%	$33\frac{1}{3}$%	**15.**	**16.**
Fraction	**13.**	**14.**	$\frac{3}{4}$	$\frac{2}{3}$

Complete. [Obj. 8-4, pages 256–257]

0	1	2	3	4	5	6

17. $15 =$ ____% of 20   18. $30 =$ ____% of 24   19. $6 =$ ____% of 18

20. $90 =$ ____% of 90   21. $17 =$ ____% of 100   22. $16 =$ ____% of 40

0	1	2	3	4	5	6

Complete. [Obj. 8-5, pages 258–261, 264]

23. 30% of 50 = ____   24. 75% of 28 = ____   25. 16% of 38 = ____

26. 125% of 40 = ____   27. 400% of 19 = ____   28. 1% of 74 = ____

0	1	2	3	4	5	6

Complete. [Obj. 8-6, pages 262–264]

29. 50% of ____ = 10   30. 100% of ____ = 30   31. 25% of ____ = 12

32. $33\frac{1}{3}$% of ____ = 18   33. 150% of ____ = 12   34. 12% of ____ = 45

0	1	2

Solve. [Obj. 8-7, pages 257, 259, 263, 265–267]

35. A suit regularly priced at $95 was on sale at 25% off. What was the sale price?

36. Sixteen of 20 students got A on a test. What percent of the students did not get A?

_____   _____

Chapter 8
Record and Assignment Chart

Name _____

Pretest Date _____ Posttest Date _____

Objectives

		Pretest Score — Mark number correct	Posttest Score — Mark number correct
8-1	Write the ratio of two quantities.	0 1 2 3 | 4	0 1 2 3 | 4
8-2	Solve proportions.	0 1 2 | 3 4	0 1 2 | 3 4
8-3	Make conversions among fractions, decimals, and percents.	0-3 4 5 6 | 7 8	0-3 4 5 6 | 7 8
8-4	Find what percent one number is of another.	0-1 2 3 4 | 5 6	0-1 2 3 4 | 5 6
8-5	Find a given percent of a number.	0-1 2 3 4 | 5 6	0-1 2 3 4 | 5 6
8-6	Find a number when a given percent of it is known.	0-1 2 3 4 | 5 6	0-1 2 3 4 | 5 6
8-7	Solve word problems that involve percents.	0 1 | 2	0 1 | 2

Unsatisfactory Score \| Satisfactory Score   Unsatisfactory Score \| Satisfactory Score

TEACHING ASSIGNMENTS*

	Student Page	Basic Assignment	Average Assignment	Enriched Assignment	Problem Solving	RETEACHING ASSIGNMENTS†
8-1	240, 241	1–29	1–29, EW 66	1–29, EW 66		BW 66
8-2	242, 243	1–28	1–28, EW 67	1–28, EW 67		page 391 Set 71, BW 67
8-2	244, 245	1–6	1–6, EW 67	1–6, EW 67		BW 67
8-2	246, 247	1–8	1–8, EW 68	1–8, EW 68	9, 10, 11, 12, 13, 14, 15, 16	page 391 Set 72, BW 68
	248, 249	1–6	1–8, EW 69	1–8, EW 69		BW 69
8-2	250	1–28	1–30, EW 69	1–32, EW 69		BW 69
	251	1–4	1–4	1–4		BW 69
8-3	252, 253	1–56	1–56, EW 70	1–60, EW 70		page 392 Set 73, BW 70
	254, 255	1–55	1–60, EW 70	1–65, EW 70		page 392 Set 74, BW 70
8-3 8-4 8-7	256, 257	1–24	1–24, EW 71	1–24, EW 71	25, 26, 27, 28 29, 30	page 392 Set 75, BW 71
8-5	258, 259	1–27	1–27, EW 72	1–27, EW 72	28, 29, 30, 31	page 393 Set 76, BW 72
8-7	260, 261	1–35	1–35, EW 72	1–39, EW 72		page 393, Set 77, BW 72
8-6 8-7	262, 263	1–18	1–18, EW 73	1–18, EW 73	19, 20, 21, 22, 23	page 393 Set 78, BW 73
8-5 8-6	264	1–50	1–50, EW 74	1–50, EW 74		BW 74
8-2	265	1–3	1–4	1–5		BW 74
8-7	266, 267	1–8	1–10, EW 74	1–10, EW 74		BW 74
8-7	418-429	Extra Problem Solving, Sets 11-16				
	268	Chapter Checkup				
	269	Project				
	270	Chapter Review				
	271	Chapter Challenge				
	272	Major Checkup				

*Check assignments for objectives with unsatisfactory pretest scores.
†Check assignments for objectives with unsatisfactory posttest scores.

BW = Basic Worksheet
EW = Enrichment Worksheet

8
Ratios and Percent

STUDENT OBJECTIVE
To write the ratio of one quantity to another.

VOCABULARY
ratio

Suggested Lesson Plan

Introduction Ask students to count the number of girls and the number of boys in the class. If you have only students of one sex, pick some other characteristics for this activity. Suppose that there are 14 boys and 16 girls. Tell students that the *ratio* of boys to girls is 14 to 16. Write the ratio on the board in these three ways:

$$14 \text{ to } 16 \qquad 14{:}16 \qquad \frac{14}{16}$$

Tell students that each of these can be read as *14 to 16*, although the last can also be read as *fourteen sixteenths*. Ask students to write the ratio of girls to boys in three ways. Students should realize that the quantity read first gives the numerator and the quantity read second gives the denominator.

Point out that ratios can be reduced to lowest terms. For example, the ratio of boys to girls can also be written as 7 to 8. Be sure that students have an intuitive feeling for what the ratio means—there are 7 boys for every 8 girls. If you made up groups of 8 girls, there would be just as many groups of 7 boys.

Using the pages Go over the exposition on page 240 very carefully. Again, be sure that students understand that the ratio can be 2 to 3 as well as 6 to 9. They should see that there are as many groups of 2 green lures as there are groups of 3 blue lures.

In the exercises on page 241 dealing with squares and cubes, students should discover that the ratio of areas is not the same as the ratio of the lengths of the sides, and the ratio of the volumes is not the same as the ratio of the areas or the ratio of the lengths of the edges.

240 Lesson 111 (core)

Ratio

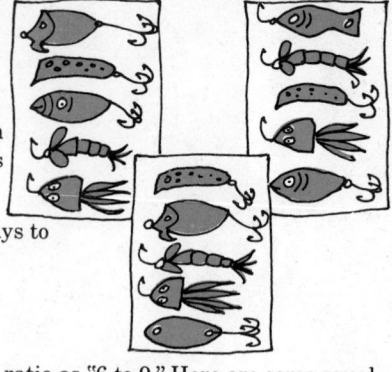

The **ratio** of green lures to blue lures is 6 to 9.

Here are some ways to write the ratio.

6 to 9 $\frac{6}{9}$ 6 : 9

We can read each ratio as "6 to 9." Here are some equal ratios that could also be used.

Looking at 1 card of lures:

2 to 3 $\frac{2}{3}$ 2 : 3

Looking at 2 cards of lures:

4 to 6 $\frac{4}{6}$ 4 : 6

We can find equal ratios by finding equivalent fractions.

$$\frac{2}{3} = \frac{4}{6} = \frac{6}{9} \qquad 2:3 = 4:6 = 6:9$$

EXERCISES
Give the ratio of

1. large flies to small flies. $\frac{6}{4}$

2. small flies to large flies. $\frac{4}{6}$

3. blue flies to red flies. $\frac{4}{3}$

4. small red to large red. $\frac{1}{2}$

5. small yellow to large blue. $\frac{2}{3}$

6. blue to not blue. $\frac{4}{6}$

7. not red to red. $\frac{7}{3}$

8. red to small yellow. $\frac{3}{2}$

Assignments

BASIC
page 240   exercises 1—8
page 241   exercises 9—29
Basic Worksheet 66

AVERAGE
page 240   exercises 1—8
page 241   exercises 9—29
Enrichment Worksheet 66

ENRICHED
page 240   exercises 1—8
page 241   exercises 9—29
Enrichment Worksheet 66

REVIEW PRACTICE
page 385   set 50

Give each ratio as a fraction in lowest terms.

9. 5 : 10 $\frac{1}{2}$ 10. 6 to 4 $\frac{3}{2}$ 11. 12 to 8 $\frac{3}{2}$ 12. 9 : 24 $\frac{3}{8}$ 13. 8 : 6 $\frac{4}{3}$ 14. 16 to 36 $\frac{4}{9}$

Copy and complete.

15. $\frac{1}{3} = \frac{12}{?}$ 36   16. $\frac{7}{2} = \frac{?}{8}$ 28   17. $\frac{8}{5} = \frac{40}{?}$ 25   18. $\frac{4}{3} = \frac{12}{?}$ 9

19. $\frac{5}{8} = \frac{15}{?}$ 24   20. $\frac{7}{8} = \frac{42}{?}$ 48   21. $\frac{4}{8} = \frac{?}{48}$ 24   22. $\frac{6}{5} = \frac{?}{30}$ 36

23. $\frac{6}{5} = \frac{30}{?}$ 25   24. $\frac{5}{8} = \frac{?}{16}$ 10   25. $\frac{3}{4} = \frac{24}{?}$ 32   26. $\frac{2}{3} = \frac{18}{?}$ 27

Solve.

27. **a.** What is the "length to width" ratio? $\frac{14}{9}$

    b. What is the "width to length" ratio? $\frac{9}{14}$

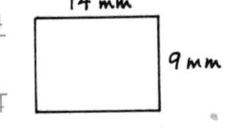

28. **a.** What is the ratio of the perimeter of A to the perimeter of B? $\frac{1}{2}$

    b. What is the ratio of the area of A to the area of B? $\frac{1}{4}$

    c. Are the ratios equal? no

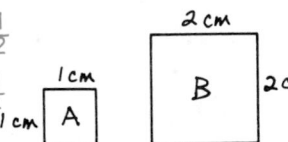

29. **a.** What is the ratio of the volume of R to the volume of S? $\frac{1}{8}$

    b. What is the ratio of the surface area of R to the surface area of S? $\frac{1}{4}$

    c. Are the ratios equal? no

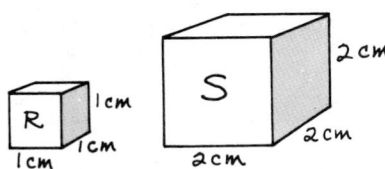

 What is the ratio of the length of the small cube to the length of the large cube?

What is the ratio of the volume of the small cube to the volume of the large cube?

1.
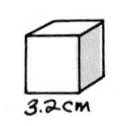 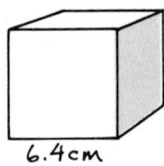
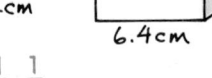
$\frac{1}{2}$, $\frac{1}{8}$

2.
 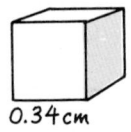
$\frac{1}{2}$, $\frac{1}{8}$

241

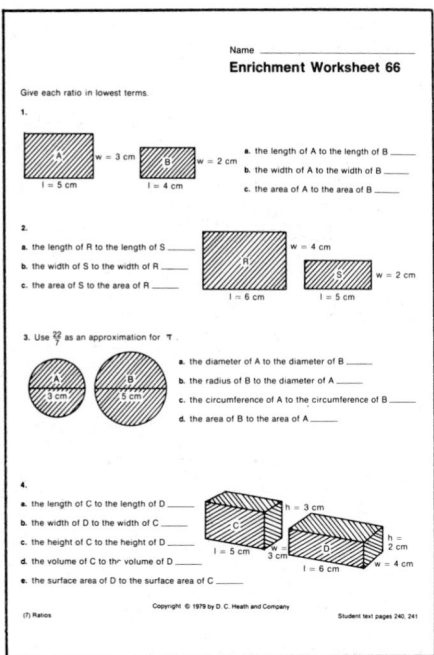

Reinforcement The lesson may be followed up by asking students to give these ratios for things in the classroom:

  the ratio of doors to windows
  the ratio of windows to doors
  the ratio of chairs to desks
  the ratio of students to desks
  the ratio of boys to all students
  the ratio of girls to all students

Continue to ask for other ratios about things found in the classroom.

Enrichment Have students place several sticks in an upright position on the school grounds, making sure that they are vertical and located in the sun. Have students record the ratio of the height of each stick to its shadow length every half hour.

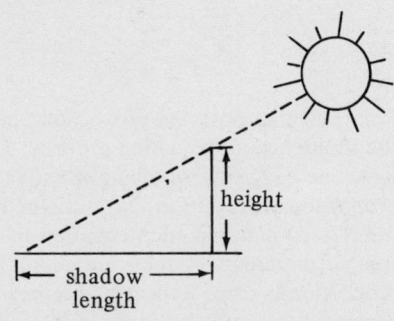

CALCULATOR ACTIVITY
When you enter a ratio in a calculator as a fraction—for example 2 to 3 is entered $2 \div 3$—the result is a decimal. This decimal can be interpreted as a ratio of the decimal to 1, .666 to 1. Have students interpret the decimals as ratios for the calculator activity on page 241.

To write a proportion given two equal ratios.
To write the related multiplication equation for a proportion.
To solve a proportion.

VOCABULARY
proportion, cross products

Suggested Lesson Plan

Introduction   Write these equations on the board and tell students that they are *proportions*:

$$\frac{1}{2} = \frac{2}{4} \qquad \frac{4}{3} = \frac{12}{9} \qquad \frac{8}{4} = 2$$

In the last case point out that 2 can be considered a ratio. "2" is a short way of writing "$\frac{2}{1}$." Next show students how to generate the related multiplication equation—the cross product equation:

$$\frac{4}{3} \diagdown\diagup \frac{12}{9}$$

$$3 \times 12 = 4 \times 9$$

Point out that both the proportion and the multiplication equation are true. In fact, one easy way of telling whether a proportion is true to to find out whether the related multiplication equation is true. If the cross products are equal, the proportion is true. Repeat with other proportions, including some like these, in which one ratio is in standard decimal form:

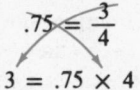

$$2 \times 4 = 8 \qquad 3 = .75 \times 4$$

Using the pages   Use the exposition on page 242 to reinforce your introduction. Be sure students know how to use cross products to write a multiplication sentence for a proportion. Work through the steps to solve the proportion on page 242. Assign exercises 1−28 for written work. At the end of the class time, have students work the Keeping Skills Sharp.

Proportions

An equation stating that two ratios are equal is called a **proportion**. Each proportion has a related multiplication equation.

Proportion	Multiplication equation
$\dfrac{3}{4} = \dfrac{9}{12}$	$3 \times 12 = 4 \times 9$

The two products 3×12 and 4×9 are often called **cross products**. The cross products and the ratios have a special relationship:

If the ratios are equal, so are the cross products
and
if the cross products are equal, so are the ratios.

Since the cross products are equal, the ratios are equal.

Since the cross products are not equal, the ratios are not equal.

EXAMPLE.   Solve: $\dfrac{3}{7} = \dfrac{12}{n}$

Step 1.   Write the related multiplication equation.

$$3n = 7 \times 12$$

Step 2.   Solve the multiplication equation.

$$3n = 7 \times 12$$
$$3n = 84$$
$$n = 28$$

$$3\overline{)84} \quad \frac{28}{}$$

Check: $\dfrac{3}{7} = \dfrac{12}{28}$

242

Assignments

BASIC
page 242   Discuss
page 243   exercises 1−28,
      Keeping Skills Sharp
Basic Worksheet 67

AVERAGE
page 242   Discuss
page 243   exercises 1−28,
      Keeping Skills Sharp
Enrichment Worksheet 67

ENRICHED
page 242   Discuss
page 243   exercises 1−28,
      Keeping Skills Sharp
Enrichment Worksheet 67

EXTRA PRACTICE
page 391   set 71

EXERCISES
= or ≠ ?

1. $\dfrac{3}{4}$ ● $\dfrac{6}{8}$ =

2. $\dfrac{2}{1}$ ● $\dfrac{3}{2}$ ≠

3. $\dfrac{9}{8}$ ● $\dfrac{6}{5}$ ≠

4. $\dfrac{6}{9}$ ● $\dfrac{4}{6}$ =

5. $\dfrac{3}{6}$ ● $\dfrac{4}{8}$ =

6. $\dfrac{9}{6}$ ● $\dfrac{6}{4}$ =

7. $\dfrac{6}{5}$ ● $\dfrac{7}{6}$ ≠

8. $\dfrac{7}{7}$ ● $\dfrac{8}{8}$ =

9. $\dfrac{9}{12}$ ● $\dfrac{6}{8}$ =

Copy and complete.

10. $\dfrac{5}{2} = \dfrac{n}{3}$
$2n = 5 \times 3$
$n = \underline{\;?\;}$ $7\dfrac{1}{2}$

11. $\dfrac{5}{6} = \dfrac{4}{n}$
$5n = 6 \times 4$
$n = \underline{\;?\;}$ $4\dfrac{4}{5}$

Hint: Divide 15 by 2.

12. $\dfrac{n}{8} = \dfrac{3}{5}$
$5n = \underline{\;?\;}$ 24
$n = \underline{\;?\;}$ $4\dfrac{4}{5}$

13. $\dfrac{4}{n} = \dfrac{6}{9}$
$6n = \underline{\;?\;}$ 36
$n = \underline{\;?\;}$ 6

Solve each proportion.

14. $\dfrac{n}{3} = \dfrac{5}{9}$ $1\dfrac{2}{3}$

15. $\dfrac{7}{n} = \dfrac{4}{6}$ $10\dfrac{1}{2}$

16. $\dfrac{4}{8} = \dfrac{2}{n}$ 4

17. $\dfrac{6}{n} = \dfrac{4}{3}$ $4\dfrac{1}{2}$

18. $\dfrac{9}{n} = \dfrac{7}{4}$ $5\dfrac{1}{7}$

19. $\dfrac{8}{n} = \dfrac{5}{6}$ $9\dfrac{3}{5}$

20. $\dfrac{n}{8} = \dfrac{6}{5}$ $9\dfrac{3}{5}$

21. $\dfrac{3}{3} = \dfrac{n}{3}$ 3

22. $\dfrac{n}{8} = \dfrac{3}{4}$ 6

23. $\dfrac{5}{16} = \dfrac{n}{11}$ $3\dfrac{7}{16}$

24. $\dfrac{17}{23} = \dfrac{n}{15}$ $11\dfrac{2}{23}$

25. $\dfrac{8}{5} = \dfrac{6}{n}$ $3\dfrac{3}{4}$

26. $\dfrac{13}{38} = \dfrac{24}{n}$ $70\dfrac{2}{13}$

27. $\dfrac{9}{100} = \dfrac{n}{50}$ $4\dfrac{1}{2}$

28. $\dfrac{n}{100} = \dfrac{5}{6}$ $83\dfrac{1}{3}$

Give each product in lowest terms.

1. $4 \times \dfrac{1}{3}$ $\dfrac{4}{3}$

2. $\dfrac{3}{4} \times 3$ $\dfrac{9}{4}$

3. $\dfrac{1}{2} \times \dfrac{4}{5}$ $\dfrac{2}{5}$

4. $\dfrac{2}{3} \times \dfrac{5}{2}$ $\dfrac{5}{3}, 1\dfrac{2}{5}$

5. $\dfrac{3}{8} \times \dfrac{4}{5}$ $\dfrac{3}{10}$

6. $\dfrac{5}{8} \times 8$ 5

7. $6 \times \dfrac{2}{3}$ 4

8. $\dfrac{5}{9} \times \dfrac{9}{5}$ 1

9. $\dfrac{3}{4} \times \dfrac{4}{3}$ 1

10. $\dfrac{5}{6} \times \dfrac{3}{4}$ $\dfrac{5}{8}$

11. $\dfrac{1}{5} \times \dfrac{1}{3}$ $\dfrac{1}{15}$

12. $\dfrac{4}{9} \times \dfrac{3}{4}$ $\dfrac{1}{3}$

13. $\dfrac{1}{8} \times 2$ $\dfrac{1}{4}$

14. $\dfrac{5}{6} \times \dfrac{9}{10}$ $\dfrac{3}{4}$

15. $\dfrac{2}{3} \times \dfrac{3}{4}$ $\dfrac{1}{2}$

243

Follow-up Activities

Reinforcement You may wish to have students work with the following activity to provide them with further experiences with proportions. Have students set up some sticks in the direct sunlight on the school grounds. Have them make sure that the sticks are vertical.

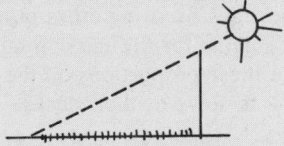

Ask them to measure the height of each stick and the length of each shadow. Finally, have them compare the ratios of the height to shadow length for all the sticks. They can see whether they are the same by checking the cross products of a proportion. The ratios should be equal.

Enrichment Have pairs of students toss two dice 100 times and record each sum. They might keep a record like this:

Sum	Tally	Ratio
2		
3		
4		
5		
6		
7		
8		
9		
10		
11		
12		

When they have finished have them give the ratio of 2s to number of tosses, 3s to number of tosses, etc. Ask students to explain their results. They will probably find that they got more 7s than 2s. This is because there are 6 ways to get the sum of 7, and there is only 1 way to get the sum of 2.

CALCULATOR ACTIVITY
Have students use calculators to total each team's results in the Enrichment activity. After all the outcomes are recorded, students should change the ratios to decimals by dividing the number of individual outcomes by the total number of throws. The results should be near the following: ratio of 2 : .03; 3 : .05; 4 : .08; 5 : .1; 6 : .14; 7 : .16; 8 : .14; 9 : .1; 10 : .08; 11 : .09; and 12 : .03.

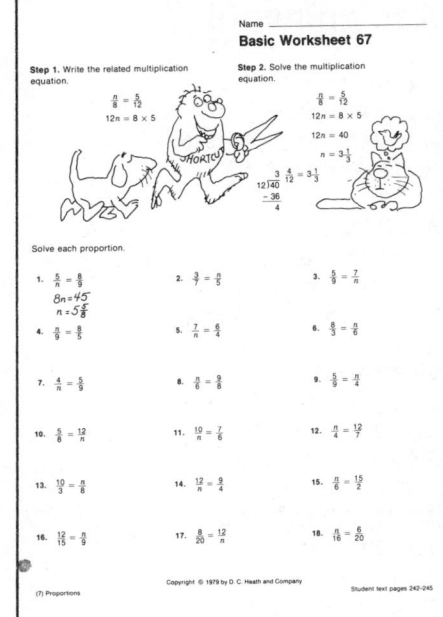

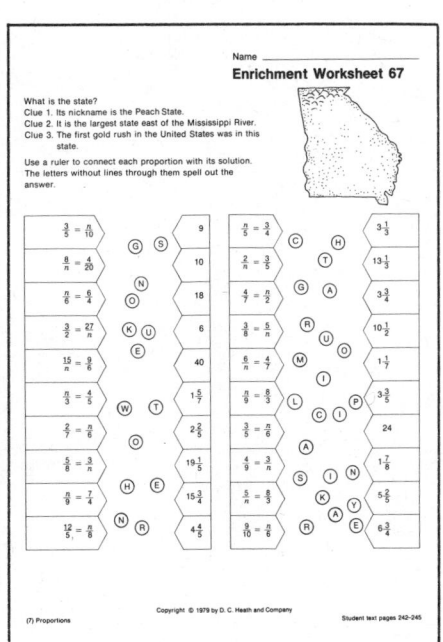

To write a proportion for a word
problem involving ratios.
To solve the word problem by solving
the proportion.

Suggested Lesson Plan

Introduction Quickly review solving
proportions by using cross products and
then solving for the missing number.
Write these proportions on the board for
pupils to solve at their desks.

$$\frac{5}{7} = \frac{m}{38}; \quad \frac{9}{12} = \frac{24}{n}; \quad \frac{4}{14} = \frac{p}{30}.$$

Have them check their answers:

$$m = 27\frac{1}{7}; \quad n = 32; \quad p = 8.57.$$

Using the pages Use the exposition
on 244 to develop the idea of how to set
up a proportion from a word problem.
Point out that there are several correct
proportions that can be written for this
example. The key is to be sure the same
things are contained in each ratio. For
this example, emphasize that the ratios
compare model airplane to real airplane
and model airplane to real airplane.

Assign exercises 1—6 for written
work, but start exercise 1 together. After
letting pupils read the problem and think
about the proportion, have them write a
proportion for finding the length of the
wingspan for the model. Their
proportion should be

$$\frac{1}{10} = \frac{n}{13.3}$$

Then see whether they can write a
proportion for finding the length of the
model.

The students will work
independently, but observe their work
closely to be sure they are setting up
their proportions correctly.

Proportions in problem solving

The first man to fly nonstop across
the Atlantic alone was Charles A.
Lindbergh.

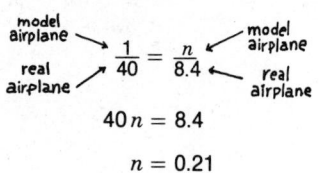

A model is to be $\frac{1}{40}$ the size of Lindbergh's airplane. The length of
Lindbergh's airplane is 8.4 meters. We
can solve a proportion to find how long
the model should be.

$$\begin{array}{c} \text{model} \\ \text{airplane} \end{array} \rightarrow \frac{1}{40} = \frac{n}{8.4} \leftarrow \begin{array}{c} \text{model} \\ \text{airplane} \end{array}$$
$$\begin{array}{c} \text{real} \\ \text{airplane} \end{array} \nearrow \qquad \qquad \leftarrow \begin{array}{c} \text{real} \\ \text{airplane} \end{array}$$

$$40n = 8.4$$

$$n = 0.21$$

The length of the model should be 0.21
meters.

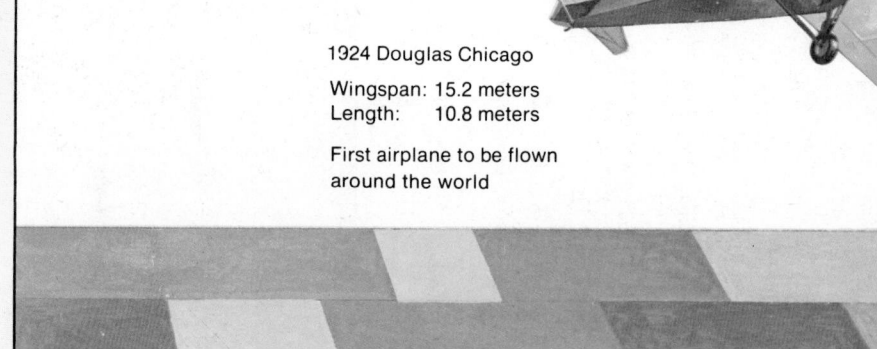

1903 Wright Brothers

Wingspan: 13.3 meters
Length: 6.4 meters

First airplane to make
a successful flight

1924 Douglas Chicago

Wingspan: 15.2 meters
Length: 10.8 meters

First airplane to be flown
around the world

244

Assignments

BASIC
page 244 Discuss
page 245 exercises 1—6
Basic Worksheet 67

AVERAGE
page 244 Discuss
page 245 exercises 1—6
Enrichment Worksheet 67

ENRICHED
page 244 Discuss
page 245 exercises 1—6
Enrichment Worksheet 67

REVIEW PRACTICE
page 385 set 51

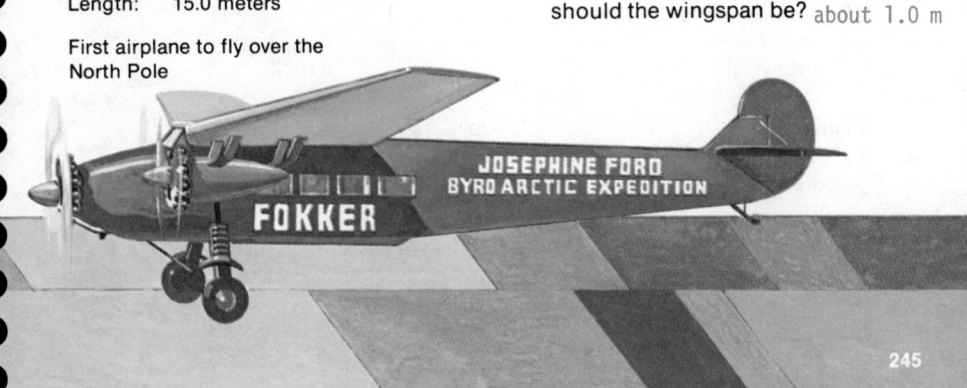

1923 Fokker T-2

Wingspan: 24.3 meters
Length: 15.0 meters

First airplane to fly nonstop
across the United States

1926 Fokker Josephine Ford
Wingspan: 19.3 meters
Length: 15.0 meters

First airplane to fly over the
North Pole

EXERCISES
Solve.

1. A model of the Wright brothers' plane is to be $\frac{1}{10}$ the size of the real airplane. Find its wingspan and length. w: 1.33 m, ℓ: 0.64 m

2. What are the wingspan and length of a model Douglas Chicago if it is $\frac{1}{25}$ the actual size?
w: 0.608 m, ℓ: 0.432 m

3. Compute the wingspan and length of a Fokker T-2 model if it is $\frac{1}{80}$ the actual size.
w: 0.30375 m, ℓ: 0.1875 m

4. What is the ratio of wingspan to length of the Fokker Josephine Ford? What is the length of a model that has a wingspan of 3.0 meters?
193/150, about 2.3 m

5. To get a special shade of green for painting the Douglas Chicago, 2 bottles of midnight blue are mixed with 3 bottles of canary yellow. How much canary yellow should be mixed with 1 bottle of midnight blue to get the same color? $1\frac{1}{2}$ bottles

6. A model of the Wright brothers' airplane is to be 0.5 meter long. What should the wingspan be? about 1.0 m

245

Follow-up Activities

Reinforcement The following game provides further practice with ratios and proportions. Write the ten digits 0−9 on index cards. Divide the class into pairs of students. Thoroughly shuffle the cards and place 6 cards on the chalkboard. One student from each pair should build as many true proportions as possible that use some or all of the 6 digits without using any digit twice. If, for example, these digits were picked:

students could build these true proportions:

$$\frac{1}{2} = \frac{3}{6} \qquad \frac{1}{3} = \frac{2}{6}$$

Award one point for each proportion built. Reshuffle the cards and pick 6 digits for the opposing player. Continue to play. The player with the greater number of points wins the game.

Enrichment Display some items purchased at the grocery store. Have students set up proportions to determine the cost per unit weight of each item. If possible, have two identical items that are packaged in different sizes so that students can determine which size is the better buy.

EXCURSION
If a cone is cut like this, the cut edge is a circle.

Draw each of the cut edges.

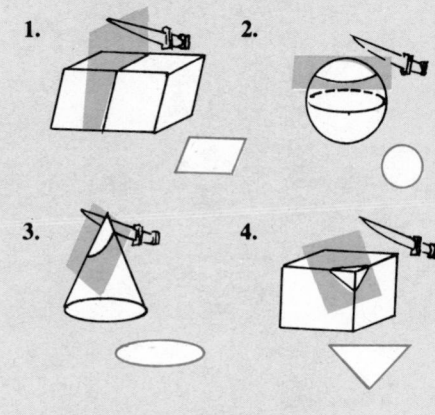

1.   2.

3.   4.

(core) Lesson 113   **245**

Suggested Lesson Plan

Introduction Whereas a ratio is usually defined as a comparison of like quantities, a rate compares such unlike quantities as miles and time, items and cost, miles and gallons, etc. Equal rates can be used to make proportions just like ratios. Likewise, cross products can be used to solve the proportions.

Introduce the concept of rates by asking students to name some rates such as the examples named above. After a pupil names a rate, say 10 miles in 6 minutes, ask how long it would take to go 50 miles at that rate. Have a student set up a proportion for the problem, $\frac{10}{6} = \frac{50}{n}$. Have a student solve the proportion at the board using cross products.

Using the pages Use the exposition on page 246 to reinforce the introduction. For examples 1–4, the proportions come directly from the number line in the same relative positions as shown. Assign exercises 1–16 for written work. As students work on the word problems, set aside a special area where students can come to you for help in reading the problem or in setting up the proportion.

Rates

Here a proportion is used to solve a problem involving **rates**. You might think of a rate as a ratio of two quantities.

In 1932 Hubert Opperman set a 24-hour distance record for a bicycle rider when he rode 1380 kilometers. At that rate, how far did he ride in 7 hours?

$$\overset{\text{kilometers}}{\underset{\text{hours}}{\frac{1380}{24} = \frac{n}{7}}}$$

$$24n = 9660$$

$$n = 402.5$$

He rode 402.5 km in 7 h.

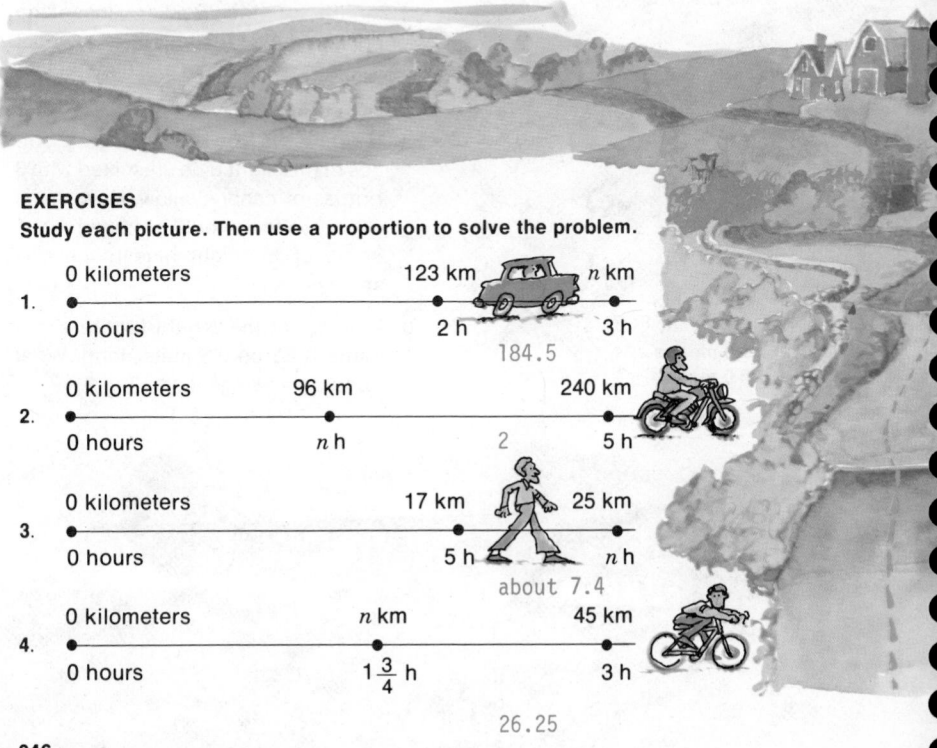

0 km   *n* km   1380 km

0 h   7 h   24 h

EXERCISES
Study each picture. Then use a proportion to solve the problem.

1. 0 kilometers   123 km   *n* km
    0 hours   2 h   3 h
                            184.5

2. 0 kilometers   96 km   240 km
    0 hours   *n* h   5 h
                            2

3. 0 kilometers   17 km   25 km
    0 hours   5 h   *n* h
                    about 7.4

4. 0 kilometers   *n* km   45 km
    0 hours $1\frac{3}{4}$ h   3 h
                    26.25

246

Assignments

BASIC
page 246 exercises 1–4
page 247 exercises 5–10
Basic Worksheet 68

AVERAGE
page 246 exercises 1–4
page 247 exercises 5–14
Enrichment Worksheet 68

ENRICHED
page 246 exercises 1–4
page 247 exercises 5–16, Excursion
Enrichment Worksheet 68

EXTRA PRACTICE
page 391 set 72

Use the given rate to solve each problem. Round each answer to the nearest tenth.

5. 30 kilometers in 7 hours
   How far in 3 hours?   12.9 km

6. 62 kilometers in 2.5 hours
   How far is 4 hours?   99.2 km

7. 96 kilometers in 1.6 hours
   How long to go 60 kilometers? 1 h

8. 168 kilometers in 3.25 hours
   How long to go 240 kilometers? 4.6 h

Solve.

9. A 0.5-kilogram package of hamburger costs $2.00. At that rate what would a 0.8-kilogram package of hamburger cost? $3.20

10. 1.6 kilograms of apples cost $1.19. What would 2.3 kilograms of apples cost? $1.71

11. In 3 days, members of the Drama Society sold 72 tickets to their play. At that rate, how many tickets would they sell in 5 days?   120

12. An automobile used 15.3 liters of gasoline to go 80 kilometers. How much gasoline would it use to go 142 kilometers? Give your answer to the nearest tenth liter.   27.2 L

13. Jill earned $3.35 for baby-sitting $3\frac{1}{2}$ hours. How much would she earn for $1\frac{3}{4}$ hours? Give your answer to the nearest cent. $1.68

14. Jeff mowed $\frac{2}{3}$ of a lawn in 52 minutes. At that rate, how long would it take him to mow the whole lawn? 78 minutes

15. Andrew typed 180 words in $6\frac{1}{2}$ minutes. At that rate, how many words could he type in 10 minutes?   277

16. Nineteen members of a wilderness club ate 92 marshmallows. At that rate, how many marshmallows would be needed for 36 people? Round answer to the nearest whole number.   174

Excursion ■□■□■□■□■□■□■□■□■□■□■□■□■□■□■□■□

Get a paper cup and toss it onto the floor 50 times.

What fraction of the tosses landed on the bottom? On the top? On the side? Estimate how many times in 1000 tosses the cup would land on its top, bottom, and side.

247

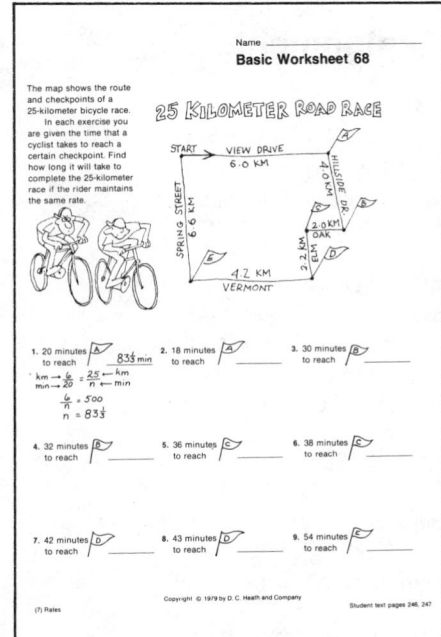

Follow-up Activities

Reinforcement The following project provides further experiences with rates. Have students walk at a normal pace for one minute and measure the distance they walked. From the data have them compute how far they can walk in an hour. Of course, they can determine this by multiplying the distance walked in one minute by 60. Then have them convert the distance walked in one hour to miles. You may have to write this on the chalkboard:

$$1760 \text{ yd} = 1 \text{ mile}$$
$$\text{or}$$
$$5280 \text{ ft} = 1 \text{ mile}$$

Point out that their final answers are their walking rates (at a normal pace) in miles per hour.

Enrichment Have more able students do the project described above, but ask them to make a graph of their findings. Have them discuss their graphs with other classmates.

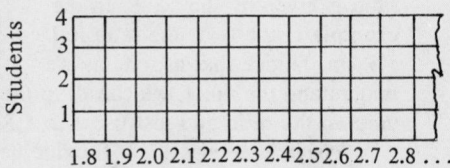

Average Walking Rate
in Miles per Hour

EXCURSION
By using these two squares:

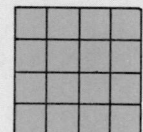 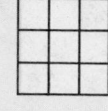

this square can be made:

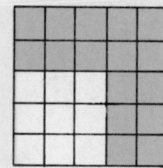

Use graph paper to find some other squares that can be used to build a third square. You must use all of each square.

To read scale drawings and maps.
To compute true dimensions and
distances given a scale drawing or a
map.

VOCABULARY
scale drawing

Suggested Lesson Plan

Introduction Try to find several maps
of small areas. Also ask students to
bring in maps of interesting areas they
have visited. Examine the different maps
with students, having them note the
scale used for each map. Ask questions
about the maps that will encourage the
use of proportions to determine actual
distances represented.

Using the pages Go over the
exposition on page 248. Be sure that
students understand the proportion for
the example. The ratio of the scale
drawing to the real distance is always
the same in a given scale drawing. That
ratio is given by the scale. In the
example in the text, the ratio is 1 cm to
5.5 km. Notice that as long as we
understand the units, we can drop the
units in the ratio and just use 1 to 5.5.

Assign exercises 1−8. Provide help
as the students work on exercises 1−3,
but let them proceed on their own for
exercises 4−8. Leave some time near
the end of the class period for the
Keeping Skills Sharp. Have students
work the exercises and then correct their
own work.

Scale drawing

A map is an example of a scale drawing.
For example, 1 centimeter on the map stands for
5.5 kilometers on the trail.

Since we know the scale, we can measure a distance on the map
and solve a proportion to find the corresponding distance
on a trail.

EXAMPLE.
The distance from Barabo to East Fork
on the map is 6 centimeters. How long is
the trail from Barabo to East Fork?

The distance from Barabo to East Fork
is 33 kilometers.

$$\text{cm on map}$$
$$\frac{1}{5.5} = \frac{6}{n}$$
$$\text{km on trail}$$

$$n = 6 (5.5)$$
$$= 33$$

EXERCISES

1. On the map, measure the distance
between Barabo and Yorke to the
nearest millimeter. Compute the distance from Barabo to Yorke.
46.75 km

2. What is the actual distance from
Huntsville to Yorke? 27.5 km

3. What is the actual straight-line distance from East Fork to Yorke?
57.75 km

Assignments

BASIC
page 248 exercises 1−3
page 249 exercises 4−6,
    Keeping Skills Sharp
Basic Worksheet 69

AVERAGE
page 248 exercises 1−3
page 249 exercises 4−8, Project
    Keeping Skills Sharp
Enrichment Worksheet 69

ENRICHED
page 248 exercises 1−3
page 249 exercises 4−8, Project
    Keeping Skills Sharp
Enrichment Worksheet 69

REVIEW PRACTICE
page 386 set 52

Here is the floor plan of a house.

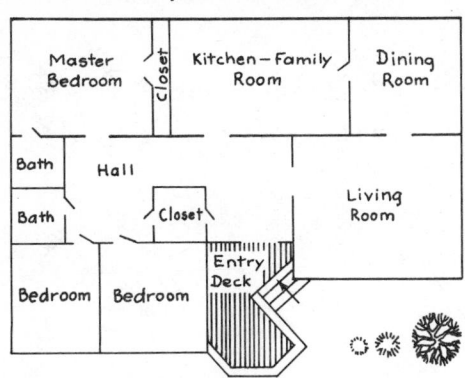

Scale: 1 cm = 2.5 meters

Find each of the following lengths by carefully measuring the drawing and solving a proportion.

4. the length of the living room   7.5 m

5. the width of the kitchen–family room   5 m

6. the dimensions (length and width) of the dining room   5 m by 5 m

Solve.

7. The floor of the kitchen–family room is to be covered with tile costing $9.95 a square meter. How much will the tile cost? $398

8. The floors of the living and dining rooms are to be carpeted. If the carpet costs $12.75 a square meter, how much will the carpet cost for these two rooms? $916.41

Decide on a scale and draw a floor plan of your classroom.

Follow-up Activities

Reinforcement Get some road maps of your state from a gas station. Show students how to determine the distance between two cities via a certain highway by adding the miles printed on the map. List several pairs of cities and have students determine the minimum distance between the cities via a highway.

Enrichment Provide each small group of students with a road map. Have them find the scale used in making the map. Ask them to suppose that they were flying an airplane from one city to another "as the crow flies." Have them compute the distance by carefully measuring the distance on the map and then solving a proportion. Here is an example:

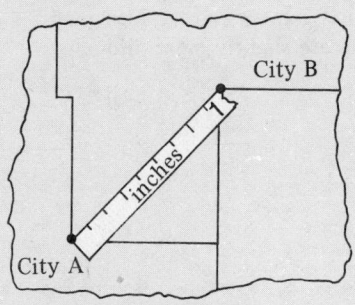

Scale: 1 in. = 100 mi

EXCURSION
Give the next number.

1, 2, 5, 14, 41, 122, ?   365

Multiply by 3, then subtract 1.

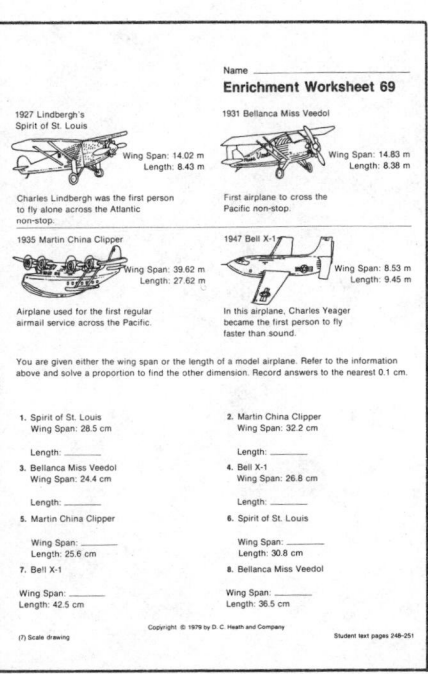

STUDENT OBJECTIVES
To practice solving proportions.
To solve word problems involving
    mathematics and careers.

Suggested Lesson Plan

Introduction If you have a student whose parent works in construction, ask that student to discuss page 251 with his or her parent and report back to the class.

Using the pages Assign exercises 1–32 on page 250 without further discussion. Check on the work of students to see that they are using cross products correctly to solve the proportions.

Assign exercises 1–4 on page 251. You may want students to work in pairs on these exercises since the reading content is greater and the ideas and notation are slightly more difficult.

Practice exercises

Solve.

1. $\frac{5}{2} = \frac{n}{4}$ 10
2. $\frac{6}{n} = \frac{3}{5}$ 10
3. $\frac{28}{12} = \frac{n}{3}$ 7
4. $\frac{8}{n} = \frac{24}{18}$ 6

5. $\frac{n}{6} = \frac{15}{30}$ 3
6. $\frac{3}{4} = \frac{15}{n}$ 20
7. $\frac{13}{8} = \frac{39}{n}$ 24
8. $\frac{12}{42} = \frac{n}{7}$ 2

9. $\frac{3}{5} = \frac{n}{6}$ $3\frac{3}{5}$
10. $\frac{7}{9} = \frac{4}{n}$ $5\frac{1}{7}$
11. $\frac{5}{2} = \frac{8}{n}$ $3\frac{1}{5}$
12. $\frac{7}{9} = \frac{3}{n}$ $3\frac{6}{7}$

13. $\frac{6}{4} = \frac{5}{n}$ $3\frac{1}{3}$
14. $\frac{n}{12} = \frac{9}{5}$ $21\frac{3}{5}$
15. $\frac{3}{8} = \frac{n}{2}$ $\frac{3}{4}$
16. $\frac{7}{16} = \frac{4}{n}$ $9\frac{1}{7}$

17. $\frac{n}{8} = \frac{3}{7}$ $3\frac{3}{7}$
18. $\frac{5}{2} = \frac{n}{9}$ $22\frac{1}{2}$
19. $\frac{n}{6} = \frac{1}{8}$ $\frac{3}{4}$
20. $\frac{8}{5} = \frac{n}{9}$ $14\frac{2}{5}$

21. $\frac{n}{\frac{1}{2}} = \frac{3}{4}$ $\frac{3}{8}$
22. $\frac{\frac{2}{3}}{4} = \frac{5}{n}$ 30
23. $\frac{2\frac{1}{2}}{3} = \frac{n}{6}$ 5
24. $\frac{4}{n} = \frac{1\frac{1}{2}}{2}$ $5\frac{1}{3}$

25. $\frac{3\frac{2}{3}}{4} = \frac{7\frac{1}{3}}{n}$ 8
26. $\frac{n}{2\frac{3}{4}} = \frac{4}{5}$ $2\frac{1}{5}$
27. $\frac{1\frac{1}{4}}{2} = \frac{\frac{3}{4}}{n}$ $1\frac{1}{5}$
28. $\frac{n}{\frac{5}{8}} = \frac{\frac{1}{5}}{3}$ $\frac{1}{24}$

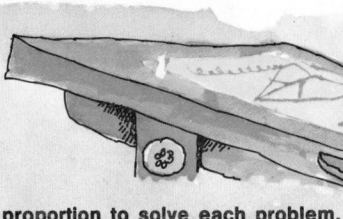

Use a proportion to solve each problem.

29. Joan jogged 400 m in 2 minutes. At that rate, how long would it take her to jog 1500 m? $7\frac{1}{2}$ minutes

30. Jerry hiked 1.6 km in 14 minutes. At that rate, how long would it take him to hike 7.2 km? 63 minutes

31. If 11.2 liters of gasoline cost $3.05, how much do 16 liters cost? Round your answer to the nearest cent. $4.36

32. Bill wants to make a scale drawing of an airplane. He decides to use the scale 1 cm = 1.5 m. How long should his drawing be if the length of the airplane is 20.5 m? about 13.7 cm

250

Assignments

BASIC
page 250 exercises 1–28
page 251 exercises 1–4
Basic Worksheet 69

AVERAGE
page 250 exercises 1–30
page 251 exercises 1–4
Enrichment Worksheet 69

ENRICHED
page 250 exercises 1–32
page 251 exercises 1–4
Enrichment Worksheet 69

REVIEW PRACTICE
page 386 set 53

Mathematics in careers

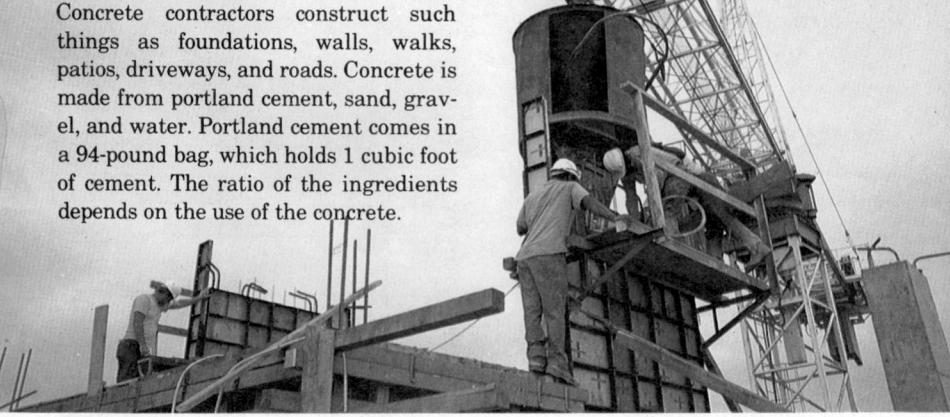

Concrete contractors construct such things as foundations, walls, walks, patios, driveways, and roads. Concrete is made from portland cement, sand, gravel, and water. Portland cement comes in a 94-pound bag, which holds 1 cubic foot of cement. The ratio of the ingredients depends on the use of the concrete.

EXERCISES

Use your completed table in exercises 2 and 3.

1. Copy and complete the following table.

Makes 1 Cubic Yard of Concrete

Mix ratio cement:sand: gravel	Portland cement (ft³)	Sand (ft³)	$\frac{3}{4}$-inch gravel (ft³)
$1:1:1\frac{3}{4}$	10	10	$17\frac{1}{2}$
$1:3:5$	$4\frac{1}{2}$	$13\frac{1}{2}$	$22\frac{1}{2}$
$1:2\frac{1}{2}:3\frac{1}{2}$	6	15	21

3. The $1:2\frac{1}{2}:3\frac{1}{2}$ mix can be used for driveways. How much of each material is needed for a driveway having a volume of 5 cubic yards?

$19\frac{2}{7}$ ft³, $48\frac{3}{14}$ ft³, $67\frac{1}{2}$ ft³

2. It is recommended that the 1 : 3 : 5 mix be used for footings (the bases on which foundation walls rest). How many cubic feet of each material are needed for a footing having a volume of 3 cubic yards?

9 ft³, 27 ft³, 45 ft³

4. Here is a scale drawing of a patio.

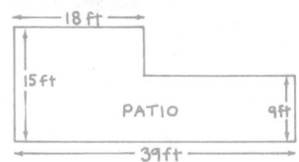

If concrete costs $38 a cubic yard, how much will a 4-inch slab for this patio cost? Round the volume up to the nearest $\frac{1}{2}$ cubic yard.

$228

251

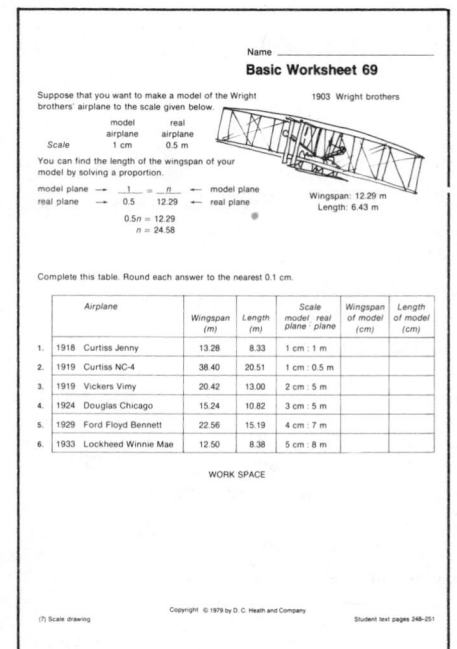
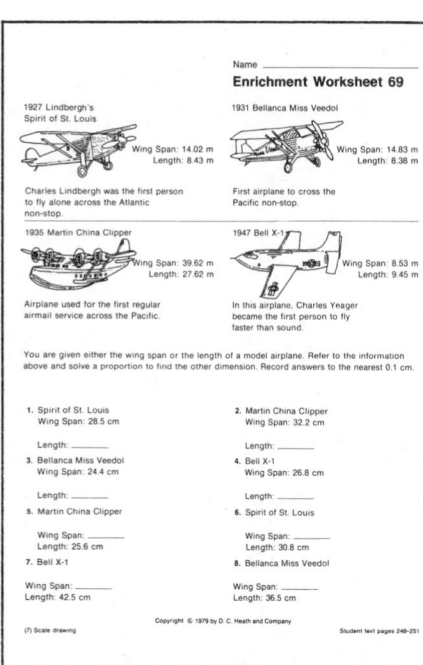
Follow-up Activities

Reinforcement To provide further problem-solving experiences, have students write at least two stories for these headlines:

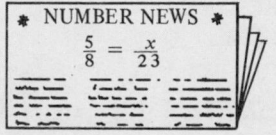

NUMBER NEWS
$\frac{5}{8} = \frac{x}{23}$

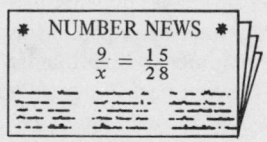

NUMBER NEWS
$\frac{9}{x} = \frac{15}{28}$

Enrichment Have students write several stories for each of the following headlines:

NUMBER NEWS
$\frac{8}{5} = \frac{19}{x}$

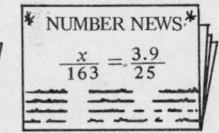

NUMBER NEWS
$\frac{x}{163} = \frac{3.9}{25}$

If time permits, have students create their own headlines for others to write stories for.

EXCURSION

Copy and fill in the missing digits.

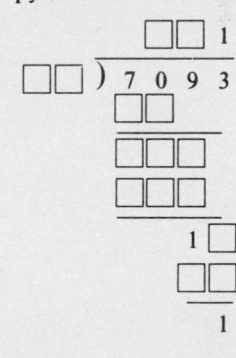

$$
\begin{array}{r}
591 \\
12\overline{)7093} \\
60 \\
\hline
109 \\
108 \\
\hline
13 \\
12 \\
\hline
1
\end{array}
$$

STUDENT OBJECTIVES
To use percents to name hundredths.
To change fractions and decimals to
  percents.
To change percents to fractions and
  decimals.

VOCABULARY
percent (%)

Suggested Lesson Plan

Introduction Ask students to suggest
where they have seen percent used. Ask
what percent means. (per hundred) Point
out that the first part of percent is "per"
which is used in rates: miles *per* gallon,
miles *per* hour, etc. Percent means *per*
one hundred.

Using the pages Read through the
exposition on page 252 with your class.
Point out that percent is just another
way to write a number. Assign exercises
1–60 for written work. Quickly review
the instruction for each set of exercises,
and then monitor individual students as
they work the exercises.

Percent

So far, you have learned three ways to write about hundredths: words, fractions, and decimals. Now we add a fourth
way—percents. **Percent** means "per hundred." We write about
percents with a percent sign:

$$\%$$

Here is an example.

A seventh-grade student surveyed 100
students to find out their favorite individual sports.

The graph shows that 21 out of 100 students liked tennis best. Here are some
ways to write about that.

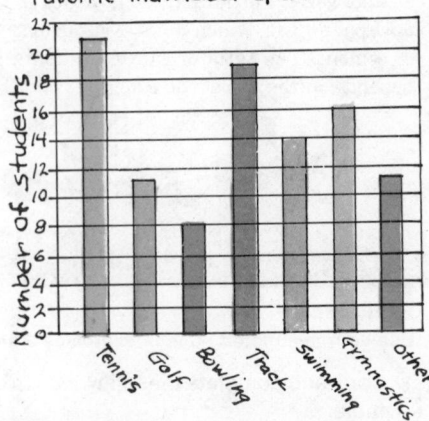
Favorite individual sport.

21 hundredths of the students
liked tennis best.

$\frac{21}{100}$ of the students liked tennis best.

0.21 of the students liked tennis best.

21% of the students liked tennis best.

EXERCISES
Refer to the graph above. What part of the total number of
students liked the given sport best? Write the answers as
fractions, decimals, and percents.

1. golf **2.** bowling **3.** swimming
4. What does 100% mean? $\frac{100}{100}$ or 1 or the whole thing

252   1. $\frac{11}{100}$, 0.11, 11%   2. $\frac{8}{100}$, 0.08, 8%   3. $\frac{14}{100}$, 0.14, 14%

Assignments

BASIC
page 252 exercises 1–4
page 253 exercises 5–56
Basic Worksheet 70

AVERAGE
page 252 exercises 1–4
page 253 exercises 5–56
Enrichment Worksheet 70

ENRICHED
page 252 exercises 1–4
page 253 exercises 5–60
Enrichment Worksheet 70

EXTRA PRACTICE
page 392 set 73

Copy and complete.

	5.	6.	7.	8.	9.	10.
Decimal	0.41	0.37	0.13	0.73	0.87	0.06
Fraction						
Percent	41%	37%	13%	73%	87%	6%

5. $\frac{41}{100}$ 6. $\frac{37}{100}$ 7. $\frac{13}{100}$
8. $\frac{73}{100}$ 9. $\frac{87}{100}$ 10. $\frac{6}{100}$

Write as a percent.

11. 0.37 _37%_ 12. 0.42 _42%_ 13. 0.63 _63%_ 14. 0.40 _40%_ 15. 0.82 _82%_ 16. 0.56 _56%_

17. 0.72 _72%_ 18. 0.35 _35%_ 19. 0.60 _60%_ 20. 0.90 _90%_ 21. 0.10 _10%_ 22. 0.09 _9%_

23. 0.03 _3%_ 24. 0.05 _5%_ 25. 0.01 _1%_ 26. 0.25 _25%_ 27. 0.18 _18%_ 28. 0.45 _45%_

Write each fraction as a percent. *Hint:* **First change to an equivalent fraction having a denominator of 100.**

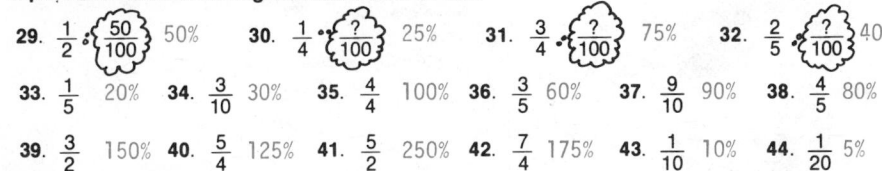

29. $\frac{1}{2}$ · $\frac{50}{100}$ _50%_ 30. $\frac{1}{4}$ · $\frac{?}{100}$ _25%_ 31. $\frac{3}{4}$ · $\frac{?}{100}$ _75%_ 32. $\frac{2}{5}$ · $\frac{?}{100}$ _40%_

33. $\frac{1}{5}$ _20%_ 34. $\frac{3}{10}$ _30%_ 35. $\frac{4}{4}$ _100%_ 36. $\frac{3}{5}$ _60%_ 37. $\frac{9}{10}$ _90%_ 38. $\frac{4}{5}$ _80%_

39. $\frac{3}{2}$ _150%_ 40. $\frac{5}{4}$ _125%_ 41. $\frac{5}{2}$ _250%_ 42. $\frac{7}{4}$ _175%_ 43. $\frac{1}{10}$ _10%_ 44. $\frac{1}{20}$ _5%_

Write each percent as a fraction in lowest terms.

45. 10% · $\frac{10}{100}$ _$\frac{1}{10}$_ 46. 20% _$\frac{1}{5}$_ 47. 50% _$\frac{1}{2}$_ 48. 60% _$\frac{3}{5}$_ 49. 75% _$\frac{3}{4}$_ 50. 80% _$\frac{4}{5}$_

51. 5% _$\frac{1}{20}$_ 52. 32% _$\frac{8}{25}$_ 53. 48% _$\frac{12}{25}$_ 54. 64% _$\frac{16}{25}$_ 55. 25% _$\frac{1}{4}$_ 56. 65% _$\frac{13}{20}$_

Here are the results of a comic-strip survey of seventh-grade students. What percent read

57. no comic strip? _20%_

58. two comic strips? _28%_

59. more than four? _8%_

60. more than one? _64%_

Number of Comic Strips Read

0	‖‖‖
1	‖‖‖
2	‖‖‖ ‖‖
3	‖‖‖
4	‖‖‖
More than 4	‖‖

253

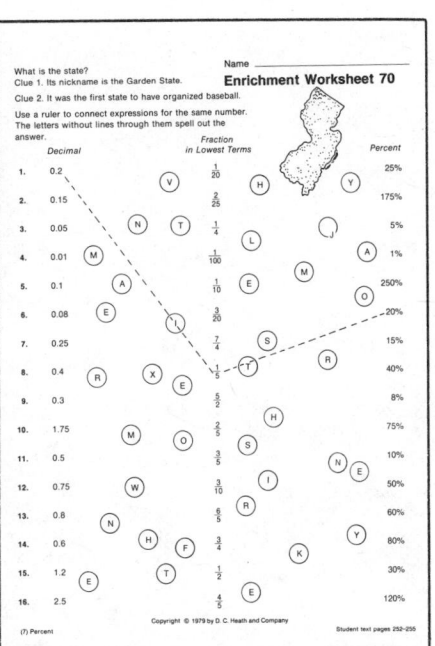

Follow-up Activities

Reinforcement You may wish to have students have some further semiconcrete experiences with percent. Prepare a grid for the overhead projector as shown:

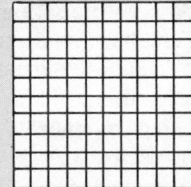

Project on the chalkboard and use chalk to shade part of the grid. For example:

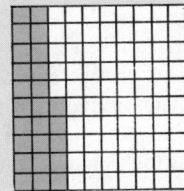

Have students tell what part of the region is shaded, using a percent, a decimal, and a fraction in lowest terms. Change the amount of shading and continue to have students tell what part of the region is shaded, using a percent, a decimal, and a fraction in lowest terms.

Enrichment Have students look in newspapers and magazines and cut out statements involving percent. Ask them to share their findings with their classmates.

EXCURSION
Copy and complete this magic square.

1.7	0.4	0.5	0.4
0.6	0.3	1.2	0.9
0.2	0.7	0.8	1.3
0.5	1.6	0.5	0.4

(core) Lesson 117   **253**

STUDENT OBJECTIVES
To change percents to decimals.
To change decimals to percents.

Suggested Lesson Plan

Introduction Write several fractions on the board and have students find equivalent fractions. Extend these to equivalent fractions with denominators of 100. Then have students write these fractions as decimals. Ask for a rule for changing a fraction with a denominator of 100 to a decimal. The rule should be something like "divide by one hundred, or just move the decimal point two places to the left."

Now put these skills together and have students change several percents to decimals. The procedure is to change the percent to a fraction with a denominator of 100, and then change that fraction to a decimal.

Using the pages Have students read the exposition on page 254. The rule for changing percents to decimals is just a shortcut for the procedure practiced in the introduction. If students have difficulty using the rule or forget part of it, have them go back to the procedure of changing to a fraction and then to a decimal.

The rule for changing from a decimal to a percent is just a reverse of the previous skill. First have students do a few decimals using the entire procedure. That is, first name the decimal as a fraction with a denominator of 100, and then drop the denominator and add the percent sign. As students become confident with this procedure, move to the shortcut rule given on page 254. If students have difficulty, then they should go back to the two-step procedure.

Assign exercises 1–65 for written work. Encourage students to use the shortcuts, but if they have difficulty they may feel more comfortable using the entire procedure.

More about percents

Percents are used in many ways. When you have to compute with percents you must change them to fractions or decimals.

To change a percent to a decimal, move the decimal point two places to the left and drop the percent sign.

28.3% = .28.3% = 0.283

37% = .37.% = 0.37

100% = 1.00.% = 1.00

4% = 0.04.% = 0.04

To change a decimal to a percent, move the decimal point 2 places to the right and write a percent sign.

0.52 = 0.52.% = 52%

0.314 = 0.31.4% = 31.4%

2 = 2.00.% = 200%

0.07 = 0.07.% = 7%

EXERCISES

Change to decimals.

1. 58%   0.58   2. 77%   0.77   3. 95%   0.95   4. 16%   0.16   5. 3%   0.03

6. 9%   0.09   7. 1%   0.01   8. 4.6%   0.046   9. 13.7%   0.137   10. 46.8%   0.468

11. 150%   1.5   12. 395%   3.95   13. 1000%   10   14. 186.3%   1.863   15. 0.4%   0.004

16. 0.6%   0.006   17. 3.8%   0.038   18. 75%   0.75   19. 0.32%   0.0032   20. 0.51%   0.0051

254

Assignments

BASIC
page 254 exercises 1–20
page 255 exercises 21–55
Basic Worksheet 70

AVERAGE
page 254 exercises 1–20
page 255 exercises 21–60
Enrichment Worksheet 70

ENRICHED
page 254 exercises 1–20
page 255 exercises 21–65
Enrichment Worksheet 70

EXTRA PRACTICE
page 392 set 74

Change to percents.

21. 0.82 82%   **22.** 0.75 75%   **23.** 0.50 50%   **24.** 0.4 40%   **25.** 0.7 70%

26. 3 300%   **27.** 2 200%   **28.** 3.6 360%   **29.** 0.02 2%   **30.** 0.07 7%

31. 0.251 25.1%   **32.** 0.384 38.4%   **33.** 0.462 46.2%   **34.** 0.8 80%   **35.** 4 400%

36. 0.001 0.1%   **37.** 0.01 1%   **38.** 0.1 10%   **39.** 1 100%   **40.** 0.173 17.3%

Change to percents. *Hint:* First change to decimals.

41. $\frac{1}{2}$ 50%   **42.** $\frac{3}{2}$ 150%   **43.** $\frac{1}{4}$ 25%   **44.** $\frac{3}{4}$ 75%   **45.** $\frac{5}{4}$ 125%

46. $\frac{7}{4}$ 175%   **47.** $\frac{1}{5}$ 20%   **48.** $\frac{2}{5}$ 40%   **49.** $\frac{3}{5}$ 60%   **50.** $\frac{4}{5}$ 80%

51. $\frac{7}{5}$ 140%   **52.** $\frac{1}{8}$ 12.5%   **53.** $\frac{3}{8}$ 37.5%   **54.** $\frac{5}{8}$ 62.5%   **55.** $\frac{7}{8}$ 87.5%

Change each number to a percent.

56. More than $\frac{1}{2}$ of the babies born are boys.   50%

57. About $\frac{3}{4}$ of the earth is covered by water.   75%

58. About 0.55 of the students in one school are girls.   55%

59. Jim scored 0.35 of the team's points.   35%

60. Karen answered $\frac{3}{5}$ of the questions correctly.   60%

61. Marcia is $\frac{4}{5}$ as tall as Mary.   80%

62. Ken earned 0.7 as much as Carl.   70%

63. Bill spent 0.65 of the money he earned.   65%

64. During a sale the price was reduced by $\frac{1}{4}$.   25%

65. There is a sales tax of $\frac{1}{20}$ of the price of a football.   5%

255

Follow-up Activities

Reinforcement Have students develop a percent chart that shows a fraction with a denominator of 100, the decimal equivalent, and the percent for all the fractions having denominators of 2, 3, 4, 5, 6, 8, 10, and 12.

Enrichment Have students extend the percent chart described above to show fractions with denominators of 16, 24, and 32. Select the best chart and post it on the mathematics bulletin board.

EXCURSION
In each picture a clock's face is shown reflected in a mirror. What is the true time for each picture?

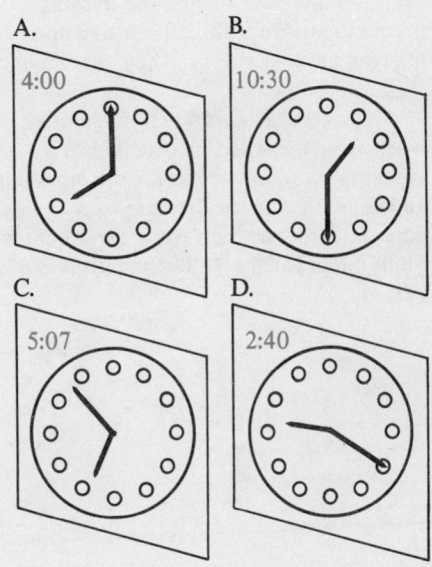

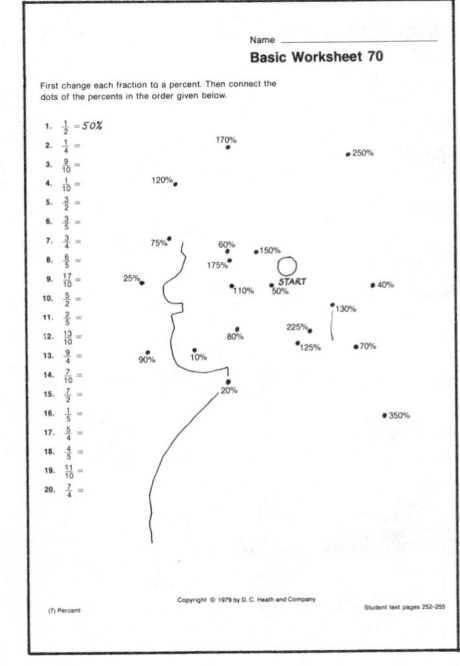

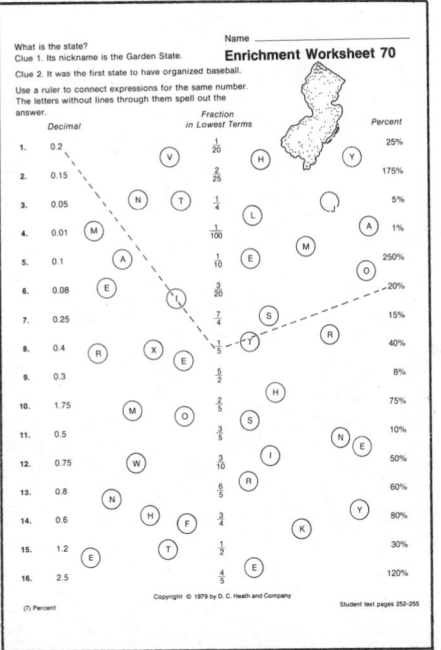

Suggested Lesson Plan

Introduction Write several fractions such as $^6/_7$, $^9/_{12}$, and $^6/_{11}$ on the board. Have students change these fractions to decimals. You may have to remind them to divide. Write the decimal equivalents on the board and then have students change them to percents. If the decimals are repeating decimals, tell students to round them to the nearest hundredth.

Using the pages Use the exposition on page 256 to reinforce your introduction. Before assigning exercises 19–24, put exercise 19 on the board and ask students how to find the missing percent. Students should see that the missing percent is $^{20}/_{40}$. They can change $^{20}/_{40}$ to a percent.

Assign exercises 1–30 for written work. For the word problems, have students write a fraction for the situation and then change the fraction to a percent. Students can work the Keeping Skills Sharp at the end of the class period.

Fractions and percents

On a mathematics test a student got 18 problems correct out of a total of 22 problems. What percent of the problems did she get correct?

Remember that you can change a fraction to a percent by first changing it to a decimal.

$$\frac{18}{22} = ?\ \%$$

$$22\overline{)18.00} \quad 0.81\frac{9}{11}$$
$$\underline{-17\,6}$$
$$40$$
$$\underline{-22}$$
$$18$$

The student got $81\frac{9}{11}\%$ of the problems correct. The teacher rounded the score to the nearest percent, 82%.

EXERCISES
Change each fraction to a percent.

1. $\frac{1}{3}$ $33\frac{1}{3}\%$
2. $\frac{1}{8}$ $12\frac{1}{2}\%$
3. $\frac{1}{6}$ $16\frac{2}{3}\%$
4. $\frac{2}{3}$ $66\frac{2}{3}\%$
5. $\frac{1}{9}$ $11\frac{1}{9}\%$
6. $\frac{5}{8}$ $62\frac{1}{2}\%$

7. $\frac{4}{9}$ $44\frac{4}{9}\%$
8. $\frac{1}{16}$ $6\frac{1}{4}\%$
9. $\frac{7}{8}$ $87\frac{1}{2}\%$
10. $\frac{5}{16}$ $31\frac{1}{4}\%$
11. $\frac{5}{3}$ $166\frac{2}{3}\%$
12. $\frac{2}{9}$ $22\frac{2}{9}\%$

13. $\frac{3}{8}$ $37\frac{1}{2}\%$
14. $\frac{4}{3}$ $133\frac{1}{3}\%$
15. $\frac{15}{8}$ $187\frac{1}{2}\%$
16. $\frac{5}{6}$ $83\frac{1}{3}\%$
17. $\frac{7}{6}$ $116\frac{2}{3}\%$
18. $\frac{9}{8}$ $112\frac{1}{2}\%$

Solve.

19. $20 = \underline{\ ?\ }\%$ of 40 50
20. $7 = \underline{\ ?\ }\%$ of 28 25
21. $9 = \underline{\ ?\ }\%$ of 27 $33\frac{1}{3}$

22. $11 = \underline{\ ?\ }\%$ of 53 $20\frac{40}{53}$
23. $12 = \underline{\ ?\ }\%$ of 8 150
24. $50 = \underline{\ ?\ }\%$ of 86 $58\frac{6}{43}$

256

Assignments

BASIC
page 256 exercises 1–24
page 257 exercises 25–26,
 Keeping Skills Sharp
Basic Worksheet 71

AVERAGE
page 256 exercises 1–24
page 257 exercises 25–30,
 Keeping Skills Sharp
Enrichment Worksheet 71

ENRICHED
page 256 exercises 1–24
page 257 exercises 25–30,
 Keeping Skills Sharp
Enrichment Worksheet 71

EXTRA PRACTICE
page 392 set 75

Solve.

25.

WEAVER JUNIOR HIGH SCHOOL

Starting Line-up	Shots Made	Shots Attempted
Jones	40	96
Casey	36	80
Allen	36	72
Davis	50	112
Garcia	34	64

a. What percent of his shots did Jones make? $41\frac{2}{3}\%$

b. How many players made less than 50% of their shots?   3

c. Who made the higher percent of shots, Jones or Davis?   Davis

26. A boys' club sold 325 out of 450 boxes of candy. What percent of the candy did they sell? $72\frac{2}{9}\%$

27. Janice spent $1.60 of her $3.00 allowance for a book. What percent of her allowance did she spend for the book? $53\frac{1}{3}\%$

28. Stan read 126 pages of a 240-page book. What percent of the book did he read? $52\frac{1}{2}\%$

29. In a large city there are 567,344 people who are 21 years old or older and 487,398 people who are under 21 years old. What percent of the people are under 21? about 46.2%

30. Ralph wants to buy a car that costs $4576.95. He has saved $2985.64. What percent of the cost of the car has he saved? about 65.2%

Follow-up Activities

Reinforcement Give each student four or five of his or her own scores with instructions to find their average percent. Have them change each score to a percent and find the average percent by dividing the sum of all the percents by the number of percents.

Enrichment Let students write several word problems similar to those on page 257. Each can select his or her best problem and write it on a duplicating master. Run off the master and use the problems for extra practice.

EXCURSION
Who am I?

1. I am a 3-digit number.

2. I have three different digits.

3. I am divisible by 3.

4. I am an even number.

5. I am the closest such number to 600.

594

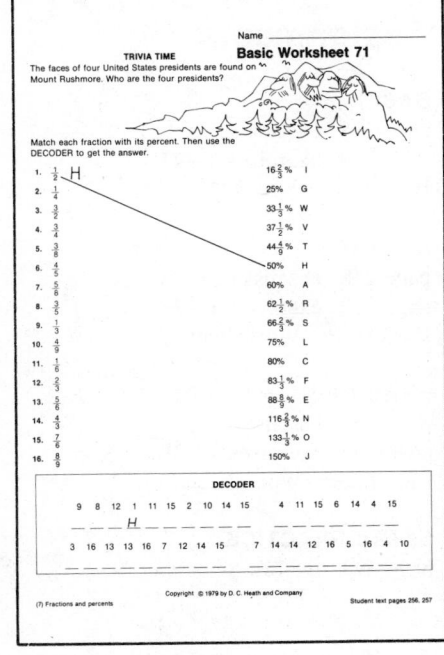

STUDENT OBJECTIVE
To find a percent of a number by
changing the percent to a fraction.

Suggested Lesson Plan

Introduction Quickly review changing
percents to fractions. Use percents that
students generally know, such as 40%,
75%, 33$\frac{1}{3}$%, etc. Also try a few
percents that are greater than 100%,
such as 150%, 160%, etc.

Using the pages Since students know
how to find a fraction of a number, they
can find a percent of a number by
changing the percent to a fraction and
then multiplying. Use the exposition on
page 258 to review the entire procedure.
Since these are common percents, the
fractional equivalents should be known.
If students are not sure of the fractional
equivalent, have them go through the
entire procedure of writing the percent
as a fraction with a denominator of 100
and then reducing the fraction. Read and
work through the three examples
together. Assign exercises 1–31 for
written work.

Finding a percent of a number

Most of the percent problems that you
will have to solve involve finding a percent of a number. Here is an example.

What is the sale price of the bicycle?

Equation: 75% of 160 = n

Since you already know how to find a
fraction of a number, you can solve the
percent equation by solving a fraction
equation.

$$\left(\frac{75}{100}\right)$$

$$75\% \text{ of } 160 = \frac{3}{4} \text{ of } 160$$

$$= \frac{3}{4} \times 160$$

$$= 120$$

So, the sale price is $120.

Regular
price
$160.⁰⁰
Sale price
75% of
regular
price

Here are some other examples of finding
a percent of a number.

$$\left(\frac{50}{100}\right)$$

$$50\% \text{ of } 24 = \frac{1}{2} \text{ of } 24$$

$$= \frac{1}{2} \times 24$$

$$= 12$$

$$\left(\frac{125}{100}\right)$$

$$125\% \text{ of } 36 = \frac{5}{4} \text{ of } 36$$

$$= \frac{5}{4} \times 36$$

$$= 45$$

258

Assignments

BASIC
page 258 Discuss
page 259 exercises 1–27
Basic Worksheet 72

AVERAGE
page 258 Discuss
page 259 exercises 1–29
Enrichment Worksheet 72

ENRICHED
page 258 Discuss
page 259 exercises 1–31
Enrichment Worksheet 72

EXTRA PRACTICE
page 393 set 76

EXERCISES

Solve.

1. 75% of 40 = n 30
2. 25% of 56 = n 14
3. 50% of 38 = n 19
4. 40% of 45 = n 18
5. 80% of 35 = n 28
6. 10% of 40 = n 4
7. 60% of 35 = n 21
8. 150% of 48 = n 72
9. 100% of 36 = n 36
10. 175% of 80 = n 140
11. 5% of 120 = n 6
12. 30% of 100 = n 30
13. 90% of 150 = n 135
14. 125% of 64 = n 80
15. 20% of 60 = n 12

To find 125% of a number, I add the number to $\frac{1}{4}$ the number.

25% of 20 = 5
20 + 5 = 25

SHORTCUT II

Use the shortcut to solve these equations.

16. 125% of 20 = n 25
17. 125% of 48 = n 60
18. 150% of 18 = n 27
19. 150% of 30 = n 45
20. 175% of 24 = n 42
21. 175% of 36 = n 63
22. 120% of 50 = n 60
23. 120% of 80 = n 96
24. 160% of 45 = n 72
25. 160% of 75 = n 120
26. 105% of 80 = n 84
27. 105% of 100 = n 105

Solve.

28. A 3-speed bicycle is on sale for 80% of the regular price. The regular price is $96. What is the sale price?
    $76.80

29. In a survey of 120 seventh-grade students it was found that 85% owned a bicycle. How many students was that?   102

30. The price of a certain lightweight touring bicycle is $189 plus 5% sales tax. What is the total cost?
    $198.45

31. Terry wants to trade in her old bicycle for a new 10-speed bicycle that sells for $169. The dealer will allow her $45 for her old bicycle. How much money will she need if she has to pay a 5% sales tax on the difference? $130.20

259

Follow-up Activities

Reinforcement You may wish to follow up the lesson with this activity. Display some pictures of items that are advertised in a newspaper or catalog. Have students pretend that the items are on sale for 75% of the listed price. Have them solve a proportion to determine the sale price of each item. For some items you may wish to have them pretend that the sale price is a different percentage, for example, 60% or 80%.

Enrichment Have students find out the percentage of commission charged by local real estate firms. Give students a copy of the classified ads from a local newspaper that contains houses for sale. Have each student select several houses and solve proportions to determine the commission charges for selling the houses at the advertised prices.

EXCURSION
How many isosceles triangles can you make on this 3-by-3 geoboard?   36

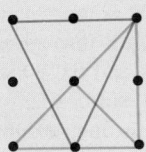

(Three have been shown.)
How many can you make on a 4-by-4 geoboard?   124

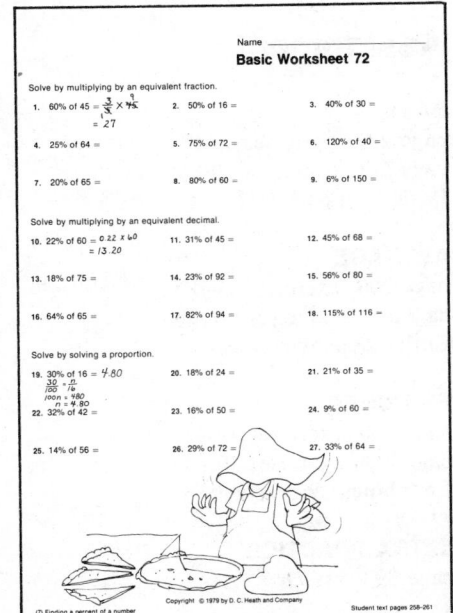

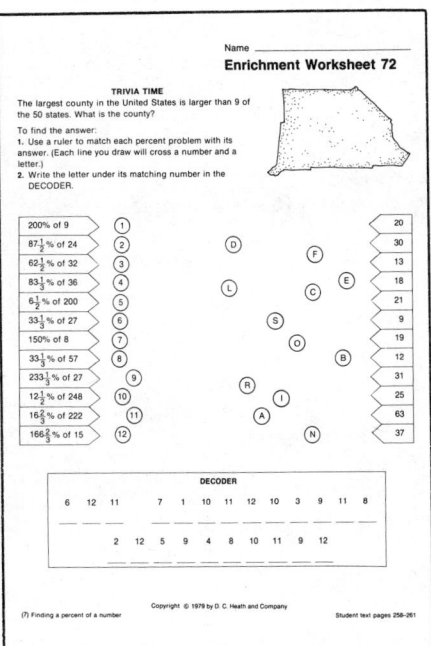

Suggested Lesson Plan

Introduction Write several percents on the board, some less than 1% and some greater than 100%. Have students change the percents to decimals. They can do this by using the shortcut—that is, drop the percent sign and move the decimal point two places to the left. Students who are not comfortable with the shortcut should change the percent to a fraction with a denominator of 100 and then change the fraction to a decimal. Follow through both procedures with the students and be sure they are comfortable and accurate in changing percents to decimals.

Using the pages Use the exposition on page 260 to review the three ways to find a percent of a number. First work through example 1 with all students. Have them work exercise 1 using that method. Next work through example 2 with all students and have them use that method to work exercise 2.

Next work through example 3 with all students. This method involves setting up a proportion and then using cross-products to solve the proportion. Have all students use this method to solve exercise 3.

After introducing the three different methods of finding a percent of a number, discuss the advantages of each method and the particular type of problem with which each method works best.

Assign exercises 1—39 for written work.

More about finding a percent of a number

In a survey of 120 seventh-grade students it was found that 20% have stereo sets. How many students have stereos?

Here are 3 ways to solve the problem.

1. Multiply by an equivalent fraction.

$$\frac{20}{100} = \frac{1}{5} \qquad \frac{1}{\cancel{5}} \times \cancel{120}^{\,24} = 24$$

$$20\% \text{ of } 120 = 24$$

2. Multiply by an equivalent decimal.

$$20\% = 0.20 \qquad \begin{array}{r} 120 \\ \times\ .20 \\ \hline 24.00 \end{array}$$

$$20\% \text{ of } 120 = 24$$

3. Solve a proportion.

$$\frac{20}{100} = \frac{n}{120}$$
$$100n = 2400$$
$$n = 24$$

$$20\% \text{ of } 120 = 24$$

The method you use will probably depend on the problem.

EXERCISES
Solve by multiplying by an equivalent fraction.

1. 25% of 32 = n 8
2. 75% of 36 = n 27
3. 50% of 60 = n 30
4. 40% of 40 = n 16
5. 80% of 35 = n 28
6. 60% of 150 = n 90
7. 150% of 60 = n 90
8. 10% of 80 = n 8
9. 120% of 75 = n 90

260

Assignments

Solve by multiplying by an equivalent decimal.

10. 18% of 25 = n 4.5   **11.** 16% of 38 = n 6.08

12. 22% of 19 = n 4.18   **13.** 25% of 56 = n 14

14. 36% of 74 = n 26.64   **15.** 17% of 58 = n 9.86

16. 8% of 83 = n 6.64   **17.** 3% of 65 = n 1.95

18. 2% of 75 = n 1.5   **19.** 6% of 142 = n 8.52

20. 9% of 108 = n 9.72   **21.** 7% of 256 = n 17.92

22. 118% of 325 = n 383.5   **23.** 126% of 378 = n 476.28

Solve by solving a proportion.

24. 8% of 51 = n 4.08   **25.** 6% of 63 = n 3.78

26. 3% of 54 = n 1.62   **27.** 15% of 29 = n 4.35

28. 29% of 78 = n 22.62   **29.** 35% of 125 = n 43.75

30. $37\frac{1}{2}$% of 77 = n 28.875   **31.** $42\frac{1}{2}$% of 61 = n 25.925

32. $18\frac{1}{4}$% of 59 = n 10.7675   **33.** $8\frac{1}{3}$% of 63 = n 5.25

34. $6\frac{3}{4}$% of 75 = n 5.0625   **35.** $9\frac{1}{2}$% of 95 = n 9.025

In another survey, 160 students were asked how many minutes each day they spent listening to their favorite radio station. The table shows the results of the survey.

How many students listened

36. between 61 and 90 minutes?   16

37. more than 3 hours?   8

38. between half an hour and an hour?   60

39. more than 30 minutes?   130

TIME SPENT LISTENING TO FAVORITE STATION	
Time in Minutes	Percent of Students Surveyed
0	$12\frac{1}{2}$
1 — 30	$6\frac{1}{4}$
31 — 60	$37\frac{1}{2}$
61 — 90	10
91 — 120	15
121 — 150	$7\frac{1}{2}$
151 — 180	$6\frac{1}{4}$
181 — 210	5

261

Follow-up Activities

Reinforcement Display the cutouts shown below:

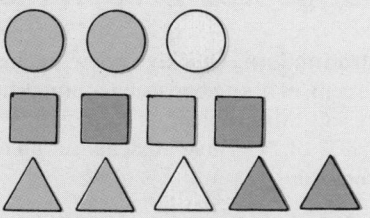

Have students solve a proportion to determine the percent of each of the following:

1. red figures $33\frac{1}{3}$%
2. blue figures $41\frac{2}{3}$%
3. figures that are circles   25%
4. figures that are squares $33\frac{1}{3}$%
5. figures that are not yellow $83\frac{1}{3}$%
6. triangles that are red   40%
7. squares that are green   25%

Enrichment Have students take a traffic survey and tally the number of cars that have only one occupant and the total number of cars. Ask them to solve a proportion that gives the percent of cars that have only one occupant.

CALCULATOR ACTIVITY
If your calculators have a % key, have students learn how to use it to do percent problems. For most calculators, the percent key is used in place of the = at the end of the sentence. For example, to find 25% of 40, you would follow this calculator code:

$25 \boxed{\times} 40 \boxed{\%}$.

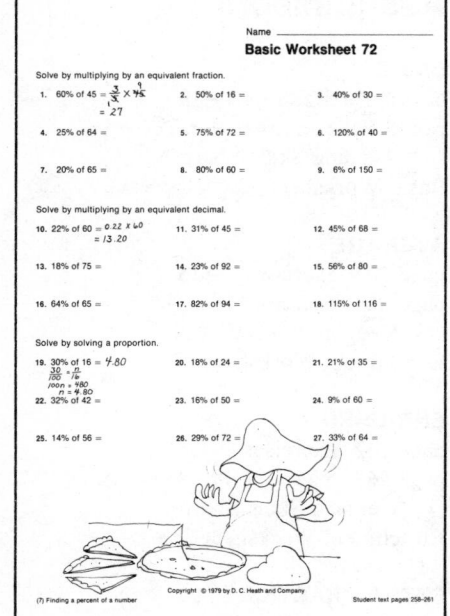

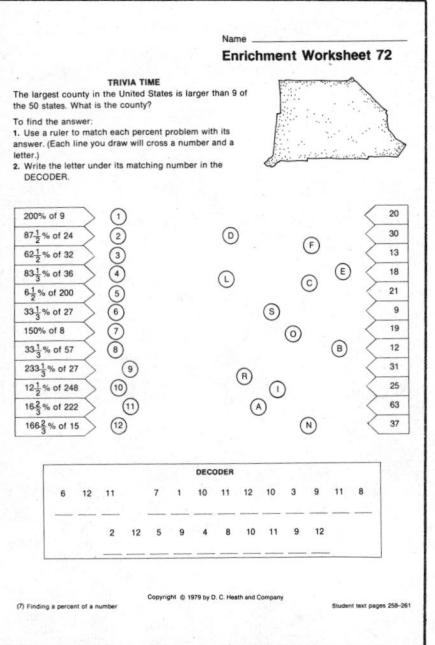

To use a proportion to find the number
when a percent is known.

Suggested Lesson Plan

Introduction Quickly review finding a
percent of a number using a proportion.
Present this problem on the board. What
is 60% of 24? Have students set up a
proportion

$$\frac{60}{100} = \frac{x}{24}$$

and then solve the proportion by cross
products.

Using the pages Use the exposition
on page 262 to show that the same
proportion can be used when the
number is unknown. For example, 60%
of what number is 24? The proportion is

$$\frac{60}{100} = \frac{24}{n}$$

The proportion is solved using cross
products just as in the example you
presented in the introduction.

Assign exercises 1–23 for written
work. Have students work the Keeping
Skills Sharp at the end of the class
period.

Finding the number
when a percent is known

We can solve a proportion to find the number when a percent
of the number is known.

Seventy-five percent of Felicia's records are jazz. If she
has 15 jazz records, how many records does she have in
all?

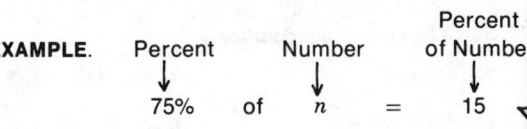

EXAMPLE.	Percent		Number		Percent of Number
	75%	of	n	$=$	15

Solution.   Part ⟶ 75   15 ← Part

Whole ⟶ 100   = n ← Whole

$$75 \times n = 1500$$
$$n = 20$$

EXERCISES
Solve by using a proportion.

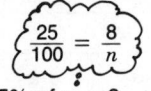

$$\frac{25}{100} = \frac{8}{n}$$

1. 25% of $n = 8$ 32
2. 20% of $n = 16$ 80
3. 30% of $n = 24$ 80
4. 75% of $n = 36$ 48
5. 60% of $n = 9$ 15
6. 25% of $n = 63$ 252
7. 30% of $n = 42$ 140
8. 75% of $n = 96$ 128
9. 15% of $n = 200$ $1333\frac{1}{3}$
10. $16\frac{2}{3}$% of $n = 45$ 270
11. $37\frac{1}{2}$% of $n = 12$ 32
12. $62\frac{1}{2}$% of $n = 45$ 72
13. $87\frac{1}{2}$% of $n = 63$ 72
14. $12\frac{1}{2}$% of $n = 15$ 120
15. $6\frac{1}{4}$% of $n = 28$ 448
16. $37\frac{1}{2}$% of $n = 33$ 88
17. 175% of $n = 49$ 28
18. 300% of $n = 81$ 27

262

Assignments

BASIC
page 262 exercises 1–18
page 263 exercises 19–21,
   Keeping Skills Sharp
Basic Worksheet 73

AVERAGE
page 262 exercises 1–18
page 263 exercises 19–23,
   Keeping Skills Sharp
Enrichment Worksheet 73

ENRICHED
page 262 exercises 1–18
page 263 exercises 19–23,
   Keeping Skills Sharp
Enrichment Worksheet 73

EXTRA PRACTICE
page 393 set 78

Solve by using a proportion.

SALE:
75% of
regular
price

Sale price
$13.00

$17.33

19. What was the regular price?

$9.36
down

Only 12%
down
payment

20. How much is the full price? $78

21. There were 72 problems on the math test. Find the percent that each student worked correctly.

Math Test Results		
Name	Number Correct	Percent
Adams, John	48	66 2/3%
Andrews, Susan	60	83 1/3%
Bartlow, Kevin	64	88 8/9%
Collins, Anne	56	77 7/9%
Cortez, Alex	66	91 2/3%

22. One week Lynn spent 60% of her allowance for a movie ticket. The ticket cost $1.20. How much was her allowance? $2

★**23.** $62\frac{1}{2}$% of the students in a seventh grade went on a field trip. If 175 students went on the field trip, how many students did not go? 105

Divide.

1. $1.5\overline{)8.70}$ 5.8

2. $0.42\overline{)1.512}$ 3.6

3. $2.7\overline{)1.215}$ 0.45

4. $0.53\overline{)3.498}$ 6.6

5. $68\overline{)510}$ 7.5

6. $7.5\overline{)292.5}$ 39

7. $40\overline{)312}$ 7.8

8. $0.23\overline{)2.139}$ 9.3

9. $1.9\overline{)5.51}$ 2.9

10. $2.7\overline{)1.566}$ 0.58

11. $6.3\overline{)2.142}$ 0.34

12. $0.34\overline{)2.142}$ 6.3

13. $8.2\overline{)10.414}$ 1.27

14. $0.64\overline{)0.8832}$ 1.38

15. $37\overline{)1587.3}$ 42.9

16. $4.5\overline{)0.36}$ 0.08

263

Follow-up Activities

Reinforcement This activity may be used to provide students with further experiences with percent. From a catalog or from an advertisement in a local newspaper, display some items with their prices. Ask students to assume that the prices listed are sale prices which are 75% of the original price. Have them determine the original price by solving a proportion. Have them round their answers to the nearest cent. Later, you may wish to have students pretend that the sale price is a different percent of the original price, say 80%.

Enrichment Have more able students try to solve these "Who am I?" puzzles:

I am 3.24 greater than 25% of 34. Who am I?

Answer. 11.74

If you take $62\frac{1}{2}$% of me, you get a number that is 4 less than the square of 8. Who am I?

Answer. 96

If time permits, have students create some "Who am I?" puzzles of their own for their classmates to work on.

CALCULATOR ACTIVITY

Students can learn to use the calculator to solve proportions quickly and efficiently. For example, to solve the proportion $^6/_{15} = {}^n/_{24}$, the student would use this calculator code:

$$6\ \boxed{\times}\ 24\ \boxed{\div}\ 15\ =$$

Have students solve several proportions with the *n* in different positions.

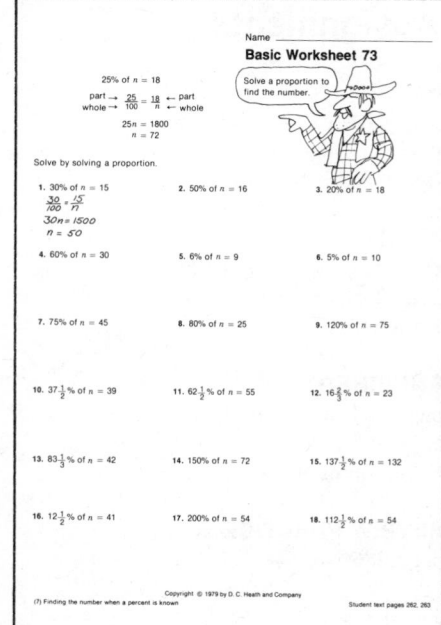

STUDENT OBJECTIVES
To practice percent problems.
To solve problems relating mathematics
and science.

Suggested Lesson Plan

Introduction If possible, have a spring
suspended from a ring stand alongside a
meter stick and several light weights.
Demonstrate to students that the greater
the weight, the more the spring
stretches. In essence, this is the
scientific basis for page 265. This
property is called *Hooke's Law*, named
after the scientist Robert Hooke.

Using the pages Have students do
exercises 1—50 on page 264. Correct the
work and make note of students who
need additional help. Assign exercises
1—5 on page 265 after you have
discussed the scientific principle.

Practice exercises

Complete this table.

	1.	2.	3.	4.	5.	6.	7.	8.
Decimal	0.31	0.17	0.89	0.5	0.75	0.03	0.01	0.09
Fraction	$\frac{31}{100}$	$\frac{17}{100}$	$\frac{89}{100}$	$\frac{1}{2}$	$\frac{3}{4}$	$\frac{3}{100}$	$\frac{1}{100}$	$\frac{9}{100}$
Percent	31%	17%	89%	50%	75%	3%	1%	9%

Solve.

9. 25% of 24 $= n$ 6
10. 50% of 38 $= n$ 19
11. 75% of 60 $= n$ 45

12. 40% of 55 $= n$ 22
13. 60% of 65 $= n$ 39
14. 10% of 150 $= n$ 15

15. 5% of 62 $= n$ 3.1
16. 125% of 38 $= n$ 47.5
17. 150% of 82 $= n$ 123

18. $6\frac{1}{4}$% of 96 $= n$ 6
19. $16\frac{2}{3}$% of 72 $= n$ 12
20. $37\frac{1}{2}$% of 45 $= n$ 16.875

21. $8\frac{1}{3}$% of 72 $= n$ 6
22. $12\frac{1}{2}$% of 112 $= n$ 14
23. $62\frac{1}{2}$% of 270 $= n$ 168.75

24. 40% of 110 $= n$ 44
25. $66\frac{2}{3}$% of 45 $= n$ 30
26. 75% of 135 $= n$ 101.25

27. $87\frac{1}{2}$% of 156 $= n$ 136.5
28. 45% of 90 $= n$ 40.5
29. $12\frac{1}{2}$% of 124 $= n$ 15.5

Solve.

30. 30% of $n = 27$ 90
31. 25% of $n = 32$ 128
32. 80% of $n = 41$ 51.25

33. 75% of $n = 48$ 64
34. 70% of $n = 42$ 60
35. 120% of $n = 96$ 80

36. 8% of $n = 15$ 187.5
37. 100% of $n = 135$ 135
38. 1% of $n = 6$ 600

39. $66\frac{2}{3}$% of $n = 34$ 51
40. $83\frac{1}{3}$% of $n = 58$ 69.6
41. $87\frac{1}{2}$% of $n = 135$ 154 2/7

42. $37\frac{1}{2}$% of $n = 150$ 400
43. $33\frac{1}{3}$% of $n = 216$ 648
44. $62\frac{1}{2}$% of $n = 352$ 563.2

45. $33\frac{1}{3}$% of $n = 124$ 372
46. 120% of $n = 36$ 30
47. 43% of $n = 19$ 44 8/43

48. $112\frac{1}{2}$% of $n = 54$ 48
49. 110% of $n = 22$ 20
50. 60% of $n = 12$ 20

Assignments

BASIC
page 264 exercises 1—50
page 265 exercises 1—3
Basic Worksheet 74

AVERAGE
page 264 exercises 1—50
page 265 exercises 1—4
Enrichment Worksheet 74

ENRICHED
page 264 exercises 1—50
page 265 exercises 1—5
Enrichment Worksheet 74

REVIEW PRACTICE
page 386 set 54

Mathematics and science

Robert Hooke (1635–1703) found that, for a particular spring, the ratio of the change in length of a spring to the force (weight) that is stretching the spring is always the same.

For example:

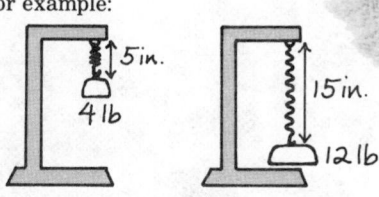

When the weight is 3 times as much, the spring is stretched 3 times as much.

The ratio is constant as long as the spring is not stretched "beyond its limit." The ratio is different for different springs.

EXERCISES

In each exercise the same spring is shown with two different weights. Solve a proportion to find the missing number.

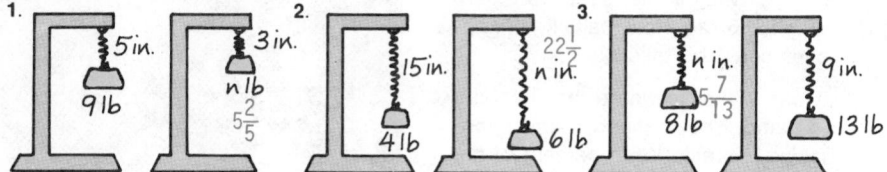

1.
5 in.
9 lb
n lb
3 in.
$5\frac{2}{5}$

2.
15 in.
n in.
4 lb

3.
$22\frac{1}{2}$
n in.
8 lb
$5\frac{7}{13}$
n in.
9 in.
13 lb

4. A force of 6 pounds stretches a spring 8.5 inches. If the force is increased by 50%, how much will the spring be stretched?   12.75 in.

★5. A 4.5-pound weight stretches a spring 12 inches. What weight would increase the stretch by 75%?
7.875 lb

265

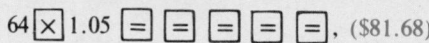
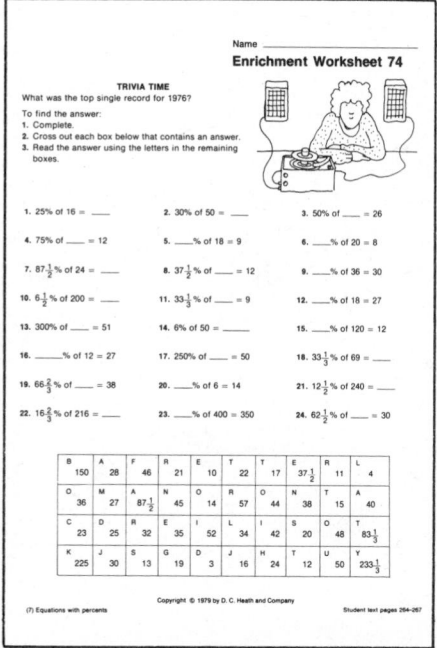

Suggested Lesson Plan

Introduction Use the situation of canoeing and camping to generate interest in the problems presented. Ask students for their personal experiences related to such activities.

Using the pages Assign problems 1–10 for written work. Request that students write an equation, a percent equation, or a proportion before they try to solve the problem. Although there are several equations that can be written for any one problem, encourage students to write the equation that describes the action in the problem.

Problem solving

1. To raise money for a canoe camping trip, a club decided to have a car wash. During the first 2 hours they washed 5 cars. At that rate, how many cars could they wash in 7 hours? $17\frac{1}{2}$

2. During the day they washed 19 cars. They charged $1.85 a car. If they spent $4.39 on supplies, how much profit did they make? $30.76

3. The fourteen boys decided that they would need $5.25 each to go on the canoe trip. If they earned $30.76 washing cars, how much more did they need? $42.74

4. Fourteen boys went on the trip. They were charged $7.35 rent for each canoe. If not more than 3 boys could be in a canoe, what was each boy's share of the canoe rental? Round your answer to the nearest cent. $2.63

5. When planning the trip, it was decided that each boy could take 40% of his weight in supplies. Sam weighed 52 kg. How many kg of supplies could he take? 20.8

6. It was 17 km to where they decided to camp. They canoed 5 km before taking a break. What percent of the trip had they completed? about 29%

Assignments

BASIC
page 266 exercises 1–6
page 267 exercises 7–8
Basic Worksheet 74

AVERAGE
page 266 exercises 1–6
page 267 exercises 7–10
Enrichment Worksheet 74

ENRICHED
page 266 exercises 1–6
page 267 exercises 7–10, Excursion
Enrichment Worksheet 74

REVIEW PRACTICE
page 386 set 55

EXTRA PROBLEM SOLVING
pages 420–421 set 12

7. At the end of 3 hours they had canoed 7 km. At that rate, how long would it take them to canoe 11 km? *about 4.7 hours*

8. For their last meal they made chili. The recipe called for 2 cups of tomatoes and 3 cups of beans. They had $7\frac{1}{2}$ cups of tomatoes. How many cups of beans should they have used? $11\frac{1}{4}$

9. The boys took a different return route. After canoeing 6 kilometers they had traveled $37\frac{1}{2}$ % of the way. How many kilometers long was the return trip? *16*

10. The first 9 kilometers of the return trip took 4 hours. At that rate, how long would it take them to return? [*Hint:* For length of return trip, see exercise 9.] *about 7.1 hours*

Excursion

Elaine wanted these five pieces of chain joined together to make one chain.

A jeweler would do the job, charging $2 for each link that was cut and rejoined. What is the minimum cost of the job? $6

267

Follow-up Activities

Reinforcement Provide a theme for the writing of problems. Have students write three word problems dealing with percents, using the theme suggested. Each student should select one of the problems and write it on a duplicating master. Run off copies of the selected problems and use them for extra practice.

Enrichment Have students work through the path to find the ending number. The answer is given in red.

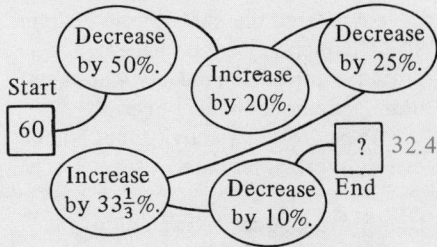

If time permits, have students create similar paths of their own. Have them exchange their paths and determine the end numbers.

CALCULATOR ACTIVITY
Have students use their calculators to solve paths of the following type.

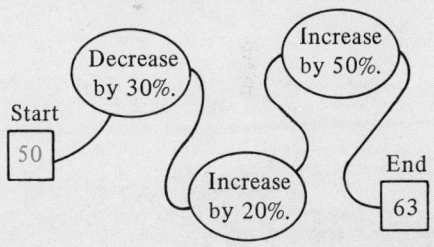

(Calculator Code:

63 ⊟ 1.5 ⊟ 1.2 ⊞ .7 ⊟)

Basic Worksheet 74 and Enrichment Worksheet 74 (reduced images)

Suggested Lesson Plan

Introduction No pre-text activity is necessary for page 268 as this is a checkup for the chapter. However, it may be valuable to briefly review the lessons in the chapter so that students are reminded of the content over which they will be tested.

This checkup will provide you with data about how well individual students have mastered the skills of the chapter. The Chapter Review on page 270 is provided for those students who need more specific individual help.

Page 269 is an activity that students can do working in pairs.

Using the pages Assign all of the exercises on page 268. As students complete the page they can work on the project on page 269.

Give the ratio. [pages 240–241]

1. triangles to circles 4/3
2. circles to squares 3/5
3. squares to circles 5/3
4. red figures to green figures 4/3
5. blue squares to red circles 3/2
6. red triangles to green figures 2/3

Solve each proportion. [pages 242–243, 250]

7. $\frac{3}{4} = \frac{n}{32}$ 24
8. $\frac{5}{9} = \frac{4}{n}$ $7\frac{1}{5}$
9. $\frac{n}{6} = \frac{3}{10}$ $1\frac{4}{5}$
10. $\frac{6}{6} = \frac{n}{7}$ 7

11. $\frac{n}{3} = \frac{5}{8}$ $1\frac{7}{8}$
12. $\frac{5}{n} = \frac{3}{7}$ $11\frac{2}{3}$
13. $\frac{n}{4} = \frac{15}{23}$ $2\frac{14}{23}$
14. $\frac{7}{n} = \frac{29}{18}$ $4\frac{10}{29}$

Solve by using a proportion. [pages 244–247]

15. Oranges cost $1.79 per dozen. How much do 20 oranges cost? $2.99

16. A passenger train traveled 215 km in $2\frac{1}{4}$ hours. At that rate, how far would it travel in 4 hours?   about 382 km

Change each fraction to a percent. [pages 252–257]

17. $\frac{1}{4}$ 25%
18. $\frac{3}{4}$ 75%
19. $\frac{5}{2}$ 250%
20. $\frac{1}{3}$ $33\frac{1}{3}$%
21. $\frac{3}{8}$ $37\frac{1}{2}$%
22. $\frac{5}{16}$ $31\frac{1}{4}$%

Solve. [pages 258–264]

23. 25% of 72 = n 18
24. 40% of 60 = n 24
25. 8% of 75 = n 6

26. $33\frac{1}{3}$% of 50 = n $16\frac{2}{3}$
27. $87\frac{1}{2}$% of 94 = n $82\frac{1}{4}$
28. $112\frac{1}{2}$% of 150 = n $168\frac{3}{4}$

29. 50% of n = 19   38
30. 18% of n = 9   50
31. 72% of n = 45 $62\frac{1}{2}$

32. 175% of n = 25 $14\frac{2}{7}$
33. $83\frac{1}{3}$% of n = 28 33.6
34. $16\frac{2}{3}$% of n = 20   120

Solve. [pages 266–267]

35. An ecology club collected a total of 8000 kg of newspaper. One team collected $33\frac{1}{3}$% of the total. How many kg did that team collect?   about 2667 kg

36. Some hiking boots are on sale for 75% of the regular price. What is the regular price if the sale price is $28.35? $37.80

268

Assignments

BASIC
page 268   exercises 1–36
page 269   Project

AVERAGE
page 268   exercises 1–36
page 269   Project

ENRICHED
page 268   exercises 1–36
page 269   Project

Reinforcement Correct the items in the Chapter Checkup. Any student who misses six or more, or any more than three problems in a section, needs additional help. It is important for each student to achieve some degree of skill in working with percents. At this point, students who are still having difficulty with percent need concentrated individual help.

Enrichment Assign these pupils to the games and activities that have been played or worked on throughout the chapter. Assign a student leader to be responsible for teaching each game or activity to the interested students and to supervise the play.

CALCULATOR ACTIVITY
Assign one student to be in charge of the calculators and the calculator activities. The calculator student is responsible for keeping track of the calculators, for explaining the activities, and for supervising the play.

Project

1. List the titles of the six songs that you think are the most popular. Order the titles from most popular to least popular.

2. Survey twenty or more students and have them pick their favorite song from your list. Be sure to keep a tally.

3. Compare the way you ordered the titles with your survey. For example, did your number 1 song get the greatest number of votes?

4. Use your survey and make a bar graph.

269

You may wish to assign some of the Creative Problem Solving Activities (pages 461-477) at this time.

STUDENT OBJECTIVE
To review or extend the skills and
  concepts taught in Chapter 8.

Suggested Lesson Plan

Introduction After checking the
Chapter Checkup you will know which
students need additional reinforcement
and which students will be able to go
ahead with the Challenge activity. Get
the better students started on page 271
first, as the students who are having
difficulty will need more of your time.

   The students who need more review
should go back and correct their errors
on the Chapter Checkup. You may want
to go over these questions orally if this
group is small enough. Carefully probe
to determine which concepts and skills
the students have not mastered and
work individually to correct their
deficiencies.

Using the pages After the identified
students have corrected the Chapter
Checkup, they should answer questions
1–38 on page 270. After they complete
these questions, read the answers and let
the students correct their own papers.
Give them an opportunity to ask
questions about those exercises they
missed.

   Assign page 271 to those students
who did well on the Chapter Checkup.
Remind students to set up proportions to
solve the problems and then to solve the
proportions by using cross products.

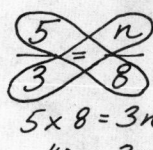

CHAPTER REVIEW

$$\frac{5}{3} = \frac{n}{8}$$

$5 \times 8 = 3n$

$40 = 3n$

$\frac{40}{3} = n$

$\frac{2}{3} = n\%$

$3\overline{)2.00}$ $.66\frac{2}{3}$
$\quad -18$
$\quad \ \ 20$
$\quad -18$
$\quad \ \ \ 2$

So, $\frac{2}{3} = 66\frac{2}{3}\%$

$37\frac{1}{2}\%$ of $60 = n$

$\frac{37\frac{1}{2}}{100} = \frac{n}{60}$

$37\frac{1}{2} \times 60 = 100n$

$2250 = 100n$

$22\frac{1}{2} = n$

$33\frac{1}{3}\%$ of $n = 8$

$\frac{33\frac{1}{3}}{100} = \frac{8}{n}$

$33\frac{1}{3}n = 100 \times 8$

$33\frac{1}{3}n = 800$

$n = 24$

Solve each proportion.

1. $\frac{5}{9} = \frac{n}{27}$ 15

2. $\frac{7}{2} = \frac{n}{5}$ $17\frac{1}{2}$

3. $\frac{3}{11} = \frac{n}{8}$ $2\frac{2}{11}$

4. $\frac{6}{5} = \frac{9}{n}$ $7\frac{1}{2}$

5. $\frac{8}{4} = \frac{5}{n}$ $2\frac{1}{2}$

6. $\frac{9}{6} = \frac{12}{n}$ 8

7. $\frac{n}{4} = \frac{12}{5}$ $9\frac{3}{5}$

8. $\frac{n}{9} = \frac{6}{5}$ $10\frac{4}{5}$

9. $\frac{n}{7} = \frac{8}{3}$ $18\frac{2}{3}$

10. $\frac{9}{n} = \frac{7}{14}$ 18

11. $\frac{6}{n} = \frac{15}{3}$ $1\frac{1}{5}$

12. $\frac{6}{n} = \frac{12}{5}$ $2\frac{1}{2}$

Change each fraction to a percent.

13. $\frac{1}{3}$ 14. $\frac{3}{8}$ 15. $\frac{7}{4}$ 16. $\frac{2}{9}$ 17. $\frac{5}{6}$ 18. $\frac{9}{8}$

$33\frac{1}{3}\%$ $37\frac{1}{2}\%$ 175% $22\frac{2}{9}\%$ $83\frac{1}{3}\%$ $112\frac{1}{2}\%$

Solve.

19. 20% of 60 = n 12

20. 25% of 48 = n 12

21. 50% of 38 = n 19

22. 75% of 36 = n 27

23. 60% of 45 = n 27

24. 150% of 72 = n 108

25. $33\frac{1}{3}\%$ of 54 = n 18

26. $37\frac{1}{2}\%$ of 72 = n 27

27. $66\frac{2}{3}\%$ of 96 = n 64

28. $12\frac{1}{2}\%$ of 18 = n $2\frac{1}{4}$

Solve.

29. 25% of n = 7 28

30. 20% of n = 12 60

31. 40% of n = 20 50

32. 75% of n = 36 48

33. 125% of n = 75 60

34. 120% of n = 72 60

35. $37\frac{1}{2}\%$ of n = 33 88

36. $33\frac{1}{3}\%$ of n = 23 69

37. $62\frac{1}{2}\%$ of n = 30 48

38. $6\frac{1}{4}\%$ of n = 15 240

270

Assignments

BASIC
page 270 exercises 1–38

AVERAGE
page 270 exercises 1–38

ENRICHED
page 271 exercises 1–4

CHAPTER CHALLENGE

The painter wants to mix a special shade of green using this ratio:

$$3 \quad : \quad 5 \quad : \quad 2$$
yellow   blue   white

She has 2 liters of yellow paint. How much of the other colors should she use?

Solution.

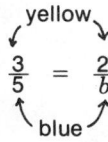

$$\overset{\text{yellow}}{\frac{3}{5}} = \frac{2}{b} \;\underset{\text{blue}}{}$$

$$\overset{\text{yellow}}{\frac{3}{2}} = \frac{2}{w} \;\underset{\text{white}}{}$$

$$3b = 10 \qquad\qquad 3w = 4$$
$$b = 3\frac{1}{3} \qquad\qquad w = 1\frac{1}{3}$$

She should mix 2 liters of yellow, $3\frac{1}{3}$ liters of blue, and $1\frac{1}{3}$ liters of white.

Tell how much of each color should be used.

1. Ratio: 2   :   3   :   4
            red   white   green

Use 1 liter of red.

2. Ratio: 3   :   4   :   2
            black   red   yellow

Use 2 liters of black.

3. Ratio: 3   :   4   :   5
            blue   white   green

Use 4 liters of green.

4. Ratio: 2   :   3   :   4
            brown   orange   yellow

Use 4 liters of orange.

271

Answers.

1. white: 1.5 L
   green: 2 L

2. red: $2\frac{2}{3}$ L

   yellow: $1\frac{1}{3}$ L

3. blue: 2.4 L
   white: 3.2 L

4. brown: $2\frac{2}{3}$ L

   yellow: $5\frac{1}{3}$ L

Follow-up Activities

Reinforcement The reinforcement at this point should be individual help focused on the skills using percents.

Enrichment Pair these students with students who are having difficulty with percents. Give them several exercises of the appropriate skill and have the student who needs help explain his or her work to the more able student.

STUDENT OBJECTIVES

To practice skills learned previously.
To practice using a standardized-test format.

Suggested Lesson Plan

Using the pages The Major Checkup at the end of each chapter of this textbook is given in standardized-test format. The answer sheet on page 448 is the type used with many standardized tests. You may duplicate it for use with the Major Checkups.

Pass out the answer sheets and be sure students understand how to use them. Allow a specified time, perhaps twenty minutes, to complete the checkup. Assign the exercises and use the results to determine what review is needed.

The table below correlates the test items and the student text pages. Assign review exercises as indicated by the Major Checkup results.

Test Item	Text Pages	Test Item	Text Pages
1	18−19	7	138−139
2	66−67	8	112−113
3	68−69	9	180−181
4	86−87	10	182−183
5	94−95	11	226−227
6	136−137	12	228−229

Chapter 8 Posttest

See page 54 for a full discussion of how to use the posttest. The table below suggests Extra Practice exercises and Basic Worksheets for those students who need further practice or reteaching.

Objectives	Extra Practice Sets	Pages	Basic Worksheets
8-1			66
8-2	71−72	391	67−69
8-3	73−74	392	70
8-4	75	392	71
8-5	76−77	393	72
8-6	78	393	73
8-7			74

MAJOR CHECKUP
Standardized Format

Choose the correct letter.

1. Six billion sixty million is

a. 6,060,000
b. 60,006,000
c. 660,000,000
(d.) none of these

2. Find the sum.

5.934 + 26.58

a. 85.92
b. 8.582
(c.) 32.514
d. none of these

3. Find the difference.

62.8 − 3.54

(a.) 59.26
b. 2.74
c. 27.4
d. none of these

4. Multiply.

3.26
×1.5

a. 0.489
(b.) 4.89
c. 48.9
d. none of these

5. Find the average of 6.8, 3.5, 9.2, 7.45, and 6.05.

a. 6.0
b. 66
(c.) 6.6
d. none of these

6. 825 g = ___?___ kg

(a.) 0.825 kg
b. 8.25 kg
c. 82.5 kg
d. none of these

7. Find the circumference. Use 3.14 as an approximation for π.

(circle labeled 1.5 cm)

a. 7.0650 cm
(b.) 9.42 cm
c. 4.71 cm
d. none of these

8. The prime factorization of 24 is

a. 6 × 4
b. 2 × 3 × 4
c. 1 × 24
(d.) none of these

9. Give the sum.

$\frac{5}{9} + \frac{5}{6}$

a. $\frac{2}{3}$
b. $\frac{5}{27}$
(c.) $\frac{25}{18}$
d. none of these

10. Give the difference.

$\frac{7}{4} - \frac{3}{7}$

(a.) $\frac{37}{28}$
b. $\frac{1}{7}$
c. $\frac{3}{4}$
d. none of these

11. Give the product.

$2\frac{1}{2} \times 4\frac{1}{4}$

a. $\frac{10}{17}$
(b.) $10\frac{5}{8}$
c. $1\frac{7}{10}$
d. none of these

12. Give the quotient.

$5\frac{1}{2} \div 2\frac{1}{3}$

(a.) $2\frac{5}{14}$
b. $12\frac{5}{6}$
c. $\frac{6}{77}$
d. none of these

272

Answers for Chapter 8 Posttest

1. $\frac{4}{2}$ 2. $\frac{2}{3}$ 3. $\frac{3}{9}$ 4. $\frac{9}{3}$ 5. 12 6. 18

7. $10\frac{1}{2}$ 8. $11\frac{1}{4}$ 9. 0.83 10. 0.04 11. 51%

12. 7.3% 13. $\frac{1}{4}$ 14. $\frac{2}{3}$ 15. 50%

16. $33\frac{1}{3}$% 17. 75 18. 125 19. $66\frac{2}{3}$ 20. 50

21. 75 22. 53 23. 10 24. 18 25. 7.31

26. 25 27. 57 28. 0.63 29. 24 30. 20

31. 64 32. 45 33. 12 34. 250 35. $69.60

36. 75%

Chapter 8 Posttest

Name _____

Date _____

Write the ratios. [Obj. 8-1, pages 240–241]

1. squares to circles _____

2. circles to triangles _____

3. triangles to all figures _____

4. all figures to triangles _____

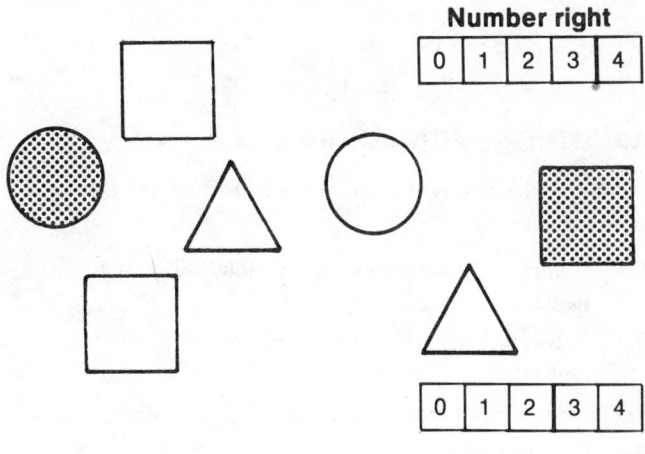

| 0 | 1 | 2 | 3 | 4 |

Solve. [Obj. 8-2, pages 242–243, 250]

5. $\frac{3}{4} = \frac{a}{16}$ 6. $\frac{5}{6} = \frac{15}{b}$ 7. $\frac{2}{3} = \frac{7}{c}$ 8. $\frac{m}{9} = \frac{5}{4}$

_____   _____   _____   _____

| 0-3 | 4 | 5 | 6 | 7 | 8 |

Complete. [Obj. 8-3, pages 252–257]

Percent	83%	4%	**11.**	**12.**
Decimal	**9.**	**10.**	0.51	0.073

Percent	25%	$66\frac{2}{3}$ %	**15.**	**16.**
Fraction	**13.**	**14.**	$\frac{1}{2}$	$\frac{1}{3}$

| 0 | 1 | 2 | 3 | 4 | 5 | 6 |

Complete. [Obj. 8-4, pages 256–257]

17. ____% of 12 = 9   18. ____% of 20 = 25   19. ____% of 30 = 20

20. ____% of 60 = 30   21. ____% of 48 = 36   22. ____% of 100 = 53

| 0 | 1 | 2 | 3 | 4 | 5 | 6 |

Complete. [Obj. 8-5, pages 258–261, 264]

23. 20% of 50 = _____   24. 75% of 24 = _____   25. 17% of 43 = _____

26. 125% of 20 = _____   27. 300% of 19 = _____   28. 1% of 63 = _____

| 0 | 1 | 2 | 3 | 4 | 5 | 6 |

Complete. [Obj. 8-6, pages 262–264]

29. 50% of _____ = 12   30. 100% of _____ = 20   31. 25% of _____ = 16

32. $33\frac{1}{3}$ % of _____ = 15   33. 150% of _____ = 18   34. 14% of _____ = 35

| 0 | 1 | 2 |

Solve. [Obj. 8-7, pages 257, 259, 263, 265–267]

35. A jacket regularly priced at $87 was on sale at 20% off. What was the sale price?

36. Seven out of 28 students failed a test. What percent of the students did not fail?

_____   _____

272a

Chapter 9
Consumer Mathematics

Pages 273 – 296

Learning Objectives

After completing this chapter, all students should be able to do the following:

9-1 Compute total earnings for various ways of being paid.

9-2 Solve problems involving budgets, discounts, and unit prices.

9-3 Write checks and balance checking accounts.

9-4 Compute simple interest.

9-5 Compute installment prices.

Students are introduced to various ways of computing income (wages, commission, salary, etc.), wise spending (unit pricing, budgets and discounts), checking accounts, and ways of borrowing (simple interest and installment interest).

Mathematics

Suppose that some item is priced at 3 for $1.00, and that someone wishes to buy just one of the items. Dividing the price of 3 by 3 gives a price of $.33⅓ for 1 item. Since it is necessary to charge a whole number of cents, the dealer must charge either $.33 or $.34. If he charges $.33, it would be cheaper to buy 3 items one at a time ($.99) rather than 3 at a time ($1.00). Therefore the price is not rounded to the *nearest cent*, but it is rounded *up*.

Teaching the Chapter

Students have had many experiences in earning and spending, and, perhaps, in borrowing and investing. Allow students to share their experiences with the class. Adjust the text problems to fit student experiences. It is possible that the wages, prices, and interest rates used in the text do not fit your particular community at this time. Feel free to change them.

We have found it very helpful to have various people from the community discuss with students their experiences in banking, the stock market, borrowing money, etc. You may also wish to take field trips to banks or other financial institutions. You should definitely have students explore stores, supermarkets, and newspaper ads to look for examples of sales, discounts, and unit prices, and to explore various lending institutions to find the wide range of rates that are available. Make this chapter as real and as close to local conditions as possible.

Vocabulary

budget
check
checking account
commission
cosigner
credit
discount
endorse
installment buying
interest
loan
principal
rate of interest
time
unit price

Materials

hand calculators
newspaper ads of sales
sales-tax table
samples of bank checks

Chapter Tests

For a discussion of how to use the chapter tests, please see page 17c.

Answers for Chapter 9 Pretest

1. $419.89   **2.** $240   **3.** $76.05   **4.** $28.78   **5.** $309.40
6. $.87   **8.** $438.97   **9.** $160   **10.** $112.50   **11.** $19.13
12. $506   **13.** $13.50

Chapter 9 Pretest

Name _____

Date _____

Number right

0	1	2

Solve. [Obj. 9-1, pages 274–275]

1. Mr. O'Brian earned $7.96 per hour plus time and a half for all time over 40 hours per week. How much did he get paid for working $48\frac{1}{2}$ hours one week? _____

2. Miss Schultz earned a salary of $200 per week plus 8% commission on all of her sales over $4500. How much would she earn if her sales one week were $5000?

_____

0	1	2	3	4

Solve. [Obj. 9-2, pages 276–283]

3. A coat regularly priced at $84.50 was sold at a 10% discount. What was the sale price? _____

4. Automobile tires were on sale for $57.55 for two tires. How much would one tire cost? _____

5. Rent accounted for 34% of one family's budget. If their monthly income was $910, how much was the rent? _____

6. Fruit juice was on sale for $1.30 for 3 cans. How much would 2 cans cost? _____

Answer. [Obj. 9-3, pages 284–285]

7. Make out this check for $37.25 to Ace Hardware. Use today's date.

8. Carl had a balance of $392.51 in his checking account. Then he wrote checks for $72.45, $2.96, and $58.57, and deposited $180.44.

   What was his new balance? _____

0	1	2

_____ 19 _____

Pay to the
order of _____ $ _____

_____ Dollars

Alcancía National Bank
6432 State Drive
Somewhere, U.S.A.   _____

⑆0112⑈053⑆ 628⑈

0	1	2	3

Find the interest. [Obj. 9-4, pages 286–287]

principal	$1000	$3000	$850
rate	8%	7.5%	9%
time	2 years	6 mo.	3 mo.
interest	**9.**	**10.**	**11.**

0	1	2

Solve. [Obj. 9-5, pages 288–289]

12. What is the total cost of a TV that can be bought for $50 down and $38 per month for a year? _____

13. A bicycle costs $112.50 cash or $30 down and $24.00 per month for 4 months. How much more is the installment cost? _____

Chapter 9
Record and Assignment Chart

Name _____

Pretest Date _____ Posttest Date _____

Objectives

		Pretest Score Mark number correct	Posttest Score Mark number correct
9-1	Compute total earnings for various ways of being paid.	0 1 | 2	0 1 | 2
9-2	Solve problems involving budgets, discounts, and unit prices.	0 1 2 | 3 4	0 1 2 | 3 4
9-3	Write checks and balance checking accounts.	0 1 | 2	0 1 | 2
9-4	Compute simple interest.	0 1 | 2 3	0 1 | 2 3
9-5	Compute installment prices.	0 | 1 2	0 | 1 2

Pretest Score: Unsatisfactory Score \| Satisfactory Score

Posttest Score: Unsatisfactory Score \| Satisfactory Score

TEACHING ASSIGNMENTS*

	Student Page	Basic Assignment	Average Assignment	Enriched Assignment	Problem Solving	RETEACHING ASSIGNMENTS†
9-1	274, 275	1–10	1–10, EW 75	1–10, EW 75		BW 75
	276, 277	1–14	1–15, EW 75	1–16, EW 75		BW 75
9-2	278, 279	1–6	1–8, EW 76	1–9, EW 76		page 393 Set 79, BW 76
	280, 281	1–6	1–8, EW 76	1–10, EW 76		page 394, Set 80, BW 76
	282, 283	1–10	1–10, EW 77	1–10, EW 77		page 394 Set 81, BW 77
9-3	284, 285	1–12	1–14, EW 78	1–14, EW 78		BW 78
9-4	286, 287	1–10	1–11, EW 79	1–13, EW 79		page 395 Set 82, BW 79
9-5	288, 289	1–6	1–8, EW 80	1–8, EW 80		BW 80
	290, 291	all	all, EW 80	all, EW 80		BW 80
	292	Chapter Checkup				
	293	Project				
	294	Chapter Review				
	295	Chapter Challenge				
	296	Major Checkup				

*Check assignments for objectives with unsatisfactory pretest scores.

†Check assignments for objectives with unsatisfactory posttest scores.

BW = Basic Worksheet

EW = Enrichment Worksheet

9
Consumer Mathematics

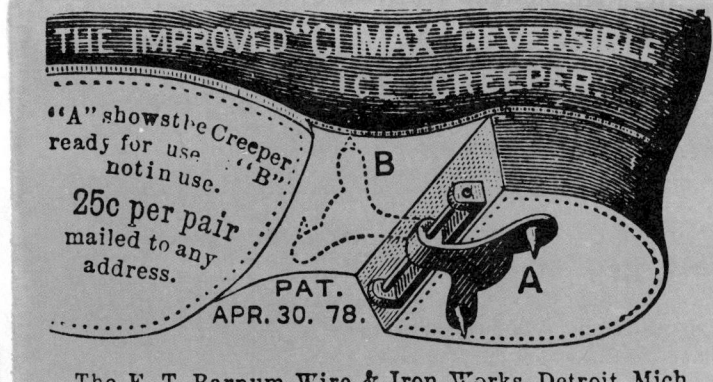

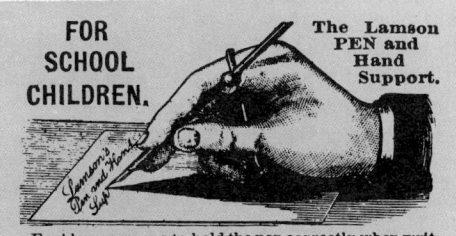

To compute the amount of money
earned when paid by the hour,
commission, and per item.

VOCABULARY
commission

Suggested Lesson Plan

Introduction Ask pupils how many
have jobs in which they earn money.
Have the students describe the types of
job and how they are paid. Treat the
amount of money they are paid very
lightly because students could be
sensitive about the amounts they earn.
Of course, there are many factors to
consider about a job, and the amount of
money earned is just one of those
factors. As students describe how they
are paid, try to classify the different
methods of determining the amount of
money earned. Some jobs, like
newspaper delivery, will pay per
subscription. Such jobs as lawn raking,
shoveling snow, etc., will pay per job,
and many will pay per hour worked.
There should be enough variety within
the class to have a good discussion.

Using the pages Use the exposition
on page 274 to summarize three different
ways of determining the amount of
money earned. After discussing the
different ways, assign exercises 1–10 on
page 275 for written work.
　　Either at the beginning or at the end
of the class period, have pupils take the
Ready or Not? inventory test. If any
pupils miss more than 3 in either
section, try to work individually with
them to improve their skill with
percents.

READY OR NOT !

Solve.

1. $\frac{3}{4}$ of $80 = n$ $60

2. $\frac{2}{3}$ of $48 = n$ $32

3. $\frac{5}{6}$ of $84 = n$ $70

4. 25% of $16 = n$ $4

5. 60% of $25 = n$ $15

6. $12\frac{1}{2}$% of $36 = n$ $4.50

Solve.

7. $\frac{1}{3}$ of $n = 13 $39

8. $\frac{3}{8}$ of $n = 24 $64

9. $\frac{4}{5}$ of $n = 56 $70

10. 20% of $n = 64 $320

11. $33\frac{1}{3}$% of $n = 35 $105

12. $137\frac{1}{2}$% of $n = 121 $88

274

Earning money

The examples show some different ways in which people
are paid.

Joan baby-sits to earn
money. She is paid
$1.25 an hour.

David sells peanuts at
a ball park. He is
paid a commission of
$12\frac{1}{2}$% of his sales.

Debbie is paid 35¢ a
week for each sub-
scriber on her paper
route.

Assignments

BASIC
page 274 Discuss
page 275 exercises 1–10
Basic Worksheet 75

AVERAGE
page 274 Discuss
page 275 exercises 1–10
Enrichment Worksheet 75

ENRICHED
page 274 Discuss
page 275 exercises 1–10, Excursion
Enrichment Worksheet 75

REVIEW PRACTICE
page 386 set 56

EXERCISES

Suppose that you charge $1.25 for an hour of baby-sitting. Study the example. Then copy and complete this table. Round each charge to the nearest cent.

	From	To	Number of hours	Charge
1.	8:00 P.M.	10:45 P.M.	$2\frac{3}{4}$	$3.44
2.	6:30 P.M.	9:30 P.M.	3	$3.75
3.	7:00 P.M.	9:15 P.M.	2 1/4	$2.81
4.	8:30 P.M.	10:00 P.M.	1 1/2	$1.88
5.	5:15 P.M.	8:30 P.M.	3 1/4	$4.06
6.	11:00 A.M.	2:30 P.M.	3 1/2	$4.38

$$2\frac{3}{4} = 2.75$$

$$
\begin{array}{r}
\$1.25 \\
\times\ 2.75 \\
\hline
625 \\
875 \\
250 \\
\hline
\$3.4375
\end{array}
$$

Pretend that you sell peanuts at a ball park and you are paid $12\frac{1}{2}$% of your total sales.

7. How much would you earn if you sold $120 worth of peanuts? $15
   [*Hint:* $12\frac{1}{2}$% = 12.5% = 0.125]

8. If you sold 264 bags of peanuts for 60¢ a bag, how much would you earn? $19.80

Suppose that you are paid 35¢ a week for each subscriber on a paper route.

9. How much would you earn per week if you had 88 subscribers? $30.80

10. If you had 104 subscribers, how much would you earn in 12 weeks? $436.80

Excursion

The price of a $200 bicycle is reduced 10% and later raised 10%. What is the final price? (The answer is not $200.) Answer the same question if the price is first raised 10% and later reduced 10%. $198 $198

275

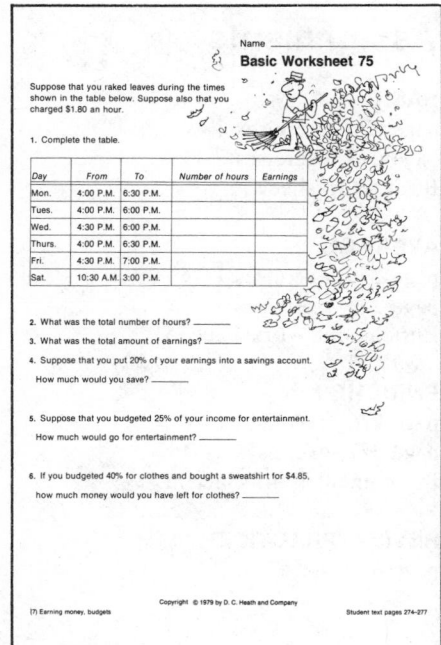

Basic Worksheet 75

Suppose that you raked leaves during the times shown in the table below. Suppose also that you charged $1.80 an hour.

1. Complete the table.

Day	From	To	Number of hours	Earnings
Mon.	4:00 P.M.	6:30 P.M.		
Tues.	4:00 P.M.	6:00 P.M.		
Wed.	4:30 P.M.	6:00 P.M.		
Thurs.	4:00 P.M.	6:30 P.M.		
Fri.	4:30 P.M.	7:00 P.M.		
Sat.	10:30 A.M.	3:00 P.M.		

2. What was the total number of hours? _____
3. What was the total amount of earnings? _____
4. Suppose that you put 20% of your earnings into a savings account. How much would you save? _____
5. Suppose that you budgeted 25% of your income for entertainment. How much would go for entertainment? _____
6. If you budgeted 40% for clothes and bought a sweatshirt for $4.85, how much money would you have left for clothes? _____

(7) Earning money, budgets.   Copyright © 1979 by D. C. Heath and Company   Student text pages 274-277

Enrichment Worksheet 75

1. Jerry earns $1.60 an hour for babysitting. The table shows the hours that she works each week. Complete the table.

Day	From — To	Number of hours	Earnings
Mon.	3:45 pm–5:15 pm		
Tues.	4:00 pm–6:00 pm		
Wed.	3:45 pm–5:30 pm		
Thurs.	4:15 pm–6:15 pm		
Fri.	3:45 pm–6:15 pm		
Sat.	10:30 am–3:45 pm		
Sun.	4:15 pm–6:00 pm		

2. What were Jerry's total earnings for the week? _____

3. The circle graph shows how Jerry budgets her earnings. How much does she spend each week for
   a. lunches? _____
   b. clothing? _____
   c. entertainment? _____

4. How much does she
   a. save each week? _____
   b. give to charity? _____

5. One week she gave $3.50 to the United Fund. How much did she go over her budget? _____

6. a. One week she bought some shoes on sale for $12. Was this within her budget? _____
   b. What percent of her weekly earnings did she spend for the shoes? _____

JERRY'S BUDGET

ENTERTAINMENT 20% SAVINGS 25%
CHARITY 5%
LUNCHES 15% CLOTHING 35%

(7) Earning money, budgets.   Copyright © 1979 by D. C. Heath and Company   Student text pages 274, 275

(core) Lesson 128   **275**

Suggested Lesson Plan

Introduction Ask students how they decide what they do with their money. After someone suggests making a plan, ask what such a plan is called. (budget) Explain that students can make a budget just as well as an adult, a family, or a company.

Ask for a volunteer to relate the details of how much money he or she has available each week, either from an allowance or working. Work out a sample budget for this student by asking the class how they would like to use the money.

Using the pages Use the exposition on page 276 to summarize your development of a student budget. Read over and discuss the reasons for developing a budget. Start through the exercises on page 276 to help students understand the questions.

Quickly direct their attention to the graph of the family budget on page 277. Take one section, say the amount budgeted for clothing, and show students that to find the actual amount, they find 10% of $16,000.

Discuss the graph and the information shown by the graph.

Assign exercises 1—16 for written work. Point out that answers will vary for exercises 15 and 16. Be prepared to assist in the construction of a circle graph for exercise 15.

Budgets

A budget is a plan for using your money. Here is a student's sample budget.

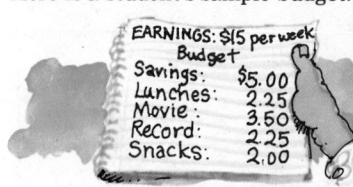

EARNINGS: $15 per week
Budget
Savings: $5.00
Lunches: 2.25
Movie: 3.50
Record: 2.25
Snacks: 2.00

Here are some reasons people use budgets.

(1) To spread out spending so that they don't run out of money between paychecks.

(2) To be sure that they put some money into savings each pay day.

(3) To control "impulsive" spending so that all necessities can be taken care of.

EXERCISES
In exercises 1–6, use the budget shown at the top of the page.

1. What percent of the earnings did the student save? $33\frac{1}{3}\%$

2. What percent of the earnings did the student spend for lunches?   15%

3. What percent was spent for movies? $23\frac{1}{3}\%$

4. What percent was spent for food? $28\frac{1}{3}\%$

5. One week the student saw two movies that cost $3.50 each. The extra money for movies came from savings. What percent was saved that week?   10%

6. One week the student earned an extra $5. Three dollars of that was spent and the rest was saved. What percent of the total earnings was saved?   35%

276

Assignments

BASIC
page 276   exercises 1—6
page 277   exercises 7—14
Basic Worksheet 75

AVERAGE
page 276   exercises 1—6
page 277   exercises 7—15
Enrichment Worksheet 75

ENRICHED
page 276   exercises 1—6
page 277   exercises 7—16
Enrichment Worksheet 75

REVIEW PRACTICE
page 387   set 57

Remember that you can find a fraction or percent of a quantity by multiplying. For example, to find the amount budgeted for utilities, you might use this method:

$$8\% \text{ of } \$16,000 = ?$$

$$\text{equivalent} \longrightarrow \begin{array}{r} \$16,000 \\ \times\ .08 \\ \hline \$1280.00 \end{array}$$

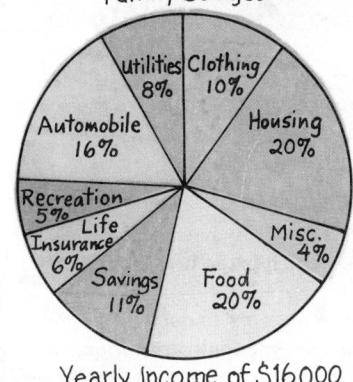

Family Budget

Utilities 8%
Clothing 10%
Automobile 16%
Housing 20%
Recreation 5%
Life Insurance 6%
Savings 11%
Food 20%
Misc. 4%

Yearly Income of $16,000

Refer to the graph of the family budget to answer the questions below.

7. How many dollars did the family budget for housing? $3200

8. How many dollars did the family budget for savings? $1760

9. What fraction of the total budget is for food and housing? Give answer in lowest terms. $\frac{2}{5}$

10. How much more money was budgeted for clothing than for life insurance? $640

11. How much money is budgeted for both recreation and automobile? $3360

12. What is the total percent budgeted for clothing, housing, and food? 50%

13. If life insurance is considered as savings, how much money is budgeted to be saved? $2720

14. The monthly car payment is $84.96. How much budgeted money a month is left for other car expenses? $128.37

15. Make a graph to show how you used your money last week.

16. Make a budget to show how you would like to use your money.

277

Follow-up Activities

Reinforcement After students have completed exercise 16, have them keep a record of their income and spending for a week. Have them construct a graph to show how they spent their money as compared to the budget they had prepared for exercise 16.

Enrichment Have students discuss their family budget with their parents. Without mentioning specific amounts, the pupils should find out the percent budgeted for the various categories, and make a circle graph for their family budget. Compare this graph with the family budget on page 277. Post the better graphs on the mathematics bulletin board.

EXCURSION

Study these examples. Can you find a shortcut for squaring numbers whose ones digit is 5?

$$25^2 = 2 \times 300 + 25 = 625$$
$$35^2 = 3 \times 400 + 25 = 1225$$
$$45^2 = 4 \times 500 + 25 = 2025$$
$$55^2 = 5 \times 600 + 25 = 3025$$

Use your shortcut to complete the following:

$$65^2 = \underline{\ ?\ } \qquad 85^2 = \underline{\ ?\ }$$
$$75^2 = \underline{\ ?\ } \qquad 95^2 = \underline{\ ?\ }$$
$$105^2 = \underline{\ ?\ }$$

4225, 7225,
5625, 9025,
11025

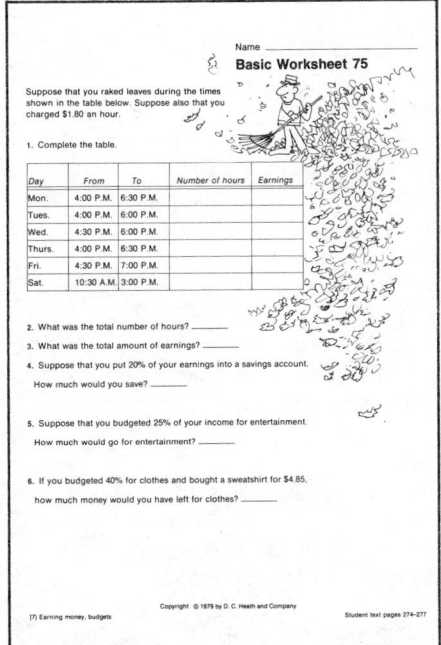

Name _____
Basic Worksheet 75

Suppose that you raked leaves during the times shown in the table below. Suppose also that you charged $1.80 an hour.

1. Complete the table.

Day	From	To	Number of hours	Earnings
Mon.	4:00 P.M.	6:30 P.M.		
Tues.	4:00 P.M.	6:00 P.M.		
Wed.	4:30 P.M.	6:00 P.M.		
Thurs.	4:00 P.M.	6:30 P.M.		
Fri.	4:30 P.M.	7:00 P.M.		
Sat.	10:30 A.M.	3:00 P.M.		

2. What was the total number of hours? _____

3. What was the total amount of earnings? _____

4. Suppose that you put 20% of your earnings into a savings account. How much would you save? _____

5. Suppose that you budgeted 25% of your income for entertainment. How much would go for entertainment? _____

6. If you budgeted 40% for clothes and bought a sweatshirt for $4.85, how much money would you have left for clothes? _____

Copyright © 1979 by D. C. Heath and Company

(7) Earning money, budgets   Student text pages 274–277

Name _____
Enrichment Worksheet 75

1. Jerry earns $1.60 an hour for babysitting. The table shows the hours that she works each week. Complete the table.

Day	From — To	Number of hours	Earnings
Mon.	3:45 pm–5:15 pm		
Tues.	4:00 pm–6:00 pm		
Wed.	3:45 pm–5:30 pm		
Thurs.	4:15 pm–5:45 pm		
Fri.	3:45 pm–6:15 pm		
Sat.	10:30 am–3:45 pm		
Sun.	4:15 pm–6:30 pm		

2. What were Jerry's total earnings for the week? _____

3. The circle graph shows how Jerry budgets her earnings. How much does she spend each week for

   a. lunches? _____

   b. clothing? _____

   c. entertainment? _____

4. How much does she

   a. save each week? _____

   b. give to charity? _____

5. One week she gave $3.50 to the United Fund. How much did she go over her budget? _____

3. a. One week she bounht some shoes on sale for $12. Was this within her budget? _____

   b. What percent of her weekly earnings did she spend for the shoes? _____

JERRY'S BUDGET

ENTERTAINMENT 20%
SAVINGS 25%
CHARITY 5%
LUNCHES 15%
CLOTHING 35%

Copyright © 1979 by D. C. Heath and Company

(7) Earning money, budgets   Student text pages 274, 275

STUDENT OBJECTIVE
To determine the better buy by
  computing the unit price of an item.

VOCABULARY
unit price

Suggested Lesson Plan

Introduction Begin the lesson by asking students what they are planning to buy in the near future. After several students have named some items, select one for your discussion. Ask leading questions about the purchase of the item, such as what qualities they look for, whether a name brand is actually better, and what other factors determine how they choose one item rather than another.

After you have discussed the comparison of the items, and assuming that the articles are comparable, turn the discussion to price. Assuming that the other factors are equal, discuss how students can decide which is the best price. If the article is a single item, of course, then a simple comparison will determine the better buy. If the items are packaged more than 1 to a package, such as notebook paper, point out to students that they need to determine the price based upon the same quantity.

Using the pages Use the exposition on page 278 to continue the discussion and to lead to the concept of unit pricing. Work several examples of unit pricing on the board so that students realize they divide the price by the number of units (each, pounds, ounces, etc.) to determine the price per unit. All other things being equal, the lower price determines the better buy.

Assign exercises 1—9 for written work. Allow some time at the end of the period for the Keeping Skills Sharp.

Spending wisely

Suppose that you are in a store and see this notebook paper. Before buying the paper you should ask yourself such questions as

(1) Is the price within my budget?
(2) Do I really need or want the paper?
(3) Which is the better buy?

If the answers to questions 1 and 2 are *yes*, then you could answer question 3 by computing the **unit price** (price per sheet) for each package.

$$120 \overline{)0.960}^{.008} \qquad 150 \overline{)1.050}^{.007}$$

Is the $1.05 package a better buy? yes

What else besides price should you think about when deciding which of two items is the better buy? how much you need, how long it takes to use it all, how much storage space it needs

EXERCISES

Suppose that both items are of equal quality. Compute the unit price and tell which is the better buy.

278

Assignments

BASIC
page 278 exercises 1—3
page 279 exercises 4—6,
  Keeping Skills Sharp
Basic Worksheet 76

AVERAGE
page 278 exercises 1—3
page 279 exercises 4—8,
  Keeping Skills Sharp
Enrichment Worksheet 76

ENRICHED
page 278 exercises 1—3
page 279 exercises 4—9,
  Keeping Skills Sharp
Enrichment Worksheet 76

EXTRA PRACTICE
page 393 set 79

In many supermarkets you don't have to compute unit prices. The store does it for you and posts those prices on their shelves. Here are some ways that unit prices are posted. Give the unit price for each item. What is the unit?

4.

UNIT PRICE	50 G	RETAIL PRICE
1.48 ✓		.74
CNTS/GRAM ✓	GROUND ALMONDS	

5.

UNIT PRICE	.475 L	RETAIL PRICE
1.03 ✓		.49
DOLS/LITER ✓	CURRANT JELLY	

6.

UNIT PRICE	340 G	RETAIL PRICE
1.68 ✓		.57
DOLS/KG ✓	CHILI SAUCE	

7.

UNIT PRICE	260 G	RETAIL PRICE
4.50 ✓		1.17
DOLS/KG ✓	TUNA	

8.

UNIT PRICE	450 G	RETAIL PRICE
1.47 ✓		.66
DOLS/KG ✓	SPAGHETTI SAUCE	

★9. Why do you think that in some cases the gram is used as a unit, while in other cases the kilogram is used? The gram is used when the quantity is very small.

Follow-up Activities

Reinforcement Give pupils a list of 3 items for which they are to find the prices at local stores. Have them prepare a list of reasons they believe a particular item is the best buy. Allow a few minutes in class for students to debate the best buys of these items.

Enrichment Have students accompany their parents food shopping and assist by noting the unit prices posted for the articles they purchase.

CALCULATOR ACTIVITY
Students should accompany their parents food shopping and list price comparisons of several items. Have them bring the lists to school and use a calculator to determine the unit price of each item of the different brands and quantities available. They can report to the class on the results when they have computed the unit prices.

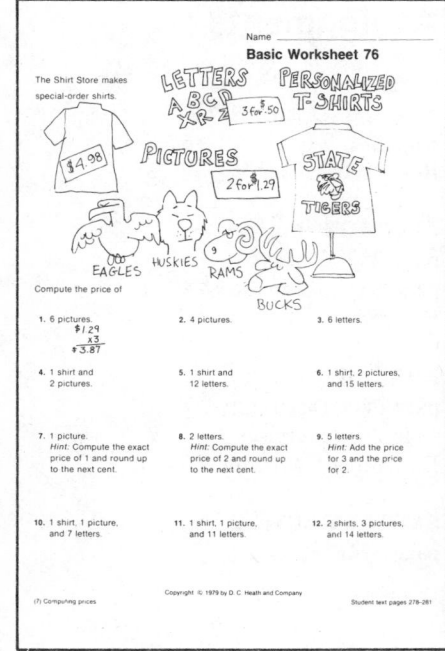

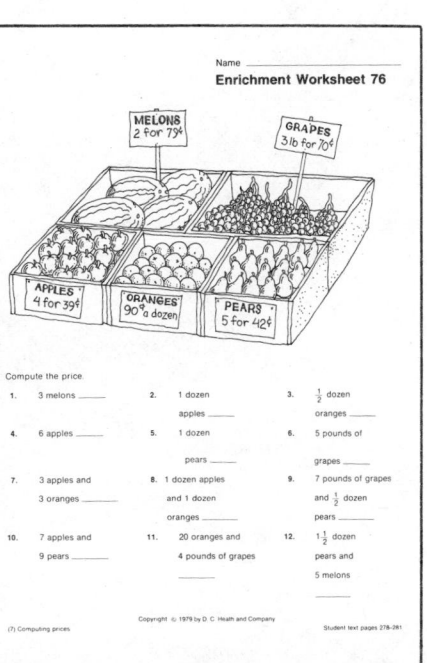

Suggested Lesson Plan

Introduction Tell students that you recently went to the food market and found grapefruit priced at 8 for $1.00. Ask pupils how much they would be charged for one grapefruit. (13¢) Some of your students may know that it is customary, when a unit price includes a fraction of a cent, to round up the actual cost of one item to the next cent. Therefore, although the cost of a single grapefruit is $12\frac{1}{2}$¢, the store would charge 13¢.

Using the pages Use the three examples to show how the costs of articles are determined. Note that for the second example a proportion is used, and the answer is then rounded up. Point out that although a single grapefruit was 13¢, 2 grapefruit would be 25¢ since $\frac{2}{8} \times \$1.00$ is 25¢.

Assign exercises 1–10 for written work.

Computing prices

Perhaps a student group at your school raises money by selling school supplies. Suppose that you had the job of computing the total amount of each sale. Below are some problems that you might have.

Pencils: 2 for 25¢
What is the price of 1 pencil?

Solution: Compute the exact price of 1 pencil and *round up* to the next cent.

$2\overline{)25}$ $12\frac{1}{2}$ The price is 13¢.

Erasers: 3 for 59¢
What is the price of 2 erasers?

Solution: Compute the exact price of 2 erasers and *round up* to the next cent.

$$\frac{3}{59} = \frac{2}{n}$$
$$3n = 118$$
$$n = 39\frac{1}{3} \quad \text{The price is 40¢.}$$

Erasers: 3 for 59¢
What is the price of 5 erasers?

Solution: Add the price of 3 erasers and the price of 2 erasers.

59¢ + 40¢ = 99¢

280

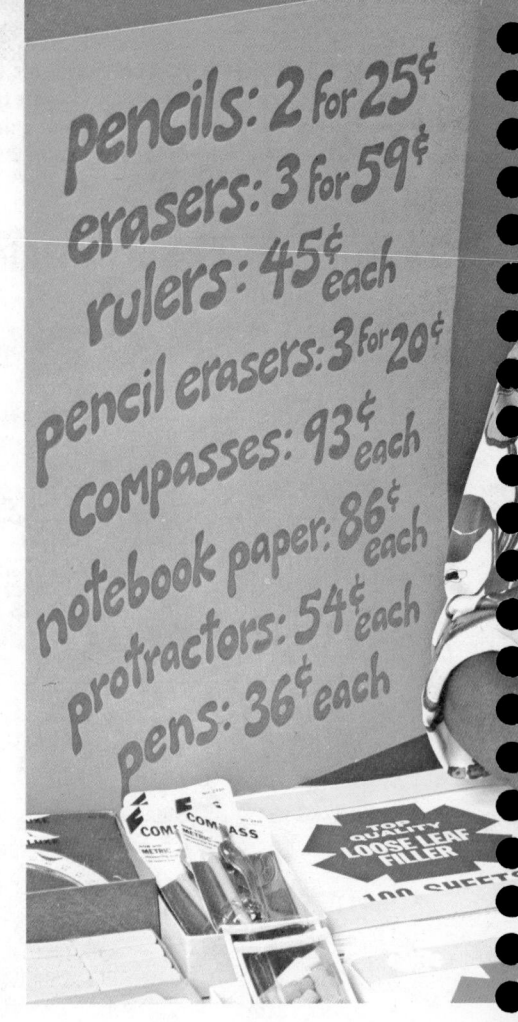

pencils: 2 for 25¢
erasers: 3 for 59¢
rulers: 45¢ each
pencil erasers: 3 for 20¢
compasses: 93¢ each
notebook paper: 86¢ each
protractors: 54¢ each
pens: 36¢ each

Assignments

BASIC
page 280 Discuss
page 281 exercises 1–6
Basic Worksheet 76

AVERAGE
page 280 Discuss
page 281 exercises 1–8
Enrichment Worksheet 76

ENRICHED
page 280 Discuss
page 281 exercises 1–10
Enrichment Worksheet 76

EXTRA PRACTICE
page 394 set 80

EXERCISES

Refer to the prices on page 280 to compute these total prices.

1. 45¢

2. 53¢

3. 38¢

4. $1.13

5. $1.13

6. 84¢

Solve.

7. A customer buys 7 pencils and gives you a dollar. How much change should you give? 12¢

8. A customer buys 3 packages of notebook paper and 5 pencils. He gives you $5. How much change should you give back? $1.79

9. Suppose someone returns a protractor and buys 1 eraser and 2 pencil erasers. How much money should you give back? 20¢

10. Another customer returns one compass and 2 pens. He then buys 4 packages of notebook paper and gives you $2. How much change should you give back? 21¢

281

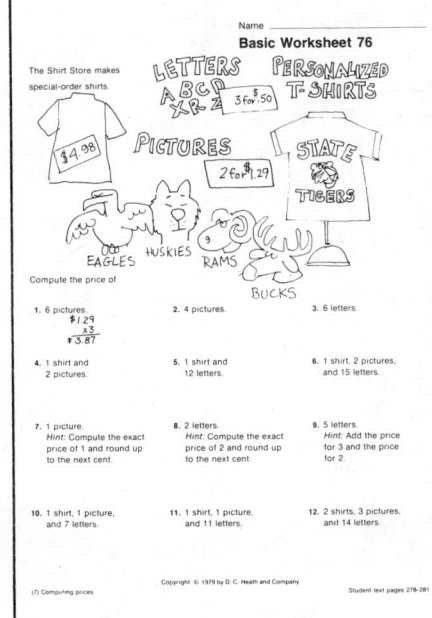

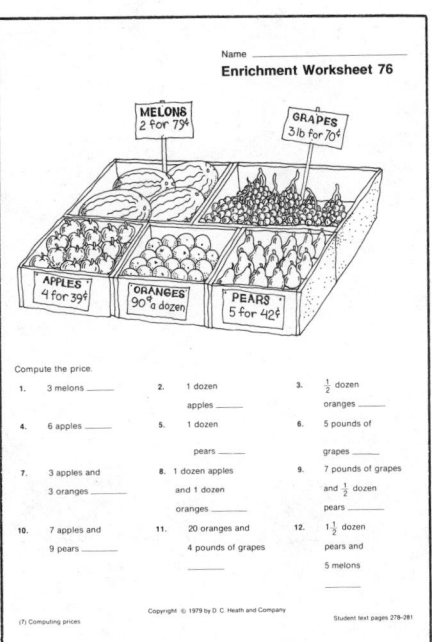

Follow-up Activities

Reinforcement Students might conduct this experiment in a food market: locating a special offer of an article that is priced 3 for a certain amount, the students can count how many people buy 3 items at a time and how many buy some other number of the items. Now ask students why food markets use such prices as 8 for $1.00, etc.

Enrichment Duplicate a chart like the one below. Have students make a check mark for each coin, to give the change in the fewest number of coins and dollars.

Purchase	Paid	Change						
			1¢	5¢	10¢	25¢	50¢	$1.00
$1.25	$2.00							

EXCURSION

Copy and fill in the missing digits.

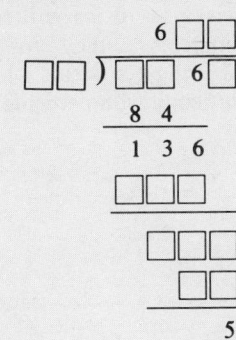

$$
\begin{array}{r}
697 \\
14\overline{)9763} \\
84 \\
\hline
136 \\
126 \\
\hline
103 \\
98 \\
\hline
5
\end{array}
$$

(core) Lesson 131 **281**

STUDENT OBJECTIVE
To compute the selling price of an
    article that is discounted.

VOCABULARY
discount

Suggested Lesson Plan

Introduction   Ask students to relate
recent experiences when they have
purchased items that were discounted.
Ask them how the discount was
computed. Did they check the discount?

Using the pages   Use the exposition
on page 282 to continue the discussion
on discounts. When discussing
discounts, point out the two ways to
determine the new selling price: (1)
compute the amount of discount and
subtract from the original price, or (2)
determine what percent the new sale
price is of the original amount and
compute this percent.

   Work through the examples on page
282, showing the work on the board.

   Assign exercises 1–10 for written
work. Observe students as they work.
Be prepared to help those students who
are still having difficulty with percents.

Discounts

Have you ever seen a sign like this in a
store?

To sell the pack frame, the merchant is
discounting (decreasing) the price 20%.
The amount a price is decreased is called
the **discount**. Here are 3 ways to find the
sale price.

If the discount is 20%, then the sale price is 80% of the regular price.

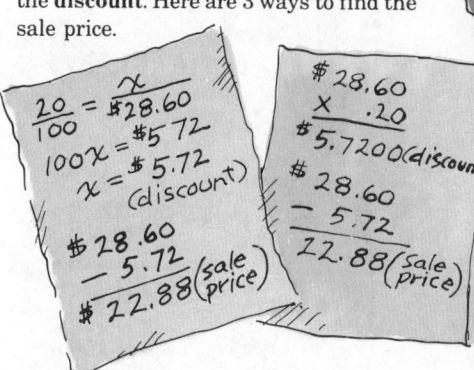

The percent a price is decreased is sometimes called the
percent of discount.

This pair of hiking boots was discounted
for a sale.

To find the percent of discount, find what
percent of the original price the discount
is.

amount of
discount $\longrightarrow$
original $\longrightarrow$ $\dfrac{6}{48} = \dfrac{n}{100}$
price $\qquad 48n = 600$
$$n = 12\tfrac{1}{2}$$

The percent of discount was $12\tfrac{1}{2}\%$.

282

Assignments

BASIC
page 282 Discuss
page 283 exercises 1–10
Basic Worksheet 77

AVERAGE
page 282 Discuss
page 283 exercises 1–10
Enrichment Worksheet 77

ENRICHED
page 282 Discuss
page 283 exercises 1–10
Enrichment Worksheet 77

EXTRA PRACTICE
page 394 set 81

EXERCISES

The regular price and the percent of discount are given. Compute the discount.

1. tent: $36.50
   discount: 25% $9.13

2. mess kit: $12.50
   discount: 10% $1.25

3. pack: $27.60
   discount: $33\frac{1}{3}$%
   $9.20

4. sleeping bag: $56.80
   discount: $12\frac{1}{2}$%
   $7.10

The regular price and the percent of discount are given. Find the total cost, including a sales tax of 5%. Refer to the table for the sales tax.

5. flashlight: $8.50
   discount: 10% $8.03

6. poncho: $16.60
   discount: 25% $13.07

7. pack frame: $29.50
   discount: 12%
   $27.26

8. stove: $24.75
   discount: $33\frac{1}{3}$%
   $17.33

Find the percent of discount.

9.
25%

10.
about 17%

Sale	Tax	Sale	Tax
6.90 – 7.09	.35	18.90 – 19.09	.95
7.10 – 7.29	.36	19.10 – 19.29	.96
7.30 – 7.49	.37	19.30 – 19.49	.97
7.50 – 7.69	.38	19.50 – 19.69	.98
7.70 – 7.89	.39	19.70 – 19.89	.99
7.90 – 8.09	.40	19.90 – 20.09	1.00
8.10 – 8.29	.41	20.10 – 20.29	1.01
8.30 – 8.49	.42	20.30 – 20.49	1.02
8.50 – 8.69	.43	20.50 – 20.69	1.03
8.70 – 8.89	.44	20.70 – 20.89	1.04
8.90 – 9.09	.45	20.90 – 21.09	1.05
9.10 – 9.29	.46	21.10 – 21.29	1.06
9.30 – 9.49	.47	21.30 – 21.49	1.07
9.50 – 9.69	.48	21.50 – 21.69	1.08
9.70 – 9.89	.49	21.70 – 21.89	1.09
9.90 – 10.09	.50	21.90 – 22.09	1.10
10.10 – 10.29	.51	22.10 – 22.29	1.11
10.30 – 10.49	.52	22.30 – 22.49	1.12
10.50 – 10.69	.53	22.50 – 22.69	1.13
10.70 – 10.89	.54	22.70 – 22.89	1.14
10.90 – 11.09	.55	22.90 – 23.09	1.15
11.10 – 11.29	.56	23.10 – 23.29	1.16
11.30 – 11.49	.57	23.30 – 23.49	1.17
11.50 – 11.69	.58	23.50 – 23.69	1.18
11.70 – 11.89	.59	23.70 – 23.89	1.19
11.90 – 12.09	.60	23.90 – 24.09	1.20
12.10 – 12.29	.61	24.10 – 24.29	1.21
12.30 – 12.49	.62	24.30 – 24.49	1.22
12.50 – 12.69	.63	24.50 – 24.69	1.23
12.70 – 12.89	.64	24.70 – 24.89	1.24
12.90 – 13.09	.65	24.90 – 25.09	1.25
13.10 – 13.29	.66	25.10 – 25.29	1.26
13.30 – 13.49	.67	25.30 – 25.49	1.27
13.50 – 13.69	.68	25.50 – 25.69	1.28
13.70 – 13.89	.69	25.70 – 25.89	1.29
13.90 – 14.09	.70	25.90 – 26.09	1.30
14.10 – 14.29	.71	26.10 – 26.29	1.31
14.30 – 14.49	.72	26.30 – 26.49	1.32
14.50 – 14.69	.73	26.50 – 26.69	1.33
14.70 – 14.89	.74	26.70 – 26.89	1.34
14.90 – 15.09	.75	26.90 – 27.09	1.35
15.10 – 15.29	.76	27.10 – 27.29	1.36
15.30 – 15.49	.77	27.30 – 27.49	1.37
15.50 – 15.69	.78	27.50 – 27.69	1.38
15.70 – 15.89	.79	27.70 – 27.89	1.39
15.90 – 16.09	.80	27.90 – 28.09	1.40
16.10 – 16.29	.81	28.10 – 28.29	1.41
16.30 – 16.49	.82	28.30 – 28.49	1.42
16.50 – 16.69	.83	28.50 – 28.69	1.43
16.70 – 16.89	.84	28.70 – 28.89	1.44
16.90 – 17.09	.85	28.90 – 29.09	1.45
17.10 – 17.29	.86	29.10 – 29.29	1.46
17.30 – 17.49	.87	29.30 – 29.49	1.47
17.50 – 17.69	.88	29.50 – 29.69	1.48
17.70 – 17.89	.89	29.70 – 29.89	1.49
17.90 – 18.09	.90	29.90 – 30.09	1.50
18.10 – 18.29	.91	30.10 – 30.29	1.51
18.30 – 18.49	.92	30.30 – 30.49	1.52
18.50 – 18.69	.93	30.50 – 30.69	1.53
18.70 – 18.89	.94	30.70 – 30.89	1.54

283

Follow-up Activities

Reinforcement Have students collect newspaper ads that give the percent of discount. When the original price and new price are given, have students check the amounts to see whether the correct percent is listed. Make a display of the ads collected and post on the mathematics bulletin board.

Enrichment Have students get a sales-tax table for your state or a neighboring state that has a sales tax. Have them explain how to use the tax table and why the tax is not always the percent listed.

EXCURSION

On graph paper, see how many different shaped cube patterns you can draw.

Example.

This pattern:

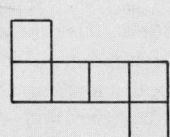

folds into this cube:

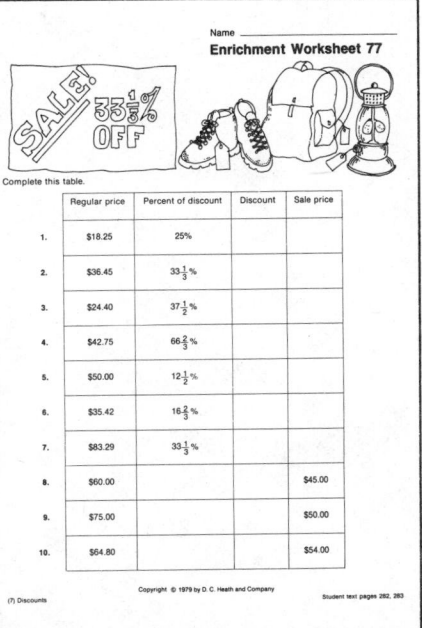

STUDENT OBJECTIVES
To answer questions concerning a
    checking account.
To write and deposit checks.

VOCABULARY
check, checking account, endorse

Suggested Lesson Plan

Introduction Try to have a parent or
friend who works in a bank talk to the
class about checking accounts. Many
students will have savings accounts, but
probably will not be familiar with the
mechanics of a checking account.

If you have a guest speaker, let that
person discuss the advantages of a
checking account and how students can
open one.

Try to obtain samples of checks and
information about checking accounts
from your local bank.

Using the pages Use the exposition
on page 284 to summarize your
discussions about checking accounts.
Work through each section, discussing
the correct way to fill out a check and
how to endorse a check given to you by
someone else.

Pay special attention to the section
on keeping records of the checks
written. You may want to add details
about the monthly statement and the
canceled checks to this discussion.

Assign exercises 1–14 for written
work. Go over the answers in class.

A checking account

It is not usually a wise idea to keep large amounts of cash in
your billfold or even in your home. It can be accidentally de-
stroyed, lost, or stolen. Millions of people put their money into
checking accounts in banks to keep it safe. Whenever they
wish to use some of the money they write a **check**. Checks are
just notes that tell the bank to give some of the money in an
account to a company or a person.

This check tells the First National Bank of Hometown,
USA, to pay Mary R. Cooper $18.25 from the checking account
of Sarah Smith.

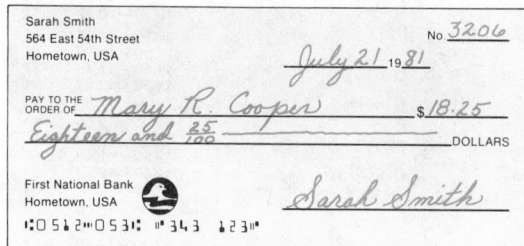

A checkbook has a section in which a record of the account is
kept. Study this part of Sarah Smith's record:

CHECK NO.	DATE	PAY TO	AMOUNT	DEPOSIT	BALANCE	
					26	42
3204	July 11	LP Records	14.20		12	22
	July 15			50.00	62	22
3205	July 18	Allan's Bookstore	8.57		53	65
3206	July 21	Mary R. Cooper	18.25		35	40

Mary R. Cooper will have to sign her name on the back of the
check before she can cash the check. This is called **endorsing**
the check. The endorsed check is proof that Sarah Smith paid
the money to Mary R. Cooper.

284

Assignments

BASIC
page 284 Discuss
page 285 exercises 1–12, Project
Basic Worksheet 78

AVERAGE
page 284 Discuss
page 285 exercises 1–14, Project
Enrichment Worksheet 78

ENRICHED
page 284 Discuss
page 285 exercises 1–14, Project
Enrichment Worksheet 78

REVIEW PRACTICE
page 387 set 58

EXERCISES
7. To prevent the amount from being changed by someone else.
Refer to the preceding page to answer the following questions.

1. What is the number of the check that was written to Mary Cooper? 3206

2. On what date was a $50 deposit made? July 15

3. Check 3204 was written for what amount? $14.20

4. How much was the check written to Allan's Bookstore? $8.57

5. What was the balance in the account after check 3206 was written? $35.40

6. To whom was a check of $14.20 written? LP Records

7. Why do you think that a check should be written in ink?

8. Why do you think the amount is written in both numerals and words?
To double-check the right amount.

9. Who can cash this check? anyone

Sarah Smith
564 East 54th Street
Hometown, USA

No. 3214

July 30 19 81

PAY TO THE
ORDER OF Cash $ 50.00

Fifty and 00/100 _____ DOLLARS

First National Bank
Hometown, USA

Sarah Smith

⑆0512⑈053⑆ ⑆343 123⑈

Write in words, as you would on a check.

10. $37.50   **11.** $42.75   **12.** $60.00   **13.** $135.45   **14.** $203.04

Project

1. Find out whether your bank charges a service charge for a checking account. If so, how do they compute the service charge?

2. Find out what "overdrawn account" means.

10. Thirty-seven and 50/100
11. Forty-two and 75/100
12. Sixty and 00/100
13. One hundred thirty-five and 45/100
14. Two hundred three and 04/100

285

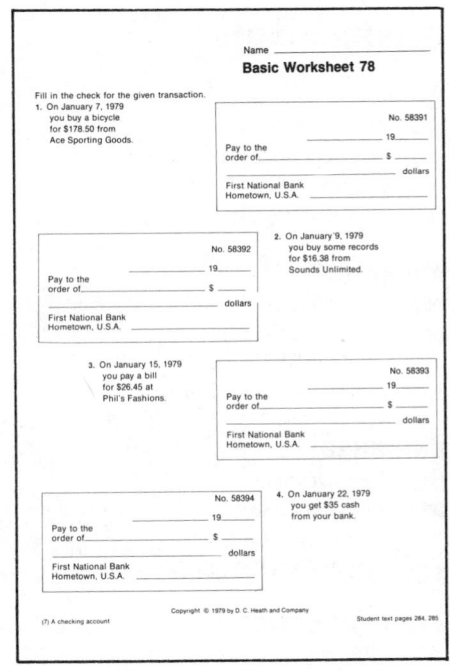

Follow-up Activities

Reinforcement On a duplicating master, prepare blank checks and stubs. Prepare a description of five checks to be written and the opening balance. Have students write the checks and fill in the stubs to show the running balance. Check their work carefully to see that they have done neat and accurate check writing.

Enrichment Have students visit a local bank and report back to the class on the different types of accounts available and the advantages of these accounts. Have students lead a discussion of the advantages of having a checking account and how to open an account.

CALCULATOR ACTIVITY
Have students write ten additional checks and make several deposits to the account started in the Reinforcement activity. Have students use a calculator to compute the balance of the account.

Suggested Lesson Plan

Introduction   Introduce the idea of borrowing (renting) money. Instead of paying a fixed fee, as with an apartment, we pay an amount that varies with the amount of money borrowed, the length of time the money is kept, and the rate of interest charged. Give examples of interest rates and introduce the words *principal*, *rate*, and *time*.

Ask students to tell what they know about borrowing.

Bring in local interest rates from banks, credit unions, small loan companies, and even loan sharks (if there are any in your community). Do examples with these rates.

Using the pages   Use the exposition on page 286 to summarize your introduction. Discuss the terms introduced.

Assign exercises 1–13. Point out that the time for a loan is figured on the period of 1 year so the time is always represented in years. For example, a loan for 6 months is $^6/_{12}$, or $^1/_2$, year.

Borrowing money

Some day you may need to borrow money. If you do, you will probably borrow the money from a bank, credit union, or loan company. You will have to pay **interest** (rent) for using the money. The amount of interest that you will pay depends on the **principal** (the amount you borrow), the **rate** (percent) of interest charged, and the **time** for which you borrow the money.

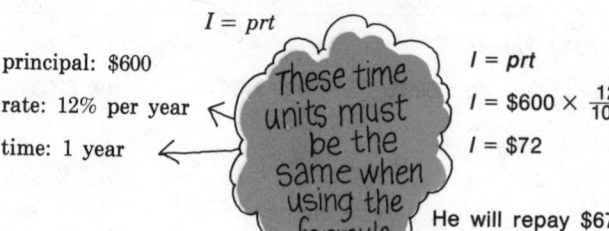

He will have to sign a note saying he will pay back the $600 plus the interest in 1 year.

The amount of interest can be computed by using this formula:

$$\text{Interest} = \text{principal} \times \text{rate} \times \text{time}$$

$$I = prt$$

principal: $600

rate: 12% per year

time: 1 year

$I = prt$

$I = \$600 \times \frac{12}{100} \times 1$

$I = \$72$

He will repay $672 at the end of 1 year.

Important: Before you borrow, you should compare the rates of several banks.

286

Assignments

BASIC
page 286 Discuss
page 287 exercises 1–10,
   Keeping Skills Sharp
Basic Worksheet 79

AVERAGE
page 286 Discuss
page 287 exercises 1–11,
   Keeping Skills Sharp
Enrichment Worksheet 79

ENRICHED
page 286 Discuss
page 287 exercises 1–13,
   Keeping Skills Sharp
Enrichment Worksheet 79

EXTRA PRACTICE
page 395 set 82

EXERCISES

Compute the interest to the nearest cent.

	Interest	Principal	Interest rate per year	Time
1.	$88	$800	11%	1 year
2.	$90	$1000	9%	1 year
3.	$120	$2000	12%	6 months
4.	$56.25	$750	10%	9 months
5.	$60	$500	18%	8 months
6.	$156.25	$1250	$12\frac{1}{2}$%	1 year
7.	$26.25	$500	$10\frac{1}{2}$%	6 months
8.	$53.83	$850	$9\frac{1}{2}$%	8 months
9.	$66.41	$1250	$12\frac{3}{4}$%	5 months
10.	$47.66	$1875	$15\frac{1}{4}$%	2 months

Solve.

11. Jane borrowed $1800 for 1 year to buy a car. If the yearly rate was $10\frac{1}{2}$%, how much interest would she owe at the end of the year? $189

12. a. A motorcycle is on sale for $1350. A bank will loan 80% of the money. How much money will the bank loan on the motorcycle? $1080
    b. If the bank will loan the money at 11% for 1 year, how much interest will be charged? $118.80

13. John saved $120 to buy a stereo set. A stereo that generally sells for $379.00 is on sale for 25% off.
    a. How much money will he have to borrow? $164.25
    b. If he borrows the money for 6 months at 12%, how much interest will he pay?

Follow-up Activities

Reinforcement Give students a copy of the classified section of a local newspaper containing automobiles for sale. Have students pick out an automobile. Ask them to pretend that they have enough cash to pay 20% of the listed price and that they borrow the rest of the money for a period of one year at a yearly interest rate of 9%. How much interest do they have to pay?

Enrichment You may wish to have some students find out what is meant by *compound interest*. Have them report the interest rates paid for deposits at a local savings and loan company. Ask them to find out how the interest is compounded.

EXCURSION
Fill in the circles with the numbers 1, 2, 3, 4, 5, 6, 8, 9, 10, and 12 so that the sum of the numbers in each row is 24.

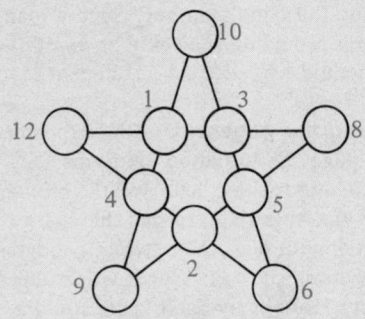

(core) Lesson 134   **287**

To find the cost of installment buying.

VOCABULARY
credit, cosigner, installment buying, loan

Suggested Lesson Plan

Introduction The cost of installment buying is an important aspect of consumer education. Installment buying has a great many advantages, and the advantages as well as the disadvantages should be known for students to become intelligent consumers. Much more time could be spent on installment buying; this lesson serves as an introduction to the topic.

Ask students if they have ever borrowed money from their parents and then paid it back on a weekly or monthly schedule. Did they have to pay interest? (probably not) Explain that when they borrow money from a bank, they have to pay *interest*, or *rent*, for using the bank's money. Such a loan, when repaid on a weekly or monthly schedule, is called an installment loan.

Using the pages Use the exposition on page 288 to define the terms associated with a loan. Work through the example given to find the cost of the installment plan. Ask students judgment questions such as: Was it worth the $18 rent? How many such loans could a person have at one time? Are credit cards like installment loans?

Assign exercises 1–8 for written work. After students complete the exercises, discuss the answers. Continue asking judgment questions as described above.

Installment buying

Suppose that you wanted to buy this television set but didn't have $180. You could pay a down payment of $30, sign the agreement to pay $14 a month for 12 payments, and take the television set with you. Until you are older and have "established credit," you will probably have to have someone sign the agreement with you. Such a person is called a **cosigner**.

When you buy an item on an installment plan, you usually have to pay more.

Cash	Installment Plan
$180	$14
	× 12
	28
	14
	$168
	+ 30
	$198

The extra $18 that you are charged on the installment plan is interest that you must pay because you borrowed from the television store.

Before buying on an installment plan, check to see if you could save money by borrowing the money from a bank or credit union.

288

Assignments

BASIC
page 288 Discuss
page 289 exercises 1–6
Basic Worksheet 80

AVERAGE
page 288 Discuss
page 289 exercises 1–8
Enrichment Worksheet 80

ENRICHED
page 288 Discuss
page 289 exercises 1–8
Enrichment Worksheet 80

REVIEW PRACTICE
page 387 set 59

EXERCISES

How much more does the installment plan cost?

1.

Cash: $68
Installment plan:
$20 down
$4.48 per month
for 12 months $5.76

2.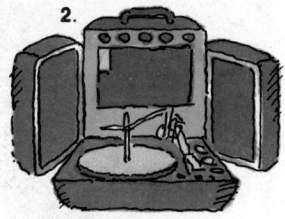

Cash: $156
Installment plan:
$30 down
$12.06 per month
for 12 months $1872

3.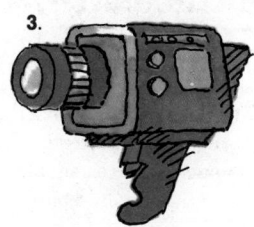

Cash: $150
Installment plan:
$35 down
$20.60 per month
for 6 months $14.25

4.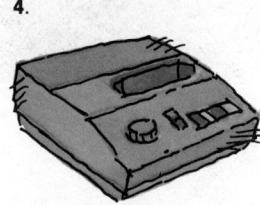

Cash: $72
Installment plan:
$15 down
$4.37 per month
for 15 months $8.55

5.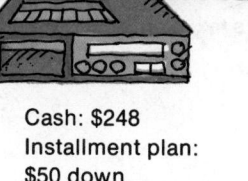

Cash: $248
Installment plan:
$50 down
$14.36 per month
for 16 months $31.76

6.

Cash: $159
Installment plan:
no down payment
$19.25 per month
for 9 months $8.60

Solve.

7. Suppose that it costs $14.88 interest to finance a $120 purchase for 1 year on an installment plan. How much could be saved by borrowing the money at a bank for $10\frac{1}{2}$ %? $2.28

8. Suppose that a merchant offers to finance $460 for 18 months at $30.35 per month. You can also borrow the money for $10\frac{1}{2}$ % at a bank. Which would cost less? How much less?
borrowing from bank, $38.00

289

Follow-up Activities

Reinforcement Have students talk to merchants that have installment loans available. Have students find out what such plans cost and how the stores obtain their money. Are the plans financed by other institutions or does the store loan its own money?

Enrichment Have students talk to the loan officer of a local bank. See whether they can arrange to have the loan officer visit your class for a lecture on loans.

EXCURSION
Each letter represents a different digit in the addition below.

$$
\begin{array}{r}
DID \\
DID \\
DID \\
DID \\
+DID \\
\hline
SAID
\end{array}
$$

Determine the digits.

The *D*s in the right column must be either 0s or 5s. The *D*s in the left column cannot be 0s. So *D* = 5. Then *I* = 0 + 2 or 5 + 2. If *I* = 2, then *S* = 2. So *I* ≠ 2. Then *I* = 7. Then *S* = 2 and *A* = 8.

$$
\begin{array}{r}
575 \\
575 \\
575 \\
575 \\
+575 \\
\hline
2875
\end{array}
$$

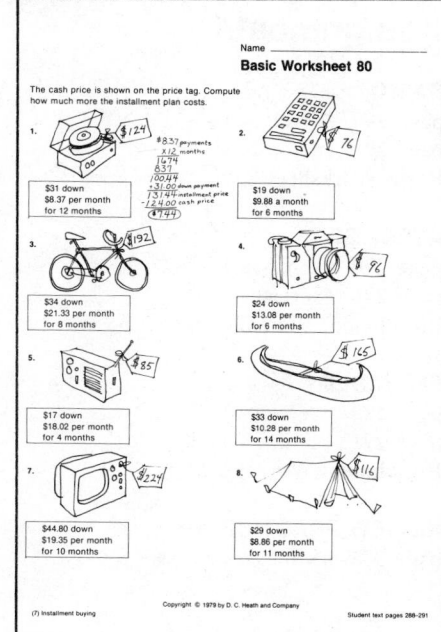

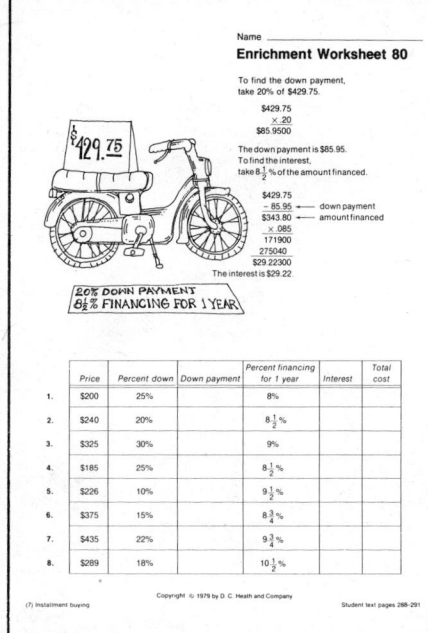

Suggested Lesson Plan

Introduction Several days before the lesson, ask whether any of the students' brothers, sisters, or parents are employed in the careers mentioned on pages 290 and 291. If so, have the student discuss the pages with that person and then lead the discussion about that career.

Using the pages Young people who work in service stations or in other retail jobs need to be able to do fast and accurate computations. Have students compute the bills on page 290.

Discuss the details of the real estate business. For these problems, have students compute to figure the commission. Be sure to point out in the discussion that although the agent gets the commission, this is not clear profit. Discuss some of the expenses associated with real estate that come out of the commission. (advertising, transportation, etc.)

Assign exercises 1−4 for written work.

Mathematics in careers

Besides selling gasoline, most gasoline station operators also sell such items as oil, tires, and batteries. They also provide such services as oil changes, wheel balancing, minor repairs and tuneups.

In a certain state, gasoline stations charge a 5% sales tax on the sale of all items except gasoline. Sales tax is not charged on labor.

EXERCISES
Compute the total. For the sales tax, refer to the table on page 283.

1.

CRAIG'S SERVICE STATION

Labor			
Minor Tune-up	$17.50	Gasoline	$9.50
Oil Change	1.50	5 L Oil	
Oil Filter	1.00	($1.25/L)	6.25
		Oil Filter	3.75
		Sales Tax	$.98
Labor Total	20.00	→	
		Total	40.48

2.

CRAIG'S SERVICE STATION

Labor			
Balance (4 wheels)	$7.00	Gasoline	$9.75
		1 L Oil	$1.25
		Sales Tax	$.55
Labor Total	$7.00	→	
		Total	18.55

3.

CRAIG'S SERVICE STATION

Labor			
Oil Change	$1.50	Gasoline	$9.95
Filter (Oil)	1.00	Oil Filter	3.75
Filter (Air)	.75	Air Filter	2.95
Lubrication	2.85	4 L Oil	
		($1.40/L)	5.60
		Sales Tax	$1.11
Labor Total	6.10	→	
		Total	29.46

290

Assignments

BASIC
page 290 exercises 1−3
page 291 exercises 1−4
Basic Worksheet 80

AVERAGE
page 290 exercises 1−3
page 291 exercises 1−4
Enrichment Worksheet 80

ENRICHED
page 290 exercises 1−3
page 291 exercises 1−4
Enrichment Worksheet 80

REVIEW PRACTICE
page 388 set 60

Mathematics in careers

Property such as houses, buildings, and land is called *real estate*. Real estate is generally sold by a real-estate agent. For selling the property, the agent receives a commission, which is generally a percentage of the selling price.

Often several real-estate agents in the same area belong to a multiple listing service. When such an agent lists (signs an agreement to try to sell) some real estate, he informs the other agents who belong to the multiple listing service. Any of these agents can then sell the property. If an agent other than the one who listed the property sells it, the commission is divided between the agent who listed the property and the one who sold it.

EXERCISES

During one week, the R. E. Johnson Real Estate Company received comissions from the sale of the properties listed below. The total commission paid was 6% of the selling price. How much commission did the R. E. Johnson Real Estate Company receive during this week? $37,038

1. Listed by R. E. Johnson
Sold by R. E. Johnson $3594

Well-maintained, professionally landscaped 3-bedroom ranch home, near schools, with living room, kitchen, utility room, and large bath. Attic with pull-down stairs, patio, attached garage. Has central air conditioning, carpet and tile floors, and maintenance-free aluminum siding. This home is a real buy at $59,900.

2. Listed by A. J. Thomas
Sold by R. E. Johnson $1947

Large exceptionally nice bi-level in Kenwood School area, with 3 large bedrooms and bath up. Lower level has big "L" shaped family room, 4th bedroom, large bath, utility area. Storm windows, carpet and tile floors, redwood sun deck off kitchen. A beautiful white aluminum-sided home in excellent condition. Will consider trade. $64,900.

3. Listed by R. E. Johnson
Sold by C. R. Davidson $2097

Beautifully cared for older air-conditioned brick-on-tile home in established area. 4 bedrooms and lovely bath on 2nd, study and family room on first. Brick fireplace in carpeted and draped living room. Beamed ceiling in magnificent dining room. Recreation room, work room, etc., in basement. Attic, 2-car garage. $69,900.

4. Listed by R. E. Johnson
Sold by R. E. Johnson $29,400

12-unit brick apartment building in good location. 8 units furnished and 4 unfurnished. Furnishings include washers and dryers, disposals in most. This apartment building has a net income of $42,000 per year. Call for more details. $490,000.

291

Follow-up Activities

Reinforcement   Have students make up sample bills for work completed at a service station. Have students exchange bills and compute the totals.

Enrichment   Have students talk to a real estate agent to discuss the mathematical skills she uses in doing her work.

EXCURSION
Find the pattern. Then copy and complete the table.

1	4	9	16	25
4	9	16	25	36
9	16	25	36	49
16	25	36	49	64

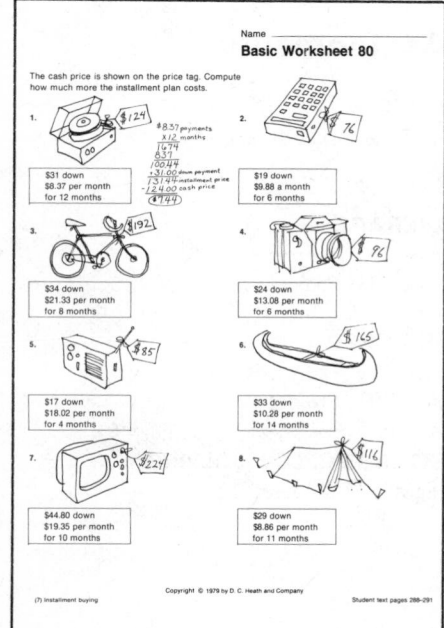

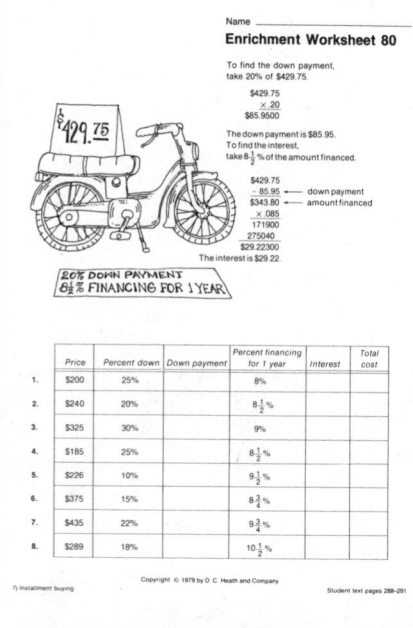

STUDENT OBJECTIVE

To review the concepts introduced in Chapter 9.

Suggested Lesson Plan

Introduction No pre-text activity is necessary for page 292 as this is a checkup for the chapter. However, it may be valuable to briefly review the lessons in the chapter so that students are reminded of the content over which they will be tested.

This Checkup will provide you with data about how well individual students have mastered the skills of the chapter. The Chapter Review on page 294 is provided for those students who need more specific individual help.

Page 293 is a project that students may do working in pairs. Students of this age are just becoming interested in cars and this activity can generate much discussion.

Using the pages Assign all of the exercises on page 292. As students complete the page they can work on the project on page 293.

Solve. [pages 274–275, 284–285]

1. John Roberto worked 3 hours for the amount shown on the check. How much did he earn per hour? $3.35

2. The balance of the account before the check was written was $142.13. What was the balance after the check was written? $132.08

3. Who wrote the check?   Robert D. Mann

[pages 280–281]

Find the price of

4. 1 record.
   $2.34
5. 2 records.
   $4.67
6. 5 records.
   $11.67

Solve. [pages 282–283]

7. A $112 bicycle was put on sale at a discount of 20%. What was the sale price? $89.60

8. A $48 camera was put on sale for $36. What was the percent of discount?   25%

Solve. [pages 286–289]

9. If you borrowed $85 for 1 year and paid 9% interest, how much interest would you pay? $7.65

10. A $156 canoe can be bought for $30 down and $11.76 a month for 12 months. Find the amount of interest. $15.12

292

Assignments

BASIC
page 292 exercises 1—10
page 293 Project

AVERAGE
page 292 exercises 1—10
page 293 Project

ENRICHED
page 292 exercises 1—10
page 293 Project

EXTRA PROBLEM SOLVING
pages 422–423 set 13

Project

1. From a classified ad in a newspaper, compute the average prices of 1-year-old Chevrolets, 2-year-old Chevrolets, 3-year-old Chevrolets, and 4-year-old Chevrolets.

2. Show your findings on a bar graph like this:

Average Price of Chevrolets

Price

$5000
$4500
$4000
$3500
$3000
$2500
$2000
$1500
$1000
$500

1   2   3   4
Years Old

3. Repeat the project for another make of automobile. Compare your results.

293

Follow-up Activities

Reinforcement Correct the items in the Chapter Checkup. Any student who misses 4 or more problems needs additional help.

Enrichment Assign these pupils to the games and activities that have been played or worked on throughout the chapter. Assign a student leader to be responsible for teaching each game or activity to the interested students and to supervise the play.

CALCULATOR ACTIVITY
Assign one student to be in charge of the calculators and the calculator activities. The calculator student is responsible for keeping track of the calculators, for explaining the activities, and for supervising the play.

You may wish to assign some of the Creative Problem Solving Activities (pages 461-477) at this time.

STUDENT OBJECTIVE

To review or extend the skills and concepts taught in Chapter 9.

Suggested Lesson Plan

Introduction After checking the Chapter Checkup you will know which students need additional reinforcement and which students will be able to go ahead with the Challenge activity. Get the better students started on page 295 first as the students who are having difficulty will need more of your time.

The students who need more review should go back and correct their errors on the Chapter Checkup. You may want to go over these questions orally if this group is small enough. Carefully probe to determine which concepts and skills the students have not mastered and work individually to correct these deficiencies.

Using the pages After the identified students have corrected the Chapter Checkup, they should answer questions 1–10 on page 294. After they complete these questions, read the answers and let the students correct their own papers. Give them an opportunity to ask questions about the exercises they missed.

Assign page 295 to those students who did well on the Chapter Checkup. Have them work individually on the computations.

To find the price of 1 or 2 birds, compute the exact price and round up to the next cent.

Find the price of

1. 1 bird 27¢
2. 2 birds 53¢
3. 5 birds $1.32

The discount is 20% of $18.50. The sale price is $18.50 minus the discount.

4. How much is the discount? $3.70
5. What is the sale price?
   $14.80

$$I = prt$$
Interest = principal × rate × time

Find the simple interest for a loan of

6. $180 at 12% for 1 year $21.60
7. $640 at 16% for 6 months $51.20

The installment cost is the down payment plus the total of the monthly payments.

8. What is the cash price? $198
9. a. What is the down payment? $18
   b. What is the total of the monthly payments? $227.64
10. How much more does the installment plan cost?
    $29.64

294

Assignments

BASIC
page 294 exercises 1–10

AVERAGE
page 294 exercises 1–10

ENRICHED
page 295 all

CHAPTER CHALLENGE

Perhaps you have a savings account. If you do, you probably know that the interest your account earns is added to your account several times during the year.

Study this example.

On January 1, $100 is deposited in a savings account that pays 6% interest per year.

At the end of 3 months ($\frac{1}{4}$ year) the interest is added to the account.

$I = p \times r \times t$

$I = \$100 \times \frac{6}{100} \times \frac{1}{4}$

$I = \$1.50$

The new balance is $101.50.

At the end of the next 3 months, the interest is figured on $101.50 and added to the account.

$I = p \times r \times t$

$I = \$101.50 \times \frac{6}{100} \times \frac{1}{4}$

$I = \$1.52$ rounded to the nearest cent

The new balance is $103.02.

Notice that "interest on interest" is being paid. This is called **compounding** the interest.

Pretend that you deposit $100 in a savings account that pays 6% interest compounded every 3 months. Find how much money you would have in your account after 2 years. $112.65

295

Follow-up Activities

Reinforcement The reinforcement at this point should be individual help on solving problems of the type presented in this chapter.

Enrichment Pair these students with students who are having difficulty with problem solving. Give these students several problems and have the student who needs help explain his or her work to the more able student.

CALCULATOR ACTIVITY

After students complete the Chapter Challenge, you may want them to use a calculator to compute new balances compounding the interest on shorter time spans.

a	b	c	d		a	b	c	d		a	b	c	d		a	b	c	d		a	b	c	d	

14 | 34 | 14 | 4 | 30
15 | | | | 31

STUDENT OBJECTIVES

To practice skills learned previously.
To practice using a standardized-test format.

Suggested Lesson Plan

Using the pages   The Major Checkup at the end of each chapter of this textbook is given in standardized-test format. The answer sheet on page 448 is the type used with many standardized tests. You may duplicate it for use with the Major Checkups.

Pass out the answer sheets and be sure students understand how to use them. Allow a specified time, perhaps twenty minutes, to complete the checkup. Assign the exercises and use the results to determine what review is needed.

The table below correlates the test items and the student text pages. Assign review exercises as indicated by the Major Checkup results.

Test Item	Text Pages	Test Item	Text Pages
1	64–65	7	190–191
2	86–87	8	204–205
3	96–97	9	212–213
4	154–155	10	242–243
5	142–143	11	260–261
6	188–189	12	262–263

Chapter 9 Posttest

See page 54 for a full discussion of how to use the posttest. The table below suggests Extra Practice exercises and Basic Worksheets for those students who need further practice or reteaching.

Objectives	Extra Practice Sets	Pages	Basic Worksheets
9-1			75
9-2	79–81	393–394	76–77
9-3			78
9-4	82	395	79
9-5			80

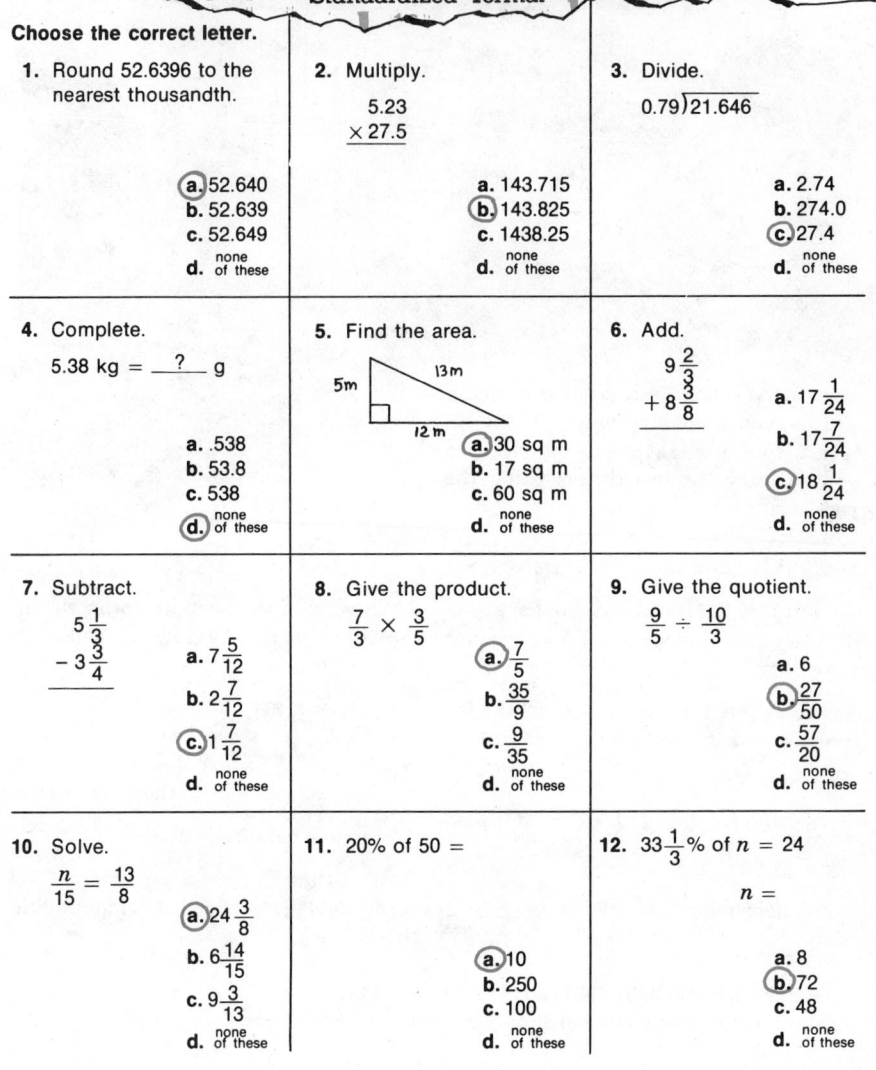

MAJOR CHECKUP
Standardized Format

Choose the correct letter.

1. Round 52.6396 to the nearest thousandth.

- **a.** 52.640
- **b.** 52.639
- **c.** 52.649
- **d.** none of these

2. Multiply.

5.23
× 27.5

- **a.** 143.715
- **b.** 143.825
- **c.** 1438.25
- **d.** none of these

3. Divide.

$0.79\overline{)21.646}$

- **a.** 2.74
- **b.** 274.0
- **c.** 27.4
- **d.** none of these

4. Complete.

5.38 kg = __?__ g

- **a.** .538
- **b.** 53.8
- **c.** 538
- **d.** none of these

5. Find the area.

5m, 13m, 12m

- **a.** 30 sq m
- **b.** 17 sq m
- **c.** 60 sq m
- **d.** none of these

6. Add.

$9\frac{2}{3}$
$+ 8\frac{3}{8}$

- **a.** $17\frac{1}{24}$
- **b.** $17\frac{7}{24}$
- **c.** $18\frac{1}{24}$
- **d.** none of these

7. Subtract.

$5\frac{1}{3}$
$- 3\frac{3}{4}$

- **a.** $7\frac{5}{12}$
- **b.** $2\frac{7}{12}$
- **c.** $1\frac{7}{12}$
- **d.** none of these

8. Give the product.

$\frac{7}{3} \times \frac{3}{5}$

- **a.** $\frac{7}{5}$
- **b.** $\frac{35}{9}$
- **c.** $\frac{9}{35}$
- **d.** none of these

9. Give the quotient.

$\frac{9}{5} \div \frac{10}{3}$

- **a.** 6
- **b.** $\frac{27}{50}$
- **c.** $\frac{57}{20}$
- **d.** none of these

10. Solve.

$\frac{n}{15} = \frac{13}{8}$

- **a.** $24\frac{3}{8}$
- **b.** $6\frac{14}{15}$
- **c.** $9\frac{3}{13}$
- **d.** none of these

11. 20% of 50 =

- **a.** 10
- **b.** 250
- **c.** 100
- **d.** none of these

12. $33\frac{1}{3}$% of n = 24

n =

- **a.** 8
- **b.** 72
- **c.** 48
- **d.** none of these

296

Answers for Chapter 9 Posttest
1. $409.94 2. $327 3. $63.60 4. $33.72
5. $84 6. $.83 8. $458.15 9. $180
10. $75 11. $20 12. $528 13. $31.05

Chapter 9 Posttest

Name _____

Date _____

Number right

0	1	2

Solve. [Obj. 9-1, pages 274–275]

1. Mrs. Carter earned $8.24 per hour plus time and a half for all time over 40 hours per week. How much did she get paid for work-

   ing $46\frac{1}{2}$ hours one week? _____

2. Mr. Holt earned a salary of $250 per week plus a 7% commission on all of his sales over $2700. How much would he earn if his sales one week were $3800?

   _____

0	1	2	3	4

Solve. [Obj. 9-2, pages 276–283]

3. A coat regularly priced at $79.50 was sold at a 20% discount. What was the sale

   price? _____

4. Automobile tires were on sale at $67.43 for two tires. How much would one tire

   cost? _____

5. Food accounted for 35% of one family's budget. If their weekly earnings were $240,

   how much was the food bill? _____

6. Fruit juice was on sale for $1.24 for 3 cans.

   How much would 2 cans cost? _____

Answer. [Obj. 9-3, pages 284–285]

7. Make out this check for $29.53 to Food City. Use today's date.

8. Sarah had a balance of $357.45 in her checking account. Then she wrote checks for $48.73, $4.57, and $77.56, and deposited $231.56. What was her new balance? _____

0	1	2

_____ 19 _____

Pay to the
order of _____ $ _____

_____ Dollars

Alcancía National Bank
6432 State Drive
Somewhere U.S.A.

⑆0⑈0⑆ 7⑂4⑊3⑈

0	1	2	3

Find the interest. [Obj. 9-4, pages 286–287]

principal	$1000	$2000	$750
rate	9%	7.5%	8%
time	2 years	6 mo.	4 mo.
interest	**9.**	**10.**	**11.**

0	1	2

Solve. [Obj. 9-5, pages 288–289]

12. What is the total cost of a stove that can be bought for $60 down and $39 per month

    for a year? _____

13. A bicycle costs $120.95 cash or $40 down and $28 per month for 4 months. How

    much more is the installment cost? _____

296a

Chapter 10
Geometry

Page 297–322

Learning Objectives

After completing this chapter, all students should be able to do the following:

10-1 Measure angles to the nearest degree.

10-2 Determine whether two lines are parallel or perpendicular.

10-3 List corresponding parts of congruent figures.

10-4 State important properties of common figures.

Students learn some simple straightedge-and-compass constructions and use them to explore angles and segments. Then they learn to measure angles with a protractor and to classify angles as acute, right, or obtuse. Perpendicular and parallel lines are defined and explored for their properties. Congruent figures are reviewed and corresponding parts defined. Then students learn about lines of symmetry and explore the properties of figures that derive from the fact that they have various lines of symmetry.

Mathematics

Geometric figures can be defined in various equivalent ways. For example, an equilateral triangle can be defined by any one of these characteristics:

1. 3 congruent sides
2. 3 congruent angles
3. 3 lines of symmetry

Usually, one uses the first as the defining characteristic and then discovers that equilateral triangles also have the other two characteristics, but to actually derive the second two from the first is quite difficult until one has the various deductive mechanisms usually learned in a tenth-grade plane geometry class. On the other hand, it is quite simple to derive 1 and 2 from 3 in the junior high school setting. For example,

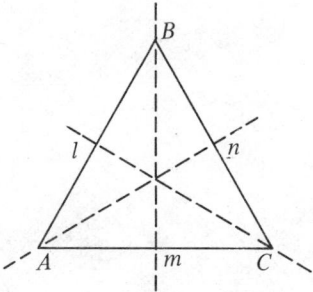

if you know that line m is a line of symmetry of the triangle, you know that when the triangle is flipped about line m the triangle fits back on itself. Obviously, if that is true, we know that $\overline{AB}$ and $\overline{BC}$ fit each other and are congruent. Similarly for angles A and C. Then, if lines n and l are also lines of symmetry, we can, in a similar manner, deduce that all sides are congruent and all angles are congruent.

While we don't expect students to give formal proofs of theorems, one reason we chose to use a symmetry approach was to give the students an opportunity to begin using deductive reasoning in simple informal situations.

Teaching the Chapter

Do not omit this chapter. Geometry is an important branch of mathematics that should be part of every school mathematics program. If this is the first opportunity you have had to teach these geometric ideas, we suggest that you teach the chapter as it is written and as it is described in the daily lessons. Work the exercises with your students. We think you will find it rewarding.

It is very important that students actually perform the activities described in the text. They should do much tracing and fitting in the work on congruence and symmetry. Students should be supplied with plenty of paper for tracing. Onionskin is good, but regular notebook paper will do quite nicely. Students should be encouraged to trace carefully, but they should not be frustrated by demands for accuracy if they do not have the dexterity necessary for neat work.

Many students have great difficulty learning to use a protractor. Part of the difficulty can be overcome by having them use protractors that have only one scale, rather than two as is quite common. One way to use a protractor is to place it (shown below) so that the vertex of the angle is at the center of the protractor and the two sides of the angle cross the protractor scale at any points.

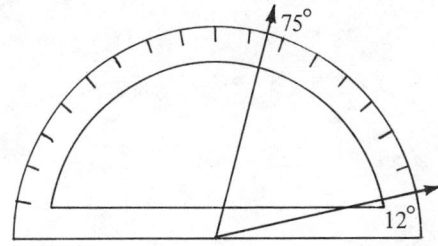

Then the angle measure is found by subtracting the two scale readings:

$$75° - 12° = 63°$$

This technique can be simplified by placing the protractor so that one of the crossing points is the 0° mark. Then the subtraction is trivial. In fact, it need not be done.

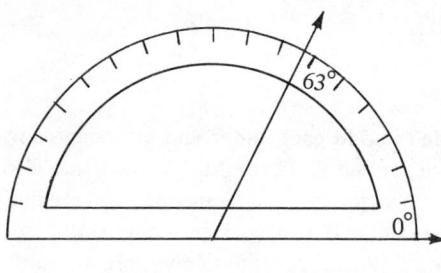

$$63° - 0° = 63°$$

Once students have had some measuring experiences, they should always estimate the measures of angles before performing the measurement. In this case, even though the protractor has two scales, the student who has made even a rough estimate should have no trouble in determining which scale to read.

Vocabulary

acute angle	octagon
bisect	opposite angles
bisector	parallel
compass	parallelogram
congruent	pentagon
corresponding parts	perpendicular
decagon	perpendicular bisector
equilateral triangle	point of symmetry
fitting	polygon
half-turn	protractor
heptagon	rectangle
hexagon	regular polygon
isosceles trapezoid	rhombus
isosceles triangle	right angle
kite	scalene triangle
line of symmetry	square
median	straightedge
midpoint	trapezoid
nonagon	vertex (vertices)
obtuse angle	

Symbols

≅   is congruent to
$\overline{AB}$ segment AB
△   triangle
∠   angle

Materials

compass for each student
straightedge for each student
protractor for each student
overhead projector and acetate
geometric figures drawn on cardboard
thin paper for tracings
straws and pipe cleaners
boxes of various sizes and shapes

Chapter Tests

For a discussion of how to use the chapter tests, please see page 17c.

Answers for Chapter 10 Pretest

1. 74°   2. 144°   3. n 4. n 5. $\overline{FG}$ 6. $\overline{DC}$ 7. $\overline{BC}$ 8. ∠E 9. ∠B 10. ∠D 11. square   12. equilateral   13. a four-sided figure with opposite sides parallel and all sides congruent   14. 0   15. parallelogram

Chapter 10 Pretest

Name _____

Date _____

Number right

Measure each angle. [Obj. 10-1, pages 298–303]

0	1	2

1.

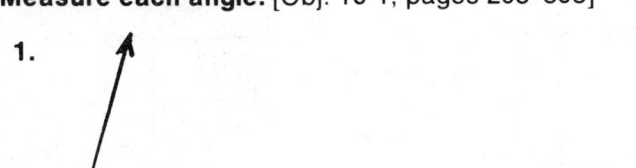

2.

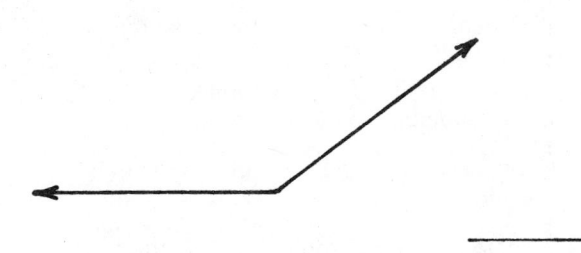

_____

_____

0	1	2

Answer. [Obj. 10-2, pages 304–305]

3. Which line is the perpendicular bisector of $\overline{AB}$? _____

4. Which line is parallel to line p? _____

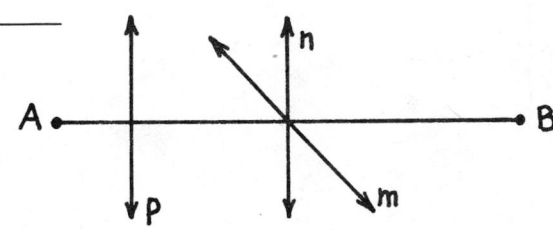

These two figures are congruent. Complete the list of corresponding parts. [Obj. 10-3, pages 306–307]

0	1	2	3	4	5	6

Corresponding Parts

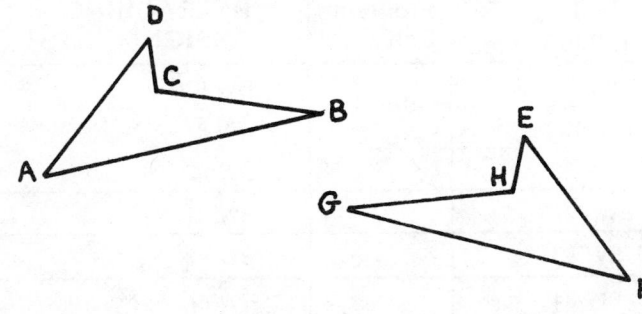

5. $\overline{AB}$ and _____   **8.** $\angle D$ and _____

6. $\overline{EH}$ and _____   **9.** $\angle G$ and _____

7. $\overline{GH}$ and _____   **10.** $\angle E$ and _____

0	1	2	3	4	5

Answer these questions. [Obj. 10-4, pages 308–316]

11. What four-sided figure has four lines of symmetry? _____

12. What kind of triangle has three congruent sides? _____

13. What is a rhombus? _____

14. How many lines of symmetry does a scalene triangle have? _____

15. What is the name of a four-sided figure that has its opposite

sides parallel? _____

297c

Chapter 10
Record and Assignment Chart

Name _____

Pretest Date _____ Posttest Date _____

Objectives

			Pretest Score — Mark number correct	Posttest Score — Mark number correct
10-1	Measure angles to the nearest degree.		`0` `1` `2`	`0` `1` `2`
10-2	Determine if 2 lines are parallel or perpendicular to each other.		`0` `1` `2`	`0` `1` `2`
10-3	List corresponding parts of congruent figures.		`0-1` `2` `3` `4` `5` `6`	`0-1` `2` `3` `4` `5` `6`
10-4	State important properties of common figures.		`0` `1` `2` `3` `4` `5`	`0` `1` `2` `3` `4` `5`

Pretest Score — Unsatisfactory Score | Satisfactory Score

Posttest Score — Unsatisfactory Score | Satisfactory Score

TEACHING ASSIGNMENTS*

	Student Page	Basic Assignment	Average Assignment	Enriched Assignment	Problem Solving	RETEACHING ASSIGNMENTS†
	298, 299	1–3	1–3, EW 81	1–3, EW 81		BW 81
10-1	300, 301	1–7	1–7, EW 81	1–7, EW 81		BW 81
	302, 303	1–17	1–17, EW 82	1–18, EW 82		BW 82
10-2	304, 305	1–3	1–3, EW 82	1–4, EW 82		BW 82
10-3	306, 307	1–10	1–10, EW 83	1–10, EW 83		BW 83
	308, 309	1–13	1–13, EW 84	1–16, EW 84		BW 84
	310, 311	1–6	1–6, EW 84	1–6, EW 84		BW 84
10-4	312, 313	1–9	1–9, EW 85	1–9, EW 85		BW 85
	314, 315	1-6	1-7, EW 85	1-7, EW 85		BW 85
	316	1-6	1-6, EW 86	1-7, EW 86		BW 86
	317	1-2	1-2	1-2		BW 86

318	Chapter Checkup
319	Project
320	Chapter Review
321	Chapter Challenge
322	Major Checkup

*Check assignments for objectives with unsatisfactory pretest scores.
†Check assignments for objectives with unsatisfactory posttest scores.

BW = Basic Worksheet
EW = Enrichment Worksheet

10
Geometry

STUDENT OBJECTIVE

To copy a line segment, copy an angle, and copy designs, using a compass and straightedge.

VOCABULARY

compass, straightedge

Suggested Lesson Plan

Introduction Begin this chapter by using the first paragraph on page 298 to start a brief discussion of geometry. Introduce geometry as the study of shapes and their properties. Have students take the Ready or Not? quiz to see whether they remember the geometric symbols and terms that they have studied before.

Using the pages Provide a compass and a straightedge for each student. Provide each student with several sheets of plain paper for their constructions. Instruct them to use all their paper beneath the sheet they are drawing on so that the compass point has something to stick into and does not damage the desk top. Remind students to draw lightly and to keep a sharp point on their pencils to make their work much neater and more accurate.

Have students do the constructions at their seats while you use a chalkboard compass. Proceed through the constructions described on pages 298 and 299. Do one step at a time and then wait for the students to do it at their seats.

After you have done the two constructions, assign exercises 1–3 on pages 299. Watch students as they continue the constructions.

Be prepared to offer help to those students having difficulty. Some students will be awkward, but they need to continue to try to use a compass and straightedge efficiently. Encourage neat and careful work, but do not demand it, because some students will just not be able to manipulate the compass as well as others.

READY OR NOT!

Match.

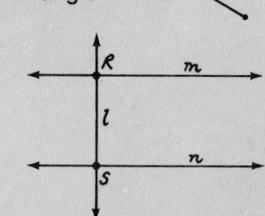
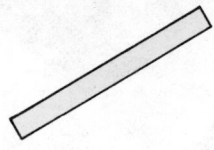

d **1.** point   **a.**

e **2.** segment   **b.**

a **3.** ray   **c.**

b **4.** line   **d.** •

c **5.** angle   **e.**

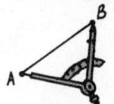

m **6.** Which line intersects line *l* at point *R*?

n **7.** Which line ‖ (is parallel to) line *m*?

l **8.** Which line ⊥ (is perpendicular to) line *m*?

298

Constructions

Look around you. What shapes can you find? Perhaps you see square tiles, a rectangular room, and a circular clock. What other shapes are there? In this chapter you will study shapes and their properties.

First let's do some work with the tools of geometry, the **compass** and **straightedge**.

Follow these steps to copy a segment, $\overline{AB}$.

Step 1. Set the compass legs on *A* and *B*.

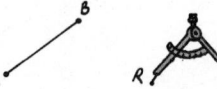

Step 2. Mark the paper with both the pencil and the point.

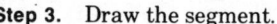

Step 3. Draw the segment.

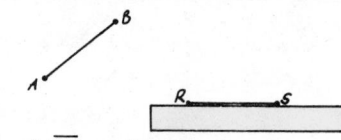

$\overline{AB}$ and $\overline{RS}$ are the same length.

Assignments

BASIC
page 298 Discuss
page 299 exercises 1–3
Basic Worksheet 81

AVERAGE
page 298 Discuss
page 299 exercises 1–3
Enrichment Worksheet 81

ENRICHED
page 298 Discuss
page 299 exercises 1–3
Enrichment Worksheet 81

REVIEW PRACTICE
page 388 set 61

Follow these steps to copy an angle, ∠B.

Step 1. Draw $\overrightarrow{TR}$.

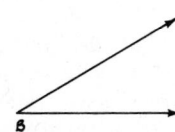

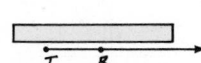

Step 2. Draw an arc that intersects the sides of ∠B.

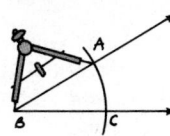

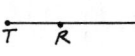

Step 3. Use the same compass setting to draw an arc as shown.

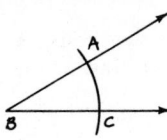

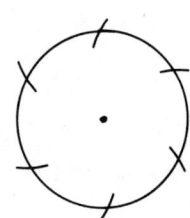

Step 4. Set the compass as shown.

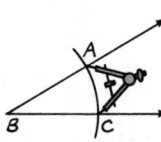

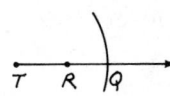

Step 5. Use the same setting to draw an arc as shown.

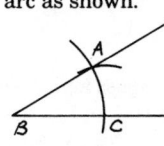

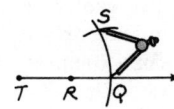

Step 6. Draw $\overrightarrow{TS}$, as shown.

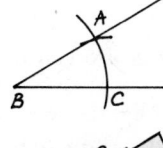

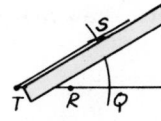

∠B and ∠T are the same size.

EXERCISES

1. First draw some segments. Then use a compass and straightedge to copy each segment.

2. First draw some angles. Then use a compass and straightedge to copy each angle.

3. Draw a circle. Do not change the compass setting. Mark off 6 equal arcs on the circle.

299

Follow-up Activities

Reinforcement Have students construct hexagons of varying sizes by connecting the marks on a circle after following the directions for exercise 3.

Enrichment Have students use the six equally spaced marks on a circle as described for exercise 3 as the basis for new designs. Encourage them to use colored pencils and shade areas to get different effects. Post the better designs on the mathematics bulletin board.

EXCURSION
Using only these weights:

2 grams on a balance,   5 grams   8 grams

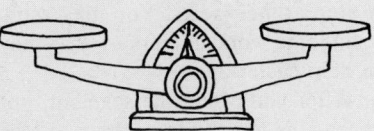

how could you weigh these amounts of sand in a single balance?

1 gram, 3 grams, 6 grams, 7 grams, 10 grams, and 11 grams.

sand + 2 g + 5 g = 8 g;
sand + 5 g = 8 g;
sand + 2 g = 8 g; sand = 2 g + 5 g;
sand = 2 g + 8 g;
sand + 2 g = 5 g + 8 g

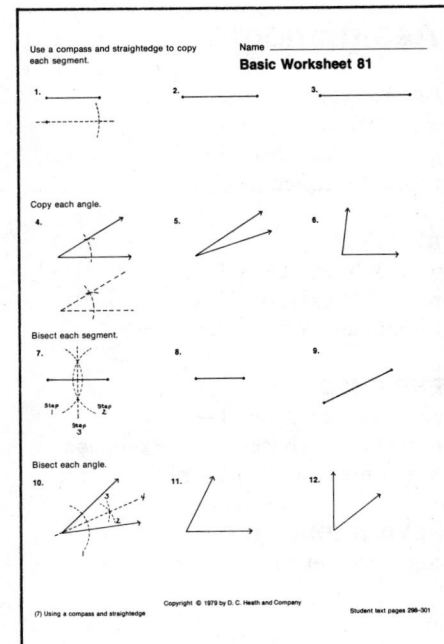

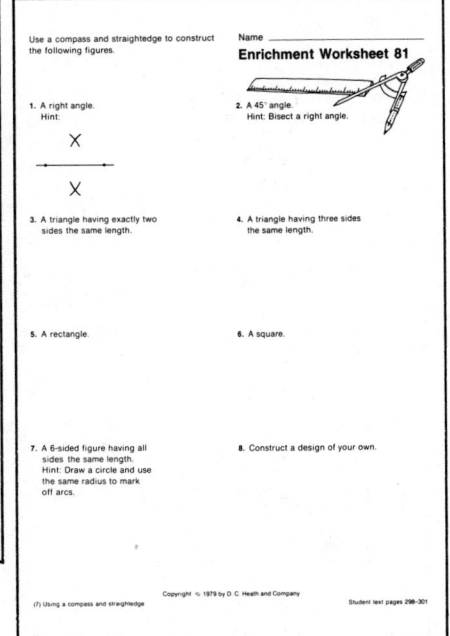

(core) Lesson 140 **299**

STUDENT OBJECTIVE
To bisect a segment and bisect an angle, using a compass and straightedge.

VOCABULARY
bisect, bisector, median, midpoint

Suggested Lesson Plan

Using the pages (compass; straightedge) Continue the instruction as in the previous lesson. Use a blackboard compass and meter stick at the board while students perform the same construction at their seats. You may want to make a master and run off copies of a segment and an angle so that each student is working on the same figure. This will avoid some difficulties such as too short a segment or obtuse angles.

Carefully show each step at the board and then wait while students do the step at their seats. You may want to let students work in pairs so that they can help each other.

After you bisect the segment, point out that the line students draw to bisect the segment is also perpendicular to the segment. This is called the *perpendicular bisector* of the segment. The construction of a perpendicular line is done with exactly the same construction.

Assign exercises 1–7 after you complete both of the constructions on page 300. Circulate around the room while students work on the exercises, since some of them will need help on the activities; you can also give them little pointers that will make their constructions easier.

For exercise 3, after students have found the point where all their lines intersect, have them use that point as the center of a circle that should touch each side of the triangle. This is called an *inscribed circle*. This is a good check to see how accurately they have done their constructions.

Bisecting segments and angles

Here is how to use a straightedge and compass to bisect (find the midpoint of) a segment.

Step 1. Using point *A* as the center, draw an arc as shown.

Step 2. Using point *B* as the center and the same compass setting, draw another arc.

Step 3. Put the straightedge on the points where the arcs cross. Mark where the straightedge crosses the segment.

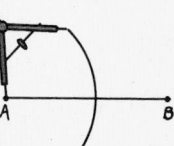 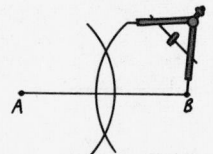 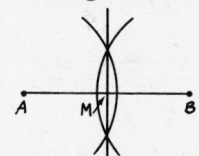

M is the midpoint of $\overline{AB}$.

You can also bisect an angle with a compass and straightedge.

Step 1. Using the vertex as the center, draw an arc as shown.

Step 2. Use points *X* and *Y* as centers. Draw two crossing arcs, using the same compass setting for both.

Step 3. Draw the ray from the vertex to the point where the arcs cross.

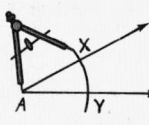 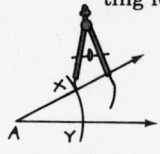 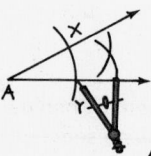

$\overrightarrow{AM}$ is the bisector of $\angle A$.

EXERCISES

1. Draw a segment and bisect it.

2. Draw an angle and bisect it.

300

Assignments

BASIC
page 300 exercises 1–2
page 301 exercises 3–7
Basic Worksheet 81

AVERAGE
page 300 exercises 1–2
page 301 exercises 3–7
Enrichment Worksheet 81

ENRICHED
page 300 exercises 1–2
page 301 exercises 3–7, Excursion
Enrichment Worksheet 81

REVIEW PRACTICE
page 389 set 62

3. Draw a triangle. Draw the bisector of each angle. If you are very careful, the three bisectors will all cross at the same point.

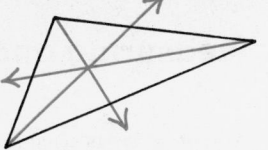

4. Draw a triangle. Bisect each side. Draw segments from a vertex to the midpoint of the opposite side. These segments are called **medians** of the triangle. If you are very careful, the three medians will all cross at the same point.

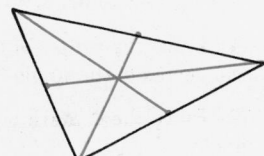

5. Draw a long segment. Bisect the segment. Bisect each half of the segment. You have divided the segment into 4 equal parts.

6. Draw a segment and divide it into 8 equal parts.

7. Draw an angle and bisect it. Bisect each of the new angles.

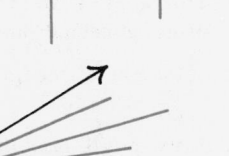

Excursion ▨▨▨▨▨▨▨▨▨▨▨▨▨▨▨▨▨▨▨▨▨▨▨▨▨▨

1. Get a strip of paper that is about 40 centimeters long.

2. Give the paper a half-twist and tape the ends together.

   This is called a Moebius strip.

3. Cut around the strip at the middle.

What happened?   You got a strip that was twice as long with 2 full twists.

301

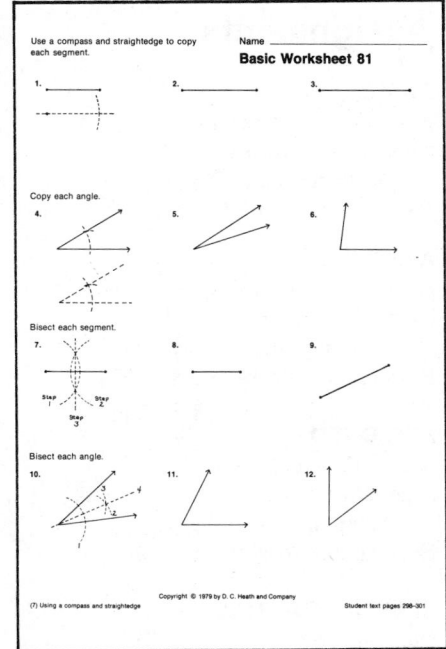
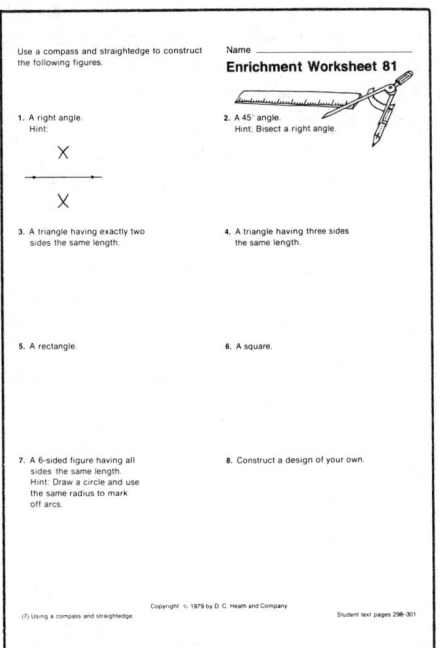
Follow-up Activities

Reinforcement   Duplicate a worksheet with several segments and several angles. Instruct students to use a compass and straightedge to bisect the segments and the angles.

Enrichment   Duplicate a worksheet with several triangles. Instruct students to use a compass and straightedge to bisect each angle in some of the triangles and to construct the median (bisect each side) in the other triangles.

EXCURSION
Which of these numbers are prime?
57, 63, 89, 97, 101, 411, 1009, 1027, 2311

VOCABULARY
protractor, acute angle, right angle,
obtuse angle

Suggested Lesson Plan

Introduction (protractor) Remind
students of other measurements they
have done as an introduction to the
concept of measurement of angles.

Before class draw various angles
(not more than 50° angles) on sheets of
acetate. On another sheet of acetate
draw this protractor. The rays are 5°
apart.

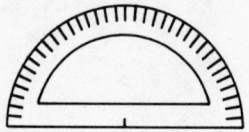

Also cut from acetate nine or ten 5°
angles.

Project one of the angles on the
board and remind students that when
you measured length, you picked a
length for a unit and "packed" the units
along the length to be measured. The
count of these units was the measure.
To measure area, you picked an area for
a unit and then "packed" the region to
be measured with the unit. The count of
these units was the measure. Now you
are going to measure the angle. So you
pick an angle for a unit. Show one of
the angles cut from the acetate. Then
you "pack" the angle to be measured
with the unit. Finally you count the
number of units. That count is the
measure of the angle.

Point out that it is rather awkward
to place all those loose copies of the
unit, so you will use a method that is
similar to putting many length units
together to form a grid. Project the
protractor on the board. Place the
protractor on one of the angles. Have
students give the measures. Repeat with
other angles. Point out that you can save
some time in using a protractor by
numbering the unit angles. Then they
won't have to be counted each time.
This is analogous to numbering the units
on a ruler.

Using the pages Go over the
exposition on page 302. Be sure that
students have protractors. Watch
students measure some angles to be sure
that they use the protractors properly.

Measuring angles

A **protractor** is used for measuring angles.
Here is how to use a protractor:

(1) Place the center of the protractor at
the vertex of the angle.

(2) Place the 0 mark on one side of the
angle.

(3) Read the measure of the angle where
the other side crosses the protractor.

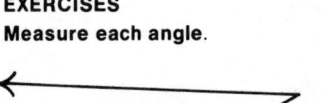

The measure of this angle is 50°. Read
"50°" as "fifty degrees."

An **acute angle** is an angle that
measures between 0° and 90°.

A **right angle** is an angle that
measures 90°.

An **obtuse angle** is an angle that
measures between 90° and 180°.

This means that the angle is a right angle.

EXERCISES
Measure each angle.

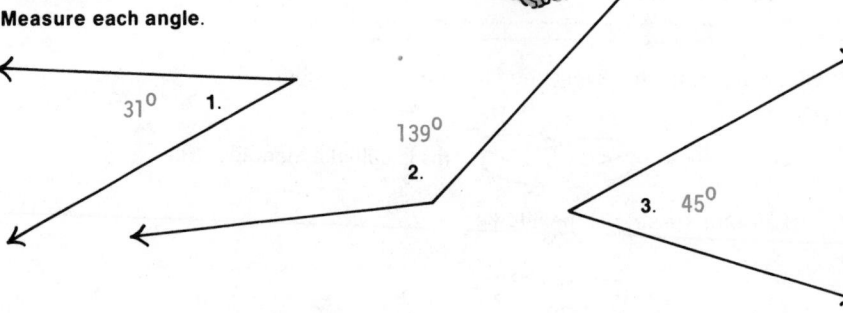

31° **1.**

139° **2.**

3. 45°

Draw angles having these measures.

4. 35°   **5.** 135°   **6.** 90°   **7.** 75°   **8.** 175°

302

Assign the exercises.
Note that most protractors have two
scales, one "running" in the clockwise
direction and the other "running" in the
counterclockwise direction. Students
must be sure to note which 0-ray they
are using and then read the angle
measure from the same scale.

Assignments

BASIC
page 302 exercises 1−8
page 303 exercises 9−17,
    Keeping Skills Sharp
Basic Worksheet 82

AVERAGE
page 302 exercises 1−8
page 303 exercises 9−17,
    Keeping Skills Sharp
Enrichment Worksheet 82

ENRICHED
page 302 exercises 1−8
page 303 exercises 9−18,
    Keeping Skills Sharp
Enrichment Worksheet 82

REVIEW PRACTICE
page 389 set 63

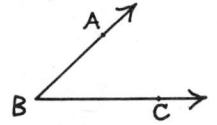

Point B is called the **vertex** of the angle. Here are 3 ways to name the angle.

∠B   "angle B"

∠ABC   "angle ABC"

∠CBA   "angle CBA"

Acute, right, or obtuse?

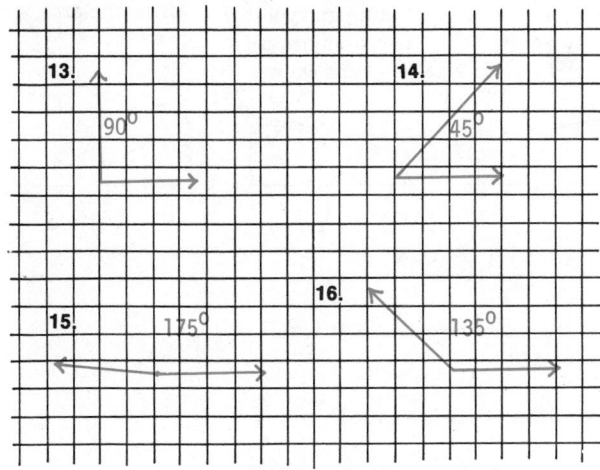

9. ∠QPT   obtuse

10. ∠SPT   acute

11. ∠SPQ   right

12. ∠RPT   acute

Some angles have been drawn on grid paper. Estimate the measure of each angle.

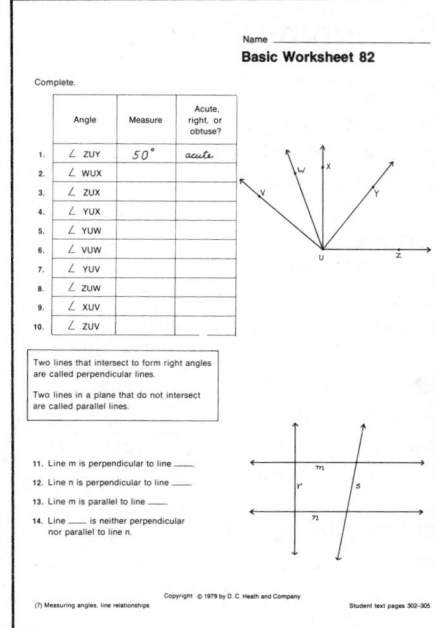

13. 90°
14. 45°
15. 175°
16. 135°

17. Draw a large triangle. Add the measures of the angles. Repeat for several other triangles. Did you always get the same sum?   Should always get 180°.

18. Repeat exercise 17 using quadrilaterals (four-sided figures).   Should always get 360°.

Keeping Skills Sharp

Give each difference.

1. 7.92 − 3.06
   4.86
2. 4.283 − 1.096
   3.187
3. 5.80 − 2.39
   3.41
4. 9.036 − 4.958
   4.078
5. 6.9 − 0.28
   6.62
6. 5.93 − 4.6
   1.33
7. 7 − 2.8
   4.2
8. 9 − 3.64
   5.36
9. 2.8 − 1.99
   0.81
10. 6.3 − 1.05
   5.25
11. 17 − 8.09
   8.91
12. 5 − 4.2
   0.8
13. 6.53 − 2.794
   3.736
14. 18.7 − 3
   15.7
15. 2.001 − 0.36
   1.641
16. 14 − 0.27
   13.73
17. 26 − 25.4
   0.6
18. 3.3 − 3.03
   0.27
19. 5.555 − 0.06
   5.495
20. 1.2 − 1.196
   0.004

303

Follow-up Activities

Reinforcement To follow up the lesson, you may wish to duplicate the following figures and have students look for angles that have the same measure:

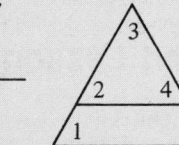

Enrichment Some students may wish to work with angles of inclination. To do so, they will first need to make an instrument by attaching a weight and drinking straw to a protractor.

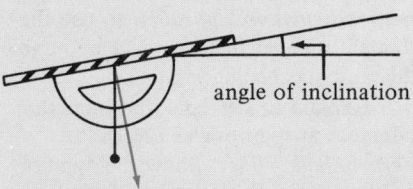

angle of inclination

When they sight through the straw, the angle of inclination is formed by the string and the ray shown in red. Have students stand at a certain location and find the angle of inclination from that point to the top of the school building, to the top of the flagpole, and so on.

EXCURSION
Find the rule and answer the question.

1 ⟶ 00
3 ⟶ 26
5 ⟶ 124
7 ⟶ (?) 440
9 ⟶ (?) 728

$n^3 - 1$

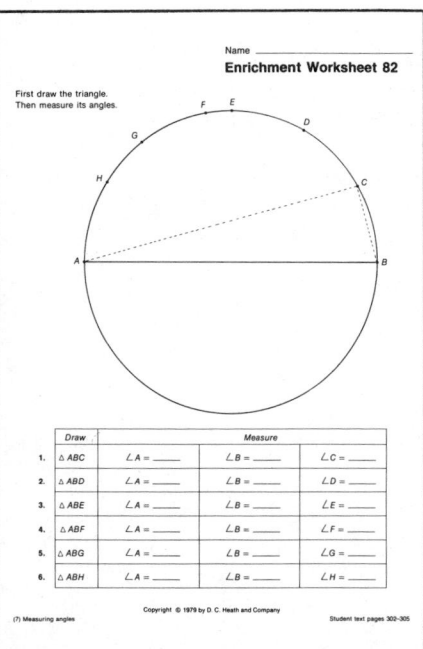

Basic Worksheet 82

Enrichment Worksheet 82

STUDENT OBJECTIVE
To construct two perpendicular lines,
using compass and straightedge.

VOCABULARY
perpendicular (⊥), perpendicular
bisector, parallel (∥)

Suggested Lesson Plan

Introduction Quickly review the
different types of angles introduced in
the previous lesson. After listing the
different angles—acute, right, and
obtuse—ask whether students know
another word to describe the lines that
form a right angle. (perpendicular) They
will probably confuse the use of
perpendicular and *parallel*, so use the
terms a number of times in the course of
this and succeeding lessons.

    Explain to students that lines that
intersect at right angles are called
perpendicular lines. Show the symbol
for perpendicular, ⊥, on the board.

Using the pages Be sure each student
has a compass and straightedge. Using a
blackboard compass, work through the
steps described on page 304 to construct
perpendicular lines. Point out to students
that this is the same construction that
they have done to bisect segments. The
result of this construction is called a
perpendicular bisector.

    Since students probably mentioned
the term *parallel*, use the opportunity to
point out that two lines in the same
plane that do not intersect are said to be
parallel lines. Write the symbol (∥) for
parallel on the board beside the symbol
for perpendicular.

    Assign exercises 1−4 for written
work. Circulate around the room,
providing help to students. Keep
reminding them to strive for neater work
by using sharp pencils, drawing their
lines lightly, and using their compasses
carefully.

    After students have found the point
where the perpendicular bisectors of the
three sides intersect (exercise 3), they
can use this point as the center of a
circle that will intersect the three
vertices of the triangle. This is a good
check to see how accurately they have
done their construction.

Perpendicular lines and parallel lines

Two lines that intersect to form right angles are called
perpendicular lines.

We say:

    line l is perpendicular to line m

we write:

    $l \perp m$

Here is how to use your straightedge and compass to construct
two perpendicular lines.

Step 1.
Draw a line.

Step 2.
Using point A as
center, draw an arc
as shown.

Step 3.
Using the same
setting and point B
as center, draw
an arc as shown.

Step 4.
Connect the points
where the arcs
cross.

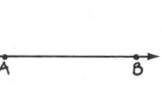 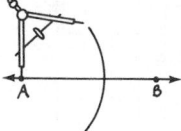 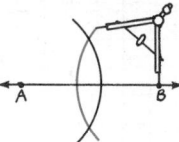 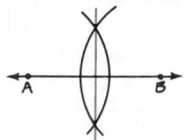

Notice that the red line in step 4 also bisects $\overline{AB}$. It is called
the **perpendicular bisector** of $\overline{AB}$.

Two lines in a plane that do not intersect are called
parallel lines.

We say:

    line r is parallel to line s

we write:

    $r \parallel s$

304

Assignments

BASIC
page 304 Discuss
page 305 exercises 1−3
Basic Worksheet 82

AVERAGE
page 304 Discuss
page 305 exercises 1−3
Enrichment Worksheet 82

ENRICHED
page 304 Discuss
page 305 exercises 1−4, Excursion
Enrichment Worksheet 82

REVIEW PRACTICE
page 389 set 64

EXERCISES

1. Use a compass and straightedge to construct two perpendicular lines.

2. Follow these steps to construct two parallel lines.

    a. Draw a line *l* and construct a perpendicular line to line *l*.

    b. Construct a second perpendicular line to line *l*.

    c. What can you say about the two lines that are perpendicular to line *l*?   They are parallel.

    d. Can you now construct a line that is parallel to line *l*?   yes

    e. How many lines do you think there are that are parallel to line *l*? Perpendicular to line *l*? an infinite number, an infinite number

3. Draw a triangle. Construct the perpendicular bisector to each side.
    If you are very careful, the three lines will all cross at the same point.

4. Draw a large triangle with sides of different lengths. Construct the three angle bisectors, the three perpendicular bisectors, and the three medians (see exercise 4 on page 301).

Excursion ▪◦▪◦▪◦▪◦▪◦▪◦▪◦▪◦▪◦
Make a Moebius strip. (See page 301.)

Cut around the strip, always staying nearer one edge than the other. Guess what will happen. What did happen?   You got a Moebius strip the same length interlocked with a strip that was twice as long with one-and-a-half twists.

305

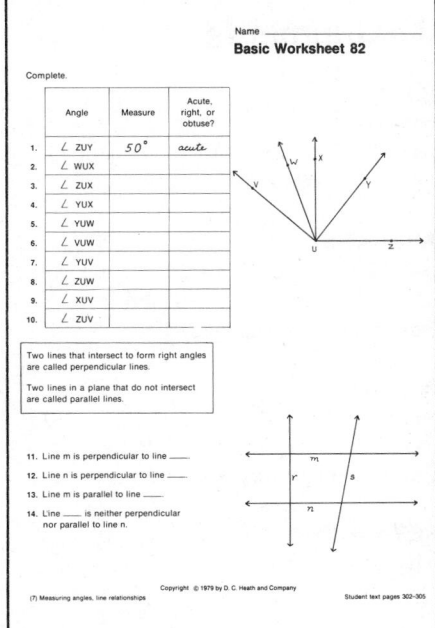

Follow-up Activities

Reinforcement Duplicate a worksheet with several segments and have students construct the perpendicular bisectors. You can vary the assignments by giving a point on the line which the perpendicular bisector should pass through. Also give a point not on the line which the perpendicular bisector is to pass through.

Enrichment Use exercise 4 for the enrichment activity. Have students start with a large triangle, since this involves many constructions that could become confusing. Make sure that the triangle is scalene so that the three points formed by the angle bisectors, the perpendicular bisectors, and the medians will be different points.

EXCURSION
Find the rule and answer the question.

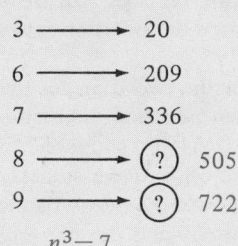

$$3 \longrightarrow 20$$
$$6 \longrightarrow 209$$
$$7 \longrightarrow 336$$
$$8 \longrightarrow \boxed{?} \; 505$$
$$9 \longrightarrow \boxed{?} \; 722$$
$$n^3 - 7$$

Basic Worksheet 82

Name _____

Complete.

	Angle	Measure	Acute, right, or obtuse?
1.	∠ ZUY	50°	acute
2.	∠ WUX		
3.	∠ ZUX		
4.	∠ YUX		
5.	∠ YUW		
6.	∠ VUW		
7.	∠ YUV		
8.	∠ ZUW		
9.	∠ XUV		
10.	∠ ZUV		

Two lines that intersect to form right angles are called perpendicular lines.

Two lines in a plane that do not intersect are called parallel lines.

11. Line m is perpendicular to line ____

12. Line n is perpendicular to line ____

13. Line m is parallel to line ____

14. Line ____ is neither perpendicular nor parallel to line n.

Copyright © 1979 by D. C. Heath and Company

(7) Measuring angles, line relationships   Student text pages 302–305

Enrichment Worksheet 82

Name _____

First draw the triangle.
Then measure its angles.

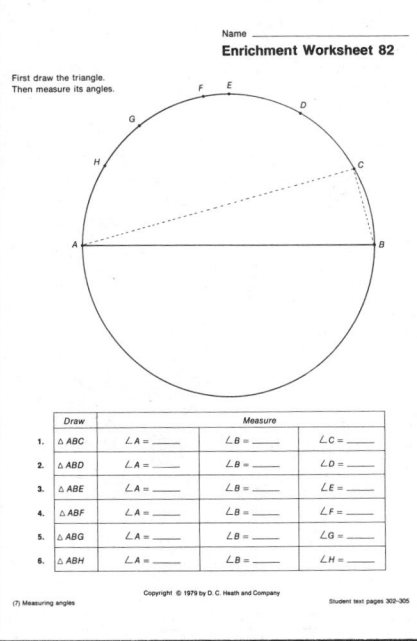

Draw	Measure		
1. △ ABC	∠ A = ____	∠ B = ____	∠ C = ____
2. △ ABD	∠ A = ____	∠ B = ____	∠ D = ____
3. △ ABE	∠ A = ____	∠ B = ____	∠ E = ____
4. △ ABF	∠ A = ____	∠ B = ____	∠ F = ____
5. △ ABG	∠ A = ____	∠ B = ____	∠ G = ____
6. △ ABH	∠ A = ____	∠ B = ____	∠ H = ____

Copyright © 1979 by D. C. Heath and Company

(7) Measuring angles   Student text pages 302–305

STUDENT OBJECTIVES

To determine whether two figures are congruent.

To name corresponding parts for congruent figures.

VOCABULARY

congruent figures (≅), corresponding parts

Suggested Lesson Plan

Introduction   On a sheet of acetate, draw two congruent scalene triangles. Project the figures on the board using an overhead projector. Ask a student to trace one figure on the board, and then move the acetate to see whether one triangle will fit exactly over the other triangle. If the two triangles fit exactly, they are said to be *congruent*.

Using the pages   Go over the exposition on page 306. Be sure to emphasize the notation for *congruent* (≅).

For the two triangles that you used in the introduction, add letters to the vertices. As you show one triangle fitted over the other, have students name the *corresponding angles*—that is, the angles that *match*—and the *corresponding sides*.

Assign exercises 1−10 for written work. Have students make tracings using onionskin paper or thin duplicating paper so they can be sure how the figures match. Have them make drawings for exercises 8, 9, and 10 to prove their answers.

Congruent figures

You have seen pairs of figures that have the same size and shape. Such figures are called **congruent figures**. For example, the two trianges below are congruent because a tracing of △ABC ("triangle ABC") fits △QPR.

We write: △ **ABC** ≅ △ **QPR**

We say: △ **ABC** is congruent to △ **QPR**

Notice that for this fitting, we have this matching of the vertices:

$$A \longleftrightarrow Q$$
$$B \longleftrightarrow P$$
$$C \longleftrightarrow R$$

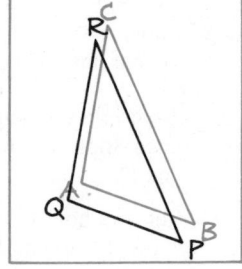

The sides and angles that match are called **corresponding parts**.

Corresponding sides	Corresponding angles
$\overline{AB} \longleftrightarrow \overline{QP}$	$\angle A \longleftrightarrow \angle Q$
$\overline{AC} \longleftrightarrow \overline{QR}$	$\angle B \longleftrightarrow \angle P$
$\overline{BC} \longleftrightarrow \overline{PR}$	$\angle C \longleftrightarrow \angle R$

EXERCISES

In each exercise the two figures are congruent. Name all pairs of corresponding parts for the congruent fitting.

1.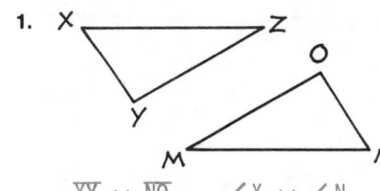

$$\overline{XY} \leftrightarrow \overline{NO} \qquad \angle X \leftrightarrow \angle N$$
$$\overline{YZ} \leftrightarrow \overline{OM} \qquad \angle Y \leftrightarrow \angle O$$
$$\overline{ZX} \leftrightarrow \overline{MN} \qquad \angle Z \leftrightarrow \angle M$$

2.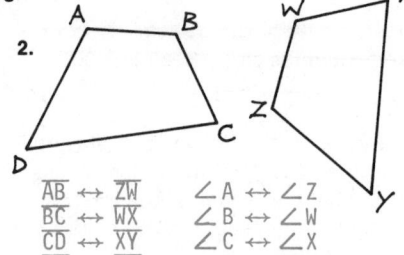

$$\overline{AB} \leftrightarrow \overline{ZW} \qquad \angle A \leftrightarrow \angle Z$$
$$\overline{BC} \leftrightarrow \overline{WX} \qquad \angle B \leftrightarrow \angle W$$
$$\overline{CD} \leftrightarrow \overline{XY} \qquad \angle C \leftrightarrow \angle X$$
$$\overline{DA} \leftrightarrow \overline{YZ} \qquad \angle D \leftrightarrow \angle Y$$

306

Assignments

BASIC

page 306   exercises 1−2
page 307   exercises 3−10, Project
Basic Worksheet 83

AVERAGE

page 306   exercises 1−2
page 307   exercises 3−10, Project
Enrichment Worksheet 83

ENRICHED

page 306   exercises 1−2
page 307   exercises 3−10, Project
Enrichment Worksheet 83

REVIEW PRACTICE

page 389   set 65

For exercises 3–6, use the figures below. The triangles are congruent.

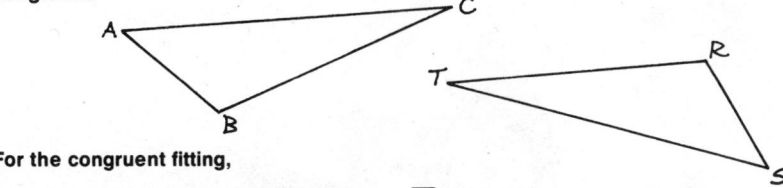

For the congruent fitting,

3. which side of △RST corresponds to $\overline{AB}$? $\overline{SR}$

4. is $\overline{RT}$ congruent to $\overline{AB}$? Why?   No; they are not corresponding parts.

5. which angle of △RST is congruent to ∠C? How do you know?   ∠T; ∠C corresponds to ∠T in the fitting.

6. which side of △ABC is congruent to $\overline{ST}$? How do you know? $\overline{AC}$; $\overline{ST}$ corresponds to $\overline{AC}$ in the fitting.

7. True or false? For a congruent fitting, the corresponding parts are congruent.   true

Some information about a pair of triangles is given. If you completed the triangles, would they be congruent?

8. The red straws are congruent.
   The green straws are congruent.
   The angles formed by the
      pipe cleaners are congruent. yes

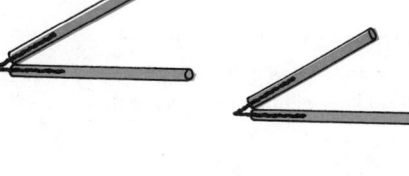

9. The angles formed by the red
      pipe cleaners are congruent.
   The angles formed by the green
      pipe cleaners are congruent.
   The straws are congruent. yes

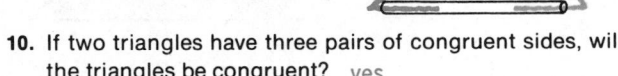

10. If two triangles have three pairs of congruent sides, will the triangles be congruent? yes

Project

1. Use a straightedge and draw a triangle.
2. Use a compass and straightedge to construct a congruent triangle.

307

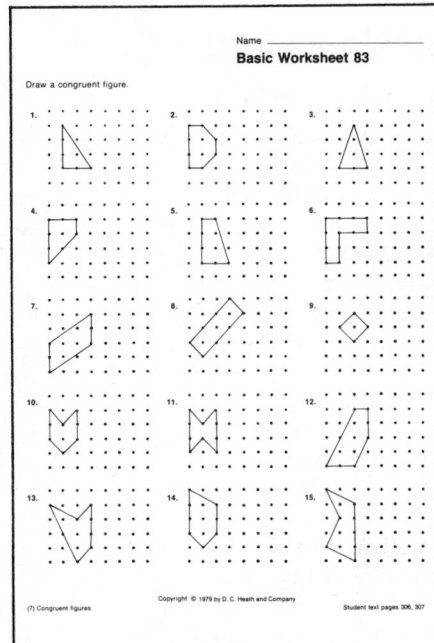

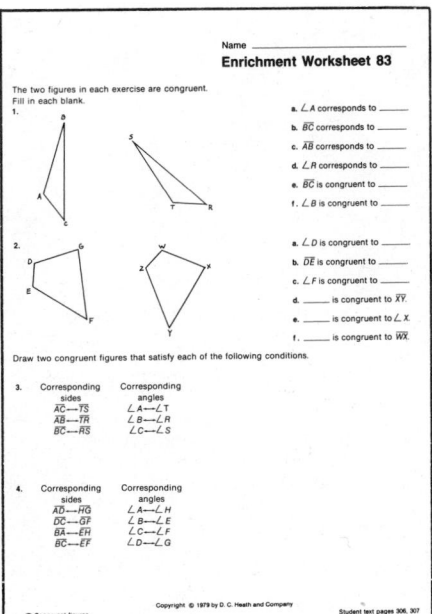

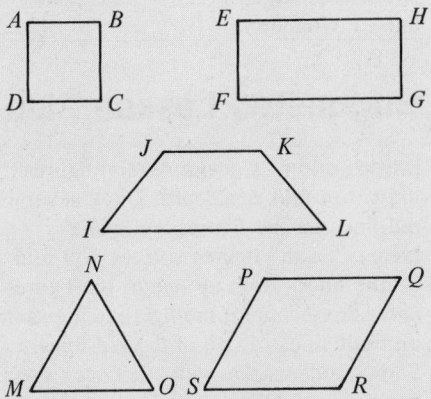

Follow-up Activities

Reinforcement Draw each of the figures on the chalkboard. Have students point out congruent segments and congruent angles in each figure.

Enrichment Encourage the more able students to solve these "Who am I?" puzzles:

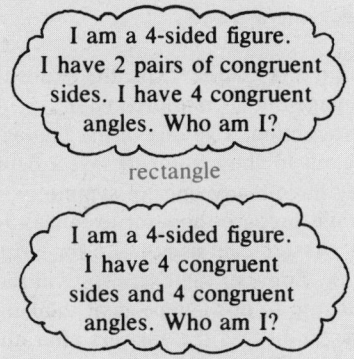

I am a 4-sided figure. I have 2 pairs of congruent sides. I have 4 congruent angles. Who am I?

rectangle

I am a 4-sided figure. I have 4 congruent sides and 4 congruent angles. Who am I?

square

If time permits, have students create some "Who am I?" puzzles of their own for other classmates to work on.

EXCURSION

I am between 60 and 80, even, and the sum of my digits is 11. Who am I?

74

(core) Lesson 144   **307**

STUDENT OBJECTIVES
To determine whether a line is a line of
   symmetry.
To find lines of symmetry of figures.
To draw or construct figures that have
   lines of symmetry.

VOCABULARY
line of symmetry

Suggested Lesson Plan

Introduction   Cut out several figures
drawn on thin cardboard. Draw several
red lines on the figures and make
creases on the figures so they will fold
on the lines. Hold up one of the figures
and ask students if the figure is the same
on both sides of one of the red lines.
Show students that you can check their
answer by folding on the line to see
whether the sides are congruent. If they
are, the line is said to be a *line of
symmetry*. Hold up the other figures and
ask students to identify the lines that are
lines of symmetry. Fold the figures to
check the answers.

Using the pages   Use the exposition
on page 308 to reinforce your
introduction. Use one of the figures you
cut out to show students that a figure
may have many lines of symmetry. This
should prepare them for exercises 7−9.
   Assign exercises 1−16 for written
work. Some of the exercises will require
students to use independent thinking.
Plan to discuss the answers after all the
students have had a chance to think
about the questions.

A line of symmetry

Notice that the two halves on each side of the fold line match.
The fold line is a **line of symmetry**.

EXERCISES

Is the dotted line a line of symmetry? *Hint:* **If you fold along the
dotted line, will the two parts match?**

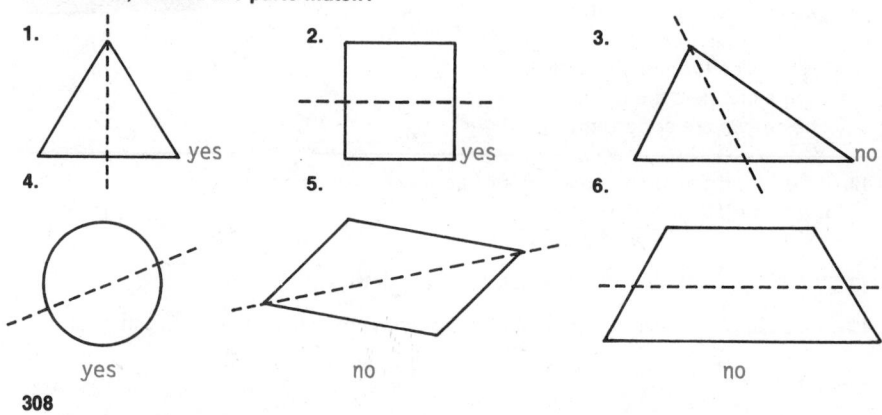

1. yes   2. yes   3. no
4. yes   5. no   6. no

308

Assignments

BASIC
page 308   exercises 1−6
page 309   exercises 7−13
Basic Worksheet 84

AVERAGE
page 308   exercises 1−6
page 309   exercises 7−13
Enrichment Worksheet 84

ENRICHED
page 308   exercises 1−6
page 309   exercises 7−16
Enrichment Worksheet 84

REVIEW PRACTICE
page 390   set 66

Trace each figure and draw all lines of symmetry.

7. 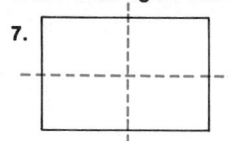   8. 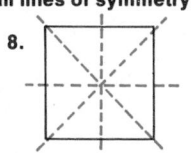   9.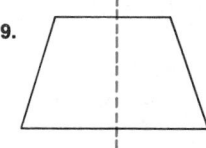

Only half of the figure is pictured. The red line is a line of symmetry. First trace the given half. Then draw the missing half.

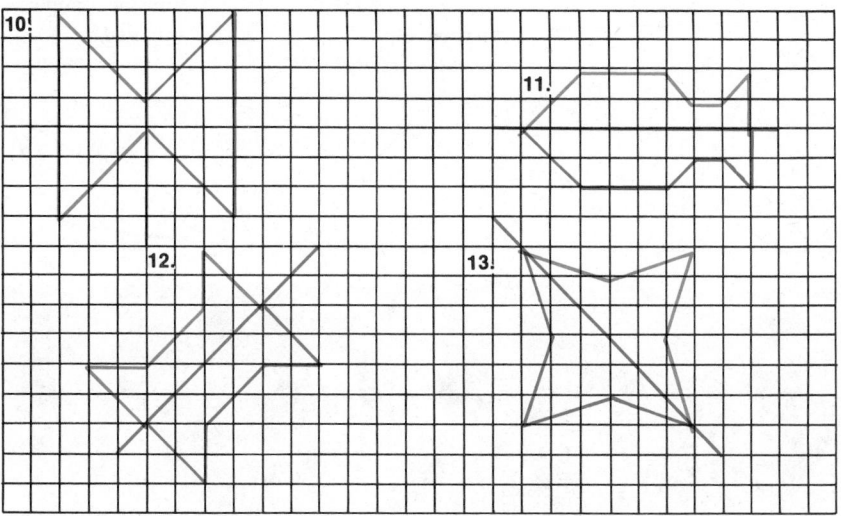

14. a. Construct a triangle having just two congruent sides.

    b. Draw all lines of symmetry.　There should be 1.

15. a. Construct a triangle having three congruent sides.

    b. Draw all lines of symmetry.　There should be 3.

16. Do you think it's possible for a triangle to have exactly two lines of symmetry?　no

309

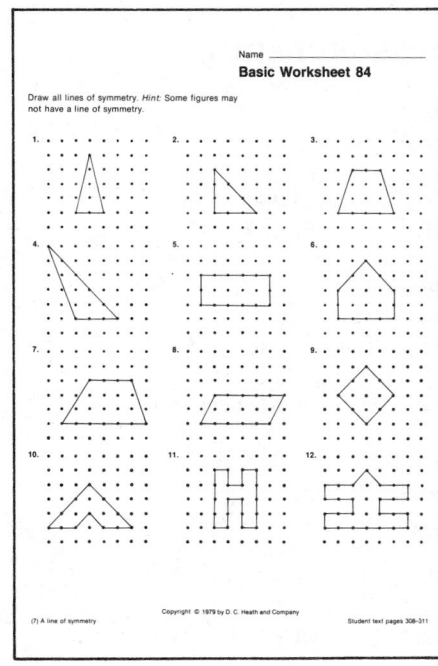

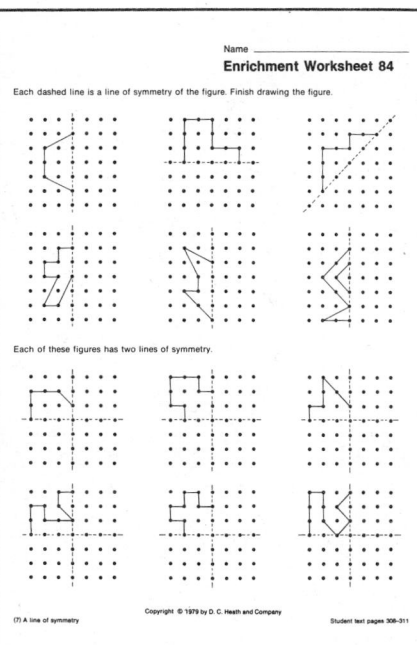

Follow-up Activities

Reinforcement　Provide students with some cutouts shaped like squares, rectangles, parallelograms, triangles, etc. Explain to students that the figures have a line of symmetry if they can be folded in such a way that the two halves match. For example, if you fold a rectangle as shown, the two parts match and the fold line is a line of symmetry:

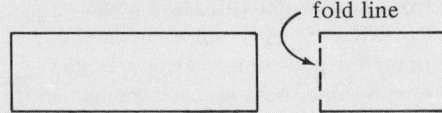

Have them determine how many lines of symmetry each figure has. (A square has 4 lines of symmetry, a rectangle has 2 lines of symmetry, a parallelogram has no lines of symmetry, and a triangle may have 0, 1, or 3 lines of symmetry.)

Enrichment　Ask students to explain why you always get a "perfect valentine" by cutting from a folded edge like this:

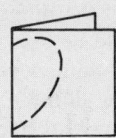

(The fold line is a line of symmetry.) Have students draw a figure that has 1 line of symmetry, 2 lines of symmetry, 3 lines of symmetry, ...

EXCURSION
Find the pattern.
Complete the table.

4	6	8	10
11	17	23	29
32	50	68	86
95	149	203	257
284	446	608	770

VOCABULARY
equilateral triangle, isosceles triangle,
scalene triangle

Suggested Lesson Plan

Introduction Cut out 8 or 9 triangles
from thin cardboard. Have some
isosceles triangles, some equilateral
triangles, and some scalene triangles.
One by one, hold up each triangle and
determine how many lines of symmetry
it has. When students identify a line of
symmetry fold the triangle to show that
it actually is a line of symmetry. As you
work through your models of triangles,
put them in groups on the tray of the
chalkboard according to the number of
lines of symmetry. Some will have no
lines, some will have one, and some will
have three lines of symmetry. When all
your triangles are sorted, ask students to
identify the common characteristics of
the triangles in the different groups.
Students should be able to perceive that
those triangles with three lines of
symmetry have all three sides equal. See
whether the students know the name for
these triangles. (equilateral) Of course,
the triangles with one line of symmetry
are isosceles triangles, and the triangles
with no lines of symmetry are *scalene*
triangles.

Using the pages Use the exposition
on page 310 to reinforce your
introduction and to restate the
generalizations.
 Assign the exercises. Have students
use onionskin paper or thin duplicating
paper for the tracings.
 Near the end of class time, have
students work the Keeping Skills Sharp.

Triangles

Now let's use the idea of a line of symmetry to study the properties of triangles. Any triangle can be classified according to
its number of lines of symmetry.

A triangle with
3 lines of symmetry
is called an
equilateral triangle.

A triangle with
1 line of symmetry
is called an
isosceles triangle.

A triangle with 0
lines of symmetry
is called a
scalene triangle.

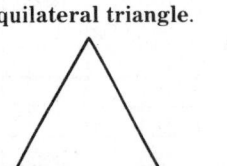
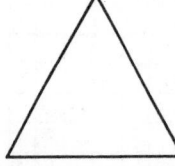
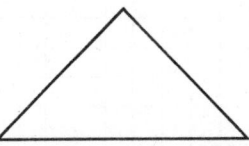
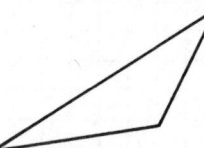

310

Assignments

BASIC
page 310 Discuss
page 311 exercises 1–6,
 Keeping Skills Sharp
Basic Worksheet 84

AVERAGE
page 310 Discuss
page 311 exercises 1–6,
 Keeping Skills Sharp
Enrichment Worksheet 84

ENRICHED
page 310 Discuss
page 311 exercises 1–6,
 Keeping Skills Sharp
Enrichment Worksheet 84

REVIEW PRACTICE
page 390 set 67

EXERCISES

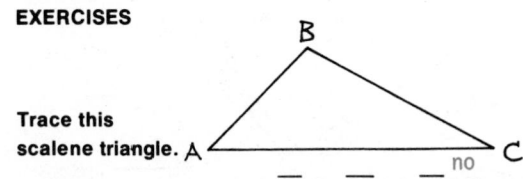

Trace this scalene triangle.

1. Does your tracing of $\overline{AB}$ fit $\overline{BC}$ or $\overline{AC}$? Does a scalene triangle have any congruent sides? no _no_

2. Does your tracing of $\angle B$ fit $\angle C$ or $\angle A$? Does a scalene triangle have any congruent angles? no _no_

> A scalene triangle has no congruent sides.

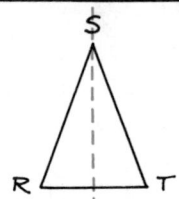

Trace this isosceles triangle.

3. Flip your drawing face-down about the line of symmetry. Does $\overline{RS}$ fit $\overline{TS}$? Does $\angle R$ fit $\angle T$? yes _yes_

4. What can you say about 2 sides of an isosceles triangle? About 2 angles of an isosceles triangle?

> An isosceles triangle has 2 congruent sides.

They are congruent. _They are congruent._

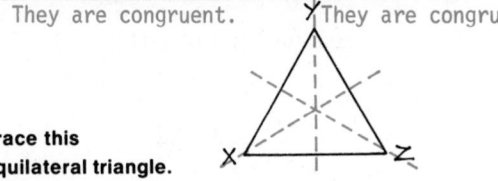

Trace this equilateral triangle.

5. If you flip your tracing face-down, does $\overline{XY}$ fit $\overline{YZ}$ and $\overline{XZ}$? Does $\angle X$ fit $\angle Y$ and $\angle Z$? _yes_ _yes_

6. What can you say about the 3 sides of an equilateral triangle? About the 3 angles?

> An equilateral triangle has 3 congruent sides.

They are congruent. _They are congruent._

Follow-up Activities

Reinforcement Have students make a 3-D bulletin-board display of the triangles studied on page 310. Have them make models of triangles using drinking straws and pipe cleaners. They should make several different triangles of each type and arrange them in groups on the bulletin board.

Enrichment Explain to students that a regular polygon has congruent sides and congruent angles. Introduce the regular pentagon, a 5-sided figure; the regular hexagon, a 6-sided figure; the regular heptagon, a 7-sided figure; and the regular octagon, an 8-sided figure. Ask them to determine how many lines of symmetry each of these polygons has.

EXCURSION
Find the path.

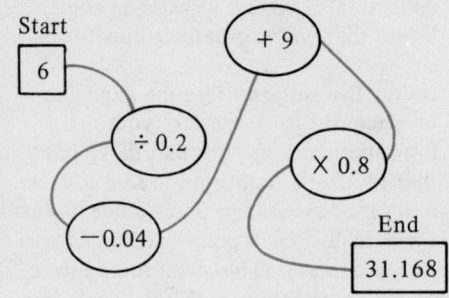

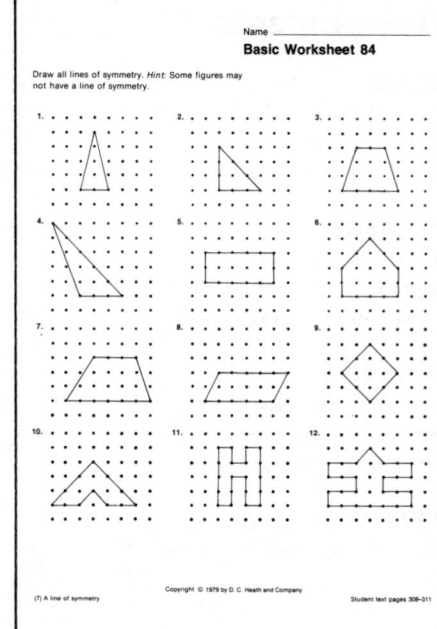

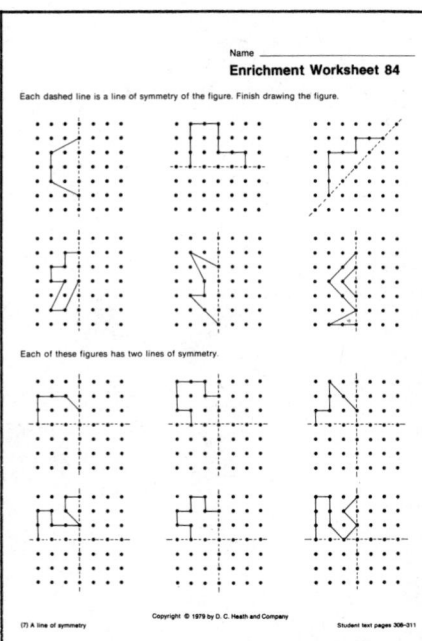

STUDENT OBJECTIVES
To determine whether a point is a point of symmetry.
To find points of symmetry for a figure.

VOCABULARY
point of symmetry, half-turn, opposite angles

Suggested Lesson Plan

Introduction Find several different sizes and shapes of boxes, such as shoe box, oatmeal box (round), valentine box, etc., to demonstrate the concept of *point of symmetry*.

Hold up one box with the lid (rectangular shoe box) and ask students whether, if you turn the lid halfway around, it will fit back on the box. Have a student demonstrate in front of the class. Take another box and lid and repeat the activity. Continue with your collection of boxes, working in some boxes that will not fit after a half-turn.

Using the pages Use the exposition on page 312 to summarize your introduction. Point out that those lids that fit after a half-turn are said to have a *point of symmetry*. Show students that there really was a point that the lid was turned around. (This point turns out to be the intersection of the diagonals, but don't tell them this now.)

Read through the examples with students. Assign exercises 1−9 for written work. Have students read and answer questions 1−9, but be prepared to discuss the answers after students have finished. You may need to help students with the notation and symbols used in the questions.

A point of symmetry

Think about taking the lid off each box and turning it halfway around.

Which lid would fit back on the box?

If a figure fits itself after a *half-turn* about a point, the point is a **point of symmetry** of the figure.

EXAMPLES.

Trace.

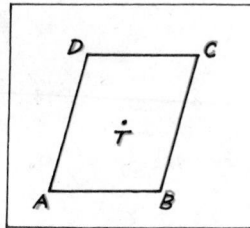

Half-turn. It fits.

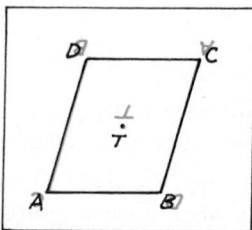

T is a point of symmetry.

Trace.

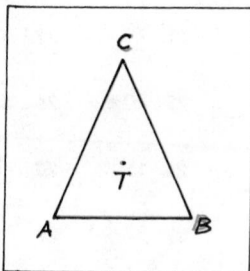

Half-turn. It does not fit.

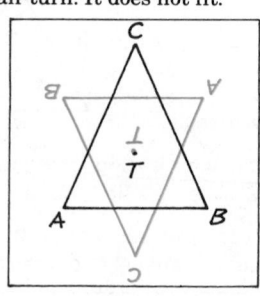

T is *not* a point of symmetry.

312

Assignments

BASIC
page 312 Discuss
page 313 exercises 1−9
Basic Worksheet 85

AVERAGE
page 312 Discuss
page 313 exercises 1−9
Enrichment Worksheet 85

ENRICHED
page 312 Discuss
page 313 exercises 1−9
Enrichment Worksheet 85

REVIEW PRACTICE
page 390 set 68

EXERCISES

Is the red point a point of symmetry of the figure? *Hint:* Trace the figure and see if the tracing fits after a *half-turn* about the red point.

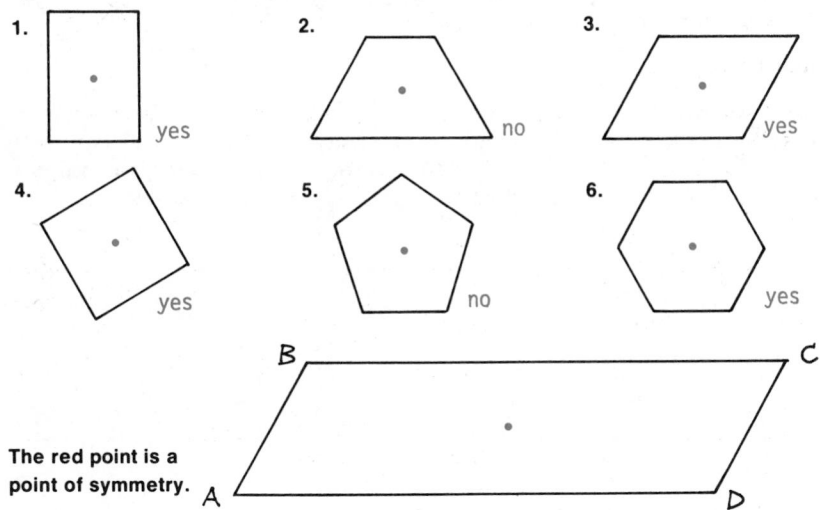

1. yes
2. no
3. yes
4. yes
5. no
6. yes

The red point is a point of symmetry.

7. a. Under a half-turn about the red point, does $\overline{AB}$ fit $\overline{CD}$?   yes

   b. Is $\overline{AB} \cong \overline{CD}$?   yes

   c. $\overline{AB}$ and $\overline{CD}$ are called **opposite sides.**
      Give the other pair of opposite sides. $\overline{BC}$ and $\overline{AD}$

   d. Are the opposite sides congruent?   yes

8. a. Under a half-turn about the red point, does $\angle A$ fit $\angle C$?   yes

   b. Is $\angle A \cong \angle C$?   yes

   c. $\angle A$ and $\angle C$ are called **opposite angles.**
      Give the other pair of opposite angles. $\angle B$ and $\angle D$

   d. Are the opposite angles congruent?   yes

9. Since the figure above has a point of symmetry, its opposite sides are parallel. Give the two pairs of parallel sides. $\overline{AB} \parallel \overline{DC}$, $\overline{BC} \parallel \overline{AD}$

313

Follow-up Activities

Reinforcement   Prepare some figures for the overhead projector that have a point of symmetry. Cover half of the figure with a piece of paper. Project it on the chalkboard and have a student go to the chalkboard and draw the half that is being covered. Uncover the half to check how accurate the drawing was. Continue the activity, using other figures that have a point of symmetry. If time permits, prepare some figures that have a line of symmetry. Project half on the chalkboard and have students draw the half that is covered.

Enrichment   Provide students with some cutouts of a square, a rectangle, a parallelogram, and a trapezoid. Have them decide which figures have a point of symmetry. (all but the trapezoid) Have them locate the points of symmetry by folding the figures.
Solution: The point of intersection of the diagonals is at the point of symmetry.

EXCURSION
Fill in the missing numbers.

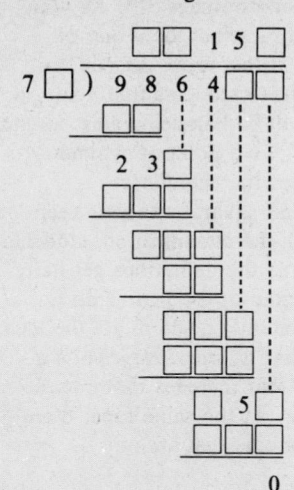

$$
\begin{array}{r}
13152 \\
75 \overline{)\,986400} \\
75 \\
\hline
236 \\
225 \\
\hline
114 \\
75 \\
\hline
390 \\
375 \\
\hline
150 \\
150 \\
\hline
0
\end{array}
$$

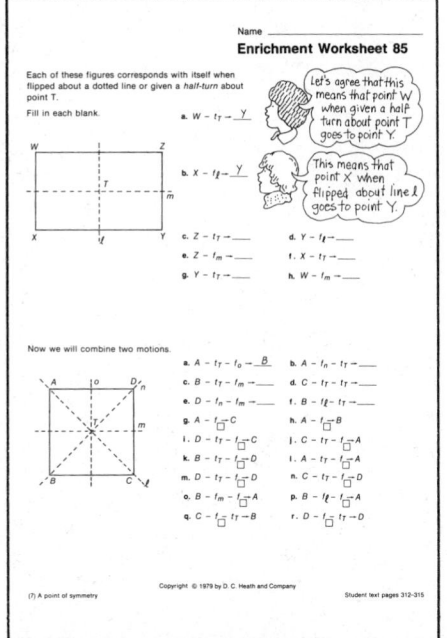

To classify quadrilaterals according to their properties.

VOCABULARY
parallelogram, rhombus, rectangle, square, isosceles trapezoid, kite

Suggested Lesson Plan

Introduction Cut several thin cardboard models of the figures shown on page 314. Without giving them names, have students classify them into groups according to whether they have a point of symmetry and how many lines of symmetry they have. Although you have probably learned to classify these figures by their sides and angles, this method of classification works well and gives students a different approach to classification of figures.

As you work through your cutouts, put them in different groups. You should end up with the different categories described on page 314.

Using the pages Start through the categories listed on page 314. As you read each term, select the group of cutouts that fit this term. As you do this, point out to students that many of the groups will be parallelograms: all the figures that have a point of symmetry, which includes the rhombuses, rectangles, and squares. As you keep going through the classification, students will see that as the definitions get more restrictive, some of the figures do not fit. Students should begin to get the idea of subsets, that is, *parallelogram* is a general term that includes rhombus, rectangle, etc. At the same time, there are parallelograms that are not rhombuses.

Assign exercises 1—7 for written work. Provide a compass and straightedge for each student who wants to try the project.

Quadrilaterals

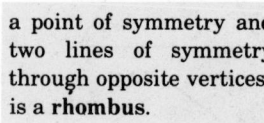

We can use points and lines of symmetry to study properties of some special quadrilaterals (4-sided figures).

A quadrilateral with:

a point of symmetry is a **parallelogram**.	a point of symmetry and two lines of symmetry through opposite vertices is a **rhombus**.	a point of symmetry and two lines of symmetry through opposite sides is a **rectangle**.

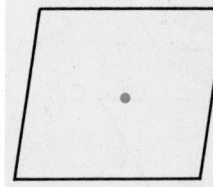   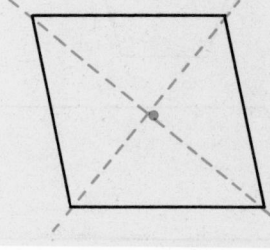   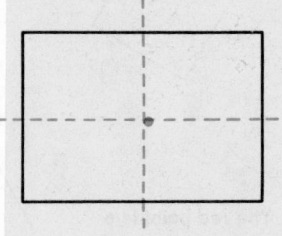

a point of symmetry and four lines of symmetry is a **square**.	one line of symmetry through opposite sides is an **isosceles trapezoid**.	one line of symmetry through opposite vertices is a **kite**.

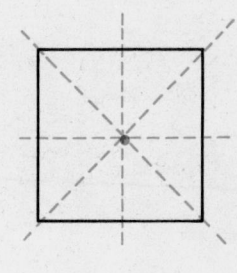   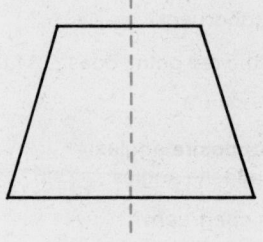   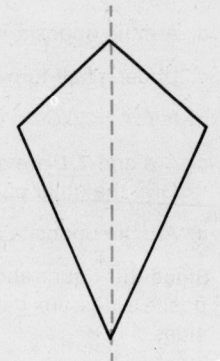

314

Assignments

BASIC
page 314 Discuss
page 315 exercises 1—6
Basic Worksheet 85

AVERAGE
page 314 Discuss
page 315 exercises 1—7
Enrichment Worksheet 85

ENRICHED
page 314 Discuss
page 315 exercises 1—7, Project
Enrichment Worksheet 85

REVIEW PRACTICE
page 391 set 69

EXERCISES

Which quadrilaterals on page 314 have

1. both pairs of opposite sides parallel? *parallelogram, rhombus, rectangle, and square*
   Hint: Which have a point of symmetry?

2. both pairs of opposite sides congruent? *parallelogram, rhombus, rectangle, and square*

3. both pairs of opposite angles congruent?
   parallelogram, rhombus, rectangle, and square

4. all four angles congruent? *rectangle and square*

5. exactly one pair of parallel sides and exactly one pair of congruent sides? *isosceles trapezoid*

6. exactly one pair of opposite angles that are congruent? *kite*

A trapezoid is a quadrilateral having just one pair of parallel sides.

7. Draw a trapezoid.

Project See which quadrilaterals you can construct with a compass and straightedge.

315

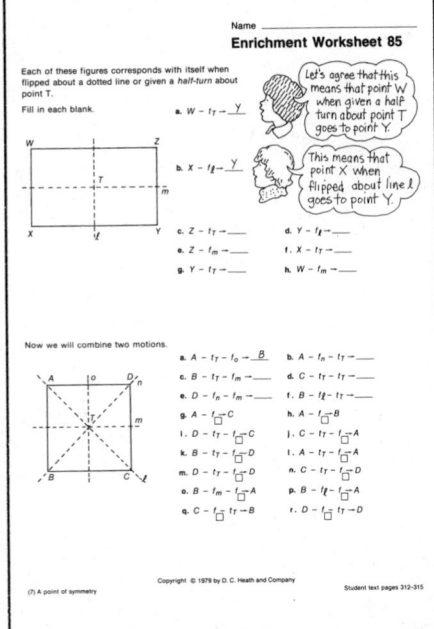

Follow-up Activities

Reinforcement Have students extend the 3-D bulletin board display of figures by building quadrilaterals of straws and pipe cleaners and grouping them in the display by their characteristics. See whether they can build in the idea that many figures are in more than one category.

Enrichment Have students make models of polygons using straws and pipe cleaners, and make mobiles showing the classification of polygons. Every figure that hangs below another figure should be of the same classification. The way to get a mobile to balance is to start at the bottom and work toward the top, balancing as you go.

EXCURSION

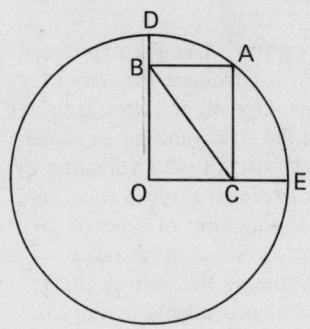

BACO is a rectangle.

Radius *OE* is 8 cm.
AC is 7 cm.
What is the length of $\overline{BC}$?

8 cm; OE = OA = BC

STUDENT OBJECTIVES
To classify polygons by the number of sides.
To identify regular polygons.
To explore surveying as an example of mathematics in careers.

VOCABULARY
polygon, pentagon, hexagon, heptagon, octagon, nonagon, decagon, regular polygon

Suggested Lesson Plan

Introduction Begin by asking students for a name that would include all the figures they have studied so far. (polygon) Explain that the prefix *poly-* means *many* and the stem *-gon* refers to sides. Thus, polygon means *many sides*. Explain to students that we can classify the polygons further just by referring to the number of sides.

Using the pages Use the exposition on page 316 to introduce the terms for the polygons. Use all of your cardboard models and the straw-and-pipe-cleaner models to classify all your polygons by the number of sides. Explain how the prefix tells the number of sides of the polygon, and continue up through decagon. Introduce the term *regular polygon* and have students identify the regular polygons from your collection.

Assign exercises 1−7 for written work.

Take some time to discuss the role of mathematics in the career of surveying. Read through the exposition on page 317 and examine the scale drawings. If you have a student whose parent is a surveyor, have that student discuss the job or, even better, have the parent come to class and discuss his or her work.

Polygons

These figures are all **polygons.** Their special names are given.

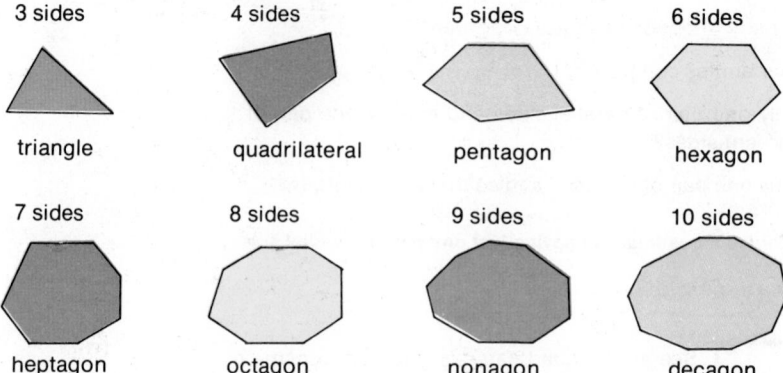

A **regular polygon** has all its sides congruent and all its angles congruent.

EXERCISES
Can you think of some real object that is shaped like

1. a pentagon? 2. a hexagon?

3. an octagon?

4. What is a regular triangle called?
   an equilateral triangle

5. What is a regular quadrilateral called?
   a square

6. Is a rhombus a regular polygon? no

7. Exercise 3 on page 299 gives directions for beginning the construction of a regular hexagon. Try to construct a regular hexagon.

316

Excursion

2 points   1 segment

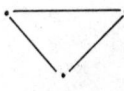
3 points   3 segments

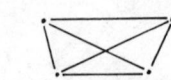
4 points   6 segments

Continue the pattern. Can you find a rule?

Answer.

Excursion

points	segments
5	10
6	15
7	21
8	28
.	.
.	.
.	.
n	$n(n - 1) \div 2$

Assignments

BASIC
page 316 exercises 1−6
page 317 exercises 1−2
Basic Worksheet 86

AVERAGE
page 316 exercises 1−6
page 317 exercises 1−2
Enrichment Worksheet 86

ENRICHED
page 316 exercises 1−7, Excursion
page 317 exercises 1−2
Enrichment Worksheet 86

REVIEW PRACTICE
page 391 set 70

Mathematics in careers

A land surveyor determines the shape and size of a part of the earth's surface. He also sets boundaries for property.

The main instrument used by a surveyor is a *transit*. It is used for sighting in a "straight line" and for determining horizontal and vertical angles. Distances are found by measuring with a steel tape. While a survey is being made, the surveyor generally records the data in a field book.

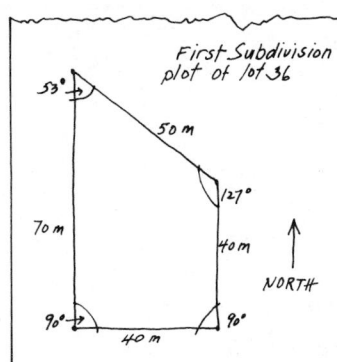

Here are two plots from a field book. Make a scale drawing of each plot. Use a protractor to draw the "corner" angles.

1.

First Subdivision plot of lot 36
53°
50 m
127°
70 m
40 m
NORTH
90°
40 m
90°

2.

First Subdivision plot of lot 43
NORTH
48m
112½°
90°
52 m
48m
67½°
90°
68 m

317

Follow-up Activities

Reinforcement Have students make models of all the polygons studied, using straws and pipe cleaners. Have them make a 3-D bulletin board or a mobile that will show the names for the polygons when classified by the number of sides.

Enrichment Have students read more about surveying and report back to the class. See if someone can bring to class an example of a surveyor's report.

EXCURSION

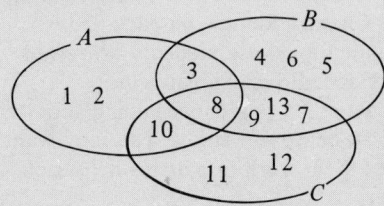

Complete. $n(A)$ means the number of elements in A.

1. $n(A) = $ _?_   2. $n(B) = $ _?_

3. $n(C) = $ _?_   4. $n(A \cap B) = $ _?_

5. $n(A \cap C) = $ _?_

6. $n(B \cap C) = $ _?_

7. $n(A \cap B \cap C) = $ _?_

8. Can you complete this rule?

$n(A \cup B \cup C) = n(A) + n(B) + \ldots$

1. 5   2. 8   3. 7

4. 2   5. 2   6. 4

7. 1

8. $n(C) - n(A \cap B) - n(A \cap C)$
$- n(B \cap C) + n(A \cap B \cap C)$

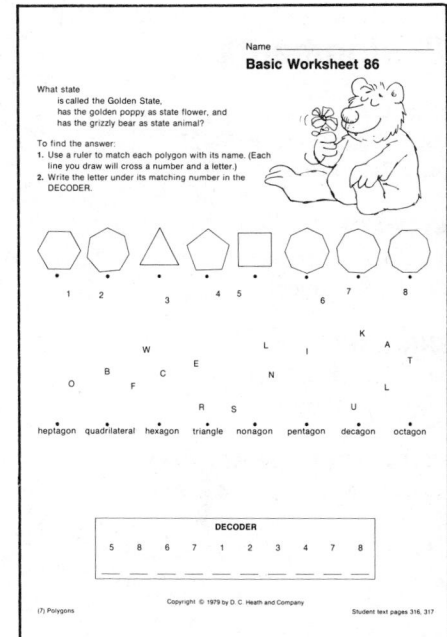

Name _____
Basic Worksheet 86

What state
is called the Golden State,
has the golden poppy as state flower, and
has the grizzly bear as state animal?

To find the answer:
1. Use a ruler to match each polygon with its name. (Each line you draw will cross a number and a letter.)
2. Write the letter under its matching number in the DECODER.

heptagon quadrilateral hexagon triangle nonagon pentagon decagon octagon

DECODER
5 8 6 7 1 2 3 4 7 8

(7) Polygons   Copyright © 1979 by D. C. Heath and Company   Student text pages 316, 317

Name _____
Enrichment Worksheet 86

First measure an angle of each of these regular polygons.
Then complete the table below.

REGULAR POLYGONS			
Number of sides	Number of angles	Measure of each angle	Sum of the measures of the angles
3	3	60°	180°
4			
5			
6			
7			
8			
9			
10			
11			
12			

(7) Polygons   Copyright © 1979 by D. C. Heath and Company   Student text pages 316, 317

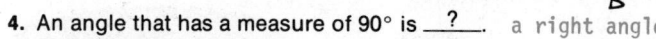

STUDENT OBJECTIVE

To review the concepts and skills introduced in Chapter 10.

Suggested Lesson Plan

Introduction No pre-text activity is necessary for page 318, as this is a checkup for the chapter. However, it may be valuable to briefly review the lessons in the chapter so that students are reminded of the content over which they will be tested.

This Checkup will provide you with data about how well individual students have mastered the skills of the chapter. The Chapter Review on page 320 is provided for those students who need more specific individual help.

Page 319 is a paper-folding activity that students will enjoy. You may want to let them work in pairs to help each other.

Using the pages Assign all of the exercises on page 318. As students complete the page, they can work on the activity on page 319.

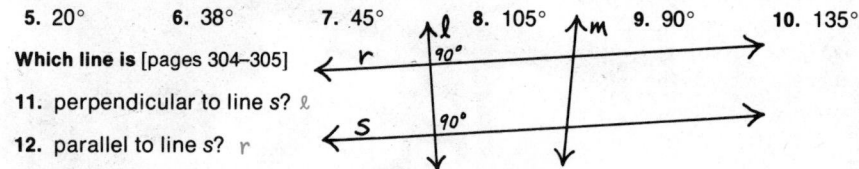

Acute, right, or obtuse?
Complete. [pages 302–303]

1. ∠ *EAB* is ___?___. obtuse

2. ∠ *BAD* is ___?___. right

3. ∠ *DAE* is ___?___. acute

4. An angle that has a measure of 90° is ___?___. a right angle

Draw angles with these measures. [pages 302–303]

5. 20° 6. 38° 7. 45° 8. 105° 9. 90° 10. 135°

Which line is [pages 304–305]

11. perpendicular to line *s*? ℓ

12. parallel to line *s*? r

These two triangles are congruent. Complete these pairs of corresponding parts for the congruent fitting. [pages 306–307]

13. $\overline{AB} \longleftrightarrow$ ___?___ $\overline{TR}$ 14. $\overline{BC} \longleftrightarrow$ ___?___ $\overline{RS}$

15. $\overline{CA} \longleftrightarrow$ ___?___ $\overline{ST}$ 16. ∠*A* $\longleftrightarrow$ ___?___ ∠T

17. ∠*B* $\longleftrightarrow$ ___?___ ∠R 18. ∠*C* $\longleftrightarrow$ ___?___ ∠S

19. Are these corresponding parts congruent? yes

True or false? [pages 308–311]

20. A scalene triangle has 1 line of symmetry. false

21. An isosceles triangle has 2 lines of symmetry. false

22. An equilateral triangle has 3 lines of symmetry. true

Name the quadrilaterals that have [pages 312–315]

23. a point of symmetry and no lines of symmetry. parallelogram

24. opposite sides parallel. 25. 4 congruent sides. rhombus, square

26. 4 right angles. 27. 4 congruent sides and 4 right angles. square
rectangle, square
    24. parallelogram, rhombus, rectangle, square

318

Assignments

BASIC
page 318 exercises 1—27
page 319 Project

AVERAGE
page 318 exercises 1—27
page 319 Project

ENRICHED
page 318 exercises 1—27
page 319 Project

EXTRA PROBLEM SOLVING
pages 424–425 set 14

1. **a.** Draw a triangle like this one using a straightedge. Cut it out.
   b. Fold the triangle so that points A and B are together. Crease the paper. The line you have folded is the perpendicular bisector of $\overline{AB}$.
   c. Fold the perpendicular bisectors of $\overline{AC}$ and $\overline{BC}$.
   d. What do you notice about the three perpendicular bisectors?
   They intersect at one point.

2. **a.** Draw another triangle like $\triangle ABC$. Cut it out.
   b. Fold the triangle so that $\overline{AC}$ falls on $\overline{AB}$. Crease. You have folded the bisector of $\angle A$.
   c. Fold the bisectors of $\angle B$ and $\angle C$.
   d. What do you notice about the three bisectors?
   They intersect at one point.

3. **a.** Draw a triangle like $\triangle ABC$. Cut it out.
   b. Fold point A over to point B. Make a small crease where the fold crosses $\overline{AB}$. This is the midpoint of $\overline{AB}$. Do not crease the whole line.
   c. Fold and crease the triangle so that the fold line goes from C to the midpoint of $\overline{AB}$. This is a median of the triangle.
   d. Fold the median that goes from A to the midpoint of $\overline{BC}$ and the median from B to the midpoint of $\overline{AC}$. What do you notice about the three medians?
   They intersect at one point.

4. Compare your results in this project with your work on pages 301 and 305.

319

You may wish to assign some of the Creative Problem Solving Activities (pages 461-477) at this time.

Follow-up Activities

Reinforcement Correct all the items in the Chapter Checkup. Any student that misses four or more exercises needs additional help.

Enrichment Assign these pupils to the activities that have been suggested throughout the chapter. Have a student leader who is responsible for each activity to explain and help with the activity.

STUDENT OBJECTIVE
To review or extend the skills and concepts taught in Chapter 10.

Suggested Lesson Plan

Introduction After checking the Chapter Checkup you will know which students need additional reinforcement and which students will be able to go ahead with the Challenge activity. Get the better students started on page 321 first as the students who are having difficulty will need more of your time.

The students who need more review should go back and correct their errors on the Chapter Checkup. You may want to go over those questions orally if this group is small enough. Carefully probe to determine which concepts and skills the students have not mastered and work individually to correct these deficiencies.

Using the pages After the identified students have corrected the Chapter Checkup, they should answer questions 1–13. After they complete these questions, read the answers and let the students correct their own papers. Give them an opportunity to ask questions about the exercises they missed.

Assign page 321 to those students who did well on the Chapter Checkup. Have students work individually to see if they can discover the relationship for determining the number of diagonals based on the number of sides of a polygon.

acute angle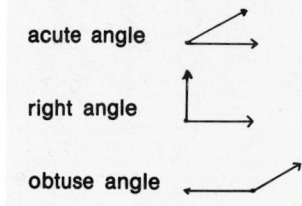

right angle

obtuse angle

Two lines in a plane that intersect to form right angles are called **perpendicular (⊥) lines**.

Two lines in a plane that do not intersect are called **parallel (ll) lines**.

Figures that are the same size and shape are called **congruent figures**.

Triangle	Lines of Symmetry
Scalene	0
Isosceles	1
Equilateral	3

320

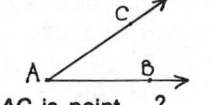

Complete.

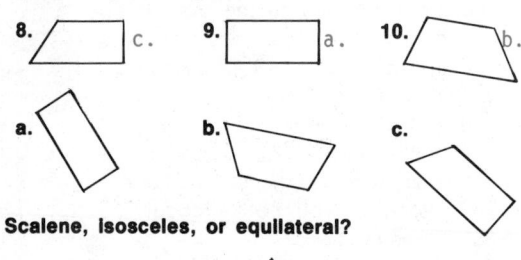

1. The vertex of ∠BAC is point __?__ . A
2. The measure of ∠A is __?__ 90°. (less than, equal to, greater than)
3. An acute angle measures between 0° and __?__ . 90°
4. A right angle measures __?__ . 90°
5. An obtuse angle measures between 90° and __?__ . 180°

Complete.

6. l ⊥ __?__ m
7. l ll __?__ n

Match congruent figures.

8. c.   9. a.   10. b.

a.   b.   c.

Scalene, isosceles, or equilateral?

11.   12.   13.

scalene   isosceles   equilateral

Assignments

BASIC
page 320 exercises 1–13

AVERAGE
page 320 exercises 1–13

ENRICHED
page 321 exercises 1–3

CHAPTER CHALLENGE

A 4-sided figure has 2 diagonals.

How many diagonals does a 5-sided figure have? 5

1. Draw a 6-sided figure. How many diagonals does it have? 9

2. Copy and complete this table. If you need to, draw each figure and its diagonals.

Number of sides	Number of diagonals
4	2
5	5
6	9
7	14
8	20

3. Study your completed table. Can you give a rule for finding the number of diagonals if you know the number of sides?

   $n(n - 3) \div 2$, where n is the number of sides

321

Reinforcement The reinforcement at this point should be individual help focused on the concepts of the chapter. Students may need help on the terms and notation introduced in the chapter. This chapter is not considered a critical skill so it is not recommended that you spend a lot of time with remedial activities.

Enrichment Pair these students with students who are having difficulty. Encourage them to review the terms and to discuss their meaning.

STUDENT OBJECTIVES

To practice skills learned previously.
To practice using a standardized-test format.

Suggested Lesson Plan

Using the pages The Major Checkup at the end of each chapter of this textbook is given in standardized-test format. The answer sheet on page 448 is the type used with many standardized tests. You may duplicate it for use with the Major Checkups.

Pass out the answer sheets and be sure students understand how to use them. Allow a specified time, perhaps twenty minutes, to complete the checkup. Assign the exercises and use the results to determine what review is needed.

The table below correlates the test items and the student text pages. Assign review exercises as indicated by the Major Checkup results.

Test Item	Text Pages	Test Item	Text Pages
1	62–63	7	190–191
2	86–87	8	226–227
3	96–97	9	220–221
4	140–141	10	260–261
5	110–111	11	282–283
6	188–189	12	286–287

Chapter 10 Posttest

See page 54 for a full discussion of how to use the posttest. The table below suggests Extra Practice exercises and Basic Worksheets for those students who need further practice or reteaching.

Objectives	Basic Worksheets
10-1	82
10-2	82
10-3	83
10-4	84–86

Answers for Chapter 10 Posttest

1. 85°   2. 136°   3. m 4. p 5. $\overline{FE}$ 6. $\overline{BC}$
7. $\overline{DA}$ 8. $\angle E$ 9. $\angle C$ 10. $\angle A$
11. equilateral triangle   12. square   13. a four-sided figure with two sides parallel
14. 0   15. isosceles

MAJOR CHECKUP
Standardized Format

Choose the correct letter.

1. Which number is greatest?
  a. 38.2906
  b. 382.145
  c. 382.735
  d. 382.905 ⟵

2. Multiply.
  8.76
  × 2.43
  a. 20.9458
  b. 2094.58
  c. 21.2868 ⟵
  d. none of these

3. Divide.
  $0.235\overline{)14.2645}$
  a. 6.7
  b. 60.7 ⟵
  c. 607
  d. none of these

4. Find the area.

  4 cm, 3 cm, 10 cm
  a. 28 sq cm
  b. 30 sq cm ⟵
  c. 40 sq cm
  d. none of these

5. The greatest common factor of 18 and 24 is
  a. 3
  b. 6 ⟵
  c. 72
  d. none of these

6. Add.
  $8\frac{1}{3}$
  $+ 3\frac{5}{6}$
  a. $11\frac{1}{6}$
  b. $10\frac{1}{6}$
  c. $12\frac{1}{6}$ ⟵
  d. none of these

7. Subtract.
  5
  $- 2\frac{3}{4}$
  a. $3\frac{3}{4}$
  b. $2\frac{1}{4}$ ⟵
  c. $2\frac{3}{4}$
  d. none of these

8. Give the product.
  $2\frac{2}{3} \times 1\frac{3}{4}$
  a. $4\frac{2}{3}$ ⟵
  b. $\frac{3}{14}$
  c. $\frac{21}{32}$
  d. none of these

9. $\frac{\frac{3}{4}}{\frac{4}{3}} = \underline{\quad?\quad}$
  a. 1
  b. $\frac{16}{9}$
  c. $\frac{9}{16}$ ⟵
  d. none of these

10. $33\frac{1}{3}\%$ of $48 = n$
  $n = \underline{\quad?\quad}$
  a. 64
  b. 16 ⟵
  c. 32
  d. none of these

11. An item that regularly sells for $30 was put on sale for $25. The percent of discount was
  a. 25%
  b. 20%
  c. $16\frac{2}{3}\%$ ⟵
  d. none of these

12. The interest at 8% for borrowing $600 for 6 months is
  a. $48
  b. $288
  c. $24 ⟵
  d. none of these

322

Chapter 10 Posttest

Name _____

Date _____

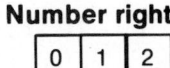
Measure each angle. [Obj. 10-1, pages 298–303]

1.

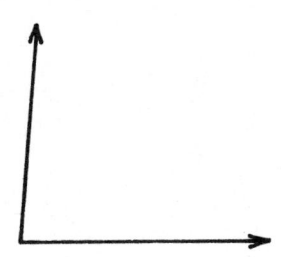

2.

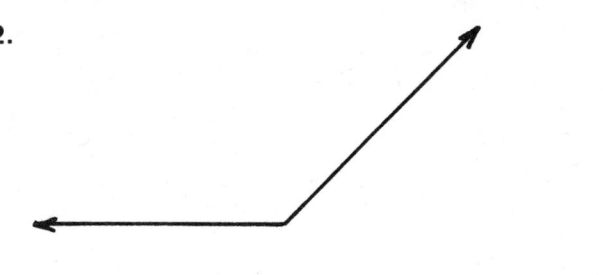

_____

_____

0 | 1 | 2

Answer. [Obj. 10-2, pages 304–305]

3. Which line is the perpendicular bisector of $\overline{AB}$? _____

4. Which line is parallel to line m? _____

These two figures are congruent. Complete the list of corresponding parts. [Obj. 10-3, pages 306–307]

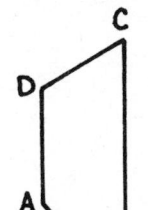

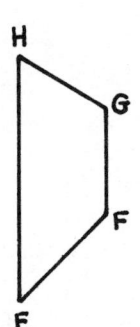

0 | 1 | 2 | 3 | 4 | 5 | 6

Corresponding Parts

5. $\overline{AB}$ and _____   8. ∠ B and _____

6. $\overline{EH}$ and _____   9. ∠ H and _____

7. $\overline{GF}$ and _____   10. ∠ F and _____

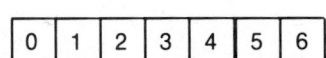

Answer these questions. [Obj. 10-4, pages 308–316]

11. What three-sided figure has three lines of symmetry? _____

12. What kind of rectangle has four congruent sides? _____

13. What is a trapezoid? _____

14. How many lines of symmetry does a scalene triangle have? _____

15. What is the name of a triangle with two congruent sides? _____

322a

NOTES

322b

Chapter 11
Probability and Statistics

Pages 323–344

Learning Objectives

After completing this chapter, all students should be able to do the following:

11-1   Count outcomes of simple and compound events.

11-2   Compute probabilities for outcomes.

11-3   Read graphs.

11-4   Compute means, medians, and ranges.

Mathematics

Counting outcomes. Counting the possible outcomes of the events used in this text is a fairly simple task. In the case of rolling a cube and looking at the top face, or spinning a spinner and looking at the number at which the arrow points, it is merely a matter of noting the numbers on the faces of the cube or on the dial of the spinner.

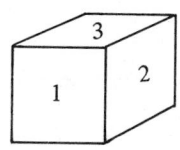   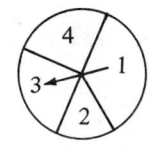

6 outcomes   4 outcomes

Notice that we do not consider that the cube will land on its edge or the spinner will land on a line of the dial.

We say that the 6 outcomes for rolling the cube are equally likely because all faces are the same size and we assume that the cube is not weighted "off center." The four outcomes for spinning the spinner shown above are not equally likely because the central angles for the regions are not the same size. There are "more stopping places" in region 1 than in the other regions. Obviously, to guess whether outcomes are equally likely or not, students must have some ideas about the forces that come into play.

When outcomes are compounded from simple outcomes, counting is somewhat more complicated. However, tree diagrams can help to show these outcomes. For example, consider tossing a coin (heads or tails) and spinning the spinner shown above. The coin can land with either heads or tails up:

If it lands heads up, there are 4 possible outcomes for spinning the spinner, 1, 2, 3, and 4:

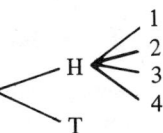

If the coin lands tails up, there are the same 4 possible outcomes for spinning the spinner:

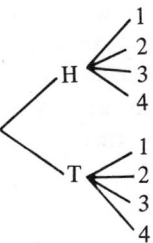

By starting at the left and following all possible paths through the diagram, we can find all possible outcomes. They are (H, 1), (H, 2), (H, 3), (H, 4), (T, 1), (T, 2), (T, 3), and (T, 4).

This diagram not only shows the outcomes but also suggests a basic counting principle.

> If a first event has m outcomes and if, after the first event, a second event has n outcomes, then the compound event of the first event followed by the second event has $m \times n$ outcomes.

Probability. If there are n *equally likely* outcomes for an event, then we say the probability of each outcome is $1/n$. In the case of the cube above there are 6 equally likely outcomes. Therefore, the probability of each is $1/6$. We use this notation for the probability of the outcome 3 when rolling the die:

$$P(3) = \frac{1}{6} \text{ (the probability of 3 equals } \frac{1}{6})$$

For tossing a coin, $P(H) = 1/2$ (the probability of heads equals $1/2$).

For tossing a cube, $P(1 \text{ or } 2) = 2/6$. Notice that we can merely add $P(1)$ and $P(2)$ to get $P(1 \text{ or } 2)$.

For the cube, $P(1, 2, 3, 4, 5, \text{ or } 6) = 1$. When the probability is 1, the outcome is certain. In this case the cube is certain to land with one of the faces up.

For tossing the cube, $P(7) = 0$. When something is impossible, its probability is 0. There is no face of the cube with 7 on it.

There is a probability principle that is a consequence of the counting principle given above.

> If the probability of a first outcome is $1/m$ and if, after that outcome occurs, the probability of a second outcome is $1/n$, then the probability of the first outcome followed by the second outcome is $1/m \times n$.

Teaching the Chapter

The material on counting outcomes and on probability should be treated lightly, but all students should be able to read data from graphs. Students should be actively involved in performing the probability experiments in the chapter. Do not skip these experiments and make probability a strictly paper-and-pencil subject.

Some experiments that you may wish to perform will involve spinners. A good spinner is difficult to make. We suggest that you get commercially made spinners such as are found in some children's games and make different dial faces for them from paper. A fairly satisfactory spinner can be made from a paper clip.

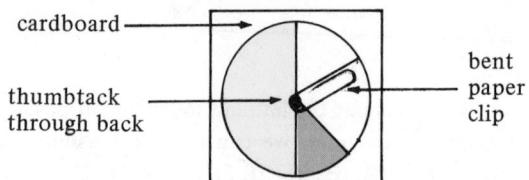

cardboard

thumbtack
through back

bent
paper
clip

Vocabulary

biased
data
demographer
equally likely
mean
median
outcome
probability
range
sample
tree diagram

Symbols

$P(2)$ the probability of the outcome 2

Materials

coins
spinners
magazines and newspapers with graphs
stock market results from newspaper
population data from the World Almanac or
    an encyclopedia

Chapter Tests

For a discussion of how to use the chapter tests, please see page 17c.

Answers for Chapter 11 Pretest

1. 4 **2.** 4 **3.** 12 **4.** $\frac{1}{2}$ **5.** $\frac{1}{4}$ **6.** $\frac{1}{3}$ **7.** $\frac{1}{2}$ **8.** $\frac{1}{2}$ **9.** 10°
10. Friday **11.** 3° **12.** 15° **13.** $18\frac{3}{7}$ 17, 9 **14.** $39\frac{5}{7}$, 37, 13

Chapter 11 Pretest

Name _____

Date _____

How many outcomes? [Obj. 11-1, pages 324–327]

1. Spin this spinner.

_____

2. Toss a dime and a quarter.

_____

3. Toss a coin and roll a die.

_____

What is the probability? [Obj. 11-2, pages 328–329]

4. $P(3) =$ _____

5. $P(1) =$ _____

6. $P(R) =$ _____

7. $P(Y) =$ _____

8. $P(R \text{ or } B) =$ _____

Answer each question. [Obj. 11-3, pages 334–335]

9. What was the noon temperature on Sunday? _____

10. On which day was the noon temperature highest? _____

11. How many degrees did the temperature rise from Tuesday to Wednesday? _____

12. What was the noon temperature on Saturday? _____

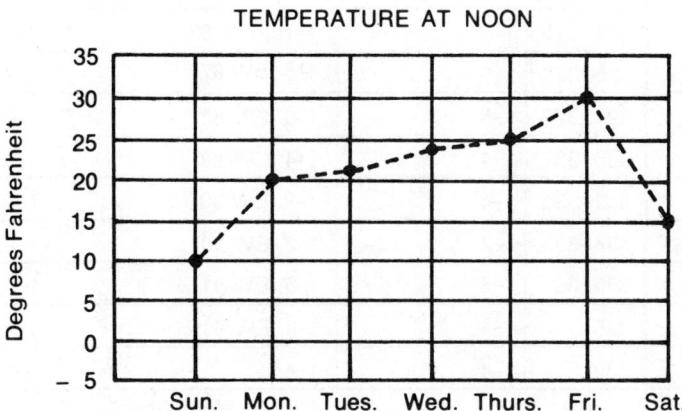

TEMPERATURE AT NOON

Find the mean, median, and range. [Obj. 11-4, pages 336–337]

13. 16, 17, 17, 17, 18, 19, 25

14. 35, 37, 48, 43, 36, 37, 42

_____ _____ _____

mean   median   range

_____ _____ _____

mean   median   range

323c

Chapter 11
Record and Assignment Chart

Name _____

Pretest Date _____ Posttest Date _____

Objectives

11-1	Count outcomes of simple and compound events.
11-2	Compute probabilities for outcomes.
11-3	Read graphs.
11-4	Compute means, medians, and ranges.

Pretest Score
Mark number correct

11-1: `0` `1` | `2` `3`

11-2: `0-1` `2` | `3` `4` `5`

11-3: `0` `1` `2` `3` | `4`

11-4: `0-1` `2` `3` `4` | `5` `6`

Unsatisfactory Score | Satisfactory Score

Posttest Score
Mark number correct

11-1: `0` `1` | `2` `3`

11-2: `0-1` `2` | `3` `4` `5`

11-3: `0` `1` `2` `3` | `4`

11-4: `0-1` `2` `3` `4` | `5` `6`

Unsatisfactory Score | Satisfactory Score

TEACHING ASSIGNMENTS*

	Student Page	Basic Assignment	Average Assignment	Enriched Assignment	Problem Solving	RETEACHING ASSIGNMENTS†
11-1	324, 325	1–8	1–10, EW 87	1–10, EW 87		BW 87
	326, 327	1–5	1–5, EW 87	1–7, EW 87		BW 87
11-2	328, 329	1–5	1–6, EW 88	1–6, EW 88		page 395 Set 83, BW 88
	330, 331	1–4	1–4, EW 89	1–5, EW 89		page 396 Set 84, BW 89
	332, 333	1–4	1–9, EW 90	1–9, EW 90		BW 90
11-3	334, 335	1–2	1–2, EW 90	1–2, EW 90		BW 90
11-4	336, 337	1–4	1–5, EW 91	1–5, EW 91		page 396 Set 85, BW 91
	338	1–4	1–4, EW 91	1–4, EW 91		BW 91
11-3	339	1–4	1–4	1–4		BW 91

340	Chapter Checkup
341	Project
342	Chapter Review
343	Chapter Challenge
344	Major Checkup

*Check assignments for objectives with unsatisfactory pretest scores.
†Check assignments for objectives with unsatisfactory posttest scores.

BW = Basic Worksheet
EW = Enrichment Worksheet

323d

11
Probability and Statistics

Suggested Lesson Plan

Introduction Toss a coin into the air and catch it in your hand. Ask students how many different ways it could land. There are only two ways—heads up or tails up. Since you are catching it, you do not allow it to land on an edge. Tell students that the different ways that it can land are called *outcomes*. Ask students if they think one outcome is more likely to occur than the other. Students may feel that one *is* more likely than the other; and, in fact, that may be true for some coins. But tell students that for the sake of simplicity we will assume that they are *equally likely*. Repeat with a die or a cube with sides numbered 1 through 6.

Using the pages Go over the exposition on page 324 with your students. Ask students to tell why the six outcomes for the die are equally likely. (The faces are the same size and shape and the cube is "balanced" in the center. This is all theoretical, of course.) Ask why the spinner has outcomes that are not equally likely. (There is not the same amount of space for the pointer in each region.)

Assign the exercises. Give students time to do the projects. The projects are designed to point out a problem to students: How do we determine whether two outcomes are equally likely in real-life situations? Suppose that a coin is tossed 100 times and there are 46 heads and 54 tails. Did this occur by chance or is it the case that for this coin tails are more likely than heads? Students should realize that there is no exact way of making that decision. If the outcomes had been 30 heads and 70 tails, we would be quite likely to say that the outcomes are not equally likely as a result of the way the coin is made or the way it is tossed. When the outcomes are near to 50−50, we have a difficult time making up our minds.

Equally likely outcomes

If you toss this coin it can land in one of these two ways.

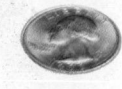

There are 2 **possible outcomes**.

Since the chance of getting heads or tails is the same, we say that the outcomes are **equally likely**.

If you toss this die it can land in one of these six ways.

1 up   2 up   3 up

4 up   5 up   6 up

There are 6 **possible outcomes**. When a die is tossed, the outcomes are **equally likely**.

If you spin this spinner, there are 4 possible outcomes. The outcomes are *not* equally likely. Why? The 4 regions have different areas.

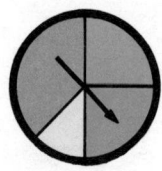

EXERCISES
First tell how many possible outcomes there are for tossing each block. Then tell whether or not the outcomes are equally likely.

1.

Cube
6, equally likely

2.

Rectangular prism
6, not equally likely

3.

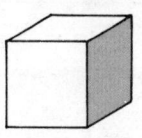

Pyramid
5, not equally likely

324

First tell how many outcomes. Then tell whether or not the outcomes are equally likely.

4.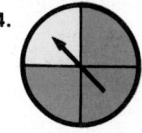

4, equally likely

5.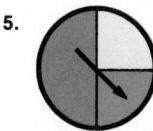

3, not equally likely

6.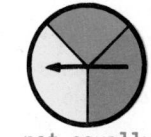

3, not equally likely

7. Think about the possible outcomes of spinning the spinner shown in exercise 5. Which color do you think you would get most often? green

8. Think about tossing a paper cup.

 a. How many ways can it land? 3
 b. Do you think the outcomes are equally likely? no

(H, 1), (T, 1),
(H, 2), (T, 2),
(H, 3), (T, 3),
(H, 4), (T, 4),
(H, 5), (T, 5),
(H, 6), (T, 6)
yes

9. Imagine tossing a coin and die at the same time. List all possible outcomes. You could list the outcome shown as (H, 1). Are the outcomes equally likely?

10. List all possible outcomes of spinning this spinner and tossing this die.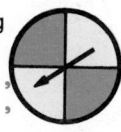
(Y,1),(Y,2),(Y,3),(Y,4),(Y,5),(Y,6),
(R,1),(R,2),(R,3),(R,4),(R,5),(R,6),
(B,1),(B,2),(B,3),(B,4),(B,5),(B,6)

Faces have from 1 through 6 dots.

Project

1. Toss a coin 100 times and record each outcome. How many heads and how many tails did you get? Compare your results with your classmates' results.

2. When a thumbtack is tossed, there are two possible outcomes:

point up   point down

Try to decide whether or not the outcomes are equally likely by tossing a thumbtack at least 50 times. Be sure to keep a tally of the outcomes.

325

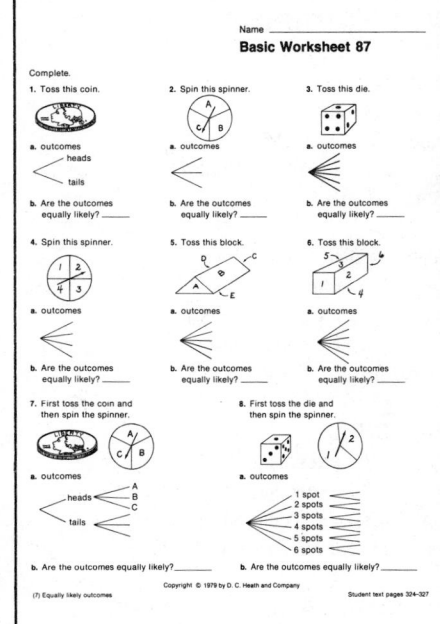

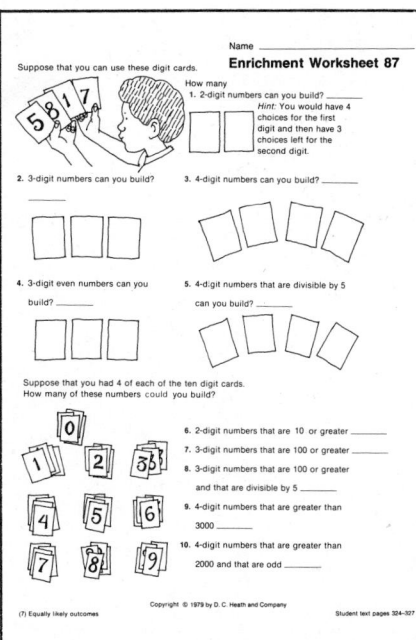

Follow-up Activities

Reinforcement You may wish to have students combine their results in Project 1. That is, have them add to find the total number of heads and the total number of tails. Discuss with students whether or not they think that the outcome of heads and the outcome of tails are equally likely. (Theoretically speaking, they are.)

Enrichment The following activity would be appropriate for more able students. Have students construct two spinners like the one shown below:

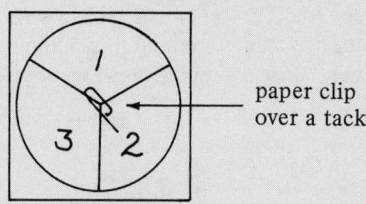

paper clip over a tack

Have them think about spinning both spinners and keeping a tally of the sum. Ask them what sums are possible. Ask them if all sums are equally likely. Have them spin their spinners and keep a record of the outcomes. (The outcome of getting 4 as the sum is more likely than getting 3 or 5. Getting the sum of 3 and 5 is more likely than getting a 2 or a 6.) They could record the outcomes on a graph like this:

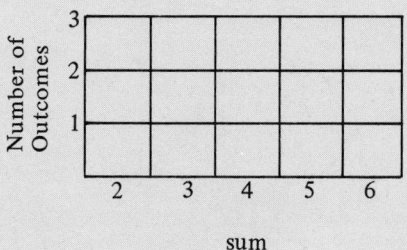

EXCURSION
Here are the first three *pentagonal numbers*.

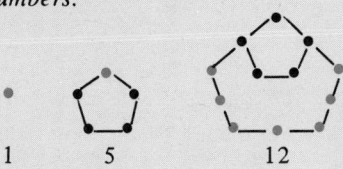

1   5   12

Find some more pentagonal numbers. Look for a pattern! 22, 35, 51

Fifty-one is a pentagonal number. What is the next pentagonal number after 51?
70

Lesson 153   **325**

STUDENT OBJECTIVE
To use a basic counting principle to
count the number of outcomes of
compound events.

VOCABULARY
tree diagram

Suggested Lesson Plan

Introduction On the board develop a
tree diagram like the one in the text on
page 326. Be sure that students see how
the tree shows all the outcomes. Ask
students how many outcomes there are
for the first event. (2) For the second
event. (6) For the first followed by the
second. (12) Repeat the above with two
other events combined into a single
event. For example, toss two coins:

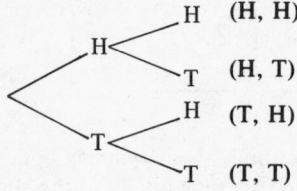

Repeat with 3 coins if you wish. (8
outcomes)

Using the pages Go over the
exposition on page 326. Students should
be aware of the counting principle from
the activities above. Assign exercises
1−7 for written work.

A basic counting principle

Tree Diagram of Outcomes

A tree diagram may be used to show
the possible outcomes of an event.
Here is an example.

Event

First tossing a coin
and then
tossing a die.

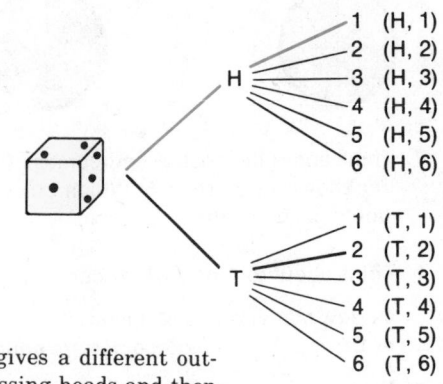

	1 (H, 1)
	2 (H, 2)
H	3 (H, 3)
	4 (H, 4)
	5 (H, 5)
	6 (H, 6)
	1 (T, 1)
	2 (T, 2)
T	3 (T, 3)
	4 (T, 4)
	5 (T, 5)
	6 (T, 6)

Notice that each "branch" of the tree gives a different outcome. The red branch stands for first tossing heads and then
tossing a 1. The tree diagram shows that there are 2 outcomes
when tossing a coin, and 6 outcomes when tossing a cube. It
also shows that if a coin is tossed and then a cube is tossed,
there are 2 × 6 (or 12) outcomes. This is an example of a basic
counting principle.

> If a first event has *m* outcomes, and if a second event has
> *n* outcomes, then the first event followed by the second
> event has *m* × *n* outcomes.

EXERCISES
**Copy and complete the tree diagram. Then tell how many
outcomes.**

1. *Event*
Toss a coin
and then spin this spinner.

Tree Diagram of Outcomes

H < R
    Y
T

2. *Event*
Spin this spinner
and then spin this spinner.

Tree Diagram of Outcomes

R < G
    Y
    B

326

Answers.

1.

```
    H < R
        Y
        B
              6
    T < R
        Y
        B
```

2.

```
        G
    R < O
        W
        P
        G
    Y < O     12
        W
        P
        G
    B < O
        W
        P
```

Assignments

BASIC
page 326 exercises 1−2
page 327 exercises 3−5,
        Keeping Skills Sharp
Basic Worksheet 87

AVERAGE
page 326 exercises 1−2
page 327 exercises 3−5,
        Keeping Skills Sharp
Enrichment Worksheet 87

ENRICHED
page 326 exercises 1−2
page 327 exercises 3−7,
        Keeping Skills Sharp
Enrichment Worksheet 87

REVIEW PRACTICE
page 391 set 72

How many outcomes?

3. *Event*
   Toss a dime
   and then toss a nickel. 4

4. *Event*
   Toss this die  36

   and then toss this die.

5. Think about building a 2-digit number by picking
   one of these cards and then another.

   | 4 | 8 | 3 | 5 | 2 |

   a. How many choices would you have for the first
      digit? 5
   b. How many choices would you have for the sec-
      ond digit? 4
   c. How many 2-digit numbers could you build? 20

6. Here is a combination lock. If the combination were
   35-42-8, you would open the lock by (1) turning the
   dial clockwise to 35, (2) turning the dial counterclockwise to 42, (3) turning the dial clockwise to 8.
   How many locks like this could be made without having any two combinations the same? 125,000

7. Suppose that you forgot a 3-number combination
   for a lock having 50 numbers. (See exercise 6.) If it
   took 10 seconds to try each combination, how long
   would it take to try them all? 1,250,000 seconds
   or about $14\frac{1}{2}$ days

Solve each proportion.

1. $\frac{n}{9} = \frac{3}{8}$ $3\frac{3}{8}$

2. $\frac{8}{n} = \frac{5}{2}$ $3\frac{1}{5}$

3. $\frac{n}{7} = \frac{1}{5}$ $1\frac{2}{5}$

4. $\frac{3}{n} = \frac{4}{9}$ $6\frac{3}{4}$

5. $\frac{n}{15} = \frac{6}{5}$ 18

6. $\frac{7}{8} = \frac{n}{16}$ 14

7. $\frac{9}{5} = \frac{n}{19}$ $34\frac{1}{5}$

8. $\frac{n}{7} = \frac{3}{5}$ $4\frac{1}{5}$

9. $\frac{12}{n} = \frac{2}{9}$ 54

10. $\frac{11}{n} = \frac{1}{6}$ 66

11. $\frac{n}{7} = \frac{0}{3}$ 0

12. $\frac{8}{3} = \frac{11}{n}$ $4\frac{1}{8}$

13. $\frac{6}{n} = \frac{2}{7}$ 21

14. $\frac{n}{8} = \frac{7}{10}$ $5\frac{3}{5}$

15. $\frac{7}{8} = \frac{n}{5}$ $4\frac{3}{8}$

16. $\frac{n}{4} = \frac{1}{6}$ $\frac{2}{3}$

17. $\frac{5}{6} = \frac{n}{3}$ $2\frac{1}{2}$

327

Follow-up Activities

Reinforcement Review the basic
counting principle as needed. The review
may be followed up with this activity.
Picture an automobile license plate. Tell
students that they are going to work on
an activity to determine how many
license plates their state could make
without having any two with the same
number. Since different states use
different numbering systems, we will
give an example of how to work through
the problem. Suppose a state numbers
its plates with two letters followed by
five digits.

> NK 56306

Assume that the letters and digits may
be repeated. *Solution:* There would be
26×26 different ways to select the
letters and $10 \times 10 \times 10 \times 10 \times 10$
different ways to select the digits. So
there are $26 \times 26 \times 10 \times 10 \times 10 \times
10 \times 10$, or 67,600,000 different license
plates.

Enrichment Ask students to compute
how many local telephone numbers the
telephone company could assign (using
their present numbering system) without
having any two numbers the same.

EXCURSION
Find the pattern. Then copy and
complete the table.

2	4	8	16
3	9	27	81
4	16	64	256
5	25	125	625

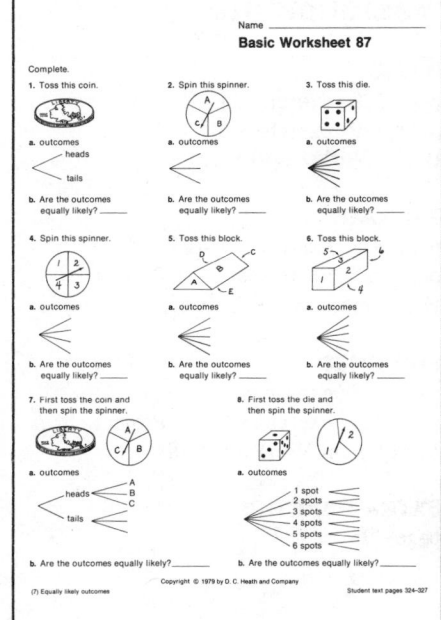

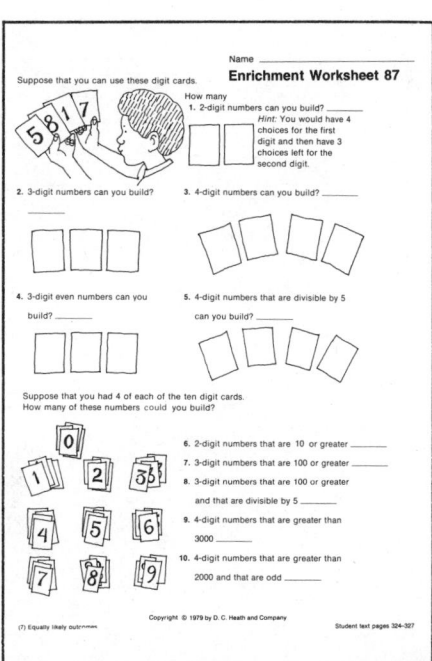

STUDENT OBJECTIVE
To determine the probability of
outcomes of simple events.

VOCABULARY
probability, $P(2)$ notation for the
probability of the outcome 2

Suggested Lesson Plan

Using the pages Go over the
exposition on page 328 to introduce the
concept of probability. Once students
can count outcomes and determine
whether they are equally likely,
assigning probabilities is quite simple.
The definition in the box on page 328 is
essential. Students should understand
that the probability of an event that is
certain to happen is 1 and the
probability of an event that is impossible
is 0. Also note the second example.
Even though the three outcomes are not
equally likely, it is easy to assign
probabilities.

Assign the exercises. You may wish
to check students' work after the first
few exercises to be sure that they are on
the right track.

In the projects, if the outcome is an
ordered pair of numbers as indicated in
the first part of Project 1, there are 36
equally likely outcomes. The probability
of each outcome is $\frac{1}{36}$. If, on the other
hand, the outcomes being considered are
the sums of the top faces, then there are
11 outcomes that are not equally likely.
These outcomes are 2, 3, 4, 5, . . ., 11,
and 12. The probabilities of these events
are simple to establish because the sums
are related to the ordered pairs. For
example, 6 of the ordered pairs have a
sum of 7. Since the probability of each
pair is $\frac{1}{36}$, the probability of the sum 7
is $\frac{6}{36}$. Here are the other probabilities
for the sums:

$$P(2) = \frac{1}{36}, \ P(3) = \frac{2}{36}, \ P(4) = \frac{3}{36},$$

$$P(5) = \frac{4}{36}, \ P(6) = \frac{5}{36}, \ P(7) = \frac{6}{36},$$

$$P(8) = \frac{5}{36}, \ P(9) = \frac{4}{36}, \ P(10) = \frac{3}{36},$$

$$P(11) = \frac{2}{36}, \ P(12) = \frac{1}{36}.$$

Probability

When a die is tossed, there are these 6
equally likely outcomes.

The **probability** of each outcome is $\frac{1}{6}$.

For example, when the die is tossed, the probability of its
landing "1 up" is $\frac{1}{6}$ We write

$P(1) = \frac{1}{6}$ (Read as "The probability of 1 equals $\frac{1}{6}$.")

What are $P(2)$, $P(3)$, and $P(6)$? What is $P(not\ 6)$? $\frac{5}{6}$

Each is $\frac{1}{6}$.

> If an event has n **equally likely** outcomes, then the
> probability of one of the outcomes is $\frac{1}{n}$.

Notice the words *equally likely* in the sentence above.
The outcomes of spinning this spinner are **not equally
likely**. Study these probabilities:

$P(\text{red}) = \frac{1}{2}$

$P(\text{green}) = \frac{1}{4}$

$P(\text{yellow}) = \frac{1}{4}$

The probability of an impossible outcome is 0.
For example, $P(\text{blue}) = 0$.

EXERCISES
Complete.

1. *Event*
Spin this spinner

a. $P(\text{red}) = ?$ 1/4
b. $P(\text{yellow}) = ?$ 1/4
c. $P(\text{green}) = ?$ 1/4
d. $P(\text{blue}) = ?$ 1/4
e. $P(\text{not blue}) = ?$ 3/4

2. *Event*
Spin this spinner

a. $P(\text{red}) = ?$ 1/2
b. $P(\text{yellow}) = ?$ 1/4
c. $P(\text{blue}) = ?$ 1/8
d. $P(\text{green}) = ?$ 1/8
e. $P(\text{purple}) = ?$ 0

328

Answer for page 329.

2.

(1,1),(1,2),(1,3),(1,4),(1,5),(1,6),
(2,1),(2,2),(2,3),(2,4),(2,5),(2,6),
(3,1),(3,2),(3,3),(3,4),(3,5),(3,6),
(4,1),(4,2),(4,3),(4,4),(4,5),(4,6),
(5,1),(5,2),(5,3),(5,4),(5,5),(5,6),
(6,1),(6,2),(6,3),(6,4),(6,5),(6,6)

Assignments

BASIC
page 328 exercises 1−2
page 329 exercises 3−5
Basic Worksheet 88

AVERAGE
page 328 exercises 1−2
page 329 exercises 3−6, Project
Enrichment Worksheet 88

ENRICHED
page 328 exercises 1−2
page 329 exercises 3−6, Project
Enrichment Worksheet 88

EXTRA PRACTICE
page 395 set 83

3. *Event*

Reach in a bag without looking and pick one of these marbles.

$P(green) = \frac{2}{7}$

a. $P(yellow) = ?$ $\frac{1}{7}$ **b.** $P(blue) = ?$ $\frac{3}{7}$

c. $P(red) = ?$ $\frac{1}{7}$ **d.** $P(not\ red) = ?$ $\frac{6}{7}$

4. *Event*

Reach in a bag and pick one of these marbles.

a. $P(red) = ?$ $\frac{1}{5}$ **b.** $P(blue) = ?$ $\frac{1}{10}$

c. $P(yellow) = ?$ $\frac{2}{5}$ **d.** $P(green) = ?$ $\frac{3}{10}$

e. $P(not\ green) = ?$ $\frac{7}{10}$ **f.** $P(purple) = ?$ 0

5. If you toss a die, what is the probability of getting

a. 6? $\frac{1}{6}$ **b.** an even number? $\frac{1}{2}$ **c.** a number less than 5? $\frac{2}{3}$

6. Suppose that these cards were thoroughly shuffled and that you picked a card without looking.

| 1 | 2 | 3 | 4 | 5 | 6 | 7 | 8 | 9 | 10 | 11 | 12 |

What is the probability of picking

a. 4? $\frac{1}{12}$ **b.** an odd number? $\frac{1}{2}$ **c.** a prime number? $\frac{5}{12}$

d. a multiple of 5? $\frac{1}{6}$ **e.** a composite number? $\frac{1}{2}$ **f.** a number less than 16? 1

Project

1. Toss two different-colored dice at least 50 times and record each outcome with a number pair. For example, the outcome shown can be recorded by using the ordered pair (1, 5).

2. List all possible outcomes of tossing two dice as shown in step 1.

3. How many times did you get a sum of 7? of 5? of 12? What other sums did you get and how many times?

4. Give the probability of tossing a sum of 7; of 5; of 12.
$\frac{1}{6}, \frac{1}{9}, \frac{1}{36}$

329

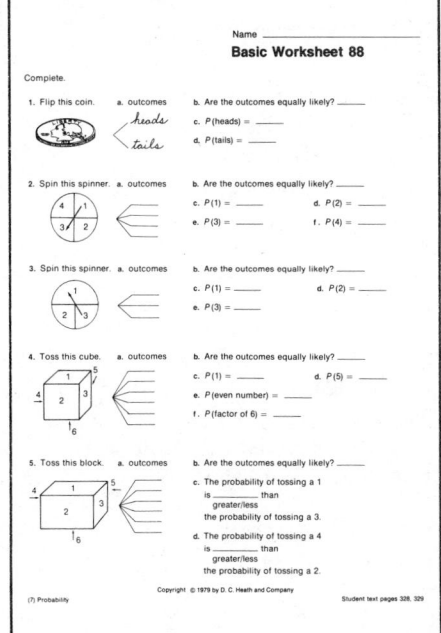

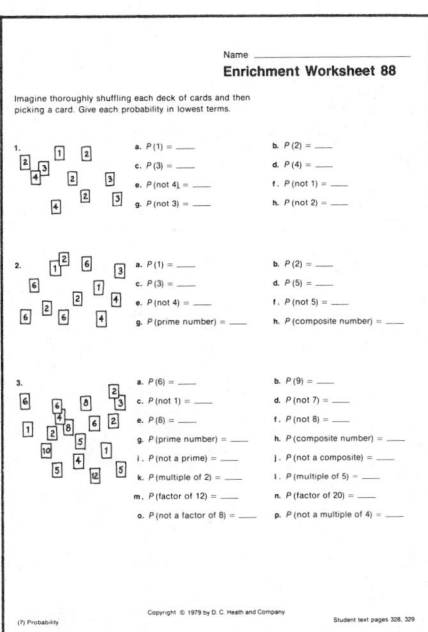

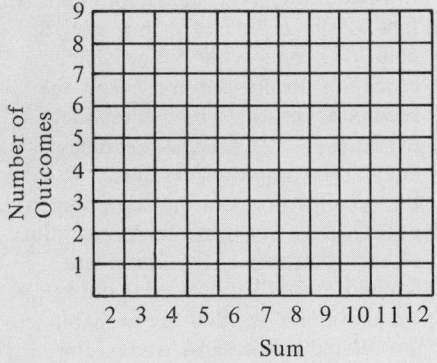
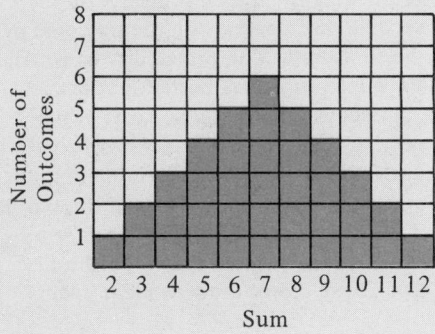
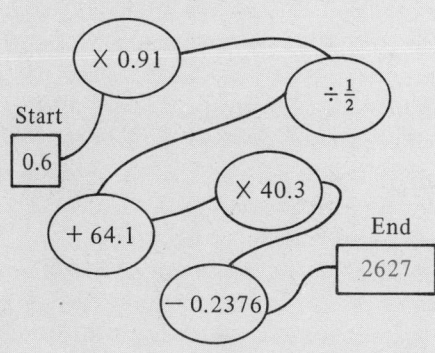

STUDENT OBJECTIVE
To compute the probabilities of
   compound independent outcomes.

Suggested Lesson Plan

Introduction Ask students to consider first tossing a die and then tossing a coin. Ask them what the possible outcomes are for the first event; the second event; the whole compound event. (6, 2, 12) Are the outcomes equally likely in the first event? (Yes) In the second? (Yes) In the compound event? (Yes) What are the probabilities of each outcome in the first event? Second event? Compound event? ($\frac{1}{6}$, $\frac{1}{2}$, $\frac{1}{12}$) Point out that the probabilities are related in the same way as the numbers of outcomes are related. That is, the probabilities of the outcomes of the compound event are the products of the probabilities of the outcomes of the first event and the second event.($\frac{1}{6} \times \frac{1}{2}$, $\frac{1}{12}$)This is always the case when the two events are independent—that is, when the outcome of the first event does not affect the outcome of the second event.

You may wish to give students an example of *dependent* events. Consider picking a card from a deck of cards and then, without replacing that card, picking another card. Obviously, the probability of drawing the queen of hearts on the second card depends on the outcome of the first draw. The probability of getting the queen of hearts on the first draw is $\frac{1}{52}$ because there are 52 cards in the deck, all with equal chances of being drawn. But the probability of getting the queen of hearts on the second draw is 0 if the queen was drawn on the first try and $\frac{1}{51}$ if it was not drawn on the first try. These are not independent events.

Using the pages Let students read the exposition at the top of page 330 and then do exercises 1–5 and the project.

Probability (independent events)

The tree diagram shows all the possible outcomes of first tossing a die and then tossing a coin.

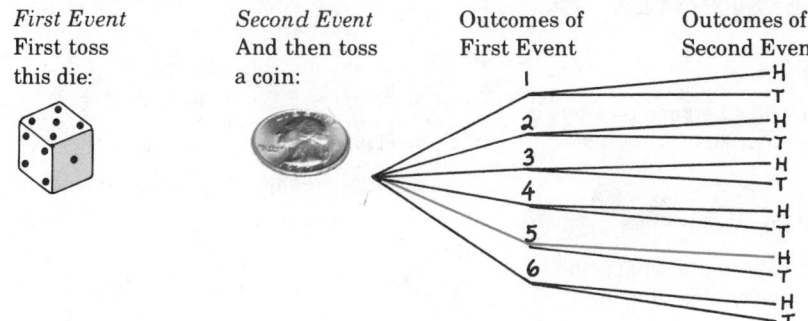

First Event
First toss this die:

Second Event
And then toss a coin:

Outcomes of First Event

Outcomes of Second Event

The red branch shows the outcome of first tossing a 5 with the die and then tossing a head with the coin. Notice that the probability of tossing a 5 is $\frac{1}{6}$, the probability of tossing heads is $\frac{1}{2}$, and the probability of first tossing a 5 **and then** tossing heads is $\frac{1}{6} \times \frac{1}{2}$, or $\frac{1}{12}$. P(5 and then H) $= \frac{1}{12}$. This is an example of the following probability principle:

> If the probability of an outcome of a first event is $\frac{a}{m}$, and if the probability of an outcome of a second event is $\frac{b}{n}$, then the probability of the first outcome followed by the second outcome is $\frac{a}{m} \cdot \frac{b}{n}$.

EXERCISES
Give each probability in lowest terms.

1. *First Event*
Spin this spinner:

Second Event
Toss a coin.

a. P(red and then heads) $= ?$ $\frac{1}{8}$

b. P(yellow and then tails) $= ?$ $\frac{1}{8}$

c. P(blue and then heads) $= ?$ $\frac{1}{4}$

330

Assignments

BASIC
page 330 exercise 1
page 331 exercises 2–4
Basic Worksheet 89

AVERAGE
page 330 exercise 1
page 331 exercises 2–4, Project
Enrichment Worksheet 89

ENRICHED
page 330 exercise 1
page 331 exercises 2–5, Project
Enrichment Worksheet 89

EXTRA PRACTICE
page 396 set 84

2. *First Event*   *Second Event*

Spin this spinner: Toss this die:

a. P(red and then 1) = ? $\frac{1}{24}$

b. P(green and then 4) = ? $\frac{1}{48}$

c. P(blue and then 6) = ? $\frac{1}{12}$

d. P(blue and then an even number) = ? $\frac{1}{4}$

3. *First Event*   *Second Event*

Toss this die: Toss the die again.

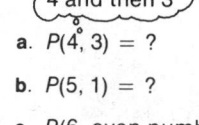
4 and then 3

a. $P(4, 3)$ = ? $\frac{1}{36}$

b. $P(5, 1)$ = ? $\frac{1}{36}$

c. P(6, even number) = ? $\frac{1}{12}$

d. P(odd number, even number) = ? $\frac{1}{4}$

4. *First Event*   *Second Event*   Possible outcomes

Toss a coin.   Toss the coin again.   (H, H), (T, H)
(H, T), (T, T)

a. What is the probability of getting both heads? $\frac{1}{4}$

b. What is the probability of getting one head and one tail? $\frac{1}{2}$

5. Imagine tossing a penny 10 times. What is the probability that you would toss heads all 10 times? $\frac{1}{1024}$

Project

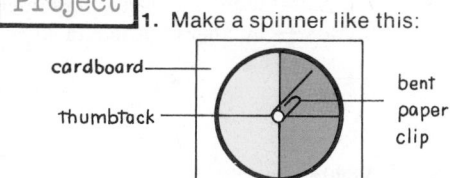

1. Make a spinner like this:

cardboard

thumbtack

bent paper clip

2. Spin the spinner twice and record the outcome by using notation like this:
yellow and then green
(Y, G)
Repeat 50 times.

3. Which outcome did you get the most? Which outcome did you get the least? Did this turn out as you expected?

4. Give the probability of each possible outcome.

331

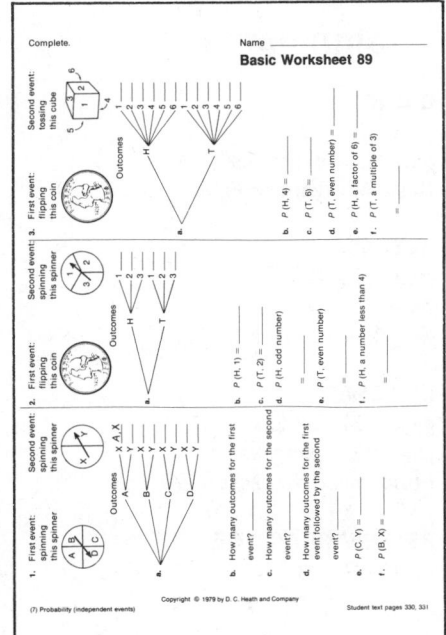

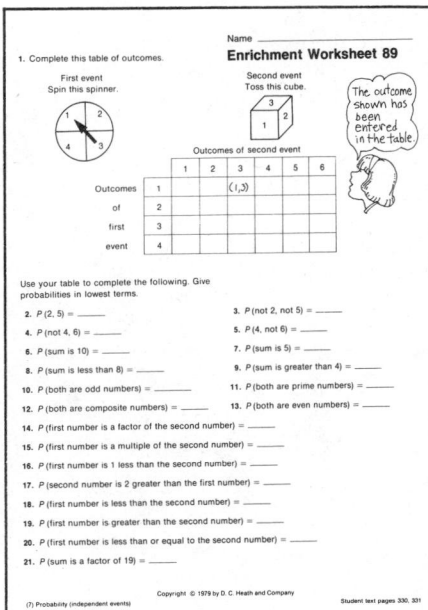

Follow-up Activities

Reinforcement You may wish to have students do the following activity to have further experiences with probability. Give them a cup and 10 pennies. Have a student shake the pennies in the cup and pour them on a table. Ask the rest of the students to record the outcome as 0 heads and 10 tails, 1 head and 9 tails, 2 heads and 8 tails, . . ., or 10 heads and 0 tails. Have them make a graph of their results. Ask them some questions about their graphs.

Enrichment Encourage more able students to compute the probability of being dealt four of a kind from an ordinary deck of playing cards. *Solution:* Any first card would be acceptable. Therefore, the probability of getting an acceptable first card is $^{52}/_{52}$. Once a first card has been dealt, the second card must match it. Therefore, the probability of getting an acceptable second card is $^{3}/_{51}$. (There are 3 cards left in the deck that match out of a total of 51 cards.) Similarly, the probability of getting an acceptable third card is $^{2}/_{50}$ and of getting an acceptable fourth card is $^{1}/_{49}$. So the solution is:

$$\frac{52}{52} \times \frac{3}{51} \times \frac{2}{50} \times \frac{1}{49} = \frac{6}{124,950} = \frac{1}{20,825}$$

EXCURSION

Each * represents a digit in the multiplication below.

$$
\begin{array}{r}
*2 \\
\times\,** \\
\hline
*** \\
** \\
\hline
2** \\
\end{array}
$$

Determine the digits.

The left-most *s must both be 1 to give a sum of 2. Then both the top * and the * beneath it must be 1. Then, to give a three-digit product, the * beneath the 2 must be 9.

$$
\begin{array}{r}
12 \\
\times 19 \\
\hline
108 \\
12 \\
\hline
228 \\
\end{array}
$$

Answer to Project.

4.

$P(Y,Y) = \frac{1}{4}$, $P(Y,B) = \frac{1}{8}$, $P(Y,G) = \frac{1}{8}$,

$P(B,Y) = \frac{1}{8}$, $P(B,B) = \frac{1}{16}$, $P(B,G) = \frac{1}{16}$,

$P(G,Y) = \frac{1}{8}$, $P(G,B) = \frac{1}{16}$, $P(G,G) = \frac{1}{16}$

Lesson 156   331

Suggested Lesson Plan

Introduction Find a report of TV program ratings or make up one. Tell students that, for example, one TV rating may say that a given TV program was watched by 15 million families. Do students think that the people who produce the ratings check every family in the country to make that rating? (No) Why not? (Not practical—perhaps not possible) Let the discussion go on to similar situations, such as political polls, surveys for advertising (3 out of 4 dentists, etc.). Use questions, if necessary, to draw from the students the fact that to get accurate data the sample must reflect the characteristics of the whole population. For example, to get TV ratings the company making the survey would not ask just people living in large cities or people living in New England. They would try to get a representative number of each kind of people. Ask students what the company would conclude if it found that 100 people out of a sample of 1000 people watched a certain TV program. (They would assume that 10% of *all* people were watching that program. By knowing how many people there are in the country, they can compute how many were watching that program.)

Using the pages Go over the exposition on page 332 carefully. Be sure that students understand that it is easy for a very small sample to be different from the population. For example, suppose that 80% of the people in a city can swim and suppose that someone were taking a sample to try to find out that fact. If the sample were only a group of two people, the most likely situation would be that they both could swim, but in that case the sampler would incorrectly conclude that 100% of the people could swim. If one could swim and the other could not, the sampler would conclude that 50% of the people could swim—also incorrect. Finally, it might be the case that both people in the sample could not swim. This is the least likely occurrence, but it could happen. Then the sampler would

332 Lesson 157

Sampling

Suppose that you want to find out how many people in your city can swim. Instead of asking each person, you could ask only some of the people (a **sample**) and then use what you found in your sample to predict how many people in your city can swim. When taking a sample, you should be sure that the sample is not too small and that the sample is not **biased**.

Notice that the second sample is biased. It is biased because most of the people who are in a swimming pool know how to swim.

Suppose that, using an unbiased sample, you found that 140 out of 200 people can swim. You could then use your sample to predict how many people in your city can swim. To do this, you could solve a proportion.

number of swimmers in sample $\longrightarrow \dfrac{140}{200} = \dfrac{n}{12{,}240} \longleftarrow$ number of swimmers in city
number of people in sample $\longrightarrow$ $\phantom{\dfrac{140}{200}}$ $\phantom{\dfrac{n}{12{,}240}}$ $\longleftarrow$ number of people in city

$$\frac{7}{10} = \frac{n}{12{,}240}$$

$$10n = 7 \times 12{,}240$$

$$10n = 85{,}680$$

$$n = 8568$$

From your sample of 200, you would predict that in this city 8568 people can swim.

332

conclude that no one could swim. Obviously, a larger sample would be much better.

Assign the exercises.

Assignments

EXERCISES

1. Suppose that you want to determine the average height of the seventh graders in your school. Tell why one of the following samples would probably be better than the other.

Range of heights would be greater in the cafeteria.

2. Suppose that you wanted to find out the average distance that students travel to get to school. Where would you be more likely to get a biased sample, at the school-bus stop, or inside the school? Explain your answer.

At the school-bus stop; students who come to school by bus have to travel farther than students who come by some other means.

Each bag contains some red marbles and some black marbles. The total number of marbles is shown on the bag. Use the sample to predict how many marbles of each color there are. (Assume that the marbles were mixed well before the sample was taken.)

3. 80 marbles R=24 B=36

4. 64 marbles R=40 B=24

5. 48 marbles R=40 B=56

6. 96 marbles R=40 B=56

7. 144 marbles R=72 B=72

8. 240 marbles R=160 B=80

9. In exercises 3–8, which sample do you consider the best? Why? Which sample do you consider the worst? Why?

Best: exercise 5; the ratio of the sample to the whole is greatest.

Worst: exercise 8; the ratio of the sample to the whole is least.

333

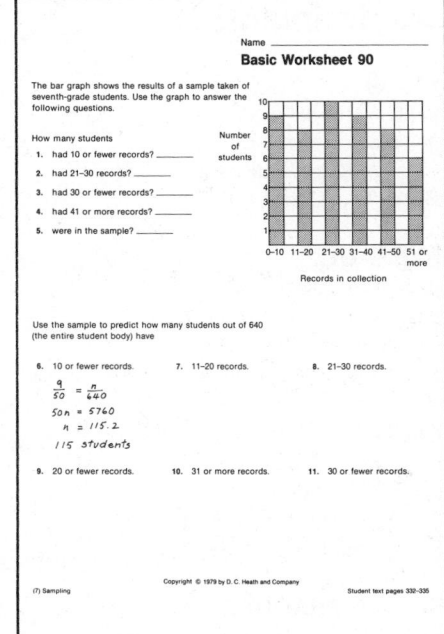

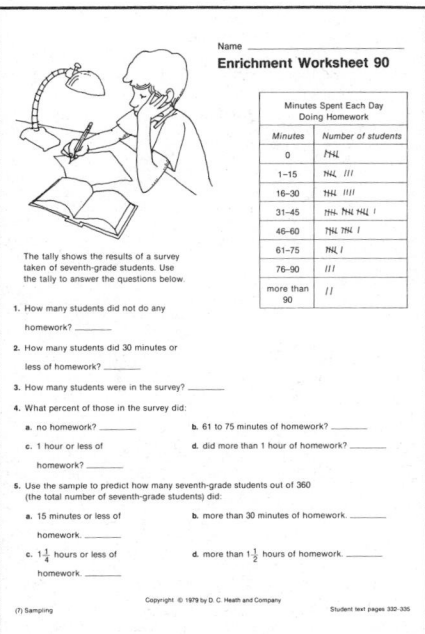

Follow-up Activities

Reinforcement You may wish to give students further sampling experiences. Suggest that students take a sample of schoolmates, asking for the number of members in their families. They could record their findings in a tally like this:

Number in Family	Tally
2	
3	
4	
5	
6	
7	

Have them take a combined sample of 100 and determine from their sample the probability of a family's having 2 members, 3 members, 4 members, etc.

Enrichment Some students may wish to follow up the work they did in the project by graphing their findings.

EXCURSION
Find the force per square centimeter on your feet. *Hint:* Divide your weight by the area of both feet.

To read data from line graphs, bar graphs, and pictographs.

VOCABULARY
data

Suggested Lesson Plan

Using the pages Students who have used the Heath Mathematics Program in earlier levels have had much experience with graphs and will have little trouble with these exercises. You may wish to go over the graphs on page 334 with your class, asking questions about the data shown to be sure that students understand.

Assign the exercises. Provide magazines and newspapers in which students can find various graphs.

Near the end of the class period, have students do the Keeping Skills Sharp.

Reporting data

> Baby-sitting service
> Call 352-6782

The seventh-grade students started a baby-sitting service to raise money for a summer camp. Jan kept this record of the money received during the first week.

Willowsprings School	
Day	Money Received
Monday	$ 6.50
Tuesday	$ 8.00
Wednesday	$ 7.75
Thursday	$ 5.50
Friday	$10.25
Saturday	$12.00
Sunday	$ 9.50

To report the money received (the data), she made these graphs:

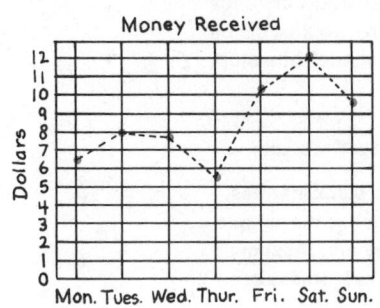

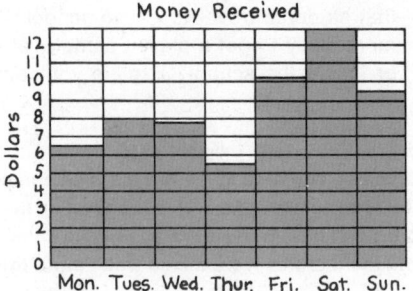

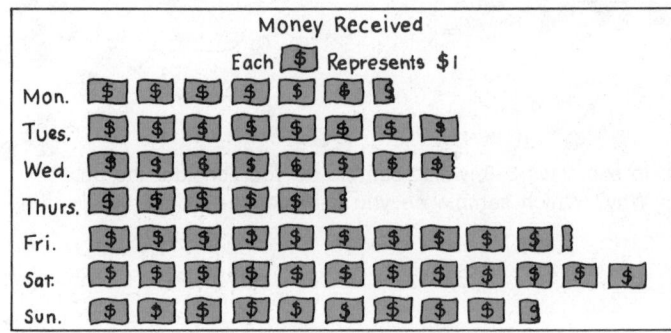

What are some things that each graph tells you?

334

Assignments

BASIC
page 334 Discuss
page 335 exercises 1–2,
  Keeping Skills Sharp
Basic Worksheet 90

AVERAGE
page 334 Discuss
page 335 exercises 1–2,
  Keeping Skills Sharp
Enrichment Worksheet 90

BASIC
page 334 Discuss
page 335 exercises 1–2,
  Keeping Skills Sharp
Enrichment Worksheet 90

REVIEW PRACTICE
page 392 set 74

EXERCISES

Look at the graph to answer the questions.

1.

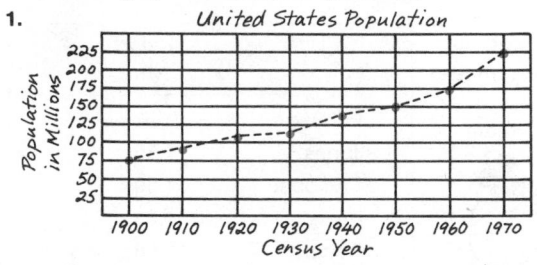

United States Population

a. Did the population increase each 10 years? yes

b. During which year was the population about 75 million? 1900

c. About what was the population in 1950?
150 million

d. During which 10-year period did the population increase about 25 million? 1930-1940, 1950-1960,

2. Television Sets In United States Households

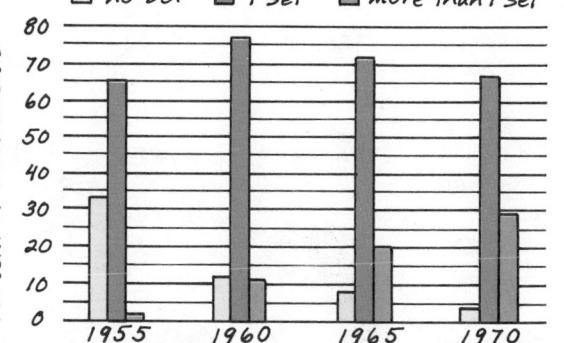
☐ no set ☐ 1 set ☐ more than 1 set

a. What percent had no set in 1955? In 1965? 33%, 8%

b. What percent had 1 set in 1960? In 1970? 77%, 67%

c. In which year did 20% of the households have more than 1 set? 1965

d. What percent of the households had at least 1 television set in 1970? 96%

Follow-up Activities

Reinforcement You may wish to follow up the lesson with this activity. Provide students with the population data for their city, county, or state in the years 1900, 1910, 1920, . . ., and 1980. Have students make a broken line graph of the data. Their graphs could look like this:

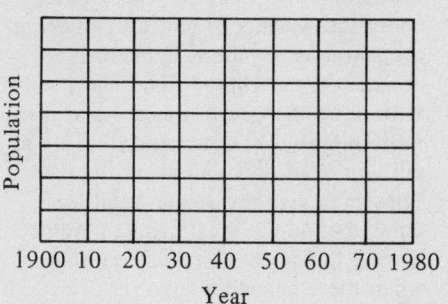

Have students list some facts shown by their graphs.

Enrichment Have students select a common stock from the New York Stock Exchange. Have them keep a graph of its performance over a period of several days. Encourage them to share their findings with their classmates.

EXCURSION

Get some graph paper and draw all the rectangles whose sides are a whole number length and whose perimeter is 24.
Example.

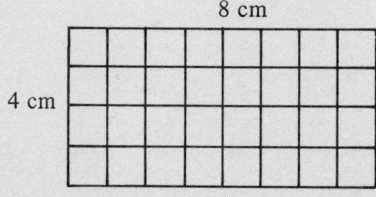

8 cm
4 cm

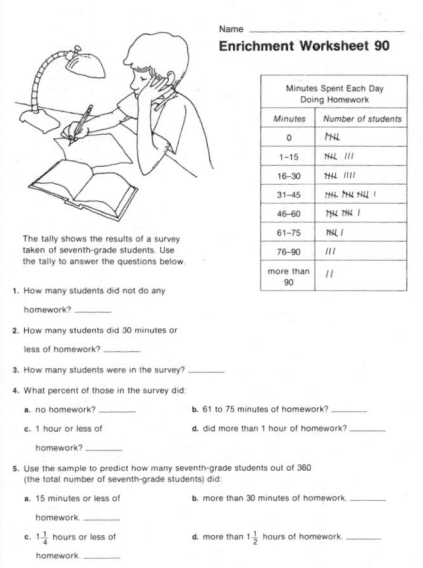

Name _____
Basic Worksheet 90

The bar graph shows the results of a sample taken of seventh-grade students. Use the graph to answer the following questions.

How many students

1. had 10 or fewer records? _____

2. had 21–30 records? _____

3. had 30 or fewer records? _____

4. had 41 or more records? _____

5. were in the sample? _____

Records in collection

Use the sample to predict how many students out of 640 (the entire student body) have

6. 10 or fewer records.   7. 11–20 records.   8. 21–30 records.

$\frac{9}{50} = \frac{n}{640}$
$50n = 5760$
$n = 115.2$
115 students

9. 20 or fewer records.   10. 31 or more records.   11. 30 or fewer records.

(7) Sampling   Copyright © 1979 by D. C. Heath and Company   Student text pages 332–335

Name _____
Enrichment Worksheet 90

Minutes Spent Each Day Doing Homework	
Minutes	Number of students
0	卌
1–15	卌 III
16–30	卌 IIII
31–45	卌 卌 卌 I
46–60	卌 卌 I
61–75	卌 I
76–90	III
more than 90	II

The tally shows the results of a survey taken of seventh-grade students. Use the tally to answer the questions below.

1. How many students did not do any homework? _____

2. How many students did 30 minutes or less of homework? _____

3. How many students were in the survey? _____

4. What percent of those in the survey did:

a. no homework? _____   b. 61 to 75 minutes of homework? _____

c. 1 hour or less of homework? _____   d. did more than 1 hour of homework? _____

5. Use the sample to predict how many seventh-grade students out of 360 (the total number of seventh-grade students) did:

a. 15 minutes or less of homework. _____   b. more than 30 minutes of homework. _____

c. $1\frac{1}{4}$ hours or less of homework. _____   d. more than $1\frac{1}{2}$ hours of homework. _____

(7) Sampling   Copyright © 1979 by D. C. Heath and Company   Student text pages 332–335

STUDENT OBJECTIVE
To compute the range, mean, and
median of a set of data.

VOCABULARY
range, mean, median

Suggested Lesson Plan

Introduction Make up a set of data
about the weights of football players or
the amounts of money individuals
donated to the United Fund, etc., and
write it on the board. Be sure that it is a
fairly large set of data. Ask students to
tell you what they can about the data.
They may give the greatest and least
numbers and the most common number.
During the discussion point out that
when there is such a large set of data, it
is difficult to comprehend. In order to
better understand the data, we usually
find several numbers, the high and low,
the most common, the middle, etc. Then
we define the range and the two kinds of
averages. Have students find these
numbers for your set of data.

Using the pages Go over the
exposition on page 336 as a review of
your discussion. Assign the exercises. If
you wish to have your students pursue
the concept of averages and why we use
different kinds, refer them to *How to Lie
with Statistics*, by Darrell Huff.

Range, mean, and median

Once data have been collected, we can
determine some numbers that tell us
something about the data. For example,
here are the heights of the members of a
certain seventh-grade basketball team:

Player	Height (m)
Peterson	**1.48**
Jones	1.55
Campbell	1.59
Davis	1.63
Roberts	1.63
Garcia	1.69
Allison	1.71
Krantz median **1.72**	range 0.34
Moore	1.74
Steinburg	1.75
Mendez	1.78
Richards	1.78
Washington	1.78
Hargrove	1.80
Cowan	**1.82**

The **range** is the difference between the
least and greatest numbers. The range,
from **1.48** to **1.82**, is **0.34**.

The **mean**, or **average**, is found by adding all the numbers and then dividing
the sum by the number of numbers.

The mean, rounded to the nearest hundredth, is **1.70 m**.

The **median** is the middle number if you
are working with an odd number of
numbers. If you are working with an
even number of numbers, the median is
the average of the two middle numbers.

The median height is **1.72 m**.

Number of players

sum of heights

$$15\overline{)25.45}$$
15
104
90
145
135
10

1.69

336

Assignments

BASIC
page 336 Discuss
page 337 exercises 1–4, Project
Basic Worksheet 91

AVERAGE
page 336 Discuss
page 337 exercises 1–5, Project
Enrichment Worksheet 91

ENRICHED
page 336 Discuss
page 337 exercises 1–5, Project
Enrichment Worksheet 91

EXTRA PRACTICE
page 396 set 85

EXERCISES

1. In seven games, Krantz scored 21, 23, 19, 21, 26, 18, and 22 points. Find the range, the mean, and the median.
8, 21 3/7, 21

2. During the first 5 games, the opposing teams scored 54, 48, 49, 56, and 50 points. Find the range, the mean, and the median. 8, 51 2/5, 50

3. One semester Jane got the following scores on her mathematics tests: 82, 75, 93, 87, 69, 81, 83, and 84. Find the range, the mean, and the median.
24, 81 3/4, 82 1/2

4. During the first 8 weeks of school, Alan averaged $3.40 per week for lunches. How much did he spend for lunches during the 8 weeks? $27.20

5. Hank Aaron holds the major-league home-run record. The table shows how many home runs he hit during each year that he was in the major leagues. Find the range, the mean and the median. 37, 32 19/23, 34

Home Runs During Regular Season			
Year	Number	Year	Number
1954	13	1965	32
1955	27	1966	44
1956	26	1967	39
1957	44	1968	29
1958	30	1969	44
1959	39	1970	38
1960	40	1971	47
1961	34	1972	34
1962	45	1973	40
1963	44	1974	20
1964	24	1975	12
		1976	10

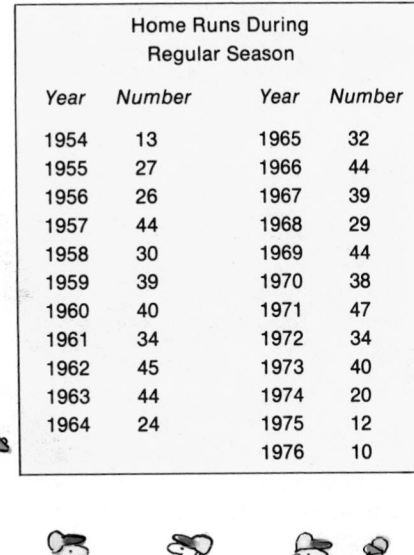

Project

1. Take your pulse to find out how many times your heart beats in one minute.

2. Determine the range, the mean, and the median of the heart rates of your class.

337

Follow-up Activities

Reinforcement You may wish to follow up the projects by having students do some graphing. Several students could compile their surveys and construct a bar graph as shown below:

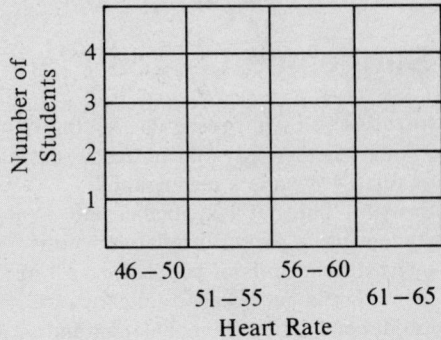

Enrichment Have students find out the yearly precipitation for their city for the past 15 years. Ask them to determine the mean, the median, and the range. If time permits, have them graph the data on a line graph.

CALCULATOR ACTIVITY

Give students 2 or 3 sets of data having 10 to 20 numbers. Have students use the calculator to compute the mean and median.

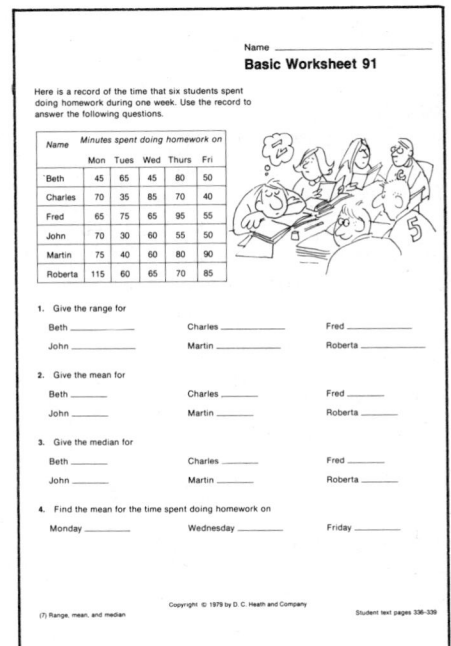

STUDENT OBJECTIVES
To solve problems involving
   mathematics and careers.
To solve problems involving
   mathematics and geography.

VOCABULARY
demographer

Suggested Lesson Plan

Introduction Introduce this lesson by
asking whether any student has a parent
or relative who is a demographer.
Probably not, but ask whether any
student has a parent or relative who is
interested in shifts of population. All of
them should be, because almost every
job depends upon the population and
shifts in the population. Discuss how
population shifts affect jobs, schools,
and towns. Discuss the population shifts
for your town or city and state. Is it
growing in population or decreasing?
How does this affect people in the state?

Using the pages With this brief
discussion, assign exercises 1–4 on
page 338 and exercises 1–4 on page
339. Be prepared to help your poor
readers. You may want to group them
together and read through the problems
together.

Mathematics
in careers

Demographers study human population.
They collect data to study such things as
birth rates and death rates. They also
study the population density (population
per square kilometer) of a region and
how population shifts from one region to
another.

1. In 1977 the population of the United
States was 216,814,000. If 30% of the
population was considered rural
population, how many people lived
in a rural area? 65,044,200

2. In a recent year, the birth rate in California was 14.8 per 1000 population.
If the population was 21,250,000,
how many births were there?
314,500

3. In 1900 the population of the United
States was 75,994,575. The land area
was 7,693,870 square kilometers.
What was the population density?
Give your answer to the nearest
tenth. 9.9

4. In 1970 the population was
203,235,298 and the area was
9,173,345 square kilometers. What
was the density then?
22.2

338

Assignments

BASIC
page 338 exercises 1–4
page 339 exercises 1–4
Basic Worksheet 91

AVERAGE
page 338 exercises 1–4
page 339 exercises 1–4
Enrichment Worksheet 91

ENRICHED
page 338 exercises 1–4
page 339 exercises 1–4
Enrichment Worksheet 91

REVIEW PRACTICE
page 392 set 75

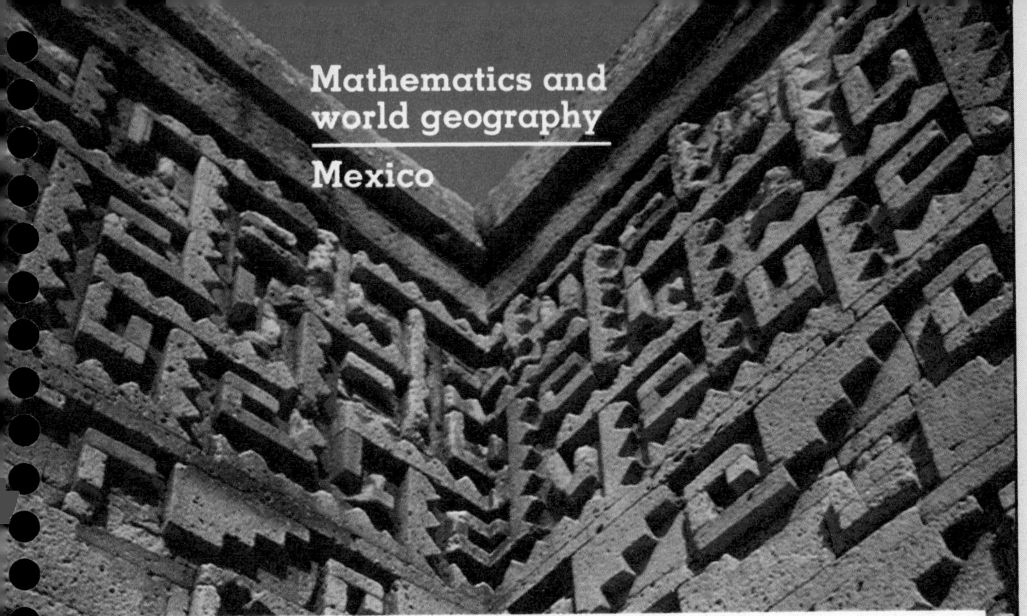

Mathematics and world geography
Mexico

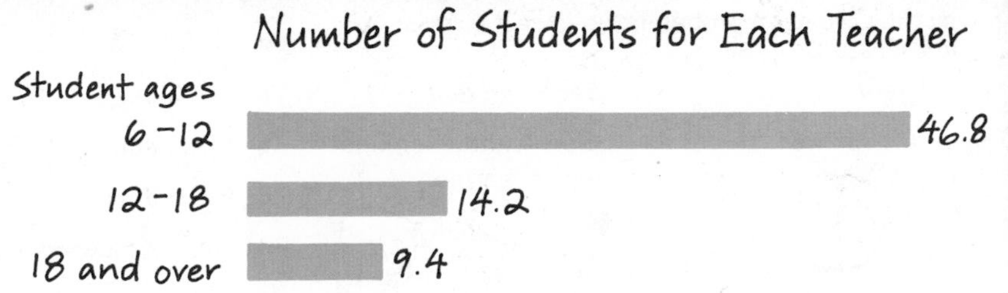

Number of Students for Each Teacher

Student ages

6–12	46.8
12–18	14.2
18 and over	9.4

1. There are about 8,948,000 students in the 6–12 age group. About how many teachers are there for this age group? 191,197

2. There are about 102,000 teachers of secondary students (12–18 age group). About how many secondary students are there? 1,448,400

3. Recently the total population of Mexico was about 51 million, with about 47% of the people under 15 years of age. How many of these young people are there in Mexico? 23,970,000

4. Only about 1.2% of the Mexican people are over 75 years of age. About how many people over 75 are there in Mexico? 612,000

339

Reinforcement Have pupils refer to an encyclopedia or the latest World Almanac for population data. Have them write 3 word problems about the data they find. Select the better problems and put them on a duplicating master. Run off copies and have pupils solve them for extra practice.

Enrichment More able students may wish to consider the following theoretical probability problem. If a segment is drawn from a given point on a circle to any other point on the circle selected at random, what is the probability that the chord will be shorter

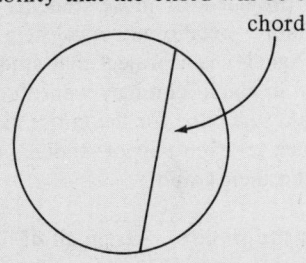
chord

than a side of an inscribed equilateral triangle? (A chord of a circle is a segment having its end points on the circle.) *Solution:* The diagram below shows that any chord having the endpoint A and having its other endpoint at any other point on the red arc, which is $2/3$ of the circle, will be shorter than a side of the equilateral triangle. Therefore the answer is $2/3$.

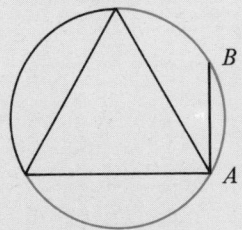

EXCURSION
See if you can construct this design with a compass.

(*Hint:* Only one compass setting was used.)

Create a design of your own.

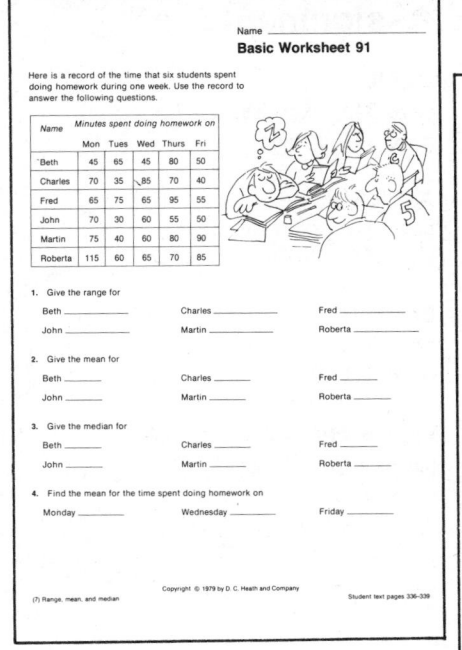

Name _____
Basic Worksheet 91

Here is a record of the time that six students spent doing homework during one week. Use the record to answer the following questions.

Name	Minutes spent doing homework on				
	Mon	Tues	Wed	Thurs	Fri
Beth	45	65	45	80	50
Charles	70	35	85	70	40
Fred	65	75	65	95	55
John	70	30	60	55	50
Martin	75	40	60	80	90
Roberta	115	60	65	70	85

1. Give the range for
   Beth _____ Charles _____ Fred _____
   John _____ Martin _____ Roberta _____

2. Give the mean for
   Beth _____ Charles _____ Fred _____
   John _____ Martin _____ Roberta _____

3. Give the median for
   Beth _____ Charles _____ Fred _____
   John _____ Martin _____ Roberta _____

4. Find the mean for the time spent doing homework on
   Monday _____ Wednesday _____ Friday _____

(7) Range, mean, and median   Copyright © 1979 by D. C. Heath and Company   Student text pages 336–339

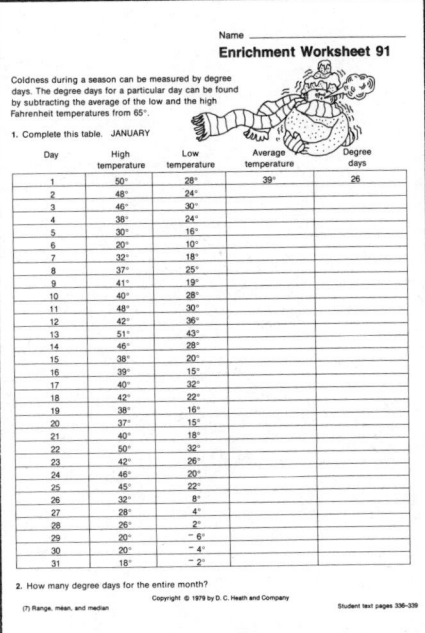

Name _____
Enrichment Worksheet 91

Coldness during a season can be measured by degree days. The degree days for a particular day can be found by subtracting the average of the low and the high Fahrenheit temperatures from 65°.

1. Complete this table. JANUARY

Day	High temperature	Low temperature	Average temperature	Degree days
1	50°	28°	39°	26
2	48°	24°		
3	46°	30°		
4	38°	24°		
5	30°	16°		
6	20°	10°		
7	32°	18°		
8	37°	25°		
9	41°	19°		
10	40°	28°		
11	48°	30°		
12	42°	36°		
13	51°	43°		
14	46°	28°		
15	38°	20°		
16	39°	15°		
17	40°	32°		
18	42°	22°		
19	38°	16°		
20	37°	15°		
21	40°	18°		
22	50°	32°		
23	42°	26°		
24	46°	20°		
25	45°	22°		
26	32°	8°		
27	28°	4°		
28	26°	2°		
29	20°	− 6°		
30	20°	− 4°		
31	18°	− 2°		

2. How many degree days for the entire month?

(7) Range, mean, and median   Copyright © 1979 by D. C. Heath and Company   Student text pages 336–339

STUDENT OBJECTIVE
To review the concepts and skills introduced in Chapter 11.

Suggested Lesson Plan

Introduction No pre-text activity is necessary for page 340 as this is a checkup for the chapter. However, it may be valuable to briefly review the lessons in the chapter so that students are reminded of the content over which they will be tested.

This Checkup will provide you with data about how individual students have mastered the concepts and skills of the chapter. The Chapter Review on page 342 is provided for those students who need more specific individual help.

Page 341 is a project that students can do in pairs. You may want to collect the data just once for the entire class and then let each pair of students use it to make their graph.

Using the pages Assign all of the exercises on page 340. As students complete the page, they can work on the project on page 341.

First tell how many outcomes. Then tell whether or not the outcomes are equally likely. [pages 324–325]

1. Toss a coin.   2. Toss a paper cup.   3. Spin this spinner:
   2, yes   3, no   4, no

Draw a tree diagram that shows the possible outcomes for these events. [pages 326–327]

4. Spin this spinner and then toss this die.

5. Think about placing these marbles in a bag, mixing them well, and then (without looking) picking one. Give each probability in lowest terms. [pages 328–329]

   a. $P(\text{green}) = ?$ $\frac{2}{5}$ b. $P(\text{blue}) = ?$ $\frac{1}{10}$ c. $P(\text{yellow}) = ?$ $\frac{3}{10}$

   d. $P(\text{red}) = ?$ $\frac{1}{5}$ e. $P(\text{not red}) = ?$ $\frac{4}{5}$ f. $P(\text{black}) = ?$ 0

6. Suppose that the first event is followed by the second event. Give each probability in lowest terms. [pages 330–331]

   First Event   *Second Event*

   Spin this spinner   then (without looking) pick a marble.

   a. $P(1, \text{blue}) = ?$ $\frac{1}{8}$

   b. $P(3, \text{green}) = ?$ $\frac{3}{40}$

   c. $P(2, \text{red}) = ?$ $\frac{1}{20}$

   d. $P(4, \text{not blue}) = ?$ $\frac{1}{8}$

7. Here are the scores of a mathematics test. Give the range, the mean, and the median. [pages 336–337]

Test Scores							
100	94	88	85	83	76	72	68
100	92	86	85	80	75	70	66
96	91	86	85	78	73	70	62

$38, 81\frac{17}{24}, 84$

340

Answer.

4.

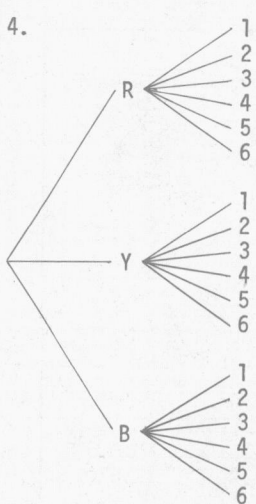

Assignments

Project

Take a sample.

1. Ask some of your classmates how far from school they live. Make sure that your sample is reasonably large. Try to include classmates from all parts of your school district.

2. Find the range, the mean, and the median of your sample.

3. Complete a bar graph like the one shown.

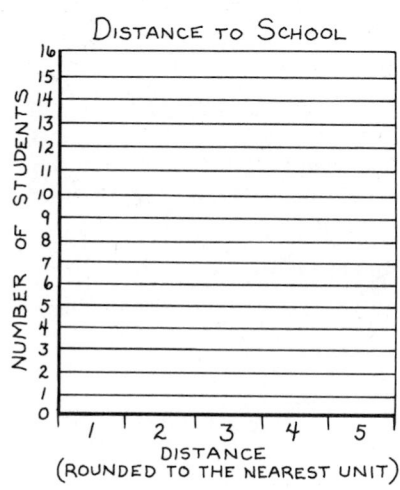

DISTANCE TO SCHOOL

NUMBER OF STUDENTS

DISTANCE
(ROUNDED TO THE NEAREST UNIT)

341

You may wish to assign some of the Creative Problem Solving Activities (pages 461–477) at this time.

Follow-up Activities

Reinforcement Correct all items in the Chapter Checkup. Any student that misses 3 or more exercises needs additional help.

Enrichment Assign these pupils to the activities that have been suggested throughout the chapter. Have a student leader who is responsible for each activity to explain and help with the activity.

STUDENT OBJECTIVE
To review or extend the skills and
concepts taught in Chapter 11.

Suggested Lesson Plan

Introduction After checking the
Chapter Checkup you will know which
students need additional reinforcement
and which students will be able to go
ahead with the Challenge activity. Get
the better students started on page 343
first as the students who are having
difficulty will need more of your time.

The students who need more review
should go back and correct their errors
on the Chapter Checkup. You may want
to go over those questions orally if this
group is small enough. Carefully probe
to determine which concepts and skills
the students have not mastered and
work individually to correct their
deficiencies.

Using the pages After the identified
students have corrected the Chapter
Checkup, they should answer questions
1−9. After they complete these
questions, read the answers and let the
students correct their own papers. Give
them an opportunity to ask questions
about the exercises they missed.
Assign page 343 to those students who
did well on the Chapter Checkup. Have
students work individually.

CHAPTER REVIEW

If a first event has *m* outcomes, and
if a second event has *n* outcomes,
then the first event followed by the
second event has $m \times n$ outcomes.

If the probability of a first outcome
is $\frac{a}{m}$ and if the probability of a second outcome is $\frac{b}{n}$, then the probability of the first outcome followed
by the second outcome is $\frac{a}{m} \cdot \frac{b}{n}$.

The range is the difference between the least and greatest numbers.

The mean is the average.

The median is the middle number.

First Event
Toss this die:

Second Event
Toss a coin:

Tell how many outcomes there are for the

1. first event.   6

2. second event.   2

3. first event and then the second event. 12

Give the probability of

4. tossing a 6. $\frac{1}{6}$

5. tossing heads. $\frac{1}{2}$

6. tossing a 6 and then tossing heads. $\frac{1}{12}$

**One week Sarah kept this record of the
number of calories in her diet.
Give the**

7. range.

8. mean.

9. median.

Daily Calories	
Sun.	1275
Mon.	1550
Tues.	1300
Wed.	1150
Thurs.	1260
Fri.	1320
Sat.	1560

410, 1345, 1300

342

Assignments

BASIC
page 342   exercises 1−9

AVERAGE
page 342   exercises 1−9

ENRICHED
page 343   exercises 1−10

CHAPTER CHALLENGE

When we wish to talk about the chances of picking a green button from the box, we can use probability. The probability of picking green is the ratio of the number of green buttons to the total number of buttons.

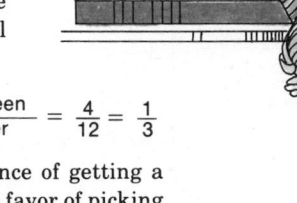

$$\text{probability of green} = \frac{\text{number of green}}{\text{total number}} = \frac{4}{12} = \frac{1}{3}$$

Another way of talking about the chance of getting a green button is to use **odds**. The odds in favor of picking green is the ratio of green buttons to not-green buttons.

$$\text{odds in favor of green} = \frac{\text{number of green}}{\text{number of not green}} = \frac{4}{8} = \frac{1}{2}$$

The odds against getting green is the reciprocal of the odds in favor of getting green.

$$\text{odds against green} = \frac{\text{number of not green}}{\text{number of green}} = \frac{8}{4} = \frac{2}{1}$$

Give the odds in favor of picking a

1. red button. $\frac{5}{7}$

2. blue button. $\frac{1}{11}$

3. yellow button. $\frac{1}{5}$

Give the odds against picking a

4. yellow button. $\frac{5}{1}$

5. blue button. $\frac{11}{1}$

6. red button. $\frac{7}{5}$

Give the odds

7. in favor of spinning yellow. $\frac{1}{1}$

8. in favor of spinning blue. $\frac{1}{7}$

9. against spinning red. $\frac{3}{1}$

10. against spinning green. $\frac{7}{1}$

343

Follow-up Activities

Reinforcement The reinforcement at this point should be individual help focused on the concepts of the chapter. This chapter is not considered a critical skill so it is not recommended that you spend a lot of time with remedial activities. It is more important that students have had a chance to explore some of the concepts and have encountered the ideas at this early stage of their mathematical development.

Enrichment Pair these students with students who are having difficulty. Encourage them to review the terms and perhaps do some of the activities together.

STUDENT OBJECTIVES
To practice skills learned previously.
To practice using a standardized-test
    format.

Suggested Lesson Plan

Using the pages   The Major Checkup at the end of each chapter of this textbook is given in standardized-test format. The answer sheet on page 448 is the type used with many standardized tests. You may duplicate it for use with the Major Checkups.

Pass out the answer sheets and be sure students understand how to use them. Allow a specified time, perhaps twenty minutes, to complete the checkup. Assign the exercises and use the results to determine what review is needed.

The table below correlates the test items and the student text pages. Assign review exercises as indicated by the Major Checkup results.

Test Item	Text Pages	Test Item	Text Pages
1	154−155	7	228−229
2	138−139	8	260−261
3	112−113	9	262−263
4	188−189	10	286−287
5	190−191	11	302−303
6	226−227	12	310−311

Chapter 11 Posttest

See page 54 for a full discussion of how to use the posttest. The table below suggests Extra Practice exercises and Basic Worksheets for those students who need further practice or reteaching.

Objectives	Extra Practice Sets	Pages	Basic Worksheets
11-1			87
11-2	83−84	395−396	88−89
11-3			90
11-4	85	396	91

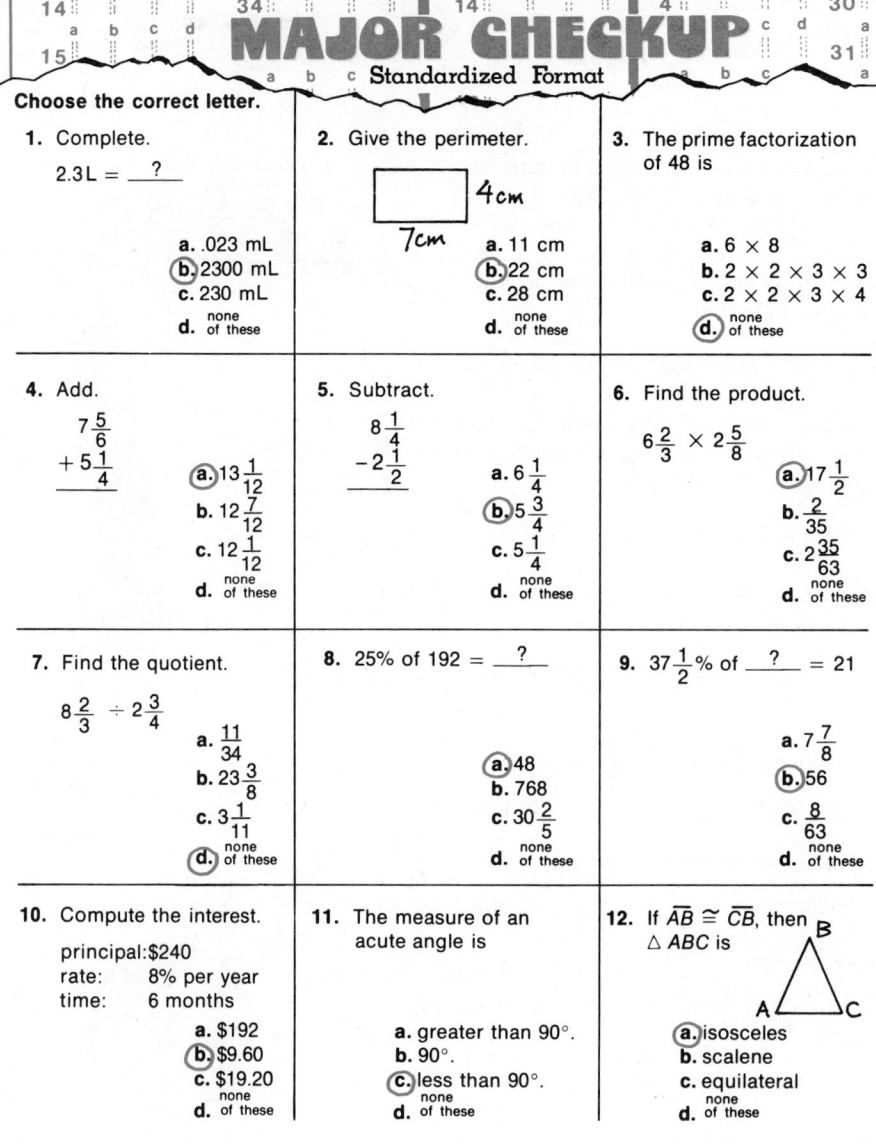

Choose the correct letter.

1. Complete.

   $2.3L = \underline{\quad?\quad}$

   a. .023 mL
   b. 2300 mL
   c. 230 mL
   d. none of these

2. Give the perimeter.

   4cm / 7cm

   a. 11 cm
   b. 22 cm
   c. 28 cm
   d. none of these

3. The prime factorization of 48 is

   a. 6×8
   b. $2 \times 2 \times 3 \times 3$
   c. $2 \times 2 \times 3 \times 4$
   d. none of these

4. Add.

   $7\frac{5}{6}$
   $+5\frac{1}{4}$

   a. $13\frac{1}{12}$
   b. $12\frac{7}{12}$
   c. $12\frac{1}{12}$
   d. none of these

5. Subtract.

   $8\frac{1}{4}$
   $-2\frac{1}{2}$

   a. $6\frac{1}{4}$
   b. $5\frac{3}{4}$
   c. $5\frac{1}{4}$
   d. none of these

6. Find the product.

   $6\frac{2}{3} \times 2\frac{5}{8}$

   a. $17\frac{1}{2}$
   b. $\frac{2}{35}$
   c. $2\frac{35}{63}$
   d. none of these

7. Find the quotient.

   $8\frac{2}{3} \div 2\frac{3}{4}$

   a. $\frac{11}{34}$
   b. $23\frac{3}{8}$
   c. $3\frac{1}{11}$
   d. none of these

8. 25% of 192 = $\underline{\quad?\quad}$

   a. 48
   b. 768
   c. $30\frac{2}{5}$
   d. none of these

9. $37\frac{1}{2}$% of $\underline{\quad?\quad}$ = 21

   a. $7\frac{7}{8}$
   b. 56
   c. $\frac{8}{63}$
   d. none of these

10. Compute the interest.

    principal: $240
    rate: 8% per year
    time: 6 months

    a. $192
    b. $9.60
    c. $19.20
    d. none of these

11. The measure of an acute angle is

    a. greater than 90°.
    b. 90°.
    c. less than 90°.
    d. none of these

12. If $\overline{AB} \cong \overline{CB}$, then △ ABC is

    a. isosceles
    b. scalene
    c. equilateral
    d. none of these

344

Answers for Chapter 11 Posttest

1. 3   2. 4   3. 36   4. $\frac{1}{4}$ 5. $\frac{1}{2}$ 6. $\frac{3}{8}$ 7. $\frac{1}{4}$

8. $\frac{3}{4}$ 9. 15°   10. 5 o'clock   11. 3°   12. 9:00

13. $19\frac{3}{7}$, 18, 9   14. $40\frac{4}{7}$, 38, 13

Chapter 11 Posttest

Name _____

Date _____

How many outcomes? [Obj. 11-1, pages 324–327]

1. Spin this spinner.

_____

2. Toss a dime and a penny.

_____

3. Roll 2 dice.

_____

| 0 | 1 | 2 | 3 | 4 | 5 |

What is the probability? [Obj. 11-2, pages 328–329]

4. $P(3) =$ _____

5. $P(1) =$ _____

6. $P(R) =$ _____

7. $P(Y) =$ _____

8. $P(R \text{ or } B) =$ _____

| 0 | 1 | 2 | 3 | 4 |

Answer each question. [Obj. 11-3, pages 334–335]

9. What was the temperature at 12:00? _____

10. When was the temperature highest? _____

11. How many degrees did the temperature rise between 2:00 and 3:00? _____

12. When was the temperature lowest? _____

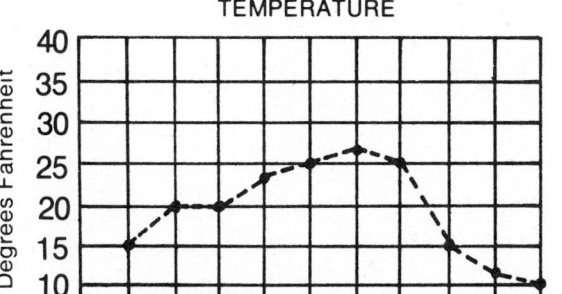

| 0 | 1 | 2 | 3 | 4 | 5 | 6 |

Find the mean, median, and range. [Obj. 11-4, pages 336–337]

13. 17, 18, 18, 18, 19, 20, 26

14. 36, 37, 49, 44, 37, 38, 43

_____   _____   _____
mean   median   range

_____   _____   _____
mean   median   range

344a

Chapter 12
Computing with Integers

Pages 345–366

Learning Objectives

After completing this chapter, all students should be able to do the following:

12-1   Add integers.

12-2   Subtract integers.

12-3   Multiply integers.

12-4   Divide integers.

12-5   Graph ordered pairs of integers in the coordinate plane.

In this chapter students become acquainted with the integers—positive and negative and 0. They learn to compute with the integers. They are also introduced to graphing ordered pairs of integers on the coordinate plane.

Mathematics

Positive and negative numbers are used to measure quantities with opposite directions. For example, if $^+6$ represents earning \$6, then $^-6$ represents spending \$6. If $^-4$ represents going down 4 stories, then $^+4$ represents going up 4 stories. Two quantities are opposites if together they involve no change—earning \$6 and spending \$6 leaves one's financial situation unchanged, and going down 4 stories and then up 4 stories leaves one's position unchanged.

Teaching the Chapter

Addition of integers is easy to teach using any model that involves opposites—number line, trips on a road, gaining and losing money, etc. Subtraction of integers, on the other hand, is a different matter because in the minds of most students subtraction involves "taking away." Therefore, to be intuitively satisfying to students, the model used to explain subtraction should allow us to think in terms of taking away both positive and negative quantities. The text uses such a model.

We ask students to imagine small bodies that have electrical charges on them (electrons and protons, perhaps). There are two kinds of charges, which are opposites. That is, if a body with one charge is with a body with the opposite charge, they neutralize each other. They still keep their respective charges, however. Since the charges are opposites, we can call one positive and the other negative.

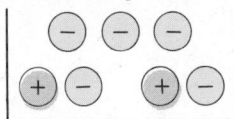

In the figure above, the total charge on the container is $^-3$ because there are 3 "extra" negatively charged bodies.   The neutral pairs do not contribute to the total charge in any way.   Students find it easy to give the total charge on a container.

Addition is described in terms of joining two collections of charges. This diagram shows a charge of $^+4$ being added to a charge of $^-3$.

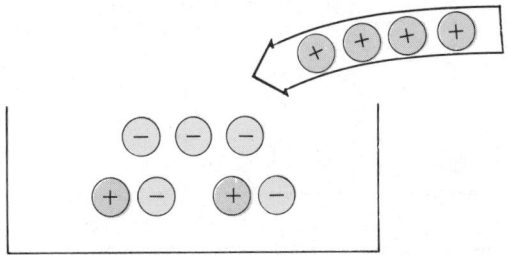

Notice that 3 of the positives neutralize the 3 negatives and the resultant charge is $^+1$.

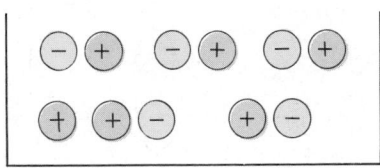

$$^-3 + {}^+4 = {}^+1$$

Other addition problems can be explained in a similar manner.

Subtraction is defined as taking out charges. For example, the diagram below shows a container with a charge of $^-3$.

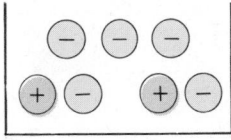

Now we take out a charge of $^-4$. Notice that we get one of the negative charges from a neutral pair. The resultant charge is $^+1$.

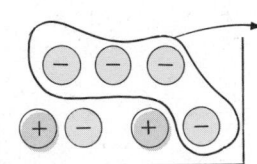

$$^-3 - {}^-4 = {}^+1$$

345a

Other subtractions can be explained in a similar manner. When doing subtractions with students, always be sure to include many neutral pairs.

Notice in the two examples above that subtracting ⁻4 and adding ⁺4 give the same results. Other examples will show your students that subtracting a number is the same as adding the opposite of the number.

Multiplication is easily explained using the same model. In the case of multiplication we always start with a charge of 0. The first diagram below shows 3 groups of ⁻2 being put into a container. If we consider "putting in 3 groups" to be represented by ⁺3, the diagram shows:

$$^+3 \times {}^-2 = {}^-6$$

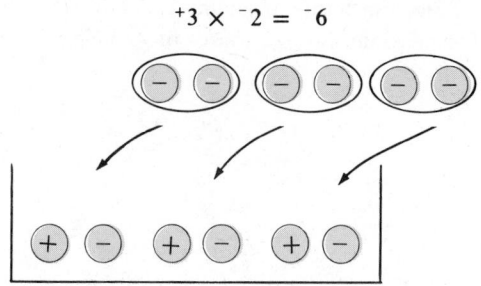

If we consider taking out 3 groups as represented by ⁻3, the diagram below shows the multiplication fact:

$$^-3 \times {}^-2 = {}^+6$$

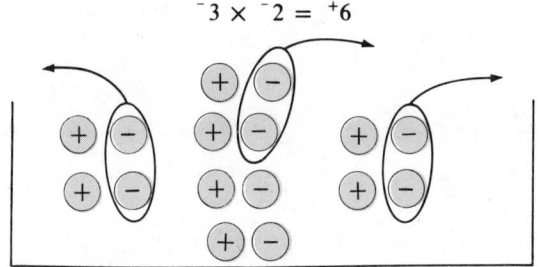

All multiplication situations are as easily explained to students.

Division is treated as the inverse of multiplication and a model is not used.

Vocabulary

axis
coordinate plane
coordinates
first coordinate axis
graph
integer
negative
opposite
ordered pair
origin
positive
second coordinate axis

Symbols

⁺6   (positive 6)
⁻6   (negative 6)

Materials

chips or disks of two colors

Chapter Tests

For a discussion of how to use the chapter tests, please see page 17c.

Answers for Chapter 12 Pretest

1. ⁺9   2. ⁻3   3. ⁺4   4. ⁻10   5. ⁺5   6. ⁻21   7. ⁺32
8. ⁻59   9. ⁺3   10. ⁻2   11. ⁻10   12. ⁺10   13. ⁻2   14. ⁺15
15. ⁻7   16. 0   17. ⁺12   18. ⁻35   19. ⁻24   20. ⁺40
21. ⁻30   22. ⁻91   23. ⁺153   24. ⁺90   25. ⁺5   26. ⁻3
27. ⁻4   28. ⁺8   29. ⁺8   30. ⁻6   31. ⁻7   32. ⁺6
33. (⁺2, ⁺1)   34. (⁺3, 0)   35. (0, ⁺2)   36. (0, ⁻2)
37. (⁻3, ⁻2)   38. (⁻3, ⁺2)

Chapter 12 Pretest

Name _____

Date _____

Add. [Obj. 12-1, pages 346–348, 352]

1. $^+4 + {}^+5 =$ _____   **2.** $^+5 + {}^-8 =$ _____   **3.** $^-4 + {}^+8 =$ _____   **4.** $^-7 + {}^-3 =$ _____

5. $^+18 + {}^-13 =$ _____   **6.** $^-36 + {}^+15 =$ _____   **7.** $^-18 + {}^+50 =$ _____   **8.** $^-17 + {}^-42 =$ _____

Subtract. [Obj. 12-2, pages 350–352]

| 0-2 | 3 | 4 | 5 | 6 | 7 | 8 |

9. $^+8 - {}^+5 =$ _____   **10.** $^+8 - {}^+10 =$ _____   **11.** $^-3 - {}^+7 =$ _____   **12.** $^+7 - {}^-3 =$ _____

13. $^-5 - {}^-3 =$ _____   **14.** $^+8 - {}^-7 =$ _____   **15.** $^+24 - {}^+31 =$ _____   **16.** $^-31 - {}^-31 =$ _____

Multiply. [Obj. 12-3, pages 354–355, 358]

| 0-2 | 3 | 4 | 5 | 6 | 7 | 8 |

17. $^+2 \times {}^+6 =$ _____   **18.** $^+7 \times {}^-5 =$ _____   **19.** $^-6 \times {}^+4 =$ _____   **20.** $^-8 \times {}^-5 =$ _____

21. $^-6 \times {}^+5 =$ _____   **22.** $^+13 \times {}^-7 =$ _____   **23.** $^+17 \times {}^+9 =$ _____   **24.** $^-9 \times {}^-10 =$ _____

Divide. [Obj. 12-4, pages 356–358]

| 0-2 | 3 | 4 | 5 | 6 | 7 | 8 |

25. $^+15 \div {}^+3 =$ _____   **26.** $^+12 \div {}^-4 =$ _____   **27.** $^-24 \div {}^+6 =$ _____   **28.** $^-32 \div {}^-4 =$ _____

29. $^+24 \div {}^+3 =$ _____   **30.** $^+36 \div {}^-6 =$ _____   **31.** $^-42 \div {}^+6 =$ _____   **32.** $^-18 \div {}^-3 =$ _____

Give the coordinates of the points. [Obj. 12-5, pages 360–361]

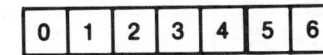

| 0 | 1 | 2 | 3 | 4 | 5 | 6 |

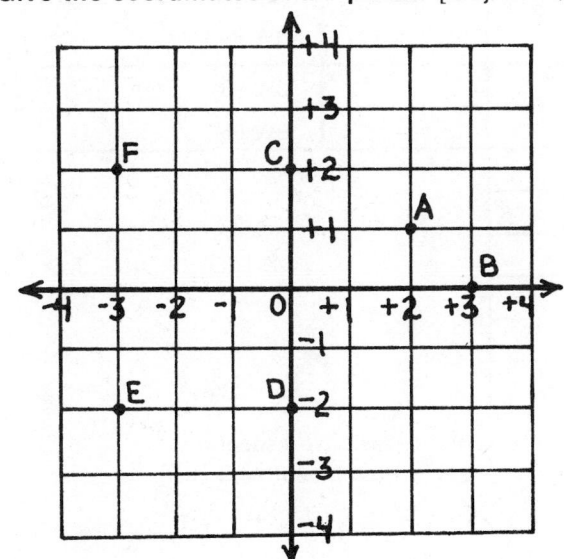

33. A: (_____ , _____)   **34.** B: (_____ , _____)

35. C: (_____ , _____)   **36.** D: (_____ , _____)

37. E: (_____ , _____)   **38.** F: (_____ , _____)

Chapter 12
Record and Assignment Chart

Name _____

Pretest Date _____   Posttest Date _____

Objectives

		Pretest Score
		Mark number correct

		Pretest Score	Posttest Score
12-1	Add integers.	0-3 | 4 | 5 | 6 | 7 | 8	0-3 | 4 | 5 | 6 | 7 | 8
12-2	Subtract integers.	0-3 | 4 | 5 | 6 | 7 | 8	0-3 | 4 | 5 | 6 | 7 | 8
12-3	Multiply integers.	0-3 | 4 | 5 | 6 | 7 | 8	0-3 | 4 | 5 | 6 | 7 | 8
12-4	Divide integers.	0-3 | 4 | 5 | 6 | 7 | 8	0-3 | 4 | 5 | 6 | 7 | 8
12-5	Graph pairs of positive and negative numbers in the coordinate plane.	0-2 | 3 | 4 | 5 | 6	0-2 | 3 | 4 | 5 | 6

Pretest Score — Mark number correct: Unsatisfactory Score | Satisfactory Score

Posttest Score — Mark number correct: Unsatisfactory Score | Satisfactory Score

TEACHING ASSIGNMENTS*

	Student Page	Basic Assignment	Average Assignment	Enriched Assignment	Problem Solving	RETEACHING ASSIGNMENTS†
	346, 347	1–29	1–30, EW 92	1–31, EW 92		page 396 Set 86, BW 92
12-1	348, 349	1–24	1–33, EW 92	10–36, EW 92		page 396 Set 87, BW 92
12-2	350, 351	1–30	1–40, EW 93	1–44, EW 93		page 396 Set 88, BW 93
12-1 12-2	352	1–64	1–64, EW 93	1–64, EW 93		BW 93
	353	1–5	1–5	1–5		BW 93
12-3	354, 355	1–44	1–50, EW 94	1–56, EW 94		page 397 Set 89, BW 94
12-4	356, 357	1–30	1–38, EW 95	1–5, 16–40, EW 95		page 397 Set 90, BW 95
12-3 12-4	358	1–64	1–64, EW 96	1–64, EW 96		BW 96
	359	1–4	1–4	1–4		BW 96
12-5	360, 361	1–31	1–33, EW 96	1–35, EW 96		BW 96
	362	Chapter Checkup				
	363	Project				
	364	Chapter Review				
	365	Chapter Challenge				
	366	Major Checkup				
	367, 368	Final Test				

*Check assignments for objectives with unsatisfactory pretest scores.

†Check assignments for objectives with unsatisfactory posttest scores.

BW = Basic Worksheet

EW = Enrichment Worksheet

12
Computing with Integers

To use integers to describe number
situations.
To locate integers on a number line.
To compare integers.

VOCABULARY
integer, positive, negative

Suggested Lesson Plan

Introduction Draw a number line on
the board and label the whole numbers.
Indicate that the number line extends to
the left, but don't show the numbers
yet. Ask students such questions as,
What is the temperature today? Locate
this number on the number line. Then
ask what the temperature would be if it
dropped 20 degrees. Continue this line of
questioning until you get answers that
are below zero. At this point, have a
student locate the point for the number
by extending the number line to the left.
Ask students what this number would be
called. (negative 6°, etc.)

Using the pages Use the exposition
on page 346 to reinforce your
introduction. Ask students for examples
of other situations where negative
integers occur. Point out that there are
negative numbers between consecutive
negative integers—they are negative
rational numbers.

Show students how they can use the
number line to tell which of two
numbers is greater. They locate the two
numbers and the greater number is the
one to the right.

Assign exercises 1–31 for written
work. Have students refer to the number
line if they become confused in
comparing the numbers.

Integers

When the temperature is 8° below 0°,
the weather report might say that the
temperature is $^-8$° ("negative eight
degrees"). When the temperature is 15°
above 0°, the report might say that the
temperature is $^+15$° ("positive fifteen
degrees").

Positive numbers and negative numbers
like these (and 0) are called **integers**.

Integers	Not Integers
0 $^-6$ $^+45$ $^-876$ $^-17{,}358$	$^-\frac{1}{2}$ $^+\frac{7}{8}$ $^-3.97$ $^+17.3$

The integers can be shown on the number line like this:

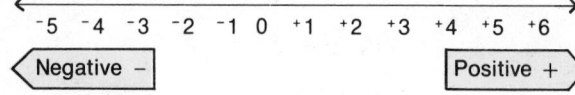

$^-5$ $^-4$ $^-3$ $^-2$ $^-1$ 0 $^+1$ $^+2$ $^+3$ $^+4$ $^+5$ $^+6$

Negative −   Positive +

You can use a number line to compare two integers. Notice
that the greater of two integers is always to the right. The
number line above shows that

$$^-4 < {}^-3 \qquad {}^+2 < {}^+3 \qquad 0 < {}^+1 \qquad {}^+4 > {}^+3 \qquad {}^+1 > {}^-5$$

is less than   is greater than

EXERCISES

< or > ?

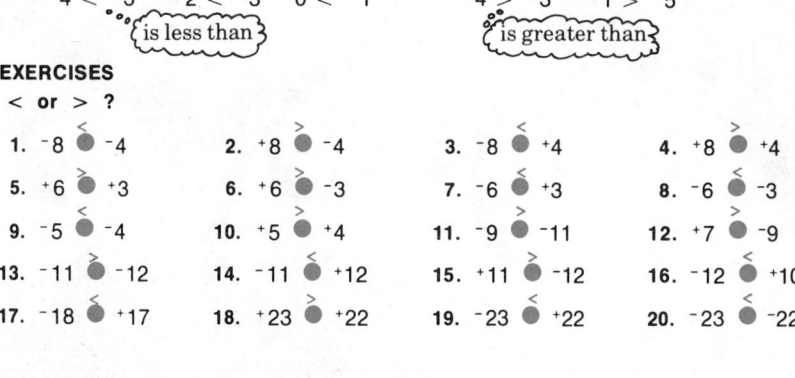

1. $^-8$ ● $^-4$ 2. $^+8$ ● $^-4$ 3. $^-8$ ● $^+4$ 4. $^+8$ ● $^+4$

5. $^+6$ ● $^+3$ 6. $^+6$ ● $^-3$ 7. $^-6$ ● $^+3$ 8. $^-6$ ● $^-3$

9. $^-5$ ● $^-4$ 10. $^+5$ ● $^+4$ 11. $^-9$ ● $^-11$ 12. $^+7$ ● $^-9$

13. $^-11$ ● $^-12$ 14. $^-11$ ● $^+12$ 15. $^+11$ ● $^-12$ 16. $^-12$ ● $^+10$

17. $^-18$ ● $^+17$ 18. $^+23$ ● $^+22$ 19. $^-23$ ● $^+22$ 20. $^-23$ ● $^-22$

346

Assignments

BASIC
page 346 exercises 1–20
page 347 exercises 21–29
Basic Worksheet 92

AVERAGE
page 346 exercises 1–20
page 347 exercises 21–30
Enrichment Worksheet 92

ENRICHED
page 346 exercises 1–20
page 347 exercises 21–31
Enrichment Worksheet 92

EXTRA PRACTICE
page 396 set 86

Complete.

21. __?__ is neither positive nor negative. 0

22. All __?__ integers are greater than 0. positive

23. All __?__ integers are less than 0. negative

24. Zero is __?__ than any negative integer. greater

25. A negative integer is __?__ than any positive integer.
    less

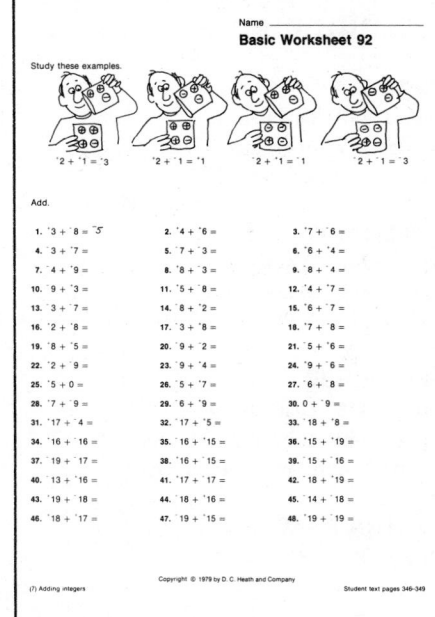

Solve.

26. If ⁺8 stands for a gain of 8 meters, what does ⁻4 stand for? a loss of 4 meters

27. If ⁻10 stands for 10° below zero, what does ⁺16 stand for? 16° above zero

28. If ⁺50 stands for $50 profit, then what stands for a loss of $28? ⁻28

29. If ⁻40 stands for 40 meters below sea level, then what stands for 220 meters above sea level? ⁺220

Solve.

30. If ⁺3 stands for 3 centimeters above the average height, then what stands for 2 centimeters below the average height? ⁻2

31. Gerry used integers to keep a record of how much she earned or spent each day. The table shows that she earned 75¢ on Monday. Did Gerry have more or less money at the end of the week than at the beginning? How much more or less? more, $2.10

Monday	⁺75¢
Tuesday	⁺60¢
Wednesday	⁻50¢
Thursday	⁺75¢
Friday	⁻80¢
Saturday	⁺80¢
Sunday	⁺50¢

347

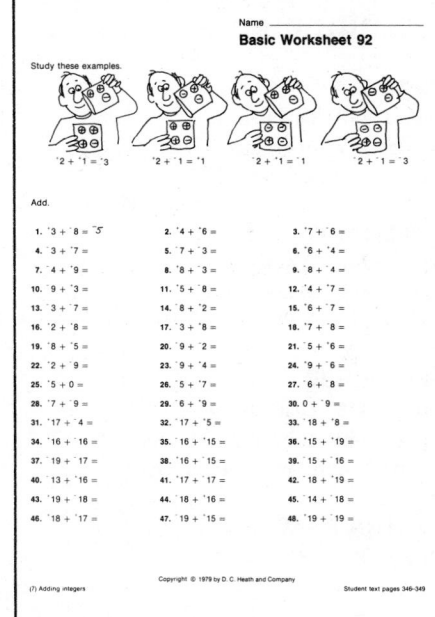

Follow-up Activities

Reinforcement You may wish to prepare the following worksheet for students to complete. (Answers are given in red.)

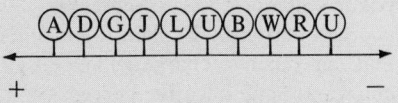

Start	Trip	End	
A	+6	?	B
B	⁻6	?	A
R	⁻5	?	J
J	+3	?	B
D	?	U	+4
W	?	A	⁻7
G	?	R	+6
R	?	G	⁻6

Enrichment Have students use the given information to label the sign markers. (Answers are given in red.)

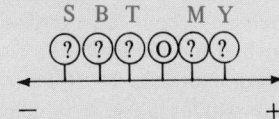

Start	Trip	End
O	+2	Y
S	+3	O
Y	⁻4	B
M	⁻1	O
T	+2	M

EXCURSION
Give the next number.

$\frac{1}{2}, \frac{3}{4}, \frac{7}{8}, \frac{15}{16}, \frac{31}{32}, ?$ $\frac{63}{64}$

Add 1, then divide by 2; or divide by 2, then add $\frac{1}{2}$

Name _____
Basic Worksheet 92

Study these examples.

⁻2 + ⁺1 = ⁻3   ⁻2 + ⁺1 = ⁻1   ⁻2 + ⁻1 = ⁻3   ⁻2 + ⁻1 = ⁻3

Add.

1. ⁻3 + ⁻8 = ⁻⁵   2. ⁻4 + ⁻6 =   3. ⁻7 + ⁻6 =
4. ⁻3 + ⁻7 =   5. ⁻7 + ⁻3 =   6. ⁻6 + ⁻4 =
7. ⁻4 + ⁻9 =   8. ⁻8 + ⁻3 =   9. ⁻8 + ⁻4 =
10. ⁻9 + ⁻3 =   11. ⁻5 + ⁻8 =   12. ⁻4 + ⁻7 =
13. ⁻3 + ⁻7 =   14. ⁻8 + ⁻2 =   15. ⁻6 + ⁻7 =
16. ⁻2 + ⁻8 =   17. ⁻3 + ⁻8 =   18. ⁻7 + ⁻8 =
19. ⁻8 + ⁻5 =   20. ⁻9 + ⁻2 =   21. ⁻5 + ⁻6 =
22. ⁻2 + ⁻9 =   23. ⁻9 + ⁻4 =   24. ⁻9 + ⁻6 =
25. ⁻5 + 0 =   26. ⁻5 + ⁻7 =   27. ⁻6 + ⁻8 =
28. ⁻7 + ⁻9 =   29. ⁻6 + ⁻9 =   30. 0 + ⁻9 =
31. ⁻17 + ⁻4 =   32. ⁻17 + ⁻5 =   33. ⁻18 + ⁻8 =
34. ⁻16 + ⁻16 =   35. ⁻16 + ⁻15 =   36. ⁻15 + ⁻19 =
37. ⁻19 + ⁻17 =   38. ⁻16 + ⁻15 =   39. ⁻15 + ⁻16 =
40. ⁻13 + ⁻16 =   41. ⁻17 + ⁻17 =   42. ⁻18 + ⁻19 =
43. ⁻19 + ⁻18 =   44. ⁻18 + ⁻16 =   45. ⁻14 + ⁻18 =
46. ⁻18 + ⁻17 =   47. ⁻19 + ⁻15 =   48. ⁻19 + ⁻19 =

Copyright © 1979 by D. C. Heath and Company

(7) Adding integers   Student text pages 346–349

Name _____
Enrichment Worksheet 92

Complete the magic squares so that the sums in the rows, columns, and diagonals are all the same.

1.

1	4	3
	1	

2.

		2
	4	
10		6

3.

3	10	0
4	7	6	1
9		12	

4.

	9	12	
3	9	12	3
	0		
6		15	

Copyright © 1979 by D. C. Heath and Company

(7) Adding integers   Student text pages 346–349

Lesson 164 347

Suggested Lesson Plan

Introduction   Use two different-colored poker chips or disks to represent charged particles. Explain to students that one positive charge will exactly counteract one negative charge, or become *neutral*. Put different numbers of the colored chips together and ask students for the total charge for the pile.

Vary the procedure by starting with a pile of one color and asking for the charge. Add chips of either color and now ask for the charge. Show a number sentence on the board to represent this action, using integers to represent the different charges.

Using the pages   Use the exposition on page 348 to reinforce your introduction. Don't attempt to generalize the rules for adding integers at this time. If students get stuck, refer them to the model of positive and negative particles. You might even give them some chips and have them represent the exercise in order to find the answer.

Assign exercises 1–36 for written work. Let students use a number line if that seems more convenient than the colored chips.

Adding integers

Think about some small objects that have either a positive electrical charge or a negative electrical charge. Positive charges and negative charges are opposites. This means that when one positive charge and one negative charge are put together, the result is no charge, or a charge of 0.

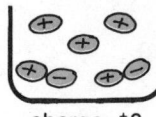

charge: $^+3$ charge: $^-4$ charge: 0

When you wish to add integers, you can think about putting charges together. Study these examples.

EXAMPLE 1. $^+3 + ^+1 = ?$

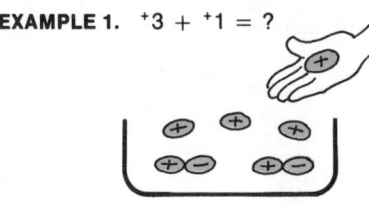

$$^+3 + ^+1 = ^+4$$

EXAMPLE 2. $^-3 + ^+4 = ?$

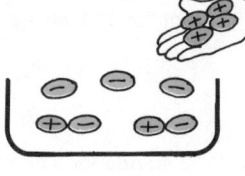

$$^-3 + ^+4 = ^+1$$

EXAMPLE 3. $^+2 + ^-5 = ?$

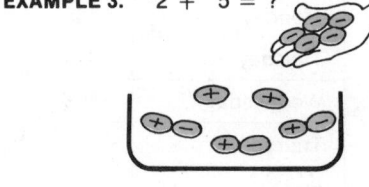

$$^+2 + ^-5 = ^-3$$

EXAMPLE 4. $^+4 + ^-4 = ?$

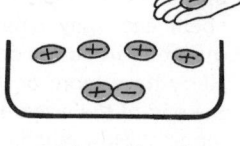

$$^+4 + ^-4 = 0$$

In Example 4, the sum of the two numbers is 0. Therefore, we say that $^+4$ and $^-4$ are **opposites**.

348

Assignments

BASIC
page 348 Discuss
page 349 exercises 1–24
Basic Worksheet 92

AVERAGE
page 348 Discuss
page 349 exercises 1–33
Enrichment Worksheet 92

ENRICHED
page 348 Discuss
page 349 exercises 10–36
Enrichment Worksheet 92

EXTRA PRACTICE
page 396 set 87

EXERCISES

Give each sum.

1. $^+8 + {}^+3$ $^+11$
2. $^+8 + {}^-3$ $^+5$
3. $^-8 + {}^+3$ $^-5$
4. $^-8 + {}^-3$ $^-11$
5. $^+6 + {}^+9$ $^+15$
6. $^+6 + {}^-9$ $^-3$
7. $^-6 + {}^+9$ $^+3$
8. $^-6 + {}^-9$ $^-15$
9. $^+7 + {}^+5$ $^+12$
10. $^+7 + {}^-5$ $^+2$
11. $-\frac{1}{7} + {}-\frac{2}{7}$ $^-\frac{3}{7}$
12. $^-7 + {}^-5$ $^-12$
13. $^+9 + {}^-9$ 0
14. $^+4 + {}^-10$ $^-6$
15. $^-4 + {}^+10$ $^+6$
16. $^-6 + {}^+11$ $^+5$
17. $^+2 + {}^-4$ $^-2$
18. $^-6 + {}^-8$ $^-14$
19. $^+5 + 0$ $^+5$
20. $0 + {}^-6$ $^-6$
21. $^-9 + {}^-2$ $^-11$
22. $^+6 + {}^+9$ $^+15$
23. $^+10 + {}^-4$ $^+6$
24. $^+12 + {}^-3$ $^+9$
25. $^-6 + {}^-7$ $^-13$
26. $^-6 + {}^+7$ $^+1$
27. $^+6 + {}^-7$ $^-1$
28. $^+6 + {}^+7$ $^+13$
29. $^-24 + {}^+39$ $^+15$
30. $^+23 + {}^+36$ $^+59$
31. $^-53 + {}^-26$ $^-79$
32. $^+74 + {}^-60$ $^+14$

Solve.

33. Central High had a metric football game. The football coach used integers to record meters gained or lost each time the ball was carried. For example, he used $^+6$ for a gain of 6 meters.

   a. What was Berry's net gain? 21 m
   b. Who netted the most meters? Berry
   c. How many meters did Martinez and Phillips net together? $^+15$

	Player		
Berry	Allan	Martinez	Phillips
$^+6$	$^-4$	$^-6$	$^+3$
$^-2$	$^+8$	$^+5$	0
$^+4$	$^+3$	$^+9$	$^-4$
0	$^+2$	$^+1$	$^+6$
$^-3$	$^-5$	$^-2$	$^+2$
$^+5$		$^+1$	$^+1$
$^+11$			$^-1$

Copy and complete these addition boxes.
Add across and add down.

34.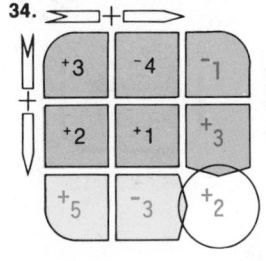

35.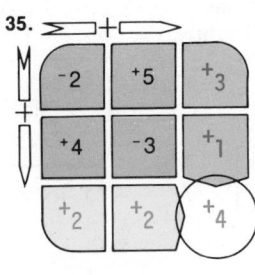

36.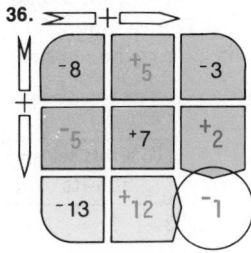

349

Follow-up Activities

Reinforcement You may wish to use the following activity for those students who need further work with adding integers. Have students think about an elevator going up and down. Call the direction up positive and the direction down negative. Ask them to think about taking two rides, one after the other. Have students give the single ride that would take them from the starting point of the first ride to the ending point of the second ride. Ask them to copy and complete this table. (Answers are given in red.)

Rides	Single ride
$^+6, {}^-3$	? $^+3$
$^-3, {}^+6$	? $^+3$
$^-3, {}^-6$	? $^-9$
$^+3, {}^+6$	? $^+9$
$^+8, {}^-8$	? 0
$^+12, {}^-14$	? $^-2$

Enrichment Remember that in a magic square the sum of the numbers in any row, column, or diagonal is the same. Have students copy and complete this magic square. (Answers are given in red.)

$^+9$	$^-4$	$^-5$	$^+6$
$^-2$	$^+3$	$^+4$	$^+1$
$^+2$	$^-1$	0	$^+5$
$^-3$	$^+8$	$^+7$	$^-6$

EXCURSION

Get 10 toothpicks.
Make 2 squares with 10.
Make 5 triangles with 9.
*Make 4 equilateral triangles with 6.

No breaking, bending, or overlapping of any toothpicks.

*Tricky

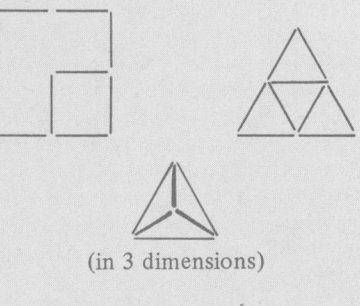

(in 3 dimensions)

Lesson 165   349

STUDENT OBJECTIVE
To subtract two integers.

Suggested Lesson Plan

Introduction Use the colored chips to develop the concept of subtraction of integers. Use the subtraction model of subtraction, that is, 10 − 6 is explained as starting with 10 and "taking away 6" leaves 4. To represent the subtraction sentence 10 − 6, start with 10 positive charges, and take away 6 positive charges; that leaves 4 positive charges. Represent ⁻10 − ⁻6, ⁻10 − ⁺6, 10 − ⁻6, etc. In order to show the taking away of 6 negative charges from 10 positive charges you need to have matched pairs of positive and negative particles with the 10. Of course, the charge of these matched particles is 0 until either the positive or negative particle is removed. Then, of course, the other charged particle remains.

Using the pages Use the exposition on page 350 to reinforce your introduction. After you have done several examples and those on page 350, show that these two sentences are equivalent:

$$10 - {}^+6 = 4 \qquad 10 + {}^-6 = 4$$

At that point you can make the generalization that to subtract an integer, we can add its opposite. Since addition is easier, we use addition to solve subtraction sentences.

Assign exercises 1−44. Do not attempt to generalize the rules for addition or subtraction except as noted above. If students become confused, give them colored chips and let them represent the sentence to find the answer.

Near the end of the class time, have students do and correct the Keeping Skills Sharp.

Subtracting integers

You can also think about electrical charges when you wish to subtract integers.

EXAMPLE 1. ⁺1 − ⁺3 = ?

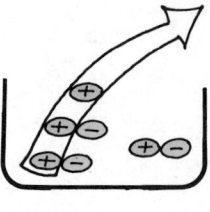

$${}^+1 - {}^+3 = {}^-2$$

EXAMPLE 2. ⁻4 − ⁻1 = ?

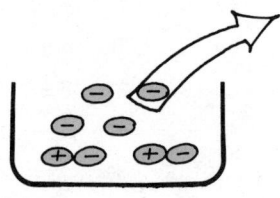

$${}^-4 - {}^-1 = {}^-3$$

EXAMPLE 3. ⁻2 − ⁻3 = ?

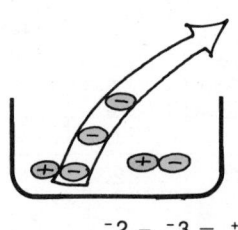

$${}^-2 - {}^-3 = {}^+1$$

EXAMPLE 4. ⁺2 − ⁻3 = ?

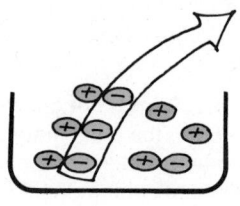

$${}^+2 - {}^-3 = {}^+5$$

Addition and subtraction are closely related. Notice that adding ⁺2 and subtracting ⁻2 give the same result.

This gives us a way to subtract.

> To subtract an integer, add its opposite.

$${}^-3 - {}^+2 = {}^-3 + {}^-2 = {}^-5$$

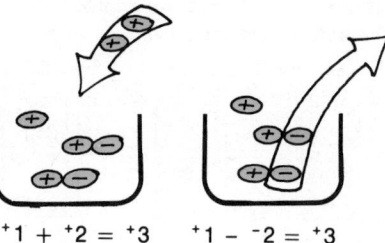

$${}^+1 + {}^+2 = {}^+3 \qquad {}^+1 - {}^-2 = {}^+3$$

350

Assignments

BASIC
page 350 Discuss
page 351 exercises 1−30,
    Keeping Skills Sharp
Basic Worksheet 93

AVERAGE
page 350 Discuss
page 351 exercises 1−40,
    Keeping Skills Sharp
Enrichment Worksheet 93

ENRICHED
page 350 Discuss
page 351 exercises 1−44,
    Keeping Skills Sharp
Enrichment Worksheet 93

EXTRA PRACTICE
page 396 set 88

EXERCISES
Complete.

1. To subtract $^+2$, add ___?___ . $^-2$
2. To subtract $^-5$, add ___?___ . $^+5$
3. To subtract an integer, add the ___?___ of the integer. *opposite*

Give each difference.

$(^+8 + ^-3 = ^+5)$ $(^-5 + ^+2 = ^-3)$

4. $^+8 - ^+3$ $^+5$ 5. $^-5 - ^-2$ $^-3$

6. $^-3 - ^+9$ $^-12$ 7. $^+12 - ^-3$ $^+15$ 8. $^-5 - ^-7$ $^+2$

9. $^+7 - 0$ $^+7$ 10. $^-8 - ^+3$ $^-11$ 11. $^-2 - ^-3$ $^+1$

12. $^+3 - ^-8$ $^+11$ 13. $^-5 - ^-6$ $^+1$ 14. $^-10 - ^+8$ $^-18$

15. $^-3 - ^-8$ $^+5$ 16. $^+3 - ^+6$ $^-3$ 17. $^-9 - ^+7$ $^-16$

18. $0 - ^-5$ $^+5$ 19. $^+15 - ^-4$ $^+19$ 20. $^-4 - ^+6$ $^-10$

21. $^-8 - ^-7$ $^-1$ 22. $^+12 - 0$ $^+12$ 23. $^+8 - ^-12$ $^+20$

24. $^-3 - ^+13$ $^-16$ 25. $^+15 - ^-6$ $^+21$ 26. $0 - ^-4$ $^+4$

27. $^+13 - ^-3$ $^+16$ 28. $^-10 - ^-12$ $^+2$ 29. $^+18 - ^+13$ $^+5$

30. $^-35 - ^-35$ 0 31. $^+35 - ^-35$ $^+70$ 32. $^-19 - ^+6$ $^-25$

33. $0 - ^-6$ $^+6$ 34. $0 - ^+19$ $^-19$ 35. $^+23 - ^-17$ $^+40$

36. $^-26 - ^-35$ $^+9$ 37. $^+38 - ^-59$ $^+97$ 38. $0 - 0$ 0

39. $^+16 - ^+4$ $^+12$ 40. $^+13 - ^-14$ $^+27$ 41. $^-8 - ^+3$ $^-11$

42. $^-18 - ^+13$ $^-31$ 43. $^+18 - ^-13$ $^+31$ 44. $^-18 - ^-13$ $^-5$

[calculator icon] $1 - 2 + 3 - 4 + 5 - 6 + 7 - \ldots + 1001 = ?$
501

Keeping Skills Sharp

Change to a percent.

1. $\frac{1}{2}$ 2. $\frac{1}{4}$

3. $\frac{3}{4}$ 4. $\frac{3}{5}$

5. $\frac{1}{3}$ 6. $\frac{2}{3}$

7. $\frac{1}{8}$ 8. $\frac{9}{8}$

9. $\frac{5}{6}$ 10. $\frac{11}{6}$

11. $\frac{1}{9}$ 12. $\frac{9}{16}$

13. $\frac{8}{5}$ 14. $\frac{7}{9}$

15. $\frac{5}{8}$ 16. $\frac{7}{6}$

17. $\frac{4}{5}$ 18. $\frac{3}{10}$

19. $\frac{11}{9}$ 20. $\frac{7}{8}$

21. $\frac{3}{2}$ 22. $\frac{4}{15}$

23. $\frac{8}{5}$ 24. $\frac{5}{12}$

25. $\frac{2}{5}$ 26. $\frac{3}{8}$

27. $\frac{4}{9}$ 28. $\frac{2}{9}$

29. $\frac{7}{15}$ 30. $\frac{11}{20}$

351

Follow-up Activities

Reinforcement To provide further experiences with addition and subtraction of integers, have students copy and complete these addition-subtraction boxes. (The answers are in red.)

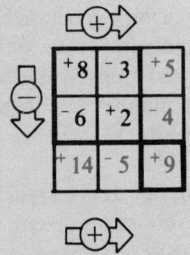

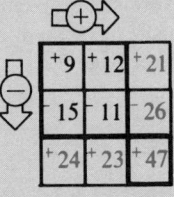

Enrichment Copy all the following path on the chalkboard. Explain to students that they are to determine what goes where the question mark is.

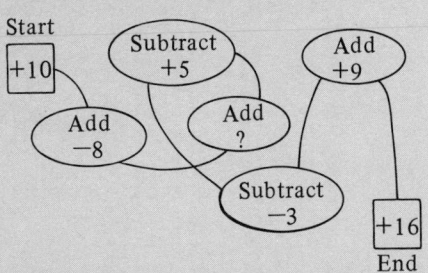

The solution is $^+7$. You may need to suggest to some students that they will need to first work forward to the question mark and then work backward to the question mark. They can then use the results to determine the answer.

CALCULATOR ACTIVITY
Have students try to add and subtract integers on their calculators. Some calculators will handle positive and negative numbers while others will not. Give students several addition and subtraction sentences with integers and see if they can work out a calculator code to use.

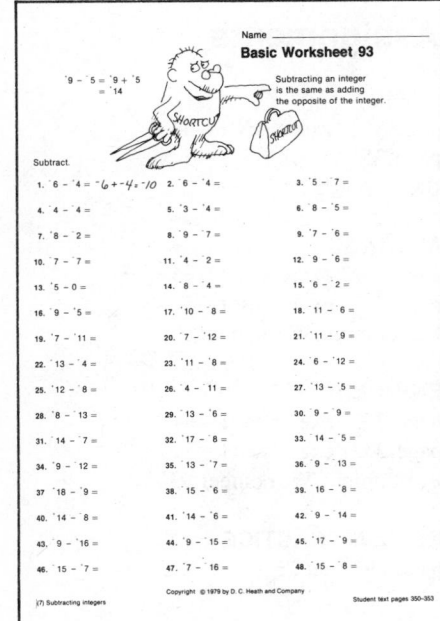

STUDENT OBJECTIVES

To practice addition and subtraction of integers.

To solve problems involved with mathematics and science.

Suggested Lesson Plan

Introduction Don't generalize the rules for addition and subtraction of integers. Make the colored chips available or have students use a number line if they become confused.

Using the pages Have students do the practice exercises on page 352. When they finish, have them do exercises 1–5 on page 353.

Practice exercises

Give each sum.

1. $^+2 + {}^+6$ $^+8$
2. $^-5 + {}^-9$ $^-14$
3. $^+3 + {}^-7$ $^-4$
4. $0 + {}^-9$ $^-9$
5. $^-7 + {}^+8$ $^+1$
6. $^+3 + {}^+5$ $^+8$
7. $^+4 + {}^-5$ $^-1$
8. $^-9 + {}^-5$ $^-14$
9. $^-5 + {}^-8$ $^-13$
10. $^-7 + {}^-9$ $^-16$
11. $^-2 + {}^+8$ $^+6$
12. $^+6 + {}^+4$ $^+10$
13. $0 + {}^+8$ $^+8$
14. $^-8 + {}^+5$ $^-3$
15. $^-6 + {}^-9$ $^-15$
16. $^-8 + {}^+8$ 0
17. $^+8 + {}^+9$ $^+17$
18. $^+3 + {}^-9$ $^-6$
19. $^+7 + {}^+4$ $^+11$
20. $0 + 0$ 0
21. $^+9 + {}^-9$ 0
22. $^-6 + {}^+8$ $^+2$
23. $^-9 + {}^-8$ $^-17$
24. $^+8 + {}^+8$ $^+16$
25. $^+10 + {}^+7$ $^+17$
26. $^+15 + {}^-9$ $^+6$
27. $^+13 + {}^-10$ $^+3$
28. $^-9 + {}^-15$ $^-24$
29. $^-23 + 0$ $^-23$
30. $^+28 + {}^+19$ $^+47$
31. $^+21 + {}^-21$ 0
32. $^-24 + {}^-16$ $^-40$

Give each difference.

33. $^+9 - {}^+2$ $^+7$
34. $^-5 - 0$ $^-5$
35. $^+8 - {}^+5$ $^+3$
36. $^-6 - {}^+6$ $^-12$
37. $^-6 - {}^-7$ $^+1$
38. $^+6 - {}^-5$ $^+11$
39. $^-8 - {}^-7$ $^-1$
40. $^-5 - {}^+6$ $^-11$
41. $^-9 - {}^+9$ $^-18$
42. $^+3 - {}^+9$ $^-6$
43. $^-4 - {}^-9$ $^+5$
44. $^+8 - {}^+4$ $^+4$
45. $^+8 - {}^-3$ $^+11$
46. $^-9 - {}^-8$ $^-1$
47. $^+2 - {}^-9$ $^+11$
48. $0 - {}^+9$ $^-9$
49. $^-9 - {}^+6$ $^-15$
50. $^+3 - {}^-8$ $^+11$
51. $^+8 - {}^+8$ 0
52. $^-6 - {}^-6$ 0
53. $^+5 - {}^-7$ $^+12$
54. $^+6 - {}^+8$ $^-2$
55. $^+7 - {}^-6$ $^+13$
56. $^-5 - {}^+9$ $^-14$
57. $^+15 - {}^-6$ $^+21$
58. $^+18 - {}^-9$ $^+27$
59. $^-17 - {}^-9$ $^-8$
60. $^+15 - {}^+6$ $^+9$
61. $^+23 - {}^+5$ $^+18$
62. $^-26 - {}^+24$ $^-50$
63. $^-25 - {}^+28$ $^-53$
64. $^+28 - {}^-21$ $^+49$

352

Assignments

BASIC
page 352 exercises 1–64
page 353 exercises 1–5
Basic Worksheet 93

AVERAGE
page 352 exercises 1–64
page 353 exercises 1–5
Enrichment Worksheet 93

ENRICHED
page 352 exercises 1–64
page 353 exercises 1–5
Enrichment Worksheet 93

REVIEW PRACTICE
page 393 set 76

Mathematics and science

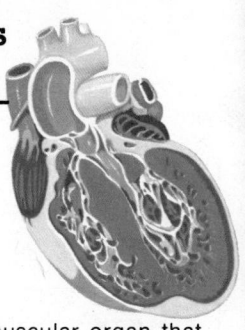

1. The heart is a muscular organ that pumps blood through the body. Take your pulse and compute about how many times a day your heart beats.

2. A man's heart weighs about 312 grams. A woman's heart weighs about $\frac{5}{6}$ as much. How much does a woman's heart weigh? 260 g

3. a. An adult weighing 75 kilograms has about 4.7 liters of blood. At that ratio, how many liters of blood do you have?
   b. Blood is made up of plasma, white cells, and platelets. About 55% of the volume of blood is plasma. About how many liters of plasma do you have?

4. In an adult the heart pumps about 4.7 liters of blood through the body every minute. How many liters of blood does it pump through the body in a day? 6768 L

5. A 75-kilogram adult has about 160,000 kilometers of blood vessels. At that ratio, how many kilometers of blood vessels do you have?

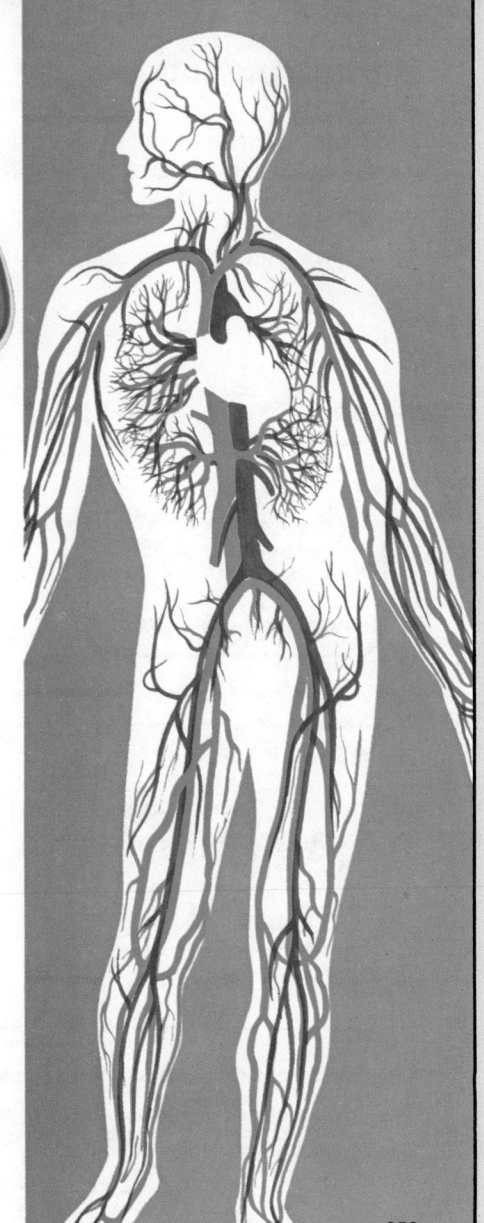

353

Follow-up Activities

Reinforcement You may wish to review and practice the computational skills that have been thus far introduced. Consider the following game. Divide the students into two well-balanced teams. Call a member from one of the teams to write a specified kind of exercise on the chalkboard. Next, call on a volunteer from the opposing team to go to the chalkboard and work the problem. If her work is correct, award her team one point. If her work is incorrect, the player who made up the problem can earn one point for his team by working the problem correctly. Have a member from the other team make up a problem, and continue to play the game until each player has worked on at least one problem. The team getting the greater number of points wins the game.

Enrichment The game described above may also be used for more able students, since they generally make up more difficult problems.

EXCURSION
Suppose you have a bag of dimes that weighs the same as you. How much would the bag be worth?

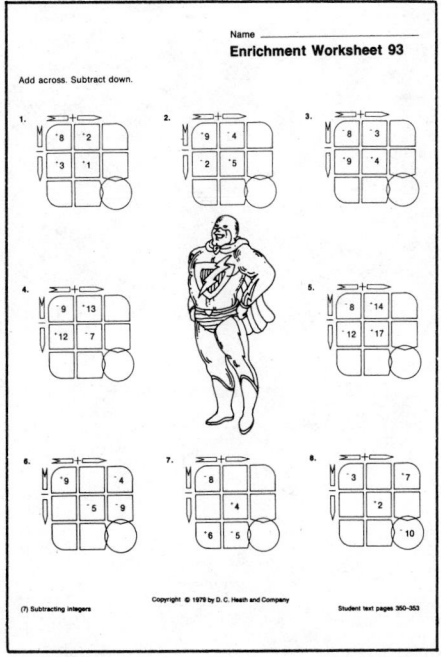

Suggested Lesson Plan

Introduction Use the colored chips and charged-particles model to develop the rules for multiplication of integers.

Using the pages Show students how a multiplication sentence such as $^+3 \times {}^+2$ can be represented using charged particles. When the first number (the multiplier) is positive we think of "putting charges in" and when it is negative we think of "taking charges out." Thus, $^+3 \times {}^+2$ means put in 3 groups of 2 positive charges. Of course students know the answer and the model shows the answer of $^+6$. Now continue with sentences such as $^+3 \times {}^-2$ and $^-3 \times {}^+2$. For the second sentence you will have to have matched charges available so that you can remove 3 groups of 2 positive charges.

After modeling such sentences as these, work through $^-3 \times {}^-2$ to show that the answer is positive. At this point, generalize the rules for multiplication of integers. Have students write them down. Make colored chips available so that if they become confused they can use the chips to find the answers. Practically speaking, many of these numbers are too large to represent; therefore, after the rules are generalized, students should refer to them rather than try to count large numbers of chips.

Assign exercises 1–56. Have students work exercises 45–56 from a multiplication standpoint. For $? \times {}^-3 = {}^-24$, ask what times $^-3$ gives $^-24$.

Multiplying integers

To multiply integers we will think of "putting charges in" as positive and "taking charges out" as negative.

EXAMPLE 1. $^+3 \times {}^+2 = ?$

Start with a 0 charge.

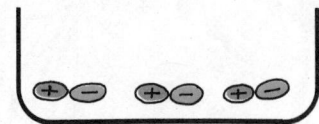

Put in 3 sets of $^+2$ charges.

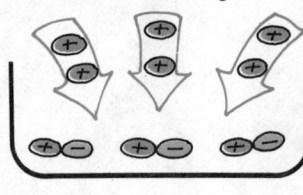

$$^+3 \times {}^+2 = {}^+6$$

EXAMPLE 3. $^+3 \times {}^-2 = ?$

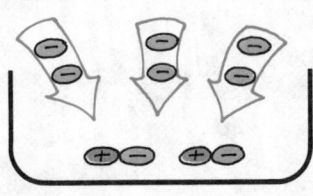

$$^+3 \times {}^-2 = {}^-6$$

EXAMPLE 2. $^-3 \times {}^-2 = ?$

Start with a 0 charge.

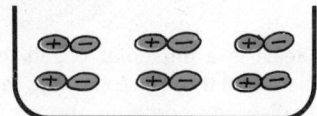

Take out 3 sets of $^-2$ charges.

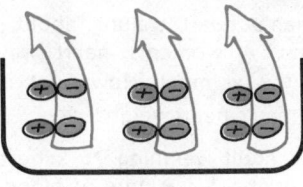

$$^-3 \times {}^-2 = {}^+6$$

EXAMPLE 4. $^-3 \times {}^+2 = ?$

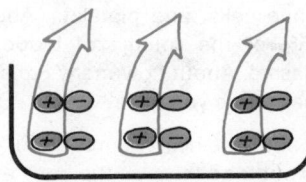

$$^-3 \times {}^+2 = {}^-6$$

The product of two integers with the *same* sign is *positive*.

The product of two integers with *different* signs is *negative*.

The product of any integer and 0 is 0.

354

Assignments

BASIC
page 354 Discuss
page 355 exercises 1–44
Basic Worksheet 94

AVERAGE
page 354 Discuss
page 355 exercises 1–50
Enrichment Worksheet 94

ENRICHED
page 354 Discuss
page 355 exercises 1–56
Enrichment Worksheet 94

EXTRA PRACTICE
page 397 set 89

Complete.
Positive, negative, or zero?

1. The product of two positive integers is a __?__ integer. *positive*

2. The product of two negative integers is a __?__ integer. *positive*

3. The product of a positive integer and a negative integer is a __?__ integer. *negative*

4. The product of an integer and 0 is __?__. *0*

Give each product.

5. $^+3 \times {}^+4$ $^+12$ 6. $^+3 \times {}^-4$ $^-12$ 7. $^-3 \times {}^+4$ $^-12$ 8. $^-3 \times {}^-4$ $^+12$

9. $^+5 \times {}^+6$ $^+30$ 10. $^+5 \times {}^-6$ $^-30$ 11. $^-5 \times {}^+6$ $^-30$ 12. $^-5 \times {}^-6$ $^+30$

13. $^+7 \times {}^+5$ $^+35$ 14. $^+7 \times {}^-5$ $^-35$ 15. $^-7 \times {}^+5$ $^-35$ 16. $^-7 \times {}^-5$ $^+35$

17. $^+8 \times {}^+6$ $^+48$ 18. $^+8 \times {}^-6$ $^-48$ 19. $^-8 \times {}^+6$ $^-48$ 20. $^-8 \times {}^-6$ $^+48$

21. $^+9 \times {}^+6$ $^+54$ 22. $^+9 \times {}^-6$ $^-54$ 23. $^-9 \times {}^+6$ $^-54$ 24. $^-9 \times {}^-6$ $^+54$

25. $^+9 \times {}^+9$ $^+81$ 26. $^-7 \times {}^+7$ $^-49$ 27. $^-6 \times 0$ 0 28. $^-7 \times {}^-8$ $^+56$

29. 0×0 0 30. $0 \times {}^+5$ 0 31. $^-8 \times {}^+8$ $^-64$ 32. $^+8 \times {}^-9$ $^-72$

33. $^-7 \times {}^-9$ $^+63$ 34. $^+9 \times {}^+8$ $^+72$ 35. $^-6 \times {}^-7$ $^+42$ 36. $^+3 \times {}^-9$ $^-27$

37. $^-12 \times {}^+5$ $^-60$ 38. $^-16 \times {}^+3$ $^-48$ 39. $^+9 \times {}^+15$ $^+135$ 40. $^-16 \times {}^+4$ $^-64$

41. $^+24 \times {}^-3$ $^-72$ 42. $^+12 \times {}^+18$ $^+216$ 43. $^+15 \times {}^-15$ $^-225$ 44. $^-19 \times 0$ 0

Give the missing factor.

45. $? \times {}^-3 = {}^-24$ $^+8$ 46. $^+6 \times ? = {}^+18$ $^+3$ 47. $? \times {}^-8 = {}^-72$ $^+9$

48. $? \times {}^+7 = {}^+35$ $^+5$ 49. $^-3 \times ? = {}^+3$ $^-1$ 50. $? \times {}^+3 = 0$ 0

51. $^+12 \times ? = 0$ 0 52. $^-11 \times ? = {}^-55$ $^+5$ 53. $? \times {}^-5 = {}^-5$ $^+1$

54. $^+8 \times ? = {}^-72$ $^-9$ 55. $? \times {}^-10 = {}^+100$ $^-10$ 56. $? \times {}^+3 = {}^-27$ $^-9$

355

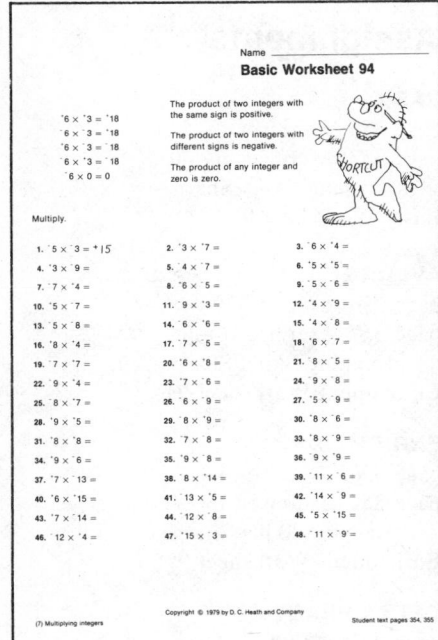

(7) Multiplying integers   Copyright © 1979 by D. C. Heath and Company   Student text pages 354, 355

Follow-up Activities

Reinforcement You may wish to follow up the lesson by having students copy and complete the following multiplication boxes. (The answers are given in red.)

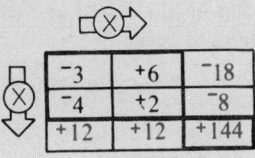

×→		
$^-3$	$^+6$	$^-18$
$^-4$	$^+2$	$^-8$
$^+12$	$^+12$	$^+144$

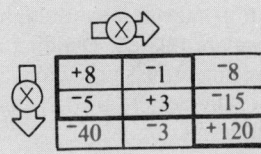

×→		
$^+8$	$^-1$	$^-8$
$^-5$	$^+3$	$^-15$
$^-40$	$^-3$	$^+120$

Enrichment The concept of division may be foreshadowed by having students copy and complete the following multiplication boxes. In these boxes we are asking students to find missing factors, which is really asking them to do a division problem. (The answers are given in red.)

×→		
$^+3$	$^-2$	$^-6$
$^-4$	$^-5$	$^+20$
$^-12$	$^+10$	$^-120$

×→		
$^-4$	$^-6$	$^+24$
$^+7$	$^+8$	$^+56$
$^-28$	$^-48$	$^+1344$

EXCURSION

$A = \{1, 3, 5, 7, 9, \ldots\}$
$B = \{\text{all primes}\}$

What is $A \cup B$? $A \cup \{2\}$
What is $A \cap B$? B without 2
True or false?

$A \cup B = A$ false
$A \cap B = B$ false

Suggested Lesson Plan

Introduction Quickly review multiplication of integers. Then write this equation on the board and ask students how to solve it:

$$9a = 576$$

Most students should know that it can be solved by dividing 576 by 9. Repeat with several similar equations. Use these examples to point out how multiplication and division are related: Dividing is the same as finding a missing factor. So, if you wish to divide $^+16$ by $^+2$, you can think about a missing factor:

$$^+16 \div {}^+2 = d \qquad {}^+2d = {}^+16$$

Since students know how to multiply, they should be able to solve the missing factor problem and, therefore, the division problem.

Using the pages Go over the exposition on page 356 to reinforce what has already been said. Do the examples orally to see that students have the idea. Students will easily discover the usual rules, which they state explicitly in exercises 1–5 on page 356.

Assign exercises 1–40 for written work. Have students do the Keeping Skills Sharp and then correct their work. Note any students who miss more than four exercises.

Dividing integers

Division is finding a missing factor.
Notice that you can find the quotient of two integers by finding a missing factor.

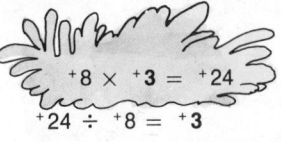

$^+8 \times {}^+3 = {}^+24$
$^+24 \div {}^+8 = {}^+3$

$^+8 \times {}^-3 = {}^-24$
$^-24 \div {}^+8 = {}^-3$

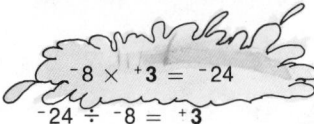

$^-8 \times {}^+3 = {}^-24$
$^-24 \div {}^-8 = {}^+3$

$^-8 \times {}^-3 = {}^+24$
$^+24 \div {}^-8 = {}^-3$

The quotient of two integers with the *same* sign is *positive*.
The quotient of two integers with *different* signs is *negative*.
The quotient of 0 divided by any nonzero integer is 0.

EXERCISES
Positive, negative, or zero?

1. If you divide a positive integer by a positive integer the quotient is __?__. positive

2. If you divide a negative integer by a negative integer the quotient is __?__. positive

3. The quotient of a positive integer divided by a negative integer is __?__. negative

4. The quotient of a negative integer divided by a positive integer is __?__. negative

5. The quotient of 0 divided by any integer is __?__. 0

356

Assignments

BASIC
page 356 exercises 1–5
page 357 exercises 6–30,
    Keeping Skills Sharp
Basic Worksheet 95

AVERAGE
page 356 exercises 1–5
page 357 exercises 6–38,
    Keeping Skills Sharp
Enrichment Worksheet 95

ENRICHED
page 356 exercises 1–5
page 357 exercises 16–40,
    Keeping Skills Sharp
Enrichment Worksheet 95

EXTRA PRACTICE
page 397 set 90

Give each quotient.

6. $^+12 \div ^+6$ $^+2$ 7. $^-16 \div ^-2$ $^+8$ 8. $^-18 \div ^+9$ $^-2$

9. $^+12 \div ^-4$ $^-3$ 10. $^-20 \div ^-4$ $^+5$ 11. $^+21 \div ^+7$ $^+3$

12. $^-40 \div ^-8$ $^+5$ 13. $^+24 \div ^-3$ $^-8$ 14. $^-18 \div ^+3$ $^-6$

15. $^-28 \div ^+7$ $^-4$ 16. $^+64 \div ^+8$ $^+8$ 17. $^+42 \div ^-7$ $^-6$

18. $^-36 \div ^-9$ $^+4$ 19. $^+48 \div ^-6$ $^-8$ 20. $0 \div ^-6$ 0

21. $^-63 \div ^-9$ $^+7$ 22. $^+36 \div ^+4$ $^+9$ 23. $^-54 \div ^-9$ $^+6$

24. $0 \div ^-8$ 0 25. $^+72 \div ^-8$ $^-9$ 26. $^-45 \div ^+5$ $^-9$

27. $^+81 \div ^+9$ $^+9$ 28. $^-49 \div ^+7$ $^-7$ 29. $^+56 \div ^-7$ $^-8$

30. $^-32 \div ^+2$ $^-16$ 31. $^+45 \div ^-3$ $^-15$ 32. $^+84 \div ^+4$ $^+21$

33. $^-52 \div ^-4$ $^+13$ 34. $^+95 \div ^+5$ $^+19$ 35. $^-72 \div ^-6$ $^+12$

36. $^-96 \div ^+24$ $^-4$ 37. $^-98 \div ^-14$ $^+7$ 38. $^+65 \div ^-13$ $^-5$

Find the end number.

39.

Find the starting number.

40.

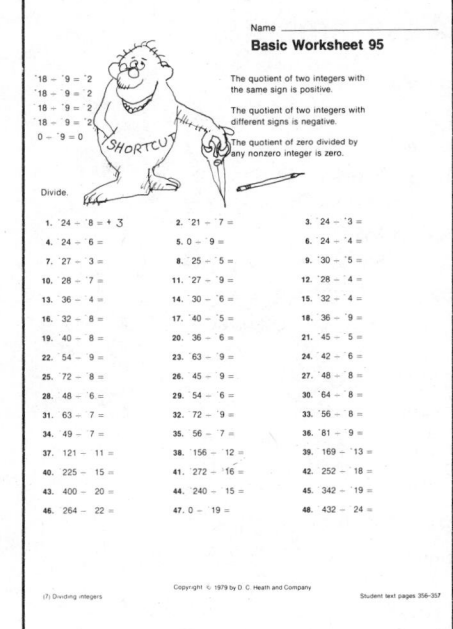

Solve.

1. 18% of 50 = n   9
2. 46% of 150 = n   69
3. 36% of 25 = n   9
4. $37\frac{1}{2}$% of 96 = n   36
5. $66\frac{2}{3}$% of 81 = n   54
6. 110% of 80 = n   88
7. 16% of 50 = n   8
8. $83\frac{1}{3}$% of 300 = n   250
9. 1% of 1000 = n   10
10. 200% of 25 = n   50

11. 15% of n = 15   100
12. 23% of n = 46   200
13. 20% of n = 16   80
14. $33\frac{1}{3}$% of n = 18   54
15. $62\frac{1}{2}$% of n = 55   88
16. $83\frac{1}{3}$% of n = 95   114
17. 40% of n = 28   70
18. 75% of n = 93   124
19. $16\frac{2}{3}$% of n = 13   78
20. 128% of n = 128   100

357

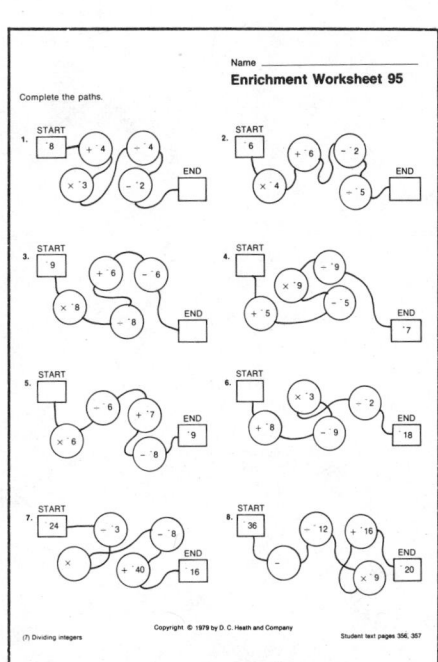

Follow-up Activities

Reinforcement You may wish students to review adding, subtracting, multiplying, and dividing integers at this time. If so, have them work through the following path to find the ending number. (The answer is given in red.)

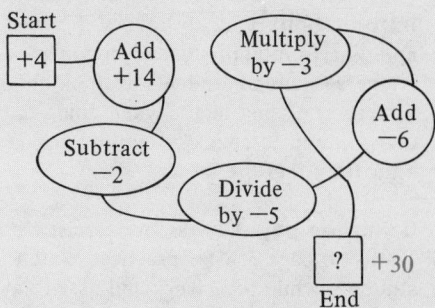

If time permits, have students create some paths of their own for their classmates to determine ending numbers for.

Enrichment Ask the more able students to determine the starting number by working through the following path backwards. Notice that to do this they will need to think of inverse operations. For example, the ending number was obtained by subtracting $^+6$ from some number. So, to find the number, we can add $^+6$ to the ending number. Have students continue backwards through the path in that manner. (The answer is in red.)

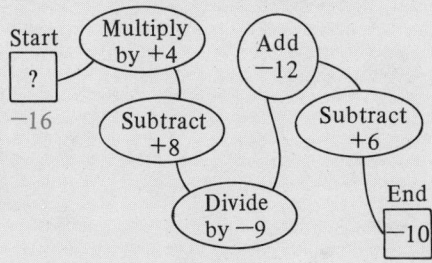

If time permits, have students create some paths for their classmates to find the starting or ending numbers for.

EXCURSION

Find 14 fractions between $\frac{1}{2}$ and $\frac{1}{3}$.

$$\frac{31}{90}, \frac{32}{90}, \frac{33}{90}, \cdots \frac{44}{90}$$

Lesson 169   357

STUDENT OBJECTIVES
To practice multiplication and division of
  integers.
To solve problems involving
  mathematics and geography.

Suggested Lesson Plan

Introduction Quickly review the rules
applying to multiplying and dividing
integers. Remind students to think about
finding a missing factor when doing the
division and to check by multiplying
after they find the factor.

Using the pages Assign exercises
1—64 on page 358 for practice. Watch
students while they work and assist any
student who has difficulty.
    Assign exercises 1—4 on pages 359
for problem-solving skills.

Practice exercises

Give each product.

1. $+9 \times +5$ $+45$ 2. $-9 \times +6$ -54 3. -7×-6 $+42$ 4. $+6 \times -5$ -30

5. -7×-8 $+56$ 6. $+4 \times -8$ -32 7. $+7 \times -7$ -49 8. -8×-9 $+72$

9. $+9 \times -4$ -36 10. $+8 \times +8$ $+64$ 11. $-3 \times +9$ -27 12. 0×-7 0

13. -6×-8 $+48$ 14. 0×0 0 15. $-9 \times +8$ -72 16. $+4 \times +7$ $+28$

17. $-9 \times +9$ -81 18. $+5 \times +5$ $+25$ 19. -6×0 0 20. $-8 \times +4$ -32

21. $+10 \times -5$ -50 22. -11×-3 $+33$ 23. -12×-2 $+24$ 24. $+5 \times -11$ -55

25. $-13 \times +4$ -52 26. $+6 \times +15$ $+90$ 27. $+19 \times 0$ 0 28. $-15 \times +12$ -180

29. $+16 \times -16$ -256 30. $-18 \times +20$ -360 31. $+23 \times +13$ $+299$ 32. 0×-22 0

Give each quotient.

33. $+21 \div +7$ $+3$ 34. $+24 \div -3$ -8 35. $-45 \div +5$ -9 36. $-25 \div -5$ $+5$

37. $-72 \div -9$ $+8$ 38. $+54 \div +6$ $+9$ 39. $-28 \div +4$ -7 40. $+48 \div -6$ -8

41. $+30 \div -5$ -6 42. $-36 \div +6$ -6 43. $-72 \div -8$ $+9$ 44. $+32 \div +8$ $+4$

45. $-63 \div +7$ -9 46. $+35 \div +7$ $+5$ 47. $-36 \div -9$ $+4$ 48. $+56 \div -8$ -7

49. $+42 \div -6$ -7 50. $-81 \div +9$ -9 51. $+49 \div +7$ $+7$ 52. $-42 \div -7$ $+6$

53. $-24 \div +2$ -12 54. $0 \div -8$ 0 55. $+45 \div +5$ $+9$ 56. $+42 \div -21$ -2

57. $0 \div +25$ 0 58. $+36 \div +3$ $+12$ 59. $+72 \div -18$ -4 60. $-75 \div +25$ -3

61. $+45 \div -15$ -3 62. $-60 \div -20$ $+3$ 63. $-96 \div +24$ -4 64. $+96 \div +12$ $+8$

358

Assignments

BASIC
page 358 exercises 1—64
page 359 exercises 1—4
Basic Worksheet 96

AVERAGE
page 358 exercises 1—64
page 359 exercises 1—4
Enrichment Worksheet 96

ENRICHED
page 358 exercises 1—64
page 359 exercises 1—4
Enrichment Worksheet 96

REVIEW PRACTICE
page 393 set 77

Mathematics and world geography

China

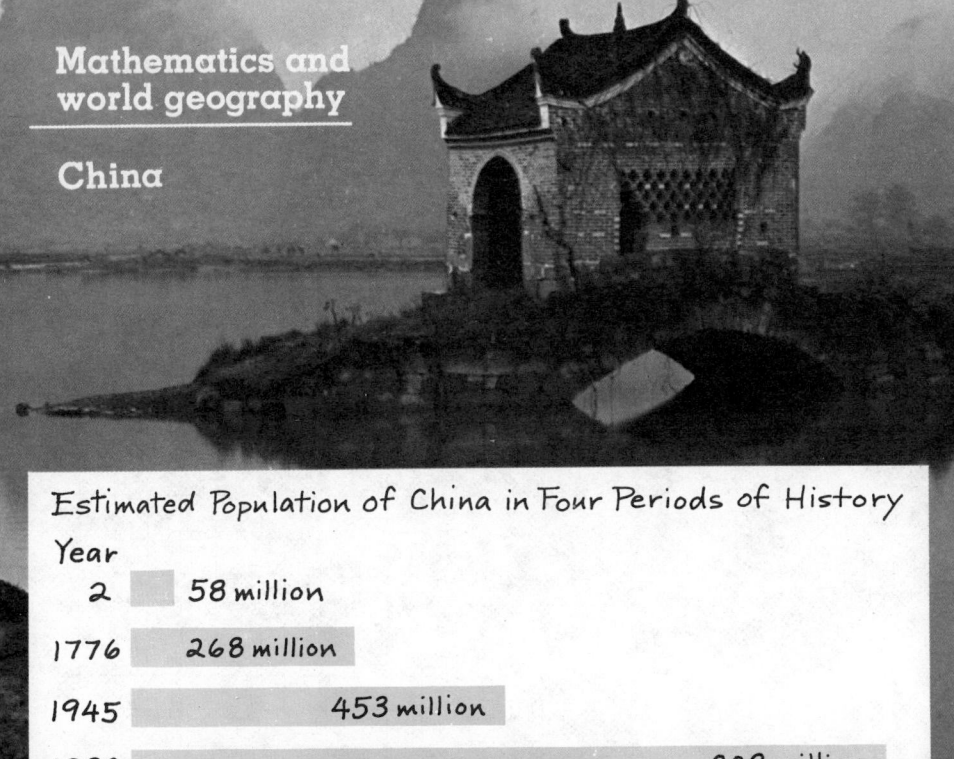

Estimated Population of China in Four Periods of History

Year	Population
2	58 million
1776	268 million
1945	453 million
1980	908 million

1. How many times greater is the estimated population in 1980 than the estimated population in the year 2?

   $15\frac{19}{29}$

2. The population of the United States of America is about 24% of the population of China. About how many people lived in the U.S.A. in 1945?

   108.7 million

3. China has the highest population of any country in the world. About 21% of all people live in China. What is the estimated population of the world in 1980?

   about 4323.8 million

4. The Chinese population doubled between 1945 and 1980. If the population continues to grow at the same rate, when will it be double the 1980 population?

   2015

359

Student text pages 358, 361

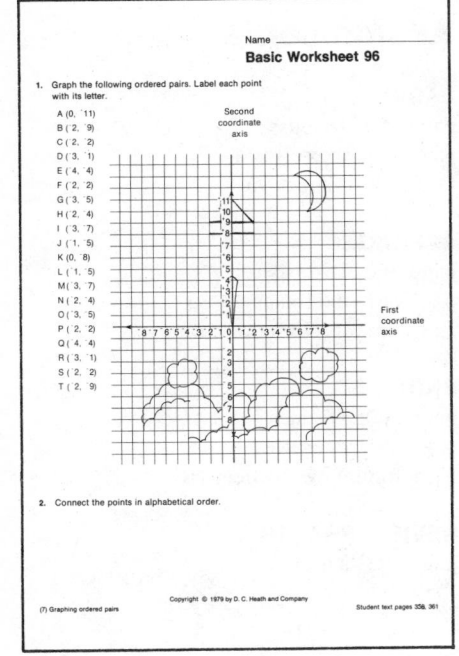

Basic Worksheet 96

1. Graph the following ordered pairs. Label each point with its letter.

A (0, ¯11)
B (2, ¯9)
C (2, 2)
D (3, ¯1)
E (4, 4)
F (2, 2)
G (3, 5)
H (2, 4)
I (3, 7)
J (1, 5)
K (0, 8)
L (1, 5)
M (3, 7)
N (2, ¯4)
O (3, 5)
P (2, 2)
Q (4, 4)
R (3, ¯1)
S (2, 2)
T (2, 9)

2. Connect the points in alphabetical order.

(7) Graphing ordered pairs
Copyright © 1979 by D. C. Heath and Company

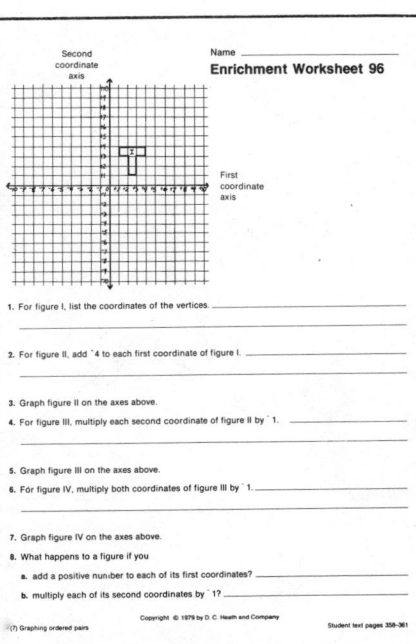

Enrichment Worksheet 96

1. For figure I, list the coordinates of the vertices. _____

2. For figure II, add ¯4 to each first coordinate of figure I. _____

3. Graph figure II on the axes above.

4. For figure III, multiply each second coordinate of figure II by ¯1. _____

5. Graph figure III on the axes above.

6. For figure IV, multiply both coordinates of figure III by ¯1. _____

7. Graph figure IV on the axes above.

8. What happens to a figure if you
   a. add a positive number to each of its first coordinates? _____
   b. multiply each of its second coordinates by ¯1? _____

(7) Graphing ordered pairs
Copyright © 1979 by D. C. Heath and Company
Student text pages 358–361

Follow-up Activities

Reinforcement To provide further problem-solving experiences have students write at least two stories for each of the following headlines:

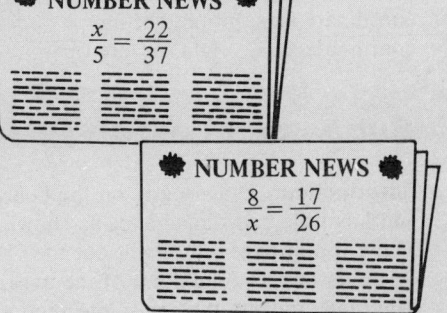

❀ **NUMBER NEWS** ❀
$$\frac{x}{5} = \frac{22}{37}$$

❀ **NUMBER NEWS** ❀
$$\frac{8}{x} = \frac{17}{26}$$

Enrichment Have more able students determine the starting number in the following path. To do this, they will need to think about inverse operations. For example, the end number is the result of adding ¯6 to some number. To find the number, we can subtract ¯6 from the end number. Have students continue backward through the path in the same manner.

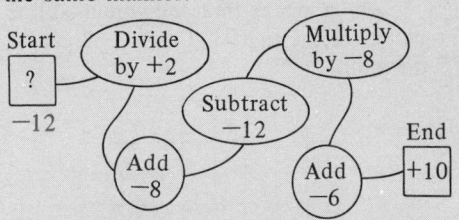

Start ? −12 — Divide by +2 — Multiply by ¯8 — Subtract ¯12 — Add ¯8 — Add ¯6 — End +10

If time permits, have students create some paths for their classmates to find the start or end numbers for.

EXCURSION

Here is a table. (See page 147.)

1	2	3	4	5
6	7	8	9	10
11	12	13	14	15
16	17	18	19	20

Pick a number on the table.

Make this move: ↓

Is the ending number 5 greater than your starting number? This means that the move ↓ and the rule $n \rightarrow n + 5$ give the same results.

Make rules for these moves.

1. →   2. ↓↘   3. ↙

4. →↘   5. ↖←

Make up other exercises.

add 1, add 6, add 4, add 7, subtract 8

Lesson 170   359

Suggested Lesson Plan

Introduction   Draw a grid on the board
and label the coordinate axes as shown
at the top of page 360. Point out the
origin as the crossing point of the axes.
Then tell students that each intersection
point of two grid lines has a location
that can be described in relation to the
origin. We describe a location as if we
were telling someone how to walk along
city streets from the origin to the given
point. We *always* tell the number of
blocks right or left first and then tell the
number of blocks up or down. Mark the
point labeled *A* below and tell students
that the directions for this point are $^+2$,
$^-3$, which means that one would walk 2
blocks to the right and then 3 blocks
down.

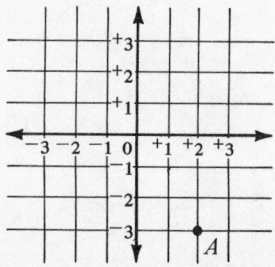

Indicate other points and ask students to
give directions as above. Be sure to pick
points in all parts of the grid. Next give
pairs of integers and ask students to
point to the points.

Using the pages   Go over the
exposition on page 360 with your
students. Be sure to emphasize the
vocabulary, especially that a point is the
graph of an ordered pair and the
numbers of the ordered pair are the
coordinates of the point.
   Assign the exercises. Watch
students to be sure that they do the
work correctly.

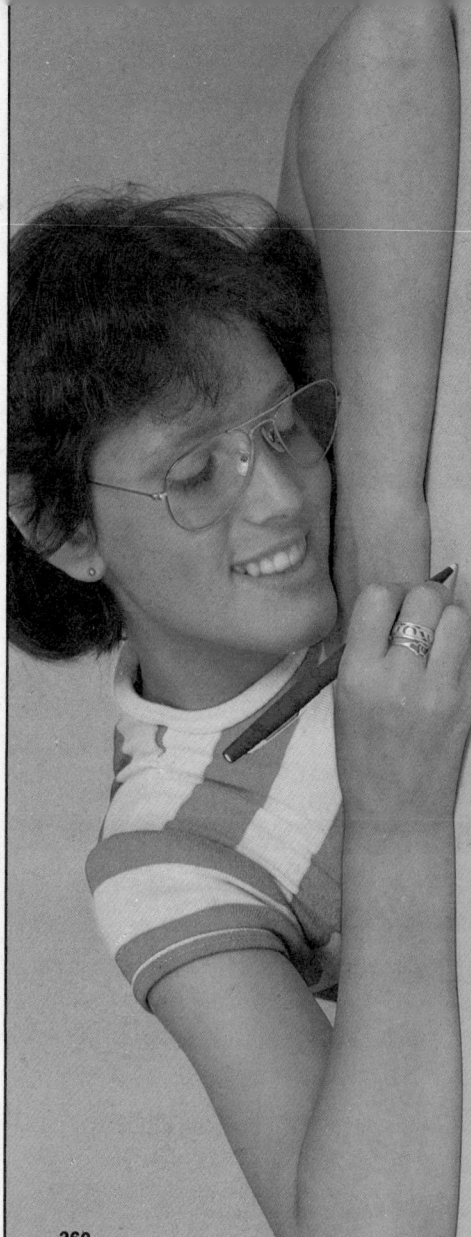

360

Graphing ordered pairs

Here is a **coordinate plane**. The red
horizontal number line is the **first coordinate axis**. The red vertical number
line is the **second coordinate axis**. The
point where the axes intersect is called
the **origin**.

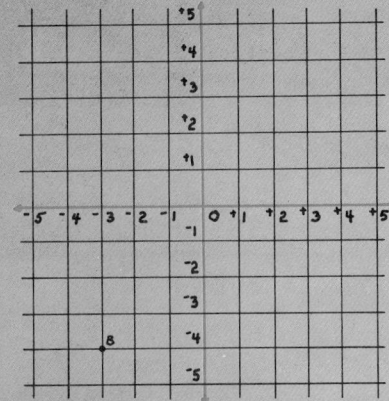

Ordered pairs of numbers may be
graphed on a coordinate plane. Here is
how to graph the ordered pair ($^-3$, $^-4$).

Step 1.   Start at the origin. Move along
the first coordinate axis to $^-3$.

Step 2.   Then move parallel to the second coordinate axis to $^-4$.

The ordered pair ($^-3$, $^-4$) gives the coordinates of point *B*. Point *B* is the graph
of the ordered pair ($^-3$, $^-4$).

Assignments

360   Lesson 171

EXERCISES

Give the coordinates of each point.

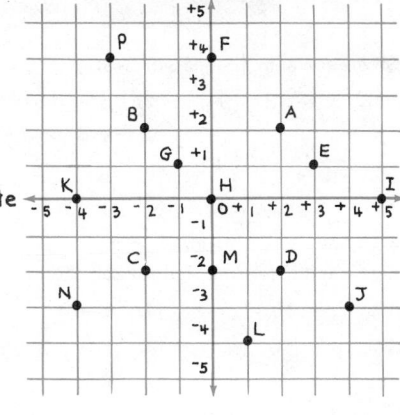

Second coordinate axis

First coordinate axis

1. *A*   2. *B*   3. *C*

4. *D*   5. *E*   6. *F*

7. *G*   8. *H*   9. *I*

10. *J*   11. *K*   12. *L*

13. *M*   14. *N*   15. *P*

Graph the following ordered pairs.
Label each point with its coordinates.

16. ($^+$3, $^+$2)   17. ($^+$3, $^-$2)   18. ($^-$3, $^+$2)   19. ($^-$3, $^-$2)

20. (0, 0)   21. ($^-$4, 0)   22. ($^-$4, $^-$1)   23. ($^-$4, $^+$1)

24. ($^+$4, $^-$1)   25. ($^+$4, $^+$1)   26. (0, $^-$4)   27. ($^+$1, $^-$2)

28. ($^-$3, $^+$3)   29. ($^-$2, $^-$2)   30. ($^+$3, 0)   31. ($^+$4, $^-$3)

32. Copy the triangle on graph paper and give the coordinates of each vertex.

33. Add $^+$3 to the first number of each ordered pair. Graph the new ordered pairs. Connect the points to make a new triangle.

34. Multiply the second number of each original pair by $^-$1. Graph the ordered pairs and draw the triangle.

35. Draw the triangle that you get by multiplying all the original numbers by $^-$2.

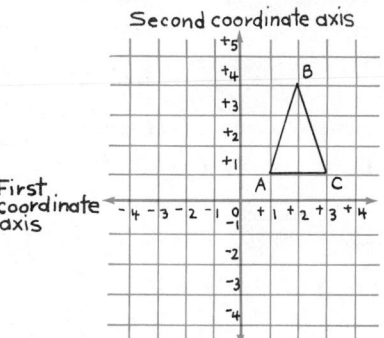

Second coordinate axis

First coordinate axis

361

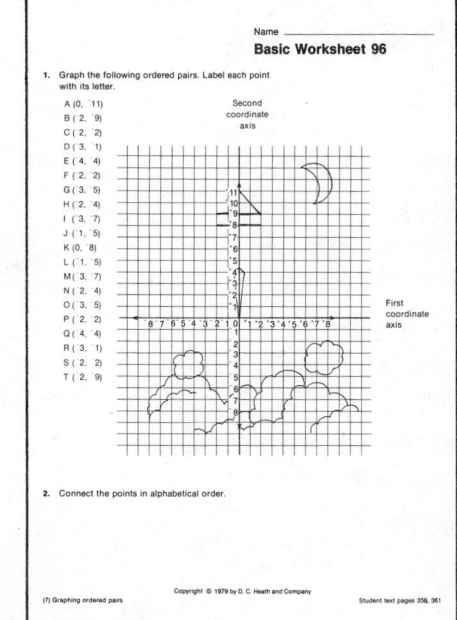

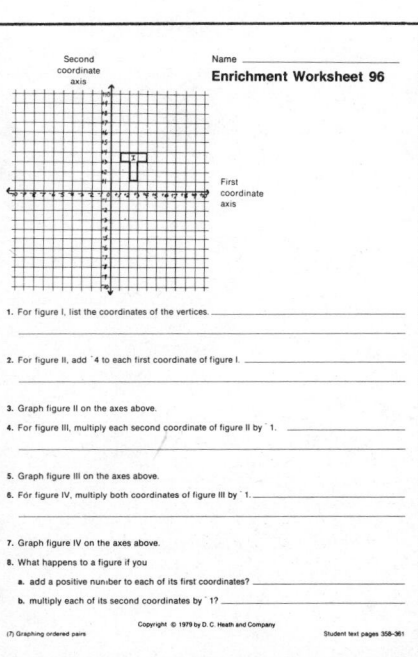

Follow-up Activities

Reinforcement You may wish to give students some ordered pairs of numbers to graph. Another activity would be to give students some ordered pairs to graph and then have them connect certain points to determine a figure. Here is an example. Have students first graph these ordered pairs and label each point with the proper letter. A ($^-$1, 0); B (0, 0); C ($^+$1, 0); D ($^+$5, 0); E ($^-$2, $^+$1); F ($^-$2, $^-$1); G ($^-$1, $^+$1); H ($^-$1, $^-$1); I (0, $^+$1); J (0, $^-$1); K ($^+$4, $^+$1); L ($^+$4, $^-$1)

Then ask students to draw these line segments to determine the figure: $\overline{AD}$, $\overline{EA}$, $\overline{FA}$, $\overline{GB}$, $\overline{HB}$, $\overline{IC}$, $\overline{JC}$, $\overline{KD}$, $\overline{LD}$. When completed, their work should look like this:

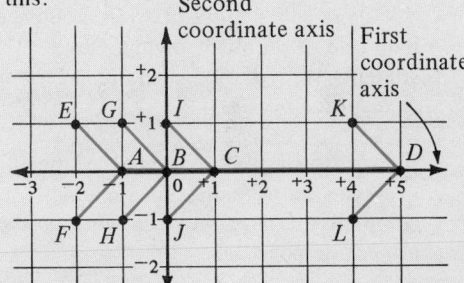

Second coordinate axis | First coordinate axis

Enrichment Some students may wish to create directions for drawing figures using ordered pairs as suggested in the activity above. Have students exchange their directions and draw each other's figures.

EXCURSION

Find the greatest four-digit number that has no two digits alike. 9876

Find the smallest five-digit number that has no two digits alike. 10,234

Answers.

1. ($^+$2, $^+$2)   2. ($^-$2, $^+$2)

3. ($^-$2, $^-$2)   4. ($^+$2, $^-$2)

5. ($^+$3, $^+$1)   6. (0, $^+$4)

7. ($^-$1, $^+$1)   8. (0, 0)

9. ($^+$5, 0)   10. ($^+$4, $^-$3)

11. ($^-$4, 0)   12. ($^+$1, $^-$4)

13. (0, $^-$2)   14. ($^-$4, $^-$3)

15. ($^-$3, $^+$4)

32. A:($^+$1, $^+$1), B:($^+$2, $^+$4), C:($^+$3, $^+$1)

33. ($^+$4, $^+$1), ($^+$5, $^+$4), ($^+$6, $^+$1)

34. ($^+$1, $^-$1), ($^+$2, $^-$4), ($^+$3, $^-$1)

35. ($^-$2, $^-$2), ($^-$4, $^-$8), ($^-$6, $^-$2)

STUDENT OBJECTIVE
To review the concepts and skills
introduced in Chapter 12.

Suggested Lesson Plan

Introduction No pre-text activity is
necessary for page 362, as this is a
checkup for the chapter. However, it
may be valuable to briefly review the
lessons in the chapter so that students
are reminded of the content over which
they will be tested.

    This Checkup will provide you with
data about how individual students
have mastered the skills of the chapter.
The Chapter Review on page 364 is
provided for those students who need
more specific individual help.

    Page 363 is more of a research page
than one of problem solving. Have
students study the page and read further
in resource books.

Using the pages Assign all of the
exercises on page 362. As students
complete the page they can work on the
project on page 363.

CHAPTER CHECKUP

Give each sum. [pages 348–349]

1. $^+6 + {}^+3$ $^+9$ 2. $^-5 + {}^+5$ 0 3. $^-3 + {}^-9$ $^-12$ 4. $^-6 + {}^+3$ $^-3$

5. $^+5 + {}^-5$ 0 6. $^-1 + {}^-6$ $^-7$ 7. $0 + {}^-2$ $^-2$ 8. $^+9 + {}^+7$ $^+16$

9. $^+10 + {}^-3$ $^+7$ 10. $^+8 + {}^+9$ $^+17$ 11. $^-4 + {}^+10$ $^+6$ 12. $^-5 + {}^-8$ $^-13$

Give each difference. [pages 350–351]

13. $^-5 - {}^+3$ $^-8$ 14. $^-2 - {}^-1$ $^-1$ 15. $^+3 - {}^+5$ $^-2$ 16. $^-4 - {}^+5$ $^-9$

17. $^+6 - {}^+6$ 0 18. $^-6 - {}^+2$ $^-8$ 19. $^+8 - {}^-8$ $^+16$ 20. $^-3 - {}^-6$ $^+3$

21. $^-9 - {}^-2$ $^-7$ 22. $^+6 - 0$ $^+6$ 23. $^-8 - {}^+3$ $^-11$ 24. $^+7 - {}^-9$ $^+16$

Give each product. [pages 354–355]

25. $^-6 \times {}^-4$ $^+24$ 26. $^+5 \times {}^+5$ $^+25$ 27. $^-5 \times {}^+7$ $^-35$ 28. $^+10 \times 0$ 0

29. $^+8 \times {}^-6$ $^-48$ 30. $^+8 \times {}^+7$ $^+56$ 31. $^-4 \times 0$ 0 32. $^-6 \times {}^-9$ $^+54$

33. $0 \times {}^-3$ 0 34. $^-8 \times {}^-9$ $^+72$ 35. $^-9 \times {}^+8$ $^-72$ 36. $^+6 \times {}^+9$ $^+54$

Give each quotient. [pages 356–357]

37. $^+45 \div {}^-9$ $^-5$ 38. $^-49 \div {}^+7$ $^-7$ 39. $^-40 \div {}^+8$ $^-5$ 40. $^+64 \div {}^-8$ $^-8$

41. $^+36 \div {}^+4$ $^+9$ 42. $^+56 \div {}^+7$ $^+8$ 43. $0 \div {}^-9$ 0 44. $^-40 \div {}^-8$ $^+5$

45. $^-72 \div {}^+8$ $^-9$ 46. $^-81 \div {}^-9$ $^+9$ 47. $^-48 \div {}^-6$ $^+8$ 48. $^+42 \div {}^+7$ $^+6$

Give the coordinates of each point. [pages 360–361]

49. A 50. B

51. C 52. D

53. E 54. F

55. G 56. H

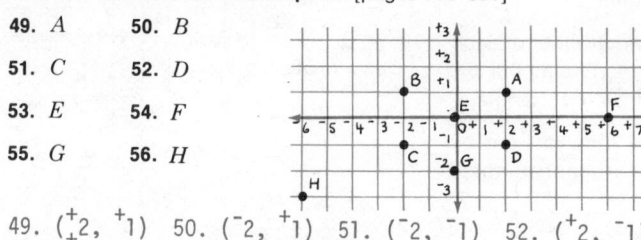

49. $(^+2, {}^+1)$ 50. $(^-2, {}^+1)$ 51. $(^-2, {}^-1)$ 52. $(^+2, {}^-1)$ 53. $(0, 0)$
54. $(^+6, 0)$ 55. $(0, {}^-2)$ 56. $(^-6, {}^-3)$

362

Assignments

BASIC
page 362 exercises 1—56
page 363 Project

AVERAGE
page 362 exercises 1—56
page 363 Project

ENRICHED
page 362 exercises 1—56
page 363 Project

EXTRA PROBLEM SOLVING
pages 428–429 set 16

Project

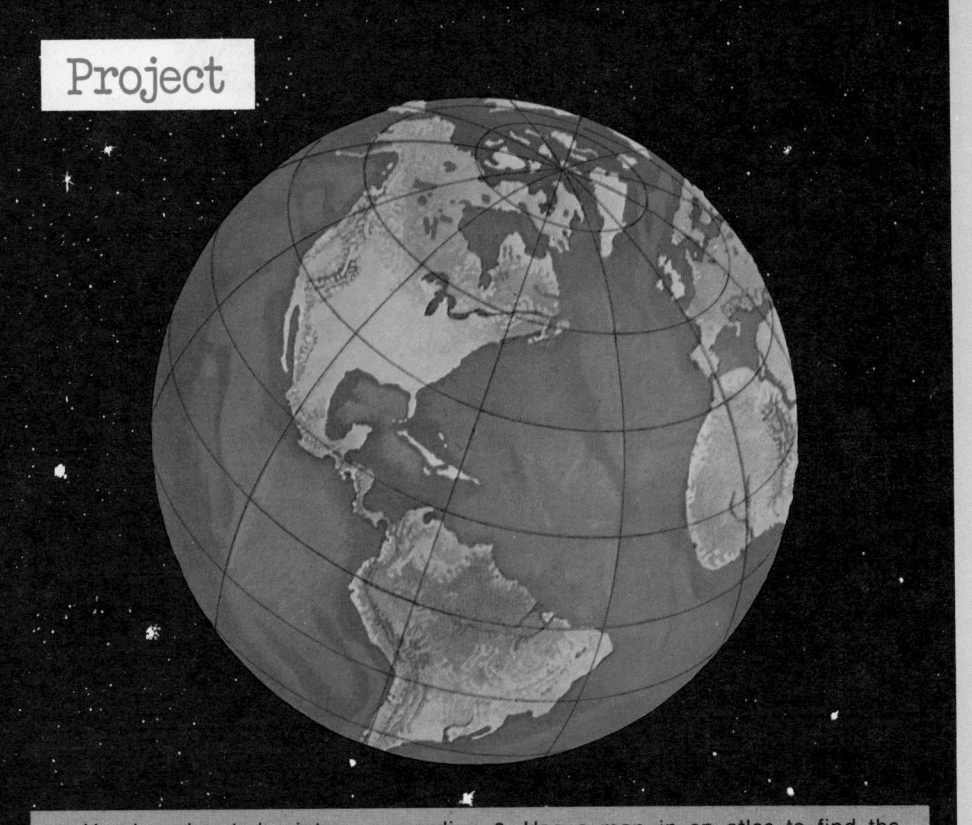

1. You have located points on a coordinate plane by referring to two lines, or axes. Circles around the earth called lines of latitude and longitude are used to locate places on the earth's surface. In an encyclopedia, see what you can learn about latitude and longitude.

2. Use a map in an atlas to find the latitude and longitude of the place where you live. What are the latitude and longitude of the point on the side of the earth opposite the place where you live?

3. The earth is divided into 24 time zones based on the lines of longitude. In an encyclopedia, see what you can learn about time zones. Which time zone do you live in?

363

You may wish to assign some of the Creative Problem Solving Activities (pages 461-477) at this time.

Follow-up Activities

Reinforcement Correct all items in the Chapter Checkup. Any student who misses 8 exercises, or more than three exercises on any one section needs additional help.

Enrichment Assign these pupils to the activities that have been suggested throughout the chapter. Have a student leader who is responsible for each activity to explain and help with the activity.

STUDENT OBJECTIVE
To review or extend the skills and concepts taught in Chapter 12.

Suggested Lesson Plan

Introduction After checking the Chapter Checkup you will know which students need additional reinforcement and which students will be able to go ahead with the Challenge activity. Get the better students started on page 365 first as the students who are having difficulty will need more of your time.

The students who need more review should go back and correct their errors on the Chapter Checkup. You may want to go over those questions orally if this group is small enough. Carefully probe to determine which concepts and skills the students have not mastered and work individually to correct these deficiencies.

Using the pages After the identified students have corrected the Chapter Checkup, they should answer questions 1—36. After they complete these questions, read the answers and let the students correct their own papers. Give them an opportunity to ask questions about those exercises they missed.

Assign page 365 to those students who did well on the Chapter Checkup. Have students work individually.

To subtract an integer, add its opposite.

$$-4 - {}^-5 = {}^-4 + {}^+5$$
$$= {}^+1$$

The product or quotient of 2 integers with the same sign is positive.

$$^-8 \times {}^-3 = {}^+24$$
$$^+12 \div {}^+4 = {}^+3$$

The product or quotient of 2 integers with different signs is negative.

$$^+8 \times {}^-2 = {}^-16$$
$$^-18 \div {}^+9 = {}^-2$$

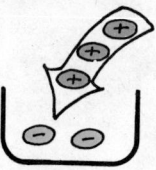 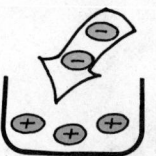

Give each sum.

1. $^-2 + {}^+3$ $^+1$
2. $^+3 + {}^-2$ $^+1$
3. $^-2 + {}^-2$ $^-4$
4. $^+5 + {}^-4$ $^+1$
5. $^-5 + {}^+4$ $^-1$
6. $^-8 + {}^-3$ $^-11$
7. $^+6 + {}^+2$ ^{8}
8. $^-7 + 0$ $^-7$
9. $0 + {}^+6$ $^+6$

Give each difference.

10. $^-8 - {}^-2$ $^-6$
11. $^+7 - {}^+2$ $^+5$
12. $^+5 - 0$ $^+5$
13. $^+9 - {}^-4$ $^+13$
14. $^-7 - {}^-3$ $^-4$
15. $^-10 - {}^+8$ $^-18$
16. $^+15 - {}^+7$ ^{8}
17. $^+16 - {}^-8$ $^+24$
18. $^-12 - {}^+4$ $^-16$

Give each product.

19. $^+9 \times {}^+8$ $^+72$
20. $^-6 \times {}^-7$ $^+42$
21. $^-6 \times {}^+8$ $^-48$
22. $0 \times {}^-7$ 0
23. $^+7 \times {}^+9$ $^+63$
24. $^+5 \times {}^-9$ $^-45$
25. $^-6 \times {}^+9$ $^-54$
26. 0×0 0
27. $^-8 \times {}^-7$ $^+56$

Give each quotient.

28. $^+63 \div {}^+9$ ^{7}
29. $^-56 \div {}^+8$ $^-7$
30. $^-54 \div {}^-6$ $^+9$
31. $^-42 \div {}^-6$ $^+7$
32. $^+48 \div {}^+6$ $^+8$
33. $^-36 \div {}^+4$ $^-9$
34. $^+32 \div {}^-4$ $^-8$
35. $0 \div {}^-8$ 0
36. $^-27 \div {}^-9$ $^+3$

364

Assignments

BASIC
page 364 exercises 1—36

AVERAGE
page 364 exercises 1—36

ENRICHED
page 365 exercises 1—2

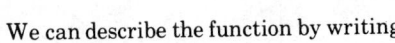

CHAPTER CHALLENGE

To get the **output number**, this function machine adds ⁻3 to the **input number**.

We can describe the function by writing

$$f : n \longrightarrow n + {}^-3$$

input number → output number

Read as "f takes n to $n + {}^-3$."

To graph a function, we graph the ordered pairs of the function. Here we have graphed some ordered pairs of the function

$$f : n \longrightarrow n + {}^-3$$

What do you notice about the points of the graph? What are some other points that belong to the graph of this function?
They are in a straight line.

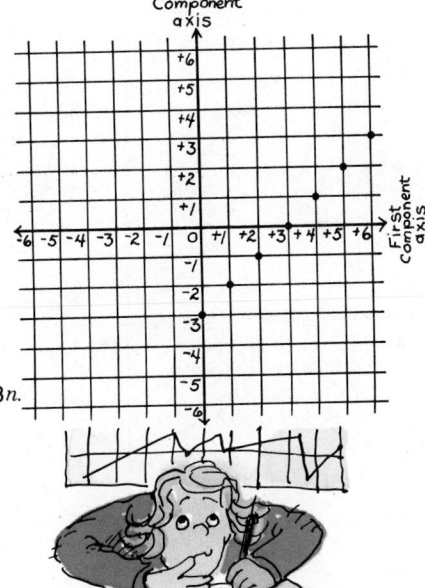

1. Copy and complete these ordered pairs of the function $f : n \longrightarrow {}^-3n$.

   a. $({}^-3, ?)$ ⁺9 **b.** $({}^+1, ?)$ ⁻3 **c.** $(0, ?)$ 0

   d. $({}^-4, ?)$ ⁺12 **e.** $({}^-2, ?)$ ⁺6 **f.** $({}^+3, ?)$ ⁻9

   g. $({}^+2, ?)$ ⁻6 **h.** $({}^+4, ?)$ ⁻12 **i.** $({}^-1, ?)$ ⁺3

   j. Graph your ordered pairs for $f : n \longrightarrow {}^-3n$.

2. Graph some ordered pairs of these functions.

   a. $g : n \longrightarrow {}^+2n$ **b.** $h : n \longrightarrow n - {}^-4$

   c. $j : n \longrightarrow n^2$

365

a b c d | a b c d | 13 a b c d | 3 a b c d | 29 a b c d
14 | 34 | 14 | 4 | 30 a b c d
a b c d | a b c d | a b c d | c d | a b c d
15 | a b c | 31 b c | a b c

STUDENT OBJECTIVES

To practice skills learned previously.
To practice using a standardized-test format.

Suggested Lesson Plan

Using the pages The Major Checkup at the end of each chapter of this textbook is given in standardized-test format. The answer sheet on page 448 is the type used with many standardized tests. You may duplicate it for use with the Major Checkups.

Pass out the answer sheets and be sure students understand how to use them. Allow a specified time, perhaps twenty minutes, to complete the checkup. Assign the exercises and use the results to determine what review is needed.

The table below correlates the test items and the student text pages. Assign review exercises as indicated by the Major Checkup results.

Test Item	Text Pages	Test Item	Text Pages
1	64–65	7	212–213
2	86–87	8	260–261
3	96–97	9	262–263
4	188–189	10	282–283
5	190–191	11	310–311
6	204–205	12	330–331

Chapter 12 Posttest

See page 54 for a full discussion of how to use the posttest. The table below suggests Extra Practice exercises and Basic Worksheets for those students who need further practice or reteaching.

Objectives	Extra Practice Sets	Pages	Basic Worksheets
12-1	87	396	92
12-2	88	396	93
12-3	89	397	94
12-4	90	397	95
12-5			96

MAJOR CHECKUP
Standardized Format

Choose the correct letter.

1. Round 42.0385 to the nearest thousandth.
a. 42.04
b. 42.038
c. 42.039
d. none of these

2. Multiply.
59.2×4.83
a. 8.880
b. 2859.36
c. 285.936
d. none of these

3. Divide.
$0.016\overline{)7.568}$
a. 47.3
b. 4.73
c. 473
d. none of these

4. Add.
$8\frac{5}{6} + 3\frac{3}{4}$
a. $11\frac{7}{12}$
b. $11\frac{1}{12}$
c. $12\frac{7}{12}$
d. none of these

5. Subtract.
$12 - 5\frac{3}{4}$
a. $7\frac{3}{4}$
b. $7\frac{1}{4}$
c. $6\frac{1}{4}$
d. none of these

6. Find the product.
$\frac{3}{8} \times \frac{2}{3}$
a. $\frac{1}{4}$
b. $\frac{9}{16}$
c. 4
d. none of these

7. Give the quotient.
$\frac{5}{6} \div \frac{5}{4}$
a. $\frac{3}{2}$
b. $\frac{25}{24}$
c. $\frac{2}{3}$
d. none of these

8. $33\frac{1}{3}\%$ of $96 = $ ___?___
a. 32
b. 64
c. 288
d. none of these

9. 40% of ___?___ = 54
a. 90
b. 135
c. $21\frac{3}{5}$
d. none of these

10. A bicycle that regularly sells for $96 was put on sale for $80. The percent of discount was
a. 24%
b. 25%
c. 16%
d. none of these

11. How many lines of symmetry does a parallelogram have?
a. 1
b. 2
c. 4
d. none of these

12. Imagine tossing a dime and then tossing a nickel. The probability of getting both tails is
a. $\frac{1}{2}$
b. $\frac{3}{4}$
c. $\frac{1}{4}$
d. none of these

366

Answers for Chapter 12 Posttest

1. $^+7$ **2.** $^-4$ **3.** $^+2$ **4.** $^-9$ **5.** $^+7$
6. $^-11$ **7.** $^+26$ **8.** $^-32$ **9.** $^+3$ **10.** $^-2$
11. $^-8$ **12.** $^+10$ **13.** $^-1$ **14.** $^+17$ **15.** $^-9$
16. 0 **17.** $^+12$ **18.** $^-24$ **19.** $^-21$
20. $^+42$ **21.** $^-30$ **22.** $^-84$ **23.** $^+135$
24. $^+80$ **25.** $^+4$ **26.** $^-3$ **27.** $^-6$ **28.** $^+4$
29. $^+7$ **30.** $^-7$ **31.** $^-5$ **32.** $^+8$
33. $(^+1, ^+2)$ **34.** $(0, ^+2)$ **35.** $(0, ^+1)$
36. $(0, ^-1)$ **37.** $(^-2, ^-2)$ **38.** $(^-3, ^+3)$

Chapter 12 Posttest

Name _____

Date _____

Number right

0-2	3	4	5	6	7	8

Add. [Obj. 12-1, pages 346–348, 352]

1. $^+3 + {}^+4 =$ _____
2. $^+3 + {}^-7 =$ _____
3. $^-4 + {}^+6 =$ _____
4. $^-6 + {}^-3 =$ _____

5. $^+19 + {}^-12 =$ _____
6. $^-25 + {}^+14 =$ _____
7. $^-12 + {}^+38 =$ _____
8. $^-17 + {}^-15 =$ _____

Subtract. [Obj. 12-2, pages 350–352]

0-2	3	4	5	6	7	8

9. $^+6 - {}^+3 =$ _____
10. $^+7 - {}^+9 =$ _____
11. $^-2 - {}^+6 =$ _____
12. $^+8 - {}^-2 =$ _____

13. $^-4 - {}^-3 =$ _____
14. $^+9 - {}^-8 =$ _____
15. $^+27 - {}^+36 =$ _____
16. $^-25 - {}^-25 =$ _____

Multiply. [Obj. 12-3, pages 354–355, 358]

0-2	3	4	5	6	7	8

17. $^+3 \times {}^+4 =$ _____
18. $^+6 \times {}^-4 =$ _____
19. $^-7 \times {}^+3 =$ _____
20. $^-7 \times {}^-6 =$ _____

21. $^-5 \times {}^+6 =$ _____
22. $^+14 \times {}^-6 =$ _____
23. $^+15 \times {}^+9 =$ _____
24. $^-8 \times {}^-10 =$ _____

Divide. [Obj. 12-4, pages 356–358]

0-2	3	4	5	6	7	8

25. $^+12 \div {}^+3 =$ _____
26. $^+12 \div {}^-4 =$ _____
27. $^-18 \div {}^+3 =$ _____
28. $^-24 \div {}^-6 =$ _____

29. $^+28 \div {}^+4 =$ _____
30. $^+35 \div {}^-5 =$ _____
31. $^-40 \div {}^+8 =$ _____
32. $^-56 \div {}^-7 =$ _____

Give the coordinates of the points. [Obj. 12-5, pages 360–361]

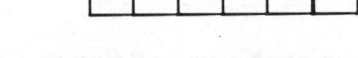

0	1	2	3	4	5	6

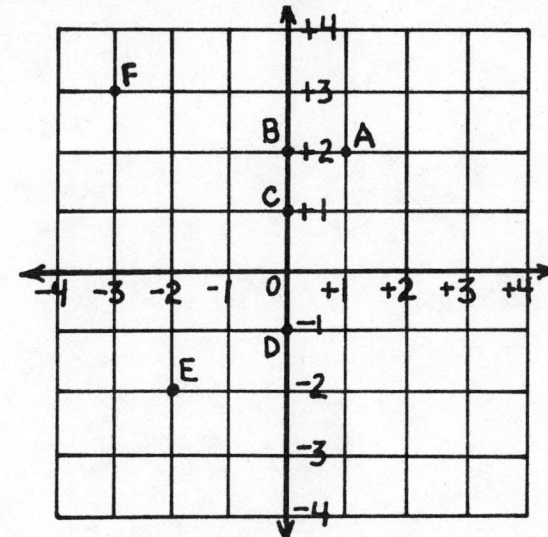

33. A: (_____, _____)
34. B: (_____, _____)

35. C: (_____, _____)
36. D: (_____, _____)

37. E: (_____, _____)
38. F: (_____, _____)

Final Test

Add, subtract, multiply, or divide.

1. 296
    58
  341
+ 67

2. 8402
− 1597

3. 504
× 261

4. 326)‾18256‾

Round 59.8956 to the nearest

5. hundredth　　　**6.** tenth

Complete.

7. 9.382 + 6.88 = ___?___

8. 7.43 − 2.286 = ___?___

Multiply or divide.

9. 0.74
× 0.06

10. 32.1
× 6.23

11. 0.04)‾3.904‾

12. 3.02)‾7.7312‾

Complete.

13. The greatest common factor of 24 and 36 is ___?___.

14. The prime factorization of 48 is ___?___.

15. The least common multiple of 12 and 9 is ___?___.

16. The standard numeral for 4^3 is ___?___.

Complete.

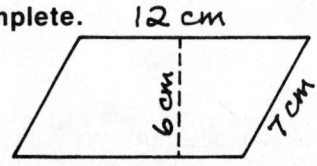

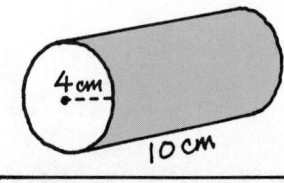

Use 3.14 as an approximation for π.

17. The perimeter is ___?___.

18. The area is ___?___.

19. The surface area is ___?___.

20. The volume is ___?___.

Give each sum or difference in lowest terms.

21. $\frac{1}{3} + \frac{1}{4}$　　　**22.** $\frac{2}{3} - \frac{1}{2}$　　　**23.** $4\frac{3}{5} + 2\frac{1}{2}$　　　**24.** $9\frac{3}{8} - 6\frac{3}{4}$

Continued on the next page

Answers.

1. 762　2. 6805　3. 131,544　4. 56　5. 59.90　6. 59.9　7. 16.262　8. 5.144　9. 0.0444　10. 199.983　11. 97.6
12. 2.56　13. 12　14. 2 x 2 x 2 x 2 x 3　15. 36　16. 64　17. 38 cm　18. 72 cm²　19. 351.68 cm²　20. 502.4 cm³
21. 7/12　22. 1/6　23. 7 1/10　24. 2 5/8

Give each product or quotient.

25. $\frac{3}{4} \times \frac{2}{5}$ **26.** $\frac{5}{6} \div \frac{3}{2}$ **27.** $2\frac{1}{4} \times 3\frac{1}{2}$ **28.** $3\frac{1}{2} \div 2\frac{2}{3}$

Solve.

29. $\frac{n}{4} = \frac{5}{8}$ **30.** $\frac{5}{n} = \frac{3}{8}$ **31.** 25% of 10 = n **32.** 20% of n = 17

Solve.

33. Apples are on sale at 6 for 98¢. How much will 1 apple cost?

34. Oranges are priced at 6 for 89¢. How much will 5 oranges cost?

35. Jim bought a $40 tennis racket on sale for 20% off. What was the sale price of the racket?

36. How much interest will be charged on a loan of $2000 at 8% per year for 6 months?

True or false?

37. An acute angle is an angle that measures 90°.

38. Figures that have the same size and shape are called congruent figures.

39. An isosceles triangle has 1 line of symmetry.

40. A parallelogram has a point of symmetry.

Think about putting these marbles in a sack, mixing, and picking one without looking. Give each probability in lowest terms.

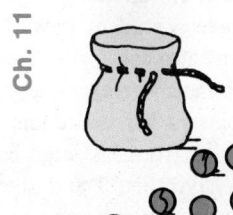
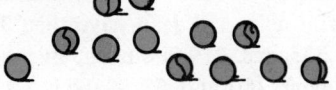

41. P(green)

42. P(not green)

43. P(red or green)

Answer each question about the test data.

Test Scores			
99	90	83	80
99	90	83	76
99	90	83	70
96	86	82	65
95	85	81	50
93	84	81	43
90	84	81	43

44. What is the mean?

45. What is the median?

46. What is the range?

Add, subtract, multiply, or divide.

47. $^+8 + {}^-9$ **48.** $^-3 - {}^+7$ **49.** $^-9 \times {}^-6$ **50.** $^+24 \div {}^-3$

Answers.
25. 3/10 26. 5/9 27. 7 7/8 28. 1 5/16 29. 2 1/2 30. 13 1/3 31. 2 1/2 32. 85 33. 17¢ 34. 75¢ 35. $32
36. $80 37. false 38. true 39. true 40. true 41. 1/6 42. 5/6 43. 2/3 44. 81 13/28 45. 83 1/2 46. 56
47. ⁻1 48. ⁻10 49. ⁺54 50. ⁻8

Student Text Resources

This section, pages 369–437 of the student's text, can help you diagnose computational weaknesses and provide additional practice in computation and problem solving. It also contains a glossary with a list of symbols and formulas introduced and used at Level 7.

Skill Test 369–373

This is a criterion-referenced test for all the computational skills covered in Level 7. For each of the 49 skills, the objective, the pages in the text on which the skill is taught, and the appropriate sets of extra practice for reinforcement are listed in this teacher's edition. The Skill Test may be used in several ways:

1) To periodically evaluate previously learned computational skills
2) To determine the computational proficiency of a transfer student
3) As a "midyear" or "final" on computational skills

Extra Practice 374–397

This section consists of 90 sets of extra practice exercises on all the basic computational skills. There are several ways the teacher's guide helps you assign these sets. The assignment guide for each lesson where a skill is introduced lists the corresponding set as *Extra Practice*. The same set is listed in a later assignment guide as *Review Practice* to help maintain the previously learned skill. The Record and Assignment charts also reference the sets. And, as mentioned above, the sets are correlated with the Skill Test.

Extra Problem Solving 398–429

Sixteen Extra Problem Solving sets are provided for your students. Each set has some problems that are quite easy so that less able students can have some success, and most sets have some problems that are more difficult so that better students can be challenged. A more complete description of the sets and their use in the classroom may be found starting on page 398 in this teacher's edition.

Extra Problem Solving can be used in more than one way. Students generally need both instruction and practice in problem solving, so we offer an additional suggestion for using an Extra Problem Solving set.

Remember that in the text we introduce these problem-solving steps:

1. Read the problem and find the question.
2. What are the facts?
3. Decide what to do.
4. Answer the question.
5. Estimate. Does your answer seem right?

You can emphasize step 1 by reading the problem aloud and having students give the question. To emphasize step 2, read the problem several times and have the students give the facts. For step 3, you might ask whether one would add, subtract, multiply, or divide. Another option is to copy the problem on the chalkboard, omitting the numbers, and ask students what operation they would use. To emphasize step 5, you can first read a problem to the class and then write two answers on the chalkboard. Reread the problem and have a student pick the more reasonable answer. You might also ask for an explanation of why that answer was chosen. For example, for the problem "Jean had 277 coins in her collection. Her grandfather gave her 58 coins from his large collection. How many coins did Jean have then?" and the possible answers 335 and 219, a student might estimate and say 277 is about 280 and 58 is about 60, so the answer should be about 280 + 60, or 340. Since the answer should be about 340, the answer 219 could not be correct.

Glossary, Symbols, Formulas 430–437

The Glossary can be used to review the key mathematical terms that are used at this level, but students should first learn most concepts through use and from examples. Wordy descriptions can be confusing unless the concept has already been developed. We have tried to give understandable descriptions rather than precise mathematical definitions. Such precision can be obtained only in a rigorous deductive development of mathematics, which is not appropriate for this level.

Following the Glossary is a list of the symbols and formulas used in Level 7. Again, this page can be used to review the symbols and formulas, but students should first learn them through use and examples.

Skill Test

See page 373 for a correlation of these skills with the learning objectives, student text pages, and Extra Practice Sets.

	skill objective	**test items**			
1	Add two or more numbers	475 + 312	296 + 352	596 628 + 327	3758 5863 + 9479
2	Subtract any two numbers	352 – 121	462 – 139	526 – 347	6000 – 2382
3	Multiply by a 1-digit number	241 × 2	28 × 3	516 × 6	2371 × 8
4	Multiply by 10 or 100	67 × 10	38 × 100	576 × 10	3241 × 100
5	Multiply by a 2-digit number	431 × 26	358 × 34	544 × 61	8075 × 85
6	Multiply by a 3-digit number	543 × 122	308 × 496	615 × 204	8312 × 426
7	Divide by a 1-digit number	3)252	6)594	8)462	5)4295
8	Divide by a 2-digit number	23)713	45)1080	93)5762	42)8320
9	Divide by a 3-digit number	200)4600	120)960	431)13392	486)2483
10	Add any two decimals	3.51 + 2.81	4.75 + 2.68	67.5 + 9.8	4.832 + .96

Answers.

1. 787; 648; 1551; 19,100 / 2. 231; 323; 179; 3618 / 3. 482; 84; 3096; 18,968 / 4. 670; 3800; 5760; 324,100 /
5. 11,206; 12,172; 33,184; 686,375 / 6. 66,246; 152,768; 125,460; 3,540,912 / 7. 84; 99; 57 R6; 859 /
8. 31; 24; 61 R89; 198 R4; / 9. 23; 8; 31 R31; 5 R53 / 10. 6.32; 7.43; 77.3; 5.792

	skill objective	test items			
11	Subtract any two decimals	$\begin{array}{r}.483\\-.265\end{array}$	$\begin{array}{r}2.67\\-.88\end{array}$	$\begin{array}{r}35.2\\-17.8\end{array}$	$\begin{array}{r}18.6\\-9.83\end{array}$
12	Multiply by a whole number	$\begin{array}{r}5.6\\\times 3\end{array}$	$\begin{array}{r}7.24\\\times 8\end{array}$	$\begin{array}{r}1.59\\\times 12\end{array}$	$\begin{array}{r}3.68\\\times 142\end{array}$
13	Multiply by a decimal	$\begin{array}{r}5.3\\\times 2.7\end{array}$	$\begin{array}{r}.41\\\times .08\end{array}$	$\begin{array}{r}.62\\\times .37\end{array}$	$\begin{array}{r}1.46\\\times 3.8\end{array}$
14	Divide by a whole number	$3\overline{)85.2}$	$5\overline{)6.25}$	$56\overline{)71.68}$	$200\overline{)4.6}$
15	Divide by a decimal	$.9\overline{)1.08}$	$.06\overline{).192}$	$2.3\overline{)1.334}$	$.46\overline{)1.426}$
16	Divide and round to the nearest tenth	$.6\overline{)5.23}$	$.9\overline{)1}$	$1.6\overline{)59.2}$	$.45\overline{)17.6}$
17	Find an equivalent fraction	$\frac{2}{3}=\frac{?}{12}$	$\frac{5}{8}=\frac{?}{64}$	$\frac{5}{6}=\frac{?}{30}$	$\frac{5}{4}=\frac{?}{32}$
18	Reduce a fraction to lowest terms	$\frac{6}{12}$	$\frac{18}{24}$	$\frac{15}{35}$	$\frac{45}{63}$
19	Compare fractions	$<$ **or** $>$? $\frac{3}{7}\bullet\frac{4}{7}$	$\frac{2}{3}\bullet\frac{3}{5}$	$\frac{4}{8}\bullet\frac{4}{7}$	$\frac{4}{7}\bullet\frac{5}{8}$
20	Add fractions	$\frac{1}{8}+\frac{3}{4}$	$\frac{1}{6}+\frac{1}{3}$	$\frac{2}{3}+\frac{2}{5}$	$\frac{3}{4}+\frac{2}{3}$
21	Subtract fractions	$\frac{3}{4}-\frac{1}{8}$	$\frac{1}{3}-\frac{1}{6}$	$\frac{2}{3}-\frac{2}{5}$	$\frac{3}{4}-\frac{2}{3}$
22	Change a fraction to a mixed number	$\frac{7}{2}=\underline{\ ?\ }$	$\frac{8}{3}=\underline{\ ?\ }$	$\frac{15}{4}=\underline{\ ?\ }$	$\frac{23}{8}=\underline{\ ?\ }$

Answers.

11. 0.218; 1.79; 17.4; 8.77 / 12. 16.8; 57.92; 19.08; 522.56 / 13. 14.31; 0.0328; 0.2294; 5.548 /
14. 28.4; 1.25; 1.28; 0.023 / 15. 1.2; 3.2; 0.58; 3.1 / 16. 8.7; 1.1; 37; 39.1 / 17. 8; 40; 25; 40 /
18. 1/2; 3/4; 3/7; 5/7 / 19. <; >; <; < / 20. 7/8; 1/2; 16/15; 17/12 / 21. 5/8; 1/6; 4/15; 1/12 /
22. 3 1/2; 2 2/3; 3 3/4; 2 7/8

	skill objective	test items			
23	Change a mixed number to a fraction	$2\frac{1}{2} = \underline{?}$	$3\frac{2}{3} = \underline{?}$	$5\frac{3}{4} = \underline{?}$	$4\frac{7}{8} = \underline{?}$
24	Add mixed numbers	$3\frac{5}{7}$ $+2\frac{3}{7}$	$4\frac{2}{3}$ $+1\frac{1}{3}$	$12\frac{5}{6}$ $+4\frac{3}{8}$	$5\frac{2}{3}$ $+4\frac{3}{4}$
25	Subtract mixed numbers	$5\frac{2}{7}$ $-1\frac{1}{7}$	$6\frac{2}{9}$ $-3\frac{5}{9}$	$6\frac{3}{4}$ $-4\frac{5}{6}$	$8\frac{2}{3}$ $-3\frac{3}{4}$
26	Multiply fractions	$\frac{2}{3} \times \frac{4}{7}$	$\frac{3}{5} \times \frac{5}{8}$	$\frac{6}{7} \times \frac{5}{3}$	$\frac{12}{15} \times \frac{5}{4}$
27	Find a fraction of a number	$\frac{1}{2}$ of 18	$\frac{2}{3}$ of 21	$\frac{4}{3}$ of 12	$\frac{5}{6}$ of 18
28	Divide fractions	$\frac{3}{4} \div \frac{5}{2}$	$\frac{3}{4} \div \frac{3}{8}$	$\frac{2}{3} \div \frac{3}{4}$	$\frac{5}{7} \div \frac{3}{7}$
29	Simplify fractions	$\frac{\frac{2}{3}}{\frac{2}{5}}$	$\frac{\frac{3}{4}}{\frac{3}{8}}$	$\frac{\frac{2}{3}}{\frac{3}{4}}$	$\frac{\frac{5}{9}}{\frac{2}{3}}$
30	Change a fraction to a decimal	$\frac{1}{4} = \underline{?}$	$\frac{2}{5} = \underline{?}$	$\frac{9}{10} = \underline{?}$	$\frac{3}{2} = \underline{?}$
31	Change a mixed number to a decimal	$2\frac{1}{2} = \underline{?}$	$1\frac{3}{4} = \underline{?}$	$2\frac{5}{8} = \underline{?}$	$3\frac{3}{8} = \underline{?}$
32	Change a decimal to a fraction	$0.5 = \underline{?}$	$0.25 = \underline{?}$	$0.65 = \underline{?}$	$0.75 = \underline{?}$
33	Change a decimal to a mixed number	$1.5 = \underline{?}$	$2.75 = \underline{?}$	$1.375 = \underline{?}$	$2.05 = \underline{?}$
34	Change a fraction to a mixed decimal	$\frac{1}{3} = \underline{?}$	$\frac{2}{3} = \underline{?}$	$\frac{5}{6} = \underline{?}$	$\frac{4}{9} = \underline{?}$

Answers.

23. 5/2; 11/3; 23/4; 39/8 / 24. 6 1/7; 6; 17 5/24; 10 5/12 / 25. 4 1/7; 2 2/3; 1 11/12; 4 11/12 /
26. 8/21; 3/8; 10/7; 1 / 27. 9; 14; 16; 15 / 28. 3/10; 2; 8/9; 5/3 / 29. 5/3; 2; 8/9; 5/6 /
30. 0.25; 0.4; 0.9; 1.5 / 31. 2.5; 1.75; 2.625; 3.375 / 32. 1/2; 1/4; 13/20; 3/4 / 33. 1 1/2; 2 3/4; 1 3/8; 2 1/20 /
34. 0.33 1/3; 0.66 2/3; 0.83 1/3; 0.44 4/9

skill objective		test items	

35 Multiply mixed numbers
$$3\frac{1}{2} \times 2 \qquad 1\frac{1}{4} \times 1\frac{1}{2}$$
$$2\frac{1}{3} \times 3\frac{2}{3} \qquad 1\frac{2}{3} \times 2\frac{3}{4}$$

36 Divide mixed numbers
$$3\frac{1}{2} \div 2 \qquad 2\frac{3}{4} \div 1\frac{1}{3}$$
$$2\frac{1}{3} \div 1\frac{1}{2} \qquad 4\frac{2}{3} \div 2\frac{3}{8}$$

37 Solve a proportion
$$\frac{5}{3} = \frac{n}{4} \qquad \frac{2}{n} = \frac{3}{8}$$
$$\frac{4}{5} = \frac{6}{n} \qquad \frac{n}{5} = \frac{6}{7}$$

38 Change a fraction to a percent
$$\frac{3}{10} = \underline{?} \qquad \frac{1}{4} = \underline{?} \qquad \frac{2}{5} = \underline{?} \qquad \frac{3}{4} = \underline{?}$$

39 Change a percent to a fraction
$$60\% = \underline{?} \quad 5\% = \underline{?} \quad 25\% = \underline{?} \quad 90\% = \underline{?}$$

40 Change a decimal to a percent
$$0.1 = \underline{?} \quad 0.15 = \underline{?} \quad 2.36 = \underline{?} \quad 1.7 = \underline{?}$$

41 Change a percent to a decimal
$$18\% = \underline{?} \; 12.2\% = \underline{?} \; 65.3\% = \underline{?} \; 8.6\% = \underline{?}$$

42 Change a fraction to a mixed percent
$$\frac{1}{3} = \underline{?} \qquad \frac{2}{3} = \underline{?} \qquad \frac{5}{6} = \underline{?} \qquad \frac{5}{9} = \underline{?}$$

43 Find a percent of a number
$$25\% \text{ of } 28 = n \qquad\qquad 35\% \text{ of } 50 = n$$
$$33\frac{1}{3}\% \text{ of } 51 = n \qquad\qquad 83\frac{1}{3}\% \text{ of } 72 = n$$

44 Find the number when a percent is given
$$10\% \text{ of } n = 6 \qquad\qquad 75\% \text{ of } n = 45$$
$$12\frac{1}{2}\% \text{ of } n = 16 \qquad\qquad 32\% \text{ of } n = 8$$

Answers.

35. 7; 1 7/8; 8 5/9; 4 7/12 / 36. 1 3/4; 2 1/16; 1 5/9; 1 55/57; / 37. 6 2/3; 5 1/3; 7 1/2; 4 2/7 /
38. 30%; 25%; 40%; 75% / 39. 3/5; 1/20; 1/4; 9/10 / 40. 10%; 15%; 236%; 170% / 41. 0.18; 0.122; 0.653; 0.086 /
42. 33 1/3%; 66 2/3%; 83 1/3%; 55 5/9% / 43. 7; 17 1/2; 17; 60 / 44. 60; 60; 128; 25

	skill objective	test items

45	Compare integers	< or >?
		$^+3$ ● $^-2$ 0 ● $^-5$ $^+6$ ● $^-8$ $^-5$ ● $^-6$

46	Add two integers	$^+8 + {}^+6$ $^-4 + {}^+7$ $^+9 + {}^-3$ $^-5 + {}^-7$

47	Subtract two integers	$^+5 - {}^+2$ $^+6 - {}^-4$ $^-5 - {}^-2$ $^-7 - {}^+3$

48	Multiply two integers	$^+8 \times {}^-3$ $^+2 \times {}^+7$ $^-6 \times {}^-4$ $^-3 \times {}^+7$

49	Divide two integers	$^-8 \div {}^+2$ $^+18 \div {}^-6$ $^+9 \div {}^+3$ $^-28 \div {}^-7$

Answers.

45. >; >; >; > / 46. $^+14$; $^+3$; $^+6$; $^-12$ / 47. $^+3$; $^+10$; $^-3$; $^-10$ / 48. $^-24$; $^+14$; $^+24$; $^-21$ / 49. $^-4$; $^-3$; $^+3$; $^+4$

Skill	Objective	Student pages	Extra Practice Sets	Skill	Objective	Student pages	Extra Practice Sets
1	1-3	26, 27, 30	18	26	7-1	204, 205, 214, 216, 217	62
2	1-4	28, 29, 30	19	27	7-1	206, 207	63
3	1-5	32, 33	20	28	7-2	212-214	65
4	1-5	34	21	29	7-2	220, 221	66
5	1-5	36, 37	22	30	7-3	222, 223	67
6	1-5	38, 39	23	31	7-3	222, 223	67
7	1-6	40, 41	24	32	7-3	222, 223	67
8	1-6	42, 43	25	33	7-3	222, 223	67
9	1-6	44, 45	26	34	7-4	224, 225	68
10	2-4	66, 67	31	35	7-5	226, 227	69
11	2-4	68, 69	32	36	7-6	228, 229	70
12	3-1	82-84, 86, 87	34, 35	37	8-2	242-250	71, 72
13	3-1	82-84, 86, 87	34, 35	38	8-3	252, 253, 255, 256	73, 75
14	3-2	90-93	36	39	8-3	252, 253	73
15	3-2	96, 97	37	40	8-3	252-255	73, 74
16	3-2	97	37	41	8-3	254	73, 74
17	6-1	172-175	54	42	8-3	256	75
18	6-1	176, 177	55	43	8-5	258-261, 264	76-77
19	6-2	178, 179	56	44	8-6	262, 264	78
20	6-3	180, 181, 184	57	45		346, 347	86
21	6-3	182-184	58	46	12-1	348, 349, 352	87
22	6-4	186, 187	59	47	12-2	350-352	88
23	6-4	186, 187	59	48	12-3	354, 355	89
24	6-5	188, 189, 192	60	49	12-4	356-358	90
25	6-6	190-192	61				

Extra Practice

Set 1   Give each sum.

1. 9 + 4   2. 6 + 8   3. 5 + 7   4. 4 + 9   5. 5 + 9

6. 9 + 7   7. 6 + 6   8. 6 + 9   9. 3 + 9   10. 5 + 6

11. 5 + 8   12. 8 + 9   13. 7 + 6   14. 8 + 5   15. 9 + 8

16. 9 + 6   17. 2 + 9   18. 7 + 7   19. 9 + 2   20. 7 + 9

21. 8 + 8   22. 7 + 8   23. 9 + 9   24. 9 + 5   25. 8 + 7

Set 2   Add.

1. 43 +26	2. 70 +28	3. 32 +32	4. 41 +35	5. 51 +20	6. 63 +31
7. 62 +33	8. 33 +62	9. 81 +12	10. 54 +62	11. 73 +55	12. 86 +21

13. 41 53 +12	14. 30 25 +84	15. 43 61 +50	16. 52 33 +24	17. 44 20 +64	18. 35 72 +22

Set 3   Add.

1. 78 +29	2. 36 +38	3. 19 +45	4. 45 +63	5. 39 +82	6. 46 +29
7. 54 +38	8. 94 +65	9. 58 +58	10. 28 +36	11. 63 +78	12. 57 +95
13. 75 +67	14. 83 +78	15. 89 +21	16. 79 +32	17. 94 +56	18. 68 +75

Set 4   Give each difference.

1. 12 − 3   2. 12 − 6   3. 11 − 9   4. 14 − 5   5. 12 − 4

6. 15 − 9   7. 13 − 4   8. 11 − 7   9. 12 − 5   10. 13 − 7

11. 12 − 8   12. 14 − 6   13. 13 − 5   14. 13 − 8   15. 16 − 8

16. 16 − 9   17. 13 − 9   18. 17 − 8   19. 14 − 8   20. 15 − 8

21. 17 − 9   22. 11 − 6   23. 18 − 9   24. 13 − 6   25. 14 − 7

Answers.

Set 1   1. 13 2. 14 3. 12 4. 13 5. 14 6. 16 7. 12 8. 15 9. 12 10. 11 11. 13 12. 17 13. 13 14. 13
15. 17 16. 15 17. 11 18. 14 19. 11 20. 16 21. 16 22. 15 23. 18 24. 14 25. 15

Set 2   1. 69 2. 98 3. 64 4. 76 5. 71 6. 94 7. 95 8. 95 9. 93 10. 116 11. 128 12. 107 13. 106
14. 139 15. 154 16. 109 17. 128 18. 129

Set 3   1. 107 2. 74 3. 64 4. 108 5. 121 6. 75 7. 92 8. 159 9. 116 10. 64 11. 141 12. 152 13. 142
14. 161 15. 110 16. 111 17. 150 18. 143

Set 4   1. 9 2. 6 3. 2 4. 9 5. 8 6. 6 7. 9 8. 4 9. 7 10. 6 11. 4 12. 8 13. 8 14. 5 15. 8 16. 7
17. 4 18. 9 19. 6 20. 7 21. 8 22. 5 23. 9 24. 7 25. 7

Set 5   Subtract.

1. 65 −23	2. 38 −15	3. 65 −22	4. 56 −14	5. 49 −23	6. 78 −35
7. 39 −15	8. 87 −24	9. 79 −32	10. 88 −43	11. 55 −40	12. 86 −32
13. 148 −82	14. 184 −91	15. 177 −93	16. 166 −84	17. 156 −92	18. 135 −83

Set 6   Subtract.

1. 82 −23	2. 75 −36	3. 64 −39	4. 53 −16	5. 45 −36	6. 72 −58
7. 76 −39	8. 82 −46	9. 60 −58	10. 75 −29	11. 42 −18	12. 93 −47
13. 164 −95	14. 143 −75	15. 132 −58	16. 120 −46	17. 165 −97	18. 174 −86

Set 7   Give each product.

1. 6×4	2. 4×7	3. 6×7	4. 6×6	5. 9×6
6. 8×7	7. 9×5	8. 3×9	9. 8×6	10. 5×6
11. 8×5	12. 8×9	13. 5×5	14. 4×9	15. 8×4
16. 3×7	17. 3×8	18. 3×6	19. 9×8	20. 6×8
21. 8×8	22. 7×6	23. 7×8	24. 5×9	25. 9×7
26. 7×7	27. 9×9	28. 4×5	29. 7×9	30. 6×9

Set 8   Multiply.

1. 23 $\times 2$	2. 34 $\times 2$	3. 21 $\times 4$	4. 23 $\times 3$	5. 22 $\times 3$	6. 20 $\times 4$
7. 21 $\times 6$	8. 42 $\times 3$	9. 30 $\times 5$	10. 42 $\times 4$	11. 82 $\times 2$	12. 61 $\times 8$
13. 84 $\times 2$	14. 30 $\times 6$	15. 51 $\times 6$	16. 41 $\times 5$	17. 64 $\times 2$	18. 70 $\times 7$

Answers.

Set 5 1. 42 2. 23 3. 43 4. 42 5. 26 6. 43 7. 24 8. 63 9. 47 10. 45 11. 15 12. 54 13. 66 14. 93 15. 84 16. 82 17. 64 18. 52

Set 6 1. 59 2. 39 3. 25 4. 37 5. 9 6. 14 7. 37 8. 36 9. 2 10. 46 11. 24 12. 46 13. 69 14. 68 15. 74 16. 74 17. 68 18. 88

Set 7 1. 24 2. 28 3. 42 4. 36 5. 54 6. 56 7. 45 8. 27 9. 48 10. 30 11. 40 12. 72 13. 25 14. 36 15. 32 16. 21 17. 24 18. 18 19. 72 20. 48 21. 64 22. 42 23. 56 24. 45 25. 63 26. 49 27. 81 28. 20 29. 63 30. 54

Set 8 1. 46 2. 68 3. 84 4. 69 5. 66 6. 80 7. 126 8. 126 9. 150 10. 168 11. 164 12. 488 13. 168 14. 180 15. 306 16. 205 17. 128 18. 490

Set 9 Multiply.

1. 29 ×2	2. 46 ×4	3. 38 ×3	4. 54 ×5	5. 63 ×7	6. 75 ×6
7. 39 ×8	8. 46 ×6	9. 74 ×3	10. 65 ×5	11. 84 ×4	12. 95 ×7
13. 65 ×6	14. 58 ×8	15. 73 ×5	16. 92 ×9	17. 83 ×7	18. 69 ×4

Set 10 Give each quotient.

1. 18 ÷ 9	2. 40 ÷ 8	3. 15 ÷ 3	4. 24 ÷ 6	5. 21 ÷ 7
6. 20 ÷ 4	7. 25 ÷ 5	8. 16 ÷ 4	9. 36 ÷ 4	10. 56 ÷ 7
11. 45 ÷ 9	12. 42 ÷ 6	13. 63 ÷ 9	14. 35 ÷ 7	15. 45 ÷ 5
16. 56 ÷ 8	17. 24 ÷ 3	18. 27 ÷ 3	19. 54 ÷ 6	20. 72 ÷ 8
21. 36 ÷ 6	22. 81 ÷ 9	23. 49 ÷ 7	24. 28 ÷ 4	25. 42 ÷ 7

Set 11 Divide.

1. 4)33	2. 3)17	3. 2)19	4. 5)33	5. 8)47	6. 7)23
7. 6)50	8. 9)37	9. 3)25	10. 5)43	11. 6)40	12. 8)44
13. 9)70	14. 7)29	15. 4)38	16. 6)46	17. 8)53	18. 7)39

Set 12 Divide.

1. 3)69	2. 2)64	3. 4)88	4. 3)66	5. 2)86	6. 3)93
7. 5)105	8. 8)168	9. 7)217	10. 6)120	11. 5)155	12. 9)279
13. 6)426	14. 8)488	15. 7)287	16. 9)369	17. 5)350	18. 8)488

Set 13 Divide.

1. 3)48	2. 4)56	3. 2)96	4. 5)70	5. 7)84	6. 3)51
7. 7)98	8. 3)87	9. 6)84	10. 5)75	11. 6)72	12. 6)96
13. 4)76	14. 4)92	15. 8)96	16. 3)84	17. 2)58	18. 5)60

Answers.

Set 9 1. 58 2. 184 3. 114 4. 270 5. 441 6. 450 7. 312 8. 276 9. 222 10. 325 11. 336 12. 665
       13. 390 14. 464 15. 365 16. 828 17. 581 18. 276
Set 10 1. 2 2. 5 3. 5 4. 4 5. 3 6. 5 7. 5 8. 4 9. 9 10. 8 11. 5 12. 7 13. 7 14. 5 15. 9 16. 7
       17. 8 18. 9 19. 9 20. 9 21. 6 22. 9 23. 7 24. 7 25. 6
Set 11 1. 8 R1 2. 5 R2 3. 9 R1 4. 6 R3 5. 5 R7 6. 3 R2 7. 8 R2 8. 4 R1 9. 8 R1 10. 8 R3 11. 6 R4
       12. 5 R4 13. 7 R7 14. 4 R1 15. 9 R2 16. 7 R4 17. 6 R5 18. 5 R4
Set 12 1. 23 2. 32 3. 22 4. 22 5. 43 6. 31 7. 21 8. 21 9. 31 10. 20 11. 31 12. 31 13. 71 14. 61
       15. 41 16. 41 17. 70 18. 61
Set 13 1. 16 2. 14 3. 48 4. 14 5. 12 6. 17 7. 14 8. 29 9. 14 10. 15 11. 12 12. 16 13. 19 14. 23
       15. 12 16. 28 17. 29 18. 12

Set 14 Give the standard numeral.

1. eight thousand   2. five thousand one hundred twenty

3. forty-two thousand, nine hundred six

4. nineteen thousand, seven hundred fifty-three

5. three hundred twenty-eight thousand, six hundred seventy-six

6. five million, two hundred twelve thousand, four hundred thirty-seven

7. two hundred forty-two million, six thousand, two hundred eighty-three

8. five billion, two hundred twenty million, two hundred eleven thousand, sixty-six

9. twenty-four billion, nine hundred forty million, five thousand eighty-two

10. seven trillion, one hundred thirty-four million, two hundred forty thousand, twenty

Set 15 Give the next three multiples.

1. 10, 20, 30, ?, ?, ?   2. 140, 150, 160, ?, ?, ?

3. 370, 380, 390, ?, ?, ?   4. 1550, 1560, 1570, ?, ?, ?

5. 200, 300, 400, ?, ?, ?   6. 1600, 1700, 1800, ?, ?, ?

7. 2300, 2400, 2500, ?, ?, ?   8. 4600, 4700, 4800, ?, ?, ?

9. 5000, 6000, 7000, ?, ?, ?   10. 36,000, 37,000, 38,000, ?, ?, ?

11. 125,000, 126,000, 127,000, ?, ?, ?   12. 96,000, 97,000, 98,000, ?, ?, ?

Set 16 Round each number to the nearest hundred, thousand, and million.

1. 6,834,527   2. 9,498,937   3. 9,672,403   4. 12,291,742

5. 233,035,555   6. 456,621,384   7. 789,125,246   8. 919,291,350

Set 17 < or >?

1. 482 ● 483   2. 590 ● 589   3. 800 ● 799

4. 4689 ● 4731   5. 6390 ● 6382   6. 4934 ● 4898

7. 26,428 ● 27,222   8. 8999 ● 10,000   9. 72,958 ● 73,094

10. 85,395 ● 83,595   11. 100,000 ● 99,999   12. 168,749 ● 168,579

13. 298,431 ● 298,341   14. 835,822 ● 843,262   15. 987,342 ● 978,342

Answers.

Set 14 1. 8000 2. 5120 3. 42,906 4. 19,753 5. 328,676 6. 5,212,437 7. 242,006,283 8. 5,220,211,066
9. 24,940,005,082 10. 7,000,134,240,020

Set 15 1. 40; 50; 60 2. 170; 180; 190 3. 400; 410; 420 4. 1580; 1590; 1600 5. 500; 600; 700
6. 1900; 2000; 2100 7. 2600; 2700; 2800 8. 4900; 5000; 5100 9. 8000; 9000; 10,000
10. 39,000; 40,000; 41,000 11. 128,000; 129,000; 130,000 12. 99,000; 100,000; 101,000

Set 16 1. 6,834,500; 6,835,000; 7,000,000 2. 9,498,900; 9,499,000; 9,000,000 3. 9,672,400; 9,672,000;
10,000,000 4. 12,291,700; 12,292,000; 12,000,000 5. 233,035,600; 233,036,000; 233,000,000
6. 456,621,400; 456,621,000; 457,000,000 7. 789,125,200; 789,125,000; 789,000,000
8. 919,291,400; 919,291,000; 919,000,000

Set 17 1. < 2. > 3. > 4. < 5. > 6. > 7. < 8. < 9. < 10. > 11. > 12. > 13. > 14. < 15. >

Set 18 Add.

1.	2.	3.	4.	5.	6.
329	509	625	978	659	746
+ 437	+ 388	+ 158	+ 388	+ 594	+ 896

7.	8.	9.	10.	11.	12.
3565	4836	9024	7477	6185	4778
+ 828	+ 565	+ 889	+ 3593	+ 6189	+ 8696

13.	14.	15.	16.	17.	18.
384	567	295	1835	7068	5347
292	308	762	6916	9383	8274
+ 743	+ 826	+ 547	+ 2159	+ 4555	+ 3339

Set 19 Subtract.

1.	2.	3.	4.	5.	6.
863	752	694	538	453	725
− 235	− 259	− 346	− 162	− 360	− 581

7.	8.	9.	10.	11.	12.
3210	5632	9322	6033	5014	7003
− 2483	− 1955	− 3996	− 1588	− 2939	− 4668

13.	14.	15.	16.	17.	18.
5032	6233	9157	7024	7335	5001
− 1486	− 2485	− 3469	− 3299	− 2467	− 2438

Set 20 Multiply.

1.	2.	3.	4.	5.	6.
23	41	52	64	83	90
× 3	× 2	× 3	× 4	× 5	× 4

7.	8.	9.	10.	11.	12.
142	238	196	370	415	467
× 5	× 9	× 8	× 7	× 6	× 5

13.	14.	15.	16.	17.	18.
4916	5328	6742	2864	8955	3780
× 7	× 2	× 4	× 5	× 8	× 9

Set 21 Give each product.

1.	2.	3.	4.
a. 24 × 10	a. 57 × 10	a. 80 × 10	a. 142 × 10
b. 24 × 100	b. 57 × 100	b. 80 × 100	b. 142 × 100
c. 24 × 1000	c. 57 × 1000	c. 80 × 1000	c. 142 × 1000

5.	6.	7.	8.
a. 200 × 10	a. 1242 × 10	a. 3450 × 10	a. 8100 × 10
b. 200 × 100	b. 1242 × 100	b. 3450 × 100	b. 8100 × 100
c. 200 × 1000	c. 1242 × 1000	c. 3450 × 1000	c. 8100 × 1000

Answers.

Set 18 1. 766 2. 897 3. 783 4. 1366 5. 1253 6. 1642 7. 4393 8. 5401 9. 9913 10. 11,070 11. 12,374 12. 13,474 13. 1419 14. 1701 15. 1604 16. 10,910 17. 21,006 18. 16,960

Set 19 1. 628 2. 493 3. 348 4. 376 5. 93 6. 144 7. 727 8. 3677 9. 5326 10. 4445 11. 2075 12. 2335 13. 3546 14. 3748 15. 5688 16. 3725 17. 4868 18. 2563

Set 20 1. 69 2. 82 3. 156 4. 256 5. 415 6. 360 7. 710 8. 2142 9. 1568 10. 2590 11. 2490 12. 2335 13. 34,412 14. 10,656 15. 26,968 16. 14,320 17. 71,640 18. 34,020

Set 21 1. 240; 2400; 24,000 2. 570; 5700; 57,000 3. 800; 8000; 80,000 4. 1420; 14,200; 142,000 5. 2000; 20,000; 200,000 6. 12,420; 124,200; 1,242,000 7. 34,500; 345,000; 3,450,000 8. 81,000; 810,000; 8,100,000

Set 22 Multiply.

1. 352	2. 592	3. 766	4. 691	5. 829	6. 527
× 24	× 91	× 48	× 63	× 83	× 38

7. 635	8. 863	9. 478	10. 409	11. 742	12. 312
× 64	× 96	× 27	× 75	× 41	× 53

Set 23 Multiply.

1. 527	2. 658	3. 492	4. 581	5. 653	6. 842
× 123	× 243	× 174	× 325	× 208	× 258

7. 952	8. 378	9. 834	10. 815	11. 706	12. 674
× 333	× 156	× 240	× 524	× 430	× 462

13. 640	14. 725	15. 534	16. 906	17. 829	18. 935
× 306	× 301	× 320	× 254	× 306	× 256

Set 24 Divide.

1. 5)706 2. 8)359 3. 5)592 4. 7)488 5. 4)969

6. 9)5218 7. 6)3961 8. 5)7438 9. 3)9064 10. 9)8213

11. 2)62943 12. 7)71826 13. 8)54391 14. 6)70658 15. 6)42653

Set 25 Divide.

1. 18)7364 2. 34)5294 3. 57)1783 4. 24)9642 5. 42)7538

6. 78)3592 7. 95)6000 8. 45)5783 9. 72)7044 10. 80)6903

11. 45)38216 12. 83)53416 13. 16)29784 14. 64)36952 15. 38)74615

Set 26 Divide.

1. 125)3956 2. 203)7834 3. 138)5916 4. 351)7538 5. 150)2964

6. 522)9678 7. 358)6398 8. 212)9000 9. 534)9008 10. 242)8634

11. 156)29783 12. 618)52006 13. 425)39481 14. 625)62934 15. 481)49538

Answers.

Set 22 1. 8448 2. 53,872 3. 36,768 4. 43,533 5. 68,807 6. 20,026 7. 40,640 8. 82,848 9. 12,906
10. 30,675 11. 30,422 12. 16,536
Set 23 1. 64,821 2. 159,894 3. 85,608 4. 188,825 5. 135,824 6. 217,236 7. 317,016 8. 58,968
9. 200,160 10. 427,060 11. 303,580 12. 311,388 13. 195,840 14. 218,225 15. 170,880 16. 230,124
17. 253,674 18. 239,360
Set 24 1. 141 R1 2. 44 R7 3. 118 R2 4. 69 R5 5. 242 R1 6. 579 R7 7. 660 R1 8. 1487 R3 9. 3021 R1
10. 912 R5 11. 31,471 R1 12. 10,260 R6 13. 6798 R7 14. 11,776 R2 15. 7108 R5
Set 25 1. 409 R2 2. 155 R24 3. 31 R16 4. 401 R18 5. 179 R20 6. 46 R4 7. 63 R15 8. 128 R23 9. 97 R60
10. 86 R23 11. 849 R11 12. 643 R47 13. 1861 R8 14. 577 R24 15. 1963 R21
Set 26 1. 31 R81 2. 38 R120 3. 42 R120 4. 21 R167 5. 19 R114 6. 18 R282 7. 17 R312 8. 42 R96
9. 16 R464 10. 35 R164 11. 190 R143 12. 84 R94 13. 92 R381 14. 100 R434 15. 102 R476

Set 27 Write in words.

1. 0.8   2. 0.08   3. 3.1   4. 0.31   5. 3.01   6. 30.1

7. 5.20   8. 50.2   9. 5.02   10. 8.40   11. 8.04   12. 80.4

Set 28 Write in words.

1. 5.002   2. 8.06   3. 3.4   4. 2.007   5. 7.024

6. 8.758   7. 45.547   8. 8.0005   9. 9.0016   10. 16.0345

Set 29 < or >?

1. .5 ● .4   2. .09 ● .08   3. .006 ● .005   4. .5 ● .05

5. .003 ● .02   6. .09 ● .1   7. .2 ● .008   8. .5 ● .004

9. 0.75 ● 0.76   10. 9.24 ● 9.42   11. 7.85 ● 7.58   12. 18.79 ● 18.8

13. .599 ● 1   14. 2 ● 1.897   15. 9.534 ● 9.0541   16. 6.375 ● 63.75

17. 56.37 ● 5.637   18. 5 ● 5.999   19. 8.001 ● 8.01   20. 19.02 ● 19.019

Set 30 Round each number to the nearest tenth, hundredth, and thousandth.

1. 16.1158   2. 43.2565   3. 82.3423

4. 65.8166   5. 58.3454   6. 9.9998

Set 31 Add.

1. 58.6 + 68.8   2. 4.63 + 0.34   3. .644 + .378   4. 91.2 + 25.9   5. 8.92 + 6.16   6. 5.39 + 0.53

7. 28.4 + 73.6   8. 22.4 + 4.78   9. 1.86 + 43

10. 4.16 + 0.379   11. 27.6 + 9.28   12. 7.88 + 0.594

13. 371 + 0.853   14. 8.62 + 5.95   15. 0.174 + 6.76

16. 99.7 + 4.89   17. 0.145 + 5.57   18. 0.0683 + 0.646

Answers.

Set 29 1. > 2. > 3. > 4. > 5. < 6. < 7. > 8. > 9. < 10. < 11. > 12. < 13. < 14. > 15. > 16. < 17. > 18. < 19. < 20. >

Set 30 1. 16.1, 16.12, 16.116 2. 43.3, 43.26, 43.257 3. 82.3, 82.34, 82.342 4. 65.8, 65.82, 65.817 5. 58.3, 58.35, 58.345 6. 10.0, 10.00, 10.000

Set 31 1. 127.4 2. 4.97 3. 1.022 4. 117.1 5. 15.08 6. 5.92 7. 102.0 8. 27.18 9. 44.86 10. 4.539 11. 36.88 12. 8.474 13. 371.853 14. 14.57 15. 6.934 16. 104.59 17. 5.715 18. 0.7143

Set 32 Subtract.

1. 95.6	**2.** 8.26	**3.** .516	**4.** 72.1	**5.** .462	**6.** 9.67
− 83.1	− 4.19	− .384	− 50.9	− .399	− 1.09

7. 46.6 − 7.4   **8.** 5.38 − 4.1   **9.** 629 − 3.84

10. 80.2 − 9.3   **11.** 92.8 − 3.56   **12.** 89 − 42.8

13. 7.3 − 7.18   **14.** 40 − 34.8   **15.** 0.3 − 0.286

16. 70.6 − 2.93   **17.** 5.6 − 0.278   **18.** 0.82 − 0.007

Set 33 Add or subtract.

1. 3.89 + 2.67   **2.** 5.08 + 0.284   **3.** 70.6 + 36.9

4. 59.8 + 0.267   **5.** 0.841 + 78.9   **6.** 5.48 + 29.9

7. 4.6 + 2.83   **8.** 7.2 + 5.94   **9.** 6 + 4.25

10. 0.29 − 0.163   **11.** 0.43 − 0.286   **12.** 5.3 − 1.92

13. 16 − 8.4   **14.** 6.62 − 0.8   **15.** 29 − 7.4

16. 2.01 − 1.99   **17.** 7.09 − 0.4   **18.** 8.64 − 3.79

Set 34 Multiply.

1. 35.8	**2.** 4.26	**3.** 57.4	**4.** 89.3	**5.** 6.52	**6.** 145
× 2.9	× 1.4	× .35	× 6.4	× 18	× 2.5

7. 3.81	**8.** 25.3	**9.** 5.64	**10.** 78.2	**11.** 9.11	**12.** 6.03
× 16	× .33	× 8.1	× 60	× 2.9	× 7.5

13. 9.38	**14.** 71.5	**15.** 6.35	**16.** 4.93	**17.** 38.5	**18.** 5.36
× 1.21	× 11.5	× 34.6	× 2.81	× 5.63	× 40.2

Set 35 Multiply.

1. .23	**2.** .081	**3.** .074	**4.** .49	**5.** .063	**6.** .29
× .3	× .7	× .5	× .03	× .08	× .04

7. .548	**8.** 70.3	**9.** 9.96	**10.** 78.3	**11.** 914	**12.** 59.6
× .005	× .004	× .007	× .38	× 1.58	× 60.8

Answers.

Set 32   1. 12.5 2. 4.07 3. .132 4. 21.2 5. .063 6. 8.58 7. 39.2 8. 1.28 9. 625.16 10. 70.9 11. 89.24
12. 46.2 13. 0.12 14. 5.2 15. 0.014 16. 67.67 17. 5.322 18. 0.813
Set 33   1. 6.56 2. 5.364 3. 107.5 4. 60.067 5. 79.741 6. 35.38 7. 7.43 8. 13.14 9. 10.25 10. 0.127
11. 0.144 12. 3.38 13. 7.6 14. 5.82 15. 21.6 16. 0.02 17. 6.69 18. 4.85
Set 34   1. 103.82 2. 5.964 3. 20.09 4. 571.52 5. 117.36 6. 362.5 7. 60.96 8. 8.349 9. 45.684
10. 4692.0 11. 26.419 12. 45.225 13. 11.3498 14. 822.25 15. 219.71 16. 13.8533 17. 216.755
18. 215.472
Set 35   1. .069 2. .0567 3. .0370 4. .0147 5. .00504 6. .0116 7. .002740 8. .2812 9. .06972 10. 29.754
11. 1444.12 12. 3623.68

Set 36 Divide.

1. $3\overline{)567}$ 2. $2\overline{)586}$ 3. $3\overline{)438}$ 4. $9\overline{)288}$ 5. $7\overline{)329}$

6. $8\overline{)8.56}$ 7. $5\overline{)3.90}$ 8. $6\overline{)4.08}$ 9. $7\overline{)11.2}$ 10. $4\overline{)5.12}$

11. $12\overline{)28.8}$ 12. $15\overline{)9.45}$ 13. $11\overline{)3.85}$ 14. $26\overline{)28.6}$ 15. $35\overline{)94.5}$

16. $73\overline{).1314}$ 17. $55\overline{)4950}$ 18. $36\overline{)26.28}$ 19. $49\overline{)2.793}$ 20. $78\overline{)397.8}$

Set 37 Divide. Round quotients to the nearest tenth.

1. $.3\overline{).386}$ 2. $.5\overline{).348}$ 3. $.6\overline{)2.97}$ 4. $.02\overline{)3.51}$ 5. $.07\overline{)6.28}$

6. $.08\overline{).347}$ 7. $.003\overline{).038}$ 8. $.05\overline{)2.97}$ 9. $.04\overline{).511}$ 10. $.9\overline{).629}$

11. $1.2\overline{)3.482}$ 12. $2.4\overline{)1.356}$ 13. $.31\overline{).9382}$ 14. $.43\overline{).3916}$ 15. $.83\overline{).1374}$

16. $.57\overline{)3.056}$ 17. $.64\overline{).2973}$ 18. $3.9\overline{)5.901}$ 19. $7.8\overline{)2.643}$ 20. $4.2\overline{).3967}$

Set 38 Give the greatest common factor.

1. 8, 12   2. 6, 9   3. 9, 12   4. 12, 16   5. 8, 16   6. 15, 20

7. 9, 15   8. 12, 24   9. 8, 14   10. 24, 48   11. 16, 24   12. 18, 24

13. 15, 30   14. 30, 36   15. 12, 20   16. 15, 25   17. 9, 18   18. 18, 42

Set 39 Give the prime factorization.

1. 4   2. 6   3. 8   4. 9   5. 10   6. 12

7. 14   8. 15   9. 16   10. 18   11. 20   12. 21

13. 22   14. 24   15. 25   16. 26   17. 27   18. 28

Set 40 Give the least common multiple.

1. 2, 5   2. 3, 9   3. 4, 6   4. 4, 8   5. 5, 3   6. 5, 21

7. 4, 7   8. 3, 8   9. 4, 9   10. 2, 10   11. 7, 6   12. 6, 14

13. 18, 12   14. 16, 8   15. 15, 20   16. 8, 10   17. 9, 10   18. 6, 8

19. 1, 10   20. 9, 11   21. 6, 16   22. 12, 5   23. 14, 20   24. 16, 24

Answers.

Set 36 1. 189 2. 293 3. 146 4. 32 5. 47 6. 1.07 7. .78 8. .68 9. 1.6 10. 1.28 11. 2.4 12. .63
13. .35 14. 1.1 15. 2.7 16. .0018 17. 90 18. .73 19. .057 20. 5.1
Set 37 1. 1.3 2. .7 3. 5.0 4. 175.5 5. 89.7 6. 4.3 7. 12.7 8. 59.4 9. 12.8 10. .7 11. 2.9 12. .6
13. 3.0 14. .9 15. .2 16. 5.4 17. .5 18. 1.5 19. .3 20. .1
Set 38 1. 4 2. 3 3. 3 4. 4 5. 8 6. 5 7. 3 8. 12 9. 2 10. 24 11. 8 12. 6 13. 15 14. 6 15. 4
16. 5 17. 9 18. 6
Set 39 1. 2 x 2 2. 2 x 3 3. 2 x 2 x 2 4. 3 x 3 5. 2 x 5 6. 2 x 2 x 3 7. 2 x 7 8. 3 x 5 9. 2 x 2 x 2 x 2
10. 2 x 3 x 3 11. 2 x 2 x 5 12. 3 x 7 13. 2 x 11 14. 2 x 2 x 2 x 3 15. 5 x 5 16. 2 x 13
17. 3 x 3 x 3 18. 2 x 2 x 7
Set 40 1. 10 2. 9 3. 12 4. 8 5. 15 6. 105 7. 28 8. 24 9. 36 10. 10 11. 42 12. 42 13. 36 14. 16
15. 60 16. 40 17. 90 18. 24 19. 10 20. 99 21. 48 22. 60 23. 140 24. 48

Set 41 Solve.

1. $n + 9 = 17$ 2. $n - 6 = 15$ 3. $n - 10 = 13$ 4. $n + 8 = 22$

5. $n - 42 = 35$ 6. $16 + n = 30$ 7. $n - 30 = 16$ 8. $n - 21 = 42$

9. $n - 32 = 15$ 10. $n + 18 = 40$ 11. $n - 14 = 23$ 12. $n + 25 = 40$

13. $16 + n = 35$ 14. $25 + n = 49$ 15. $17 + n = 51$ 16. $n - 18 = 25$

17. $n + 59 = 81$ 18. $n + 38 = 67$ 19. $n - 18 = 25$ 20. $63 + n = 94$

Set 42 Solve.

1. $3n = 12$ 2. $6n = 18$ 3. $5n = 20$ 4. $7n = 56$ 5. $9n = 81$

6. $4n = 36$ 7. $2n = 14$ 8. $6n = 36$ 9. $9n = 45$ 10. $8n = 72$

11. $10n = 40$ 12. $10n = 100$ 13. $12n = 0$ 14. $15n = 30$ 15. $16n = 64$

16. $18n = 72$ 17. $23n = 115$ 18. $15n = 180$ 19. $19n = 190$ 20. $28n = 196$

Set 43 Give the standard numeral.

1. 1^2 2. 5^2 3. 2^2 4. 2^3 5. 1^4 6. 10^2

7. 10^3 8. 4^2 9. 2^4 10. 10^4 11. 1^5 12. 6^2

13. 4^3 14. 2^5 15. 5^3 16. 1^8 17. 3^5 18. 3^3

19. 8^2 20. 2^6 21. 3^4 22. 3^2 23. 5^4 24. 1^9

Set 44 Complete.

1. $3 \text{ m} = \underline{?} \text{ dm}$ 2. $5 \text{ m} = \underline{?} \text{ cm}$ 3. $7 \text{ m} = \underline{?} \text{ mm}$

4. $200 \text{ cm} = \underline{?} \text{ m}$ 5. $4000 \text{ mm} = \underline{?} \text{ m}$ 6. $5.8 \text{ m} = \underline{?} \text{ dm}$

7. $3.9 \text{ cm} = \underline{?} \text{ mm}$ 8. $4.6 \text{ dm} = \underline{?} \text{ cm}$ 9. $5.34 \text{ m} = \underline{?} \text{ dm}$

10. $8.92 \text{ dm} = \underline{?} \text{ mm}$ 11. $3.96 \text{ dm} = \underline{?} \text{ cm}$ 12. $4.83 \text{ m} = \underline{?} \text{ cm}$

13. $5.63 \text{ cm} = \underline{?} \text{ mm}$ 14. $3.82 \text{ m} = \underline{?} \text{ dm}$ 15. $2.96 \text{ cm} = \underline{?} \text{ dm}$

16. $2.94 \text{ cm} = \underline{?} \text{ mm}$ 17. $5.42 \text{ dm} = \underline{?} \text{ cm}$ 18. $384 \text{ mm} = \underline{?} \text{ cm}$

19. $5.39 \text{ mm} = \underline{?} \text{ cm}$ 20. $2.63 \text{ m} = \underline{?} \text{ cm}$ 21. $9.8 \text{ mm} = \underline{?} \text{ dm}$

22. $38 \text{ km} = \underline{?} \text{ m}$ 23. $396 \text{ m} = \underline{?} \text{ km}$ 24. $2.4 \text{ km} = \underline{?} \text{ m}$

25. $52.3 \text{ km} = \underline{?} \text{ m}$ 26. $.74 \text{ km} = \underline{?} \text{ m}$ 27. $.385 \text{ km} = \underline{?} \text{ m}$

28. $8.56 \text{ m} = \underline{?} \text{ cm}$ 29. $.3 \text{ m} = \underline{?} \text{ mm}$ 30. $75.2 \text{ m} = \underline{?} \text{ km}$

Answers.

Set 41 1. 8 2. 21 3. 23 4. 14 5. 77 6. 14 7. 46 8. 63 9. 47 10. 22 11. 37 12. 15 13. 19 14. 24
15. 34 16. 43 17. 22 18. 29 19. 43 20. 31
Set 42 1. 4 2. 3 3. 4 4. 8 5. 9 6. 9 7. 7 8. 6 9. 5 10. 9 11. 4 12. 10 13. 0 14. 2 15. 4 16. 4
17. 5 18. 12 19. 10 20. 7
Set 43 1. 1 2. 25 3. 4 4. 8 5. 1 6. 100 7. 1000 8. 16 9. 16 10. 10,000 11. 1 12. 36 13. 64 14. 32
15. 125 16. 1 17. 243 18. 27 19. 64 20. 64 21. 81 22. 9 23. 625 24. 1
Set 44 1. 30 2. 500 3. 7000 4. 2 5. 4 6. 58 7. 39 8. 46 9. 53.4 10. 892 11. 39.6 12. 483 13. 56.3
14. 38.2 15. .296 16. 29.4 17. 54.2 18. 38.4 19. .539 20. 263 21. .098 22. 38,000 23. .396
24. 2400 25. 52,300 26. 740 27. 385 28. 856 29. 300 30. .0752

Set 45   Give the perimeter (circumference). Use 3.14 as an approximation for π.

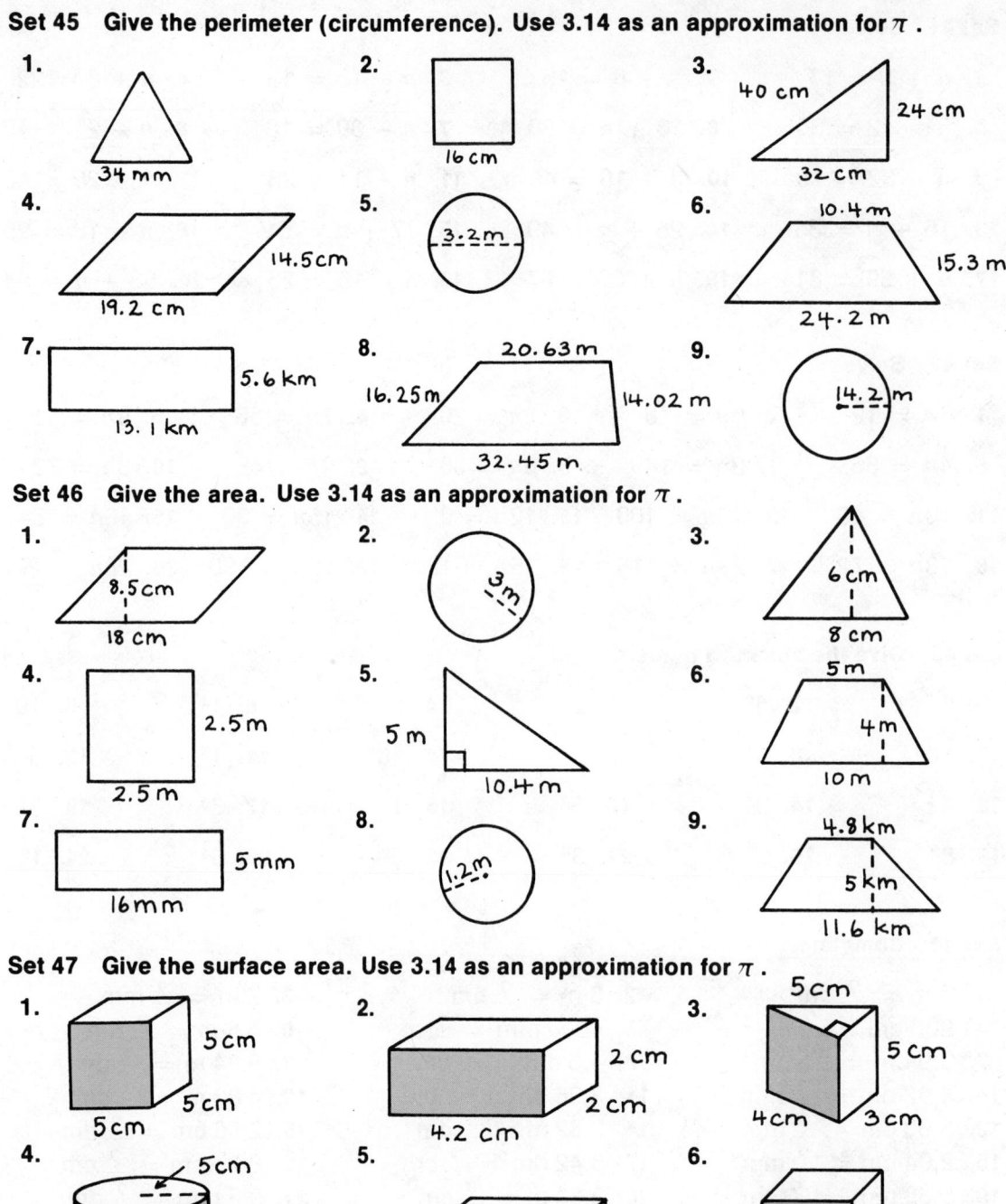

1.

34 mm

2.

16 cm

3.

40 cm   24 cm   32 cm

4.

14.5 cm   19.2 cm

5.

3.2 m

6.

10.4 m   15.3 m   24.2 m

7.

5.6 km   13.1 km

8.

20.63 m   16.25 m   14.02 m   32.45 m

9.

14.2 m

Set 46   Give the area. Use 3.14 as an approximation for π.

1.

8.5 cm   18 cm

2.

3 m

3.

6 cm   8 cm

4.

2.5 m   2.5 m

5.

5 m   10.4 m

6.

5 m   4 m   10 m

7.

5 mm   16 mm

8.

1.2 m

9.

4.8 km   5 km   11.6 km

Set 47   Give the surface area. Use 3.14 as an approximation for π.

1.

5 cm   5 cm   5 cm

2.

2 cm   2 cm   4.2 cm

3.

5 cm   5 cm   4 cm   3 cm

4.

5 cm   8 cm

5.

1.2 m   4 m   5.6 m

6.

3.5 m   2 m   4 m

Answers.

Set 45   1. 102 mm   2. 64 cm   3. 96 cm   4. 67.4 cm   5. 10.048 m   6. 65.2 m   7. 37.4 km   8. 83.35 m   9. 89.176 m
Set 46   1. 153 cm²   2. 28.26 m²   3. 24 cm²   4. 6.25 m²   5. 26 m²   6. 30 m²   7. 80 mm²   8. 4.5216 m²   9. 41 km²
Set 47   1. 150 cm²   2. 41.6 cm²   3. 72 cm²   4. 408.2 cm²   5. 67.84 m²   6. 58 m²

384

Set 48   Find each volume. Use 3.14 as an approximation for π.

1.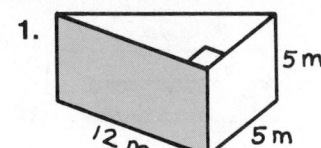
5 m
12 m
5 m

2.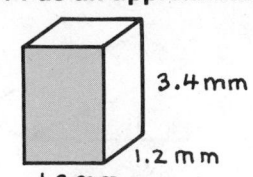
3.4 mm
1.2 mm
1.2 mm

3.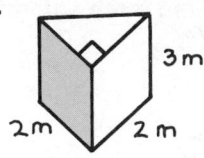
3 m
2 m   2 m

4.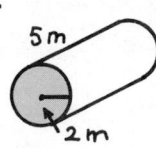
5 m
2 m

5.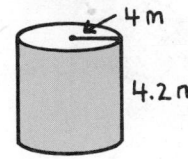
4 m
4.2 m

6.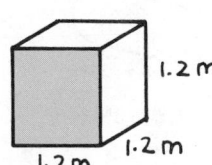
1.2 m
1.2 m   1.2 m

Set 49   Complete.

1. $3L = \underline{?}\, mL$
2. $2.4\, L = \underline{?}\, mL$
3. $3.5\, L = \underline{?}\, mL$
4. $0.24\, L = \underline{?}\, mL$
5. $.356\, L = \underline{?}\, mL$
6. $2000\, mL = \underline{?}\, L$
7. $1400\, mL = \underline{?}\, L$
8. $550\, mL = \underline{?}\, L$
9. $825\, mL = \underline{?}\, L$

10. $5\, g = \underline{?}\, mg$
11. $14\, g = \underline{?}\, mg$
12. $4000\, g = \underline{?}\, mg$
13. $5000\, g = \underline{?}\, kg$
14. $685\, g = \underline{?}\, kg$
15. $1445\, g = \underline{?}\, kg$
16. $58\, g = \underline{?}\, kg$
17. $2.4\, kg = \underline{?}\, g$
18. $.42\, kg = \underline{?}\, g$

Set 50   Complete.

1. $7\, ft = \underline{?}\, in.$
2. $3\, yd = \underline{?}\, in.$
3. $9\, yd = \underline{?}\, ft$
4. $2\, mi = \underline{?}\, ft$
5. $4\, mi = \underline{?}\, yd$
6. $1\, mi = \underline{?}\, in.$
7. $156\, in. = \underline{?}\, ft$
8. $138\, ft = \underline{?}\, yd$
9. $2232\, in. = \underline{?}\, yd$
10. $40\, ft = \underline{?}\, yd\, \underline{?}\, ft$
11. $115\, ft = \underline{?}\, yd\, \underline{?}\, ft$
12. $150\, in. = \underline{?}\, ft\, \underline{?}\, in.$
13. $205\, ft = \underline{?}\, yd\, \underline{?}\, ft$
14. $2\, ft\, 7\, in. = \underline{?}\, in.$
15. $10\, ft\, 8\, in. = \underline{?}\, in.$
16. $23\, ft\, 9\, in. = \underline{?}\, in.$
17. $9\, yd\, 2\, ft = \underline{?}\, ft$
18. $17\, yd\, 1\, ft = \underline{?}\, ft$

Set 51   Find each area. Use 3.14 as an approximation for π.

1.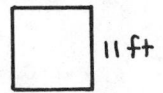
11 ft

2.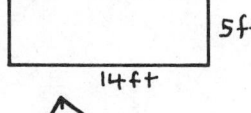
5 ft
14 ft

3.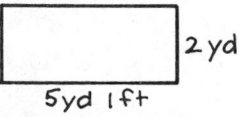
2 yd
5 yd 1 ft

4.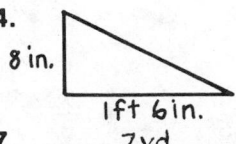
8 in.
1 ft 6 in.

5.
8 ft
16 ft

6.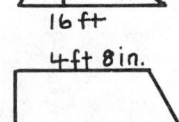
1 ft 1 in.
1 ft. 10 in.

7.
7 yd
1 yd 1 ft
9 yd 1 ft

8.
4 ft 8 in.
3 ft
6 ft 8 in.

9.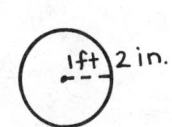
1 ft 2 in.

Answers.

Set 48   1. 150 m³   2. 4.896 mm³   3. 6 m³   4. 62.8 m³   5. 211.008 m³   6. 1.728 m³
Set 49   1. 3000   2. 2400   3. 3500   4. 240   5. 356   6. 2   7. 1.4   8. .55   9. .825   10. 5000   11. 14,000
   12. 4,000,000   13. 5   14. .685   15. 1.445   16. .058   17. 2400   18. 420
Set 50   1. 84   2. 108   3. 27   4. 10,560   5. 7040   6. 63,360   7. 13   8. 46   9. 62   10. 13, 1   11. 38, 1
   12. 12, 6   13. 68, 1   14. 31   15. 128   16. 285   17. 29   18. 52
Set 51   1. 121 ft²   2. 70 ft²   3. 96 ft²   4. 72 in.²   5. 64 ft²   6. 286 in.²   7. 98 ft²   8. 2448 in.²
   9. 615.44 in.²

Set 52 Find each volume. Use 3.14 as an approximation for π.

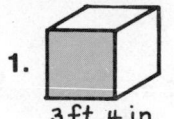

1. 3 ft   4 in.

2. 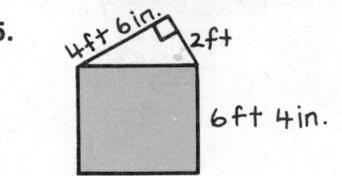 16 in.   34 in.   20 in.

3. 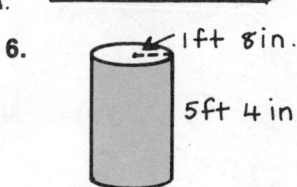 4 yd 1 ft   1 yd   1 yd 2 ft

4. 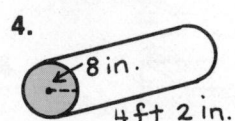 8 in.   4 ft 2 in.

5. 4 ft 6 in.   2 ft   6 ft 4 in.

6. 1 ft 8 in.   5 ft 4 in.

Set 53 Complete.

1. 36 pt = $\underline{?}$ qt
2. 8 qt = $\underline{?}$ gal
3. 24 c = $\underline{?}$ pt
4. 2 gal = $\underline{?}$ pt
5. 6 qt = $\underline{?}$ half-gallons
6. 6 gal = $\underline{?}$ half-gallons
7. 15 qt = $\underline{?}$ gal $\underline{?}$ qt
8. 27 qt = $\underline{?}$ gal $\underline{?}$ qt
9. 23 pt = $\underline{?}$ qt $\underline{?}$ pt

Set 54 Copy and complete.

1. $\frac{1}{2} = \frac{?}{4}$
2. $\frac{1}{3} = \frac{?}{12}$
3. $\frac{2}{3} = \frac{?}{9}$
4. $\frac{5}{6} = \frac{?}{30}$
5. $\frac{3}{4} = \frac{?}{16}$

6. $\frac{3}{2} = \frac{?}{12}$
7. $\frac{5}{2} = \frac{?}{20}$
8. $\frac{4}{4} = \frac{?}{8}$
9. $\frac{7}{8} = \frac{?}{32}$
10. $\frac{1}{3} = \frac{?}{18}$

11. $\frac{1}{4} = \frac{?}{20}$
12. $\frac{3}{5} = \frac{?}{15}$
13. $\frac{1}{2} = \frac{?}{10}$
14. $\frac{3}{8} = \frac{?}{24}$
15. $\frac{3}{4} = \frac{?}{24}$

Set 55 Reduce to lowest terms.

1. $\frac{4}{8}$
2. $\frac{2}{6}$
3. $\frac{4}{6}$
4. $\frac{3}{3}$
5. $\frac{5}{10}$
6. $\frac{2}{8}$
7. $\frac{9}{3}$
8. $\frac{10}{12}$

9. $\frac{12}{3}$
10. $\frac{8}{4}$
11. $\frac{0}{4}$
12. $\frac{2}{10}$
13. $\frac{9}{6}$
14. $\frac{3}{9}$
15. $\frac{10}{10}$
16. $\frac{10}{16}$

17. $\frac{4}{20}$
18. $\frac{15}{12}$
19. $\frac{15}{30}$
20. $\frac{6}{9}$
21. $\frac{5}{20}$
22. $\frac{6}{12}$
23. $\frac{14}{7}$
24. $\frac{0}{6}$

Set 56 <, =, or >?

1. $\frac{1}{3} \bullet \frac{1}{2}$
2. $\frac{1}{4} \bullet \frac{1}{5}$
3. $\frac{1}{2} \bullet \frac{6}{12}$
4. $\frac{3}{8} \bullet \frac{1}{3}$
5. $\frac{5}{6} \bullet \frac{15}{18}$

6. $\frac{3}{2} \bullet \frac{2}{3}$
7. $\frac{5}{9} \bullet \frac{1}{2}$
8. $\frac{2}{3} \bullet \frac{5}{8}$
9. $\frac{3}{4} \bullet \frac{5}{6}$
10. $\frac{6}{8} \bullet \frac{3}{4}$

11. $\frac{6}{16} \bullet \frac{3}{8}$
12. $\frac{3}{5} \bullet \frac{6}{10}$
13. $\frac{7}{4} \bullet \frac{5}{2}$
14. $\frac{5}{9} \bullet \frac{9}{5}$
15. $\frac{7}{8} \bullet \frac{5}{6}$

16. $\frac{5}{9} \bullet \frac{2}{3}$
17. $\frac{5}{4} \bullet \frac{5}{3}$
18. $\frac{3}{4} \bullet \frac{4}{3}$
19. $\frac{5}{2} \bullet \frac{15}{6}$
20. $\frac{5}{8} \bullet \frac{5}{6}$

Answers.

Set 52 1. 64,000 in.³ 2. 5440 in.³ 3. 195 ft³ 4. 10,048 in.³ 5. 49,248 in.³ 6. 80,384 in.³
Set 53 1. 18 2. 2 3. 12 4. 16 5. 3 6. 12 7. 3, 3 8. 6, 3 9. 11, 1
Set 54 1. 2 2. 4 3. 6 4. 25 5. 12 6. 18 7. 50 8. 8 9. 28 10. 6 11. 5 12. 9 13. 5 14. 9 15. 18
Set 55 1. 1/2 2. 1/3 3. 2/3 4. 1 5. 1/2 6. 1/4 7. 3 8. 5/6 9. 4 10. 2 11. 0 12. 1/5 13. 3/2
14. 1/3 15. 1 16. 5/8 17. 1/5 18. 5/4 19. 1/2 20. 2/3 21. 1/4 22. 1/2 23. 2 24. 0
Set 56 1. < 2. > 3. = 4. > 5. = 6. > 7. > 8. > 9. < 10. = 11. = 12. = 13. < 14. < 15. >
16. < 17. < 18. < 19. = 20. <

Set 57 Give each sum in lowest terms.

1. $\dfrac{1}{2}$
$+\dfrac{1}{4}$

2. $\dfrac{5}{6}$
$+\dfrac{2}{3}$

3. $\dfrac{3}{3}$
$+\dfrac{2}{2}$

4. $\dfrac{1}{4}$
$+\dfrac{5}{8}$

5. $\dfrac{6}{5}$
$+\dfrac{3}{10}$

6. $\dfrac{5}{12}$
$+\dfrac{1}{4}$

7. $\dfrac{7}{8}$
$+\dfrac{1}{3}$

8. $\dfrac{1}{2}$
$+\dfrac{5}{6}$

9. $\dfrac{3}{2}$
$+\dfrac{2}{3}$

10. $\dfrac{3}{7}$
$+\dfrac{1}{5}$

11. $\dfrac{5}{9}$
$+\dfrac{2}{3}$

12. $\dfrac{1}{2}$
$+\dfrac{1}{3}$

13. $\dfrac{4}{5}$
$+\dfrac{2}{3}$

14. $\dfrac{5}{8}$
$+\dfrac{1}{2}$

15. $\dfrac{3}{5}$
$+\dfrac{1}{3}$

16. $\dfrac{0}{5}$
$+\dfrac{2}{5}$

17. $\dfrac{3}{8}$
$+\dfrac{1}{4}$

18. $\dfrac{2}{3}$
$+\dfrac{3}{4}$

19. $\dfrac{3}{4}$
$+\dfrac{1}{8}$

20. $\dfrac{3}{8}$
$+\dfrac{2}{3}$

21. $\dfrac{5}{6}$
$+\dfrac{7}{10}$

22. $\dfrac{11}{15}$
$+\dfrac{4}{5}$

23. $\dfrac{2}{3}$
$+\dfrac{1}{2}$

24. $\dfrac{7}{3}$
$+\dfrac{7}{4}$

Set 58 Give each difference in lowest terms.

1. $\dfrac{3}{4}$
$-\dfrac{1}{4}$

2. $\dfrac{1}{2}$
$-\dfrac{1}{4}$

3. $\dfrac{5}{9}$
$-\dfrac{1}{3}$

4. 1
$-\dfrac{2}{3}$

5. $\dfrac{2}{3}$
$-\dfrac{1}{3}$

6. $\dfrac{7}{8}$
$-\dfrac{3}{4}$

7. $\dfrac{1}{2}$
$-\dfrac{3}{8}$

8. $\dfrac{3}{10}$
$-\dfrac{1}{5}$

9. $\dfrac{5}{6}$
$-\dfrac{2}{3}$

10. $\dfrac{2}{3}$
$-\dfrac{1}{4}$

11. $\dfrac{7}{4}$
-1

12. $\dfrac{3}{4}$
$-\dfrac{3}{8}$

13. $\dfrac{1}{2}$
$-\dfrac{1}{3}$

14. 2
$-\dfrac{5}{4}$

15. $\dfrac{3}{4}$
$-\dfrac{1}{2}$

16. $\dfrac{7}{2}$
-2

17. $\dfrac{7}{8}$
$-\dfrac{7}{8}$

18. $\dfrac{3}{4}$
$-\dfrac{5}{8}$

19. $\dfrac{7}{9}$
$-\dfrac{0}{3}$

20. $\dfrac{2}{3}$
$-\dfrac{3}{8}$

21. $\dfrac{5}{4}$
$-\dfrac{5}{8}$

22. $\dfrac{3}{4}$
$-\dfrac{2}{3}$

23. $\dfrac{5}{9}$
$-\dfrac{1}{2}$

24. $\dfrac{8}{9}$
$-\dfrac{3}{4}$

Set 59 Copy and complete.

	1.	2.	3.	4.	5.	6.	7.	8.	9.	10.
Fraction	$\dfrac{5}{2}$	$\dfrac{5}{3}$	$\dfrac{23}{4}$	$\dfrac{11}{2}$	$\dfrac{23}{7}$	$\dfrac{15}{4}$	$\dfrac{15}{8}$	$\dfrac{37}{5}$	$\dfrac{18}{4}$	$\dfrac{21}{6}$
Mixed number										

	11.	12.	13.	14.	15.	16.	17.	18.	19.	20.
Fraction										
Mixed number	$5\dfrac{1}{2}$	$3\dfrac{1}{4}$	$2\dfrac{2}{3}$	$3\dfrac{3}{4}$	$2\dfrac{5}{8}$	$1\dfrac{5}{9}$	$3\dfrac{7}{8}$	$5\dfrac{3}{8}$	$6\dfrac{2}{3}$	$8\dfrac{5}{6}$

Answers.

Set 57 1. 3/4 2. 3/2 3. 2 4. 7/8 5. 3/2 6. 2/3 7. 29/24 8. 4/3 9. 13/6 10. 22/35 11. 11/9 12. 5/6
13. 22/15 14. 9/8 15. 14/15 16. 2/5 17. 5/8 18. 17/12 19. 7/8 20. 25/24 21. 23/15 22. 23/15
23. 7/6 24. 49/12

Set 58 1. 1/2 2. 1/4 3. 2/9 4. 1/3 5. 1/3 6. 1/8 7. 1/8 8. 1/10 9. 1/6 10. 5/12 11. 3/4 12. 3/8
13. 1/6 14. 3/4 15. 1/4 16. 3/2 17. 0 18. 1/8 19. 7/9 20. 7/24 21. 5/8 22. 1/12 23. 1/18
24. 5/36

Set 59 1. 2 1/2 2. 1 2/3 3. 5 3/4 4. 5 1/2 5. 3 2/7 6. 3 3/4 7. 1 7/8 8. 7 2/5 9. 4 1/2 10. 3 1/2
11. 11/2 12. 13/4 13. 8/3 14. 15/4 15. 21/8 16. 14/9 17. 31/8 18. 43/8 19. 20/3 20. 53/6

Set 60 Add.

1. $6\frac{1}{3}$ $+2\frac{1}{3}$	2. $5\frac{1}{4}$ $+2\frac{1}{2}$	3. $8\frac{1}{3}$ $+2\frac{1}{4}$	4. $7\frac{3}{8}$ $+5\frac{1}{4}$	5. $8\frac{1}{2}$ $+6\frac{1}{2}$	6. $9\frac{1}{8}$ $+5\frac{1}{4}$
7. $3\frac{1}{4}$ $+7\frac{3}{4}$	8. 6 $+4\frac{2}{5}$	9. $8\frac{7}{8}$ $+5\frac{1}{4}$	10. $7\frac{5}{8}$ $+6\frac{1}{2}$	11. $9\frac{3}{4}$ $+2\frac{1}{2}$	12. $9\frac{3}{4}$ $+6\frac{3}{8}$
13. $13\frac{2}{3}$ $+7\frac{2}{3}$	14. $18\frac{3}{8}$ $+9$	15. $18\frac{2}{5}$ $+10\frac{3}{4}$	16. $20\frac{1}{6}$ $+8\frac{1}{3}$	17. $23\frac{5}{9}$ $+15\frac{2}{3}$	18. $16\frac{7}{8}$ $+3\frac{3}{8}$
19. $23\frac{3}{5}$ $+16\frac{1}{2}$	20. $31\frac{1}{3}$ $+24\frac{2}{9}$	21. $25\frac{1}{2}$ $+38\frac{3}{4}$	22. $46\frac{3}{4}$ $+56\frac{2}{3}$	23. $65\frac{1}{4}$ $+83\frac{1}{8}$	24. $35\frac{3}{4}$ $+19\frac{5}{8}$

Set 61 Subtract.

1. $6\frac{2}{3}$ $-3\frac{1}{3}$	2. $5\frac{1}{2}$ $-2\frac{1}{2}$	3. $8\frac{3}{4}$ $-6\frac{1}{2}$	4. $9\frac{4}{9}$ $-2\frac{1}{9}$	5. $9\frac{2}{5}$ $-3\frac{1}{5}$	6. 8 $-1\frac{1}{3}$
7. $9\frac{4}{5}$ $-6\frac{3}{5}$	8. $5\frac{7}{9}$ $-2\frac{4}{9}$	9. $6\frac{2}{3}$ $-3\frac{1}{6}$	10. $7\frac{3}{4}$ $-4\frac{5}{8}$	11. $9\frac{3}{4}$ $-2\frac{7}{8}$	12. $8\frac{3}{4}$ $-5\frac{7}{8}$
13. $14\frac{1}{3}$ $-5\frac{2}{3}$	14. $17\frac{1}{8}$ $-8\frac{3}{4}$	15. $15\frac{3}{5}$ $-5\frac{7}{10}$	16. $19\frac{1}{2}$ $-4\frac{3}{4}$	17. 21 $-9\frac{3}{5}$	18. $18\frac{1}{4}$ $-6\frac{3}{5}$
19. $24\frac{5}{9}$ $-17\frac{2}{3}$	20. 44 $-19\frac{5}{8}$	21. $32\frac{1}{6}$ $-18\frac{1}{8}$	22. 21 $-13\frac{2}{3}$	23. $25\frac{1}{3}$ $-16\frac{1}{2}$	24. $27\frac{2}{3}$ $-18\frac{3}{4}$

Answers.

Set 60 1. 8 2/3 2. 7 3/4 3. 10 7/12 4. 12 5/8 5. 15 8. 14 3/8 7. 11 8. 10 2/5 9. 14 1/8 10. 14 1/8
  11. 12 1/4 12. 16 1/8 13. 21 1/3 14. 27 3/8 15. 29 3/20 16. 28 1/2 17. 39 2/9 18. 20 1/4
  19. 40 1/10 20. 55 5/9 21. 64 1/4 22. 103 5/12 23. 148 3/8 24. 55 3/8
Set 61 1. 3 1/3 2. 3 3. 2 1/4 4. 7 1/3 5. 6 1/5 6. 6 2/3 7. 3 1/5 8. 3 1/3 9. 3 1/2 10. 3 1/8
  11. 6 7/8 12. 2 7/8 13. 8 2/3 14. 8 3/8 15. 9 9/10 16. 14 3/4 17. 11 2/5 18. 11 13/20
  19. 6 8/9 20. 24 3/8 21. 14 1/24 22. 7 1/3 23. 8 5/6 24. 8 11/12

388

Set 62 Give each product in lowest terms.

1. $\dfrac{1}{3} \times \dfrac{1}{3}$ 2. $\dfrac{2}{5} \times \dfrac{2}{5}$ 3. $\dfrac{4}{7} \times \dfrac{2}{5}$ 4. $\dfrac{2}{3} \times \dfrac{4}{4}$ 5. $\dfrac{5}{8} \times \dfrac{0}{6}$ 6. $\dfrac{5}{9} \times \dfrac{3}{10}$

7. $\dfrac{3}{7} \times \dfrac{1}{8}$ 8. $\dfrac{1}{2} \times \dfrac{3}{8}$ 9. $\dfrac{1}{2} \times \dfrac{1}{2}$ 10. $\dfrac{1}{4} \times \dfrac{2}{2}$ 11. $\dfrac{2}{3} \times \dfrac{3}{10}$ 12. $\dfrac{3}{4} \times \dfrac{4}{3}$

13. $\dfrac{1}{4} \times \dfrac{1}{2}$ 14. $\dfrac{7}{4} \times \dfrac{4}{10}$ 15. $\dfrac{3}{4} \times \dfrac{8}{5}$ 16. $\dfrac{2}{3} \times \dfrac{3}{7}$ 17. $\dfrac{5}{8} \times \dfrac{7}{5}$ 18. $\dfrac{1}{5} \times \dfrac{1}{4}$

19. $\dfrac{2}{3} \times \dfrac{3}{3}$ 20. $\dfrac{3}{4} \times \dfrac{8}{7}$ 21. $\dfrac{2}{3} \times \dfrac{3}{2}$ 22. $\dfrac{4}{3} \times \dfrac{9}{2}$ 23. $\dfrac{5}{8} \times \dfrac{8}{5}$ 24. $\dfrac{3}{5} \times \dfrac{10}{9}$

Set 63 Compute.

1. $\dfrac{1}{2}$ of 18 2. $\dfrac{2}{3}$ of 27 3. $\dfrac{2}{3}$ of 12 4. $\dfrac{5}{9}$ of 36 5. $\dfrac{7}{4}$ of 36

6. $\dfrac{5}{2}$ of 10 7. $\dfrac{3}{8}$ of 24 8. $\dfrac{1}{3}$ of 21 9. $\dfrac{5}{7}$ of 14 10. $\dfrac{1}{5}$ of 20

11. $\dfrac{3}{5}$ of 35 12. $\dfrac{9}{8}$ of 24 13. $\dfrac{7}{8}$ of 56 14. $\dfrac{5}{4}$ of 40 15. $\dfrac{3}{4}$ of 40

16. $\dfrac{5}{8}$ of 16.8 17. $\dfrac{1}{4}$ of 12.8 18. $\dfrac{4}{9}$ of 19.8 19. $\dfrac{5}{6}$ of 73.8 20. $\dfrac{2}{5}$ of 12

Set 64 Give the reciprocal of each number.

1. $\dfrac{1}{2}$ 2. $\dfrac{1}{4}$ 3. $\dfrac{1}{3}$ 4. $\dfrac{1}{5}$ 5. $\dfrac{2}{3}$ 6. $\dfrac{3}{4}$ 7. $\dfrac{3}{8}$ 8. $\dfrac{5}{8}$

9. $\dfrac{7}{8}$ 10. 1 11. 2 12. 3 13. 4 14. 5 15. 6 16. 7

17. $\dfrac{7}{2}$ 18. $\dfrac{7}{4}$ 19. $\dfrac{5}{6}$ 20. $\dfrac{5}{9}$ 21. $\dfrac{4}{9}$ 22. $\dfrac{5}{2}$ 23. $\dfrac{11}{6}$ 24. $\dfrac{12}{5}$

Set 65 Give the quotient in lowest terms.

1. $\dfrac{1}{2} \div \dfrac{2}{3}$ 2. $\dfrac{4}{9} \div \dfrac{1}{3}$ 3. $\dfrac{3}{2} \div \dfrac{3}{4}$ 4. $\dfrac{3}{4} \div \dfrac{1}{8}$ 5. $\dfrac{9}{5} \div \dfrac{3}{8}$ 6. $\dfrac{5}{6} \div \dfrac{1}{2}$

7. $\dfrac{1}{8} \div \dfrac{9}{5}$ 8. $\dfrac{1}{5} \div \dfrac{5}{4}$ 9. $3 \div \dfrac{2}{3}$ 10. $\dfrac{1}{3} \div \dfrac{2}{3}$ 11. $\dfrac{3}{5} \div \dfrac{3}{8}$ 12. $5 \div \dfrac{5}{3}$

13. $\dfrac{3}{10} \div \dfrac{1}{5}$ 14. $\dfrac{5}{8} \div \dfrac{1}{4}$ 15. $6 \div \dfrac{3}{8}$ 16. $\dfrac{3}{10} \div \dfrac{3}{4}$ 17. $\dfrac{1}{2} \div \dfrac{7}{2}$ 18. $\dfrac{7}{4} \div \dfrac{3}{2}$

19. $\dfrac{5}{8} \div 2$ 20. $\dfrac{3}{8} \div 5$ 21. $\dfrac{1}{4} \div \dfrac{7}{8}$ 22. $\dfrac{2}{3} \div \dfrac{1}{6}$ 23. $\dfrac{2}{5} \div 4$ 24. $\dfrac{0}{4} \div \dfrac{1}{2}$

Answers.

Set 62 1. 1/9 2. 4/25 3. 8/35 4. 2/3 5. 0 6. 1/6 7. 3/56 8. 3/16 9. 1/4 10. 1/4 11. 1/5 12. 1
13. 1/8 14. 7/10 15. 6/5 16. 2/7 17. 7/8 18. 1/20 19. 2/3 20. 6/7 21. 1 22. 6 23. 1 24. 2/3
Set 63 1. 9 2. 18 3. 8 4. 20 5. 63 6. 25 7. 9 8. 7 9. 10 10. 4 11. 21 12. 27 13. 49 14. 50
15. 30 16. 10.5 17. 3.2 18. 8.8 19. 61.5 20. 24/5
Set 64 1. 2 2. 4 3. 3 4. 5 5. 3/2 6. 4/3 7. 8/3 8. 8/5 9. 8/7 10. 1 11. 1/2 12. 1/3 13. 1/4
14. 1/5 15. 1/6 16. 1/7 17. 2/7 18. 4/7 19. 6/5 20. 9/5 21. 9/4 22. 2/5 23. 6/11 24. 5/12
Set 65 1. 3/4 2. 4/3 3. 2 4. 6 5. 24/5 6. 5/3 7. 5/72 8. 4/25 9. 9/2 10. 1/2 11. 8/5 12. 3
13. 3/2 14. 5/2 15. 16 16. 2/5 17. 1/7 18. 7/6 19. 5/16 20. 3/40 21. 2/7 22. 4 23. 1/10
24. 0

Set 66 Simplify.

1. $\dfrac{\frac{1}{2}}{\frac{1}{4}}$
2. $\dfrac{\frac{7}{8}}{\frac{1}{3}}$
3. $\dfrac{\frac{5}{2}}{\frac{3}{4}}$
4. $\dfrac{\frac{1}{2}}{\frac{5}{6}}$
5. $\dfrac{\frac{6}{5}}{\frac{3}{10}}$
6. $\dfrac{\frac{3}{2}}{\frac{2}{3}}$
7. $\dfrac{\frac{3}{5}}{\frac{1}{3}}$
8. $\dfrac{\frac{3}{8}}{\frac{1}{4}}$

9. $\dfrac{\frac{4}{5}}{\frac{2}{3}}$
10. $\dfrac{\frac{1}{4}}{\frac{5}{8}}$
11. $\dfrac{\frac{5}{6}}{\frac{2}{3}}$
12. $\dfrac{\frac{5}{8}}{\frac{1}{2}}$
13. $\dfrac{\frac{2}{3}}{\frac{3}{4}}$
14. $\dfrac{\frac{5}{12}}{\frac{1}{4}}$
15. $\dfrac{\frac{3}{8}}{\frac{3}{4}}$
16. $\dfrac{\frac{1}{2}}{\frac{1}{3}}$

17. $\dfrac{\frac{3}{4}}{\frac{1}{8}}$
18. $\dfrac{\frac{3}{7}}{\frac{1}{5}}$
19. $\dfrac{\frac{3}{8}}{\frac{2}{3}}$
20. $\dfrac{\frac{5}{6}}{\frac{7}{10}}$
21. $\dfrac{\frac{5}{9}}{\frac{2}{3}}$
22. $\dfrac{\frac{2}{3}}{\frac{1}{2}}$
23. $\dfrac{\frac{7}{3}}{\frac{7}{4}}$
24. $\dfrac{\frac{5}{9}}{\frac{5}{3}}$

Set 67 Copy and complete.

	1.	2.	3.	4.	5.	6.	7.	8.	9.	10.
Fraction or Mixed Number	$\frac{1}{5}$	$\frac{7}{20}$	$\frac{3}{8}$	$\frac{3}{5}$	$\frac{7}{8}$	$1\frac{1}{4}$	$1\frac{1}{2}$	$2\frac{3}{10}$	$2\frac{4}{5}$	$3\frac{1}{2}$
Decimal										

	11.	12.	13.	14.	15.	16.	17.	18.	19.	20.
Fraction or Mixed Number										
Decimal	0.25	0.3	0.5	0.625	0.8	1.1	1.5	1.75	2.4	2.6

Set 68 Change to a mixed decimal.

1. $\frac{1}{3}$
2. $\frac{1}{6}$
3. $\frac{5}{7}$
4. $\frac{2}{3}$
5. $\frac{1}{9}$
6. $\frac{10}{3}$
7. $\frac{5}{6}$
8. $\frac{5}{9}$

9. $\frac{11}{6}$
10. $\frac{7}{3}$
11. $\frac{4}{9}$
12. $\frac{2}{9}$
13. $\frac{5}{3}$
14. $\frac{4}{3}$
15. $\frac{10}{9}$
16. $\frac{7}{6}$

17. $\frac{13}{6}$
18. $\frac{1}{11}$
19. $\frac{1}{18}$
20. $\frac{5}{18}$
21. $\frac{2}{11}$
22. $\frac{7}{18}$
23. $\frac{11}{18}$
24. $\frac{5}{11}$

Answers.

Set 66 1. 2 2. 21/8 3. 10/3 4. 3/5 5. 4 6. 9/4 7. 9/5 8. 3/2 9. 6/5 10. 2/5 11. 5/4 12. 5/4
13. 8/9 14. 5/3 15. 1/2 16. 3/2 17. 6 18. 15/7 19. 9/16 20. 25/21 21. 5/6 22. 4/3 23. 4/3
24. 1/3

Set 67 1. 0.2 2. 0.35 3. 0.375 4. 0.6 5. 0.875 6. 1.25 7. 1.5 8. 2.3 9. 2.8 10. 3.5 11. 1/4
12. 3/10 13. 1/2 14. 5/8 15. 4/5 16. 1 1/10 17. 1 1/2 18. 1 3/4 19. 2 2/5 20. 2 3/5

Set 68 1. 0.33 1/3 2. 0.16 2/3 3. 0.71 3/7 4. 0.66 2/3 5. 0.11 1/9 6. 3.33 1/3 7. 0.83 1/3 8. 0.55 5/9
9. 1.83 1/3 10. 2.33 1/3 11. 0.44 4/9 12. 0.22 2/9 13. 1.66 2/3 14. 1.33 1/3 15. 1.11 1/9
16. 1.16 2/3 17. 2.16 2/3 18. 0.09 1/11 19. 0.05 5/9 20. 0.27 7/9 21. 0.18 2/11 22. 0.38 8/9
23. 0.61 1/9 24. 0.45 5/11

Set 69 Give each product.

1. $4\frac{1}{2} \times 2$ 2. $2\frac{1}{3} \times 7$ 3. $7\frac{1}{4} \times 6$ 4. $6\frac{1}{3} \times 5$ 5. $3\frac{1}{4} \times 4$

6. $2\frac{2}{3} \times 2\frac{1}{2}$ 7. $3\frac{1}{4} \times 3\frac{1}{3}$ 8. $3\frac{3}{4} \times 4\frac{1}{4}$ 9. $1\frac{3}{8} \times 1\frac{1}{4}$ 10. $2\frac{1}{5} \times 1\frac{1}{4}$

11. $4\frac{2}{3} \times 3\frac{1}{2}$ 12. $1\frac{1}{5} \times 2\frac{3}{4}$ 13. $1\frac{1}{2} \times 1\frac{1}{2}$ 14. $2\frac{3}{8} \times 3\frac{1}{4}$ 15. $4\frac{2}{3} \times 1\frac{3}{4}$

16. $1\frac{3}{4} \times 1\frac{1}{6}$ 17. $3\frac{1}{3} \times 2\frac{1}{5}$ 18. $2\frac{1}{9} \times 2\frac{1}{4}$ 19. $3\frac{2}{3} \times 2\frac{1}{2}$ 20. $2\frac{1}{4} \times 2\frac{3}{4}$

Set 70 Give each quotient.

1. $1\frac{1}{4} \div 1\frac{1}{4}$ 2. $3\frac{1}{2} \div 1\frac{3}{4}$ 3. $5 \div 1\frac{1}{2}$ 4. $7\frac{1}{3} \div 2\frac{1}{4}$ 5. $7\frac{2}{3} \div 4$

6. $2\frac{2}{9} \div 1$ 7. $9\frac{1}{2} \div 3\frac{1}{2}$ 8. $3\frac{3}{4} \div 3$ 9. $0 \div 5\frac{1}{3}$ 10. $3 \div 6\frac{2}{3}$

11. $6\frac{2}{3} \div 8\frac{3}{4}$ 12. $2\frac{7}{8} \div 7\frac{2}{3}$ 13. $8\frac{1}{2} \div 2\frac{1}{8}$ 14. $8\frac{1}{4} \div 4\frac{2}{3}$ 15. $9\frac{1}{3} \div 2\frac{3}{5}$

16. $4\frac{5}{8} \div 6\frac{3}{4}$ 17. $4\frac{1}{2} \div 3\frac{1}{6}$ 18. $5\frac{1}{4} \div 5\frac{4}{5}$ 19. $6\frac{1}{3} \div 7\frac{1}{5}$ 20. $6\frac{3}{5} \div 8\frac{2}{3}$

Set 71 Solve.

1. $\frac{2}{3} = \frac{x}{9}$ 2. $\frac{5}{9} = \frac{20}{x}$ 3. $\frac{5}{8} = \frac{x}{96}$ 4. $\frac{24}{x} = \frac{3}{5}$

5. $\frac{3}{8} = \frac{5}{x}$ 6. $\frac{7}{6} = \frac{8}{x}$ 7. $\frac{8}{x} = \frac{5}{6}$ 8. $\frac{9}{x} = \frac{3}{7}$

9. $\frac{6}{1} = \frac{8}{x}$ 10. $\frac{3}{4} = \frac{x}{5}$ 11. $\frac{8}{5} = \frac{7}{x}$ 12. $\frac{x}{11} = \frac{7}{8}$

13. $\frac{12}{x} = \frac{4}{3}$ 14. $\frac{x}{14} = \frac{11}{2}$ 15. $\frac{15}{x} = \frac{3}{2}$ 16. $\frac{17}{x} = \frac{5}{7}$

17. $\frac{9}{8} = \frac{x}{6}$ 18. $\frac{8}{3} = \frac{x}{9}$ 19. $\frac{13}{x} = \frac{4}{5}$ 20. $\frac{16}{x} = \frac{9}{5}$

Set 72 Solve.

1. $\frac{2}{4} = \frac{n}{2}$ 2. $\frac{5}{6} = \frac{n}{12}$ 3. $\frac{n}{9} = \frac{4}{3}$ 4. $\frac{5}{6} = \frac{11}{n}$

5. $\frac{8}{3} = \frac{13}{n}$ 6. $\frac{3}{2} = \frac{5}{n}$ 7. $\frac{3}{12} = \frac{1}{n}$ 8. $\frac{7}{2} = \frac{9}{n}$

9. $\frac{n}{11} = \frac{3}{8}$ 10. $\frac{7}{8} = \frac{n}{4}$ 11. $\frac{n}{14} = \frac{7}{4}$ 12. $\frac{20}{24} = \frac{n}{12}$

13. $\frac{6}{7} = \frac{9}{n}$ 14. $\frac{n}{18} = \frac{5}{4}$ 15. $\frac{3}{n} = \frac{4}{7}$ 16. $\frac{5}{9} = \frac{8}{n}$

Answers.

Set 69 1. 9 2. 16 1/3 3. 43 1/2 4. 31 2/3 5. 13 6. 6 2/3 7. 10 5/6 8. 15 15/16 9. 1 23/32 10. 2 3/4
     11. 16 1/3 12. 3 3/10 13. 2 1/4 14. 7 23/32 15. 8 1/6 16. 2 1/24 17. 7 1/3 18. 4 3/4 19. 9 1/6
     20. 6 3/16
Set 70 1. 1 2. 2 3. 3 1/3 4. 3 7/27 5. 1 11/12 6. 2 2/9 7. 2 5/7 8. 1 1/4 9. 0 10. 9/20 11. 16/21
     12. 3/8 13. 4 14. 1 43/56 15. 3 23/39 16. 37/54 17. 1 8/19 18. 105/116 19. 95/108 20. 99/130
Set 71 1. 6 2. 36 3. 60 4. 40 5. 13 1/3 6. 6 6/7 7. 9 3/5 8. 21 9. 1 1/3 10. 3 3/4 11. 4 3/8
     12. 9 5/8 13. 9 14. 77 15. 10 16. 23 4/5 17. 6 3/4 18. 24 19. 16 1/4 20. 8 8/9
Set 72 1. 1 2. 10 3. 12 4. 13 1/5 5. 4 7/8 6. 3 1/3 7. 4 8. 2 4/7 9. 4 1/8 10. 3 1/2 11. 24 1/2
     12. 10 13. 10 1/2 14. 22 1/2 15. 5 1/4 16. 14 2/5

Set 73 Copy and complete.

	1.	2.	3.	4.	5.	6.	7.	8.	9.	10.
Fraction	$\frac{9}{100}$	$\frac{17}{100}$	$\frac{33}{100}$							
Decimal				.43	.57	.59				
Percent							21%	37%	83%	97%

	11.	12.	13.	14.	15.	16.	17.	18.	19.	20.
Fraction	$\frac{1}{4}$	$\frac{1}{2}$	$\frac{3}{4}$	$\frac{3}{5}$						
Decimal					.8	.4	.2			
Percent								30%	85%	90%

Set 74 Copy and complete.

	1.	2.	3.	4.	5.	6.	7.	8.	9.	10.
Decimal	0.34	3.4	0.034	0.65	6.5	0.065	0.43	0.671	1.251	2
Percent										

	11.	12.	13.	14.	15.	16.	17.	18.	19.	20.
Decimal										
Percent	17.2%	1.72%	172%	38.6%	4.2%	42%	156.2%	7%	70%	.7%

Set 75 Copy and complete.

	1.	2.	3.	4.	5.	6.	7.	8.	9.	10.
Fraction	$\frac{1}{3}$	$\frac{1}{6}$	$\frac{2}{3}$	$\frac{5}{6}$	$\frac{1}{8}$	$\frac{3}{8}$	$\frac{4}{3}$	$\frac{7}{6}$	$\frac{5}{8}$	$\frac{9}{8}$
Percent										

	11.	12.	13.	14.	15.	16.	17.	18.	19.	20.
Fraction	$\frac{1}{16}$	$\frac{3}{16}$	$\frac{5}{16}$	$\frac{7}{16}$	$\frac{9}{16}$	$\frac{7}{5}$	$\frac{5}{3}$	$\frac{7}{4}$	$\frac{6}{5}$	$\frac{5}{2}$
Percent										

Answers.

Set 73 1. .09, 9% 2. .17, 17% 3. .33, 33% 4. 43/100, 43% 5. 57/100, 57% 6. 59/100, 59% 7. 21/100, .21
8. 37/100, .37 9. 83/100, .83 10. 97/100, .97 11. .25, 25% 12. .5, 50% 13. .75, 75% 14. .6, 60%
15. 4/5, 80% 16. 2/5, 40% 17. 1/5, 20% 18. 3/10, .3 19. 17/20, .85 20. 9/10, .9

Set 74 1. 34% 2. 340% 3. 3.4% 4. 65% 5. 650% 6. 6.5% 7. 43% 8. 67.1% 9. 125.1% 10. 200% 11. 0.172
12. 0.0172 13. 1.72 14. 0.386 15. 0.042 16. 0.42 17. 1.562 18. 0.07 19. 0.7 20. 0.007

Set 75 1. 33 1/3% 2. 16 2/3% 3. 66 2/3% 4. 83 1/3% 5. 12 1/2% 6. 37 1/2% 7. 133 1/3% 8. 116 2/3%
9. 62 1/2% 10. 112 1/2% 11. 6 1/4% 12. 18 3/4% 13. 31 1/4% 14. 43 3/4% 15. 56 1/4% 16. 140%
17. 166 2/3% 18. 175% 19. 120% 20. 250%

Set 76   Solve.

1. 25% of 80 = n
4. 40% of 10 = n
7. 125% of 20 = n
10. 25% of 28 = n
13. 200% of 12 = n
16. 5% of 30 = n

2. 50% of 72 = n
5. 100% of 63 = n
8. $33\frac{1}{3}$% of 15 = n
11. 75% of 78 = n
14. 500% of 30 = n
17. 30% of 60 = n

3. 20% of 60 = n
6. 150% of 8 = n
9. $12\frac{1}{2}$% of 40 = n
12. 60% of 90 = n
15. 50% of 30 = n
18. 60% of 30 = n

Set 77   Solve.

1. 6% of 100 = n
4. 12% of 25 = n
7. 125% of 200 = n
10. $87\frac{1}{2}$% of 40 = n
13. $12\frac{1}{2}$% of 40 = n
16. 40% of 8 = n

2. 50% of 39 = n
5. 175% of 12 = n
8. $37\frac{1}{2}$% of 24 = n
11. 10% of 60 = n
14. 200% of 19 = n
17. $83\frac{1}{3}$% of 24 = n

3. 20% of 45 = n
6. 8% of 50 = n
9. 25% of 48 = n
12. 150% of 52 = n
15. $16\frac{2}{3}$% of 42 = n
18. $33\frac{1}{3}$% of 37 = n

Set 78   Solve.

1. 4% of n = 2
4. 50% of n = 13
7. $33\frac{1}{3}$% of n = 23
10. 42% of n = 21
13. $62\frac{1}{2}$% of n = 25
16. $16\frac{2}{3}$% of n = 43

2. 75% of n = 12
5. 100% of n = 29
8. 25% of n = 31
11. $12\frac{1}{2}$% of n = 19
14. 80% of n = 74
17. 20% of n = 18

3. 9% of n = 9
6. $66\frac{2}{3}$% of n = 18
9. 10% of n = 8
12. $83\frac{1}{3}$% of n = 25
15. 200% of n = 39
18. $37\frac{1}{2}$% of n = 12

Set 79   Compute the unit price (cents per gram).
Round to the nearest hundredth of a cent.

1. 39 g for 78¢
4. 40 g for 92¢
7. 65 g for 48¢
10. 62.5 g for 56¢

2. 100 g for 60¢
5. 120 g for 84¢
8. 58.5 g for 52¢
11. 68.75 g for 64¢

3. 60 g for 54¢
6. 165 g for 43¢
9. 95.5 g for 75¢
12. 200 g for 72¢

Answers.

Set 76   1. 20   2. 36   3. 12   4. 4   5. 63   6. 12   7. 25   8. 5   9. 5   10. 7   11. 58 1/2   12. 54   13. 24   14. 150
15. 15   16. 1 1/2   17. 18   18. 18
Set 77   1. 6   2. 19 1/2   3. 9   4. 3   5. 21   6. 4   7. 250   8. 9   9. 12   10. 35   11. 6   12. 78   13. 5   14. 38
15. 7   16. 3 1/5   17. 20   18. 12 1/3
Set 78   1. 50   2. 16   3. 100   4. 26   5. 29   6. 27   7. 69   8. 124   9. 80   10. 50   11. 152   12. 30   13. 40
14. 92 1/2   15. 19 1/2   16. 258   17. 90   18. 32
Set 79   1. 2¢   2. 0.6¢   3. 0.9¢   4. 2.3¢   5. 0.7¢   6. 0.26¢   7. 0.74¢   8. 0.89¢   9. 0.79¢   10. 0.90¢   11. 0.93¢
12. 0.36¢

Set 80 **Compute the prices.**

1. 2 for 89¢
   a. 1 costs ?
   b. 3 cost ?

2. 3 for 71¢
   a. 1 costs ?
   b. 2 cost ?

3. 4 for 57¢
   a. 1 costs ?
   b. 3 cost ?

4. 3 for 79¢
   a. 1 costs ?
   b. 4 cost ?

5. 5 for 83¢
   a. 1 costs ?
   b. 4 cost ?

6. 4 for 95¢
   a. 1 costs ?
   b. 5 cost ?

7. 2 for 93¢
   a. 1 costs ?
   b. 5 cost ?

8. 3 for $1.13
   a. 1 costs ?
   b. 5 cost ?

9. 4 for $1.93
   a. 1 costs ?
   b. 3 cost ?

10. 2 for $1.19
    a. 1 costs ?
    b. 7 cost ?

11. 3 for $2.15
    a. 1 costs ?
    b. 8 cost ?

12. 5 for $2.74
    a. 1 costs ?
    b. 7 cost ?

Set 81 **Copy and complete.**

	1.	2.	3.	4.	5.	6.	7.	8.	9.	10.
Regular Price	$80	$60	$50	$18	$43	$62	$73	$81	$56	$42
Percent of Discount	10%	15%	12%	18%	25%	32%	30%	50%	$33\frac{1}{3}$%	$66\frac{2}{3}$%
Sale Price										

	11.	12.	13.	14.	15.	16.	17.	18.	19.	20.
Regular Price	$18.50	$16.75	$23.40	$26.80	$52.40	$36.75	$81.50	$72.30	$65.45	$72.48
Percent of Discount	10%	20%	15%	30%	50%	$37\frac{1}{2}$%	$33\frac{1}{3}$%	$66\frac{2}{3}$%	$62\frac{1}{2}$%	$12\frac{1}{2}$%
Sale Price										

Answers.

Set 80 1. a. 45¢ b. $1.34 2. a. 24¢ b. 48¢ 3. a. 15¢ b. 43¢ 4. a. 27¢ b. $1.06 5. a. 17¢ b. 67¢
6. a. 24¢ b. $1.19 7. a. 47¢ b. $2.33 8. a. 38¢ b. $1.89 9. a. 49¢ b. $1.45 10. a. 60¢ b. $4.17
11. a. 72¢ b. $5.74 12. a. 55¢ b. $3.84

Set 81 1. $72 2. $51 3. $44 4. $14.76 5. $32.25 6. $42.16 7. $51.10 8. $40.50 9. $37.33 10. $14
11. $16.65 12. $13.40 13. $19.89 14. $18.76 15. $26.20 16. $22.97 17. $54.33 18. $24.10
19. $24.54 20. $63.42

Set 82   Copy and complete.

	Principal	Rate	Time	Interest
1.	$100	6%	1 year	
2.	$300	9%	2 years	
3.	$150	8%	$1\frac{1}{2}$ years	
4.	$275	8%	6 months	
5.	$450	10%	8 months	
6.	$600	9%	9 months	
7.	$1000	$8\frac{1}{2}$%	3 months	
8.	$850	10%	2 months	
9.	$1125	10%	4 months	
10.	$3600	$9\frac{1}{2}$%	18 months	
11.	$2100	$8\frac{1}{4}$%	$2\frac{1}{2}$ years	
12.	$8000	$9\frac{3}{4}$%	$1\frac{3}{4}$ years	

Set 83   Complete.

Event

Toss this die.

1. $P(1) = \underline{?}$
3. $P(2) = \underline{?}$
5. $P(\text{odd number}) = \underline{?}$
7. $P(\text{number less than 2}) = \underline{?}$
9. $P(\text{factor of 12}) = \underline{?}$

2. $P(\text{even number}) = \underline{?}$
4. $P(\text{not 2}) = \underline{?}$
6. $P(\text{prime number}) = \underline{?}$
8. $P(\text{number greater than 3}) = \underline{?}$
10. $P(\text{multiple of 2}) = \underline{?}$

Answers.

Set 82 1. $6 2. $54 3. $18 4. $11 5. $30 6. $40.50 7. $21.25 8. $14.17 9. $37.50 10. $513 11. $433.13
12. $1365
Set 83 1. 1/6 2. 1/2 3. 1/6 4. 5/6 5. 1/2 6. 1/2 7. 1/6 8. 1/2 9. 5/6 10. 1/2

Set 84 Complete.

First Event
Spin this spinner:

Second Event
Then (without looking)
pick a marble:

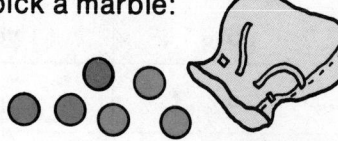

1. $P(1, red) = \underline{?}$
2. $P(2, green) = \underline{?}$
3. $P(odd, red) = \underline{?}$
4. $P(odd, blue) = \underline{?}$
5. $P(even, blue) = \underline{?}$
6. $P(even, red) = \underline{?}$

7. $P(3, blue) = \underline{?}$
9. $P(number > 3, red) = \underline{?}$

8. $P(odd, green) = \underline{?}$
10. $P(number < 3, green) = \underline{?}$

Set 85 Find the range, mean, and median.

1. 3, 5, 8, 8, 10, 11, 14
2. 5, 6, 9, 9, 11, 12
3. 32, 38, 46, 49, 50
4. 26, 32, 34, 41, 42, 42, 46
5. 68, 69, 70, 71, 72
6. 39, 43, 56, 57, 65
7. 45, 45, 45, 45, 45, 45
8. 83, 86, 86, 89, 90, 91
9. 126, 124, 132, 128, 130
10. 153, 162, 147, 165, 147

Set 86 < or >?

1. $^+5 \; \bullet \; ^+4$
2. $^-5 \; \bullet \; ^+4$
3. $^-5 \; \bullet \; ^-4$
4. $^+5 \; \bullet \; ^-4$
5. $^+9 \; \bullet \; ^-8$
6. $^+6 \; \bullet \; ^+5$
7. $^-9 \; \bullet \; ^-8$
8. $^-5 \; \bullet \; ^+4$
9. $^-14 \; \bullet \; ^+16$
10. $^+9 \; \bullet \; ^-12$
11. $^+1 \; \bullet \; 0$
12. $0 \; \bullet \; ^-1$
13. $^+12 \; \bullet \; ^-13$
14. $^+12 \; \bullet \; ^+13$
15. $^-12 \; \bullet \; ^+13$
16. $^-12 \; \bullet \; ^-13$
17. $^+18 \; \bullet \; ^+19$
18. $^+32 \; \bullet \; ^+33$
19. $^-16 \; \bullet \; ^-15$
20. $^+12 \; \bullet \; ^-12$
21. $^-36 \; \bullet \; ^+35$
22. $^-13 \; \bullet \; ^+13$
23. $^-23 \; \bullet \; ^-24$
24. $^-18 \; \bullet \; ^+19$

Set 87 Give each sum.

1. $^+5 + ^+9$
2. $^+9 + ^-5$
3. $^-8 + 0$
4. $^-5 + ^-6$
5. $^+9 + ^+3$
6. $^-9 + ^-5$
7. $^-6 + ^-6$
8. $^+9 + 0$
9. $^-15 + ^+11$
10. $^-11 + ^-3$
11. $^+8 + ^-9$
12. $^-9 + ^+13$
13. $^+11 + ^-11$
14. $^-1 + ^-10$
15. $^+7 + ^+9$
16. $^-14 + ^+14$
17. $^+13 + ^+5$
18. $^-19 + 0$
19. $^-13 + ^+13$
20. $^+13 + ^-20$
21. $^-16 + ^+16$
22. $0 + 0$
23. $^+12 + ^-5$
24. $^+11 + ^+9$

Set 88 Give each difference.

1. $^+6 - ^+4$
2. $^+6 - ^-4$
3. $^+7 - 0$
4. $^-5 - ^+7$
5. $0 - ^-6$
6. $^-5 - ^-3$
7. $^-3 - ^+9$
8. $^+12 - ^+5$
9. $^-2 - ^-6$
10. $^-9 - ^+8$
11. $^+8 - ^+3$
12. $^-8 - ^-2$
13. $^+3 - ^-9$
14. $0 - 0$
15. $^+12 - ^-3$
16. $^-2 - ^-9$
17. $^+3 - ^+8$
18. $^-4 - ^+11$
19. $^-9 - ^-4$
20. $^+4 - ^-6$
21. $^-4 - ^+6$
22. $^+13 - ^-6$
23. $^+6 - ^+14$
24. $^-1 - ^-5$

Answers.

Set 84 1. 1/6 2. 1/18 3. 1/3 4. 2/9 5. 1/9 6. 1/6 7. 1/9 8. 1/9 9. 0 10. 1/9
Set 85 1. 11, 8 3/7, 8 2. 7, 8 2/3, 9 3. 18, 43, 46 4. 20, 37 4/7, 41 5. 4, 70, 70 6. 26, 52, 56
7. 0, 45, 45 8. 8, 87 1/2, 87 1/2 9. 8, 128, 128 10. 18, 154 4/5, 153
Set 86 1. > 2. < 3. < 4. > 5. > 6. > 7. < 8. < 9. < 10. > 11. > 12. > 13. > 14. < 15. < 16. >
17. < 18. < 19. < 20. > 21. < 22. < 23. > 24. <
Set 87 1. $^+14$ 2. $^+4$ 3. $^-8$ 4. $^-11$ 5. $^+12$ 6. $^-14$ 7. $^-12$ 8. $^+9$ 9. $^-4$ 10. $^-14$ 11. $^-1$ 12. $^+4$ 13. 0
14. $^-11$ 15. $^+16$ 16. 0 17. $^+18$ 18. $^-19$ 19. 0 20. $^-7$ 21. 0 22. 0 23. $^+7$ 24. $^+20$
Set 88 1. $^+2$ 2. $^+10$ 3. $^+7$ 4. $^-12$ 5. $^+6$ 6. $^-2$ 7. $^-12$ 8. $^+7$ 9. $^+4$ 10. $^-17$ 11. $^+5$ 12. $^-6$ 13. $^+12$
14. 0 15. $^+15$ 16. $^+7$ 17. $^-5$ 18. $^-15$ 19. $^-5$ 20. $^+10$ 21. $^-10$ 22. $^+19$ 23. $^-8$ 24. $^+4$

Set 89 Give each product.

1. $^+5 \times {}^+4$ 2. $^+7 \times {}^-3$ 3. $^-8 \times {}^-8$ 4. $^-6 \times {}^+6$
5. $^-6 \times {}^+2$ 6. $0 \times {}^-4$ 7. $^+5 \times {}^+7$ 8. $^-4 \times {}^+3$
9. $^-3 \times {}^-9$ 10. $^+9 \times {}^-9$ 11. $^-5 \times {}^-8$ 12. $^-9 \times {}^-5$
13. $^-7 \times {}^+9$ 14. $^+6 \times {}^+4$ 15. $^+5 \times {}^-9$ 16. $^-8 \times {}^-9$
17. $^+9 \times {}^+8$ 18. $^+7 \times {}^-7$ 19. $^-4 \times {}^-8$ 20. $^+8 \times {}^-9$
21. $^-9 \times {}^-6$ 22. 0×0 23. $^+6 \times {}^-8$ 24. $^+6 \times {}^+9$

Set 90 Give each quotient.

1. $^+24 \div {}^-6$ 2. $^+56 \div {}^-7$ 3. $^-32 \div {}^+8$ 4. $^-27 \div {}^-3$
5. $^-35 \div {}^+7$ 6. $^-36 \div {}^-6$ 7. $0 \div {}^-7$ 8. $^+32 \div {}^+8$
9. $^+36 \div {}^+4$ 10. $^-8 \div {}^-8$ 11. $^+48 \div {}^-6$ 12. $^-45 \div {}^-9$
13. $^-36 \div {}^+9$ 14. $^+48 \div {}^+6$ 15. $^-54 \div {}^+6$ 16. $^-21 \div {}^+3$
17. $^+49 \div {}^-7$ 18. $^-28 \div {}^-4$ 19. $^+63 \div {}^-9$ 20. $0 \div {}^+9$
21. $^+81 \div {}^+9$ 22. $^+72 \div {}^-9$ 23. $^-48 \div {}^-8$ 24. $^+64 \div {}^-8$

Answers.

Set 89 1. $^+20$ 2. $^-21$ 3. $^+64$ 4. $^-36$ 5. $^-12$ 6. 0 7. $^+35$ 8. $^-12$ 9. $^+27$ 10. $^-81$ 11. $^+40$ 12. $^+45$ 13. $^-63$
14. $^+24$ 15. $^-45$ 16. $^+72$ 17. $^+72$ 18. $^-49$ 19. $^+32$ 20. $^-72$ 21. $^+54$ 22. 0 23. $^-48$ 24. $^+54$

Set 90 1. $^-4$ 2. $^-8$ 3. $^-4$ 4. $^+9$ 5. $^-5$ 6. $^+6$ 7. 0 8. $^+4$ 9. $^+9$ 10. $^+1$ 11. $^-8$ 12. $^+5$ 13. $^-4$ 14. $^+8$
15. $^-9$ 16. $^-7$ 17. $^-7$ 18. $^+7$ 19. $^-7$ 20. 0 21. $^+9$ 22. $^-8$ 23. $^+6$ 24. $^-8$

Extra Problem Solving

Sixteen two-page sets of word problems are provided so that you may give your students extra practice when you think it is needed. Each set has some problems that are quite easy so that less able students can have success, and most sets have some problems that are difficult so that better students can be challenged.

Each set of exercises is keyed to the Skill Test so that you will know which arithmetic skills are needed to solve the problems. For example, the phrase "Through Skill 9" on Set 1 indicates that no skills beyond Skill 9 of the Skill Test (page 369) are required to solve the problems of that set—that is, a student who can add, subtract, multiply, and divide whole numbers has the arithmetic skills needed to solve the problems of Set 1. Later sets involve decimals, still later sets involve fractions, and the last sets involve percents.

Answers to all exercises, and solutions to selected difficult exercises are given for your convenience. Please note that, especially in problems involving decimals, students may give answers that are slightly different from the answers we give. For example, a student may round an answer to the nearest tenth or thousandth while the provided answer is rounded to the nearest hundredth. You will, of course, have to make the final decision about the acceptability of answers, but we suggest being fairly lenient.

In most exercises students are not explicitly told how to round their answers. However, in many cases there are clues in the problems themselves that help one to decide how to round. For example, in exercise 5 of Set 4, both the safe following distance and the car length are given to the nearest tenth of a meter so it is reasonable that the final answer is, at best, correct to the nearest tenth of a meter, too. In exercise 10 of Set 4, the question is about the number of accidents that can be expected. Since a fraction of an accident can't occur, the answer should be given to the nearest whole number.

It is mathematically and logically correct to give the answer to some questions as "pure" numbers—that is, without labels. For example, the answer to the question "How many meters wide is the room?" may be correctly given as 8. However, it may help students think more carefully about a problem if they have to supply a labeled answer such as 8

Extra Problem Solving

Set 1

1. Jean had 277 coins in her collection. Her grandfather gave her 58 coins from his large collection. How many coins did Jean have then?

2. Jean went to a coin show where she sold 26 of her coins and bought 34. How many coins did she have then? (See exercise 1.)

3. At one time Jean had 172 United States coins and 86 foreign coins. How many more U.S. coins did she have?

4. At another time Jean had 329 coins. At a coin show she traded a 1973 Eisenhower silver dollar and a 1939 Jefferson nickel for 13 other coins that she needed. How many coins did she have then?

5. Ten years ago an 1884 Liberty Head silver dollar was bought for $2975. Recently it sold for $7000. How much profit was made?

6. Several years ago a coin dealer bought a roll (20 coins) of 1976 Eisenhower silver dollars for $95. Recently he sold the coins individually for $8 each. How much profit did he make?

Through Skill 9.
398 Can be used anytime after page 49.

meters. A wrong label can also give you a clue to how a student is misunderstanding a problem. Therefore you may wish to urge students to label all answers, but don't penalize them unduly for an unlabeled answer that does not logically require a label.

Note that most problems can be solved in more than one way. Solutions that we give are neither the only solutions nor necessarily the best solutions. Examine student solutions carefully before judging them.

7. Joe had 205 coins in his collection, and Carl had 371. Joe traded 13 of his coins for 32 of Carl's coins. How many coins did each boy have after the trade?

8. Virginia had 193 coins in her collection, and Barbara had 284. Virginia traded 21 of her coins for 16 of Barbara's. After the trade, how many more coins did Barbara have?

This ad appeared in a coin magazine:

CARSON CITY SILVER DOLLARS

	Fine (F)	Very fine (VF)	Extra fine (EF)	Almost uncirculated (AU)
1878	14.00	17.00	23.00	38.00
1879	33.00	75.00	190.00	---
1880	30.00	42.00	56.00	79.00
1881	---	69.00	79.00	120.00
1882	15.00	19.00	23.00	---
1883	16.00	20.00	24.00	28.00

Add $3.00 for shipping ($5.00 for orders of $300 to $499
$8.00 for orders of $500 or more.)

Find the cost of each of these orders.

9. 1 1879 VF
   1 1882 ExF
   1 1883 AU

10. 2 1878 AU
    2 1881 AU
    1 1880 AU

11. 2 1878 ExF
    3 1881 ExF

12. 10 1883 AU
    10 1881 AU

13. 1 VF dollar for each year.

14. 5 1878 AU
    5 1879 ExF
    5 1880 AU

15. Another line of the above ad offered 1 each of the ExF coins at a special price of $368. How much is saved over the individual coin prices?

16. What is the average price of an 1878 dollar?

ANSWERS

Set 1

1. 335 2. 343 3. 86 4. 340 5. $4025
6. $65 7. Joe: 224; Carl: 352 8. 101
9. $129 10. $400 11. $286 12. $1488
13. $245 14. $1543 15. $27 16. $23

Set 2

1. The earth's gravity is 6 times that of the moon's, so objects on the earth's surface weigh 6 times as much as they would weigh on the moon's surface. The astronauts of Apollo 11 collected moon rocks that weighed 49 lb back on earth. How much did these rocks weigh on the moon?

2. The crew of Apollo 17 collected rocks that weighed about 13 lb on the moon. How much did these rocks weigh back on the earth? (See exercise 1.)

3. How much would an astronaut weigh on the moon if his earth weight was 185 lb? (See exercise 1.)

4. Suppose that a lunar lander weighed 2590 lb on the moon's surface. How much would it weigh on the earth's surface? (See exercise 1.)

5. Suppose that a "moon buggy" weighed 628 lb on earth. How much did it weigh on the moon? (See exercise 1.)

6. Apollo 11 stayed on the moon for 21 hours 36 minutes 21 seconds. Apollo 17 stayed a record 75 hours. How much longer was Apollo 17 on the moon?

400   Through Skill 9.
Can be used anytime after page 49.

SELECTED SOLUTIONS

11.

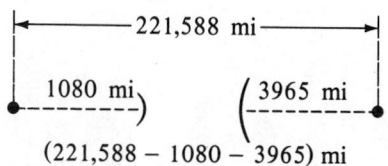

(221,588 − 1080 − 3965) mi

16. According to exercise 15, the moon travels around the earth at a speed of 2299 mi per hour. The moon takes 29 days 12 hours to make a complete orbit.

29 days 12 hours = 708 hours

708 h × 2299 mi per h = 1,627,692 mi

7. The temperature on the moon ranges from 261°F in bright sunlight to −279°F in the dark. How many degrees' difference is this?

8. The diameter of the moon is 2160 mi and the diameter of the earth is 7930 mi. How many miles greater is the diameter of the earth?

9. How much greater is the radius of the earth? (See exercise 8.)

10. At its closest point (perigee) the moon is 221,588 mi from earth. At its farthest point (apogee), it is 252,862 mi from earth. How many miles closer is the moon at perigee than at apogee?

11. The distances given in exercise 10 are from the center of the earth to the center of the moon. How far apart are the *surfaces* of the earth and moon at perigee? (See exercise 8.)

12. How far apart are the *surfaces* of the earth and moon at apogee? (See exercises 8 and 10.)

13. The average distance from the earth to the moon (center to center) is 14,005 mi less than the distance at apogee. What is the average distance between earth and moon? (See exercise 10.)

14. How much greater is the average distance than the distance at perigee? (See exercises 10 and 13.)

15. The moon travels around the earth at an average speed of 2299 mi per hour. How far does the moon travel around the earth in a day?

16. The moon takes about 29 days 12 hours to complete one orbit of the earth. How long is the orbital path? (See exercise 15.)

17. At any spot on earth the moon rises about 50 minutes later each day. Suppose that in Kansas City the moon rose at 8:00 P.M. on July 1. When would the moon next rise at about 8:00 P.M.?

401

17. One way to solve this problem is to make a table.

Date	Time of moonrise
July 1	8:00 P.M.
July 2	8:50 P.M.
July 3	9:40 P.M.
•	
•	
•	
July 29	7:20 P.M.
July 30	8:10 P.M.

Another solution: The moonrise time gets later and later as the days pass: 8:00 P.M., 8:50 P.M., 9:40 P.M., . . . The question then is: If moonrise is 50 minutes later each day, how many days will it take to be 1440 minutes later? (24 h × 60 min per h = 1440 min) We find that 29 days later the moon will rise at about 8:00 P.M. (1440 min ÷ 50 min per day = 28.8 days ≈ 29 days) In fact, 29 days later the moon will rise 1450 minutes later. (29 days × 50 min per day = 1450 min) This means that 29 days later the moon will rise at 8:10 P.M. (1450 min ÷ 60 min per hour = 24 h 10 min)

Set 3
1. 16,425,000 2. 7.5 mm per hour
3. 6.0 mm 4. 8.0 m per s 5. 219
6. 7.7 h 7. 83 cm per year
8. 31 cm per year (rounded to the nearest
cm) 9. 47.2 mm = 4.72 cm 10. 1500 cm
11. 22 cm 12. 7.8 cm 13. 98.3 cm
14. 0.38 cm 15. 25,558,000 16. 0.91 mm

Set 3

1. There are about 45,000 thunderstorms on earth each day. How many thunderstorms are there in a year?

2. A light rain is one in which the rain falls at a rate of 2.5 mm or less per hour. A heavy rain is one in which the rate is at least 3 times as great. What is the lowest rate of rainfall in a heavy rain?

3. The smallest raindrops are about 1.3 mm in diameter. The largest drops are up to 4.62 times as large. What is the diameter of the largest drop?

4. The smallest raindrops fall at about 1.5 m per second. The largest ones fall 5.33 times as fast. What is the rate of fall of the largest raindrops?

5. In Java 0.6 of all days have rainstorms. How many stormy days are there on Java in a year?

6. Suppose a moderate rain falls at the rate of 6.5 mm per hour. How long will it take to get 5 cm of rainfall?

7. The tropics average 250 cm of rain per year. The temperate regions average 0.33 as much. What is the average rainfall of the temperate regions?

8. The polar regions get 0.125 as much precipitation as the tropics. What is the average yearly precipitation in the polar regions? (See exercise 7.)

9. The driest region on earth is a part of Chile where the average rainfall for 59 years was 0.8 mm per year. What was the total rainfall in the 59 years?

10. The wettest spot on earth is Mount Waialeale on the island of Kauai in Hawaii. The yearly rainfall there is 317.8 times the total 59-year rainfall given in exercise 9. What is the yearly rainfall on Mount Waialeale?

Through Skill 16.
402 Can be used anytime after page 99.

SELECTED SOLUTIONS

15. First find the volume of the rainfall. Use cubic meters as the unit, because the weight of a cubic meter of water is 1 metric ton.

    98.3 cm = 0.983 m   26 km² = 26,000,000 m²

    The volume of the water: 0.983 m × 26,000,000 m²
    = 25,558,000 m³

    The weight of the water: 25,558,000 metric tons

16. 91,000 metric tons of water have a volume of 91,000 m³. The area covered by the rainfall: 100 km² = 100,000,000 m². The depth of the water: 91,000 m³ ÷ 100,000,000 m² = 0.00091 m
    = 0.91 mm

11. The wettest state is Hawaii, which averages 180 cm of rainfall a year. The yearly rainfall in Hawaii is 8.18 times that in the driest state, Nevada. What is the yearly rainfall in Nevada?

12. The heaviest 24-hour rainfall was 187 cm in Cilaos on the island of Réunion in the Indian Ocean on March 15–16, 1952. What was the hourly rainfall on that day?

13. The heaviest 24-hour rainfall in the U.S. was at Yankeetown, Florida, in 1950. The rainfall there was 88.7 cm less than the world record given in exercise 12. How much rain fell on Yankeetown?

14. The place with the lowest rainfall in the U.S. is Death Valley, California, with 4.52 cm per year. What is the average monthly rainfall in Death Valley?

15. The record rainfall on Yankeetown, Florida, fell on a 26-km² area. How many metric tons of water fell in that rainstorm? (1 cubic meter of water weighs 1 metric ton. See exercise 13.)

16. An average thundercloud holds 91,000 metric tons of water. If it *all* fell on a 100-km² area, what would be the depth of the rainfall? (1 metric ton = 1000 kg)

403

Set 4

1. Suppose that a car is being driven at 48 kilometers per hour and that a sudden emergency makes the driver stop the car as quickly as possible. The car will travel 10.1 m while the driver is reacting (reaction distance) and another 12.2 m while the brakes are applied (braking distance). What is the total stopping distance?

2. At 96 km per hour the reaction distance is 2 times the reaction distance at 48 km per hour. What is the reaction distance at 96 km per hour? (See exercise 1.)

3. At 96 km per hour the braking distance is 55.5 m. What is the stopping distance at 96 km per hour? (See exercise 2.)

4. At 32 km per hour the stopping distance is 12.8 m and the reaction distance is 6.7 m. What is the braking distance?

5. You must stay far enough behind another car to be able to stop without hitting it if the other driver makes an emergency stop. At 64 km per hour a safe following distance is 21.9 m. If the average car is 5.5 m long, how many car lengths is the safe following distance?

6. The safe following distance at 32 km per hour is 11 m. How many car lengths is that? (See exercise 5.)

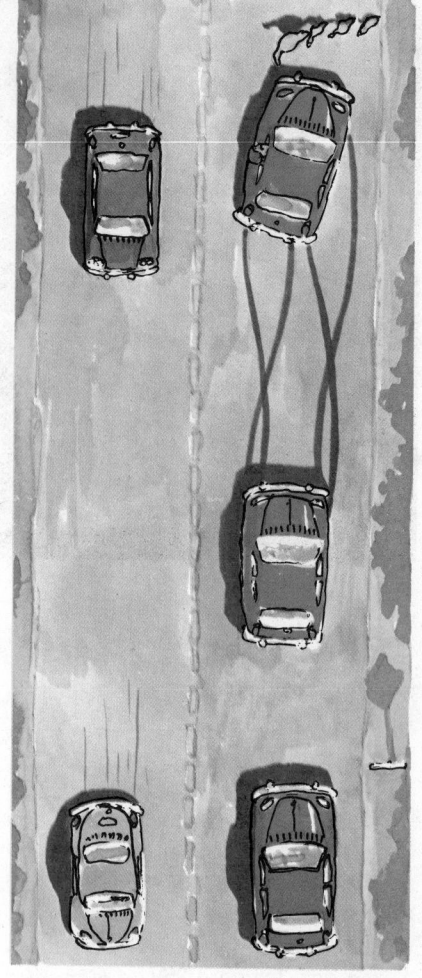

7. The safe following distance at 96 km per hour is about 6 car lengths. What is that distance in meters? (See exercise 5.)

404   Through Skill 16.
Can be used anytime after page 99.

SELECTED SOLUTIONS

8. Change the distance that teenagers drive to units of 100 million km.

$$250{,}000{,}000 \text{ km} \div 100{,}000{,}000 \text{ km} = 2.5$$

Use the accident rate.

$$2.5 \; 100 \text{ million km} \times 7.1 \text{ accidents per}$$
$$100 \text{ million km} = 17.75 \text{ accidents}$$
$$\approx 18 \text{ accidents}$$

14. $$2810 \text{ deaths} \div 75 \text{ deaths per}$$
$$100 \text{ million km} \approx 37.47 \; 100 \text{ million km}$$
$$= 3{,}747{,}000{,}000 \text{ km}$$

8. For drivers under 20 years old there are 7.1 accidents involving fatalities for each 100 million kilometers driven. In a city where teenagers drive 250,000,000 km in a year, how many fatal accidents can be expected?

9. The fatal-accident rate for teenagers is about 1.6 times the rate for all drivers. What is the fatal-accident rate for all drivers? (See exercise 8.)

10. In a large city where the total number of kilometers driven in a year is 723,000,000, how many fatal accidents can be expected? (See exercise 9.)

11. One year the overall accident rate for female drivers was 1202 accidents per 100 million kilometers driven. Suppose that in one week females drove 550 million kilometers. How many accidents would they be expected to have?

12. The overall accident rate for male drivers is 1.09 times the overall accident rate for females. What is the accident rate for males? (See exercise 11.)

13. A recent study was made of 1500 fatal accidents. It was found that 0.65 of the drivers responsible for the accidents had been drinking. In how many of these accidents was drinking not a factor?

14. One year in the state of New York the auto death rate was 75 deaths per 100 million kilometers driven. In that year there were 2810 deaths. About how many kilometers were driven in the state that year?

405

Set 5

The Patberg family was traveling in Europe one summer. Each time they entered a new country they exchanged some of their money for the money of that country. This table shows some of the exchange rates.

Exchange Rates for U.S. Dollars

Country	Unit	Units per U.S. Dollar	Country	Unit	Units per U.S. Dollar
West Germany	mark	2.413	Poland	zloty	19.05
France	franc	4.963	Russia	ruble	0.7353
Great Britain	pound	0.5831	Spain	peseta	67.11
Italy	lire	845.40	Switzerland	franc	2.509
Netherlands	guilder	2.528			

1. How many British pounds did the Patbergs get for 100 U.S. dollars?

2. How many Italian lire did they get for 100 U.S. dollars?

3. How many Polish zlotys did they get in exchange for 75 U.S. dollars?

4. How many Russian rubles did they get for 150 U.S. dollars?

5. Mr. Patberg had 50 guilders and exchanged 50 U.S. dollars for more guilders. How many guilders did he have then?

6. Mrs. Patberg gave $35 in U.S. currency for a small painting in Paris. The painting cost 125 francs. How many francs did she get in change?

Through Skill 16.
406 Can be used anytime after page 99.

SELECTED SOLUTIONS

7. 275 pesetas ÷ 67.11 pesetas per dollar ≈ 4.10 dollars

9. One way to do this problem is to change the pesetas to dollars (50 pesetas ÷ 67.11 pesetas per dollar ≈ 0.7450 dollars), and then change the dollars to dirhams (0.7450 dollars × 4.26 dirhams per dollar ≈ 3.17 dirhams). In reality, of course, there would be an exchange rate for pesetas into dirhams. This rate can be computed from the information available as follows:

4.26 dirhams per dollar ÷ 67.11 pesetas per dollar
≈ 0.06348 dirhams per peseta

Then to convert 50 pesetas to dirhams:

50 pesetas × 0.06348 dirhams per peseta
≈ 3.17 dirhams

7. When the Patbergs left Spain to return home, they still had 275 pesetas. At a bank they exchanged the Spanish money for U.S. money. How much U.S. money did they get?

8. One day during their stay in Spain the Patbergs took a 1-day tour to Tangier, Morocco. They exchanged 50 U.S. dollars for Moroccan dirhams at the rate of 4.26 dirhams per dollar. How many dirhams did they get?

9. The Patbergs also exchanged 50 pesetas for dirhams. How many dirhams did they get? (See exercise 8.)

10. Mr. Patberg flew to Zambia, where the unit of money is the kwacha. At that time 1 kwacha was worth 1.30 U.S. dollars. How many kwacha did he get for 200 U.S. dollars?

11. A hotel room in London cost the Patbergs 27 pounds per night. In Rome a hotel room cost them 29,540 lire per night. Which room was more expensive? How much more expensive?

12. When Mrs. Patberg was on a business trip to Japan, the exchange rate gradually dropped from 230 yen for the dollar to 217 yen for the dollar. What effect would that have on Mrs. Patberg?

407

11. Convert both costs to dollars.

27 pounds ÷ 0.5831 pounds per dollar
$\approx$ 46.30 dollars

29,540 lira ÷ 845.40 lira per dollar $\approx$ 34.94 dollars.

Subtract to find the difference in dollars.

12. As the exchange rate dropped, she would get fewer yen for each dollar. Since prices in yen would stay the same, the prices in dollars would go up.

Set 6

1. 2.8¢ 2. $8.45 (The computation gives $8.4388, but tolls are usually collected in multiples of 5¢.) 3. 2.1¢ 4. Will Rogers Turnpike; 0.1¢ 5. $1.35 (Computation gives $1.33.) 6. $.90 ($.92) 7. $0.70 8. 3.6¢ 9. gasoline; 2.5¢ more 10. gasoline; 2.3¢ more 11. $14.76 12. 0.9¢ 13. $69.16 14. 1.1¢

Set 6

1. The most expensive toll road in the United States in cost per kilometer is the John F. Kennedy Memorial Highway in Delaware. The toll road is only 17.7 kilometers long and costs 50¢ to drive the whole length. What is the toll per kilometer?

2. One of the most expensive toll roads in the U.S. in total cost is the Pennsylvania Turnpike, which goes from the Ohio line northwest of Pittsburgh to the New Jersey line near Philadelphia. The total length is 578 km. The cost per kilometer is 1.46¢. What is the cost of driving the full length?

3. The West Virginia Turnpike is mostly a two-lane highway through the mountains south of Charleston. It costs $3.00 to drive its 142-km length. What is the cost per kilometer?

4. The Florida Turnpike goes 427 km across south Florida. It costs $4.80 to drive its length. The Will Rogers Turnpike goes 142 km from Tulsa, Oklahoma, to the Missouri line and costs $1.75 to drive its length. Which costs more per kilometer? How much more?

5. The average cost per kilometer for driving on the Indiana toll road is 1.4 cents. What is the toll between Gary and South Bend, the home of Notre Dame University, a distance of 95 km?

6. The cost of driving the Garden State Parkway in New Jersey is about 0.99¢ per kilometer. How much does it cost to drive from near Asbury Park to near Atlantic City, a distance of 93 km?

Through Skill 16.
408 Can be used anytime after page 99.

SELECTED SOLUTIONS

8. 27¢ per liter ÷ 7.5 km per liter = 3.6¢ per km

11. One-way distance: 120 km + 76 km + 16 km = 212 km
Round-trip distance: 212 km × 2 = 424 km
Gas used: 424 km ÷ 8.3 km per liter ≈ 51.08 liters
Gas cost: 51.08 L × 28.9¢ per L ≈ 1476¢ = $14.76

12. Tolls are paid on the turnpike travel only.
Turnpike travel: 76 km × 2 = 152 km
Per km cost: $1.40 ÷ 152 km ≈ $0.009 per km = 0.9¢ per km

14. Do not average averages! Compute the cost of each segment, compute the total cost, then divide by the total number of km driven.

$$253 \text{ km} \times 1.4¢ \text{ per km} \approx 355¢$$
$$388 \text{ km} \times 0.9¢ \text{ per km} \approx 350¢$$

$$\frac{355¢ + 350¢}{253 \text{ km} + 388 \text{ km}} \approx 1.1¢ \text{ per km}$$

7. It costs about 1.5 cents per kilometer to drive the Massachusetts Turnpike. How much would it cost to drive from the New York line to Springfield, a distance of 47 km?

8. Suppose that gasoline costs 27¢ per liter and a car at highway speeds can travel 7.5 km per liter of gas. What is the cost of gasoline per kilometer of driving?

9. To drive the 121-kilometer length of the Bluegrass Parkway through "horse country" southwest of Lexington, Kentucky, costs $1.30. For the car of exercise 8, which costs more per kilometer, gasoline or the use of the Bluegrass Parkway? How much more?

10. An inexpensive toll road in the U.S. is the 64-km Everett Turnpike, which starts south of Concord, New Hampshire, and goes toward Boston. It costs 80¢ to drive the whole length. Which costs more per kilometer for the car of exercise 8, gasoline or the road toll? How much more?

11. The Scott family drove from Detroit to Cedar Point, Ohio, an amusement park on Lake Erie. They drove 120 km to the Ohio Turnpike, 76 km east on the turnpike, and then 16 km north to Cedar Point. Their car averaged 8.3 km per liter of gas. If gas cost 28.9¢ per liter, how much did gas cost for the round trip?

12. The round-trip toll paid by the Scotts on the Ohio Turnpike was $1.40. What was the cost per kilometer? (See exercise 11.)

13. Each of the four Scotts paid $8.50 to enter Cedar Point (all rides are free), and they spent an average of $4.75 per person for food and drink. What was the total cost of the trip? (See exercises 11 and 12.)

14. You can drive across Indiana and Ohio on toll roads. The Indiana east-west toll road is 253 km long and costs an average of 1.4¢ per km. The 388-km Ohio Turnpike costs an average of 0.9¢ per km. What is the average cost per kilometer for this trip?

Set 7

1. Mount Everest, the tallest mountain on earth, is 29,028 ft tall. The deepest part of the oceans is The Challenger Deep in the Pacific Ocean. It is 36,198 ft deep. What is the difference in altitude between these two points?

2. The lowest point on land is the shore of the Dead Sea, which is 1299 ft below sea level. How much higher than this is the top of Mt. Everest? (See exercise 1.)

3. The highest temperature recorded on earth was 136°F at Al Aziziyah, Libya. The lowest temperature recorded was −126.9°F at Vostok, Antarctica. What is the difference between these extreme temperatures?

4. If the temperature of the earth were to rise enough to melt the two polar ice caps, the oceans would rise 200 ft. If the average story of a high-rise building is 12 ft, how many stories of a tall building along the coast would be under water?

Through Skill 27.
410   Can be used anytime after page 207.

SELECTED SOLUTIONS

14.   11,000 mi ÷ 24,889 mi ≈ 0.44

15.   The circumference of the earth at the equator is 24,888.9 mi. This means that a point on the equator travels 24,888.9 mi during one revolution.

$$24{,}888.9 \text{ mi per day} ÷ 24 \text{ h per day}$$
$$≈ 1037.04 \text{ mi per h}$$

16.   595 million mi ÷ 365.25 days ≈ 1.63 million mi per day
1.63 million mi per day ÷ 24 h per day
≈ 0.0679 million mi per h
= 67,900 mi per h

5. The pressure at the surface of the ocean (from the atmosphere above) is about 14.7 lb per in.^{2} Water pressure increases about 0.44 lb per in.^{2} for each foot of depth below the surface of the ocean. What is the pressure at the bottom of the Challenger Deep? (See exercise 1.)

6. The deepest point in the Atlantic Ocean is the Puerto Rico Trench. The depth is 28,374 ft. What is the pressure at that depth? (See exercise 5.)

7. The greatest depth of the Indian Ocean is 25,344 ft. This is 7464 ft deeper than the deepest point in the Arctic Ocean. How deep is the deepest part of the Arctic Ocean?

8. Suppose that an experimental underwater craft is designed to withstand pressures up to 725 lb per in.^{2} What is the greatest depth to which it can go? (See exercise 5.)

9. There are 335.5 million cubic miles of water on the earth. Only $\frac{3}{100}$ of this is fresh water. How many cubic miles of fresh water are there?

10. Three fourths of the fresh water is frozen in polar ice caps and in glaciers. How many cubic miles of fresh water are frozen and unavailable for use? (See exercise 9.)

11. The total surface area of the earth is about 139,660,400 mi^2. About $\frac{7}{10}$ of the surface is covered by water. How many square miles of land are there?

12. In exercise 11 you learned that 0.7 of the earth's surface is covered by water. About 0.46 of the part covered by water is covered by the Pacific Ocean. What is the surface area of the Pacific Ocean?

13. The diameter of the earth at the equator is 7926.41 mi. Find the circumference of the earth at the equator. ($C = \pi d$, $\pi \approx 3.14$)

14. The Pacific Ocean is about 11,000 mi wide at the equator. The Pacific Ocean stretches what fraction of the way around the earth? Give your answer as a decimal correct to the nearest hundredth. (See exercise 13.)

15. The earth makes one complete rotation on its axis in about 24 hours. The diameter of the earth at the equator is 7926.41 mi. How fast does a point on the equator travel as the earth spins?

16. The earth also travels a path around the sun that is 595 million mi long. It travels this path in a year (365.25 days). What is its average speed in miles per hour?

Set 8

1. There are 250 species of sharks. One tenth of these species are dangerous to humans. How many dangerous species are there?

2. The largest shark is the whale shark, which grows up to 60 feet in length. A basking shark grows to $\frac{2}{3}$ of that length. How many feet long is a large basking shark?

3. A thresher shark grows to as much as 21 feet long, but half of this length is the shark's tail. How long is the tail?

4. The most dangerous shark is the white shark, which grows to a length of about $\frac{1}{2}$ that of a basking shark. What is the length of a large white shark? (See exercise 2.)

5. Perhaps the strangest-looking shark is the hammerhead shark. A large hammerhead shark is about $\frac{3}{4}$ as long as a white shark. How long is a large hammerhead shark? (See exercise 4.)

6. A shark has a keen sense of hearing. It can hear a swimmer up to 1000 yards away. What fraction of a mile is that?

Through Skill 27.
Can be used anytime after page 207.

7. A shark's eyesight is quite weak. It can see a moving object against a background at a distance $\frac{1}{30}$ of the distance at which it could hear the object. From how many *feet* away can a shark see a moving object? (See exercise 6.)

8. A shark has a keen sense of smell and can sense the odor of blood from $\frac{1}{4}$ mile away. How many feet is that?

9. Which sense—hearing, sight, or smell—is the most acute in a shark? (See exercises 6, 7, and 8.)

10. The largest white shark ever caught by rod and reel was caught off the coast of Australia in 1959. It weighed 2664 pounds. The largest tiger shark caught by rod and reel was caught off the coast of South Carolina in 1964. It weighed 4 pounds more than $\frac{2}{3}$ as much as the record white shark. How much did the record tiger shark weigh?

11. The record mako shark, caught off the coast of New Zealand, weighed 271 pounds less than the record white shark. What was the weight of the record mako shark?

12. The record white shark was 16'10" long. The record thresher shark, caught off the coast of New Zealand, was 5 inches longer than $\frac{1}{2}$ as long. How long was the record thresher shark?

13. The record white shark had a girth of 114 inches. The girth of the record tiger shark was 8 inches greater than $\frac{5}{6}$ of the white shark's girth. What was the girth of the record tiger shark?

14. The record porbeagle shark, caught off the coast of England, had a girth that was 8 inches less than $\frac{2}{3}$ the girth of the record white shark. What was the girth of the record porbeagle shark?

413

Set 9
1. 73¢ 2. $3.65 3. $4.55 4. $3.52
5. 11¢ 6. $2.70 7. $1.38 8. 2¾
9. $15.90 10. 13.25¢ 11. 56¢
12. 50¢ 13. $4.69 14. $3.12
15. 42¢ 16. 38¢ 17. 2¹/₁₂
18. $2.25 19. $1.08 20. $1.066

Set 9

1. How much will $\frac{1}{2}$ dozen raised doughnuts cost?

2. How much will $2\frac{1}{2}$ dozen raised doughnuts cost?

3. How much will $3\frac{1}{2}$ dozen cake doughnuts cost?

4. How much will $2\frac{3}{4}$ dozen large cookies cost?

5. How much will 1 large cookie cost?

6. How much will $1\frac{1}{2}$ dozen cupcakes cost?

7. Bill bought 6 raised doughnuts and 6 cake doughnuts. How much did they cost?

8. Sara bought $1\frac{1}{2}$ dozen small cookies and 15 large cookies. How many dozen cookies did she buy?

9. For a party Jill bought $2\frac{1}{2}$ dozen raised doughnuts, $2\frac{1}{2}$ dozen cake doughnuts, and 5 dozen cupcakes. How much did she spend?

10. What was the average cost for a piece of bakery goods in exercise 9?

RAISED DOUGHNUTS $1.46 PER DOZEN

CAKE DOUGHNUTS $1.30 PER DOZEN

SMALL COOKIES $.98 PER DOZEN

LARGE COOKIES $1.28 PER DOZEN

CUPCAKES $.15 EACH

414 Through Skill 36. Can be used anytime after page 233.

SELECTED SOLUTIONS

15. 99¢ × ⁵/₁₂ = 41.25¢. This must be rounded up to 42¢.

19. The cost of the cookies was $2.25 (exercise 18). The number of dozen was 2¹/₁₂ (exercise 17). Average cost per dozen: $2.25 ÷ 2¹/₁₂ = $1.08 Note that, because of rounding, the average cost per dozen when 5 of each kind of cookie are bought is a little greater than the average cost per dozen when a dozen of each kind is bought (exericse 20).

SUGAR COOKIES 99¢ PER DOZEN

MOLASSES COOKIES 99¢ PER DOZEN

OATMEAL-RAISIN COOKIES $1.12 PER DOZEN

DATE-FILLED COOKIES $1.34 PER DOZEN

BUTTER COOKIES 89¢ PER DOZEN

11. How much will $\frac{1}{2}$ dozen oatmeal-raisin cookies cost?

12. How much will $\frac{1}{2}$ dozen sugar cookies cost?

13. How much will $3\frac{1}{2}$ dozen date-filled cookies cost?

14. How much will $3\frac{1}{2}$ dozen butter cookies cost?

15. How much will 5 molasses cookies cost?

16. How much will 5 butter cookies cost?

17. Peggy bought 5 of each kind of cookie. How many dozen did she buy?

18. How much did the cookies in exercise 17 cost?

19. What was the average cost per dozen cookies in exercise 17?

20. Suppose that you bought 1 dozen of each kind of cookie. What would be the average price per dozen?

415

Set 10

Mary Jo is a lapidary. That is, she collects and polishes gems and makes jewelry from them. She must understand both the metric and the conventional measurement systems, because both are widely used in this hobby.

1. Mary Jo saw an ad in a lapidary magazine for blue-gold turquoise at $37.50 for a half pound. She ordered $\frac{3}{4}$ of a pound. How much did the turquoise cost?

2. Another ad offered rose quartz at $1.80 for 1 pound and $7.50 for 5 pounds. How much is saved per pound by buying the larger quantity instead of the smaller quantity?

3. Two grades of opal were advertised: Grade B for $288 per 25 grams and Grade A for $450 per 25 grams. How much more will 75 g of Grade A opal cost than 75 g of Grade B opal?

4. Spectrolite from Finland was advertised in a lapidary magazine at $8.35 for $\frac{1}{4}$ pound. How much would $1\frac{1}{2}$ pounds cost?

5. Red jasper from Africa cost $1.50 per pound. How much would $2\frac{1}{2}$ pounds cost?

6. Gold beads for making jewelry were advertised as $320 for 100 8-mm beads. This was based on a $250-an-ounce price for gold. What would the beads cost if the price of gold went to $400 per ounce?

Through Skill 36.
416 Can be used anytime after page 233.

SELECTED SOLUTIONS

6. Find what the beads would cost if gold were $1 per oz.

$$\$320 \div 250 = \$1.28$$

Then find what the beads would cost if gold were $400 per oz.

$$\$1.28 \times 400 = \$512$$

10. 3106 ct × 200 mg per ct = 621200 mg = 621.2 g

7. Korean jade was advertised for $25 per pound plus $3.75 per pound for postage, handling, and insurance. How much in all would $2\frac{1}{2}$ pounds cost?

8. Mary Jo ordered 3 pounds of golden agate at $1.75 per pound and 10 grams of Brazilian opal for $3.40 per gram. She sent a check for $50. The extra money was to cover postage. The actual postage was $5.70. How much of a refund should she get?

9. Mary Jo wanted to buy a machine for grinding and polishing stones. It cost $369.95 cash or (on the installment plan) $100 down and $24 per month for a year. How much more does the installment plan cost?

10. Fine gems are weighed in *carats*. One carat (ct) is 200 milligrams. The largest diamond ever found, the Cullinan diamond, weighed 3106 carats. How many grams did the Cullinan weigh?

11. The Cullinan diamond was cut into 9 large stones and 96 smaller stones, with about 6 carats of small chips left. What was the average weight in grams of the cut stones? (See exercise 10.)

12. Another famous diamond is the Hope diamond, which is blue. It weighs 45.52 ct. How many grams is that? (See exercise 10.)

13. An average-sized diamond in an engagement ring weighs about 67 mg. How many carats is that? (See exercise 10.)

14. The Iranian XX diamond is a peach-colored diamond weighing 10.87 grams. How many carats is that? (See exercise 10.)

15. Two emeralds were offered in a magazine ad:
    1.06 ct for $1160
    1.12 ct for $1300
    Which cost more per carat?

417

Set 11

The number of calories needed daily by a person depends on the kind of activity engaged in and the age, height, weight, and sex of the person.

1. A 75-kg male who does office work needs only $\frac{7}{9}$ of the 3600 calories needed by a 75-kg male carpenter. How many calories are needed by the office worker?

2. A 65-year-old male needs 100 calories more than $\frac{2}{3}$ of the 3600 calories needed by a 16-year-old male. How many calories does the 65-year-old male need?

3. A male 160 cm tall and weighing 59 kg needs 2700 calories daily. A 190-cm male weighing 82 kg needs $33\frac{1}{3}$% more. How many calories are needed by the larger male?

4. A 61-kg male needs 100 calories more than 1.2 times the 2500 calories needed by a female of the same size. How many calories are needed by the male?

Through Skill 43.
418 Can be used anytime after page 261.

5. A child 4 to 6 years old needs only 75% of the 2400 calories needed by a child of 7 to 10 years. How many calories are needed by the younger child?

6. Females 15 to 18 years old need $\frac{7}{8}$ of the 2400 calories needed by females 11 to 14 years old. How many calories are needed daily by the older females?

7. Males 11 to 14 years old need $16\frac{2}{3}\%$ more calories than females of the same age. How many calories are needed daily by these males? (See exercise 6.)

8. Females 11 to 14 years old need what percent of the calories needed by males of the same age? (See exercise 7.)

9. Males 15 to 18 years old need 3000 calories daily. Males 23 to 50 years old need 10% fewer calories. How many calories are needed by the older males?

10. Females 23 to 50 years old need $83\frac{1}{3}\%$ of the 2400 calories needed by 11-to-14-year-old females. How many calories are needed daily by the older females?

11. Children 4 to 6 years old need 30 grams of protein daily. Children 7 to 10 years old need 20% more. How many grams of protein do the older children need?

12. Females 15 to 18 years old need 48 g of protein daily. Females 11 to 14 years old need $8\frac{1}{3}\%$ less. How much protein is needed daily by the younger females?

13. Females 19 to 22 years old need 800 mg of calcium daily. Females 11 to 14 years old need 150% of that. How much calcium is needed by the younger females?

14. Males 11 to 14 years old need 18 mg of iron daily, and males 19 to 22 years old need 10 mg of iron daily. What is the percent of decrease in the need?

15. Females more than 50 years old need 10 mg of iron daily. Females 11 to 14 years old need 80% more. How many milligrams of iron do 11-to-14-year-old females need?

16. Males 11 to 14 years old need 44 g of protein daily, and males 15 to 18 years old need 54 g of protein daily. What is the percent of increase in the need?

419

Set 12
1. $9.9 billion 2. $6.501 billion 3. 7.3%
4. $27.3 billion 5. $150 6. 15.8%
7. 26.7% 8. 294 9. 0.375¢
10. $4.65 billion 11. $1400 12. $1.55
13. 51% 14. 7.9%

Set 12

1. Thirty percent of all money spent on advertising is spent on newspaper advertising. In 1978 a total of $33 billion was spent on advertising. How much money was spent on newspaper ads?

2. Television advertising accounts for 19.7% of the money spent on advertising. How many dollars were spent on TV advertising in 1978? (See exercise 1.)

3. In 1978 $2.4 billion was spent on radio advertising. What percent of the total advertising budget was that? (See exercise 1.)

4. In 1950 only $5.7 billion was spent on advertising. How much did advertising spending increase between 1950 and 1978? (See exercise 1.)

5. In 1978 the population of the United States was about 220 million. How much was spent per person on advertising in 1978? (See exercise 1.)

6. During the four prime evening hours there are 9.5 minutes of advertising in each hour of TV broadcasting. What percent of prime broadcasting time is taken up by advertising?

Through Skill 43.
420   Can be used anytime after page 261.

SELECTED SOLUTIONS

13. 85% of 60% = 0.85 × 60% = 51%

7. During non-prime TV broadcasting hours, advertising may take up 16 minutes of each hour. What percent is that?

8. Suppose that a TV station broadcasts from 6:00 A.M. to 2:00 A.M. on weekdays and sells as much advertising time as possible. How many minutes of advertising are there on this station in a day? (See exercises 6 and 7.)

9. A 30-second TV ad can cost $150,000 for broadcast time. If the ad is viewed by 40 million people, what is the cost per viewer?

10. Direct-mail advertising accounted for about 14.1% of the total $33 billion advertising budget in 1978. How much money was spent on direct-mail advertising?

11. Direct-mail advertisers buy lists of names and addresses. For example, a baby-food distributor bought a list of 20,000 new mothers for 7¢ per name. How much did the list cost?

12. A direct-mail advertiser bought a list of the names of 1750 horse breeders for $2712.50. What was the cost per name?

13. About 60% of a newspaper is advertising. About 85% of the advertising is *local* advertising. What percent of a newspaper is local advertising?

14. Proctor & Gamble Company spends the most on advertising in this country. One year it spent $360 million. Its total sales that year were $4.55 billion. Its advertising budget was what percent of its sales?

421

Set 13
1. 55.2%   2. 88.8%   3. $3,475,018
4. 2⁴/₅ s   5. 1⁴/₅ s   6. 40%   7. 76.7%
8. as a 7-year-old (81.8% versus 77.3%)
9. 2:00¹/₅   10. 2:01²/₅   11. 2   12. 5
13. 2:02²/₅   14. 284   15. 63.1%
16. 1³/₅

Set 13

1. Kubla Khan, a pacer, won $1959 in 1978 and $3041 in 1979. What was the percent of increase?

2. A trotter, Spinster Bull, won $41,090 in 1978 and only $4,590 in 1979. What was the percent of decrease?

3. In 1973 the leading horse-racing driver was Herve Filion, who won a total of $2,233,302. He was again the leading driver the next year when he won 55.6% more money. How much money did he win in the second year?

4. At one time the one-mile record for a trotter was $1:54\frac{4}{5}$ (1 minute and $54\frac{4}{5}$ seconds), held by Nevele Pride. The record for a pacer was 1:52, held by Steady Star. How much faster was the pace record?

5. The best time as a 4-year-old by High Bret, a pacer, was $2:04\frac{2}{5}$. His best time as a 5-year-old was $2:02\frac{3}{5}$. How much faster was his 5-year-old best time?

6. Tribune entered 10 races as a 6-year-old. He won 0, was second once, and was third 3 times. In what percent of his races was he third or better?

Through Skill 43.
422   Can be used anytime after page 261.

SELECTED SOLUTIONS

16.   1 mi ÷ ⅝ mi per lap = 1³/₅ laps

7. A pacer, Hi Ike, raced 30 times as a 5-year-old. He was first 10 times, second 8 times, and third 5 times. In what percent of his races was he third or better?

8. As a 6-year-old, Symbol Art had a record of 8 firsts, 5 seconds, and 4 thirds in 22 races. As a 7-year-old, his record was 5 firsts, 5 seconds, and 8 thirds in 22 races. In which year was his third-or-better average greater?

9. In a 1-mile pace, The Slammer paced the first quarter in 29 seconds, the second quarter in $31\frac{4}{5}$ seconds, the third quarter in $29\frac{1}{5}$ seconds, and the fourth quarter in $30\frac{1}{5}$ seconds. What was his time for the mile?

10. In a 1-mile trot, Clay Port's times for the four quarters were $29\frac{1}{5}$, $30\frac{3}{5}$, $30\frac{2}{5}$, and $31\frac{1}{5}$. What was his time for the mile?

11. In a 1-mile pace, Shelly's Hope had a time of $2{:}05\frac{3}{5}$. The winner of the race, Star of Night, had a time of $2{:}03\frac{3}{5}$. How many seconds behind the winner was Shelly's Hope?

12. At the end of a race the horses travel at a rate of speed that takes them about one length (length of a horse's body) in one fifth of a second. If a horse loses by 1 second, about how many lengths behind is it?

13. In a race the winner's time was $2{:}01\frac{3}{5}$. Swift Lad was 4 lengths behind the winner. What was Swift Lad's time? (See exercise 12.)

14. At one racetrack the favorite won in 35.5% of the 800 races. How many races did the favorite win?

15. In the 800 races the favorite placed third or better in 505 races. What percent of the time did the favorite place third or better?

16. How many laps of a $\frac{5}{8}$-mile track do horses run in a 1-mile race?

423

Set 14

1. Kent was in training for running cross-country in the fall. On one summer day he warmed up by running 7.5 km. Then to work on his speed he ran 400 m in 80 seconds 6 times, with 80-second rests between the runs. How many kilometers did he run in all?

2. At the end of wrestling season Ben weighed 43.5 kg. At the beginning of the next season he was 5.7 kg heavier. How much did he weigh then?

3. Steve weighed 57.7 kg. In order to wrestle in a lower-weight class, he lost 6% of his weight. What did he weigh then?

4. When Betty started training for track, she weighed 53 kg and 20% of her body weight was fat. How many kilograms of fat did she have?

5. After training for 4 months, Betty's weight dropped to 47 kg. At that time 13% of her body weight was fat. How much less fat did she have than when she started training? (See exercise 4.)

6. Through weight-training John increased his body weight from 51 kg to 60 kg. His body fat dropped from 19% of his body weight to 15% of his body weight. What was the change in body-fat weight in kilograms?

7. When Tomás started training, his heart rate at rest was 76 beats per minute. After 6 months of training, his at-rest heart rate was 75% of what it was before training. What was his new at-rest heart rate?

8. Marilyn's at-rest heart rate is 64 beats per minute. When she is running hard, her peak heart rate is 2.7 times as fast. What is her peak heart rate?

Through Skill 43.
424   Can be used anytime after page 261.

SELECTED SOLUTIONS

6. 19% of 51 kg = 9.69 kg
    15% of 60 kg = 9 kg
    9.69 kg − 9 kg = 0.69 kg

14. 57 min 12 s = 3432 s
    8% of 3432 s ≈ 274.6 s
    3432 s − 274.6 s = 3157.4 s = 52 min 37.4 s

9. Through training, Bill reduced his average heart rate from 75 beats per minute to 58 beats per minute. How many fewer times does his heart beat in a day now?

10. In one season Donna reduced her time in the 400-m run from 62.3 seconds to 57.5 seconds. By what percent did she reduce her time?

11. In one swimming season Terry lowered his 100-m freestyle time from 68.24 s to 65.37 s. By what percent did he lower his time?

12. Kyle's sport was power lifting. When he began, he could bench-press 37.5 kg. After a year he had increased that by 92%. How much weight could he bench-press then?

13. In the dead-lift Kyle could lift 87.5 kg when he began. After a year he could lift 208% of his beginning weight. How much could he dead-lift then?

14. Maria is a jogger. She jogged 10,000 meters in a race in a time of 57 minutes 12 seconds. In another 10,000-meter race 2 months later her time was 8% less. What was her second time?

15. In a 10,000-meter race there were 895 entries. In the same race one year later there were 1,521 entries. What was the percent of increase?

16. In a test of physical conditioning, June ran 1.9 km in 12 minutes. After 1 year of training she was tested again. This time she ran 42% farther in 12 minutes. How many kilometers did she run in the second test?

17. At the beginning of a training program James could inhale 0.84 L of air. After a year of jogging he had increased that to 1.27 L. What was the percent of increase?

Set 15

1. During the first 8 months of 1979 Tom Watson, a golfer, won $447,636. If he continued to win at the same rate for the rest of the year, how much would he win in the year?

2. Tom Watson's 8-month winnings were $203,881 more than the 8-month winnings of the golfer in second place, Larry Nelson. How much did Nelson win? (See exercise 1.)

3. Watson's 8-month winnings amounted to about 35% of the total 8-month winnings won by the top five money winners. What were the total 8-month winnings of the top five golfers? (See exercise 1.)

4. The prizes paid to women golfers are not as high as those paid to the men. Nancy Lopez, the leading woman golfer, had an 8-month winning total of about 39% of Watson's winnings. How much did Lopez win? (See exercise 1.)

5. Bjorn Borg won $442,867 in the first 8 months of 1979. This was only $34,880 more than John McEnroe won. Jimmy Connors was only $23,582 behind McEnroe. How much did Connors win?

6. The top 3 male tennis players—Borg, McEnroe, and Connors—won about 53% of the total winnings of the top 10 players. How much was won by the top 10 players? (See exercise 5.)

7. What was the average amount won by one of the top 10 male tennis players in the first 8 months of 1979? (See exercise 6.)

8. The top 10 women tennis players had an average 8-month winnings of $184,243.30. What was the total amount won by the top 10 women?

Through Skill 44.
426 Can be used anytime after page 267.

SELECTED SOLUTIONS

1. $447,636 ÷ 8 = $55,954.50 = one month's winnings (average)
   $55,954.50 × 12 = $671,454 = one year's winnings

3. $447,636 = 35% of total won
   $447,636 ÷ 0.35 = total won = $1,278,960

9. After 8 months of 1979 Martina Navratilova was the leading money-winner in women's tennis. She won about 22% of the money won by the top 10 women. How much did she win? (See exercise 8.)

10. If Navratilova continued to win at the same rate, how much would she have won in the whole year? (See exercise 9.)

11. Darrell Waltrip was the leading NASCAR driver in the first 8 months of 1979. He was $64,505 ahead of second-place driver Richard Petty, who won $312,040. How much did Waltrip win?

12. If Waltrip won at the same rate all year, how much would he have won in the first 6 months? (See exercise 11.)

13. The tenth-place NASCAR driver was Neil Barnett, who had won about 25% as much as Waltrip. How much did Barnett win? (See exercise 11.)

14. Bowling does not pay as well as golf, tennis, or auto racing. The top bowler, Mark Roth, had 8-month winnings that were $176,249 less than the third-place money-winner in women's tennis, 16-year-old Tracy Austin. Austin won $258,323. How much did Roth win?

15. Golfers, tennis players, racing drivers, and bowlers win large amounts of money, but the top thoroughbred racehorses win even more. In the first 8 months of 1979 Affirmed won $200,800 less than $1 million. How much did Affirmed win?

16. The second-place thoroughbred money-winner was Spectacular Bid, who won only about 2.2% less than Affirmed. How much did Spectacular Bid win? (See exercise 15.)

427

Set 16
1. 2.4 L   2. 308.75 g   3. 48.75 kg
4. 94,900 L   5. 85.5 L   6. 31,207.5 L
7. 3 min   8. 10,402.5 L   9. $1.25
10. 171.5 L   11. 600 L   12. 9,516.8 L
13. 250 metric tons   14. 35.0 metric
tons per hour   15. 270 metric tons
16. 6480 metric tons   17. 221 L
18. 5,516,700 L   19. 740 L

Set 16

1. According to a recent report, the average human intake of water in a lifetime is 60,600 liters. If the average life span is 69.2 years, what is the average daily intake of water?

2. Besides getting water by drinking, you get water by eating foods that contain water. For example, a tomato is 95% water. How much water is in a tomato that weighs 325 g?

3. The human body is made up of 65% water by weight. How much water is in the body of a 75-kg person? How much water is in your body?

4. The total daily use of water in an average home is 260 L. How much water is used in a year (365 days)?

5. Each minute under a shower uses 19 L of water. How much water is used in a 4.5-minute shower?

6. How much water would be used in a year if you showered for 4.5 minutes each day? (See exercise 5.)

7. Suppose that you decided to save water by reducing your shower time each day by $33\frac{1}{3}$%. How long would your shower be? (See exercise 5.)

8. How much water would you save in a year by reducing your shower time $33\frac{1}{3}$%? (See exercises 6 and 7.)

9. If you have to pay 12¢ per 1000 L for water, how much money will you save in a year by reducing your shower time $33\frac{1}{3}$%? (See exercise 8.)

428   Through Skill 44.
Can be used anytime after page 267.

SELECTED SOLUTIONS

8. 31,207.5 L are used in a year with a 4.5-min shower daily (exercise 6). That total can be reduced by ⅓ if the time of each shower is reduced by ⅓.
   31,207.5 L × ⅓ = 10,402.5 L

9. 10,402.5 L are saved by reducing shower time (exercise 8).
   10,402.5 L = 10.4025 1000-L
   10.4025 × $.12 ≈ $1.25

19. The area of the corn patch = 10 m × 20 m = 200 m².
   200 m² = $^{200}/_{10,000}$ of a hectare = $^1/_{50}$ of a hectare
   37,000 L are given off by 1 hectare, so 37,000 L × $^1/_{50}$ will be given off by the small patch. 37,000 × $^1/_{50}$ = 740 L

10. An automatic dishwasher uses about 38 L of water per load. Washing dishes by hand takes about 4.5 L of water. Suppose that you run 1 load in an automatic dishwasher per day or wash by hand 3 times per day. How much water is saved in a week by hand-washing?

11. Industries use much more fresh water than homes do. For example, water is used in the production of gasoline. The amount of water used is 10 times the amount of gasoline produced. How many liters of water are used to produce enough gasoline to fill a 60-liter gas tank?

12. At what rate is gasoline produced if a refinery uses 95,168 L of water per minute? (See exercise 11.)

13. The ratio of water used to paper produced in a paper mill is 250:1. How much water is used to produce a metric ton (1000 kg) of paper?

14. At what rate is paper produced if a paper mill uses 8756 metric tons of water per hour? (See exercise 13.)

15. Steel-making uses 8% more water than paper-making to produce a metric ton of material. How much water is used to produce 1 metric ton of steel? (See exercise 13.)

16. A small steel mill was producing 200 metric tons of steel an hour. If production is to be increased 12%, how much extra water will be used per hour? (See exercise 15.)

17. Green plants pass water into the atmosphere. For example, a birch tree gives off 260 L on a sunny summer day. It gives off 15% less water on a cloudy day. How much water is given off on a cloudy day?

18. Corn plants give off about 37,000 L of water per hectare per day. (1 hectare = 10,000 m².) How much water is given off in a week by a 21.3-hectare cornfield?

19. How much water is given off per day by a small patch of corn that is 10 m wide and 20 m long? (See exercise 18.)

429

Glossary

acute angle An angle whose measure is less than 90°.

addend A number used in an addition problem.

adding 0 property The sum of any number and zero is that number.

$$29 + 0 = 29$$

angle A figure formed by two rays with the same endpoint.

arc Part of a circle.

area The number of unit squares that cover a figure.

associative property of addition Changing the grouping of the addends does not change the sum.

$$(9 + 4) + 6 = 9 + (4 + 6)$$

associative property of multiplication Changing the grouping of the factors does not change the product.

$$(7 \times 25) \times 4 = 7 \times (25 \times 4)$$

average The average of 4, 5, 5, 7, and 9 is 6. To find the average, add the numbers and divide by the number of numbers.

axes Two perpendicular lines used as a reference for graphing number pairs (ordered pairs).

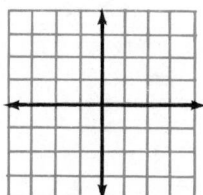

The horizontal line is the first coordinate axis and the vertical line is the second coordinate axis.

bisect To cut into halves.
The segment is bisected.

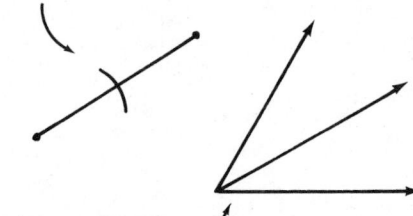

The angle is bisected.

budget A plan for using money.

canceling Dividing a numerator and a denominator in the product of two fractions by a common factor before multiplying.

$$\frac{4\,\cancel{8}}{15} \times \frac{1}{\cancel{8}\,3}$$

Celsius temperature (°C) The metric temperature scale in which 0°C is the freezing point of water and 100°C is the boiling point of water.

centimeter A metric unit of length. One centimeter is one hundredth of a meter.

circle A curved plane figure with all points a given distance from the center.

circumference The distance around a circle.

common denominator A common denominator for $\frac{1}{2}$ and $\frac{1}{3}$ is 6, because $\frac{1}{2} = \frac{3}{6}$ and $\frac{1}{3} = \frac{2}{6}$. A common denominator is a common multiple of the denominators of two fractions.

common factor 2 is a common factor of 4 and 6, because 2 is a factor of 4 and a factor of 6.

common multiple 30 is a common multiple of 5 and 6, because it is a multiple of 5 and a multiple of 6.

commutative property of addition Changing the order of the addends does not change the sum.

$$23 + 89 = 89 + 23$$

commutative property of multiplication Changing the order of the factors does not change the product.

$$19 \times 54 = 54 \times 19$$

complex fraction A fraction in which either the numerator or the denominator or both are fractions.

$$\frac{\frac{6}{7}}{\frac{2}{3}} \qquad \frac{8}{\frac{3}{4}} \qquad \frac{\frac{5}{2}}{6}$$

composite number A whole number other than 0 having more than two factors.

4, 6, 8, 9
1, 2, 4   1, 2, 3, 6

congruent figures Figures that have the same size and shape.

conversion fraction A fraction equivalent to 1 that is multiplied by a measurement to convert the measurement from one unit to another unit.

$$2 \text{ ft} \times \frac{12 \text{ in.}}{1 \text{ ft}} = 24 \text{ in.}$$

coordinates A pair of numbers that locates a point on a grid.

corresponding parts In congruent figures, the parts that fit are called corresponding parts.

cube A rectangular solid with all edges the same length.

customary system The system of measurement that uses foot, quart, pound, and Fahrenheit temperature.

cylinder A three-dimensional figure formed by two congruent circular regions in parallel planes and a "curved" rectangular region.

decagon A polygon with ten sides.

decimal A number written in our place-value system with a decimal point before the tenths place.

degree A unit for measuring angles. This is a 1° (1 degree) angle.

denominator In $\frac{2}{3}$, the denominator is 3.

diameter The distance across a circle through its center.

difference The answer to a subtraction problem.

digits The basic symbols used to write numerals in a place-value system. In our base ten system the digits are 0, 1, 2, 3, 4, 5, 6, 7, 8, and 9.

discount An amount subtracted from the regular price of an item.

distributive property of multiplication A product can be written as the sum of two products.

$$3 \times (10 + 2) = (3 \times 10) + (3 \times 2)$$

dividend The number that is divided.

$$\begin{array}{r} 6 \\ 3\overline{)18} \end{array} \qquad 18 \div 3 = 6$$

dividend

divisor The number that one divides by.

$$\begin{array}{r} 9 \\ 4\overline{)36} \end{array} \qquad 36 \div 4 = 9$$

divisor

down payment The first amount paid when buying on an installment plan.

equally likely outcomes Outcomes such that each has the same chance of occurring.

equation A sentence with an equals sign, such as $3 \times 9 = 27$.

equilateral triangle A triangle with all sides congruent.

equivalent fractions Fractions for the same number. $\frac{1}{2}$, $\frac{2}{4}$, and $\frac{3}{6}$ are equivalent fractions.

error of measurement The difference between the measurement of a quantity and the quantity itself.

even number A multiple of 2.

expanded numeral A numeral used to show the place value of each digit in a standard numeral.

$$248 = 200 + 40 + 8$$

exponent An exponent tells the number of factors.

exponent

$$2^3 = \underbrace{2 \times 2 \times 2}_{3 \text{ factors}}$$

factors Numbers used in a multiplication problem.

$$\begin{array}{r} 8 \leftarrow \text{factor} \\ \times 6 \leftarrow \text{factor} \\ \hline 48 \leftarrow \text{product} \end{array}$$

formula A general rule expressed by using symbols.

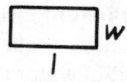

$$A = l \times w$$

function A set of number pairs of which no two first numbers are the same.

Function rule
$n \rightarrow n + 3$
(0, 3)
(1, 4)
(2, 5)

gram A metric unit of weight (mass). One gram is one thousandth of a kilogram.

graph A picture used to show numerical information.

greatest common divisor The greatest factor of each of two or more whole numbers.

greatest common factor (GCF) The greatest number that is a factor of each of two or more numbers.

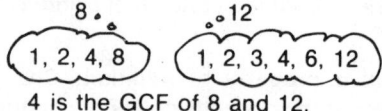

4 is the GCF of 8 and 12.

greatest possible error Half of the unit used in making the measurement.

hectare A metric unit of area. One hectare is 10,000 square meters.

heptagon A polygon with seven sides.

hexagon A polygon with six sides.

installment buying A way of buying expensive items. You pay part of the cost (the down payment) when you get the item and then agree to pay a certain amount each month for a certain number of months.

integers The numbers . . ., $^-5$, $^-4$, $^-3$, $^-2$, $^-1$, 0, $^+1$, $^+2$, $^+3$, $^+4$, $^+5$, ...

interest A payment for the use of money.

intersecting lines Lines that meet at a point.

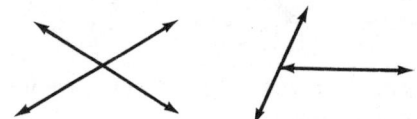

intersection of sets
The intersection of set A and set B, A ∩ B, is the set of all elements that belong to both A and B.

A = {0, 1, 2, 3}
B = {2, 3, 4, 5}
A ∩ B = {2, 3}

isosceles trapezoid A trapezoid with 2 congruent sides.

isosceles triangle A triangle with two congruent sides.

kilogram A unit of weight (mass) in the metric system. A kilogram is 1000 grams.

kiloliter A unit of volume in the metric system. One kiloliter is 1000 liters.

kilometer A unit of length in the metric system. A kilometer is 1000 meters.

kite A quadrilateral with 2 pairs of congruent sides.

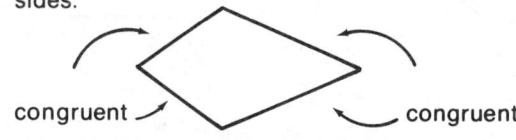

congruent   congruent

least common denominator The least common multiple of the denominators of two or more fractions.

least common multiple The least (smallest) common multiple of two or more numbers. The least common multiple of 6 and 15 is 30.

line of symmetry If a figure can be folded along a line so the two parts of the figure match, the fold line is a line of symmetry.

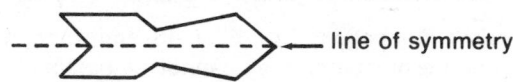
line of symmetry

liter A unit of volume in the metric system.

mean The average of a set of numbers.

median The median of a set of numbers is a number such that half of the numbers in the set are less and half are greater.

{63, 68, 74, 81, 86}

The median is 74.

median of a triangle A segment joining a vertex of a triangle with the midpoint of the opposite side.

meter A unit of length in the metric system. A meter is 100 centimeters.

metric system An international system of measurement that uses meter, liter, gram, and Celsius temperature.

midpoint The point that bisects a segment.

milligram A metric unit of weight (mass). One milligram is one thousandth of a gram.

milliliter A metric unit of volume. One milliliter is one thousandth of a liter.

millimeter A metric unit of length. One millimeter is one thousandth of a meter.

mixed number A number that has a whole-number part and a fraction part. $2\frac{3}{4}$ is a mixed number.

multiple A product. 0, 4, 8, 12, 16, 20, and so on, are multiples of 4.

multiplying by 1 property The product of any number and 1 is that number.

$8 \times 1 = 8$

multiplying by 0 property The product of any number and 0 is 0.

$24 \times 0 = 0$

nonagon A polygon with nine sides.

number line A line with its points labeled with numbers.

$0 \ \frac{1}{3} \ \frac{2}{3} \ 1 \ \frac{4}{3} \ \frac{5}{3} \ 2\frac{1}{3}$

number pair An ordered pair of numbers.

(5, 6), (8, 2)

numeral A name or symbol for a number.

Numerals for ten: 10, 2 × 5, 12 − 2

numerator In $\frac{2}{3}$, the numerator is 2.

obtuse angle An angle whose measure is greater than 90°.

octagon A polygon with eight sides.

odd number A whole number that is not divisible by 2. The numbers 1, 3, 5, 7, 9, 11, and so on, are odd.

odds The ratio of the number of ways that an outcome can occur to the number of ways that the outcome cannot occur.

opposites Two numbers are opposites if their sum is 0.

$$^-3 + {}^+3 = 0$$

opposites

origin The point where axes intersect.

outcome A possible result.

parallel lines Lines in a plane that do not cross.

parallelogram A quadrilateral with opposite sides parallel.

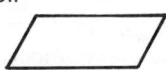

pentagon A polygon with five sides.

percent (%) Percent means per hundred. 5% is a percent. It equals $\frac{5}{100}$.

perimeter The distance around a figure. The sum of the lengths of the sides.

The perimeter is 9 cm.

2 cm   3 cm
4 cm

perpendicular bisector A line that bisects and is perpendicular to a segment.

perpendicular lines Lines that intersect to form right angles.

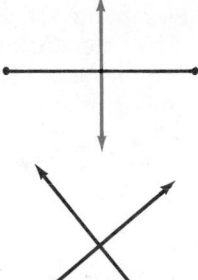

pi The number that is the ratio of the circumference of a circle to its diameter. It is represented by the Greek letter π and is approximately equal to $\frac{22}{7}$ or 3.14.

place value A system for writing numbers in which the value of a digit is determined by its position.

plane A flat surface that extends endlessly in all directions.

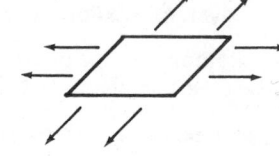

point of symmetry If a figure fits itself after a half-turn about a point, the point is a point of symmetry of the figure.

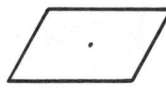

polygon A plane figure made up of segments.

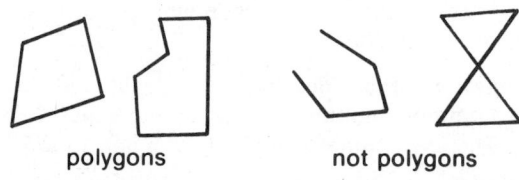

polygons   not polygons

prime factorization Writing a composite number as a product of prime numbers. The prime factorization of 18 is 2 × 3 × 3.

prime number 2, 3, 5, 7, 11, 13, and so on, are prime numbers. They cannot be obtained by multiplying smaller whole numbers.

principal An amount of money on which interest is paid.

prism A three-dimensional figure with two congruent parallel faces that are polygons and with the remaining faces parallelograms.

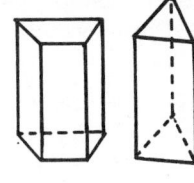

probability of an outcome The ratio of the number of ways that an equally likely outcome can occur to the total number of ways that all the equally likely outcomes can occur.

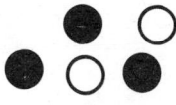

probability of picking black $= \frac{3}{5}$.

proportion An equation stating that two ratios are equal.

$$\frac{5}{8} = \frac{30}{48}$$

protractor An instrument used for measuring angles.

pyramid A three-dimensional figure with a face (known as the base) that is any polygon and with all other faces, which are triangles, sharing a common vertex.

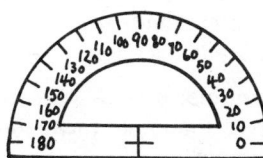

quadrilateral A polygon with four sides.

quotient The answer to a division problem.

radius The distance from the center of a circle to the circle.

range The highest and lowest numbers in a set of numbers. Can also be thought of as the difference of the highest and lowest numbers.

$$\{8, 13, 23, 27, 42, 51, 55\}$$

The range is from 8 to 55, or 47.

rate A comparison by division of two quantities.

$$\frac{87 \text{ kilometers}}{2 \text{ hours}}$$

ratio A comparison of two quantities by division. In a quadrilateral, the ratio of sides to diagonals is 4 to 2, 4 : 2, or $\frac{4}{2}$.

ray A part of a line that has one endpoint. This is ray *AB*.

$$A \bullet\!\!-\!\!\!-\!\!\!-\!\!\!-\!\!\!-\!\!\!-\!\!\!\to B$$

reciprocal Two numbers are reciprocals if their product is 1.

$$\frac{3}{4} \times \frac{4}{3} = 1$$

reciprocals

rectangle A parallelogram with four right angles.

rectangular prism A prism whose faces are rectangles.

reduced to lowest terms A fraction such that the greatest common factor of its numerator and denominator numbers is 1.

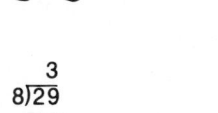

$\frac{5}{6}$ is in lowest terms.

remainder In a division problem the number that is "left over." When it is added to the product of the divisor and quotient, the sum is the dividend.

$$\begin{array}{r} 3 \\ 8\overline{)29} \\ -24 \\ \hline 5 \end{array} \leftarrow \text{remainder}$$

435

repeating decimal A decimal in which a digit or a group of digits repeats forever.

$$0.3333\ldots \qquad 1.47474747\ldots$$

rhombus A parallelogram with 4 congruent sides.

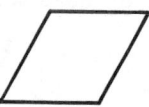

right angle An angle whose measure is 90°

round a number To replace a number by another one that is easier to use. You round a number to the nearest ten by choosing the nearest multiple of ten. (5 is rounded up.)

$$13 \rightarrow 10 \qquad 27 \rightarrow 30 \qquad 45 \rightarrow 50$$

You round a number to the nearest hundred by choosing the nearest multiple of one hundred.

$$487 \rightarrow 500 \qquad 1238 \rightarrow 1200 \qquad 550 \rightarrow 600$$

sample A small group, chosen from a larger group, that is examined carefully in order to make predictions about the larger group.

scale drawing A drawing of an object such that the ratio of a unit of length on the drawing to a unit of length on the object is fixed.

scalene triangle A triangle with no congruent sides.

scientific notation A notation for writing a number as the product of a number between 1 and 10 and a power of ten.

$$186.3 = 1.863 \times 10^2$$

segment A part of a line that has two endpoints.

set A collection of things.

solve an equation Find the numbers that make an equation true.

square A rectangle with four congruent sides.

statistics A branch of mathematics that studies numerical facts as a basis for drawing general conclusions and making predictions.

standard numeral A numeral written in its simplest place-value form. 248

subset Set A is a subset of set B, $A \subseteq B$, if all the members of A are also members of B.

$$A = \{0, 2, 4\} \quad B = \{0, 1, 2, 3, 4, 5\}$$
$$A \subseteq B$$

substitute Replace a variable with a numeral.

$$7a + 3$$
$$7 \cdot 6 + 3$$

surface area The total area of the surface of a three-dimensional figure.

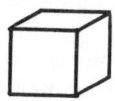

terms (of a fraction) The numerator and denominator numbers of a fraction.

trapezoid A quadrilateral with two parallel sides.

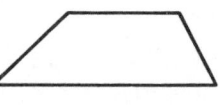

triangular prism A prism with two triangular faces in parallel planes.

union of sets The union of set A and set B, $A \cup B$, is the set of all elements in either A or B.

$$A = \{3, 5, 7\} \quad B = \{1, 2, 3\}$$
$$A \cup B = \{1, 2, 3, 5, 7\}$$

unit A fixed quantity used as a standard for measuring length, area, volume, weight, etc.

variable A symbol, usually a letter, that holds the place for a number.

$$8x + 19 = 23$$

vertex The point at the "corner" of an angle, plane figure, or solid figure.

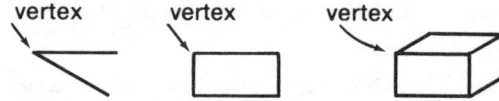

volume The measure of the space inside a three-dimensional figure. A cube is used as a unit.

whole number Any of the numbers 0, 1, 2, 3, 4, and so on.

Symbols

{ }	set
∅	the empty set
⊆	is a subset of
∪	union
∩	intersection
<	is less than
>	is greater than
(a, b)	number pair
%	percent
.34̄	.34343434 . . .
$^+6$	positive 6
$^-6$	negative 6
$P(2)$	the probability of the outcome 2

′	foot
″	inch
≈	is approximately equal to
π	pi
°	degree
$a : b$	the ratio of $a : b$
≅	is congruent to
$\overline{AB}$	segment AB
$\overrightarrow{AB}$	ray AB
△	triangle
‖	is parallel to
⊥	is perpendicular to

Formulas

$P = 4s$	Perimeter of a square
$P = 2l + 2w$	Perimeter of a rectangle
$C = \pi d$	Circumference of a circle
$A = lw$	Area of a rectangle
$A = s^2$	Area of a square
$A = bh$	Area of a parallelogram
$A = \frac{1}{2} bh$	Area of a triangle
$A = \frac{1}{2} h(b_1 + b_2)$	Area of a trapezoid
$A = \pi r^2$	Area of a circle
$V = lwh$	Volume of a rectangular prism
$V = Bh$	Volume of a prism
$V = \pi r^2 h$	Volume of a cylinder
$I = prt$	Interest

Teaching Resources

This section provides teaching support for Level 7. Many of the pages are copy masters that can be reproduced. Since they can be used throughout the school year, you may want to duplicate an ample supply at one time.

Final Checkup 439–445

These pages are a final test covering the year's work. The test is in standardized format similar to the Major Checkups. Pages 439–441 cover Chapters 1–5, pages 442–444 cover Chapters 6–10, and page 445 covers Chapters 11 and 12. Use these pages to suit your convenience. For example, pages 439 and 440 could be used as a midyear test.

Standardized Test Format 446–449

Page 446 is a standardized format answer sheet for your students to use with the final checkup. Page 447 is a quick-score answer key for the final checkup. You can fold a copy of the page to bring the correct responses close to the responses you are checking, or you can punch holes where the correct responses are located and align the punched sheet over the sheet you are correcting. Some of the exercises are marked with an asterisk on the quick-score sheet. These exercises test objectives which we consider to be very important for this level and proficiency with these skills should be stressed. You should feel free to modify this selection to meet your local situation.

Pages 448 and 449 provide a standardized answer sheet and a quick-score answer key for the twelve Major Checkups in the student text.

The Calculator 450–459

These pages discuss various ways that you might wish to use the calculator to enhance your mathematics program. Eight pages of calculator activities (a sample of the Calculator Worksheets available on duplicating masters) are also provided for you to copy.

Creative Problem Solving Activities 461–477

Fourteen problems are provided that require careful thought and analysis. Detailed suggestions for using these problems with students are given, and several methods for solving such problems are introduced.

Parent Involvement 478–491

Eight Parent Involvement Activity Sheets of topics of interest to both students and parents are available to copy and send home after students have mastered certain skills. A Parent Report of Student Progress in the learning objectives of Level 7 is also provided.

Bibliographies 492–495

Student's literature and professional literature suitable for your school, classroom, or personal library.

FINAL CHECKUP
Standardized Format

Choose the correct letter.
Sample

A. Two thousand fifty-
seven is

    a. 2507
    b. 20,057
    c. 2057
    d. 257

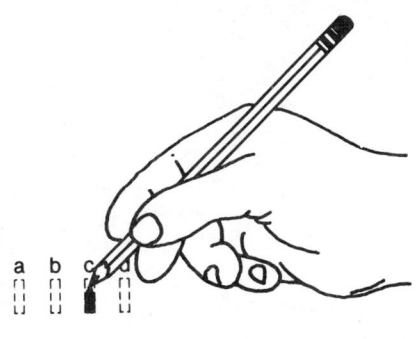

Each question is followed by four possible answers. You decide which
is correct. Then find the row of spaces with the same number as the
problem. Fill in the space under the letter of the answer you chose.
For example, the sample problem is labeled A. Since two thousand
fifty-seven is 2057, c. is the correct answer. Be sure to make your
mark heavy enough.

1. Sixty-two billion, forty-
nine million, two hundred
thousand, one hundred
twelve is

    a. 62,490,200,112
    b. 62,049,200,112
    c. 62,409,200,112
    d. none of these

---

2. 18,502,379 rounded to the
nearest ten thousand is

    a. 19,000,000
    b. 18,502,000
    c. 18,502,400
    d. none of these

3. Add.

    5321
    8465
    4907
  +3218

    a. 21,911
    b. 21,910
    c. 20,891
    d. 20,890

4. Subtract.

    59026
  −34789

    a. 24,327
    b. 24,237
    c. 25,337
    d. 25,763

---

5. Multiply.

    2504
  ×156

    a. 30,048
    b. 367,404
    c. 390,624
    d. none of these

6. Divide.

    246)26330

    a. 17 R8
    b. 108
    c. 107 R8
    d. none of these

7. Each of 36 students sold 18
adult tickets and 27
children's tickets for the
school carnival. How many
tickets were sold?

    a. 675
    b. 990
    c. 522
    d. 1620

---

8. Eight hundred forty
and twenty-nine ten-
thousandths is

    a. 804.0029
    b. 840.29
    c. 840.0029
    d. 840.029

9. 93.0481 < _?_

    a. 93.05
    b. 93.04
    c. 93.0048
    d. 92.0482

10. 243.0154 rounded to the
nearest hundredth is

    a. 200
    b. 243.02
    c. 243.01
    d. 243.015

11. Give the sum.
59.03 + 252.8 = _?_

a. 84.31
b. 843.1
c. 311.83
d. none of these

12. Give the difference.
84.01 − 2.593 = _?_

a. 82.417
b. 5.808
c. 58.08
d. none of these

13. Estimate the answer by rounding each number to the nearest whole number.
(29.8 − 4.89) + 20.09 = _?_

a. 45
b. 46
c. 44
d. none of these

---

14. David had $20. He bought a book for $5.79 and a record for $6.59. How much money did he have left?

a. $13.41
b. $7.62
c. $14.21
d. none of these

15. Multiply.
5.62
×14.7

a. 6.744
b. 826.14
c. 82.614
d. none of these

16. Divide.

6.3)‾3‾.‾6‾5‾4

a. 58
b. 5.8
c. 0.58
d. none of these

---

17. Paige hiked at the rate of 6.4 km per hour for 3.25 hours. How far did she hike?

a. 2.08 km
b. 20.8 km
c. 32.5 km
d. none of these

18. Sandra hiked 20.3 km in 3.5 hours. How many km per hour did she average?

a. 71.05
b. 23.8
c. 5.8
d. none of these

19. {1, 3, 5} is a subset of _?_

a. {1, 2, 3, 4}
b. {1, 3}
c. {1, 2, 3, 4, 5, 6}
d. {3, 5, 7}

---

20. {0, 2, 4, 6} ∩ {0, 3, 6, 9} = _?_

a. {0, 2, 3, 4, 6, 9}
b. {0, 2, 4, 6}
c. {0, 6}
d. {6}

21. {0, 2, 4} ∪ {1, 3, 4} = _?_

a. {0, 1, 2, 3, 4}
b. {0, 1, 2, 3}
c. {4}
d. {0, 2, 4}

22. The greatest common factor of 24 and 36 is

a. 6
b. 8
c. 12
d. 18

---

23. The least common multiple of 12 and 16 is

a. 4
b. 8
c. 32
d. 48

24. Substitute and simplify.

a	b	c
8	3	5

$(a \times c) - b$

a. 19
b. 7
c. 37
d. none of these

25. Solve.
$n - 13 = 42$

a. 55
b. 39
c. 29
d. none of these

26. Give the length to the nearest millimeter.

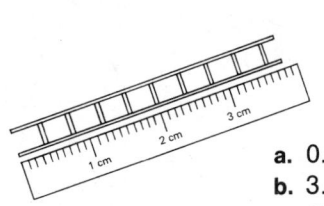

a. 0.38 mm
b. 3.8 mm
c. 38 mm
d. 380 mm

27. 58.4 cm = _?_ mm

a. 584
b. 5.84
c. 0.584
d. none of these

28. 378.5 m = _?_ km

a. 37,850
b. 37.85
c. 3.785
d. 0.3785

---

29. Give the perimeter.

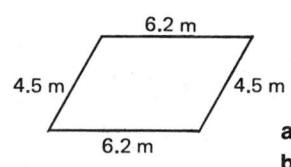

6.2 m
4.5 m   4.5 m
6.2 m

a. 10.7 m
b. 21.4 m
c. 27.9 m
d. 2.79 m

30. Give the circumference. Use 3.14 for π.

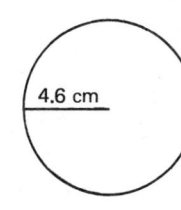

4.6 cm

a. 90.70832 m
b. 14.444 m
c. 28.888 cm
d. none of these

31. Find the area of the rectangle.

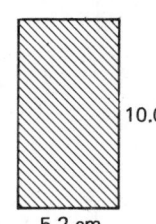

10.0 cm
5.2 cm

a. 52 cm^2
b. 15.2 cm^2
c. 30.4 cm^2
d. none of these

---

32. Give the surface area. Use 3.14 for π.

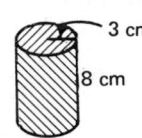

3 cm
8 cm

a. 150.72 cm^2
b. 178.98 cm^2
c. 207.24 cm^2
d. none of these

33. Give the volume.

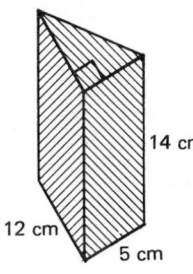

14 cm
12 cm
5 cm

a. 420 cm^3
b. 840 cm^3
c. 238 cm^3
d. none of these

34. Give the volume. Use 3.14 for π.

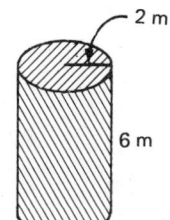

2 m
6 m

a. 37.68 m^2
b. 75.36 m^3
c. 100.48 m^3
d. none of these

---

35. 354 mL = _?_ L

a. 3540
b. 35.4
c. 3.54
d. 0.354

36. 0.735 kg = _?_ g

a. 7.35
b. 73.5
c. 735
d. 7350

37. Give the area of the rectangle.

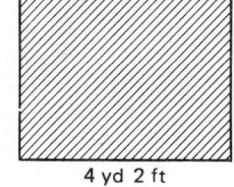

3 yd 1 ft
4 yd 2 ft

a. 140 ft^2
b. 140 yd^2
c. 70 ft^2
d. none of these

---

38. Give the volume.

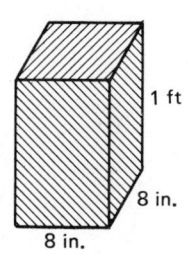

1 ft
8 in.
8 in.

a. 64 in.^{3}
b. 64 ft^3
c. 768 in.^{3}
d. none of these

39. 5 qt 1 pt = _?_ pt

a. 21
b. 11
c. 16
d. 41

40. 4 lb 6 oz = _?_ oz

a. 38
b. 54
c. 66
d. 70

41. Reduce $\frac{18}{24}$ to lowest terms.

    a. $\frac{9}{12}$

    b. $\frac{6}{8}$

    c. $\frac{3}{4}$

    d. none of these

42. $\frac{3}{4} > \underline{?}$

    a. $\frac{7}{8}$

    b. $\frac{3}{2}$

    c. $\frac{2}{3}$

    d. none of these

43. Give the sum in lowest terms.

$$\frac{5}{6} + \frac{3}{4} = \underline{?}$$

    a. $\frac{38}{24}$

    b. $\frac{19}{12}$

    c. $\frac{4}{5}$

    d. none of these

44. Give the difference in lowest terms.

$$\frac{5}{6} - \frac{1}{3} = \underline{?}$$

    a. $\frac{4}{3}$

    b. $\frac{2}{3}$

    c. $\frac{1}{2}$

    d. none of these

45. $\frac{14}{3} = \underline{?}$

    a. $4\frac{1}{3}$

    b. $4\frac{2}{3}$

    c. $3\frac{2}{3}$

    d. none of these

46. $2\frac{5}{8} = \underline{?}$

    a. $\frac{15}{8}$

    b. $\frac{42}{8}$

    c. $\frac{80}{8}$

    d. $\frac{21}{8}$

47. Add.

$$11\frac{2}{3}$$
$$+3\frac{4}{5}$$

    a. $15\frac{7}{15}$

    b. $15\frac{3}{4}$

    c. $14\frac{3}{4}$

    d. $14\frac{7}{15}$

48. Subtract.

$$9\frac{1}{3}$$
$$-3\frac{3}{4}$$

    a. $5\frac{5}{12}$

    b. $5\frac{7}{12}$

    c. $6\frac{7}{12}$

    d. $6\frac{5}{12}$

49. Terry needs a total of $8\frac{1}{2}$ feet of leather shoe strings for a craft project. He has two strings that are each $2\frac{3}{4}$ feet in length. How many feet more does he need?

    a. $5\frac{3}{4}$

    b. $11\frac{1}{4}$

    c. 3

    d. 14

50. Give the product in lowest terms.

$$\frac{5}{8} \times \frac{4}{5} = \underline{?}$$

    a. $\frac{20}{13}$

    b. $\frac{25}{32}$

    c. $\frac{1}{2}$

    d. none of these

51. Give the quotient in lowest terms.

$$\frac{6}{5} \div \frac{2}{3} = \underline{?}$$

    a. $\frac{9}{5}$

    b. $\frac{5}{9}$

    c. $\frac{4}{5}$

    d. none of these

52. $3\frac{4}{5} = \underline{?}$

    a. 3.45

    b. 3.6

    c. 3.75

    d. 3.8

53. $4.625 = \underline{?}$

    a. $4\frac{3}{5}$

    b. $4\frac{3}{8}$

    c. $4\frac{5}{8}$

    d. $4\frac{3}{4}$

54. $\frac{5}{9} = \underline{?}$

    a. $0.55\frac{5}{9}$

    b. $0.44\frac{4}{9}$

    c. 0.18

    d. 1.8

55. Give the product.

$$3\frac{2}{3} \times 2\frac{1}{2} = \underline{?}$$

    a. $8\frac{1}{3}$

    b. $9\frac{1}{6}$

    c. 11

    d. 6

56. Give the quotient.

$5\frac{1}{4} \div 1\frac{2}{3} = \underline{\ ?\ }$

     a. $3\frac{3}{20}$

     b. $8\frac{3}{4}$

     c. $3\frac{15}{16}$

     d. 7

57. Ruth can jog $4\frac{1}{2}$ miles in an hour. At that rate, how many miles can she jog in $2\frac{1}{4}$ hours?

     a. 2

     b. $\frac{1}{2}$

     c. $10\frac{1}{8}$

     d. none of these

58. Marla jogged $7\frac{3}{4}$ miles in $2\frac{1}{2}$ hours. How many miles did she average each hour?

     a. $10\frac{1}{4}$

     b. $3\frac{1}{10}$

     c. $19\frac{7}{8}$

     d. none of these

---

59. Give the ratio of squares to triangles.

     a. $\frac{2}{5}$

     b. $\frac{3}{5}$

     c. $\frac{2}{3}$

     d. $\frac{3}{2}$

60. $\frac{6}{n} = \frac{8}{5}$

$n = \underline{\ ?\ }$

     a. $9\frac{3}{5}$

     b. $3\frac{3}{4}$

     c. $6\frac{2}{3}$

     d. none of these

61. $22.5\% = \underline{\ ?\ }$

     a. 22.5

     b. 2.25

     c. 0.225

     d. 0.0225

---

62. $0.084 = \underline{\ ?\ }$

     a. 8.4%

     b. 84%

     c. 0.84%

     d. 0.084%

63. $\frac{5}{6} = \underline{\ ?\ }$

     a. 120%

     b. 1.20%

     c. $0.83\frac{1}{3}\%$

     d. $83\frac{1}{3}\%$

64. Solve.

$24 = n\%$ of 32

$n = \underline{\ ?\ }$

     a. $66\frac{2}{3}$

     b. 75

     c. $133\frac{1}{3}$

     d. none of these

---

65. 60% of $75 = n$

$n = \underline{\ ?\ }$

     a. 60

     b. 45

     c. 125

     d. none of these

66. $37\frac{1}{2}\%$ of $60 = n$

$n = \underline{\ ?\ }$

     a. 160

     b. 22.5

     c. 225

     d. none of these

67. 125% of $n = 100$

$n = \underline{\ ?\ }$

     a. 80

     b. 12.5

     c. 125

     d. none of these

---

68. Allison took a math test of 80 problems. She got 70% of the problems correct. How many problems did she get correct?

     a. 24

     b. 50

     c. 56

     d. none of these

69. John answered 126 questions correctly on his science test. His score was 84%. How many questions were there?

     a. 84

     b. 106

     c. 150

     d. none of these

70. Paul charges $2.40 an hour for doing yard work. How much should he charge for working from 8:30 A.M. to 1.15 P.M.?

     a. $11.40

     b. $12.60

     c. $10.20

     d. none of these

71. Ms. Clark sold a house for $62,500. She was paid a 4% commission. How much did she earn?

a. $2400
b. $2500
c. $3000
d. none of these

72. The Adams family budget 32% of their income for food. If their weekly income is $380, how much do they budget for food each week?

a. $243.20
b. $121.60
c. $12.16
d. none of these

73. What is the price of 5 pencils?

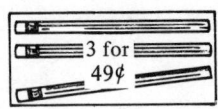

a. $1.47
b. $.83
c. $.81
d. none of these

74. A pair of blue jeans that regularly sells for $24.80 is on sale for 30% off. What is the sale price?

a. $7.44
b. $17.36
c. $32.24
d. none of these

75. Who endorses a check?

a. the bank
b. the person who wrote the check
c. the person who received the check
d. none of these

76. Ann had a balance of $118.29 in her checking account. She made a deposit of $48.25 and then wrote a check for $39.67. What was her balance then?

a. $30.37
b. $126.87
c. $109.71
d. none of these

77. Mr. Wilson borrowed $435 for 8 months at 9% interest. How much interest did he pay?

a. $26.10
b. $29.36
c. $39.15
d. none of these

78. How much *more* does the installment plan cost?

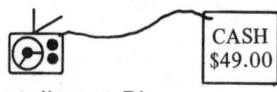

Installment Plan
$10 down
$7.25 per month
for 6 months

a. $53.50
b. $44.50
c. $4.50
d. none of these

79. The measure of $\angle DEF$ is __?__ .

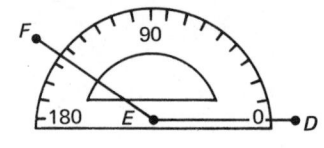

a. 145°
b. 135°
c. 45°
d. 35°

80. Line *l* is perpendicular to line __?__ .

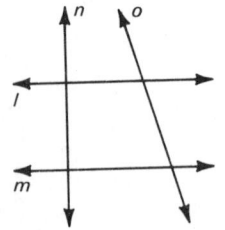

a. *m*
b. *n*
c. *o*
d. none of these

81. $\triangle ABC \cong \triangle TSR$
Corresponding sides
$\overline{AC} \leftrightarrow$ __?__

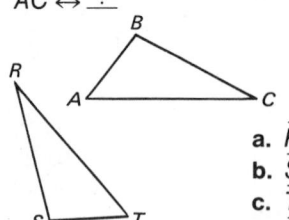

a. $\overline{RS}$
b. $\overline{ST}$
c. $\overline{TR}$
d. $\overline{AB}$

82. An isosceles triangle has __?__ lines of symmetry.

a. 0
b. 1
c. 2
d. 3

83. A quadrilateral has __?__ sides.

a. 6
b. 5
c. 4
d. 3

84. Which quadrilateral does not have a point of symmetry?

a. square
b. parallelogram
c. rhombus
d. isosceles trapezoid

85. Which of these quadrilaterals has just one pair of parallel sides?

a. square
b. parallelogram
c. rhombus
d. isosceles trapezoid

86. How many outcomes are there for tossing this die?

   a. 2
   b. 3
   c. 5
   d. 6

87. If you first toss a coin and then toss a die, how many possible outcomes are there?

   a. 8
   b. 10
   c. 11
   d. 12

88. If you spin this spinner, what is the probability it will stop on a number greater than 5?

   a. 3
   b. $\frac{1}{4}$
   c. $\frac{3}{4}$
   d. none of these

89. What is the probability of first tossing heads and then tossing a 5?

   a. 8
   b. $\frac{1}{8}$
   c. $\frac{1}{6}$
   d. $\frac{1}{12}$

90. From an unbiased sample of 120 students, it was found that 84 bought their lunch. Predict how many students out of 720 would buy their lunch.

   a. 504
   b. 216
   c. 605
   d. none of these

91. How much savings in May?

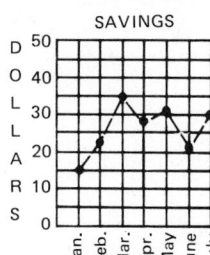

   a. $20
   b. $30
   c. $35
   d. $32

92. See Test Item 91. For how many months was there a decrease in savings?

   a. 4
   b. 3
   c. 2
   d. none of these

93. What is the mean of 9.18, 8.62, 9.25, 8.73, and 9.07?

   a. 45.85
   b. 8.97
   c. 9.07
   d. none of these

94. What is the median of 46, 54, 49, 45, 50, and 44?

   a. 47.5
   b. 49
   c. 48
   d. none of these

95. What is the mode of 26, 23, 19, 21, 19, 19, and 20?

   a. 21
   b. 20
   c. 19
   d. none of these

96. $^-16 + {}^+5 = \underline{\ ?\ }$

   a. $^+11$
   b. $^-21$
   c. $^+21$
   d. none of these

97. $^-9 - {}^+13 = \underline{\ ?\ }$

   a. $^-22$
   b. $^+4$
   c. $^-4$
   d. none of these

98. Give the product.
$^-11 \times {}^-5 = \underline{\ ?\ }$

   a. $^-16$
   b. $^-55$
   c. $^+55$
   d. none of these

99. Give the quotient.
$^+36 \div {}^-12 = \underline{\ ?\ }$

   a. $^-3$
   b. $^+3$
   c. $^+24$
   d. none of these

100. Which point has coordinates $(^-2, {}^+1)$?

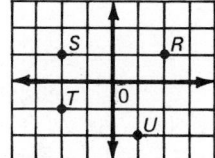

   a. R
   b. S
   c. T
   d. U

Answer Sheet for Final Checkup

Name _____

School _____

Date _____

Score _____

---

page 1

	a	b	c	d
1.	□	□	□	□

	a	b	c	d		a	b	c	d		a	b	c	d
2.	□	□	□	□	3.	□	□	□	□	4.	□	□	□	□
5.	□	□	□	□	6.	□	□	□	□	7.	□	□	□	□
8.	□	□	□	□	9.	□	□	□	□	10.	□	□	□	□

---

page 2

	a	b	c	d		a	b	c	d		a	b	c	d
11.	□	□	□	□	12.	□	□	□	□	13.	□	□	□	□
14.	□	□	□	□	15.	□	□	□	□	16.	□	□	□	□
17.	□	□	□	□	18.	□	□	□	□	19.	□	□	□	□
20.	□	□	□	□	21.	□	□	□	□	22.	□	□	□	□
23.	□	□	□	□	24.	□	□	□	□	25.	□	□	□	□

page 5

	a	b	c	d		a	b	c	d		a	b	c	d
56.	□	□	□	□	57.	□	□	□	□	58.	□	□	□	□
59.	□	□	□	□	60.	□	□	□	□	61.	□	□	□	□
62.	□	□	□	□	63.	□	□	□	□	64.	□	□	□	□
65.	□	□	□	□	66.	□	□	□	□	67.	□	□	□	□
68.	□	□	□	□	69.	□	□	□	□	70.	□	□	□	□

---

page 3

	a	b	c	d		a	b	c	d		a	b	c	d
26.	□	□	□	□	27.	□	□	□	□	28.	□	□	□	□
29.	□	□	□	□	30.	□	□	□	□	31.	□	□	□	□
32.	□	□	□	□	33.	□	□	□	□	34.	□	□	□	□
35.	□	□	□	□	36.	□	□	□	□	37.	□	□	□	□
38.	□	□	□	□	39.	□	□	□	□	40.	□	□	□	□

page 6

	a	b	c	d		a	b	c	d		a	b	c	d
71.	□	□	□	□	72.	□	□	□	□	73.	□	□	□	□
74.	□	□	□	□	75.	□	□	□	□	76.	□	□	□	□
77.	□	□	□	□	78.	□	□	□	□	79.	□	□	□	□
80.	□	□	□	□	81.	□	□	□	□	82.	□	□	□	□
83.	□	□	□	□	84.	□	□	□	□	85.	□	□	□	□

---

page 4

	a	b	c	d		a	b	c	d		a	b	c	d
41.	□	□	□	□	42.	□	□	□	□	43.	□	□	□	□
44.	□	□	□	□	45.	□	□	□	□	46.	□	□	□	□
47.	□	□	□	□	48.	□	□	□	□	49.	□	□	□	□
50.	□	□	□	□	51.	□	□	□	□	52.	□	□	□	□
53.	□	□	□	□	54.	□	□	□	□	55.	□	□	□	□

page 7

	a	b	c	d		a	b	c	d		a	b	c	d
86.	□	□	□	□	87.	□	□	□	□	88.	□	□	□	□
89.	□	□	□	□	90.	□	□	□	□	91.	□	□	□	□
92.	□	□	□	□	93.	□	□	□	□	94.	□	□	□	□
95.	□	□	□	□	96.	□	□	□	□	97.	□	□	□	□
98.	□	□	□	□	99.	□	□	□	□	100.	□	□	□	□

Quick-score Answer Key for Final Checkup

Name _____

School _____

Date _____

Score _____

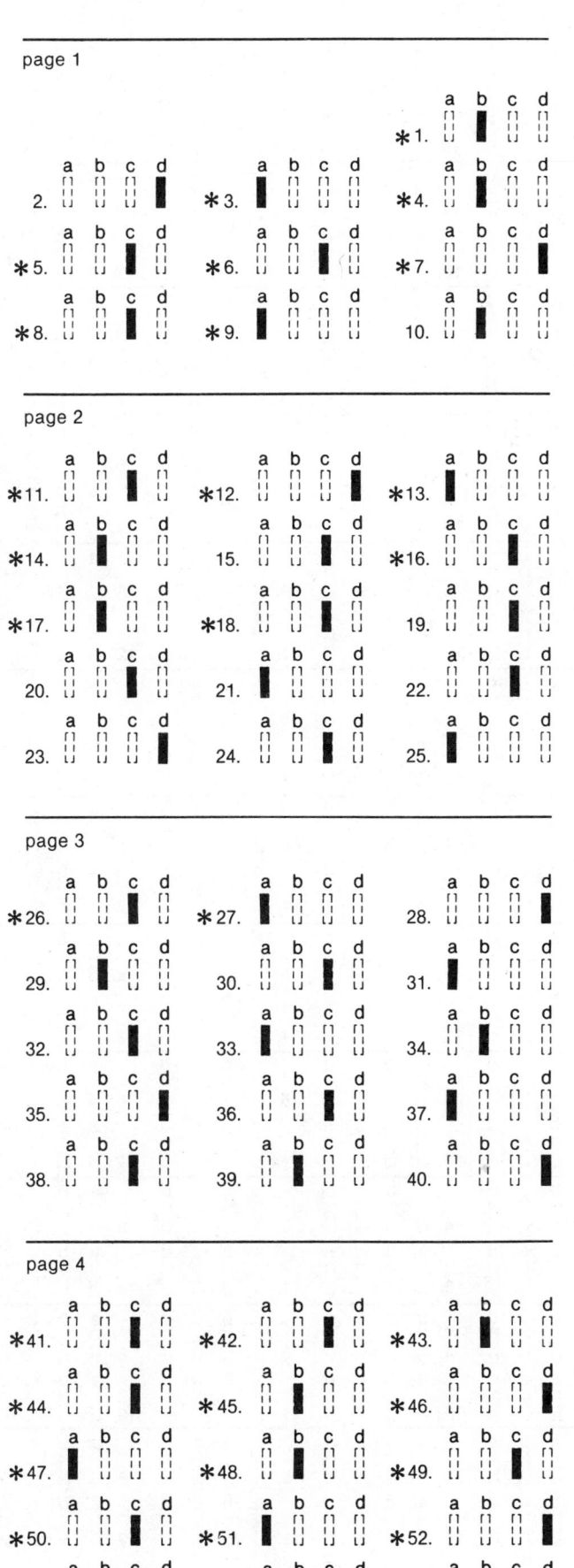

page 1

*1. b
2. d   *3. a   *4. a
*5. c   *6. c   *7. d
*8. c   *9. c   10. c

page 2

*11. c   *12. d   *13. a
*14. b   15. b   *16. a
*17. b   *18. a   19. a
20. c   21. a   22. a
23. c   24. c   25. a

page 3

*26. c   *27. a   28. d
29. b   30. d   31. a
32. b   33. a   34. c
35. c   36. b   37. a
38. b   39. b   40. d

page 4

*41. c   *42. c   *43. b
*44. b   *45. b   *46. d
*47. a   *48. a   *49. a
*50. b   *51. a   *52. a
*53. c   *54. a   55. d

page 5

56. a   57. c   58. b
59. c   60. b   *61. c
*62. a   *63. a   *64. a
*65. a   *66. b   *67. a
*68. b   *69. b   *70. a

page 6

*71. b   *72. b   *73. d
*74. a   75. c   *76. a
77. a   *78. c   79. a
80. a   81. c   82. a
83. b   84. b   85. d

page 7

86. c   87. d   88. d
89. b   90. a   91. d
92. a   93. b   94. a
95. a   96. b   97. a
98. c   99. a   100. b

Chapter 1

	a b c d	a b c d	a b c d	a b c d	a b c d	a b c d
1.		2.	3.	4.	5.	6.
7.		8.	9.	10.	11.	12.

Chapter 2

	a b c d	a b c d	a b c d	a b c d	a b c d	a b c d
1.		2.	3.	4.	5.	6.
7.		8.	9.	10.	11.	12.

Chapter 3

	a b c d	a b c d	a b c d	a b c d	a b c d	a b c d
1.		2.	3.	4.	5.	6.
7.		8.	9.	10.	11.	12.

Chapter 4

	a b c d	a b c d	a b c d	a b c d	a b c d	a b c d
1.		2.	3.	4.	5.	6.
7.		8.	9.	10.	11.	12.

Chapter 5

	a b c d	a b c d	a b c d	a b c d	a b c d	a b c d
1.		2.	3.	4.	5.	6.
7.		8.	9.	10.	11.	12.

Chapter 6

	a b c d	a b c d	a b c d	a b c d	a b c d	a b c d
1.		2.	3.	4.	5.	6.
7.		8.	9.	10.	11.	12.

Chapter 7

	a b c d	a b c d	a b c d	a b c d	a b c d	a b c d
1.		2.	3.	4.	5.	6.
7.		8.	9.	10.	11.	12.

Chapter 8

	a b c d	a b c d	a b c d	a b c d	a b c d	a b c d
1.		2.	3.	4.	5.	6.
7.		8.	9.	10.	11.	12.

Chapter 9

	a b c d	a b c d	a b c d	a b c d	a b c d	a b c d
1.		2.	3.	4.	5.	6.
7.		8.	9.	10.	11.	12.

Chapter 10

	a b c d	a b c d	a b c d	a b c d	a b c d	a b c d
1.		2.	3.	4.	5.	6.
7.		8.	9.	10.	11.	12.

Chapter 11

	a b c d	a b c d	a b c d	a b c d	a b c d	a b c d
1.		2.	3.	4.	5.	6.
7.		8.	9.	10.	11.	12.

Chapter 12

	a b c d	a b c d	a b c d	a b c d	a b c d	a b c d
1.		2.	3.	4.	5.	6.
7.		8.	9.	10.	11.	12.

Quick Score Answer Sheet for Major Checkups

Each chapter has questions 1–12, with answer choices a, b, c, d.

Chapter	1	2	3	4	5	6	7	8	9	10	11	12
Chapter 1	b	d	a	c	c	a	b	c	a	c	a	c
Chapter 2	b	b	b	d	d	d	a	a	b	c	a	c
Chapter 3	b	b	a	b	c	a	c	b	d	d	c	d
Chapter 4	b	c	a	b	a	d	b	a	c	a	b	b
Chapter 5	d	a	c	c	c	a	c	a	a	a	c	a
Chapter 6	d	c	d	a	a	a	b	c	d	a	c	c
Chapter 7	c	c	a	b	b	d	b	a	c	a	d	b
Chapter 8	a	c	a	a	a	a	b	b	b	a	b	a
Chapter 9	a	a	a	a	a	d	b	a	b	a	c	a
Chapter 10	d	c	a	a	a	c	b	d	c	b	b	d
Chapter 11	b	a	b	a	c	a	c	a	a	a	c	c
Chapter 12	c	c	a	c	c	a	c	a	a	c	d	d

The Calculator

There are many ways that the hand calculator can be used to support today's mathematics program. The calculator can extend and reinforce the objectives of the program or it can be the basis for a different approach to building a concept or practicing a skill. It can summarize a sequence of experiences or it can give new insights into problem-solving skills, even if the problems exceed the grade level computation skills.

Using a calculator creatively to enhance a mathematics program requires having appropriate calculator activities that are correlated with the program. Therefore, we have prepared 60 worksheets that are available as duplicating masters in the booklet entitled CALCULATOR WORKSHEETS for Level 7. A sample of eight of these worksheets is reproduced on the following pages. You may duplicate these worksheets for use with your class.

Using Calculators in Your Classroom

You do not need a calculator for every student. Many teachers have gotten started with calculator instruction just by asking students to bring calculators from home. You can purchase a few calculators at a time as the budget allows and eventually acquire enough for every pair of students. Good calculators are available for less than ten dollars. We suggest a 9-volt battery-powered, four function ($+$, $-$, $\times$, $\div$) machine that has algebraic logic. It is better not to use machines that are more complex than necessary for the calculations your students will be doing.

The way you use the calculator worksheets will depend upon the number of calculators available. If you have only a few calculators, you may want to place copies of the worksheets and the calculators in the "Mathematics Corner" when they are appropriate. You may also want to use the sheets for "early finishers" or for enrichment activities for a few students. If you have enough calculators so that students can work in pairs, give each student a copy of the activity and have each student work with a partner.

The calculator sheets can also be used as homework. Students like to work with calculators and many students have calculators available at home. Not only will the students enjoy the activity, but they will learn at the same time.

Using the Worksheets

Calculator Worksheets: Multiplication Estimation (after student page 39)
Students develop estimation skills and a "feel" for numbers by having experiences such as this worksheet provides. Here students look at three problems and, by estimation, try to circle the problem with the largest product. They then do the multiplications using the calculator. Rather than competing against anyone, they are striving to score as many points as they can.

Estimation skills will improve when students have incentive to estimate accurately and when the estimation is verified immediately after being made.

> *Answers:* 54×39, 46×39, 724×49, 73×63, 321×52, 474×53, 706×55, 403×71, 753×62, 291×307

Calculator Worksheet: Reading Decimals (after student page 59)
It is difficult to provide students with meaningful practice in reading decimals. With this worksheet students get practice reading decimals and the calculator provides immediate reinforcement.

This sheet can also be used by a pair of students. One student reads the decimal name aloud while the other student enters the number in the calculator and adds. Every four numbers are checked by comparing the sum with the check number. The students then reverse their roles and do the exercises again.

Calculator Worksheet: How Far? (after student text page 75)
Problem-solving skills are developed and supported with the calculator. The calculator frees students from computational restrictions and allows them to focus on solving the problems. Using a calculator encourages students to become "risk-takers." That is, rather than just sit there, students are more willing to make a try when using the calculator. This is an important problem-solving attitude that students need to develop. Many times when solving a problem a first guess will be wrong, but the guess will lead to new insights to the problem that will in turn lead to the answer.

> *Answers:* 1. 122.8 2. 137.3 3. Cedar and Harding 4. 13.6 5. 55.9 6. Harding, 5.4 kilometers

Calculator Worksheet: Fill the Holes (after student text page 93)

The calculator can help motivate practice and at the same time encourage new insights in familiar patterns such as the division algorithm. In filling in the holes, students are forced to analyze the division algorithm and to figure out what number comes from where. When a variety of digits are missing, the student is forced to really "look" at the pattern in the algorithm.

The use of the calculator with this activity illustrates how the calculator can move the attention of the student away from just getting an answer and focus that attention on the concept or, as in this case, the algorithm.

Answers: 3, 90, 22, 22; 4, 606, 3, 03; 0, 84, 1792; 3, 1252, 7, 7; 0.26, 3.10, 0.14, 0.06, 0.45, 1.35

Calculator Worksheet: Finding Averages (after student text page 95)

Many basic topics taught in the textbook can be enhanced and extended using the calculator. In this worksheet students are given additional exposure to finding averages. When using a calculator, answers don't have to "come out even." Thus the data can be more realistic, and large numbers are no more difficult than small numbers. The calculator allows students to concentrate on the concepts involved rather than the size or the difficulty of the numbers.

Answers: 17.5, 12.1 seconds, 146, 6.75 yards, 81, 1.84

Calculator Worksheet: Divisibility (after student text page 116)

The calculator encourages exploration and experimentation with mathematics. Many concepts when "discovered" are much more meaningful than when explained by a teacher. Shortcuts such as divisibility rules are much more likely to be remembered after a student has done an activity like this which points out the convenience of knowing the rules.

Answers: Divisible by 2: 94, 102, 68

Divisible by 3: 237, 135, 813;
Divisible by 4: 316, 832, 572; winner: o

Divisible by 6: 324, 210, 534;
Divisible by 8: 296, 472, 392; winner: X

Divisible by 7: 203, 798, 644:
Divisible by 9: 468, 360, 171; winner: X

Divisible by 4: 532, 724, 820;
Divisible by 6: 918, 594, 726; winner: o

Calculator Worksheet: How Far, How Much, or How Many? (after student text page 123)

The calculator aids development of problem-solving skills since it takes the emphasis away from the computation and puts it on the relationship between the numbers in the problem. For this page, the student fills in the calculator path and then follows the path to find the answer. Problem solving is difficult for many students and they need many and varied experiences to develop these skills.

Answers: $1126 - 475 = 651$; $2395 + 3170 = 5565$; $212 - 57 = 155$; $407 - 132 = 275$; $905 - 621 = 284$

Calculator Worksheet: Circumference (after student text page 139)

The calculator can be used to do the computation when the conceptual development pertains to geometric concepts. For this page, the calculator is used to evaluate the formulas which relate the radius, diameter, and circumference of a circle.

Answers: 18.84 cm; 12.5 cm, 78.5 cm; 16 cm, 50.24 cm; 15 cm, 7.5 cm; 50 cm, 314 cm

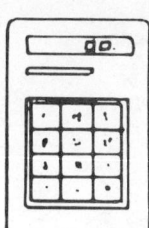

Multiplication Estimation

Estimating

Use your estimation skills. On each card, circle the exercise with the largest answer.

Check with your calculator.

Score 1 point for each correct estimate.

82	54	64
× 21	× 39	× 19

58	46	74
× 21	× 39	× 23

724	593	812
× 49	× 36	× 21

92	86	73
× 41	× 52	× 63

321	406	712
× 52	× 31	× 22

474	326	216
× 53	× 49	× 84

812	706	916
× 43	× 55	× 32

403	563	319
× 71	× 22	× 65

753	812	549
× 62	× 21	× 35

291	406	586
× 307	× 211	× 115

Score yourself:

9 or 10 points — *Pat yourself on your back!!*   7 or 8 points — *Shake your hand!*   6 or less — *Sharpen your pencil!*

Calculator Worksheet

(7) Student text page 39

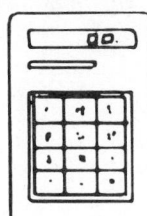

Reading Decimals

Name _____

Add these decimals on your calculator.
Check your answer with the ✔ number.

---

two tenths
nine tenths
three and eight tenths
twenty-one and two tenths

✔ number
26.1

---

fourteen hundredths
thirty-two hundredths
one and nineteen hundredths
eight and fifty-four hundredths

✔ number
10.19

---

twenty-five and seven tenths
six and eighty-three hundredths
fifty-three hundredths
forty-two and one tenth

✔ number
75.16

---

three hundred sixteen and nine tenths
twelve and nineteen hundredths
thirty-three hundredths
five and two hundredths

✔ number
334.44

---

two hundred fifteen thousandths
one and eighty-one hundredths
six hundred and two tenths
four hundred sixty-three thousandths

✔ number
602.688

Calculator Worksheet

Permission to reproduce this page is granted to users of Heath Mathematics.

How Far?

Problem Solving

Name _____

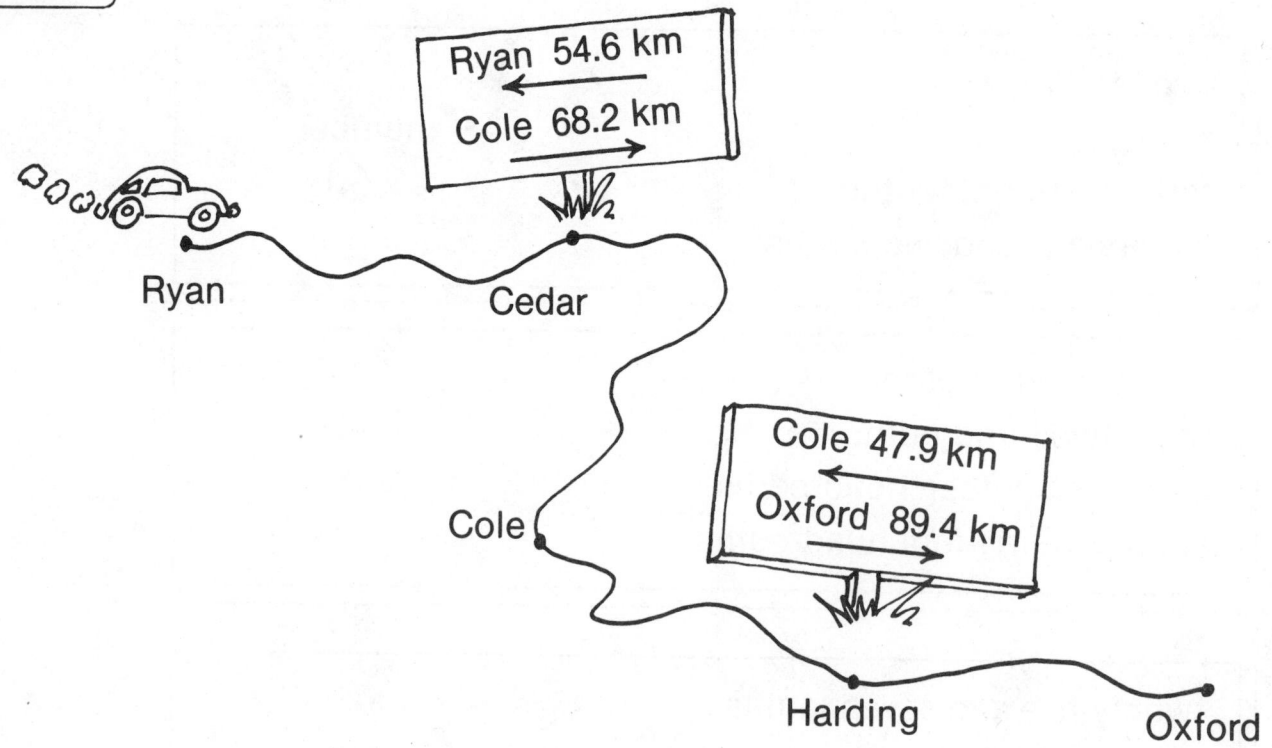

1. How many kilometers from Ryan to Cole? _____

2. How many kilometers from Cole to Oxford? _____

3. Which two cities are 116.1 kilometers apart? _____

4. My family drove from Cedar to Ryan. My friend's family drove from Cedar to Cole. How many kilometers farther did they drive? _____

5. We started at Harding and drove 15 kilometers toward Oxford. Our friend started at Oxford and drove 18.5 kilometers toward Harding. How many kilometers apart are we? _____

6. We started at Cedar and drove toward Oxford. After driving 121.5 kilometers we ran out of gas. Where should we go to get gasoline and how far is it? _____

Calculator Worksheet

(7) Student text page 75

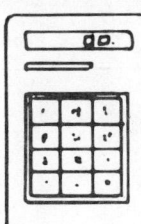

Fill the Holes

Division

Name _____

Use your calculator to "fill the holes."

$$
\begin{array}{r}
2\square.5 \\
45\overline{)1057.5} \\
\square\square \\
157 \\
135 \\
\square5 \\
5 \\
\end{array}
$$

$$
\begin{array}{r}
\square.47 \\
129\overline{)576.63} \\
516 \\
\square\square \\
516 \\
90\square \\
9\square \\
\end{array}
$$

$$
\begin{array}{r}
0.4\square2 \\
896\overline{)360.192} \\
35\square \\
1792 \\
\square\square \\
\end{array}
$$

$$
\begin{array}{r}
\square58 \\
216\overline{)77328} \\
648 \\
\square\square \\
1080 \\
1\square28 \\
1\square28 \\
\end{array}
$$

Use your calculator. Round answers to hundredths.

$12.58 \div 49 =$ _____

$96 \div 31 =$ _____

$1 \div 7 =$ _____

$2.6 \div 41.2 =$ _____

$1.35 \div 3 =$ _____

$129.6 \div 96 =$ _____

Calculator Worksheet

Finding Averages

Problem Solving

Name _____

Round your answers to hundredths.

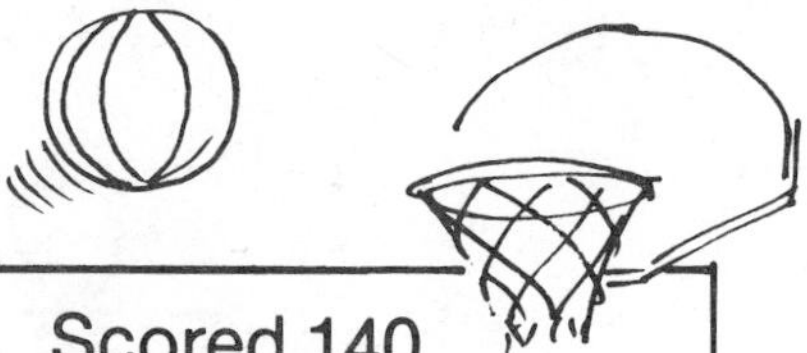

Scored 140
points in
8 games.
Average score
was _____

Ran 100-meter dash
four times.

12.2 s	11.9 s
12.9 s	11.4 s

Average time was _____

Bowled three games.
My scores were 135,
142, and 161. What
was my average? _____

Carried the ball 12 times
and gained 81 yards. What
was the average gain per
carry? _____

Averaged 4.5 strokes per
hole for 18 holes. What
was my total number of
strokes? _____

Our team hit 46 home runs
in 25 games. What was
the average number of
home runs per game? _____

To check — circle your answers. (Ignore the decimal points)

1	7	5	1	4	8	5	6	7	5	9
6	5	9	1	2	1	6	1	1	8	4
2	1	4	6	7	7	2	8	1	4	1

Calculator Worksheet

(7) Student text page 95

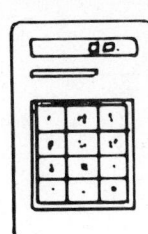

Divisibility

Explore

Which numbers on the tic-tac-toe board are divisible by 2? Mark them with an X.

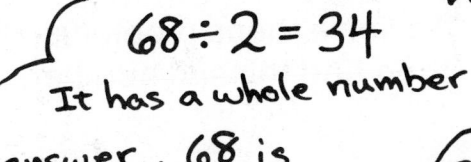

$68 \div 2 = 34$
It has a whole number answer... 68 is divisible by 2.

51	73	68
33	102	121
94	209	127

Find out who won these games.

Mark numbers divisible by 3 with an X.

Mark numbers divisible by 4 with an O.

316	237	135
238	832	813
526	817	572

Who won, X or O? _____

Mark numbers divisible by 6 with an X.

Mark numbers divisible by 8 with an O.

324	214	296
530	210	472
392	326	534

Who won? _____

X: numbers divisible by 7
O: numbers divisible by 9

468	214	633
360	552	171
203	798	644

Who won? _____

X: numbers divisible by 4
O: numbers divisible by 6

532	918	724
322	594	715
820	726	263

Who won? _____

Calculator Worksheet

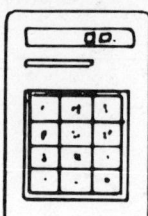

How Far, How Much, or How Many?

Name _____

Problem Solving

To solve these problems, fill in the calculator path and then find the end number.

It's 1126 kilometers from the mountains to Chicago. How many more kilometers are there to drive?

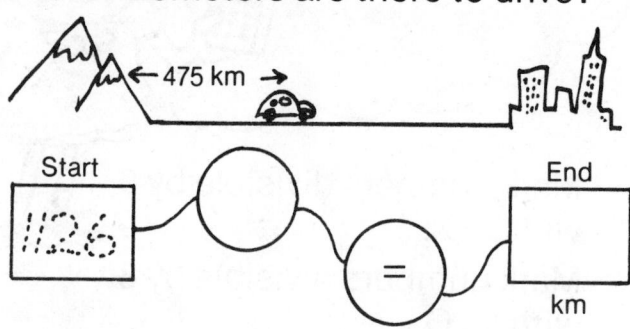

My friend has 212 baseball cards. This is 57 cards more than I have. How many cards do I have?

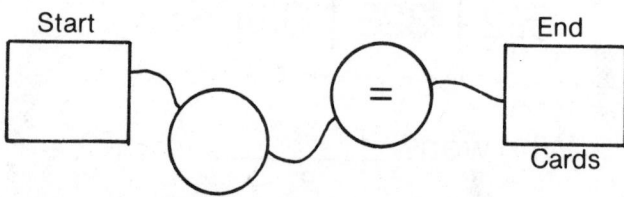

Our basketball team scored 407 points this season. I scored 132 of these points. How many points were scored by my team members?

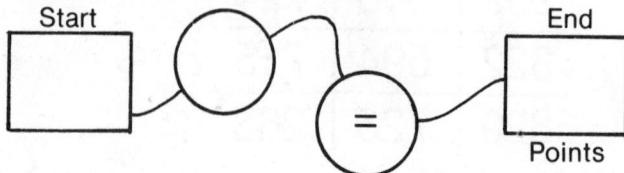

Our old car sold for $2395. This is $3170 less than the price of a new car. What is the price of the new car?

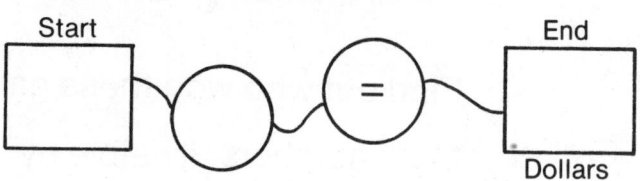

Karen is carrying $905. How much money is in the second bag?

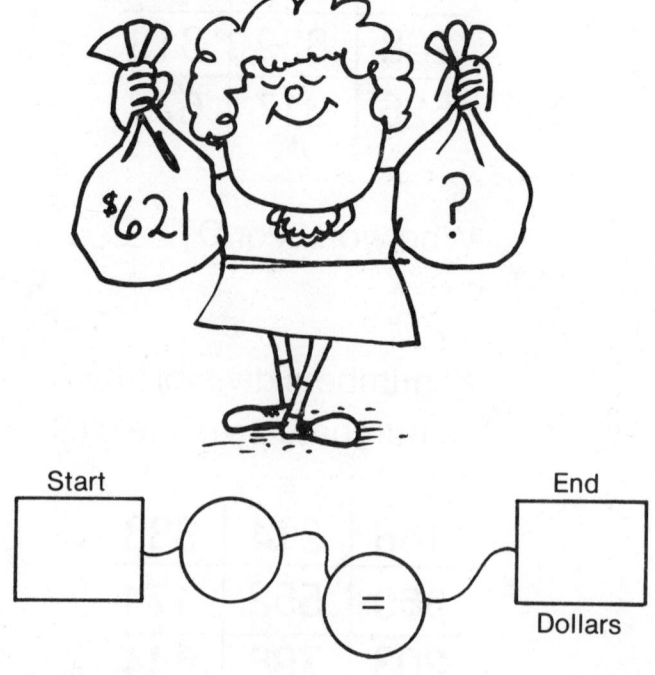

Calculator Worksheet

(7) Student text page 123

Circumference

Geometry

Check these paths on your calculator.

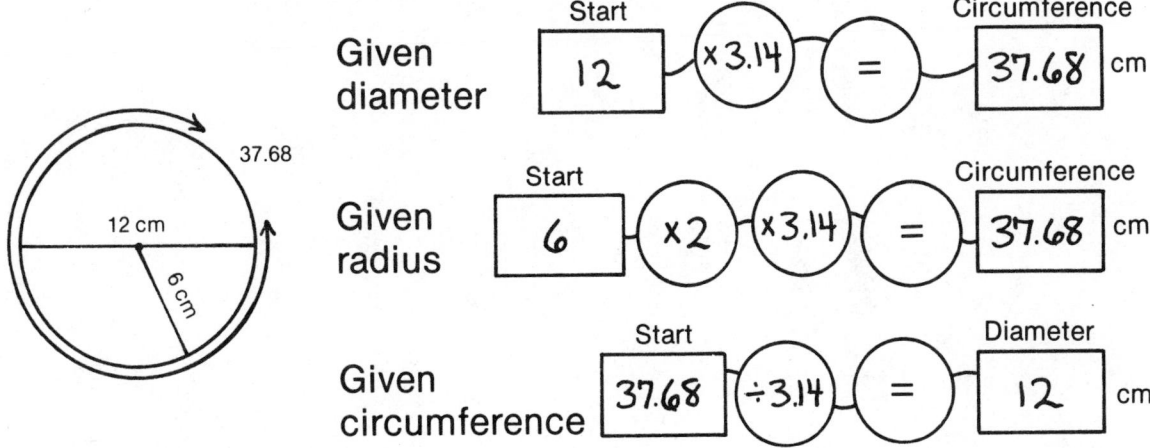

Choose a path to complete the table.

	Diameter	Radius	Circumference
6 cm circle	6 cm	3 cm	
25 cm circle	25 cm		
8 cm circle		8 cm	
47.1 cm circle			47.1 cm
100 cm circle	100 cm		

Calculator Worksheet

Creative Problem-Solving Activities

Introduction

The student texts of the HEATH MATHEMATICS PRO-GRAM contain many word or story problems that help teach students how to apply the mathematics they have learned to everyday types of problems. There are, however, other higher-level problem-solving skills that students ought to develop. These skills involve analyzing new problem situations, selecting methods of solving the problems, carrying out the methods, and evaluating the results. The activities in this section are intended to help you teach students such problem-solving skills.

The problem-solving processes suggested by Polya and others are:

1. understanding the problem,
2. selecting a method for solving the problem,
3. solving the problem, and
4. reviewing the problem and solution.

In step 3 students utilize such subskills as collecting and organizing data, forming hypotheses, testing hypotheses, and drawing conclusions. These, then, are the problem-solving skills that this section is intended to teach.

In this section you will find 14 problems, a very detailed discussion of how you can work with students in solving the first problem, brief discussions of the other 13 problems, and general suggestions for incorporating these materials into your teaching.

Using Problem 1

Suppose that seven people meet at a family party and that each person shakes hands with each of the other people once. How many handshakes will there be?

Understanding the Problem

You can help students understand the problem by asking questions that focus on the key points.

If Alan is one of the seven people, how many hands will he shake?
If Alan shakes hands with Betty, will Betty later shake hands with Alan?

Note that the two questions do not suggest answers or methods of solution. Instead they point out two important facts—you do not shake hands with yourself, and when you shake hands with someone, that person is also shaking hands with you.

Selecting a Method for Solving the Problem

One important fact that students should discover is that each problem can be solved in several ways. They should also learn to use several of the different ways.

Five methods for solving Problem 1 are described below. Students may discover other methods or combinations of methods.

Experiment Some students may suggest that seven students get into a group and actually shake hands with each other while someone counts the handshakes.

Explore simpler but similar problems looking for a pattern Other students may think about looking at the handshakes in smaller groups—groups of 1, 2, 3, etc. Then they can make a table of the data.

Number of people	1	2	3	4	
Number of handshakes	0	1	3	6	

Make a list Some students may choose names for the seven people and try making a list of all of the possible pairs.

  Alan & Betty
  Alan & Carl Betty & Carl
  Alan & Dan   ⋮
   ⋮

Make a diagram Students can make a diagram of the handshakes by drawing seven dots representing the people and joining the dots by segments representing the handshakes.

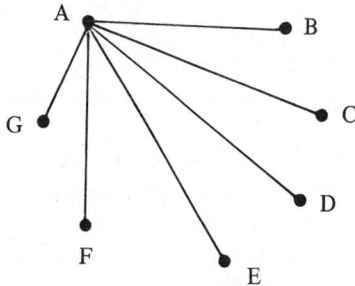

Use logical reasoning Finally, some students may try to solve the problem by reasoning without resorting to any of the above strategies. For example, they may *begin* by reasoning that each of the seven people would shake hands with each of the six other people, thus giving 42 handshakes.

Other methods such as systematic trial and error and manual labor will be suggested for some problems. Some of these procedures are tedious with pencil and paper, but sometimes are quite easy with a calculator.

Solving the Problem

Once a method of solving the problem is chosen, most students will be able to carry out that method and actually solve the problem. There are two primary sources of difficulty. Students using one of the first four methods suggested above may have trouble finding a systematic way of organizing and counting. Unless they are systematic, they may count some handshakes more than once and others not at all.

Students using the last method (logical reasoning) may count each handshake twice. That is, they may count Alan shaking hands with Betty and then later count Betty shaking hands with Alan.

As most students solve this problem, they probably will use a mixture of methods. That is, they will start by actually listing all the handshakes or performing the handshakes. But as they get data from these beginnings, they probably will see patterns and guess that the patterns continue. These guesses are hypotheses. While some students will immediately accept the hypotheses as true, most students will test the hypotheses by gathering more data. Even better, some students will recognize that these kinds of data never will be *proof* of the hypotheses and will search for acceptable ways of explaining their rules. Note the examples of this in the following review of the methods of solution.

Reviewing the Problem and Solution

Since it is important for students to become aware of different methods of attacking problems and of the strengths and weaknesses of the methods, allot sufficient time for classroom discussion.

The following are sample discussions for Problem 1:

Experiment
First student: We put seven people into a group and had them shake hands with each other. I tried to count the handshakes. At first there were too many handshakes at one time, and I couldn't count. So I asked the people to do one handshake at a time.

Second student: We still had trouble because we kept losing track of which people had shaken hands with which other people.

Teacher: What did you do to be more systematic?

Second student: We had one person shake hands with each of the others and then leave the group. Then a second person shook hands with each of the remaining people and then left the group. We continued this until there was no one left in the group. We counted 21 handshakes.

Teacher: Are you sure of your answer?

First student: Of course. We didn't miss any handshakes, and we know that we didn't count any twice. We also repeated the experiment an extra time to be sure.

Teacher: Do you like the method you used?

Second student: Yes. It was fun trying to do the experiment. We learned right away that we had to be systematic. Also, it was nice knowing for sure that we had the right answer.

Simpler problems

First student: We started with simpler situations that involved fewer than seven people. We made this table:

Number of people	1	2	3	4	5	6	7
Number of handshakes	0	1	3	6			
Increase in the number of handshakes		1	2	3			

We noticed a pattern in the way the number of handshakes increased. We guessed that the number of handshakes for a group of 5 people would be 4 more than the number for a group of 4 people. We checked that out and it was correct.

Second student: We were sure of our pattern, so we added 5 to 10 to get the number of handshakes for a group of 6 and then added 6 to that to get the number for a group of 7. Our answer was also 21.

Teacher: Are you sure that your pattern will continue as the size of the group gets larger?

Second student: Yes, it is quite obvious when you think about it. Suppose that you have a group of 5, and they all shake hands with each other. There will be 10 handshakes. Now if a 6th person joins the group, she will shake hands with each of the other 5, and then all of the handshakes will be completed. There will be only 5 new handshakes.

First student: The same reasoning can be used with bigger groups. Suppose that there is a group of 25 people and they do all of the handshaking. I don't know how many handshakes there will be, but if a 26th person joins the group, the only new handshakes will be the 25 he makes with the 25 people who were in the group to begin with.

Teacher: Good thinking. Could you use your method to find how many handshakes there would be in a group of 26?

First student: Yes, we would just add 1, 2, 3, 4, . . . , 24, and 25.

Teacher: Good. Do you like your method?

Second student: Yes. We actually experimented as the first group did, but we did it in such simple cases that it was easy. It was fun to find the pattern in the table, and it was even more fun to find a good explanation for the pattern.

List
First student: We made this list:

Alan and Betty
Alan and Carl   Betty and Carl
Alan and Dan   Betty and Dan   Carl and Dan
Alan and Emma   Betty and Emma   Carl and Emma
Alan and Fred   Betty and Fred   Carl and Fred
Alan and Ginny   Betty and Ginny   Carl and Ginny

We stopped before we listed all handshakes, because we could see a pattern. There are 6 in the first column, 5 in the second, and 4 in the third. There will be 3 in the next column, 2 in the next, and 1 in the last.

Second student: We just added 6, 5, 4, 3, 2, and 1, and also got 21 handshakes.

Teacher: Were you convinced that your pattern was correct?

First student: Yes, we were. It makes sense, too. For example, if there were 10 people in the group, one person would shake hands with 9 others. Then one of the 9 would shake hands with the 8 others. Then one of the 8 would shake hands with the 7 others, etc. So the total number of handshakes would be $9 + 8 + 7 + 6 + 5 + 4 + 3 + 2 + 1$.

Teacher: Good thinking. Do you like your method?

Second student: Oh yes. We wouldn't really like to make a complete list for a big group, but the list was a good way to start. The pattern became clear right away.

Diagram

First student: Our way was a lot like making a list, but it was simpler because we had to do less writing. We made this diagram:

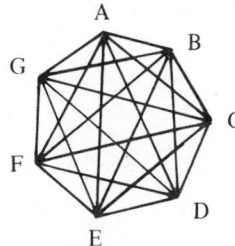

The dots were the 7 people and the segments were the handshakes. At first we had the same problem that the first group had. We tried to draw in all of the segments, but as it turned out we missed some. Also, it was hard to count them without counting some twice or missing some. So we started over. We connected A to each of the other 6 dots. Then we connected B to each of the dots except A. (A was already connected to B.) That took 5 segments. We did the same at C and got 4 new segments. Then we saw the pattern and just added.

$$6 + 5 + 4 + 3 + 2 + 1 = 21$$

Teacher: Were you sure of your answer?

First student: Yes. We didn't consider groups of other sizes, but we were sure that 21 was the correct answer.

Teacher: Do you like your method?

Second student: Yes. The picture was really simple to make, and it helped us get the answer.

Logical reasoning

First student: At first we thought that the answer was 42 because we reasoned that each of the 7 people would shake hands with each of the other 6 people. That gave 6×7, or 42 handshakes. Then we heard that the other groups were getting 21 as their answer.

Second student: We thought that we might have made a mistake, but we didn't know what it was. We tried our reasoning for a group of 3. According to our rule, each of the 3 would shake hands with 2 others, giving 6 handshakes. But when we actually tried it, we got only 3 handshakes. We knew for sure that our rule was wrong. We went back to the original problem and started to make a list. Right away we saw that we had counted

every handshake twice. The 42 handshakes included Alan shaking hands with Dan and Dan shaking hands with Alan as 2 separate handshakes.

First student: Since each handshake was counted twice, we knew that we should have divided 42 by 2 to get the correct answer, 21.

Teacher: Were you sure of your answer?

First student: Yes. But we were also sure of 42 for a while. The thing that made us most sure that 21 was correct was the fact that the other groups also got 21.

Teacher: Do you like your method?

Second student: Yes. It was harder to be sure that we hadn't overlooked something, but our method will help us to easily find the number of handshakes in a group of any size.

Teacher: Why is your way easier than the other ways?

Second student: For example, suppose that you want to know the total number of handshakes in a group of 26 people. The other groups would have to find this sum:

$$25 + 24 + 23 + 22 + \cdots + 3 + 2 + 1$$

We would just multiply 26 by 25 and then divide by 2.

$$\frac{26 \times 25}{2} = 325$$

Teacher: Very good. You have all done good work. Keep in mind the methods that were used so that you can use them on the next problem.

Teaching Creative Problem Solving

Using the Problems

We suggest that these problems be used over a long period of time, perhaps most of the school year. Give students a problem and let them work on it individually or in small groups for a few weeks. Occasionally give students some time in class to work on a problem. They can also use whatever free time is available. Then let students share solutions.

Introducing a Problem

There are several ways of introducing a problem to students. You can duplicate the problem and give each student a copy, post it on a bulletin board, or put it on a transparency and project it on an overhead projector. Let students read the problem and then ask them questions to be sure they understand the problem. Sample questions are given for each of the problems in this unit. Ask other questions, if you wish, but do not guide students toward a way to solve the problem at this time.

Ideally, of course, students should read a problem, think about what they have read, and ask themselves questions as they seek to understand what is expected. That is, the students should learn to read and understand without your help. Therefore, as the year progresses you should gradually wean the students away from depending on you.

Selecting a Method

Once students understand the problem, let them think about it and work on it by themselves for a few days. Then check with them individually to see if they have made progress in finding a way of solving it. At this point, if some students have not found a way of solving the problem, you may wish to suggest one. For example, you could ask if they have thought of trying an experiment or of drawing a diagram.

Solving the Problem

As students work on the problem, look for two things: frustration and generalization based on insufficient or incorrect data. Frustration may be indicated by mild anger or by lack of interest. In such situations you should help students move forward. Discuss with them what they have tried and what they have accomplished. Look for the point of difficulty and try to help students over that difficulty. You should do as little as you can and still get students working again by themselves. Be sure that you don't solve the problem for them.

Students who generalize too quickly may be incorrect in their generalizations, or they may actually be correct. In the former case you can suggest that they check their generalization or you may suggest a specific counterexample. A more difficult situation is the one in which students make a correct generalization from two or three pieces of information and accept it without question. While it is good that they found a correct generalization, they should learn not to trust completely any snap judgment. Encourage these students to find an explanation for the pattern.

Reviewing the Problem and Solution

As students discuss their solutions, be sure to ask questions that force them to look at the strengths and weaknesses of their methods. Ask them to think about where they had trouble, where the work was tedious, how they found patterns, how they enjoyed using the method, etc.

Note that students may have difficulty trying to state the rules or generalizations that they used. You may have to help them find the proper language to state the rules clearly. For example, the easiest way of stating the rule used by the "logical reasoning" group in Problem 1 and the way we will state such generalizations is this:

The number of handshakes in a group of n people = $\dfrac{n(n-1)}{2}$.

Students may use words in place of algebraic symbols. For example, they may suggest this:

To get the number of handshakes, you multiply the number in the group by the next smaller number and then divide by 2.

The rule used by the other groups for the same problem can be stated in this way:

If there are n people in a group, the number of handshakes is $1 + 2 + 3 + \cdots + (n - 1)$.

A third rule that might be stated by the group that made the table tells how to find the number of handshakes in terms of the number of handshakes in the next smaller group.

To get the number of handshakes for a group of n people, you add $(n - 1)$ to the number of handshakes for the next smaller group.

For example, if you wish to know the number of handshakes for a group of 6, you add 5 to the number of handshakes for a group of 5.

Using Problem 2

Understanding

What is the area to be mowed? (2880 square ft)
How much must each person mow? (1440 square ft)
If Mary mows one strip down the short side of the yard, what area has she mowed? (2 ft × 48 ft = 96 square ft)

Selecting a Method

Diagram Make a rectangle to represent the yard, and shade parts to represent what is mowed until half is left unmowed.

Table After each full round the unmowed part is a rectangle. The areas of these rectangles are easy to compute.

	Start	After 1 time around	After 2 times around	After 3 times around	After 4 times around
Rectangle left	48 ft by 60 ft	44 ft by 56 ft	40 ft by 52 ft	36 ft by 48 ft	32 ft by 44 ft
Area left	2880 square ft	2464 square ft	2080 square ft	1728 square ft	1408 square ft

less than half left

Answer

Mary would mow 3 times around and all but a 16-foot strip the fourth time around.

PROBLEM 1

Hearty Handshakes

Suppose that seven people meet at a family party and that each person shakes hands with each of the other people once. How many handshakes will there be?

PROBLEM 2

Mow, Mow, Mow the Lawn

Mary and her brother have agreed that each will mow half of their backyard, which is a 48-foot by 60-foot rectangle. The mower cuts a 2-foot-wide path. If Mary starts at a corner and mows around and around the yard toward the center, when will she have mowed her half?

PROBLEM 3

Special Segments

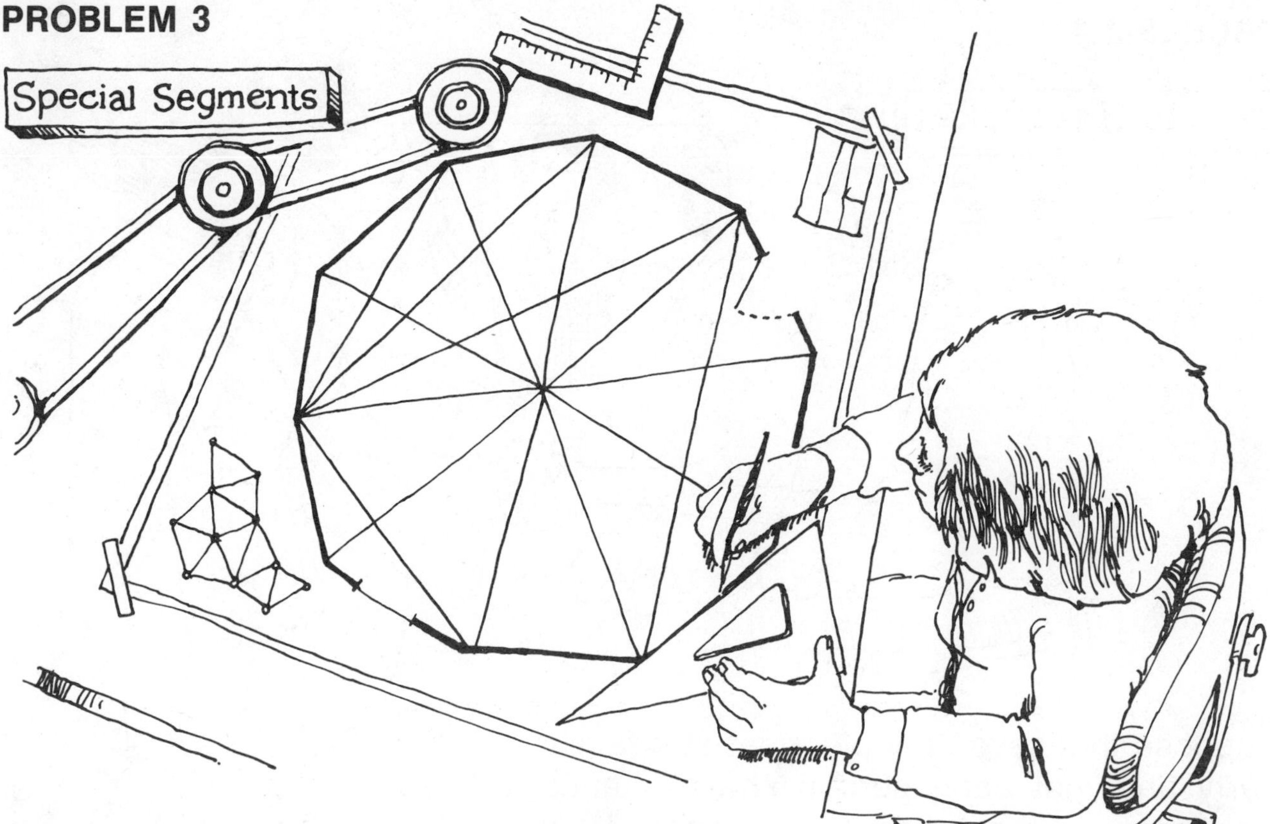

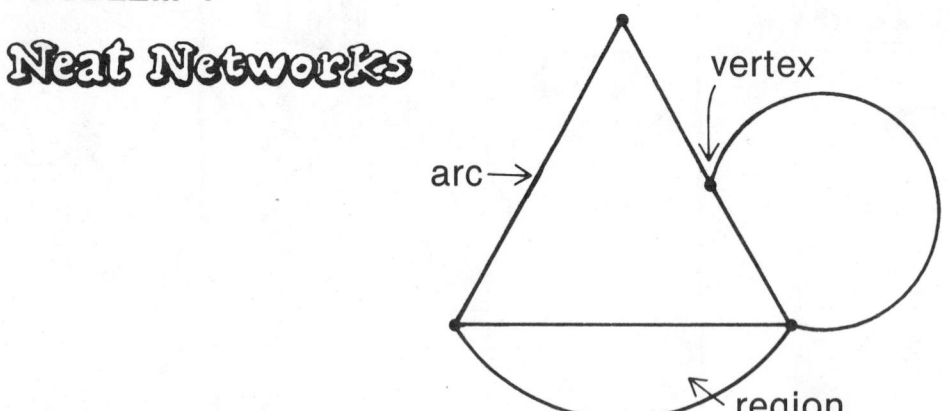

Suppose that a 10-sided polygon and all of its diagonals are drawn. How many segments (sides and diagonals) will there be?

PROBLEM 4

Neat Networks

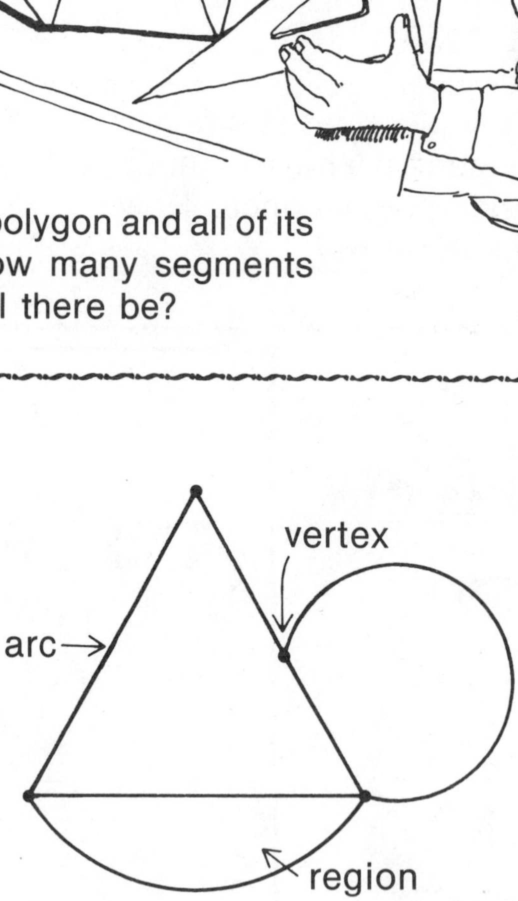

vertex

arc →

← region

Here is an example of a closed network made up of *arcs, vertices,* and enclosed *regions.* There is a simple rule that relates the number of arcs, the number of vertices, and the number of regions for all closed networks. Find that rule.

Using Problem 3

Understanding

Draw a 4-sided polygon and its diagonals. What is a diagonal? (A segment that is not a side that joins two vertices)

Selecting a Method

Simpler problems

Kind of polygon	3-sided	4-sided	5-sided	6-sided
Number of segments (sides and diagonals)	3	6	10	15

Logical reasoning There are 9 segments from each of the 10 vertices. It appears that there are 90 segments, but this counts each of the segments twice. So, there are 45 segments in all.

Answer

45 segments (sides and diagonals)

Students who use the table may notice that the numbers of segments increase in a regular way.

Number of segments (sides and diagonals) | 3 | 6 | 10 | 15 |
                             3   4   5

They can find the solution by adding 6 to 15 and then, in turn, adding 7, 8, and 9.

Rule: The number of segments in an n-sided polygon $= 3 + 3 + 4 + 5 + \cdots + (n - 1)$.

Students who use the logical reasoning suggested above may see this rule:

Rule: The number of segments in an n-sided polygon $= \dfrac{n(n - 1)}{2}$.

Students should note that this problem is really the same as Problem 1, because in both cases the real question deals with the number of ways in which some elements can be paired.

Using Problem 4

Understanding

How many regions are in the network? (3)
How many arcs? (6)
How many vertices? (4)

Selecting a Method

Table Draw a variety of networks.

Network	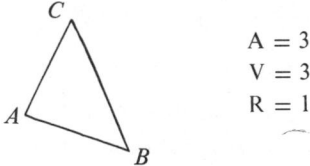			
Number of arcs	3	4	8	6
Number of vertices	3	4	5	4
Number of regions	1	1	4	3

Logical Reasoning
Start with a very simple network such as this:

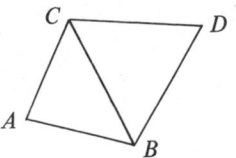

A = 3
V = 3
R = 1

Now build onto the network:

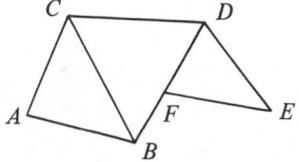

This added 2 arcs, 1 vertex, and 1 region.

Build again:

This added 3 arcs ($\overline{BD}$ was cut into two parts), 2 vertices, and 1 region. In both cases the number of arcs added equaled the sum of the numbers of vertices and regions. Try others. The same thing happens. This suggests that there is a relationship, between the number of arcs and the sum of the numbers of vertices and regions, that does not change from the beginning simple situation. From that situation we can see that $V + R$ is 1 more than A.

Answer

$A + 1 = V + R$

Students are not likely to think of the logical reasoning suggested above; but after the problem is solved, you may wish to show the method—starting with a simple situation and building on it.

Using Problem 5

Understanding

How many 45-year-old people are in the parade? (45)
How many people 3 years old or less are in the parade? (6)

Selecting a Method

Manual Labor Find the number of people at each of the ages and add the numbers.

Simpler Problems

Greatest age	1	2	3	4	5	6	7
Number of people marching	1	3	6	10	15	21	28
Increase in number marching		2	3	4	5	6	7

Answer   1275

Rule: The number of people marching who are n years old or younger is $\dfrac{n(n + 1)}{2}$.

Rule: To find the total number of people marching who are n years old or less, you add n to the total number who are $n - 1$ years old or less.

Using Problem 6

Understanding

Demonstrate several moves for students (moving 2 disks at a time, putting a large one on a small one, putting a small one on a large one) and ask if the moves are permitted. (No. No. Yes.)

Selecting a Method

Experiment Make a model and actually make the moves.

Simpler problems

Number of disks	1	2	3	4	5	6
Number of moves	1	3	7	15	31	63
Increase in number of moves		2	4	8	16	32

Answer   1023 moves ($2^{10} - 1$)

Rule: The number of moves required to move n disks = $2^n - 1$.

Rule: The number of moves required to move n disks = $1 + 2^1 + 2^2 + 2^3 + 2^4 + \cdots + 2^{n-1}$.

PROBLEM 5

Parade of the Ages

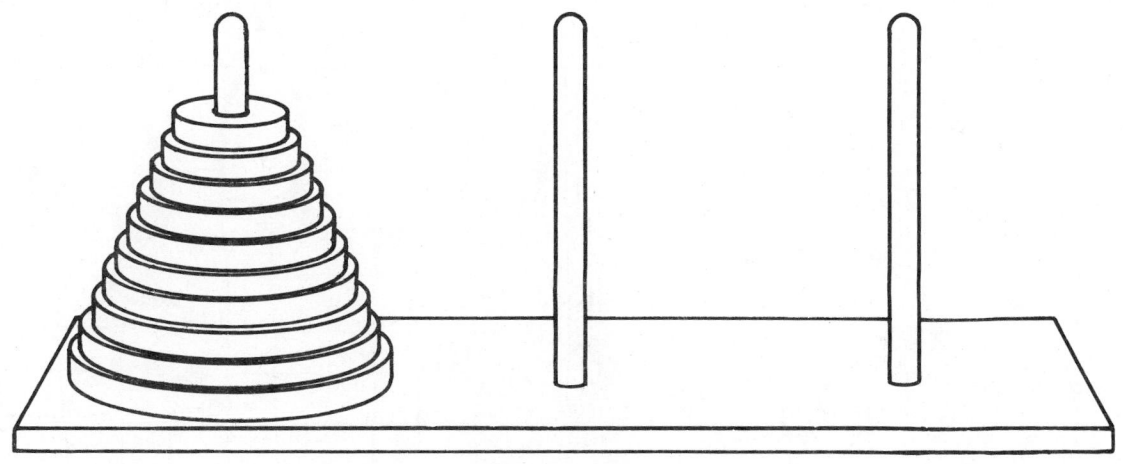

In a faraway land all people celebrate their births on the same day. On that day there is a "Parade of the Ages." At the head of the parade (riding in a wagon, of course) is 1 one-year-old child. Next are 2 two-year-olds. Then there are 3 three-year-olds, 4 four-year-olds, 5 five-year-olds, 6 six-year-olds, etc. How many people 50 years old or under are in the parade?

PROBLEM 6

Tower of Hanoi

There are 10 round disks with different diameters piled in order on one of three rods. By moving one disk at a time from one rod to another, the whole pile is to be moved to another rod. No disk is ever placed on a smaller one. How many moves will this task take?

PROBLEM 7

The Triangle Trap

How many triangles are in this figure?

PROBLEM 8

The Case of the Colored Cube

Suppose that a 10-cm by 10-cm by 10-cm cube is painted red and then cut into 1-cm by 1-cm by 1-cm cubes. How many of the little cubes are painted on 4 faces? On 3 faces? On 2 faces? On 1 face? On 0 faces?

Using Problem 7

Understanding

Look at the small triangle at the top. How many triangles of that size are in the next "layer"? (3)

Find a bigger triangle. (Many answers)

Find a triangle that looks like the bigger one but is "upside down." (Many answers)

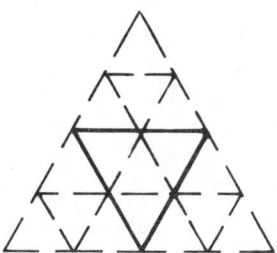

Selecting a Method

Systematic counting This is probably the only method that will be fruitful in this problem.

One systematic method is to count all of the small triangles (49); then count all of the next larger size (21 plus 10 "upside down"); etc.

Simpler problems Students may try looking at simpler but similar situations, but they are not likely to find a usable pattern. It is important to learn that some problems do not easily yield a pattern.

	△	⬙	⬙		
Number of "layers"	1	2	3	4	5
Number of triangles	1	5	13	27	48

Answer 118

Using Problem 8

Understanding

How many small cubes are there in all? (1000)

Where are the cubes with 3 painted faces located? (In the corners of the big cube)

Where are the cubes with 2 painted faces located? (Along the edges of the cube)

Selecting a Method

Experiment Get 1000 small cubes, arrange them into a big cube, paint the outside, take it apart, and count the various kinds of cubes.

Diagram Some students may be able to solve the problem by carefully drawing a 10 by 10 by 10 cube and coloring it.

Simpler problems

Size of cube	2x2x2	3x3x3	4x4x4	5x5x5	6x6x6
Total number of small cubes	8	27	64	125	216
Number of cubes with 3 painted faces	8	8	8	8	8
Number of cubes with 2 painted faces	0	12	24	36	48
Number of cubes with 1 painted face	0	6	24	54	96
Number of cubes with 0 painted faces	0	1	8	27	64

Students should note these patterns:

a. The numbers in the first and last rows are cubic numbers (2^3, 3^3, 4^3, etc.).

b. The numbers in the second row are the same (8).

c. The numbers in the third row are multiples of 12.

d. The numbers in the fourth row are multiples of 6.

Logical reasoning The cubes with 3 painted faces are in the corners, so there are always 8 of them.

The cubes with 2 painted faces are located along the edges. The number of these cubes on each edge is 2 less than the length of the edge, because of the 2 in the corners. So there are 8 cubes with 2 painted faces along each of the 12 edges. So, ...

The cubes with 1 painted face form squares on the faces of the big cube. The dimensions of the square are 2 less than the dimensions of the big cube. So there are 8 × 8 cubes with 1 painted face on each of the 6 faces. So, ...

The cubes with 0 painted faces form another cube inside the big cube. The dimensions of the inside cube are 2 less than the dimensions of the big cube. So, ...

Answer
3 painted faces: 8
2 painted faces: 96
1 painted face: 384
0 painted faces: 512

Rule: In an n by n by n cube,

the number of cubes with 3 painted faces = 8,
the number of cubes with 2 painted faces = $12(n - 2)$,
the number of cubes with 1 painted face = $6(n - 2)^2$, and
the number of cubes with 0 painted faces = $(n - 2)^3$.

Using Problem 9

Understanding

Draw this figure and ask if it is a solution. (No. Some segments are not crossed.)

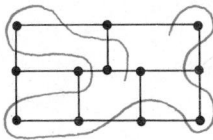

Selecting a Method

Experiment Most students will attack the problem head on and try different ways of tracing until they find one that works. They should be encouraged to keep some kind of record of the various attempts so that they don't repeat the same ones over and over. (Students should notice the symmetry of the figure and be aware that this reduces the number of ways of trying to draw the path. For example, the two paths below are really alike.)

 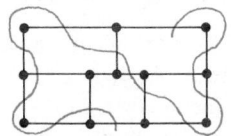

Logical reasoning Students are not likely to think of this argument, but you may wish to acquaint them with it during the review session.

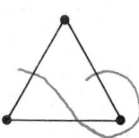  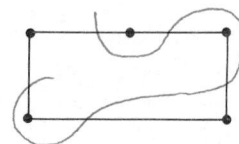

If you start *inside* a simple closed figure made of an odd number of segments, you end outside it. If you start *outside* such a figure with an odd number of segments, you end inside it. In the puzzle figure there are 3 parts with an odd number of segments.

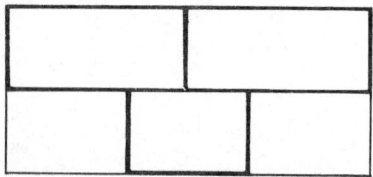

If you start outside the three parts, the path would have to end inside *each* of the three parts—which is impossible. If you start inside one of the three parts, the path would end outside that part; then the path would start outside the other two odd parts and would have to end inside *each* of them—which is impossible. So, no such path is possible.

Answer Impossible

Rule: The task is impossible if there are more than 2 parts of such a puzzle that have an odd number of segments.

Using Problem 10

Understanding

How many even vertices does this network have? (2)
How many odd vertices? (2)

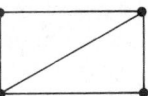

Draw a network that has 1 even and 2 odd vertices.

Draw a network that has 1 odd and 2 even vertices. (Impossible)

Selecting a Method

Experiment and table In this experiment students draw many networks and count each kind of vertex.

Network						
Number of odd vertices	0	0	0	0	0	2
Number of even vertices	2	3	4	5	3	1

Experiment and table In this experiment students choose a number of even vertices and a number of odd vertices and try to draw such a network.

Possible					
Number of odds	0	0	2	4	6
Number of evens	3	4	7	1	2

Impossible					
Number of odds	1	1	1	3	7
Number of evens	0	3	5	7	2

Logical reasoning Students are not likely to think of this argument, but you may wish to acquaint them with it during the review session.

Each arc contributes 2 "ends."

This means that no matter how many arcs and vertices, there are an even number of "ends." That is, if you should add the numbers of "ends" for the vertices, you get an even number.

$$2 + 4 + 4 + 3 + 3 = \text{even number}$$

This, in turn, means that there must be an even number of odd addends and, therefore, an even number of odd vertices.

Answer

No such network is possible, because each closed network must have an even number of odd vertices.

472

PROBLEM 9

Puzzling Path

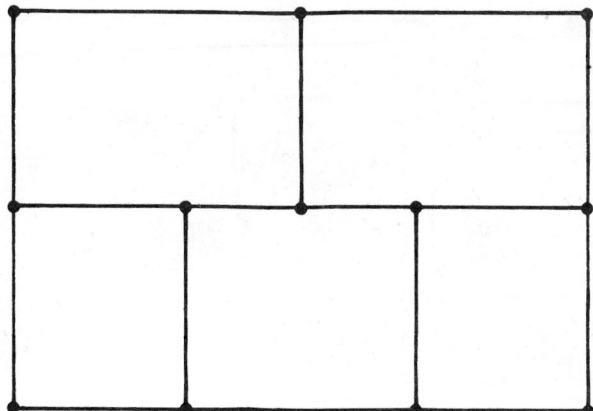

Draw a path that crosses each of the segments in this figure exactly once. Do not lift your pencil as you draw the path.

PROBLEM 10

Network Work

A closed network is made up of arcs and vertices.

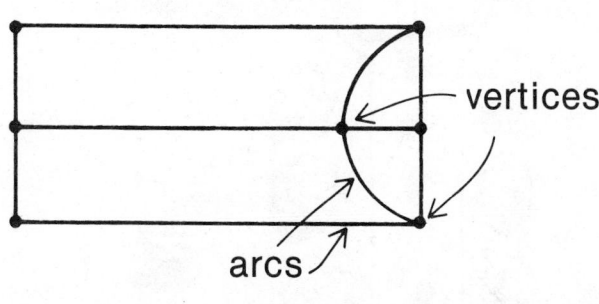

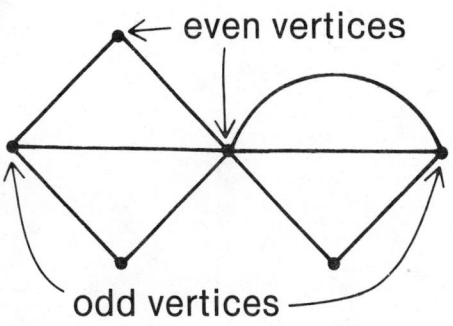

If a vertex has an even number of arcs going from it, it is called an even vertex. If a vertex has an odd number of arcs going from it, it is called an odd vertex.

Find a closed network that has 5 even vertices and 3 odd vertices.

PROBLEM 11

The Road Inspector

A road inspector must inspect the roads in this network. Can he drive over all the roads without ever retracing his path? He may start anywhere and end anywhere.

PROBLEM 12

A Peach of a Pear

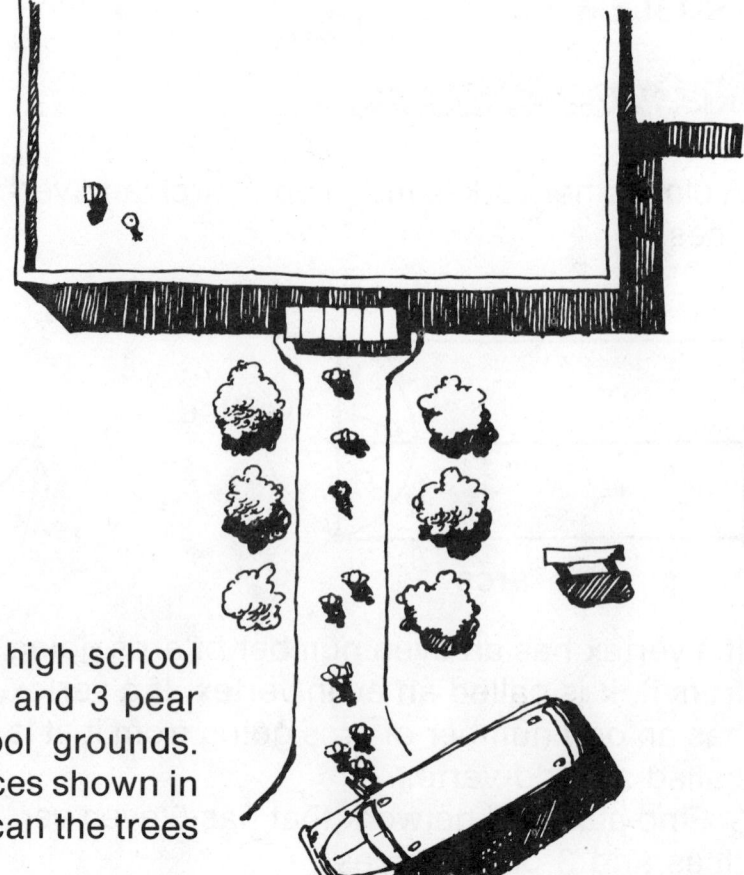

The graduating class of a junior high school wishes to donate 3 peach trees and 3 pear trees to help beautify the school grounds. They are to be planted in the places shown in the diagram. In how many ways can the trees be arranged?

Using Problem 11

Understanding

Can this network be traced? (Yes.)

Can this network be traced? (No.)

Selecting a Method

You may wish to give students a hint that there is a rule for traceability that is related to the numbers of odd and even vertices.

Experiment Students can use a pencil to try to trace the network in various ways until they succeed or until they decide that it is impossible.

Simpler problems

Network	⊖	⊕	△	▱	⊞
Number of odd vertices	2	4	0	2	4
Number of even vertices	0	0	3	2	5
Traceable?	yes	no	yes	yes	no

Logical reasoning Students are not likely to think of this argument, but you may wish to give it to them during the review session.

Each time the road inspector passes through an intersection (vertex) he traces two arcs, one while going to the vertex and one while leaving it. If he passes through a vertex 1 time, he traces 2 arcs; if he passes through a vertex 2 times, he traces 4 arcs; if he passes through a vertex 3 times, he traces 6 arcs; etc. The only way that he can trace through an odd number of arcs at a vertex is to start at that vertex or end there. Since there can be at most two starting and ending places, there can be at most two odd vertices in a traceable network.

Answer

There are many solutions, but in all cases the inspector must start at one of the marked vertices and end at the other.

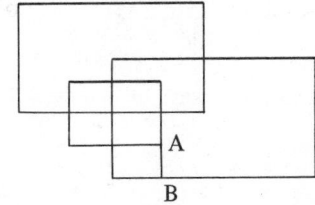

Rule: A network is traceable if it has at most 2 odd vertices.

Using Problem 12

Understanding

This problem is easily understood without help.

Selecting a Method

Experiment Use 3 objects to represent peach trees and another 3 objects to represent pear trees. Arrange them in different ways and count the ways.

The difficulty here is to be sure that all arrangements have been found without counting any arrangement twice.

Diagram

1 ○	○ 4
2 ○	○ 5
3 ○	○ 6

Position 1	Position 2	Position 3	Position 4	Position 5	Position 6

H: Peach
R: Pear

The total number of paths through the tree diagram (which is also the same as the number of endpoints in the last column) gives the total number of arrangements of the trees. Note that there are usually 2 choices for each position—peach or pear—but after all of one kind are used up there is no longer a choice.

Answer

20 arrangements

Using Problem 13

Understanding

Is this a solution?

    water—8 kg   vinegar—31 kg   oil—13 kg, 15 kg
                                     17 kg, 19 kg

(No. The amount of oil is not twice the amount of vinegar.)

Does the fact that the above suggestion is not a solution mean that the 8-kg barrel does not have water in it? (No. There may be another way of arranging the other barrels so that one amount is twice the other.)

Selecting a Method

Probably the only way that students can do this problem is by trial and error tempered by some logical reasoning.

Trial and error Select one barrel to be water. Combine the other amounts in different ways, trying to find one arrangement in which one amount is twice the other.

Logical reasoning Logical reasoning may show some students that the number of kg of oil must be an even number. (It is 2 times the number of kg of vinegar, and 2 times a whole number is an even number.) Therefore, if the oil is in 2 barrels, each contains an odd number of kg. If the oil is in 3 barrels, 2 have an odd number of kg and the third contains an even number of kg. (In this case the third barrel must be the 8-kg barrel.) This kind of reasoning will reduce the number of combinations that must be tried.

Answer

water—19 kg   oil—8 kg, 17 kg, 31 kg   vinegar—13 kg, 15 kg

Using Problem 14

Understanding

Look at the second picture. If you put another kitten on the left side, what could you put on the right side to balance it? (1 mouse and 1 chicken, or 1 kitten)

Selecting a Method

Trial and error Either mentally or using some real objects to represent the animals, make various substitutions, trying to eliminate the puppies and the chickens.

Logical reasoning Since the problem is to balance 1 kitten with some mice, it is necessary to make substitutions that gradually eliminate two kinds of animals. In the first picture, 1 puppy balances 1 kitten and 1 mouse. So in the third picture, replace 2 puppies by 2 kittens and 2 mice.

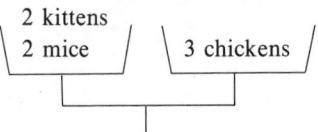

Now in the second picture, 1 kitten balances 1 mouse and 1 chicken. So, in the above picture, replace 2 kittens by 2 mice and 2 chickens.

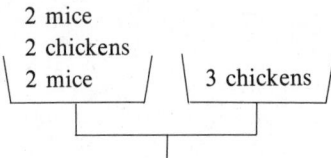

Now take 2 chickens off each side.

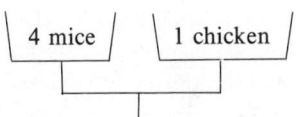

Finally, in the second picture, the 1 chicken can be replaced by its equivalent, 4 mice.

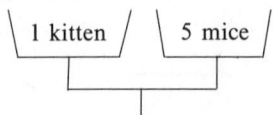

(Students may find other ways of making substitutions.)

Answer

5 mice will balance with 1 kitten.

PROBLEM 13

Salad Dressing

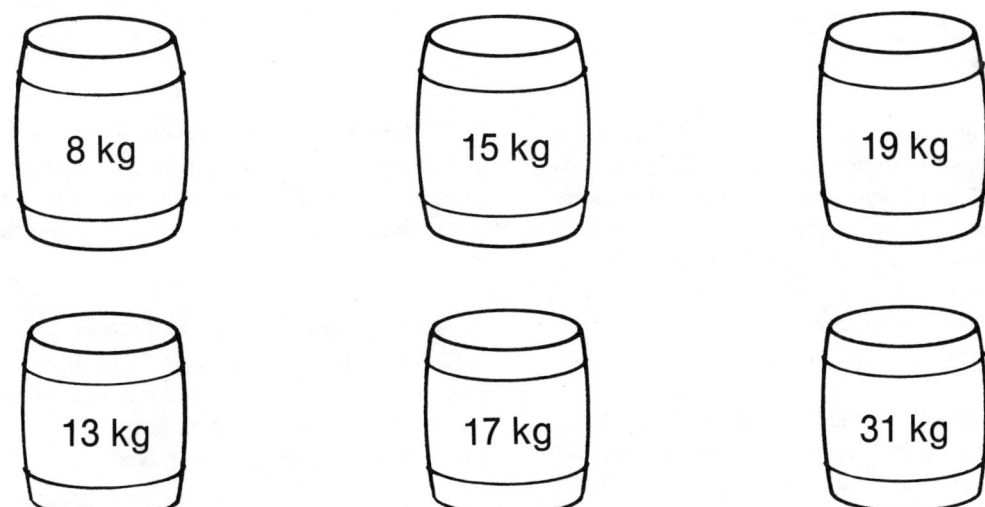

One of the six barrels contains water. Each of the other five barrels contains either oil or vinegar. There is twice as much oil as vinegar in the barrels. Which barrel contains water?

PROBLEM 14

How many mice will balance with the kitten?

PARENT INVOLVEMENT

There is a growing trend toward involvement of parents in all aspects of school operation. The end result should be the furthering of educational opportunities and achievement of children. This is possible because parents have such an in-depth and long-term knowledge of their children—their strengths and weaknesses, their needs and their problems. The exchange of such information with trained professionals can help in planning a better, more relevant, school program.

Another advantage of parental involvement is that it can improve student motivation. As children see their parents become more involved in school affairs, they will be encouraged to take a more active interest in school themselves.

Publishers can assist the total parental involvement program by providing teachers and administrators with information that is easy to share with parents. This information should help explain the goals and objectives of the school curriculum and help teachers share individual pupil progress with parents. Therefore, we have developed a Parent Involvement Packet that provides the following duplicating masters:

1. Eight Activity Sheets

There are two major objectives for these activity sheets:

- To provide an easy way of sharing individual student progress with parents.

- To demonstrate the usefulness of mathematics in dealing with relevant topics of interest to students and parents.

The sheets should be sent home *after* the student has mastered the skill. This provides a positive contact between home and school and demonstrates the student's progress. The eight activity sheets for Level 7 are:

Skill	Taught in Chapters	Use after Student Page
Add, subtract, multiply, and divide whole numbers	1	50
Add, subtract, multiply, and divide decimals	2, 3	100
Metric measurement using decimals	5	166
Add and subtract mixed numbers	6	196
Multiply and divide mixed numbers	7	234
Ratio, proportion, and percent	8	268
Consumer mathematics	9	292
Reading and interpreting graphs	11	340

2. A Parent Report of Student Progress

The objectives of each chapter are listed, with space to check a student's level of performance. This can be used in parent conferences or sent home as a supplement to a report card.

3. An Introductory Letter to Parents

All of the duplicating masters from the Parent Involvement Packet are reproduced on the following pages and the letter is shown reduced below. You can reproduce these pages for use with your class.

Dear Parent,

The enclosed activity sheet is one of several "checkpoints" in mathematics that your child will share with you this year.

Children's achievement can be greatly influenced by their parents' interest in day-to-day progress. You can demonstrate your interest and, at the same time, become aware of your child's mastery of concepts and skills by working with your child on the activity sheets.

The activity provides motivation (answer a riddle, find a hidden picture, play a game) and also makes any wrong answers obvious because the message would be scrambled or the picture distorted. Read the directions with your child and explain the format of the activity. Then watch your child do the computations or join in the game.

Thank you for your cooperation and assistance.

Sincerely,

Chapter 1   Whole Numbers

		Needs Improve-ment	Satis-factory	Outstand-ing
1-1	Write large numbers using words or digits. five billion, six hundred fifty-seven thousand $\longrightarrow$ 5,000,657,000			
1-2	Round whole numbers to any place. 6474 rounded to the nearest ten is 6470 6474 rounded to the nearest hundred is 6500 6474 rounded to the nearest thousand is 6000 6474 rounded to the nearest ten thousand is 10,000			
1-3	Add any two or more whole numbers. 83,432 1,796 $+9,623$			
1-4	Subtract any two whole numbers. 10,005 $-8,937$			
1-5	Multiply any two whole numbers. 4362 $\times 195$			
1-6	Divide any two whole numbers. $383\overline{)56923}$			
1-7	Solve word problems using whole numbers.			

Chapter 2   Decimals—Addition and Subtraction

2-1	Write decimals using words or digits. four hundred eighty-two thousandths $\longrightarrow 0.482$			
2-2	Determine which of two decimals is greater. $0.482 > 0.428$			
2-3	Round decimals to any place. 0.4825 rounded to the nearest one is 0 0.4825 rounded to the nearest tenth is 0.5 0.4825 rounded to the nearest hundredth is 0.48 0.4825 rounded to the nearest thousandth is 0.483			
2-4	Add and subtract decimals. 9.36 10.005 8.4 $+1.937$ -7.037			
2-5	Estimate sums and differences. 9.36 $\longrightarrow$ 9 10.005 $\longrightarrow$ 10 8.4 $\longrightarrow$ 8 $+1.937 \longrightarrow$ 2 $-7.037 \longrightarrow$ 7 21 1			
2-6	Solve word problems using decimals.			

Chapter 3   Decimals—Multiplication and Division

3-1	Multiply any two decimals. 4.37 $\times 1.03$			

	Needs Improve-ment	Satis-factory	Outstand-ing
3-2 Divide any two decimals. $0.46\overline{)0.0392}$			
3-3 Solve word problems using decimals.			

Chapter 4   Number Theory

	Needs Improve-ment	Satis-factory	Outstand-ing
4-1 Tell whether a set is a subset of another set. The set $\{1, 2, 3, 4, 5\}$ is a subset of the set of whole numbers $\{0, 1, 2, \ldots\}$.			
4-2 Give the intersection ($\cap$) and union ($\cup$) of two sets. If set A $= \{1, 2, 3, 4\}$ and set B $= \{4, 5, 6\}$ then A $\cap$ B $= \{4\}$ and A $\cup$ B $= \{1, 2, 3, 4, 5, 6\}$.			
4-3 Give the greatest common factor (GCF) of two numbers. The GCF of 4 and 10 is 2.			
4-4 Give the least common multiple (LCM) of two numbers. The LCM of 4 and 10 is 20.			
4-5 Substitute numbers for letters in mathematical expressions, then give the answer. If $n = 3$, then $2n + 7 = 6 + 7 = 13$			
4-6 Solve a simple equation. $3n + 4 = 10$ $n = 2$			

Chapter 5   Measurement

	Needs Improve-ment	Satis-factory	Outstand-ing
5-1 Measure lengths with a millimeter ruler.			
5-2 Make conversions among metric units. $2\,\text{kg} = \underline{\ ?\ }\,\text{g}$			
5-3 Compute perimeter (distance around a figure) and circumference (distance around a circle). 2 cm 5 cm Perimeter is 14 cm			
5-4 Compute areas of figures, including circles. 2 cm 5 cm Area is 10 square cm			
5-5 Compute surface areas of some three-dimensional figures, including cylinders. 4 cm 2 cm 3 cm Surface area is 52 square cm			
5-6 Compute volumes of some three-dimensional figures, including cylinders. 4 cm 2 cm 3 cm Volume is 24 cubic cm			

Name_____

	Needs Improvement	Satisfactory	Outstanding
5-7 Make conversions among customary units. $2\,\text{ft} = \underline{\ ?\ }\,\text{in.}$			

Chapter 6   Fractions—Addition and Subtraction

	Needs Improvement	Satisfactory	Outstanding
6-1 Reduce a fraction to lowest terms. $\dfrac{8}{12} = \dfrac{2}{3}$			
6-2 Determine which of two fractions is greater ($>$). $\dfrac{5}{8} > \dfrac{1}{2}$			
6-3 Add and subtract fractions. $\dfrac{1}{2} + \dfrac{3}{5}$ $\quad \dfrac{9}{10} - \dfrac{2}{3}$			
6-4 Make conversions between fractions and mixed numbers. $4\dfrac{1}{2} = \dfrac{9}{2}$ $\quad \dfrac{8}{3} = 2\dfrac{2}{3}$			
6-5 Add mixed numbers. $7\dfrac{5}{8} + 2\dfrac{2}{3}$			
6-6 Subtract mixed numbers. $7\dfrac{5}{8} - 2\dfrac{2}{3}$			
6-7 Solve word problems using fractions and mixed numbers.			

Chapter 7   Fractions—Multiplication and Division

	Needs Improvement	Satisfactory	Outstanding
7-1 Multiply any two fractions. $\dfrac{1}{5} \times \dfrac{10}{11}$			
7-2 Divide any two fractions. $\dfrac{4}{9} \div \dfrac{2}{3}$			
7-3 Change fractions to terminating (ending) decimals and vice versa. $\dfrac{1}{2} = 0.5 \quad 0.625 = \dfrac{5}{8}$			
7-4 Change fractions to repeating (unending) decimals and vice versa. $\dfrac{1}{3} = 0.33333\ldots = 0.\overline{3} \quad 0.\overline{5} = 0.55555\ldots = \dfrac{5}{9}$			
7-5 Multiply mixed numbers. $4\dfrac{1}{2} \times 2\dfrac{2}{3}$			

	Needs Improvement	Satisfactory	Outstanding
7-6 Divide mixed numbers. $4\frac{1}{2} \div 2\frac{2}{3}$			
7-7 Solve word problems using fractions and mixed numbers.			

Chapter 8   Ratios and Percent

8-1 Write the ratio of two quantities. 25 girls out of 52 students $\longrightarrow \frac{25}{52}$			
8-2 Solve a proportion for a missing term. $\frac{3}{9} = \frac{2}{x}$ $x = 6$			
8-3 Make conversions among fractions, decimals, and percents. $\frac{3}{4} = 0.75 = 75\%$ $33\frac{1}{3}\% = 0.33\frac{1}{3} = \frac{1}{3}$			
8-4 Find what percent one number is of another. 3 is what percent of 18?			
8-5 Find the percent of a given number. What is 50% of 12?			
8-6 Find the number given a percent of it. 4 is $33\frac{1}{3}\%$ of what number?			
8-7 Solve word problems using percents.			

Chapter 9   Consumer Mathematics

9-1 Compute earnings for various ways of being paid. If you are paid $5.60 an hour, how much will you earn for 37.5 hours?			
9-2 Solve problems about budgets, discounts, and unit pricing.			
9-3 Write checks and balance checking accounts.			
9-4 Compute simple interest.			
9-5 Compute installment prices.			

Chapter 10   Geometry

10-1 Measure angles to the nearest degree. A ∠ ———→ The measure of angle A is 45°.			

Name _____

	Needs Improve-ment	Satis-factory	Outstand-ing
10-2 Determine whether two lines are parallel or perpendicular. parallel lines perpendicular lines			
10-3 List corresponding parts of congruent (same size and shape) figures. Triangle *ABC* is congruent to triangle *DEF*. Angle *A* is congruent to angle *D*. Side *AB* is congruent to side *DE*.			
10-4 State some important properties of common figures. A square has all its sides congruent and all its angles congruent.			

Chapter 11   Probability and Statistics

	Needs Improve-ment	Satis-factory	Outstand-ing
11-1 Count outcomes of events. Tossing a coin has two outcomes—heads and tails. Rolling one standard die ( ) has six outcomes—1, 2, 3, 4, 5, and 6.			
11-2 Compute probabilities of outcomes. The probability of getting a head when a coin is tossed is $\frac{1}{2}$. The probability of getting 3 when one die is rolled is $\frac{1}{6}$.			
11-3 Read information from graphs.			
11-4 Compute average, median (middle value), and range for a set of numbers. 5, 3, 2, 1, 9 Average is 4 ($5 + 3 + 2 + 1 + 9 = 20$, $20 \div 5 = 4$). Median is 3. Range is 8($9 - 1$).			

Chapter 12   Computing with Integers

	Needs Improve-ment	Satis-factory	Outstand-ing
12-1 Add integers (signed numbers). $^+3 + {}^-1 = {}^+2$			
12-2 Subtract integers. $^+3 - {}^-1 = {}^+4$			
12-3 Multiply integers. $^+3 \times {}^-1 = {}^-3$			
12-4 Divide integers. $^+3 \div {}^-1 = {}^-3$			
12-5 Graph pairs of integers on a grid. *A* is at ($^-2$, $^+1$).			

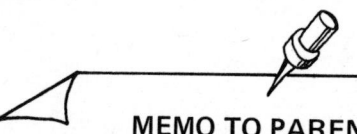

MEMO TO PARENTS

Our math class recently finished a chapter on adding, subtracting, multiplying, and dividing whole numbers. This activity sheet gives your child an opportunity to demonstrate these skills.

NAME _____

ELECTRICITY USED IN FOOD PREPARATION

1. How much more power is needed for a range than for a microwave oven?

   8200 W
   −1500 W   *Subtraction*

Appliance	Average wattage (power)	Estimated kilowatt-hours (energy) used monthly
Blender	390 W	1 kW·h
Coffee maker	890 W	9 kW·h
Frying pan	1200 W	15 kW·h
Range	8200 W	97 kW·h
Toaster	1150 W	3 kW·h
Microwave oven	1500 W	25 kW·h

2. How many kilowatt-hours of electricity would be consumed by a range in 12 months?

   97 kW·h
   ×12   *Multiplication*

3. a. How much power is needed to use the coffee maker, the frying pan, the toaster, and the microwave oven all at the same time?

   Addition

   890 W
   1200 W
   1150 W
   +1500 W

   b. What is the average amount of power required by these four appliances?

   Division   4)‾‾‾‾‾ W

OPERATION OBSERVATION _____

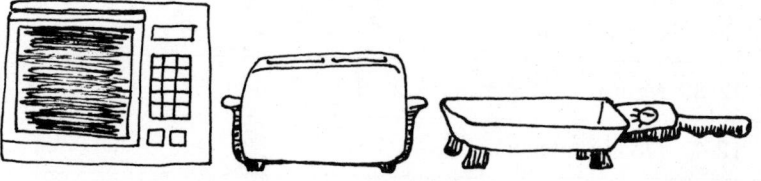

Examine the appliances in your kitchen. Each one should have a label that tells the number of watts required. If all the appliances in your kitchen are used at once, what is the total number of watts required?

(7) Chapter 1. Whole numbers

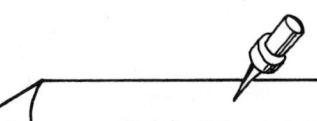

MEMO TO PARENTS

Our math class has studied adding, subtracting, multiplying, and dividing decimals. This activity sheet gives your child an opportunity to demonstrate these skills.

Name _____

1. How many kilowatt-hours of energy are used in one month by a refrigerator, freezer, washing machine, and clothes dryer?

$$\begin{array}{r} 91.7 \\ 99.6 \\ 8.6 \\ +82.8 \\ \hline \end{array}$$

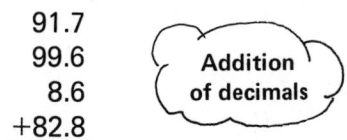
Addition of decimals

ELECTRIC ENERGY CONSUMED BY HOUSEHOLD APPLIANCES

Appliance	Average kilowatt-hours consumed monthly
Refrigerator	91.7
Freezer	99.6
Washing machine	8.6
Clothes dryer	82.8
Television (black & white)	9.0
Television (color)	36.9
Clock	1.4

2. How many more kilowatt-hours are used monthly by the clothes dryer than by the washing machine?

$$\begin{array}{r} 82.8 \\ - 8.6 \\ \hline \end{array}$$

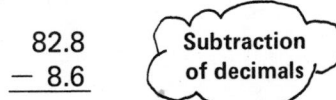
Subtraction of decimals

3. How many kilowatt-hours are used each month by 4 electric clocks?

$$\begin{array}{r} 1.4 \\ \times 4 \\ \hline \end{array}$$

Multiplication of decimals

4. How many times as many kilowatt-hours are used by a color TV than by a black and white TV?

$$9\overline{)36.9}$$

Division of decimals

OPERATION OBSERVATION

1. Count the number of times your refrigerator door is opened in preparing a meal.

   a. Each opening of the door uses 0.02 kilowatt-hours of electricity. How many kilowatt-hours were used?

   number of times door opened × 0.02 = total kilowatt-hours used

   b. Estimate the number of times your refrigerator door is opened each day. At that rate, how many kilowatt-hours of electricity would be used in a year?

   number of times door opened × 0.02 × 365 = total kilowatt hours used

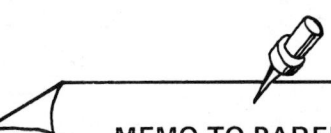

MEMO TO PARENTS

Our math class recently completed a chapter on measurement. This activity sheet gives your child an opportunity to demonstrate these skills.

Name _____

Attic insulation is one of the most important energy-saving home improvements you can make.

The following examples can help you determine the cost of insulating your attic.

Insulation costs are approximately $2.00 per square meter of attic area if there is *no* insulation. If there is already 5 centimeters of insulation, the cost drops to $1.00 per square meter.

> No insulation
> $2.00
> per square meter

> With 5 cm of
> insulation
> $1.00
> per square meter

What would it cost to insulate

a. an attic that is 9 m long and 7 m wide?

9 m × 7 m × $2.00 = _____

> Find the AREA in square meters and multiply by $2.00.

b. an attic that is 765 cm wide and 915 cm long?

> Change the dimensions to meters.

765 cm = 7.65 m
915 cm = 9.15 m

> Multiply

7.65 m × 9.15 m × $2.00 = _____

c. What would the cost be if the attics above already had 5 cm of insulation?

a. _____   b. _____

BE AN ENERGY NUT _____

What would it cost you to insulate your attic? Find the area of your attic (it may be the same as the area of your first floor) and measure the depth of the insulation. Then compute the cost of insulating your attic.

NOTE: The yearly savings in fuel cost will usually pay the insulation cost in two or three years.

MEMO TO PARENTS

Our math class recently studied adding and subtracting mixed numbers. This activity sheet gives your child an opportunity to demonstrate these skills.

Name _____

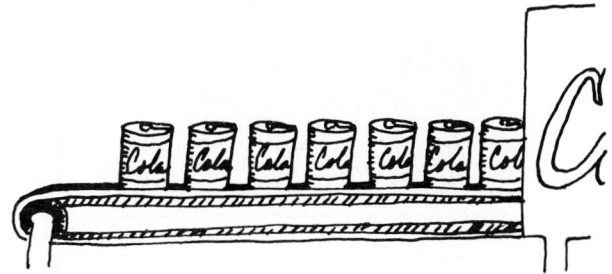

The United States uses a great deal of energy in the production of soft drink containers. This chart gives the amounts of energy necessary to produce the more common ones.

1. If you purchased a soft drink in each of the containers listed and threw them in the trash, how many energy units would be wasted?

$3\frac{9}{10}$
$6\frac{3}{5}$ Add.
$9\frac{7}{10}$
$+5\frac{4}{5}$

$3\frac{9}{10}$
$6\frac{6}{10}$ Change to a common denominator.
$9\frac{7}{10}$
$+5\frac{8}{10}$

Container	Energy units
Steel can	$3\frac{9}{10}$
Aluminum can	$6\frac{3}{5}$
Bottle (returnable)	$9\frac{7}{10}$
Bottle (nonreturnable)	$5\frac{4}{5}$

2. How many more energy units are used to produce a returnable bottle than an aluminum can?

$9\frac{7}{10}$
$-6\frac{3}{5}$ Subtract.

$9\frac{7}{10}$
$-6\frac{6}{10}$ Change to a common denominator.

3. How many more energy units are used to produce a returnable bottle than a non-returnable bottle?

$9\frac{7}{10}$
$-5\frac{4}{5}$ Change to a common denominator and regroup.

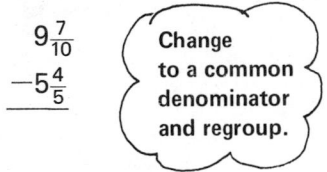

OPERATION OBSERVATION _____

Estimate the number of cans and nonreturnable bottles your family uses in a month.
Figure out how many energy units would be saved if you used returnable bottles instead.

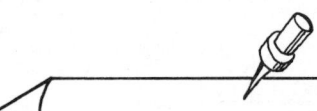

MEMO TO PARENTS

Our math class recently studied multiplying and dividing mixed numbers. This activity sheet gives your child an opportunity to demonstrate these skills.

Name _____

Many of our natural resources can be conserved by recycling. The most common materials that can be recycled are newspapers, glass bottles, and aluminum. The prices paid for these items varies and the chart is based on a recent price list.

	Price per pound
Newspapers	1¢
Glass	$1\frac{1}{2}$¢
Aluminum	$16\frac{3}{4}$¢

1. Most recycling centers accumulate their materials in large quantities. What would the price per ton be for
   a. newspapers? _____   b. glass? _____   c. aluminum? _____

   Hint!
   Multiply each price by 2000 to get the price per ton.

   $1\frac{1}{2} \times 2000$

   $16\frac{3}{4} \times 2000$

   Change to fractions and multiply.

   $\frac{3}{2} \times 2000 =$

   $\frac{67}{4} \times \frac{2000}{1} =$

2. A junior high school band collected aluminum cans to raise money for new uniforms. They collected 2400 pounds. How much did they earn?

   $16\frac{3}{4} \times 2400 =$

   Change to fractions and multiply.

3. How many times as much money is paid for aluminum cans than is paid for glass?

   $16\frac{3}{4} \div 1\frac{1}{2} =$

   Change to fractions, invert the divisor and multiply.

OPERATION OBSERVATION

Collect all the newspapers delivered to your home for one week, weigh them, and figure out how much they are worth. Do the same with all the aluminum cans used by your family in two weeks.

Name _____

A major waste of energy is high-speed driving. The chart compares fuel economy of two compact and two intermediate automobiles.

FUEL ECONOMY IN MILES PER GALLON				
Driving speed in miles per hour	Compact A	Compact B	Intermediate A	Intermediate B
40	60	57	26.2	25.5
50	50	49.6	23.8	24.4
60	40	40.5	21.4	20.7

1. What is the ratio of the fuel economy of Intermediate A at 60 mph to its fuel economy at 40 mph?

$$\frac{\text{economy at 60 mph}}{\text{economy at 40 mph}} = \frac{?}{?}$$

Write this ratio as a percent.

2. What is the ratio of the fuel economy of Intermediate B at 60 mph to the fuel economy of Compact A at 60 mph?

$$\frac{\text{economy Intermediate B}}{\text{economy Compact A}} = \frac{?}{?}$$

Write this ratio as a percent.

3. Compact B gets 49.6 miles per gallon at 50 mph. How many miles would it go on 8.6 gallons at this speed?

 Write a proportion.

$$\frac{\text{miles driven}}{\text{gallons used}} = \frac{\text{miles}}{\text{gallons}}$$

Substitute.

$$\frac{?}{8.6} = \frac{49.6}{1}$$

$$? = 8.6 \times 49.6$$

OPERATION OBSERVATION

The fuel economy of Compact A increases when the speed is reduced from 50 mph to 40 mph. Assume that your family car would show a similar increase. What fuel economy would you expect to get at 40 mph?

Hint: Figure your fuel economy at 50 mph. (Do this on your next family outing; mpg = $\frac{\text{miles driven}}{\text{gallons used}}$)

Then solve this proportion: $\dfrac{\text{family car mpg @ 50 mph}}{? \text{ mpg @ 40 mph}} = \dfrac{50 \text{ mpg}}{60 \text{ mpg}}$

MEMO TO PARENTS

Our math class recently completed a chapter on consumer mathematics. This activity sheet gives your child an opportunity to demonstrate these skills.

Name _____

TABLE OF WITHHOLDING TAX WEEKLY PAYROLL PERIODS

And the wages are —		And the number of withholding exemptions claimed is —					
At least	But less than	0	1	2	3	4	5
		The amount of income tax to be withheld shall be —					
90	92	11.20	9.20	7.10	5.00	2.90	1.20
92	94	11.60	9.60	7.50	5.30	3.20	1.40
94	96	11.90	9.90	7.80	5.70	3.60	1.70
96	98	12.20	10.20	8.10	6.00	3.90	2.00
98	100	12.50	10.50	8.50	6.40	4.20	2.30
100	105	13.10	11.10	9.10	7.00	4.80	2.80
105	110	13.90	11.90	9.90	7.80	5.70	3.60
110	115	14.70	12.70	10.70	8.70	6.50	4.40
115	120	15.50	13.50	11.50	9.50	7.40	5.30
120	125	16.30	14.30	12.30	10.30	8.20	6.10
125	130	17.10	15.10	13.10	11.10	9.10	7.00
130	135	17.90	15.90	13.90	11.90	9.90	7.80
135	140	18.70	16.70	14.70	12.70	10.70	8.70
140	145	19.50	17.50	15.50	13.50	11.50	9.50
145	150	20.30	18.30	16.30	14.30	12.30	10.30
150	160	21.50	19.50	17.50	15.50	13.50	11.50
160	170	23.10	21.10	19.10	17.10	15.10	13.10
170	180	25.00	22.70	20.70	18.70	16.70	14.70
180	190	26.90	24.50	22.30	20.30	18.30	16.30
190	200	28.80	26.40	24.10	21.90	19.90	17.90
200	210	30.70	28.30	26.00	23.60	21.50	19.50
210	220	32.60	30.20	27.90	25.50	23.10	21.10
220	230	34.50	32.10	29.80	27.40	25.00	22.70
230	240	36.40	34.00	31.70	29.30	26.90	24.50
240	250	38.30	35.90	33.60	31.20	28.80	26.40

1. Federal and state income taxes are withheld from employees' salaries. The table shows the tax withheld in one state in a recent year. How much tax is withheld each week from a person's weekly wages of

   a. $94 when 1 exemption is claimed?

   _____

   b. $235 when 3 exemptions are claimed?

   _____

2. How much tax is withheld in a year if a person's weekly wages are $105 and 1 exemption is claimed?

   52 weeks × _____ weekly amt. = _____

3. Employees also pay a federal tax for social security. In a recent year, it was 7.8% of the first $12,000 of annual income. Compute the social security tax for that year if an employee earned $250 each week.

   a. $250 × 52 weeks = _____ annual salary

   b. taxable salary × 0.078 = _____ social security

OPERATION OBSERVATION

Ask your parents if you may see the record of deductions that they receive with their paychecks. How much is withheld for federal and state income taxes each pay period? How much is withheld for a year? What are the total deductions in a year? What percent is this of the total salary?

(7) Chapter 9. Consumer mathematics

MEMO TO PARENTS

Our math class recently completed a chapter on reading graphs. This activity sheet gives your child an opportunity to demonstrate these skills.

Name _____

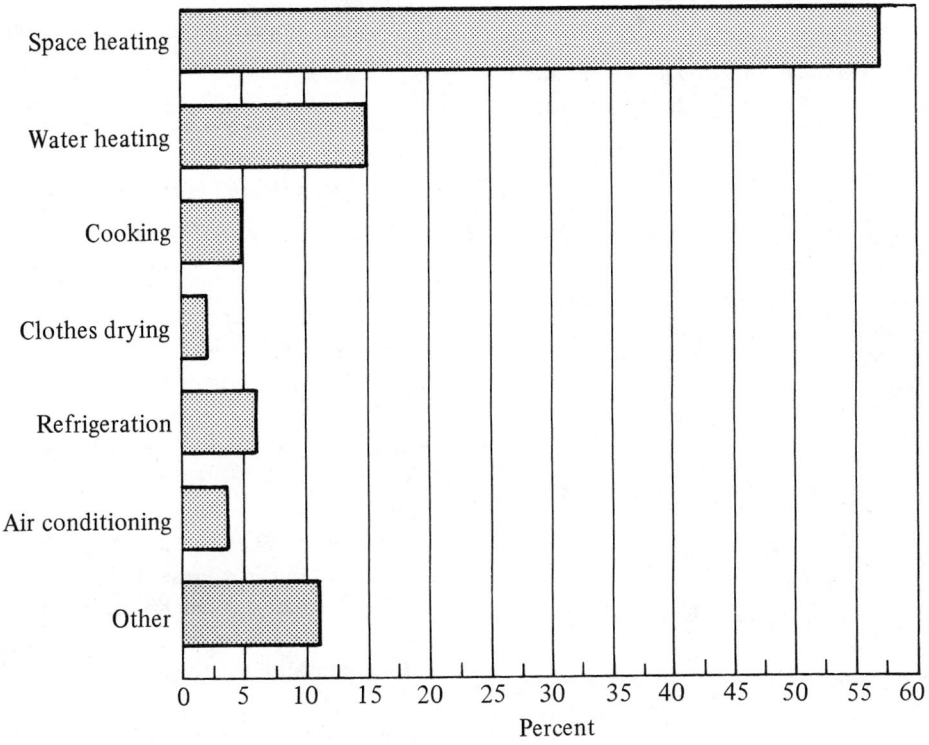

AVERAGE PERCENT OF ENERGY USE IN THE HOME

1. The largest use of energy in the home is for _____. It uses _____% of the home energy.

2. Space heating and water heating together use approximately _____% of the home energy.

3. What percent of the energy used in the home goes for cooking, clothes drying, refrigeration, and air conditioning? _____

4. Which category uses 6% of the energy? _____

OPERATION OBSERVATION

Find out how much your family spent on energy last month. Include the cost of electricity, fuel oil, and natural gas used in your home. Assume your family uses the national average and determine the approximate amount spent for each category.

Student's Bibliography

The selections that follow are a sample of the current children's literature suitable for use in the mathematics classroom. The selections can be used in classroom activities or given as individual reading. These stories and illustrated books will help reinforce basic concepts and will help foster an interest in mathematical ideas.

Abbott, Edwin A. *Flatland: A Romance of Many Dimensions.* 5th rev. ed. New York: Barnes & Noble, Inc., 1963.

Adler, Irving. *Logic for Beginners.* New York: The John Day Company, Inc., 1964.

—— *The Magic House of Numbers,* rev. ed. New York: The John Day Company, Inc., 1974.

—— *Probability and Statistics for Everyman,* rev. ed. New York: The John Day Company, Inc., 1963.

Alterman, Hyman. *Numbers at Work: The Story and Science of Statistics.* New York: Harcourt Brace Jovanovich, Inc., 1966.

Anderson, John T., and Ogilvy, C.T. *Excursions in Number Theory.* New York: Oxford University Press, 1966.

Andrews, F. Emerson. *Numbers, Please.* Boston: Little, Brown and Company, 1961.

Asimov, Isaac. *Quick and Easy Math.* Boston: Houghton Mifflin Company, 1964.

—— *The Realm of Numbers.* Boston: Houghton Mifflin Company, 1959.

Bakst, Aaron. *Mathematics, Its Magic and Mastery.* New York: Van Nostrand Reinhold Company, 1967.

Barbow, Louis E. *What About Metric?* Washington, D. C.: The National Bureau of Standards, 1973.

Barr, Stephen. *Experiments in Topology.* New York: Thomas Y. Crowell Company, 1964.

Bell, Eric T. *Men of Mathematics.* New York: Simon & Schuster, Inc., 1937.

Bendick, Jeanne, and Levin, Marcia. *The Mathematics Ilustrated Dictionary.* New York: McGraw-Hill Book Company, 1965.

—— *Take Shapes, Lines, and Letters: New Horizons in Mathematics.* New York: McGraw-Hill Book Company, 1962.

Bernstein, Jeremy. *Einstein.* New York: The Viking Press, Inc., 1972.

Brindze, Ruth. *Investing Money: The Facts About Stocks and Bonds.* New York: Harcourt Brace Jovanovich, Inc., 1968.

Buckeye, Donald A. *Experiments in Probability and Statistics.* Troy, Michigan: Midwest Publications Company, Inc., 1970.

—— *Introducing the Metric System with Activities.* Troy, Michigan: Midwest Publications Company, Inc., 1972.

Burlingame, Roger. *Dictator Clock: 5000 Years of Telling Time.* New York: Macmillan, Inc., 1966.

Clark, Frank. *Contemporary Math.* New York: Franklin Watts, Inc., 1964.

—— *Speed Math.* New York: Franklin Watts, Inc., 1968.

Davis, Philip J., and Chinn, William G. *3.1416 and All That.* New York: Simon & Schuster, Inc., 1969.

Deming, Richard. *Metric Power, Why and How We Are Going Metric.* Camden, N.J.: Thomas Nelson, Inc., 1974.

Diggins, Julia E. *String, Straightedge and Shadow: The Story of Geometry.* New York: The Viking Press, Inc., 1965.

Dilson, Jesse. *The Abacus: A Pocket Computer.* New York: St. Martin's Press, Inc., 1968.

Dwyer, Thomas A., and Kaufman, Michael S. *A Guided Tour of Computer Programming in BASIC.* Boston: Houghton Mifflin Company, 1973.

Ellison, Elsie C. *Fun with Lines and Curves.* New York: Lothrop, Lee & Shepard Co., Inc., 1972.

Feravolo, Rocco V. *The Wonders of Mathematics.* New York: Dodd, Mead & Co., 1963.

Fouke, George R. *A First Book of Space Form Making.* San Francisco: Geo Books, 1974.

Friend, J. Newton. *Numbers: Fun with Facts,* reprint of 1954 edition. New York: Charles Scribner's Sons, 1972.

Fults, John Lee. *Magic Squares.* La Salle, Ill.: Open Court Publishing Co., 1974.

Gallant, Roy A. *Man the Measurer: Our Units of Measure and How They Grew.* Garden City, N.Y.: Doubleday & Company, Inc., 1972.

Gardner, Martin. *Codes, Ciphers and Secret Writing.* New York: Simon & Schuster, Inc., 1972.

—— *Perplexing Puzzles and Tantalizing Teasers.* New York: Simon & Schuster, Inc., 1969.

Greenhood, David. *Mapping.* Chicago: University of Chicago Press, 1964.

Gross, Jonathan L., and Brainerd, Walter S. *Fundamental Programming Concepts*. New York: Harper & Row, Publishers, 1972.

Hirsch, S. Carl. *Meter Means Measure: The Story of the Metric System*. New York: The Viking Press, Inc., 1973.

Hogben, Lancelot. *Mathematics in the Making*. Garden City, N.Y.: Doubleday & Company, Inc., 1960.

——— *The Wonderful World of Mathematics*, rev. ed. Garden City, N.Y.: Doubleday & Company, Inc., 1968.

Holt, Michael, and Ridout, Ronald. *The Second Big Book of Puzzles*. New York: Alfred A. Knopf, Inc., 1975.

Holton, Jean L. *Algebra: A New Way of Looking at Numbers*. New York: David McKay Co., Inc., 1968.

——— *Geometry: A New Way of Looking at Space*. New York: David McKay Co., Inc., 1971.

Hoyt, Edwin P. *Arab Science: Discoveries and Contributions*. Nashville, Tenn.: Thomas Nelson, Inc., 1975.

Irwin, Keith G. *The Romance of Weights and Measures*. New York: The Viking Press, Inc., 1960.

Jones, Madeline. *The Mysterious Flexagons*. New York: Crown Publishers, Inc., 1965.

Juster, Norton. *The Dot and the Line*. New York: Random House, Inc., 1963.

——— *The Phantom Tollbooth*. New York: Random House, Inc., 1961.

Karush, William. *The Crescent Dictionary of Mathematics*. New York: Macmillan, Inc., 1962.

Kline, Morris. *Mathematics and the Physical World*. New York: Thomas Y. Crowell Company, 1959.

Lewis, Alfred. *The New World of Computers*. New York: Dodd, Mead & Co., 1965.

Lewis, W. D. *Mathematics Makes Sense*. New York: Arco Publishing Co., Inc., 1966.

Lieber, Lillian. *The Education of T. C. Mits*. New York: W. W. Norton & Company, Inc., 1944.

——— *Mits, Wits, and Logic*. New York: W. W. Norton & Company, Inc., 1960.

Linn, Charles F. *The Golden Mean: Mathematics and the Fine Arts*. Garden City, N.Y.: Doubleday & Company, 1974.

——— *Probability*. New York: Thomas Y. Crowell Company, 1972.

——— *Puzzles, Patterns, and Pastimes*. Garden City, N.Y.: Doubleday & Company, 1969.

Lohberg, Rolf, and Lutz, Theo. *Computers at Work*. New York: Sterling Publishing Co., Inc., 1969.

——— *Electronic Brains*. New York: Sterling Publishing Co., Inc., 1965.

Lowenstein, Dyno. *Graphs*. rev. ed. New York: Franklin Watts, Inc., 1976.

Menninger, Karl W. *Mathematics in Your World*. New York: The Viking Press, Inc., 1962.

Moore, William. *Metric Is Here!* New York: G.P. Putnam's Sons, 1974.

Navarra, John G. *Clocks, Calendars, and Carousels*. Garden City, N.Y.: Doubleday & Company, Inc., 1967.

Neal, Harry E. *Money*. New York: Julian Messner, Inc., 1967.

Neely, Henry M. *Triangles: Getting Ready for Trigonometry*. New York: Thomas Y. Crowell Company, 1962.

Newman, James R., ed. *The World of Mathematics*. New York: Simon & Schuster, Inc., 1956.

Olney, Ross, and Olney, Pat. *Pocket Calculator Fun and Games*. New York: Franklin Watts, Inc., 1977.

Pallas, Norvin. *Calculator Puzzles, Tricks and Games*. New York: Sterling Publishing Co., Inc., 1976.

Paradis, Adrian A. *The Bulls and the Bears: How the Stock Exchange Works*. New York: Hawthorn Books, Inc., 1967.

Piper, Roger. *The Story of Computers*. New York: Harcourt Brace Jovanovich, Inc., 1964.

Razzell, Arthur G., and Watts, K.G.O. *Probability: The Science of Chance*. Garden City, N.Y.: Doubleday & Company, Inc., 1967.

——— *This Is 4: The Idea of a Number*. Garden City, N.Y.: Doubleday & Company, Inc., 1967.

Rogers, James T. *The Pantheon Story of Mathematics*. New York: Pantheon Books, Inc., 1966.

Ruchlis, Hyman. *Clear Thinking*. New York: Harper & Row, Publishers, 1962.

Sawyer, W.W. *Mathematicians's Delight*. Baltimore: Penguin Books, Inc., 1943.

——— *Prelude to Mathematics*. Baltimore: Penguin Books, Inc., 1955.

Schlein, Miriam. *Metric: The Modern Way to Measure*. New York: Harcourt Brace Jovanovich, 1977.

Silverberg, Robert. *Clocks for the Ages—How Scientists Date the Past*. New York: Macmillan, Inc., 1971.

Smith, George O. *Mathematics: The Language of Science*. New York: G.P. Putnam's Sons, 1961.

Srivastava, Jane Jonas. *Statistics*. New York: Thomas Y. Crowell Company, 1973.

Steinberg, Fred. *The First Book of Computers*. New York: Franklin Watts, Inc., 1969.

Steinhaus, Hugo. *Mathematical Snapshots*, 2nd ed. New York: Oxford University Press, Inc., 1969.

Summers, George J. *New Puzzles in Logical Deduction*. New York: Dover Publications, Inc., 1968.

——— *Test Your Logic*. New York: Dover Publications, Inc., 1972.

Tannenbaum, Beulah, and Stillman, Myra. *Understanding Maps*, rev. ed. New York: McGraw-Hill Book Company, 1969.

—— *Understanding Time: The Science of Clocks and Calendars*. New York: McGraw-Hill Book Company, 1958.

Tarshis, Barry. *Barter, Bills and Banks*. New York: Julian Messner, Inc., 1970.

Valens, Evans G. *The Number of Things: Pythagoras, Geometry and Humming Strings*. E.P. Dutton & Co., Inc., 1964.

Vorwald, Alan, and Clark, Frank. *Computers: From Sand Table to Electronic Brain*, 3rd ed. New York: McGraw-Hill Book Company, 1970.

Zaslavaky, Claudia. *Africa Counts*. Boston: Prindle, Weber & Schmidt, Inc., 1973.

Teacher's Bibliography

The selections that follow are a sample of the current literature that would be of particular interest to the junior high school teacher. Included are professional books dealing with methods of teaching, child development, and the modern school. There are also enrichment books that can be adapted for classroom use.

We also suggest *The Arithmetic Teacher* and *The Mathematics Teacher*, monthly journals published by the National Council of Teachers of Mathematics, Reston, Virginia 22091. These journals contain timely articles specifically designed and written for use by classroom teachers of mathematics.

AAAS Science Book List for Children, 3rd ed. Washington, D.C.: American Association for the Advancement of Science, 1972.

Barnett, I. A. *Elements of Number Theory*, rev. ed. Boston: Prindle, Weber & Schmidt, Inc., 1972.

Biggs, Edith. *Mathematics for Older Children*. New York: Citation Press, 1972.

Biggs, Edith E., and MacLean, James R. *Freedom to Learn*. Don Mills, Ontario: Addison-Wesley (Canada), Ltd., 1969.

Brumfiel, Charles F., and Vance, Irvin E. *Algebra and Geometry for Teachers*. Reading, Mass.: Addison-Wesley Publishing Co., Inc., 1970.

Butts, Thomas. *Problem Solving in Mathematics*. Glenview, Ill.: Scott, Foresman and Company, 1973.

Copeland, Richard W. *How Children Learn Mathematics*. New York: Macmillan, Inc., 1970.

Cundy, H.M. and Rollett, A.P. *Mathematical Models*, 2nd ed. New York: Oxford University Press, Inc., 1961.

DeSimone, Daniel V. *A Metric America: A Decision Whose Time Has Come*. (SD Catalog No. C13.10:345) Washington, D.C.: U.S. Government Printing Office, 1971.

Dienes, Zoltan P. *Building Up Mathematics*. New York: Humanities Press, Inc., 1960.
—— *Experimental Study of Mathematics Learning*. New York: Humanities Press, Inc., 1963.

Featherstone, Joseph. *Schools Where Children Learn*. New York: Liveright, 1971.

Gattegno, Caleb. *The Common Sense of Teaching Mathematics*. New York: Educational Solutions, Inc., 1974.

Hafner, Lawrence E. *Improving Reading in Middle and Secondary Schools*. New York: Macmillan, Inc., 1974.

Hardgrove, Clarence Ethel, and Miller, Herbert F. *Mathematics Library: Elementary and Junior High School*, 2nd ed. Reston, Va.: National Council of Teachers of Mathematics, 1973.

Henderson, George L., and Glunn, Lowell D. *Let's Play Games in Metrics*. Skokie, Ill.: National Textbook Co., 1974.

Herndon, James. *How to Survive in Your Native Land*. New York: Simon & Schuster, Inc., 1971.

Hertzberg, Alvin, and Stone, Edward. *Schools Are for Children*. New York: Schocken Books Inc., 1971.

Higgins, Jon L., ed. *A Metric Handbook for Teachers*. Reston, Va.: National Council of Teachers of Mathematics, 1974.

Holden, Alan. *Shapes, Space, and Symmetry*. New York: Columbia University Press, 1971.

Holt, John. *What Do I Do Monday?* New York: E.P. Dutton & Co., Inc., 1970.

Holt, Michael, and Dienes, Zoltan. *Let's Play Math*. New York: Walker & Co., 1973.

Hopkins, Robert A. *The International (SI) Metric System and How It Works*, rev. ed. Tarzana, Calif.: Polymetric Services, Inc., 1975.

Humphrey, James H., and Sullivan, Dorothy D. *Teaching Slow Learners Through Active Games.* Springfield, Ill.: Charles C. Thomas, Publisher, 1970.

Jacobs, Harold R. *Mathematics: A Human Endeavor.* San Francisco: W.H. Freeman and Company Publishers, 1976.

James, Glenn, and James, Robert C., eds. *Mathematics Dictionary,* 4th ed. New York: Van Nostrand Reinhold Company, 1976.

Johnson, Donovan A. *Excursions in Outdoor Measurement.* Portland, Me.: J. Weston Walch, Publisher, 1974.

Johnson, Donovan A., and Rising, Gerald R. *Guidelines for Teaching Mathematics,* 2nd ed. Belmont, Calif.: Wadsworth Publishing Co., Inc., 1972.

Kane, Robert B.; Byrne, Mary Ann; and Hater, Mary Ann. *Helping Children Read Mathematics.* New York: American Book Company, 1974.

Kidd, Kenneth P.; Myers, Shirley S.; and Cilley, David M. *A Laboratory Approach to Mathematics.* Chicago: Science Research Associates, Inc., 1970.

Kordemsky, Boris A. *The Moscow Puzzles: 359 Mathematical Recreations.* Translated by Albert Parry. New York: Charles Scribner's Sons, 1972.

Krulik, Stephen. *A Handbook of Aids for Teaching Junior and Senior High School Mathematics.* Philadelphia: W.B. Saunders Company, 1971.

Krulik, Stephen, and Weise, Ingrid. *Teaching Secondary School Mathematics.* Philadelphia: W.B. Saunders Company, 1975.

Kurtz, V. Ray. *Teaching Metric Awareness.* St. Louis, Missouri: C.V. Mosby Company, 1976.

McFarland, Dora, and Lewis, Eunice M. *Introduction to Modern Mathematics,* 2nd ed. Lexington, Mass.: D.C. Heath and Company, 1973.

Moore, Carolyn C. *Why Don't We Do Something Different?* Boston: Prindle, Weber & Schmidt, Inc., 1973.

National Council of Teachers of Mathematics *Yearbooks.* Reston, Va.: National Council of Teachers of Mathematics.
—— *Developing Mathematical Skills, 1978 Yearbook,* 1978.

—— *Geometry in the Mathematics Curriculum, Thirty-sixth Yearbook,* 1973.
—— *Historical Topics for the Mathematics Classroom, Thirty-first Yearbook,* 1969.
—— *Instructional Aids in Mathematics, Thirty-fourth Yearbook,* 1973.
—— *Measurement in School Mathematics, 1976 Yearbook,* 1976.
—— *Organizing for Mathematics Instruction, 1977 Yearbook,* 1977.
—— *The Slow Learner in Mathematics, Thirty-fifth Yearbook,* 1972.

Paige, Donald, *Elementary Mathematical Methods.* New York: John Wiley and Sons, Inc., 1977.

Pedoe, Dan. *The Gentle Art of Mathematics,* Reprint of 1958 edition. New York: Dover Publications, Inc., 1973.

Pemberton, John E. *How to Find Out in Mathematics,* 2nd ed. Elmsford, N.Y.: Pergamon Press, Inc., 1970.

Polya, Gyorgy. *How to Solve It.* Princeton, N.J.: Princeton University Press, 1971.
—— *Mathematical Discovery: On Understanding, Learning and Teaching Problem Solving.* New York: John Wiley & Sons. Inc., 1962.

Rade, Lennart, and Kaufman, Burt A. *Adventures with Your Hand Calculator.* St. Louis, Missouri: CERMEL, 1977.

Schaaf, William L. *The High School Mathematics Library,* 5th ed. Reston, Va.: National Council of Teachers of Mathematics, 1973.

Skemp, Richard R. *The Psychology of Learning Mathematics.* Baltimore: Penguin Books, Inc., 1972.

Smart, James R. *Metric Math: The Modernized Metric System (SI).* Monterey, Calif.: Brooks Cole Publishing Co., 1974.

Sobel, Max A., and Maletsky, Evan M. *Teaching Mathematics: A Source Book of Aids, Activities and Strategies.* Englewood Cliffs, N.J.: Prentice-Hall, Inc., 1974.

Suydam, Marilyn N., and Dessart, Donald J. *Classroom Ideas from Research on Computational Skills.* Reston, Va.: National Council of Teachers of Mathematics, 1976.

Index

1 2 3 4 5 6 7 8 9 0